WINDOWS
TO ALGEBRA AND GEOMETRY
AN INTEGRATED APPROACH

© 1 9 9 6

Teacher's Edition

ROLAND E. LARSON

LAURIE BOSWELL

TIMOTHY KANOLD

LEE STIFF

CONTENTS

Published simultaneously in Canada

Printed in the United States of America

International Standard Book Number: 0-669-37691-4

1 2 3 4 5 6 7 8 9 10 RRD 00 99 98 97 96 95

Math that's meaningful. Math that engages.

Math that's meaningful.
Math that engages.

We wrote *Windows to Algebra and Geometry* with several goals in mind.

One goal is to help students recognize and appreciate the role math plays in the real world. At every opportunity, we demonstrate the usefulness and vitality of math, making it accessible to every student. We feel that students respond more enthusiastically to a subject that connects directly to their lives.

In addition to demonstrating the connections between mathematics and students' own world, *Windows to Algebra and Geometry* also helps students make connections between different areas of mathematics.

Finally, to help students move from elementary math to high school math, *Windows to Algebra and Geometry* provides a broad yet solid foundation in both algebra and geometry—and a comfortable bridge from the concrete to the abstract.

Roland E. Larson is a professor of mathematics at the Behrend College of Pennsylvania State University at Erie. He is a member of NCTM and an author of many well known high school and college mathematics textbooks, including D.C. Heath's *Calculus, Precalculus,* and *Algebra-Geometry* series. He is a pioneer of interactive textbooks, and his calculus textbook is published in a CD-ROM version.

Laurie Boswell is a mathematics teacher at Profile Junior-Senior High School in Bethlehem, New Hampshire and has taught mathematics at the middle school and high school levels. She is active in NCTM and local mathematics associations and is a frequent convention speaker. A 1986 recipient of the Presidential Award for Excellence in Mathematics Teaching, she is also the 1992 Tandy Technology Scholar and the 1991 recipient of the Richard Balomenos Mathematics Education Service Award presented by the New Hampshire Association of Teachers of Mathematics. She is also an author of D.C. Heath's *Geometry*.

Timothy Kanold is Director of Mathematics and Science and a teacher at Adlai Stevenson High School in Lincolnshire, Illinois. He is a 1986 recipient of the Presidential Award for Excellence in Mathematics Teaching, the 1991 recipient of the Outstanding Young Alumni Award from Illinois State University, and the 1993 recipient of ICTM's Outstanding Leadership Award. A member of NCTM, he served on NCTM's *Professional Standards for Teaching Mathematics* Commission and served as a speaker for *New Dimensions in Leadership*. He has published numerous articles on effective teaching practices and is an author of D.C. Heath's *Algebra* texts.

Lee Stiff is an associate professor of mathematics education in the College of Education and Psychology of North Carolina State University at Raleigh and has taught mathematics at the high school and middle school levels. He was a member of the NCTM Board of Directors and the writing team for NCTM's *Professional Standards for Teaching Mathematics*. He was the 1992 recipient of the W.W. Rankin Award for Excellence in Mathematics Education presented by the North Carolina Council of Teachers of Mathematics. He is an author of D.C. Heath's *Algebra-Geometry* series and a contributing author to *Heath Mathematics CONNECTIONS*.

What to look for in Windows to Algebra and Geometry

A broad yet solid foundation for algebra and geometry

Windows to Algebra and Geometry makes math accessible and interesting to all students through development of topics that lead to an understanding of algebra and geometry. Frequent use of visual models, manipulatives, and technology helps students understand the mathematical content. *Windows to Algebra and Geometry* also provides a smooth transition in mathematics from concrete experiences to more abstract experiences, using multiple modes of learning: concrete, visual, and abstract.

Integration: a bridge between algebra, geometry, and data analysis

Windows to Algebra and Geometry integrates the major themes outlined in the NCTM Standards: relevancy, communication, reasoning, connections, problem solving, and use of technology. To help students see the larger picture of mathematics, *Windows to Algebra and Geometry* connects important concepts in algebra and geometry, makes links to other math topics, such as data analysis, and incorporates continual review.

Meaningful applications to real life

Above all, *Windows to Algebra and Geometry* strives to make math interesting—and memorable. To illustrate the meaning behind mathematics, the text provides scores of real-life applications and demonstrates, again and again, how math can help solve real-life problems, so students sense the need for math. In addition to an inviting writing style and the frequent use of real data, *Windows to Algebra and Geometry* also profiles people in all walks of life who use math on the job, at home, and at play.

Opportunities for active learning

Windows to Algebra and Geometry gets students involved in mathematics by encouraging them to **communicate** their ideas, to learn along with their peers, and to **explore** and discover. The Student Text offers numerous opportunities for **hands-on** investigation, **cooperative learning**, **communication**, ideas for incorporating **research and writing**, and the **use of manipulatives**. In the Teacher's Edition, you'll find ideas for even deeper student involvement and self-assessment.

Pacing chart

Suggestions on pacing are provided at the beginning of each chapter. A comprehensive pacing chart for the entire text is found on pages T18 -19.

CHAPTER 2 OVERVIEW

PACING CHART

Lesson	Basic/ Average Course	Above Average Course	Advanced Course
2.1	2 days	1 day	1 day
2.2	2 days	1 day	1 day
2.3	2 days	1 day	1 day
2.4	2 days	1 day	1 day
2.5	2 days	1 day	1 day
2.6	2 days	1 day	1 day
2.7	2 days	1 day	1 day
2.8	2 days	1 day	1 day
2.9	0 days	1 day	1 day

About the Chapter

The concepts and skills of this course are taught in the context of real-life modeling. The students' ability to solve equations is, of course, central to this approach. This chapter lays early foundations for solving equations. After learning in Lessons 2.1 and 2.2 how the Distributive Property is used to help simplify and evaluate expressions, students will begin in Lesson 2.3 to solve the simplest equations with mental math and to check their solutions. In Lessons 2.4 and 2.5, students learn how the properties of equality are applied in order to maintain equivalent expressions on both sides of an equation. They see how this technique is applied in solving single-operation equations using addition, subtraction, multiplication, and division.

Meanwhile, Goal 2 of each of these lessons serves to remind students of the ongoing real-life context of these techniques. Algebraic modeling becomes the primary goal in Lessons 2.6 and 2.7, when students learn to translate verbal phrases into algebraic expressions and verbal sentences into equations. They learn to identify and label whatever numerical constants and variables are involved in such phrases and sentences. Lesson 2.8 introduces students to the technique of a systematic algebraic problem-solving plan that will be used throughout this course as a powerful tool in modeling real-life problems, from the simplest to the most complex. Lesson 2.9, alerting students to the fact that real-life situations often require an inequality model rather than an equation, offers students some practice in solving simple inequalities.

48

CHAPTER 2

Investigations in Algeb

LESSONS

2.1 The Distributive Property ▪ 51

2.2 Simplifying by Adding Like Terms ▪ 55

2.3 Solving Equations: Mental Math ▪ 59

2.4 Solving Equations: Addition or Subtraction ▪ 65

2.5 Solving Equations: Multiplication or Division ▪ 71

2.6 Modeling Verbal Expressions ▪ 76

2.7 Real-Life Modeling with Equations ▪ 81

2.8 A Problem-Solving Plan ▪ 85

2.9 Exploring Variables and Inequalities ▪ 89

Apparel and accessory stores in the United States generate sales in excess of $95 million. However, each individual store must take in enough money to pay for the goods it is selling, to cover its operating costs (rent, insurance, advertising, salaries, etc.), and to pay off any outstanding debts or loans.

Meaningful Math

Relevance to real life

Each chapter begins with a two-page **Opener** that shows the relevance of math to daily life and real-life occupations. The example connects data and facts about the world to what students will learn later in the chapter—and ultimately answers the question "Why do I have to learn this?"

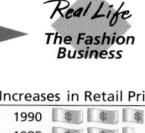

Real Life
The Fashion Business

Increases in Retail Prices

1990	
1985	
1980	
1975	
1970	

Each ▦ represents the retail price of an item in 1960

The amount you pay for any item in a store is called the **retail price.** The graph at the left shows how clothing prices have changed over the years. The amount the store paid for the item is called the **wholesale price.** The **markup** is the amount the store adds to the wholesale price to get the retail price. So, in words,

retail price = wholesale price + markup.

In this chapter, you will learn how to assign variables and write verbal and algebraic models to describe real-life situations as part of a problem-solving plan.

Using the Page

Encourage students to ask questions about the mathematics of real-life situations found in the text. For example, using the photo caption, students might ask how much of the $95 million dollars is a result of shoe sales and how much is a result of athletic apparel sales. They may question whether there were more sales of children's, teen's or adult clothing.

Introduce students to verbal models by asking them to use words to describe how a store's profit is related to its sales.

Multimedia Resources

🔘 Interactive CD-ROM Projects A project for this chapter combines print, animation, sound and video presentations to capture students' interest in Clothes Patterns. This interactive approach shows students how the math concepts and problem-solving strategies they are learning will be used in the future in dealing with important personal, national, and world issues.
The theme of Clothes Patterns correlates to examples and exercises on pages 52, 84, and 96.

🔘 Interactions: Real Math—Real Life
The theme of this chapter, The Fashion Business, correlates with an episode of **Interactions** which is a videodisc-based multimedia resource that connects middle school math topics with real-life careers. In each of the twelve episodes, students go on-site with a variety of professionals to witness real-life applications of the math they are studying. Students see math concepts and problem-solving strategies in a context that helps them connect what they are studying to the world outside the classroom. **Interactions** was developed by the Foundation for Advancements in Science and Education (FASE) and is published by D.C. Heath and Company.
The theme of the Fashion Business is continued throughout the chapter on pages 52, 60, 82, 84, and 96.

Performance Assessment Resource The **PACKETS® Program: Performance Assessment for Middle School Mathematics** was developed by Educational Testing Service and is published by D.C. Heath. **PACKETS** helps you assess your students' performances as they learn. You can use a wide variety of **PACKETS** Activity Units with this chapter because, in every activity, students will use ideas from all topic areas of mathematics. However, you can use the chart on page T16 to help you choose the **PACKETS** Activity Unit(s) that may fit best with this chapter.

49

Active Learning

Using the Chapter Opener

About the Page helps you present the real-life connections in the Chapter Openers. You'll also find references to using multimedia resources (*Interactions* videodiscs and *CD-ROM Projects*) and performance assessment (*The PACKETS® Program*).

Meeting individual needs

The **Meeting Individual Needs** notes provide suggestions for using concrete, visual, and abstract approaches and help you tailor the lesson to the different performance levels of your students.

INVESTIGATION Notes

Materials
Teaching Tools
   Algebra tiles, pp. T4, C5
Overhead Manipulatives Kit

The goal of this investigation is to help students visualize the idea of dividing each side of an equation by the same nonzero number.

▶ **MEETING INDIVIDUAL NEEDS**
For some students, solving the equation $2x = 6$ may be a mental math exercise. But for other students, the idea of grouping tiles may help them understand the concept of isolating the variable by using multiplication and division as modeled in Lesson 2.5. Note that the concept of removing tiles in order to divide is a reminder that division can be viewed as repeated subtraction.

Before assigning the exercises, be sure to demonstrate several examples of removing a group of tiles from each side. Remind students that the idea is to remove equal groups of tiles until only one variable tile remains.

EXTENSION
Ask students to create their own tile equation models.

Answers
1. $3x = 6$
   $x = 2$
2. $2x = 8$
   $x = 4$

3.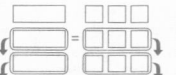

4.

5.

Materials Needed: algebra tiles

In this investigation, you will use algebra tiles to model and solve equations involving multiplication.

Example   *Using Algebra Tiles*

Model the equation $2x = 6$ with algebra tiles. Then use the tiles to solve the equation. Finally, check your solution.

Solution

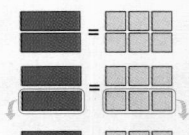

Original equation: $2x = 6$

To isolate x, divide each side into 2 groups and remove one group from each side.

Solution is $x = 3$.

You can check that $x = 3$ is a solution as follows.

$$2x = 6 \qquad \text{Write original equation.}$$
$$2(3) \overset{?}{=} 6 \qquad \text{Substitute 3 for } x.$$
$$6 = 6 \qquad x = 3 \text{ is a solution. } ✔ \qquad ■$$

Exercises

In Exercises 1 and 2, an equation has been modeled and solved with algebra tiles. Write the equation and its solution. Then check the solution. See margin.

1.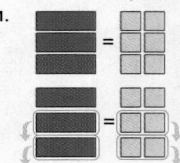

2.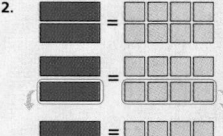

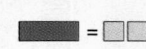

In Exercises 3–6, use algebra tiles to model and solve the equation.   For models, see margin.

3. $2x = 10$ 5   4. $3n = 9$ 3   5. $4y = 12$ 3   6. $2b = 12$ 6

6.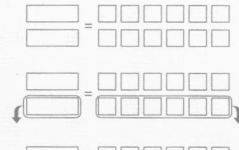

Active Learning

Starting with investigation

Several **Lesson Investigations** per chapter let students explore new concepts in a concrete, hands-on way before learning them formally in subsequent lessons.

2.5 Solving Equations: Multiplication or Division

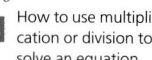

What you should learn:

Goal 1 How to use multiplication or division to solve an equation

Goal 2 How to use equations to solve real-life problems

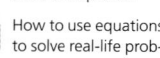

Why you should learn it:

You can use multiplication or division to solve equations that model real-life situations, such as finding the hourly rate for baby-sitting.

Goal 1 Using Multiplication or Division

In Lesson 2.4 you learned how to use addition or subtraction to solve an equation. In this lesson you will learn how to use multiplication or division to solve an equation.

> **Multiplication and Division Properties of Equality**
>
> Multiplying both sides of an equation by the same nonzero number or dividing both sides of an equation by the same nonzero number produces an equivalent equation.

Example 1 *Solving Equations*

Solve the equations **a.** $5x = 20$ and **b.** $12 = \frac{n}{4}$.

Solution

a. $5x = 20$ *Rewrite original equation.*

   $\frac{5x}{5} = \frac{20}{5}$ *Divide both sides by 5.*

   $x = 4$ *Simplify.*

The solution is 4. Check this in the original equation.

b. $12 = \frac{n}{4}$ *Rewrite original equation.*

   $4 \cdot 12 = 4 \cdot \frac{n}{4}$ *Multiply both sides by 4.*

   $48 = n$ *Simplify.*

The solution is 48. Check this in the original equation. ∎

In Example 1, notice that you can simplify a fraction that has a **common** factor in its numerator and denominator. Here are two other examples.

Fraction	Factor	Divide	Simplify
$\frac{6}{4}$	$\frac{2 \cdot 3}{2 \cdot 2}$	$\frac{2 \cdot 3}{2 \cdot 2}$	$\frac{3}{2}$
$\frac{3x}{3}$	$\frac{3 \cdot x}{3}$	$\frac{3 \cdot x}{3}$	$\frac{x}{1}$ or x

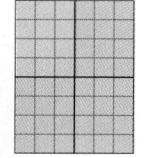

This is an area model for part b of Example 1. One-fourth of the area is 12. The entire area is 48.

2.5 • Solving Equations: Multiplication or Division **71**

PACING the Lesson

Suggested Number of Days
Basic/Average 2   **Above Average** 1
Advanced 1

PLANNING the Lesson

Lesson Plan 2.5, p. 13

ORGANIZER

Starters (reproduced below)
  Problem of the Day 2.5, p. 5
  Warm-Up Exercises 2.5, p. 5
Lesson Resources
  Math Log, p. 8
  Technology, pp. 9, 10
  Answer Masters 2.5, pp. 31, 32
  Extra Practice Copymaster 2.5, p. 13
  Reteaching Copymaster 2.5, p. 13
  Calculator
Special Populations
  Suggestions, Teacher's Edition, p. 48D

LESSON Notes

Point out how the Golden Rule of Equality applies here for multiplication and division. That is, if we multiply (or divide) one side of an equation by a number (a nonzero number for division), then an equivalent equation is produced when we multiply (or divide) the other side by the same number.

Example 1

In the Warm-Up Exercises, we used mental math to solve equations similar to these examples. Stress the importance of using algebra to solve simple equations now. Later, we will encounter more complex equations in which having equation-solving skills will really pay off. Also, note the use of the fraction bar to indicate division. Discuss the "—" versus "÷".

Make sure that students recognize that canceling works because:

$$\frac{2 \cdot 3}{2 \cdot 2} = \frac{2}{2} \cdot \frac{3}{2} = 1 \cdot \frac{3}{2} = \frac{3}{2}$$

Have students complete the following exercises and record their work in their journal using the same headings as found at the bottom of page 71.

a. $\frac{8}{6}$ **b.** $\frac{10}{4}$ **c.** $\frac{4x}{8}$

d. $\frac{16a}{4}$ **e.** $\frac{12y}{18}$ **f.** $\frac{14x}{8}$

"What you should learn" and "Why you should learn it"

Each lesson begins with objectives that spell out the point of the lesson and the usefulness of the material in real life.

Organizing the lesson

The **Organizer** helps you plan each lesson, with ideas for starter exercises, a list of resources, and hints on meeting the needs of diverse populations.

STARTER: Problem of the Day

Write five equations in the form $x + a = c$ whose solution is 10.

Answers will vary.

Also available as a copymaster, page 5

STARTER: Warm-Up Exercises

1. Use mental math to solve each equation.
   a. $3 + x = 10$ **b.** $m - 5 = 16$
   c. $4y = 16$ **d.** $6x = 24$
   e. $\frac{y}{2} = 6$ **f.** $\frac{m}{8} = 4$
   a. 7, b. 21, c. 4, d. 4, e. 12, f. 32

2. Model each product using an area model for multiplication.
   a. $y = 5 \cdot 4$ **b.** $m = 4 \cdot 3$ **c.** $x = 3 \cdot 5$
   a.   b.   c.

Also available as copymasters

Integration

Visual/graphical approach

Lessons incorporate visual models as needed to develop students' understanding of abstract concepts.

Teaching the lesson

Lesson Notes throughout the Teacher's Edition give suggestions for teaching the lesson, including alternate approaches, common student errors, and much more.

Meaningful Math

Modeling with math

Real-life connections help students see math as a language for modeling the real world. Throughout the program, many examples incorporate real data and data analysis techniques.

Integration

Problem solving

The text presents problem solving as a continuing process—one that helps students reach the goals of the lesson. A consistent problem-solving plan is used throughout the text.

After completing Example 2, have students create models for the type of after-school work they may be aware of.

Example 2

Go over the relationship that determines income for hourly work. Help students see why the relationship holds.

Vocabulary Alert!

Using units of measures to check solutions is called *unit analysis* or *dimensional analysis*. The quotient of two numbers having different units is called a *rate*. If the units are the same, the quotient is called a *ratio*.

Communicating
about **MATHEMATICS**

Challenge students to identify other expressions in which unit analysis is used.

Writing Prompt

Assign students the task of bringing to class a magazine photo of a favorite product. In class, give them five to ten minutes to create their own word problems that model information from the photo. Suggest that they refer to exercise 58 as an example.

Answers to Communicating
A–D. Situations vary.
A. Driving a truck at 50 mph for 3 hours
B. Riding on a train that is traveling at 80 km per hour for 2.5 hours
C. Buying 4 pounds of meat at $2.50 per pound
D. Buying 10 gallons of gas for a car that uses a gallon of gas for every 28 miles driven

Technology

EXAMPLE Converting Units of Volume

Use a calculator to convert 12,000 milliliters to gallons.

SOLUTION

From the table, you can see that 1 liter is equivalent to 1000 milliliters and is also approximately 0.264 gallons. Therefore, you can determine how many gallons are in a 12,000 milliliters by evaluating the following expression using your calculator

$$12{,}000 \text{ milliliters} \cdot \frac{1 \text{ liter}}{1000 \text{ milliliters}} \cdot \frac{0.264 \text{ gallons}}{1 \text{ liter}}$$

Note that when you evaluate this expression, the milliliters and liters units cancel and the final answer is in gallons. To evaluate this expression, enter 12,000 ÷ 1000 × 0.264 = on your calculator. The display should show 3.168, which means that 12,000 milliliters is approximately 3.17 gallons. 9. The U.S., 100 km/hr ≈ 62.15 mph which means than approximately in Canada is about 2.85 mph less than in the U.S.

EXAMPLE Converting Units of Speed

Use a calculator to convert 25 meters per second to miles per hour.

SOLUTION In Exercises 1-10, answers vary slightly.
From the table, you can see that 1000 meters is equivalent to 1 kilometer and 1 kilometer is approximately 0.6214 miles. Also, you should know that there are 60 seconds in 1 minute and 60 minutes in 1 hour. Thus, to determine how many miles per hour is equivalent to 25 meters per second, evaluate the following expression using your calculator

$$\frac{25 \text{ meters}}{1 \text{ second}} \cdot \frac{1 \text{ kilometer}}{1000 \text{ meters}} \cdot \frac{0.6214 \text{ mile}}{1 \text{ kilometer}} \cdot \frac{60 \text{ seconds}}{1 \text{ minute}} \cdot \frac{60 \text{ minutes}}{1 \text{ hour}}$$

Note that after evaluating this expression, the only units that are left are miles per hour. To evaluate this expression, enter 25 ÷ 1000 × 0.6214 × 60 × 60 = on your calculator. The display should show 55.926, which means that 25 meters per second is approximately 55.93 miles per hour. 10. At Supermarket B, 2.5 kilograms per dollar = 5.51 pounds per dollar. You get 1/2 pound more for the same price.

EXERCISES
In Exercises 1–6, use a calculator to perform the unit conversion. Round answers to two decimal places.

1. 15 feet to meters ≈ 4.57 m
2. 32 quarts to gallons 8 gal
3. 5 ounces to grams ≈ 142.86 grams
4. 15,000 millimeters to feet ≈ 49.23 ft
5. 14 pints to liters ≈ 6.62 liters
6. 4.5 kilograms to ounces ≈ 157.5 oz
7. 18 meters per second to miles per hour ≈ 40.27 mph
8. 110 miles per hour to kilometers per hour ≈ 176.99 km/hr
9. In the United States, the maximum speed limit is 65 miles per hour. In Canada, the maximum speed limit is 100 kilometers per hour. In which country can you drive the fastest? Explain your reasoning.
10. At Supermarket A, the price of a product is 5 pounds per dollar. At Supermarket B, the price of the same product is 2.5 kilograms per dollar. At which supermarket do you get the best buy? Explain your reasoning.

10 Technology Using Calculators and Computers

D. C. Heath and Company

72 Chapter 2

Goal 2 **Modeling Real Life with Equations**

Real Life
Baby-Sitting

In 1991, 2000 eighth-grade students were surveyed about after-school work. The 4 most common types of work were lawn work, restaurant work, newspaper deliveries, and baby-sitting. (Source: Teacher Magazine, May/June 1991)

Example 2 *Using an Equation as a Real-Life Mo*

You are baby-sitting for a neighbor. You arrive at 3:30 P.M. a leave at 8:00 P.M. Your neighbor pays you $13.50. How muc you get paid per hour?

Solution From 3:30 to 8:00 is a total of 4.5 hours.

Verbal Model	Total time	·	Hourly rate	=	Total pay

Labels Total time = 4.5 (b
Hourly rate = x (dollars per
Total pay = 13.5 (do

Algebraic Model $4.5 \cdot x = 13.5$
$\frac{4.5x}{4.5} = \frac{13.5}{4.5}$
$x = 3$

You got paid $3 per hour. You can check this by multiplying see that 4.5(3) = 13.5.

Problem Solving: Checking Solutions Using Unit Analysis
When you are solving real-life problems that involve divisio be sure to check that your units of measure make sense. Fo instance, you can check that the units of measure in Examp make sense as follows.

$$4.5 \text{ hours} \cdot \frac{3 \text{ dollars}}{\text{hour}} = 13.5 \text{ dollars}$$

Communicating *about* **MATHEMATICS**

▷ **SHARING IDEAS about the Lesson**

Unit Analysis Each of the following expressions was take from a real-life situation. Simplify the expression, statin the units for the simplified result.

A. $\frac{50 \text{ miles}}{\text{hour}} \cdot 3 \text{ hours}$ 150 miles
B. $\frac{80 \text{ kilometers}}{\text{hour}} \cdot 2.5 \text{ hours}$ 200 kilomete
C. $\frac{2.5 \text{ dollars}}{\text{pound}} \cdot 4 \text{ pounds}$ 10 dollars
D. $\frac{28 \text{ miles}}{\text{gallon}} \cdot 10 \text{ gallons}$ 280 miles

For each of the above expressions, describe a real-life situ tion that the expression could represent. See margin.

72 Chapter **2** • Investigations in Algebra

OPTION: Extra Examples
Here are additional examples similar to Example 1.
Solving Equations
Solve the equations.

a. $15a = 45$ b. $\frac{a}{3} = 42$

Solution
a. $15a = 45$ Rewrite original equation.
$\frac{15a}{15} = \frac{45}{15}$ Divide both sides by 15.
$a = 3$ Simplify.
The solution is 3. Check this in the original equation.

b. $\frac{a}{3} = 42$ Rewrite original equation.
$3 \cdot \frac{a}{3} = 3 \cdot 42$ Multiply both sides by 3.
$a = 126$ Simplify.
The solution is 126. Check this in the original equation.

Communication and self-assessment

Communicating about Mathematics exercises and writing prompts in every lesson offer rich opportunities for sharing ideas and justifying reasoning. Throughout the program, math logs and math journals provide other opportunities for self-assessment and active involvement.

Active Learning

EXERCISES

Guided Practice

CHECK for Understanding

In your own words, state the Multiplication and Division Properties of Equality. Give an example of how the Division Property of Equality can be used. See margin.

P **2.** Give an example of how the Multiplication Property of Equality can be used. See margin.

In Exercises 4 and 5, state whether you would multiply or divide to solve the equation.

4. $6x = 54$ Divide by 6, or multiply by $\frac{1}{6}$

5. $\frac{x}{3} = 12$ Multiply by 3

6. **Problem Solving** Describe a real-life situation that can be modeled with an equation. Answers vary.

Independent Practice

In Exercises 7–10, write the equation as a verbal sentence. Then solve the equation. For verbal sentences, see margin.

7. $2x = 4$ 2

8. $3x = 21$ 7

9. $\frac{b}{2} = 3$ 6

10. $\frac{a}{3} = 3$ 9

In Exercises 11–34, solve the equation. Check your solution.

11. $4x = 16$ 4

12. $12y = 144$ 12

13. $56 = 7n$ 8

14. $6s = 48$ 8

15. $6 = \frac{x}{5}$ 30

16. $\frac{m}{2} = 2$ 4

17. $\frac{t}{8} = 9$ 72

18. $5y = 100$ 20

19. $2z = 50$ 25

20. $10a = 240$ 24

21. $\frac{b}{20} = 2$ 40

22. $16 = \frac{x}{4}$ 64

23. $\frac{n}{4} = 25$ 100

24. $\frac{m}{3} = 33$ 99

25. $5x = 625$ 125

26. $7s = 175$ 25

27. $6.3 = 3y$ 2.1

28. $5t = 6.5$ 1.3

29. $524 = \frac{a}{1}$ 524

30. $\frac{y}{6} = 345$ 2070

31. $\frac{z}{3.2} = 8$ 25.6

32. $\frac{t}{7.4} = 6$ 44.4

33. $4.8b = 36$ 7.5

34. $9.6x = 72$ 7.5

35. Sketch an area model for $\frac{x}{3} = 36$.

☿ **36.** Sketch an area model for $\frac{n}{5} = 20$.

35., 36. See Additional Answers.

In Exercises 37–44, use a calculator to solve the equation.

37. $456x = 1368$ 3

38. $824x = 1648$ 2

39. $23x = 966$ 42

40. $55x = 3025$ 55

41. $\frac{x}{9} = 1025$ 9225

42. $\frac{x}{8} = 624$ 4992

43. $\frac{x}{136} = 17$ 2312

44. $\frac{x}{189} = 19$ 3591

Geometry In Exercises 45–48, find the width of the rectangle.

45. 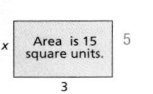 x | Area is 15 square units. | 5
3

46. 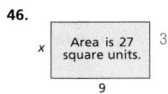 x | Area is 27 square units. | 3
9

47. x | Area is 38 square units. | 19
2

48. 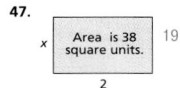 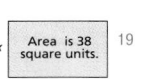 x | Area is 48 square units. | 8
6

More difficult exercises
Portfolio Opportunity

2.5 • Solving Equations: Multiplication or Division **73**

EXERCISE Notes

ASSIGNMENT GUIDE

Basic/Average:
Day 1: Ex. 7–21 odd, 35–39 odd, 45, 46, 49–51
Day 2: Ex. 52–55, 58, 59–63 odd

Above Average:
Ex. 25–33 odd, 36, 40, 42, 47, 48, 55–58, 63

Advanced: Ex. 25–33 odd, 36, 40, 42, 47, 48, 55–58, 63

Selected Answers: Ex. 1–6, 7–61 odd

Guided Practice

▶ **Ex. 1–6**
MATH JOURNAL
Use these exercises as a ten-minute journal activity at the end of the class period. Ask students to examine Example 2 for insight. For Exercises 2 and 3, students could create problems similar to Exercises 11–34.

Independent Practice

▶ **Ex. 7–10**
MENTAL MATH
Encourage students to try mental math for these exercises.
▶ **Ex. 11–34** For these exercises students should pay careful attention to the format of their solutions, following the format of Example 1. For exercises 30–34, encourage the use of a calculator.
▶ **Ex. 35, 36**
GROUP ACTIVITY
Assign these exercises as a two-minute in-class activity for small groups. A model is provided next to Example 1.
▶ **Ex. 37–44** Remind students that these exercises are marked with the calculator icon.

Answers
2. Answers vary. If $\frac{n}{3} = 6$, then $3 \cdot \frac{n}{3} = 3 \cdot 6$ and $n = 18$.
3. Answers vary. If $3n = 6$, then $\frac{3n}{3} = \frac{6}{3}$ and $n = 2$.
7. The product of 2 and x is 4.
8. The product of 3 and x is 21.
9. The quotient of b and 2 is 3.
10. The quotient of a and 3 is 3.

Lesson 2.5 **73**

Check for understanding

In **Guided Practice** exercises, students check their understanding by using their own words, writing their own examples, and describing a real-life situation.

Plenty of practice

Independent Practice reviews essential skills developed in the lesson and provides opportunities for self-checking using a visual approach, a graphical approach, or technology. **Extra Practice worksheets** provide further practice of skills developed in the lesson. For students who have not grasped the concepts, **Reteaching copymasters** provide additional opportunities to learn the essential concepts.

Connections within mathematics

Opportunities to integrate algebra, geometry, data analysis, and technology are found in both the lesson instruction and the exercises.

Integration

Alternative/ self-assessment

Every lesson provides **portfolio opportunities** —math logs, math journals, and writing prompts—as ongoing self-assessment tools.

Meaningful Math

Connections to real life

High-interest topics and rich data sets in exercises motivate students to do mathematics.

Integrating continued review

Integrated Review exercises help students fit new material into the larger picture of math by integrating mental math, estimation, probability, coordinate geometry, computation sense, and measurement.

Integrated Review

Review of customary units of weight, length, capacity, and time is provided in the Student Handbook, page 681.

Exploration and Extension

Students will need help setting up the proper expressions for these exercises. They may find the placing of the appropriate conversion factors confusing.

Portfolio Opportunity: Math Log

What happens to an equation when both sides are multiplied by 0? Explain why you cannot divide both sides of an equation by 0.

Also available as a copymaster, page 8, Ex. 5

In Exercises 49–54, write an equation that represents the sentence. **52.** $\frac{t}{6} = 10, 60$
Then solve the equation. **50.** $4d = 100, 25$

49. The number of football players f times 4 equals 28 players. $4f = 28, 7$

50. The product of the number of dancers d and 4 is 100 dancers.

51. The number of bicycles b divided by 12 equals 2 bicycles. $\frac{b}{12} = 2, 24$

52. The quotient of the number of telephones t and 6 is 10 telephones.

53. 5 comic books times x dollars is \$3.75. $5x = 3.75, 0.75$

54. The number of board games g times 20 dollars is 100 dollars. $20g = 100, 5$

☺ 55. *Basketball Court*   The area of a basketball court is 4700 square feet. The width of a basketball court is 50 feet.

   a. Write an equation that represents the area of a basketball court. $4700 = 50L$

   b. Solve the equation to find the length of a basketball court. 94 ft

Basketball   **In Exercises 56 and 57, use the following information.**   **56.** $24 \times 15.75 =$ Points scored this season

You play on your school's basketball team. This season your team played 24 games. You averaged 15.75 points per game.

☺ 56. Use the number of games played and your points-per-game average to write a verbal model that represents the points you scored this season.

☺ 57. Write an algebraic model that represents your total points scored this season. Then solve the equation to find your total. $24 \times 15.75 = t, 378$

☺ 58. *Rollerblading*   You rollerblade 5 days a week. Each day you rollerblade the same distance in miles. How many miles a day do you rollerblade if you rollerblade a total of 20.5 miles in 5 days? 4.1

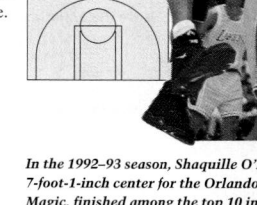

In the 1992–93 season, Shaquille O'N 7-foot-1-inch center for the Orlando Magic, finished among the top 10 in ing for his first season. O'Neal score points per game, ranking eighth.

Integrated Review   *Making Connections within Mathematics*

Computing with Measures   **In Exercises 59–62, perform the indicated operation.**

59. 1 hr 50 min + 37 min 2 hr 27 min

60. 20 lb − (3 lb 4 oz + 1 lb 14 oz) 14 lb 14 o

61. $3\frac{1}{2}$ yd ÷ 6 $\frac{7}{12}$ yd = 21 in. = 1 ft 9 in.

62. 126 gal ÷ 8 $15\frac{3}{4}$ gal = 15 gal 3 qt

Exploration and Extension

Measurement Sense   **In Exercises 63 and 64, perform the indicated conversion.**

☺ 63 Convert 4.5 dollars per pound to cents per ounce. $\frac{28.125\ \text{cents}}{\text{ounce}}$

☺ 64 Convert 55 miles per hour to feet per second. $\frac{80.6\ \text{feet}}{\text{second}}$

Extending the lesson

Exploration and Extension exercises ask all students to go beyond the lesson material in interesting ways.

spreadsheet is a computer program that creates tables. The following ample shows how a spreadsheet can be used to help solve a real-life oblem.

Example *Creating a Wage Table*

ake a table that shows your total pay for working from 1 to 8 hours at urly rates ranging from $2.00 per hour to $4.50 per hour.

lution The table is shown below.

Hourly Rate

	$2.00	$2.50	$3.00	$3.50	$4.00	$4.50
1.0	$2.00	$2.50	$3.00	$3.50	$4.00	$4.50
1.5	$3.00	$3.75	$4.50	$5.25	$6.00	$6.75
2.0	$4.00	$5.00	$6.00	$7.00	$8.00	$9.00
2.5	$5.00	$6.25	$7.50	$8.75	$10.00	$11.25
3.0	$6.00	$7.50	$9.00	$10.50	$12.00	$13.50
3.5	$7.00	$8.75	$10.50	$12.25	$14.00	$15.75
4.0	$8.00	$10.00	$12.00	$14.00	$16.00	$18.00
4.5	$9.00	$11.25	$13.50	$15.75	$18.00	$20.25
5.0	$10.00	$12.50	$15.00	$17.50	$20.00	$22.50
5.5	$11.00	$13.75	$16.50	$19.25	$22.00	$24.75
6.0	$12.00	$15.00	$18.00	$21.00	$24.00	$27.00
6.5	$13.00	$16.25	$19.50	$22.75	$26.00	$29.25
7.0	$14.00	$17.50	$21.00	$24.50	$28.00	$31.50
7.5	$15.00	$18.75	$22.50	$26.25	$30.00	$33.75
8.0	$16.00	$20.00	$24.00	$28.00	$32.00	$36.00

ou can use the table to find your total pay. For instance, if you work 5.5 urs at $3.50 per hour, then your total pay is $19.25 ■

ercises

Make a table that shows the distance traveled for several different times and speeds.
Tables vary.

2. Make a table that shows the areas of several
rectangles of different widths and heights.
Tables vary.

Materials
A spreadsheet computer program or a TI-82

The table shown for total pay can be demonstrated using a computer spreadsheet, or the
TABLE feature on a TI-82 overhead graphing
calculator.
On the TI-82, set
$Y_1 = 2X$,
$Y_2 = 2.5X$,
$Y_3 = 3X$,
$Y_4 = 3.5X$,
$Y_5 = 4X$, and
$Y_6 = 4.5X$.
Select TblSet, set TblMin = 1.0, ΔTbl = 0.5,
and the other entries Auto.
Select TABLE to see parts of the wage table
visually displayed.

For the exercises, help students to correctly
format and label the table. Students will need
help in getting started—choosing times and
distances, and so on.

Have students discuss any previous connection to a similar spreadsheet table they might
recall, for example, multiplication tables, IRS
tax tables, banking interest rate tables, and so
on.

You could verbally connect this type of table
to a matrix, a concept that will be discussed
later.

The *copy, fill down,* and/or *fill right* features
of spreadsheet software enable you to create
tables without having to enter each entry by
hand. Familiarize yourself with the spreadsheet software before trying this activity with
your students. After entering the formulas in
the second row, show students how to use the
fill down feature to create each column of the
table. To create column B, highlight cells B2
through B16 and choose the *fill down* command from the edit menu.

	A	B	C	D
1		2	2.5	...
2	1	=2*A2	=2.5*A2	...
3	1.5	=2*A3	=2.5*A3	...
4	2	=2*A4	=2.5*A4	...

Ask students how they could adapt the
spreadsheet so that it calculated the total pay
for 1 to 8 hours at hourly rates from $5.00 to
$8.00 per hour. Have students suggest other
changes they could make to the spreadsheet.

Another spreadsheet application is available
on page 11 of the Technology supplement to
be used with Lesson 2.6.

Use of technology

Opportunities for using
technology appear throughout the text in lessons, exercises, and special features such as
the one shown. The lessons
and exercises provide a
balance of calculator skills
and mental math skills.
Technology features use
scientific calculators, graphing
calculators, and computers
to teach students how to use
technology as a tool in
applications.

Resources that support a variety of teaching and learning styles

TEACHER'S RESOURCE PACKAGE

- **Teaching Tools: Transparencies and Copymasters**
  Transparencies of coordinate grids, geoboards, algebra tiles, fraction strips, models, etc. Copymasters of the transparencies and of diagrams for use in investigations and exercises.

- **Reteaching Copymasters**
  Teacher-directed and independent activities.

- **Extra Practice Copymasters**
  One worksheet per lesson, with additional exercises similar to those in the Student Text.

- **Formal Assessment**
  Quizzes, Mid-Chapter Tests (2 forms), Chapter Tests (3 forms), and Cumulative Tests.

- **Alternative Assessment**
  Projects, Group and Individual Assessments, Partner Quizzes, and suggestions for assessing student work.

- **Lesson Plans**

- **Math Log**
  A tool for alternative assessment.

- **Problem of the Day**
  Puzzles, brain teasers, and problem solving. One activity per lesson.

- **Enrichment Projects**
  Independent research and projects that extend classroom learning.

- **Answer Masters**

- **Warm-Up Exercises**

ADDITIONAL RESOURCES

- **Teacher's Edition**
  Includes comprehensive teaching strategies in a wrap-around format.

- **Complete Solutions Manual**

- **Technology: Using Calculators and Computers**
  Teacher's Guide and Copymasters for using calculators, graphing calculators, spreadsheets, and drawing programs.

- **60 Color Transparencies for Real-Life Applications**

- **Overhead Manipulatives Kit**
  Algebra tiles and number counters to model integers.

- **Computerized Testing Program**
  For IBM and Macintosh. Teacher's Guide included.

- **Interactions: Real Math— Real Careers**
  Videodisc-based resource that connects math to actual careers and on-the-job problem solving.

- **Interactive CD-ROM Projects**
  Interactive projects for solving real-world problems using multimedia. Correlated to each chapter.

The PACKETS® Program: Performance Assessment for Middle School Mathematics

The PACKETS® Program: Performance Assessment for Middle School Mathematics was developed and extensively field tested by Educational Testing Service (ETS) and is published by D.C. Heath. It is a performance assessment program that links assessment and instruction.

You can use a wide variety of PACKETS Activity Units with each chapter because, in every activity, students use ideas from all the topic areas of mathematics. However, you can use the chart at right to help you choose the PACKETS Activity Units that may fit best with your program.

Using the PACKETS tools, you can assess your students' performance as they learn. Students' learning is sparked by a math-rich newspaper and a variety of real-life activities that encourage them to use higher-level thinking, reasoning, and problem-solving strategies. In the process, students learn how to evaluate and revise their own work. And they enjoy it!

PROJECTS	Geometry and Measurement	Whole Numbers and Computation	Fractions and Decimals	Ratios, Rates, and Proportions	Functions, Algebra, and Graphing	Data Analysis, Probability, Statistics	Continuity and Change	Discrete Math, Logic, and Proof
PACKETS Post								
Million Dollar Getaway	✔	✔	✔					
Bike-a-thon	✔	✔					✔	✔
Thanksgiving Dinner			✔					✔
Dream Quilt	✔			✔				
Back to the Future					✔	✔	✔	✔
One Block Away	✔							✔
Walkabouts		✔	✔			✔		
Making Money				✔	✔	✔		
PACKETS Sun								
Shape	✔			✔			✔	
Arranging Booths	✔		✔					✔
Snakes Alive!		✔			✔	✔		
Leapin' Lizards	✔							✔
You Count		✔		✔		✔		
Resizing Recipes	✔		✔		✔		✔	
Mousetrap Tractor		✔	✔	✔				
CD Toss				✔	✔	✔		
PACKETS Times								
The Inheritance			✔	✔	✔		✔	
Fast Track				✔	✔	✔	✔	
Jolly Green Giant???	✔			✔			✔	
Easy Does It			✔	✔	✔	✔		
Smart Shadows	✔							✔
Singing Balloons		✔			✔	✔		
Better Bouillon Boxes	✔	✔	✔					
Walking Papers		✔						✔

The table is headed **BIG IDEAS IN MATH**.

Interactions:
Real Math—Real Careers™

Developed by FASE, the Foundation for Advancements in Science and Education

Interactions: Real Math—Real Careers™ is an easy-to-use, interactive tool that links math concepts to real-world applications. *Interactions* videodiscs are for teachers and students who are just beginning to use technology as well as those already skilled in its use.

Each of the six *Interactions* modules contains two episodes that are each approximately twelve minutes in length. The episodes focus on professionals who take students "behind the scenes" to share some of the excitement and challenges related to their careers.

Interactions worksheets engage students in reality-based problem-solving exercises using the information in the videos. The chart below shows the math topics involved in the activities for each episode.

Episode	Fractions	Decimals	Powers of Ten	Percent	Ratios	Geometry	Statistics	Measurements	Patterns & Functions
Solar Energy				✔		✔		✔	
Water Resources	✔			✔	✔	✔	✔	✔	✔
Endangered Species				✔	✔	✔	✔	✔	
Recycling	✔	✔		✔		✔			✔
Digital Communication			✔		✔		✔	✔	
Making Music	✔				✔				✔
The Fashion Business		✔		✔	✔	✔	✔	✔	✔
Coaching an Athlete		✔		✔	✔		✔		✔
Designing a Product	✔	✔		✔		✔	✔	✔	
Building a Rover				✔	✔	✔			✔
Voyage to Mars	✔	✔		✔	✔	✔		✔	
Deep Sea Missions				✔	✔	✔		✔	

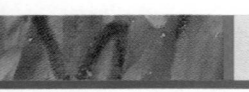

SUGGESTED PACING CHART

* Suggestions for omitting lessons are given at the beginning of each chapter. Adjust the choice of lessons to meet your local requirements.

	Basic/Average Course		Above Average Course		Advanced Course	
	72 lessons*	170 days	110 lessons*	170 days	117 lessons	170 days
Chapter 1 *Exploring Patterns*	6 lessons	15 days	8 lessons	11 days	8 lessons	11 days
Chapter 2 *Investigations in Algebra*	8 lessons	19 days	9 lessons	12 days	9 lessons	12 days
Chapter 3 *Modeling Integers*	8 lessons	19 days	8 lessons	12 days	8 lessons	11 days
Chapter 4 *Exploring the Language of Algebra*	5 lessons	12 days	8 lessons	12 days	8 lessons	11 days
Chapter 5 *Exploring Data and Graphs*	6 lessons	13 days	8 lessons	13 days	8 lessons	13 days
Chapter 6 *Exploring Number Theory*	4 lessons	10 days	4 lessons	7 days	9 lessons	12 days
Chapter 7 *Rational Numbers and Percents*	5 lessons	12 days	9 lessons	12 days	9 lessons	12 days
Chapter 8 *Proportion, Percent, and Probability*	6 lessons	14 days	8 lessons	13 days	8 lessons	11 days
Chapter 9 *Real Numbers and Inequalities*	4 lessons	10 days	8 lessons	11 days	8 lessons	11 days
Chapter 10 *Geometry Concepts and Spatial Thinking*	6 lessons	14 days	9 lessons	14 days	9 lessons	12 days
Chapter 11 *Congruence, Similarity, and Transformations*	4 lessons	9 days	9 lessons	16 days	9 lessons	16 days
Chapter 12 *Measurements in Geometry*	7 lessons	16 days	8 lessons	14 days	8 lessons	14 days
Chapter 13 *Exploring Linear Equations*	0 lessons	0 days	8 lessons	13 days	8 lessons	11 days
Chapter 14 *Exploring Data and Polynomials*	3 lessons	7 days	6 lessons	10 days	8 lessons	13 days

Notes on Pacing

The Pacing Chart on page T18 must be considered as only a suggestion that can help you tailor the pace of *Windows to Algebra and Geometry* to the special needs of your class.

Each chapter has an Overview with a chapter pacing chart. Refer to those charts for suggestions on which lessons to omit and the number of days to spend on each lesson. These suggestions were made with a hypothetical class in mind. You must select the lessons and timing that suit the needs of your class.

Basic/Average Course

The pacing scheme for this course provides for 72 two-day lessons. The suggestions for this ability level try to strike a balance between geometry and some of the more mechanical skills of basic algebra. You should decide which way you need to tip this balance. For example, if you teach *Windows to Algebra and Geometry* to a middle school population who will likely take a full geometry course later on, you may wish to devote more days to the basic algebra skills in Chapters 6 and 7, omitting transformations, some of the solid geometry in Chapter 12, the more sophisticated data analysis topics, and so on. However, if you teach the text to a high school population for whom this course may be their only exposure to geometry, you may wish to tip the balance toward geometry and offer your students ready access to calculators to supplement any shortfall in mechanical skills.

Above Average Course

The pacing scheme for this course is similar to that suggested for the advanced course. However, some additional two-day lessons are suggested to allow more time for coordinate geometry, multi-step equations, exploring percent equations, probability simulations, and some of the geometry topics in Chapter 10.

Advanced Course

In general, this course consists of one-day lessons. However, two-day lessons have been suggested for the more sophisticated data analysis topics in Chapters 5 and 14, transformations and problem solving with geometry and trigonometry in Chapter 11, and some of the solid geometry in Chapter 12. Two-day lessons may also be appropriate for some lessons that are preceded by a lab.

Special Populations

Also see the article on special populations in the Professional Handbook at the end of this book.

Students Acquiring English Proficiency

These students may need help mastering the key mathematics vocabulary and understanding word problems. Pair these students with students who know English and place them in supportive cooperative learning groups.

Students with Various Learning Styles

These are students who have various learning disabilities and various learning styles: auditory learners, tactile learners, and kinesthetic learners. Suggestions include using manipulatives, acting out concepts, and referring to the alternative teaching strategies suggested with some lessons.

Underachieving Students

These students do not have any diagnosed learning disabilities, but they are not performing well and may be in danger of dropping out. Their attendance may be poor. They need motivation and encouragement to build upon whatever mathematics they know. For these students, the engaging writing style, real-life applications, use of technology, and numerous opportunities for hands-on learning enable them to actively and successfully do the mathematics.

Gifted and Talented Students

These students will enjoy the rich variety of high-interest topics in the Student Edition and activities provided in the Teacher's Resource Package, such as Enrichment Projects, Alternative Assessment, Technology, and multimedia. The Teacher's Edition also highlights the more challenging problems, makes references to various ways to extend problems, and provides tips on extending exercises sets, such as Exploration and Extension.

WINDOWS

TO ALGEBRA AND GEOMETRY

AN INTEGRATED APPROACH

Roland E. Larson

Laurie Boswell

Timothy D. Kanold

Lee Stiff

HEATH

D.C. Heath and Company
Lexington, Massachusetts / Toronto, Ontario

About the Cover

Each chapter has a theme which is used in the chapter introduction, in several examples and exercises throughout the chapter, and for the last page of the Chapter Review. Water resources is the theme for Chapter 7 (see pages 292, 293, 307, 331, and 340) and it is also the theme of the cover.

Acknowledgements

Editorial Development Jane Bordzol, Anne M. Collier,
   Rita Campanella, Tamara Gorman, Susan E. Kipp,
   Albert S. Jacobson, James O'Connell, George J. Summers
Marketing Jo DiGiustini
Advertising Phyllis Lindsay
Design Jane Bigelow-Orner, Robert Botsford, Carmen Johnson
Production Pamela Tricca

D. C. Heath is committed to publishing educational materials that accurately and fairly reflect the diversity of all peoples; that promote a better understanding of one another; that acknowledge the contributions of all groups; and that avoid stereotypes, ridicule, and bias. Our instructional materials foster an appreciation of differences in culture, religion, age, gender, ability, and socio-economic background. Our products promote respect for the intrinsic worth of all individuals and prepare people to live and work together in a diverse world. D. C. Heath believes that in order to flourish in a changing world, we must value diversity.

Roland E. Larson is a professor of mathematics at the Behrend College of Pennsylvania State University at Erie. He is a member of NCTM and author of many well-known high school and college mathematics textbooks, including D. C. Heath's *Calculus*, *Pre-Calculus*, and *Algebra-Geometry* series. He is a pioneer of interactive textbooks, and his calculus textbook is published in a CD-ROM version.

Laurie Boswell is a mathematics teacher at Profile Junior-Senior High School in Bethlehem, New Hampshire. She is active in NCTM and local mathematics associations and is a frequent convention speaker. A 1986 recipient of the Presidential Award for Excellence in Mathematics Teaching, she is also the 1992 Tandy Technology Scholar and the 1991 recipient of the Richard Balomenos Mathematics Education Service Award, presented by the New Hampshire Association of Teachers of Mathematics. She is also an author of D. C. Heath's *Geometry*.

Timothy D. Kanold is Director of Mathematics and Science and a teacher at Adlai Stevenson High School in Lincolnshire, Illinois. He is the 1986 recipient of the Presidential Award for Excellence in Mathematics Teaching, the 1991 recipient of the Outstanding Young Alumni Award from Illinois State University, and the 1993 recipient of ICTM's Outstanding Leadership Award. A member of NCTM, he served on NCTM's *Professional Standards for Teaching Mathematics* Commission and served as a speaker for *New Dimensions in Leadership.* He has published numerous articles on effective teaching practices and is a co-author of D. C. Heath's *Algebra* series.

Lee Stiff is an associate professor of mathematics education in the College of Education and Psychology of North Carolina State University at Raleigh and has taught mathematics at the high school and middle school levels. He was a member of both the NCTM Board of Directors and the writing team of NCTM's *Professional Standards for Teaching Mathematics.* He is the 1992 recipient of the W. W. Rankin Award for Excellence in Mathematics Education presented by the North Carolina Council of Teachers of Mathematics. He is an author of D. C. Heath's *Algebra-Geometry* series and a contributing author to *Heath Mathematics CONNECTIONS.*.

Linda Bailey
Putman City Schools
Oklahoma City, OK

David S. Bradley
Thomas Jefferson Junior High School
Kearns, UT

Blanche S. Brownley
Mathematics, Science, Technology Initiative
District of Columbia Public Schools

John A. Carter
West Chicago Community High School
West Chicago, IL

Susan Currier
Pioneer Valley Regional School
Northfield, MA

Anthony C. Dentino
Plainfield School District
Plainfield, NJ

Susan E. Ewart
Centreville Middle School
Centreville, MD

John Paul Fox
Clinton Middle School
Columbus, OH

Gregory J. Fry and Keith Tuominen
White Bear Lake High School
White Bear Lake, MN

Sue D. Garriss
Millbrook Senior High School
Raleigh, NC

Linda Gojak
Hawken School
Lyndhurst, OH

Leigh M. Graham
Awtrey Middle School
Cobb County, GA

Judy Hall
St. John School
Seattle, WA

Sandra A. Hinker
Marshfield Junior High School
Marshfield, WI

Audrey M. Johnson
Luke O'Toole Elementary School
Chicago, IL

Kathy Johnson
East Paulding Middle School
Dallas, GA

Lieshen Johnson
Schimelpfenig Middle School
Plano, TX

Scott Hemingway Killam
Carter Junior High School
Arlington, TX

Charlene M. Kincaid
Gulf Breeze High School
Gulf Breeze, FL

Marsha W. Lilly
Alief Independent School District
Alief, TX

Christine S. Losq
The Whole Math™ Project
Palo Alto, CA

Veronica G. Meeks
Western Hills High School
Fort Worth, TX

Joyce E. Nitz
Kellogg Middle School
Portland, OR

Eileen Paul and Ellen Silbert
Adlai E. Stevenson High School
Lincolnshire, IL

Clementine Sherman
Dade County Public Schools
Miami, FL

Robyn Silbey
Math Specialist
Montgomery County Public Schools, MD

Tomas M. Tobiasen
Parsippany–Troy Hills Township Schools
Parsippany, NJ

Ricardo Torres
M. B. Lamar Middle School
Laredo, TX

Linda Tucci
Rice Avenue Middle School
Girard, PA

Marianne Weber
Middle School Mathematics Consultant
Chesterfield, MO

Betsy L. Wiens
Washburn Rural Middle School
Topeka, KS

To the Students

Mathematics evolved over thousands years in many stages. The early stages were concerned with using mathematics to answer questions about real life. We wrote this book in much the same way. We centered the concepts around the real-life use of mathematics.

As more and more mathematics was discovered, people began to collect and categorize the different rules, formulas, and properties. This took place independently in many different parts of the world: Africa, Asia, Europe, North America, and South America. The mathematics that we use today is a combination of the work of literally thousands of people.

As you study our book, be sure you understand the value and purpose of what you are learning. Knowing how and why a concept is used helps you master it. That's why we begin each lesson explaining what you should learn and why you should learn it.

Remember, math is not a spectator sport It's a valuable tool you can use in everyday life, and the more you use it the more useful it becomes!

Roland E. Larson

Laurie Boswell

Timothy D. Kanold

Lee Stiff

Mathematics is more fun and more understandable when you can play around with mathematical ideas and discover how things work before you are told the formal definitions and rules. There are many opportunities in this text to explore mathematical ideas through hands-on investigations and using technology. The full-page investigations that precede lessons are listed below. In addition, shorter investigations are built into many of the lessons. Also listed below are the full-page technology activities.

Look through this list for things that interest you. Then find out how they are linked to mathematics.

People

Places

United States Facts

World Facts

Integrating Patterns and Relationships

In **Chapter 1**, students visualize and communicate a variety of patterns by use of words, tables, symbols, and graphs—setting the foundation for the study of algebra and geometry.

C Integrates Coordinate Geometry **D** Integrates Data Analysis or Probability
P/F Integrates Patterns and Functions

Using Problem Solving to Model Math in Real Life
Windows introduces you to a problem-solving plan for writing algebraic models—the major problem-solving strategy of the program. By introducing the plan early, problem solving becomes an integral part of every lesson.

Introducing the Coordinate Plane
Windows introduces the coordinate plane beginning in Lesson 3.8. It is a pictorial model to help you discover the patterns and relationships of algebra and geometry. Introducing the coordinate plane early prepares you for future study of mathematics.

A Variety of Problem-Solving Approaches
Windows provides many ways to look at problems: arithmetically, graphically, and algebraically using the problem-solving plan first introduced in **Lesson 2.8**. **Chapter 4** also provides opportunities for using other problem-solving skills, strategies, and tools—organizing and interpreting data in real life through graphs, charts, tables; and looking for patterns and relationships in algebra and geometry. Underlying all problem solving in the program is the appropriate use of technology.

Integrating Data Analysis
Windows integrates authentic data from a variety of real-life situations—making students informed citizens about their world. Beginning in Chapter 1, special **"Exploring Data"** lessons expose students to data presented in charts, tables, and graphs. **Chapter 5** provides students with more formal methods for interpreting data; **Chapter 14** develops further data-analysis techniques.

Emphasis on Communication
Communicating about Mathematics—a feature found in every lesson—offers opportunities for you to share your ideas about the lesson and to do cooperative learning activities.

C Integrates Coordinate Geometry **D** Integrates Data Analysis or Probability
P/F Integrates Patterns and Functions

Connections Across Content Strands

Windows provides connections within mathematics—between data analysis and probability, patterns and functions, algebra, geometry and coordinate geometry—and to other disciplines, such as social sciences, physical sciences, music, and many more.

Integrating Technology
Windows integrates technology, using scientific and graphing calculators, and computer drawing programs. Technology is integrated throughout the program in lessons, exercises, and features—allowing students to continually reinforce, explore, and discover mathematical concepts.

Portfolio/Journal Opportunities
Windows provides a variety of opportunities for students to take responsibility for their own learning: portofolio opportunities, writing activities and journal entries, research projects, and critical thinking questions. Additional suggestions for student portfolio performance can be found in the Teacher's Edition.

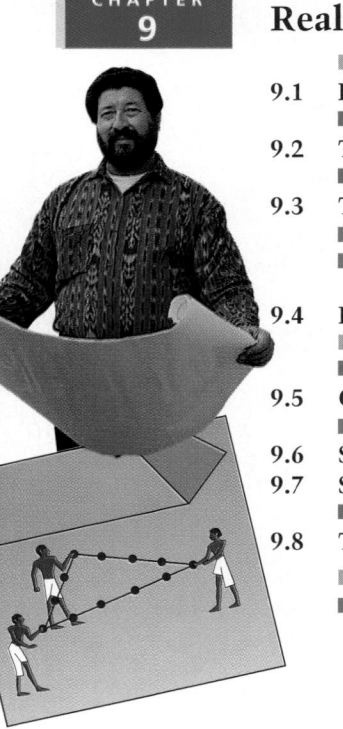

People of all Walks of Life
Windows celebrates the contributions of men and women past and present—not just in special features but as an integral part of problems and applications.

C Integrates Coordinate Geometry D Integrates Data Analysis or Probability
P/F Integrates Patterns and Functions

Career Interviews
Career Interviews, which feature people of various backgrounds who use math on the job, demonstrate the utility of math in daily life.

The Underpinnings of Plane Geometry
Chapter 10 gives students the tools necessary to describe geometric phenomena regardless of previous experiences with geometry. **Chapter 11** integrates two fundamental concepts in geometry —congruence and similarity—with the study of three types of transformations: line reflections, rotations, and translations.

C Integrates Coordinate Geometry D Integrates Data Analysis or Probability
P/F Integrates Patterns and Functions

CHAPTER 1 GOALS

Lesson	Pages	Goals	Meeting the NCTM Standards
1.1	2–5	1. Use numbers to identify and measure objects 2. Recognize and describe number patterns	Problem Solving, Communication, Connections, Patterns and Functions, Measurement
Lesson Investigation 1.2	6	Computation Practice	Communication, Computation and Estimation
1.2	7–10	1. Use the four basic number operations 2. Use multiplication models	Problem Solving, Communication, Connections, Number Relationships, Computation and Estimation, Technology, Patterns and Functions, Statistics
1.3	11–15	1. Use powers 2. Use square roots	Problem Solving, Communication, Reasoning, Connections, Number Relationships, Computation and Estimation, Technology, Patterns and Functions, Geometry, Measurement
Mixed Review	15	Review of arithmetic, algebra and geometry	Computation and Estimation, Technology, Patterns and Functions
Using a Calculator	16	Problem Solving: Using a *Guess, Check and Revise* Strategy	Problem Solving, Computation and Estimation, Technology, Geometry, Measurement
1.4	17–21	1. Use order of operations 2. Use order of operations on a calculator	Problem Solving, Communication, Reasoning, Connections, Computation and Estimation, Technology
Mid-Chapter Self-Test	22	Diagnose student weaknesses and remediate with correlated Reteaching Copymasters	Assessment
Lesson Investigation 1.5	23	Finding patterns	Problem Solving, Computation and Estimation, Patterns and Functions, Geometry, Measurement
1.5	24–27	1. Evaluate variable expressions 2. Use variable expressions in formulas to model real-life situations	Problem Solving, Communication, Reasoning, Connections, Computation and Estimation, Algebra
1.6	28–31	1. Use tables to organize data 2. Use graphs to model data visually	Problem Solving, Communication, Connections, Computation and Estimation, Patterns and Functions, Algebra, Statistics, Geometry, Measurement
Mixed Review	32	Review of arithmetic, algebra, and geometry	Computation and Estimation, Algebra
Career Interview	32	Robotics Engineer	Connections, Geometry
Lesson Investigation 1.7	33	Perimeter and Area	Patterns and Functions, Geometry, Measurement
1.7	34–37	1. Identify polygons and parts of polygons 2. Discover properties of polygons	Problem Solving, Communication, Reasoning, Connections, Patterns and Functions, Algebra, Geometry, Measurement
1.8	38–41	1. Use a calculator to discover number patterns 2. Use diagrams to discover number patterns in real-life situations	Communication, Connections, Computation and Estimation, Technology Patterns and Functions, Algebra
Chapter Summary	42	A restatement of what has been learned, why it has been learned, and how it fits into the structure of mathematics	Communication, Connections
Chapter Review	43–46	Review of concepts and skills learned in the chapter	Problem Solving, Connections
Chapter Test	47	Diagnose student weaknesses and remediate with correlated Reteaching Copymasters	Assessment

CHAPTER 1 ■ OVERVIEW

RESOURCES ORGANIZER

Lesson Pages	1.1 2–5	1.2 7–10	1.3 11–15	1.4 17–21	1.5 24–27	1.6 28–31	1.7 34–37	1.8 38–41
Lesson Plans	1	2	3	4	5	6	7	8
Problem of the Day	1	1	1	2	2	2	3	3
Warm-Up Exercises	1	1	1	2	2	2	3	3
Color Transparencies	—	2	—	—	3	4, 5	5, 6	—

Teaching Tools:
  Transparencies
  Copymasters
	—
	—
		T1
		C2
			—
			—
				T1
				C3, C4
					—
					—
						T1
						C2
							—
							—
								—
								—

Math Log	4	4	5	5	5	6	6	6
Technology	—	3	4	5	—	—	6	—
Answer Masters	1–3	4, 5	6–8	9	10	11–13	14	15–17
Extra Practice Copymasters	1	2	3	4	5	6	7	8
Reteaching Copymasters	1	2	3	4	5	6	7	8
Enrichment Projects	—	—	—	—	—	2, 3	4, 5	6, 7

Alternative Assessment:
  Projects
  Partner Quizzes
  Group Assessment
	15
	—
	—
		—
		—
		—
			15
			—
			—
				16
				44
				—
					—
					—
					—
						16
						—
						—
							—
							—
							59, 60
								—
								—
								—

Formal Assessment:
  Short Quizzes
  Tests
	—
	—
		1
		—
			—
			—
				2
				3, 4
					—
					—
						5
						—
							—
							—
								6
								7–15

Overhead Manipulatives Kit	—	—	—	—	—	—	—	—
Complete Solutions Manual	Includes step-by-step solutions for all exercises in the student text							
Computerized Test Bank	Creates customized tests that include graphics							
Interactive CD-ROM Project	Provides an interactive and interdisciplinary chapter project							

STARTERS

Problem of the Day

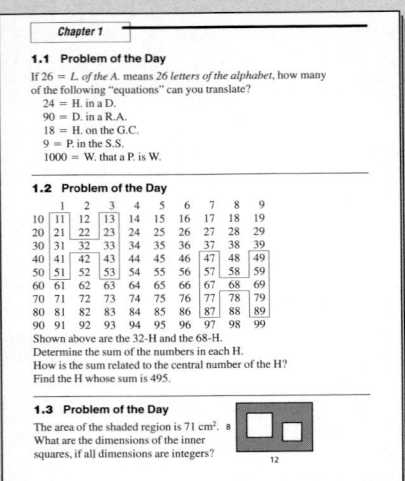

Warm-Up Exercises

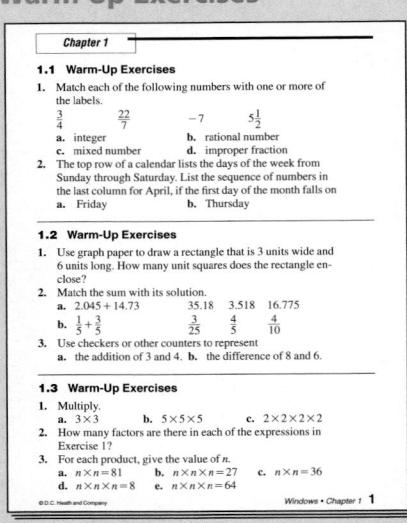

FOR TEACHERS

Answer Masters

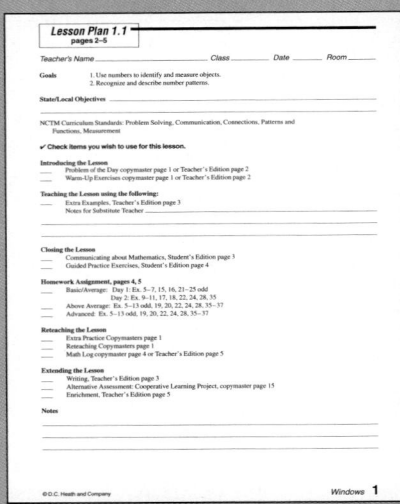

Lesson Plans

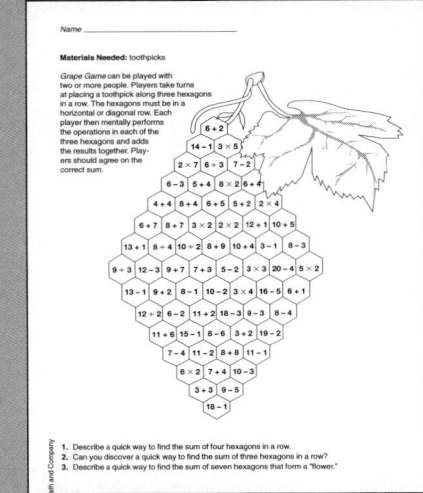

Teaching Tools

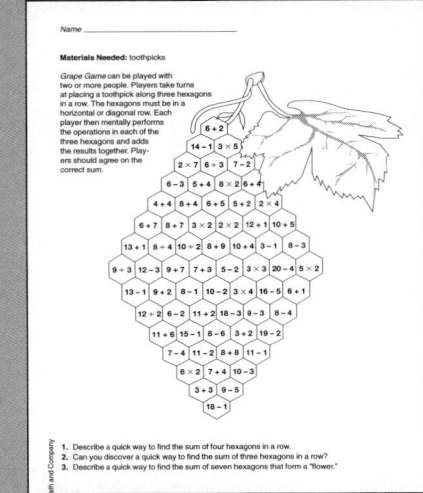

Teaching Tools includes:
Transparencies and Copymasters for classroom activities and study skills:

- Graph Paper
- Dot Paper (Geoboards)
- Algebra Tiles
- Number Counters
- Fraction Strips
- Models

REAL LIFE

Color Transparencies for Real-Life Applications

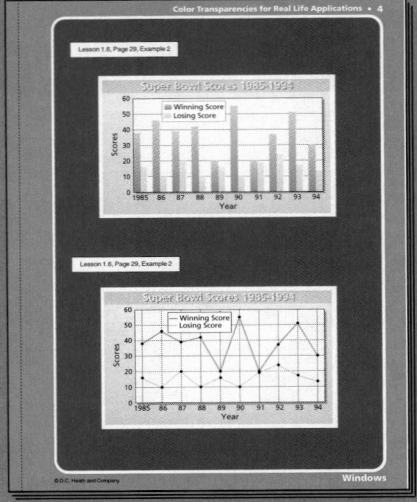

Technology: Using Calculators and Computers

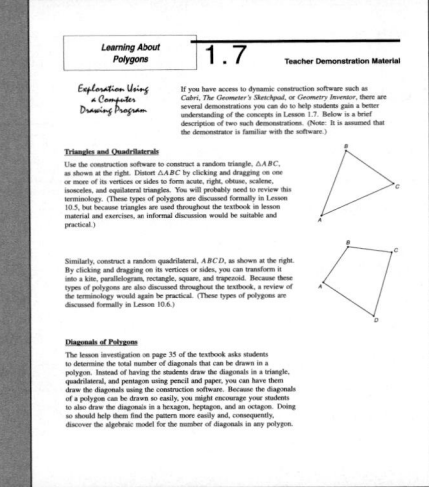

Also Available:

- Complete Solutions Manual
- Overhead Manipulatives Kit
- Computerized Testing Program

- **Interactive CD-ROM Projects**
  Interactive projects for solving real-world problems using multimedia

- **Interactions: Real Math–Real Careers**
  A videodisc–based resource that connects math to real careers and on-the-job problem solving

- **PACKETS® Performance Assessment for Middle School Mathematics**
  A program that links assessment and instruction

ASSESSMENT

Alternative Assessment

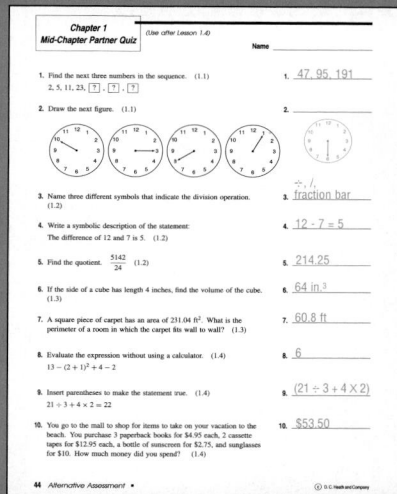

Alternative Assessment includes:
- Scoring Rubrics
- Portfolios
- Math Journals
- Projects
- Partner Quizzes
- Individual and Group Assessment

Formal Assessment

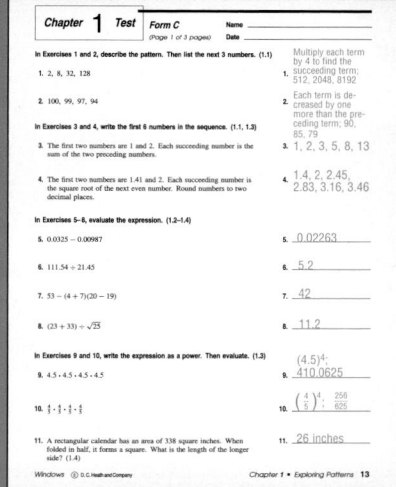

Formal Assessment includes:
- Short Quizzes (after every 2 lessons)
- Mid-Chapter Tests (2 forms)
- Chapter Tests (3 forms)
- Cumulative Tests (after every 3 Chapters)

MEETING INDIVIDUAL NEEDS

Extra Practice Copymasters

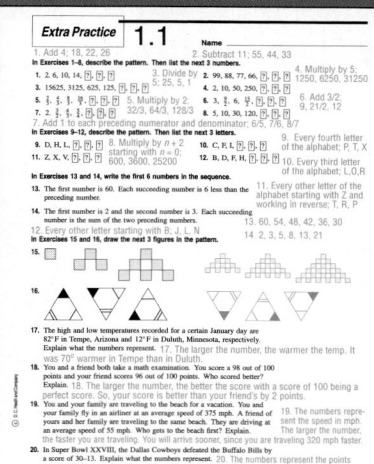

Reteaching Copymasters

Enrichment Projects

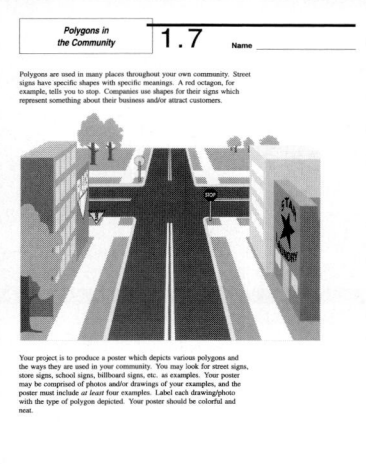

Math Log

Special Populations
Suggestions for providing equal access for:

Students Acquiring English Proficiency*
In Lesson 1.2, make sure that students know the vocabulary for the basic operations. It may be helpful to display a poster with this information.

Add

$3 + 5 = 8$

plus sum

Subtract

$8 - 5 = 3$

minus difference

Multiply

$3 \times 5 = 15$

times product

Divide

$15 \div 5 = 3$

divided quotient
by

For Lesson 1.7, display a poster showing the various polygons and their names.

Students with Various Learning Styles*
Many patterns in this chapter are modeled as arrangements of circles, squares, and triangles. Some students will benefit from a **tactile** approach by using blocks and tiles to match illustrated patterns. Also, many number patterns can be modeled with blocks and tiles; for example, using squares to model the sequence of even numbers.

Underachieving Students*
In Lesson 1.2, allow students to use calculators to compensate for any lack of computation skills, but encourage them to learn the basic facts, and use mental math. These students may also be intrigued and motivated by using a calculator that handles fractions.

Sports fans may be motivated by the analysis of sports data in Lesson 1.6. Help them find data on their favorite sport, pose questions about the data, and use graphs to find patterns in the data.

Gifted and Talented Students*
Challenge students to develop a game similar to the grape game on page 6.

Encourage students to analyze the patterns in exercises 9–12 on page 40 and develop similar patterns of their own.

* See page T19 for descriptions of these special populations.

Exploring Patterns

Rocky IV is a smart robot that can explore places that are too dangerous for humans. It is designed to withstand the temperatures on Mars that get as low as −190°F.

CHAPTER 1 OVERVIEW

PACING CHART

Lesson	Basic/ Average Course	Above Average Course	Advanced Course
1.1	2 days	1 day	1 day
1.2	2 days	1 day	1 day
1.3	2 days	1 day	1 day
1.4	2 days	1 day	1 day
1.5	2 days	1 day	1 day
1.6	2 days	1 day	1 day
1.7	0 days	1 day	1 day
1.8	0 days	1 day	1 day

About the Chapter

A distinctive feature of the text is its readability. Lessons provide clear and concise instruction. You may choose to build class presentations around them. Encourage students to read the text. It has been found that when you use the textbook lessons as the basis for your own lessons, students find it easier to read and follow classroom instructions.

This opening chapter requires students to look for patterns in numbers (especially in numbers that express real-life data), and to look for patterns in the geometric shapes and properties that make up the visible world around us. From the beginning, students are encouraged to use a calculator where appropriate in identifying such patterns. Students will then learn that observation of a pattern can be taken a giant step further. The pattern may be described or modeled in a formula, and this is what algebra is all about. As will be evident in Goal 2 of Lessons 1.2, 1.5, and 1.8, the concepts and skills of this course will be taught in the context of real-life modeling.

In Lessons 1.2–1.5, students learn or revisit some of the basic rules and operations underlying the language of algebra. Then, since this language is to be applied to analyzing and modeling real-life data, several standard methods of organizing that data are presented in Lesson 1.6.

As early as Lesson 1.2, students will be exposed to the thorough integration of algebra and geometry that is characteristic of this text. Just as mathematical patterns and algebraic relationships can often be better understood by a geometrical representation or model (Lesson 1.2, Goal 2), similarly, many geometric patterns can be described or modeled by algebraic expressions (Lesson 1.7, Goal 2).

Real Life
Building a Rover

3.3 ft / min

Distance (in feet)
Time (in minutes)

Because of size and weight limits in modern space exploration, this Mars rover will be under 2 feet long, and weigh less than 17 pounds. It recognizes patterns and makes decisions by using a computer program based on a guess-and-check strategy.

In this chapter, you will study number patterns and ways to present data, such as this graph of distance, rate, and time for Rocky IV.

PACING THE LESSON

Suggested Number of Days
Basic/Average 2 Above Average 1
Advanced 1

PLANNING THE LESSON

Lesson Plan 1.1, p. 1

ORGANIZER

Starters (reproduced below)
Problem of the Day 1.1, p. 1
Warm-Up Exercises 1.1, p. 1

Lesson Resources
Math Log, p. 4
Answer Masters 1.1, pp. 1–3
Extra Practice Copymaster 1.1, p. 1
Reteaching Copymaster 1.1, p. 1
Calculator

Special Populations
Suggestions, Teacher's Edition, p. 1D

LESSON Notes

Ask students to identify uses of numbers in their classroom. Then go to the Lesson Investigation. The goal of the investigation is to make students realize how important numbers are to their lives.

Lesson Investigation
You might expect lists that include telephone numbers, social security numbers, student IDs, shoe sizes, computer memory sizes, weights, heights, and grades. Have students decide which numbers are used for identification and which for measurement. Encourage them to use a variety of types of numbers including fractions. A good follow-up activity is to let them make a bulletin board of the uses of numbers in daily living.

MATH JOURNAL
Encourage students to keep journals in which they may record useful and interesting information from class—perhaps the uses of numbers in daily living qualifies.

1.1

Number Patterns

 What you should learn:

Goal 1 How to use numbers to identify and measure objects

Goal 2 How to recognize and describe number patterns

 Why you should learn it:

You can use numbers to identify and measure real-life objects, such as the numbers in a zip code or the waist size of a pair of jeans.

Nebraska's Zip Codes

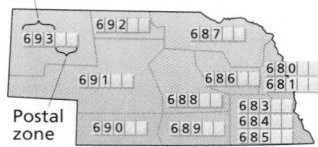

Zip codes identify the state, sectional center, and postal zone of an address.

Goal 1 — Identifying and Measuring

Mathematics is not just the study of numbers. Mathematics is also the study of how numbers are *used* in real life. For instance, numbers can be used as zip codes to identify addresses. Numbers can also be used to measure distances on a highway.

Highway signs indicate the distance to a city or town.

LESSON INVESTIGATION

■ **Investigating Number Uses**

Group Activity With the other students in your group, make 4 different lists of numbers that are used for identification. Then make 4 different lists of numbers used for measurement. (Each list should contain at least five numbers.)

Share the numbers from one of your group's lists with the other groups in your class. Ask the groups if they can tell what the numbers identify or measure. For instance, the numbers

10199, 20066, 60607, 75260, and 94188

are the postmaster zip codes for New York City; Washington D.C.; Dallas; San Francisco; and Chicago.

STARTER: Problem of the Day

If 26 = *L. of the A.* means *26 letters of the alphabet,* how many of the following "equations" can you translate?

24 = H. in a D. hours in a day
90 = D. in an R.A. degrees in a right angle
18 = H. on the G.C. holes on the golf course
9 = P. in the S.S. planets in the solar system
1000 = W. that a P. is W. words that a picture is worth

Also available as a copymaster, page 1

STARTER: Warm-Up Exercises

Warm-Up Exercises are designed to quickly get students ready for the day's lesson.

1. Match each of the following numbers with one or more of the labels.
$\frac{3}{4}$ b. $\frac{22}{7}$ b., d. -7 a., b. $5\frac{1}{2}$ c.
a. integer **b.** rational number
c. mixed number **d.** improper fraction

2. The top row of a calendar lists the days of the week from Sunday through Saturday. List the sequence of numbers in the last column for April, if the first day of the month falls on
a. Friday 2, 9, 16, 23, 30
b. Thursday. 3, 10, 17, 24

Also available as a copymaster, page 1

The most common shoe sizes for women are 7, $7\frac{1}{2}$, 8, and $8\frac{1}{2}$. The most common shoe sizes for men are $9\frac{1}{2}$, 10, and $10\frac{1}{2}$.

Goal 2 **Describing Number Patterns**

Sometimes when you see numbers in real life, the numbers form a pattern. For instance, when you go into a shoe store, you might see numbers representing shoe sizes.

$5, 5\frac{1}{2}, 6, 6\frac{1}{2}, 7, 7\frac{1}{2}, 8, 8\frac{1}{2}, 9, 9\frac{1}{2}, 10, 10\frac{1}{2}$ *Shoe Sizes*

An ordered list of numbers is called a **sequence**. The pattern for the sequence above is that each number is $\frac{1}{2}$ more than the preceding number.

Example *Describing Number Patterns*

Describe a pattern for each sequence. Then use the pattern to write the next three numbers in the sequence.

a. 4, 8, 12, 16, ?, ?, ?

b. 128, 64, 32, 16, ?, ?, ?

Solution

a. One pattern for this sequence is that each number is 4 more than the preceding number. The next three numbers are shown below.

4, 8, 12, 16, 20, 24, 28

$16 + 4 \nearrow 20 + 4 \nwarrow 24 + 4$

b. One pattern for this sequence is that each number is half the preceding number. The next three numbers are shown below.

128, 64, 32, 16, 8, 4, 2

$\frac{1}{2} \cdot 16 \nearrow \frac{1}{2} \cdot 8 \nwarrow \frac{1}{2} \cdot 4$ ∎

Communicating about **MATHEMATICS**

▶ **SHARING IDEAS about the Lesson**

Describing Patterns In Example 1, only one pattern was described for each list of numbers. Often, however, a list of numbers can be described by two or more patterns. For instance, suppose that you are given the numbers

2, 3, 5, ?, ?, ?, ?, ?.

Describe several possible patterns for this list. For each pattern, write the next five numbers in the list.

To get the next number:
1. Add 1 to preceding number, add 2 to preceding number, add 3 … etc.; 8, 12, 17, 23, 30
2. Add two preceding numbers; 8, 13, 21, 34, 55
3. Name the next prime number; 7, 11, 13, 17, 19
4. Subtract 1 from 2 times preceding number; 9, 17, 33, 65, 129

Many number patterns arise from real-life situations. Let students make their own number patterns and challenge classmates to extend the patterns.

Point out that when students identify and extend patterns, they are using inductive reasoning, which is essential to scientific and mathematical inquiry.

Example

You may want to describe the general term of each sequence in both words and symbols. For example, in **a.** you might say, "If a given term is n, then the next term is $n + 4$."

Make students aware that sequences of numbers can often be extended in more than one way.

Communicating about **MATHEMATICS**

For each pattern, ask students to state how they constructed it. They may want to record their sequences in their journals.

Writing Prompt
You may want to use this feature as a lesson closure. It is intended to encourage students to share insights or concerns that they have about the lesson or about the course as a whole.

Today's lesson was . . . because . . .

Here are additional examples similar to those of the lesson.

Describing Number Patterns
Describe a pattern for each sequence. Then use the pattern to write the next three numbers of the sequence.
a. 3, 8, 13, 18, …   **b.** 1, 2, 4, 8, 16, …

Solution
a. One pattern is that each number is 5 more than the preceding number. The next three terms are shown below.
3, 8, 13, 18, 23,   28   33
                  (18 + 5)   (23 + 5)   (28 + 5)

b. One pattern is that each number is twice the preceding number. The next three terms are shown below.
1, 2, 4, 8, 16, 32,   64   128
                  (2 × 16)   (2 × 32)   (2 × 64)

EXERCISE Notes

Guided Practice

Guided Practice exercises are designed to help you check students' understanding of the skills and concepts of the lesson. You are encouraged to make these exercises a whole-class activity so that all students can benefit. The answers to all Guided Practice exercises are found in the Selected Answers section of the student text. Look for the Portfolio Opportunity logo P for suggested items you and your students may wish to include in Assessment Portfolios.

▶ **Ex. 2, 3** Encourage students to think beyond examples given in class.

Independent Practice

Answers to the odd-numbered exercises of the Independent Practice and Integrated Review sections are found in the Selected Answers section of the student's text.

▶ **Ex. 21, 22**

Have groups write rules for generating sequences on index cards to challenge other groups.

▶ **Ex. 23** This is a visual model of the triangular numbers: 1, 1+2, 1+2+3, 1+2+3+4, etc.

▶ **Ex. 24** Have students determine the number of turns necessary to bring the square back to the starting position.

4 Chapter 1

EXERCISES

Guided Practice

▶ **CHECK for Understanding** Answers vary.

P **1.** *Writing* In your own words, describe what mathematics is. … the study of numbers and their uses.

2. State several examples of how numbers are used to identify objects in real life. Phone numbers, house numbers, auto license plates

3. State several examples of how numbers are used to measure objects in real life. Name some units of measure, such as centimeters or pounds. Heights of people in feet and inches, weights of packages in pounds and ounces, speeds of cars in miles per hour, liter, yard, second

4. State an example of a real-life number sequence. Describe its pattern. Hat sizes: $7, 7\frac{1}{8}, 7\frac{1}{4}, 7\frac{3}{8}, 7\frac{1}{2}$, etc. Each number is $\frac{1}{8}$ more than preceding number.

Independent Practice

Exercises 5–20: For descriptions, see Additional Answers.
In Exercises 5–14, describe the pattern. Then list the next 3 numbers.

5. 1, 3, 5, 7, ⬚, ⬚, ⬚   9, 11, 13

6. 5, 10, 15, 20, ⬚, ⬚, ⬚   25, 30, 35

7. 1, 3, 6, 10, ⬚, ⬚, ⬚   15, 21, 28

8. 60, 57, 53, 48, ⬚, ⬚, ⬚   42, 35, 27

9. $\frac{1}{2}, \frac{2}{3}, \frac{3}{4}, \frac{4}{5}$, ⬚, ⬚, ⬚ $\frac{5}{6}, \frac{6}{7}, \frac{7}{8}$

10. $\frac{2}{3}, \frac{4}{5}, \frac{6}{7}, \frac{8}{9}$, ⬚, ⬚, ⬚ $\frac{10}{11}, \frac{12}{13}, \frac{14}{15}$

11. $2, \frac{7}{2}, 5, \frac{13}{2}$, ⬚, ⬚, ⬚ $8, \frac{19}{2}, 11$

12. 100, 81, 64, 49, ⬚, ⬚, ⬚   36, 25, 16

13. 2, 6, 18, 54, ⬚, ⬚, ⬚   162, 486, 1458

14. 4096, 1024, 256, 64, ⬚, ⬚, ⬚   16, 4, 1

In Exercises 15–20, describe the pattern. Then list the next 3 letters.

15. A, C, E, G, ⬚, ⬚, ⬚   I, K, M

16. A, Y, C, W, ⬚, ⬚, ⬚   E, U, G

17. Z, A, Y, B, X, C, ⬚, ⬚, ⬚   W, D, V

18. A, N, B, O, ⬚, ⬚, ⬚   C, P, D

✪ **19.** O, T, T, F, F, S, ⬚, ⬚, ⬚   S, E, N

✪ **20.** T, F, S, E, T, ⬚, ⬚, ⬚   D, S, C; T, F, S

Number Sense **In Exercises 21 and 22, write the first 6 numbers in the sequence.**

21. The first number is 50. Each succeeding number is 3 less than the preceding number.   50, 47, 44, 41, 38, 35

22. The first number is 1 and the second number is 2. Each succeeding number is the sum of the two preceding numbers.   1, 2, 3, 5, 8, 13

Visualizing Patterns **In Exercises 23 and 24, draw the next 3 figures in the pattern.** See Additional Answers.

23.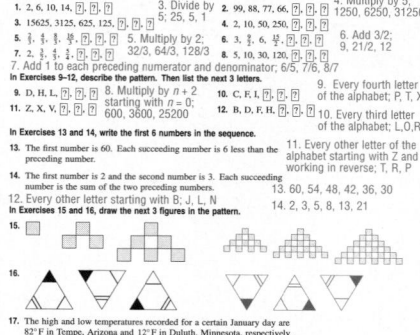

24.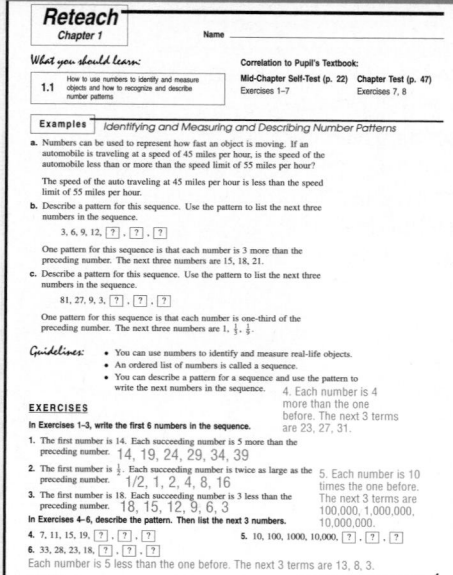

4 Chapter 1 ▪ Exploring Patterns

✪ More difficult exercises
P Portfolio Opportunity

Extra Practice

Extra Practice 1.1   Name _____

1. Add 4; 18, 22, 26   2. Subtract 11; 55, 44, 33
In Exercises 1–8, describe the pattern. Then list the next 3 numbers.
1. 2, 6, 10, 14, ?, ?, ?   3. Divide by 5; 25, 5, 1   4. Multiply by 5; 1250, 6250, 31250
2. 99, 88, 77, 66, ?, ?, ?
3. 15625, 3125, 625, 125, ?, ?, ?   4. 2, 10, 50, 250, ?, ?, ?
5. $\frac{1}{4}, \frac{2}{5}, \frac{3}{6}, \frac{4}{7}$, ?, ?, ?   5. Multiply by 2; 32/3, 64/3, 128/3   6. 3, $\frac{3}{2}$, 6, $\frac{9}{2}$, ?, ?, ?   6. Add 3/2; 9, 21/2, 12
7. 2, $\frac{4}{3}$, $\frac{2}{3}$, $\frac{1}{6}$, ?, ?, ?   7. Add 1 to each preceding numerator and denominator; 6/5, 7/6, 8/7
8. 5, 10, 30, 120, ?, ?, ?   9, 21/2, 12
In Exercises 9–12, describe the pattern. Then list the next 3 letters.
9. D, H, L, ?, ?, ?   8. Multiply by n + 2 starting with n = 0; 600, 3600, 25200   9. Every fourth letter of the alphabet; P, T, X
11. Z, X, V, ?, ?, ?   10. C, F, I, ?, ?, ?   10. Every third letter of the alphabet; L, O, R
12. B, D, F, H, ?, ?, ?   11. Every other letter of the alphabet starting with Z and working in reverse; T, R, P
In Exercises 13 and 14, write the first 6 numbers in the sequence.
13. The first number is 60. Each succeeding number is 6 less than the preceding number.   12. Every other letter starting with B; J, L, N
14. The first number is 2 and the second number is 3. Each succeeding number is the sum of the two preceding numbers.   13. 60, 54, 48, 42, 36, 30   14. 2, 3, 5, 8, 13, 21
In Exercises 15 and 16, draw the next 3 figures in the pattern.
15.
16.
17. The high and low temperatures recorded for a certain January day are 82°F in Tempe, Arizona and 12°F in Duluth, Minnesota, respectively. Explain what the numbers represent.   17. The larger the number, the warmer the temp. It was 70° warmer in Tempe than in Duluth.
18. You and a friend both take a math examination. You score a 98 out of 100 points and your friend scores 96 out of 100 points. Who scored better? Explain.   18. The larger the number, the better the score with a score of 100 being a perfect score. So, your score is better than your friend's by 2 points.
19. You and your family are traveling to the beach for vacation. You and yours and her family are traveling to the same beach. They are driving at an average speed of 55 miles per hour. Who gets to the beach first? Explain.   19. The numbers represent the speed in mph. You will arrive sooner, since you are traveling 320 mph faster.
20. In Super Bowl XXVIII, the Dallas Cowboys defeated the Buffalo Bills by a score of 30–13. Explain what the numbers represent.   20. The numbers represent the points scored for a particular team. Dallas scored more than Buffalo, so Dallas won the game.

Windows   1.1 ▪ Number Patterns **1**

Reteaching

Reteach Chapter 1   Name _____

What you should learn: **Correlation to Pupil's Textbook:**
1.1 How to use numbers to identify and measure objects and how to recognize and describe number patterns   Mid-Chapter Self-Test (p. 22)   Chapter Test (p. 47)
Exercises 1–7   Exercises 7, 8

Examples *Identifying and Measuring and Describing Number Patterns*

a. Numbers can be used to represent how fast an object is moving. If an automobile is traveling at a speed of 45 miles per hour, is the speed of the automobile less than or more than the speed limit of 55 miles per hour?

The speed of the auto traveling at 45 miles per hour is less than the speed limit of 55 miles per hour.

b. Describe a pattern for this sequence. Use the pattern to list the next three numbers in the sequence.
3, 6, 9, 12, ?, ?, ?
One pattern for this sequence is that each number is 3 more than the preceding number. The next three numbers are 15, 18, 21.

c. Describe a pattern for this sequence. Use the pattern to list the next three numbers in the sequence.
81, 27, 9, 3, ?, ?, ?
One pattern for this sequence is that each number is one-third of the preceding number. The next three numbers are 1, $\frac{1}{3}$, $\frac{1}{9}$.

Guidelines: • You can use numbers to identify and measure real-life objects.
• An ordered list of numbers is called a sequence.
• You can describe a pattern for a sequence and use the pattern to write the next numbers in the sequence.   4. Each number is 4 more than the one before. The next 3 terms are 23, 27, 31.

EXERCISES
In Exercises 1–3, write the first 6 numbers in the sequence.
1. The first number is 14. Each succeeding number is 5 more than the preceding number.   14, 19, 24, 29, 34, 39
2. The first number is $\frac{1}{2}$. Each succeeding number is twice as large as the preceding number.   1/2, 1, 2, 4, 8, 16   5. Each number is 10 times the one before. The next 3 terms are 100,000, 1,000,000, 10,000,000.
3. The first number is 18. Each succeeding number is 3 less than the preceding number.   18, 15, 12, 9, 6, 3
In Exercises 4–6, describe the pattern. Then list the next 3 numbers.
4. 7, 11, 15, 19, ?, ?, ?   5. 10, 100, 1000, 10,000, ?, ?, ?
6. 33, 28, 23, 18, ?, ?, ?
Each number is 5 less than the one before. The next 3 terms are 13, 8, 3.

Windows   Chapter 1 ▪ Exploring Patterns **1**

27. They decrease. Exercises 25–26: For explanations, see Additional Answers.

25. *Race Times* You run a 400-meter race with a time of 2:39.4. Your friend's time is 2:41.8. Explain how these numbers measure your times. Who won the race? You

26. *Long Jump* You and a friend are in a standing long-jump contest. You jump 4 feet 9 inches and your friend jumps 4 feet 11 inches. Who won the contest? Explain. Your Friend

27. *Vacation Travel* You and your family travel to an amusement park. As you near the park, you begin seeing signs that state the number of miles to the park. What can you say about the numbers on the signs as you get closer and closer to the park? See above.

28. *Amusement Park* Imagine that you are at an amusement park. Describe several ways that numbers are used to identify objects at the park and measure objects at the park. See Additional Answers.

In 1994, approximately 255 million people visited a theme park in North America. The most popular of these was the Magic Kingdom at Walt Disney World in Florida.

Integrated Review

Making Connections within Mathematics

Measurement Sense **In Exercises 29–34, rewrite the measure as indicated. (Measurement tables are found on pages 680 and 681.)**

29. 1.5 feet = [?] inches 18

30. 1.5 hours = [?] minutes 90

31. 1.5 meters = [?] centimeters 150

32. 1.5 kilometers = [?] meters 1500

33. 30 inches = [?] feet 2.5

34. 90 seconds = [?] minutes 1.5

Exploration and Extension

Making a Table **In Exercises 35 and 36, imagine that you have completed a homework assignment. Without a penalty, your score would be 94. Complete the table to show what your score would be with penalties.**

35. 1 day late: Lose 5 points.
2 days late: Lose 10 points.
3 days late: Lose 15 points.

84 79 74 69

Days Late	0	1	2	3	4	5
Score	94	89	?	?	?	?

36. 1 day late: Lose 4 points.
2 days late: Lose 4 + 8 points.
3 days late: Lose 4 + 8 + 12 points.

82 70 54 34

Days Late	0	1	2	3	4	5
Score	94	90	?	?	?	?

37. *It's Up to You* If you were the teacher, which penalty system would you use: the one described in Exercise 35 or in Exercise 36? Explain. Answers vary.

Integrated Review

Exercises in this section provide students with an opportunity to review previously learned skills and concepts in the context of the current lesson.

Exploration and Extension

The exercises in this section are not necessarily difficult problems, nor are they designated only for gifted students. They often provide an interesting extension of the lesson goals.
▶ **Ex. 37** Have students share their comments. Have groups determine a "fair" policy for late homework, keeping in mind that students should be rewarded for completing homework on time (full credit) and should be penalized for late work.

Portfolio Opportunity: Math Log

Find four real-life uses for the number 55 when different units of measurement are used.

Also available as a copymaster, page 4, Ex. 1

Alternative Assessment

A cooperative learning project that evaluates students' knowledge of how numbers and sequences are used to identify and measure real-world objects.

Available as a copymaster, page 15

Enrichment

Activities in this section of the teacher's edition typically require students to go beyond the lesson goals.

Have students investigate the Braille alphabet, used by persons who cannot see. These people must use their fingertips to recognize the patterns of raised dots on paper. Some braille symbols frequently used in mathematics are shown here.

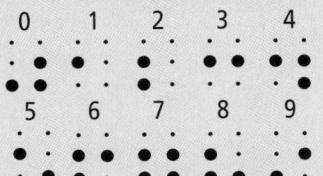

| Numeric indicator | Decimal point | x | y | Plus | Minus | Equal |

Examples: 3.5 + 6

x − 9 = 7

Materials
Color Transparencies
Transparency of grape game, p. 1
Teaching Tools
Copymaster of grape game, p. C1

The goal of this activity is for students to do some mental arithmetic, look for patterns, and to have fun.

EXTENSION
Have students design their own Grape Game with a new magic number for the sum of four hexagons. For instance, subtracting 2 from each hexagon will yield a magic number of 30. Students would then have to invent the different operations to yield the number within each hexagon.

Materials Needed: toothpicks

Grape Game can be played with two or more people. Players take turns at placing a toothpick along three hexagons in a row. The hexagons must be in a horizontal or diagonal row. Each player than mentally performs the operations in each of the three hexagons and adds the results together. Players should agree on the correct sum.

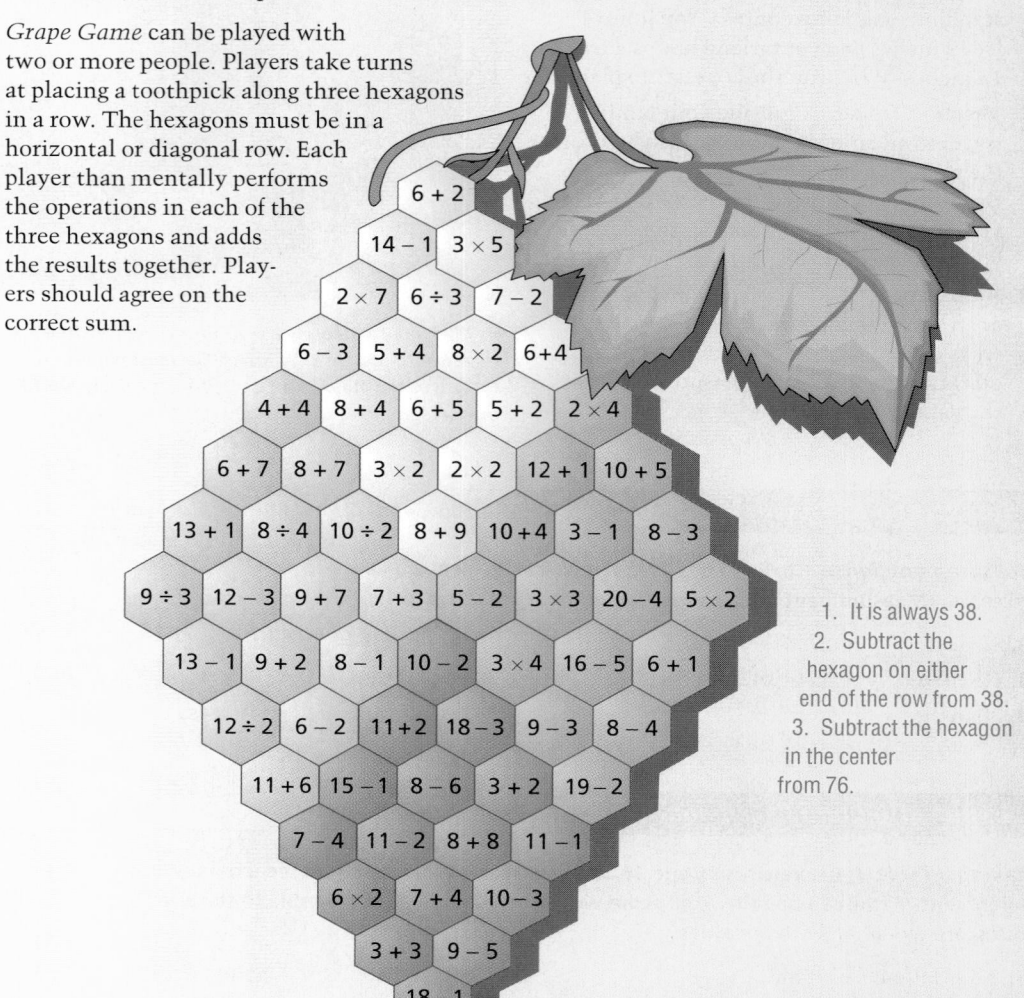

1. It is always 38.
2. Subtract the hexagon on either end of the row from 38.
3. Subtract the hexagon in the center from 76.

1. Describe a quick way to find the sum of four hexagons in a row. **1.–3.** See above.
2. Can you discover a quick way to find the sum of three hexagons in a row?
3. Describe a quick way to find the sum of seven hexagons that form a "flower."

1.2 Number Operations

▶ PACING the Lesson

Suggested Number of Days
Basic/Average 2   **Above Average** 1
Advanced 1

▶ PLANNING the Lesson

Lesson Plan 1.2, p. 2

What you should learn:

Goal 1 How to use the four basic number operations

Goal 2 How to use multiplication models

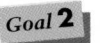

Why you should learn it:

Many real-life uses of numbers require number operations, such as multiplication to find the area of a rectangle.

Hindu-Arabic Numerals
Mathematical symbols that are used ...ay came from many different cultures. ...instance, the numerals 0, 1, 2, 3, . . . , 9 ...re invented in India and Arabia more ...2000 years ago. The fraction bar was ...st introduced by the Arabic author al-Hassar in about A.D. 1202.

Goal 1   Using Number Operations

There are four basic number operations: **addition, subtraction, multiplication,** and **division.** Each of these operations can be described verbally or symbolically.

The symbol "+" signifies addition and the symbol "−" signifies subtraction. Multiplication can be specified by "×", or by "•", or by parentheses. Division can be specified by "÷", or by "/", or by a fraction bar, as in $\frac{1}{2}$.

Example 1   *Finding Sums and Differences*

a. *Addition:*

The **sum** of 5 and 13 is 18.   *Verbal description*

$5 + 13 = 18$ *Symbolic description*

b. *Subtraction:*

The **difference** of 9 and 6 is 3.   *Verbal description*

$9 - 6 = 3$ *Symbolic description* ∎

Example 2   *Finding Products and Quotients*

a. *Multiplication:*

The **product** of 3 and 5 is 15.   *Verbal description*

$3 \times 5 = 15$ *Symbolic description*

$3 \cdot 5 = 15$ *Symbolic description*

$3(5) = 15$ *Symbolic description*

b. *Division:*

The **quotient** of 14 and 7 is 2.   *Verbal description*

$14 \div 7 = 2$ *Symbolic description*

$14/7 = 2$ *Symbolic description*

$\frac{14}{7} = 2$ *Symbolic description* ∎

1.2 ▪ *Number Operations*   **7**

ORGANIZER

Starters (reproduced below)
   Problem of the Day 1.2, p. 1
   Warm-Up Exercises 1.2, p. 1
Lesson Resources
   Color Transparencies
      Diagrams for Communicating about
      Mathematics, p. 2
      Graph for Ex. 49–52, p. 2
   Teaching Tools
      Graph paper, pp. T1, C2
   Math Log, p. 4
   Technology, p. 3
   Answer Masters 1.2, pp. 4, 5
   Extra Practice Copymaster 1.2, p. 2
   Reteaching Copymaster 1.2, p. 2
Special Populations
   Suggestions, Teacher's Edition, p. 1D

LESSON Notes

Make certain that students recognize the symbols for addition, subtraction, multiplication, and division. Point out that calculators and computers usually use an asterisk for multiplication. Frequently, multiplication is denoted by the dot symbol (•). Common symbols for division include / and ÷.

Throughout the text, visual and concrete models have been used to help students understand the variety of concepts presented. The area model of multiplication is a particularly important representation for students to understand.

Example 1

Note that the order in which we add 5 and 3 is unimportant because addition is commutative. The order in which we subtract 9 and 6, however, is important because subtraction is not a commutative operation. Stress that the "difference of 9 and 6" implies an order, 9 (first) subtract 6.

Example 2

Ask students if the order in which we multiply 3 and 5 is important. Ask if the order in which we divide 14 and 7 is important. Stress that the "quotient of 14 and 7" implies an order, 14 (first) divided by 7.

Lesson 1.2   **7**

Models are an important part of making mathematics fun, interesting, and understood!

Connections
Geometry

Length

Width

Area = 18 square units

Goal 2 Using Multiplication Models

A **model** is something that helps you visualize or understand an actual process or object. For instance, drawing a family tree helps you understand how your cousins are related to you. The next example shows how area can be used as a model for multiplication.

Example 3 *Using Area as a Multiplication Model*

Show how to use area to model the product of 3 and 6.

Solution One way to model the product is to use squares to form a rectangle that is 3 units wide and 6 units long. Each square has an area of 1 square unit. By counting the squares, you can see that the rectangle has an area of 18 square units. Because the area of a rectangle is the product of its width and length,

(Area of rectangle) = (Width) × (Length),

you can see that $3 \times 6 = 18$. ∎

Communicating *about* MATHEMATICS

Cooperative Learning

▶ **SHARING IDEAS about the Lesson**

Multiplication Models Each of the multiplication models shown below represents a multiplication sentence. Work with a partner. Write the sentence verbally and symbolically. Describe other ways to model multiplication. See below.

A. The product of 3 and 6 is 18. $3 \times 6 = 18$

B. The product of 5 and 7 is 35. $5 \times 7 = 35$

C. The product of 6 and 5 is 30. $6 \times 5 = 30$

A.
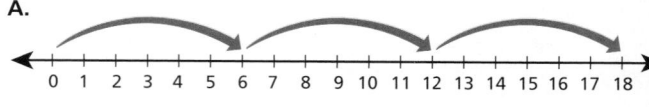
0 1 2 3 4 5 6 7 8 9 10 11 12 13 14 15 16 17 18

B.
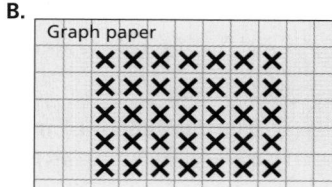
Graph paper

C.
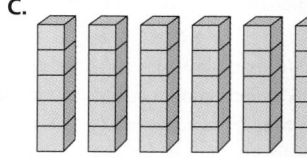

Answers vary. Number of seats in an auditorium section, total cost of identical items

8 *Chapter 1 • Exploring Patterns*

OPTION: Extra Examples

Here are additional examples similar to some of those of the lesson.

1. Finding Sums and Differences

a. Addition
The sum of 3 and 8 is 11.   Verbal description
$3 + 8 = 11$ Symbolic description

b. Subtraction
The difference of 18 and 11 is 7.   Verbal description
$18 - 11 = 7$ Symbolic description

2. Finding Products and Quotients

a. Multiplication
The product of 4 and 9 is 36.   Verbal description
$4 \times 9 = 36$ Symbolic description
$4 \cdot 9 = 36$ Symbolic description
$4(9) = 36$ Symbolic description

b. Division
The quotient of 12 and 6 is 2.   Verbal description
$12 \div 6 = 2$ Symbolic description
$12/6 = 2$ Symbolic description
$\frac{12}{6} = 2$ Symbolic description

EXERCISES

Guided Practice

▶ CHECK for Understanding

1. State the four basic number operations.   Addition, subtraction, multiplication, divison
2. State the symbol or symbols that represent each number operation. $+$, $-$, $\times$ or $\bullet$ or $(\ )$, $\div$ or $/$
3. What is a model? Describe a model that can be used to represent multiplication.   See page 8.
4. *Problem Solving*   Describe a real-life example of a number operation.   Answers vary. A cash register adds the prices of various products bought in a store.

Independent Practice

Computation Sense   **In Exercises 5-12, write a verbal description of the number sentence.**   See margin.

5. $6 \times 8 = 48$ **6.** $25 \div 5 = 5$ **7.** $3 + 14 = 17$ **8.** $9(7) = 63$
9. $111 - 56 = 55$ **10.** $\frac{12}{4} = 3$ **11.** $2 \bullet 54 = 108$ **12.** $\frac{132}{11} = 12$

Computation Sense   **In Exercises 13–28, find the sum or difference.**   **21.** 905.43 **22.** 4327.02 **23.** 0.151

13. $659 + 23$ 682   **14.** $350 + 211$ 561   **15.** $746 - 27$ 719   **16.** $858 - 349$ 509
17. $75 + 40 + 98$ 213 **18.** $352 + 67 + 20$ 439 **19.** $10.9 - 8.6$ 2.3   **20.** $112.7 - 72.9$ 39.8
21. $316.41 + 589.02$ **22.** $4203.9 + 123.12$ **23.** $0.248 - 0.097$ **24.** $2.385 - 0.597$ 1.788
25. $\frac{5}{6} + \frac{1}{6}$ 1   **26.** $\frac{3}{8} + \frac{1}{8}$ $\frac{1}{2}$ **27.** $\frac{9}{12} - \frac{5}{12}$ $\frac{1}{3}$ **28.** $\frac{6}{13} - \frac{3}{13}$ $\frac{3}{13}$

Number Sense   **In Exercises 29–44, find the product or quotient.**

29. 16×7 112   **30.** 21×14 294   **31.** $527 \div 31$ 17   **32.** $1435 \div 35$ 41
33. $(4.7)(8.9)$ 41.83   **34.** $(13.2)(5.1)$ 67.32   **35.** $3 \bullet \frac{4}{9}$ $\frac{4}{3}$ **36.** $7 \bullet \frac{1}{8}$ $\frac{7}{8}$
37. $\frac{256}{32}$ 8   **38.** $\frac{1024}{64}$ 16   **39.** 321×156 50,076 **40.** 497×38 18,886
41. $76.97 \div 4.3$ 17.9 **42.** $145.2 \div 33$ 4.4   **43.** $1977/15$ 131.8   **44.** $2125/34$ 62.5

In Exercises 45–48, write a number sentence for each model.

45.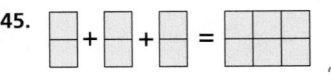
$2 + 2 + 2 = 6$

46.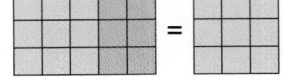
$15 = 9 + 6$

47.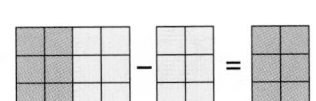
$12 - 6 = 6$

48.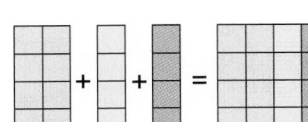
$8 + 4 + 4 = 16$

This symbol indicates exercises where you should choose the appropriate method of calculation: mental math, paper and pencil, or calculator.

Extra Practice

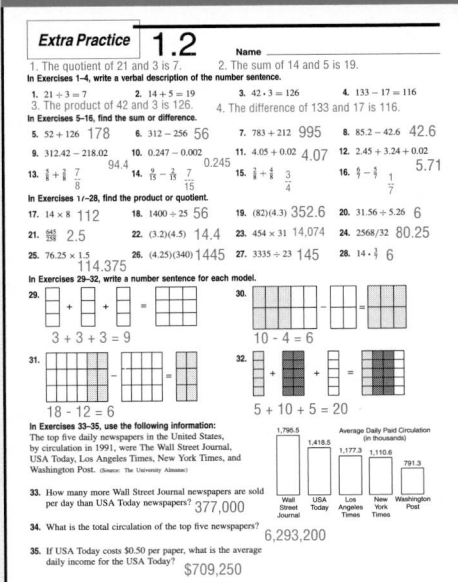

Reteaching

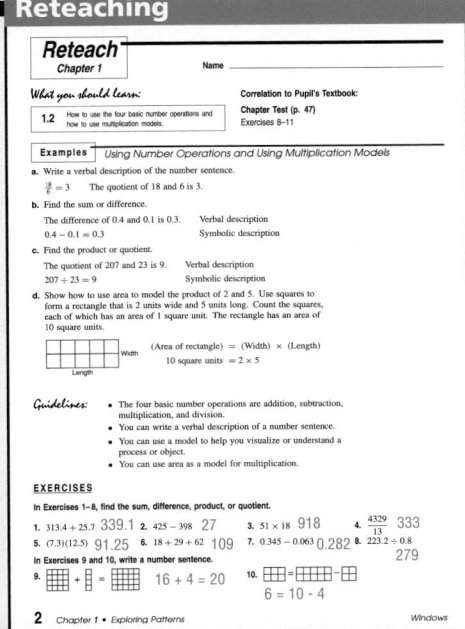

ASSIGNMENT GUIDE
Basic/Average:
  Day 1: Ex. 5–8, 13, 17, 21, 25, 31, 35, 39, 43
  Day 2: Ex. 45, 47, 49–52, 54, 55–61 odd, 63
Above Average: Ex.5–7, 9, 23, 27, 34, 41, 44, 45, 54, 55–61 odd, 63–66
Advanced: Ex. 5–7, 9, 23, 27, 34, 41, 44, 45, 54, 55–61 odd, 63–66
Selected Answers: Ex. 1–4, 5–61 odd

Guided Practice
▶ **Ex. 4** Encourage students to consider as many real-life contexts as possible.

Independent Practice
▶ **Ex. 10, 12** Check to see if students see only fractions or the operation of division as well.
▶ **Ex. 13–44**
ASSESSMENT
Although later chapters address operations with decimals and fractions, these problems will give an early indication of what exposure your students have had to these topics. Lack of computational skill should not be a barrier for students to be successful in this course. Use of calculators is encouraged for all students.
▶ **Ex. 45–58** These are a preview of later work with algebra tiles.

Answers
  5. The product of 6 and 8 is 48.
  6. The quotient of 25 and 5 is 5.
  7. The sum of 3 and 14 is 17.
  8. The product of 9 and 7 is 63.
  9. The difference of 111 and 56 is 55.
  10. The quotient of 12 and 4 is 3.
  11. The product of 2 and 54 is 108.
  12. The quotient of 132 and 11 is 12.

Lesson 1.2 **9**

▶ Ex. 49–52

EXTENSION

Gather data in your class by asking about the number of CDs and cassettes purchased or received by students in the last year.

▶ Ex. 54 Have students explain their reasoning. Students could be asked to draw in their journals models for their answers.

Possible models:

Odd + Even = Odd

Odd + Odd = Even

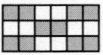

This odd × even rectangle could be covered with pairs of tiles as shown, therefore the product is even.

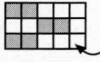

This odd × odd rectangle could be covered with pairs of tiles as shown, except that there is a single tile left over, therefore the product is odd.

Integrated Review

ASSESSMENT

These questions assess previous exposure to the topics, and they preview content to come later.

Exploration and Extension

The use of calculators is encouraged.

COOPERATIVE LEARNING

You may wish to change the given numbers and have groups determine if there is a strategy that should be used for each operation in order to maximize or minimize the result.

Portfolio Opportunity: Math Log

1. Write a verbal description, not used in Lesson 1.2, for each of the four basic number operations.
2. In your own words, define a model. Describe or draw a model that could be used to understand a real-life process, object, or relationship.

Also available as a copymaster, page 4, Ex. 2, 3

Short Quiz

Covers Lessons 1.1 and 1.2

Available as a copymaster, page 1

CDs and Cassettes **In Exercises 49–52, use the graph.** *(Source: Sound Scan)*

49. In 1993, how many more CDs were sold than cassettes? 36 million

50. How many more CDs were sold in 1993 than in 1992? 56 million

51. How many CDs and cassettes were sold in 1993? 572 million

52. *It's Up to You* What do you predict will happen in years to come with regard to CDs and cassettes? See below.

53. *Collecting CDs* You have a CD storage unit that holds 5 stacks of 14 CDs. How many CDs does it hold? 70

54. *Number Sense* Complete the table. Is the result of the sentence odd or even?

First number	Operator	Second number	Result	
Odd	+	Even	?	Odd
Odd	+	Odd	?	Even
Odd	×	Even	?	Even
Odd	×	Odd	?	Odd

CDs OUTSELL CASSETTES

Number sold in millions

1992
CDs — 248
Cassettes — 300

1993
CDs — 304
Cassettes — 268

52. More and more CDs, and fewer and fewer cassettes, will be sold.

Integrated Review — *Making Connections within Mathematics*

Fraction Sense **In Exercises 55–58, simplify the fraction.**

55. $\frac{2}{4}$ $\frac{1}{2}$

56. $\frac{6}{3}$ 2

57. $\frac{12}{8}$ $\frac{3}{2}$ or $1\frac{1}{2}$

58. $\frac{6}{20}$ $\frac{3}{10}$

Decimal Sense **In Exercises 59–62, write the fraction as a decimal.**

59. $\frac{1}{2}$ 0.5

60. $\frac{1}{4}$ 0.25

61. $\frac{2}{3}$ $0.\overline{6}$

62. $\frac{2}{5}$ 0.4

Exploration and Extension

Guess, Check, and Revise **In Exercises 63–66, find the largest number that can be made using each of the digits 2, 4, 6, 8, and 9 only once. Then find the smallest.**

✪ 63. [?][?][?]
− [?][?]   962; 148

✪ 64. [?][?][?]
+ [?][?]   1046; 317

✪ 65. [?][?][?]
× [?][?]   81,028; 12,714

✪ 66. [?][?][?] ÷ [?][?] $41\frac{1}{12}$; $2\frac{25}{49}$

✪ More difficult exercises

1.3 Powers and Square Roots

► PACING the Lesson
Suggested Number of Days
Basic/Average 2   Above Average 1
Advanced 1
► PLANNING the Lesson
Lesson Plan 1.3, p. 3

What you should learn:

Goal 1 How to use powers

Goal 2 How to use square roots

Why you should learn it:

You can use powers and square roots to solve real-life problems, such as finding the area of a square room.

Study Tip...

When you encounter new symbols in mathematics, be sure you can state the symbols verbally. For instance, the statement

$$2^5 = 32$$

is read as "2 raised to the 5th power is 32."

Technology
Using a Calculator

Goal 1 Using Powers

The squares shown below have sides whose lengths are 1, 2, 3, 4, and 5. The areas of the squares are

$$1 \times 1, 2 \times 2, 3 \times 3, 4 \times 4, \text{ and } 5 \times 5.$$

These areas can also be written as **powers.** For instance, 1×1 can be written as 1^2, 2×2 can be written as 2^2, and so on.

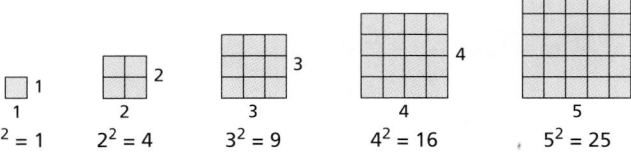

1	2	3	4	5
$1^2 = 1$	$2^2 = 4$	$3^2 = 9$	$4^2 = 16$	$5^2 = 25$

A power has two parts, a **base** and an **exponent.** For instance, the base of 4^2 is 4 and the exponent of 4^2 is 2.

Base ⟶ 4^2 ⟵ Exponent

Power

Any natural number (1, 2, 3, ...) can be used as an exponent.

$4^2 = 4 \times 4 = 16$	*4 raised to the 2nd power or 4 squared*
$5^3 = 5 \times 5 \times 5 = 125$	*5 raised to the 3rd power or 5 cubed*
$3^4 = 3 \times 3 \times 3 \times 3 = 81$	*3 raised to the 4th power*
$6^1 = 6$	*6 raised to the 1st power*

Example 1 Raising Numbers to Powers

Use a calculator to evaluate the powers.

a. 1.5^2 b. 4.2^3 c. 6^5

Solution

Calculator Steps	Display	Written Result
a. 1.5 $\boxed{x^2}$	2.25	$1.5^2 = 2.25$
b. 4.2 $\boxed{y^x}$ 3 $\boxed{=}$	74.088	$4.2^3 = 74.088$
c. 6 $\boxed{y^x}$ 5 $\boxed{=}$	7776	$6^5 = 7776$ ∎

1.3 • *Powers and Square Roots* **11**

ORGANIZER

Starters (reproduced below)
   Problem of the Day 1.3, p. 1
   Warm-Up Exercises 1.3, p. 1
Lesson Resources
   Math Log, p. 5
   Technology, p. 4
   Answer Masters 1.3, pp. 6–8
   Extra Practice Copymaster 1.3, p. 3
   Reteaching Copymaster 1.3, p. 3
Special Populations
   Suggestions, Teacher's Edition, p. 1D

LESSON Notes

Be careful to distinguish among the terms: *base, exponent,* and *power.* It is interesting to note that the geometric model (a square) of "4 raised to the 2nd power" is the reason we often say "the square of 4" to mean 4^2. The numbers 1, 4, 9, 16, 25, ... are appropriately called "square numbers."

Example 1

Have students multiply 1.32 and 1.22 using paper and pencil. Let them check their work using calculators.

Not every calculator has the keys pictured in the example. Question students to determine whether different keystrokes are necessary for some calculators that students are using.

Study Tip Extension
Give students an opportunity to identify the component parts of expressions such as $3^3 = 27$ or $8^2 = 64$.

STARTER: Problem of the Day

The area of the shaded region is 71 cm². What are the dimensions of the inner squares, if all dimensions are integers?
4 cm × 4 cm, 3 cm × 3 cm

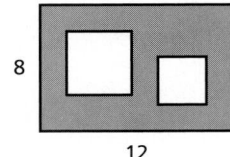

Also available as a copymaster, page 1

STARTER: Warm-Up Exercises

1. Multiply.
a. 3×3 9   b. $5 \times 5 \times 5$ 125
c. $2 \times 2 \times 2 \times 2$ 16

2. How many factors are there in each of the expressions in Exercise 1?
a. 2   b. 3   c. 4

3. For each product, give the value of *n*.
a. $n \times n = 81$ 9   b. $n \times n \times n = 27$ 3
c. $n \times n = 36$ 6   d. $n \times n \times n = 8$ 2
e. $n \times n \times n = 64$ 4

Also available as a copymaster, page 1

Finding square roots is like solving a puzzle: "What number times itself is 16?" or "If $n \times n = 16$, what's n?" Once students are comfortable with the relationship between a square and its square root, introduce the symbol $\sqrt{}$.

Communicating about MATHEMATICS

Direct students to identify other perfect squares and their square roots. Ask students whether they notice anything about the decimal parts of square roots that are not from perfect squares, for example, $\sqrt{2}$, $\sqrt{3}$, $\sqrt{5}$, $\sqrt{6}$, $\sqrt{7}$, etc. Possible answer: None of these seems to terminate or repeat.

Writing Prompt

Have students define in their own words "the square root of a number" and write the definition in their journals.

The **square root** of a number is denoted by the symbol $\sqrt{}$, which is called a **radical** or **square root symbol.** When you square the square root of a number, you obtain the original number. For instance, $\sqrt{9} = 3$ because $3^2 = 9$.

Real Life
Architecture

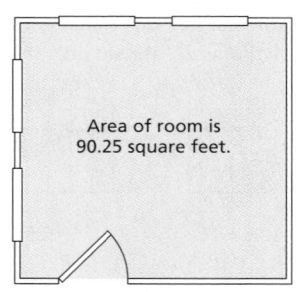

Area of room is 90.25 square feet.

The perimeter of a room is the sum of the lengths of the four sides.

Example 2   *Designing a Room*

You are designing a bedroom for an apartment. You want the room to be square and have an area of 90.25 square feet. How long should each side of the room be? What is the perimeter?

Solution   You need to find a number whose square is 90.25.

$$(\text{Side})^2 = 90.25$$

The solution of this equation is the square root of 90.25.

$$\text{Side} = \sqrt{90.25}$$

With a calculator, you can obtain the following.

Calculator Steps	Display	Written Result
90.25 $\boxed{\sqrt{x}}$	9.5	$\sqrt{90.25} = 9.5$

Each side of the room should be 9.5 feet long. The perimeter is the sum of the lengths of the four sides, which is 4(9.5) or 38 feet.

Communicating about MATHEMATICS

▶ **SHARING IDEAS about the Lesson**

Rounding Numbers The square root of a **perfect square** can be written as an exact decimal. Two examples of perfect squares are $\sqrt{49} = 7$ and $\sqrt{1.44} = 1.2$. The square root of a number that is not a perfect square can only be approximated by a decimal. Here are two examples.

$$\sqrt{2} \approx 1.4142136 \quad \text{and} \quad \sqrt{5.5} \approx 2.3452079$$

(The symbol $\approx$ means "is approximately equal to.") Rounded to two decimal places, these square roots are 1.41 and 2.35. Round each of the following to two decimal places. Explain how to check your answers.
To check, square each answer.

A. $\sqrt{6}$	**B.** $\sqrt{10}$	**C.** $\sqrt{6.5}$	**D.** $\sqrt{140.3}$
2.45	3.16	2.55	11.84

EXERCISES

Guided Practice

CHECK for Understanding

1. Fill in the blanks.   A power has two parts, a [?] and an [?]. base, exponent
2. State a verbal description of the number sentence $3^4 = 81$. 3 raised to the 4th power is 81.

In Exercises 3–5, find the value of the expression.

3. $\sqrt{16}$ 4   4. $\sqrt{49}$ 7   5. $\sqrt{81}$ 9

6. State a verbal description of the number sentence $\sqrt{36} = 6$. The square root of 36 is 6.

Independent Practice

In Exercises 7–10, write a verbal description of the number sentence. See margin.

7. $6^4 = 1296$ 8. $2.9^2 = 8.41$ 9. $\sqrt{1.21} = 1.1$ 10. $\sqrt{225} = 15$

In Exercises 11–16, write each expression as a power. Then use a calculator to find the value of the power.

11. 12×12 12^2, 144   12. $8 \times 8 \times 8 \times 8$ 8^4, 4096   13. $(3.4)(3.4)(3.4)$ 3.4^3, 39.304

14. $(9.7)(9.7)(9.7)(9.7)(9.7)$ 15. $\frac{1}{5} \cdot \frac{1}{5} \cdot \frac{1}{5} \cdot \frac{1}{5}$ $\left(\frac{1}{5}\right)^4$, $\frac{1}{625}$ 16. $\frac{2}{3} \cdot \frac{2}{3} \cdot \frac{2}{3} \cdot \frac{2}{3} \cdot \frac{2}{3}$ $\left(\frac{2}{3}\right)^5$, $\frac{32}{243}$
9.7^5; 85,873.40257

In Exercises 17–22, find the value of the expression using a calculator. Round your result to two decimal places.

17. $\sqrt{169}$ 13   18. $\sqrt{441}$ 21   19. $\sqrt{117}$ 10.82

20. $\sqrt{372}$ 19.29   21. $\sqrt{5.5}$ 2.35   22. $\sqrt{8.26}$ 2.87

Guess and Check   In Exercises 23–28, find the number that is represented by △.

23. $\triangle \cdot \triangle \cdot \triangle = 512$ 8   24. $\triangle \cdot \triangle \cdot \triangle \cdot \triangle = 625$ 5   25. $\triangle \cdot \triangle = 4.41$ 2.1

26. $\triangle \cdot \triangle \cdot \triangle = 42.875$ 3.5   27. $\sqrt{\triangle} = 9$ 81   28. $\sqrt{\triangle} = 17$ 289

Guess and Check   In Exercises 29–32, replace each [?] with >, <, or =. (The symbol < means "is less than" and the symbol > means "is greater than.")

29. 2^3 [?] 3^2 <   30. 2^4 [?] 4^2 =   31. 4^3 [?] 3^4 <   32. 5^2 [?] 2^5 <

33. *Estimation*   Without using a calculator, predict which is greater 10^2 or 2^{10}. Then use a calculator to check your answer. 2^{10}

34. Find the greatest power of 5 that is less than 20,000. Explain how you did this. 5^6 Explanations vary. Keeping track of the number of 5's, press 5 and then press $\times$ and 5 repeatedly until the result is over 20,000.

Extra Practice

Extra Practice 1.3   Name _____

In Exercises 1 and 2, write a verbal description of the number sentence.
1. $3^4 = 81$ 2. $\sqrt{1.69} = 1.3$
3 raised to the 4th power is 81.   Square root of 1.69 is 1.3.
In Exercises 3–8, write each expression as a power. Then use a calculator to find the value of the power. 7^5; 16,807
3. 10.5×10.5 10.5^2; 110.25   4. $7 \times 7 \times 7 \times 7$ 5. $(1.2)(1.2)(1.2)$ 1.2^3; 1.728
6. $(8.2)(8.2)(8.2)$ 7. $\frac{3}{8} \cdot \frac{3}{8} \cdot \frac{3}{8} \cdot \frac{3}{8} \cdot \frac{3}{8}$ 8. $\frac{1}{9} \cdot \frac{1}{9} \cdot \frac{1}{9} \cdot \frac{1}{9}$
8.2^3; 4521.2176 $(2/5)^6$; 64/15,625 $(1/9)^4$; 1/6561
In Exercises 9–14, find the value of the expression using a calculator. Round your results to two decimal places.
9. $\sqrt{625}$ 25   10. $\sqrt{676}$ 26   11. $\sqrt{243.36}$ 15.6
12. $\sqrt{596}$ 24.41   13. $\sqrt{73}$ 2.74   14. $\sqrt{4.25}$ 2.06
In Exercises 15–20, find the number that is represented by △.
15. $\triangle \cdot \triangle \cdot \triangle = 729$ 9   16. $\triangle \cdot \triangle \cdot \triangle \cdot \triangle \cdot \triangle = 3125$ 5   17. $\triangle \cdot \triangle = 33.64$ 5.8
18. $\triangle \cdot \triangle \cdot \triangle = 42.875$ 3.5   19. $\sqrt{\triangle} = 12$ 144   20. $\sqrt{\triangle} = 27$ 729
In Exercises 21–24, replace each [?] with >, <, or =.
21. 4^2 [?] 2^4 =   22. 3^5 [?] 5^3 >
23. 7^3 [?] 3^7 <   24. 3^2 [?] 2^3 >
25. The floor plan at the right shows three square rooms. The area of the kitchen is 400 square feet. The area of the bathroom is 64 square feet. The perimeter of the living room is 112 feet. Find the perimeter of both the kitchen and the bathroom, and find the area of the living room. Find the total floor area.
Kitchen perimeter: 80 ft; bathroom perimeter: 32 ft; living room area: 784 sq ft; total area: 1248 sq ft.
26. The closed box shown at right has dimensions 8 in. by 8 in. by 8 in.
  a. Find the volume of the box.
  b. What is the surface area of the box?
  c. Is it possible to place another box of volume 420 cubic inches inside of the box shown? Explain.
  a. 512 cubic inches; b. 384 square inches; c. Yes, if neither the length, width, nor height of the "smaller box" is greater than 8 inches.

Windows   *1.3* ▪ *Powers and Square Roots* **3**

Reteaching

Reteach Chapter 1   Name _____

What you should learn: Correlation to Pupil's Textbook:
1.3 How to use powers and how to use square roots.   Mid-Chapter Self-Test (p. 22) Chapter Test (p. 47)
                    Exercises 12, 13   Exercise 16

Examples *Using Powers and Using Square Roots*
a. Write a verbal description of the number sentence.
  $6^3 = 216$ 6 raised to the 3rd power or 6 cubed is 216.
b. Write each expression as a power. Then use a calculator to find the value of the power.
  $4 \times 4 \times 4$ 4^3 Calculator steps: 4 [y^x] 3 [=] 64
  $(0.5)(0.5)(0.5)(0.5)$ $(0.5)^4$ Calculator steps: 0.5 [y^x] 4 [=] 0.0625
c. Find the value of the expression using a calculator. Round your result to two decimal places.
  $\sqrt{6.27}$ Calculator steps: 6.27 [√] $\approx$ 2.50
d. Find the number that is represented by △.
  $\sqrt{\triangle} = 11$ △ = 121
e. Find the side of a square which has an area of 44.89 square units.
  $(\text{Side})^2 = 44.89$
  Side $= \sqrt{44.89} = 6.7$ units

Guidelines: • A power has two parts, a base and an exponent.
  • Any number can be used as an exponent.
  • When you square the square root of a number n, you get the original number n. $\left(\sqrt{n}\right)^2 = n$
  • The square root of a perfect square can be written as an exact decimal.

EXERCISES 1. The square root of   2. 2 raised to the fifth
      0.09 is 0.3.   power is 32.
In Exercises 1–3, write a verbal description of each number sentence.
1. $\sqrt{0.09} = 0.3$ 2. $2^5 = 32$ 3. $\sqrt{484} = 22$ The square root of 484 is 22.
In Exercises 4–6, write each expression as a power. Then use a calculator when appropriate to find the value of the power. 6.7^4, 2015.1121
4. $\frac{1}{3} \cdot \frac{1}{3}$ $(1/3)^2$, $0.\overline{1}$ 5. $(6.7)(6.7)(6.7)(6.7)$ 6. $(15)(15)(15)$ 15^3, 3375
In Exercises 7–9, find the value of the expression using a calculator. Round your result to two decimal places.
7. $\sqrt{201}$ 14.18   8. $\sqrt{4.6}$ 2.14   9. $\sqrt{1.44}$ 1.2

Windows   Chapter 1 ▪ *Exploring Patterns* **3**

EXERCISE Notes

ASSIGNMENT GUIDE

Basic/Average:
  Day 1: Ex. 7, 9, 12, 13, 17–19, 23–33 odd
  Day 2: Ex. 35–39, 41–47 odd, 51, 52
Above Average: Ex. 3, 8, 10, 13, 16, 20–22, 23–31 odd, 33, 34, 39, 40, 42, 49, 51–53
Advanced: Ex. 3, 8, 10, 13, 16, 20–22, 23–31 odd, 33, 34, 39, 40, 42, 49, 51–53
Selected Answers: Ex. 1–6, 7–49 odd

Guided Practice

Refer to the Writing Prompt on page 12. This project will be helpful both for you and the students as a reference later if they incorrectly evaluate 10^2 as 20, or $\sqrt{20}$ as 10.

Independent Practice

▶ **Ex. 15, 16** Students may need additional instruction in using the calculator to raise a fraction to a power.
▶ **Ex. 19–22**
ESTIMATION
Have students estimate between what two whole numbers the answer will be.
▶ **Ex. 23–27** The small triangle is being used as a *variable* (this concept will be introduced in Lesson 1.5).
▶ **Ex. 29–34** Assign these as a group in order to help students develop number sense.

Answers
7. 6 raised to the 4th power is 1296.
8. 2.9 squared is 8.41.
9. The square root of 1.21 is 1.1.
10. The square root of 225 is 15.

37. False; $\sqrt{5} \approx 2.24$, $\sqrt{2} + \sqrt{3} \approx 3.15$

Reasoning In Exercises 35–38, determine whether the statement is true or false. Explain your reasoning.

35. $5^3 = 5 \times 5 \times 5$ True, by meaning of power

36. $5^3 = 2^3 + 3^3$ False; $5^3 = 125$, $2^3 + 3^3 = 35$

37. $\sqrt{5} = \sqrt{2} + \sqrt{3}$ See above.

38. $\sqrt{5} = \sqrt{2+3}$ True, $5 = 2 + 3$

39. *Geometry* Each edge of the cube shown at the right is 7 inches. The surface area of a cube is the sum of the areas of the faces.

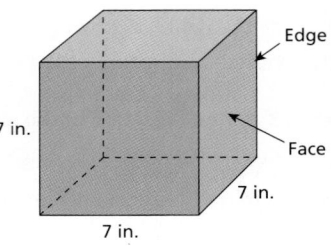

a. How many faces does a cube have? 6

b. What is the area of one face of the cube? 49 in.²

c. Find the surface area of the cube. Explain how you obtained your answer. 294 in.², 6 (7 in.)²

d. If you double the length of each edge of the cube, does its surface area double? Explain your reasoning. No, $6(14^2) \neq 2[6(7^2)]$

40. *Geometry* Volume is a measure of the amount of space that an object occupies. A formula for the volume of a cube is

Volume = (Edge)³.

Use the cube in Exercise 39 to answer the following questions.

a. What is the length, width, and height of the cube? Each is 7 in.

b. Write an expression that gives the volume of the cube. (7 in.)³

c. What is the volume? 343 in.³

41. *Designing a Room* You are designing a computer classroom. You want the classroom to be square and have an area of 420.25 square feet. **b.** 82 ft

a. Find the length and width of the classroom. Each is 20.5 ft.

b. Find the perimeter of the classroom.

c. If you double the area of the classroom, does its perimeter double? Explain your reasoning. No, $4 \times \sqrt{2(420.25)} \neq 2(82)$

✪ **42.** The classroom in Exercise 41 must be divided into nine equal square work areas.

a. Sketch a simple diagram of the classroom. Check students' work.

b. What is the area of each work area? $46\frac{25}{36}$ ft²

c. Explain how you can find the side length of each work area. Compare your explanation to others in the class. Do you all agree? See below.

d. What is the side length of a work area? $6\frac{5}{6}$ ft

c. Find $(20\frac{1}{2} \text{ ft}) \div 3$ or find $\sqrt{46\frac{25}{36} \text{ ft}^2}$.

I. M. Pei is an American architect known for his imaginative and creative designs. Born in China, Pei became a United States citizen in 1954. Some o his works include the John Hancock Building and the John F. Kennedy Library. Both are in Boston, Massachusetts.

Estimation   **In Exercises 43–48, round the number to two decimal places.**

43. 2.5914 2.59   **44.** 11.3496 11.35   **45.** 318.067 318.07

46. 42.8934 42.89   **47.** 26.1966 26.20   **48.** 285.095 285.10

49. *How Many Buses?*   216 students and 9 teachers are boarding buses to go on a field trip. Each bus holds 50 people. How many buses are needed? 5

50. *Fundraiser*   Your band club is selling T-shirts to raise money for a trip. The profit from each shirt is $9.00. Your club needs to raise $5000. How many shirts must be sold? 556

Exploration and Extension

51. Complete the table.

80 ≈ 25.298   8 ≈ 2.5298   0.8 ≈ 0.25298

Expression	$\sqrt{6400}$	$\sqrt{640}$	$\sqrt{64}$	$\sqrt{6.4}$	$\sqrt{0.64}$	$\sqrt{0.064}$
Value	?	?	?	?	?	?

52. *Finding a Pattern*   Describe a pattern of the values you obtained in the table. See margin.

53. *Making a Prediction*   Use the pattern to predict the value of $\sqrt{64,000}$ and $\sqrt{0.0064}$. Verify your answers by using a calculator. ≈ 252.98, 0.08

Mixed R E V I E W

Exercises 1–6: For descriptions, see Additional Answers.

In Exercises 1–6, describe the pattern. Then list the next 3 numbers (1.1)

1. 2, 4, 6, 8, ?, ?, ? 10, 12, 14   **2.** 30, 27, 24, 21, ?, ?, ? 18, 15, 12

3. 1, 6, 11, 16, ?, ?, ? 21, 26, 31   **4.** 3, 1, $\frac{1}{3}$, $\frac{1}{9}$, ?, ?, ? $\frac{1}{27}$, $\frac{1}{81}$, $\frac{1}{243}$

5. 1, 3, 7, 15, ?, ?, ? 31, 63, 127   **6.** 2, 5, 14, 41, ?, ?, ? 122, 365, 1094

In Exercises 7–14, perform the operation. (1.2)

7. 724 + 693 1417   **8.** 415 + 219 634   **9.** 532 − 421 111   **10.** 864 − 179 685

11. 84 × 31 2604   **12.** (243)(16) 3888   **13.** 4472 ÷ 52 86   **14.** 2327 ÷ 13 179

In Exercises 15–20, use a calculator to find the value of the expression. Round your answer to two decimal places. (1.3)

15. 5^7 78,125   **16.** 7^5 16,807   **17.** $\left(\frac{1}{3}\right)^3$ 0.04

18. $\sqrt{3}$ 1.73   **19.** $\sqrt{22}$ 4.69   **20.** $\sqrt{45.28}$ 6.73

Integrated Review

▶ **Ex. 49** Check to see that students understand that 4.5 buses cannot be rented! This is also an application where the regular rules of rounding do not apply. If only 8 teachers chaperone (224 ÷ 50 = 4.48), five buses are still needed.

▶ **Ex. 50** A whole number of T-shirts must be sold. See the notes on Ex. 49.

Exploration and Extension

▶ **Ex. 51–53** Assign these as a group in order to help students develop number sense.

Portfolio Opportunity: Math Log

Describe the pattern and list the next three numbers. 1, 8, 27, 64, ?, ?, ?

Also available as a copymaster, page 5, Ex. 4

Alternative Assessment

A cooperative learning project in which students discover the effect of the square root operation.

Available as a copymaster, page 15

Mixed Review exercises help students check their understanding of previous lessons and prior courses. Answers to the odd numbered exercises are provided in the Selected Answers section of the student text. The Mixed Review exercises include a reference to the lesson in which each skill, strategy, or concept was presented. Students may use these references as a study aid if they are uncertain about how to do a given exercise.

Answer
52. Each odd-numbered expression after the first is $\frac{1}{10}$ the previous one; each even-numbered expression after the first is $\frac{1}{10}$ the previous one.

Lesson 1.3 **15**

Materials

Any kind of calculator (students are asked not to use a square root key)

The primary goal of this activity is to practice the problem-solving strategy of "guess, check, and revise." This is done in a context that allows students to develop a greater understanding of powers and roots. Students gain an appreciation of the square root and cube root keys found on scientific calculators, while also developing the number sense necessary to be successful with this problem-solving strategy.

For additional problems, ask groups to determine solutions to the following problems, accurate to the nearest thousandth.

a. $?^3 = 400$ ≈ 7.368

b. $?^4 = 400$ ≈ 4.472

c. $?^2 = 680$ ≈ 26.077

d. $?^2 = 6800$ ≈ 82.462

Problem Solving

Guess, Check, Revise

Guess a reasonable solution based on data in the problem.

↓

Check the guess.

↓

Revise the guess and continue until a correct solution is found.

Problem solving is a process for discovering relationships. It is not simply a process for finding answers. In this text, problem solving is something you will do while you learn new skills. To solve problems successfully, you should consider using different strategies, such as *making a table, looking for a pattern, using a model, drawing a diagram,* and *guessing, checking, and revising.*

Example   *Designing a Testing Ground*

You are part of a team that is designing a moon rover. You are in a desert location and want to design a testing ground for the rover. The testing ground should be square and have an area of 10 square kilometers. You have only a simple calculator—one that doesn't have a square root key. Explain how to use the calculator to find the dimensions of the testing ground.

Solution   Because the area of the square testing ground is

$$\text{Area} = (\text{Side})^2$$

you need to find a number whose square is 10. With your calculator, you can try **guessing, checking,** and **revising.**

Guess	Calculator Steps	Display	Conclusion
3.1	3.1 $\boxed{\times}$ 3.1 $\boxed{=}$	9.61	Too small
3.2	3.2 $\boxed{\times}$ 3.2 $\boxed{=}$	10.24	Too large
3.15	3.15 $\boxed{\times}$ 3.15 $\boxed{=}$	9.9225	Too small
3.16	3.16 $\boxed{\times}$ 3.16 $\boxed{=}$	9.9856	Too small
3.17	3.17 $\boxed{\times}$ 3.17 $\boxed{=}$	10.0489	Too large

From these guesses and revisions, you can see that each side should be between 3.16 kilometers and 3.17 kilometers. ∎

Exercises   1. Between 2.23 km and 2.24 km; No, between 2.23 and 2.24 $\neq \frac{1}{2}$ (Between 3.16 and 3.17).

1. Use a guess, check, and revise strategy to find the dimensions of a square testing ground that has an area of 5 square kilometers. Are the dimensions half the dimensions of the testing ground described in the Example? Explain your reasoning.

2. You are designing a cubical storage container for the moon rover. The storage container should have a volume of 2 cubic feet. Find the dimensions of the container. (*Hint:* Use the fomula Volume = (Edge)^3).
Each dimension (Edge): ≈ 1.26 ft

1.4 Order of Operations

What you should learn:

 Goal 1 How to use order of operations

 Goal 2 How to use order of operations on a calculator

Why you should learn it:

When more than one operation is used in an expression, it is important to know the order in which the operations must be performed.

Goal 1 | ### Using the Order of Operations

One of your goals as you study this book is to learn to read and write about numbers. One way to avoid confusion when you are communicating mathematical ideas is to establish an **order of operations.**

LESSON INVESTIGATION

■ Investigating Order of Operations

Group Activity Individually perform the following operations. Then compare your results with those obtained by other members in your group.

1. $3 \times 8 + 2 = \boxed{?}$ 26
2. $2 + 8 \times 3 = \boxed{?}$ 26
3. $12 \div 4 \times 3 = \boxed{?}$ 9
4. $3 \div 12 = \boxed{?}$ $\frac{1}{4}$
5. $40 - 4^2 \times 2 = \boxed{?}$ 8
6. $2 \times 3^2 = \boxed{?}$ 18
7. $16 + 12 - 20 = \boxed{?}$ 8
8. $20 - 12 + 16 = \boxed{?}$ 24

Because the value of an expression can change by performing the operations in different orders, we give a different priority to each of the operations. First priority is given to exponents, second priority is given to multiplication and division, and third priority is given to addition and subtraction.

Numerical Expression
A **numerical expression** is a collection of numbers, operations, and grouping symbols. When you perform the operations to obtain a single number or value, you are **evaluating** the expression.

| **Example 1** | *Priority of Operations* |

a. $2 + \overbrace{8 \times 3} = 2 + 24$
   $= 26$

   First priority: multiplication
   Second priority: addition

b. $4 \times \overbrace{3^2} = 4 \times 9$
   $= 36$

   First priority: exponent
   Second priority: multiplication

1.4 ▪ Order of Operations **17**

▶**PACING** the Lesson
Suggested Number of Days
Basic/Average 2   **Above Average** 1
Advanced 1

▶**PLANNING** the Lesson
Lesson Plan 1.4, p. 4

ORGANIZER

Starters (reproduced below)
 Problem of the Day 1.4, p. 2
 Warm-Up Exercises 1.4, p. 2
Lesson Resources
 Teaching Tools
  Graph paper and dot paper, pp. T1–T3, C2–C4
 Math Log, p. 5
 Technology, p. 5
 Answer Masters 1.4, p. 9
 Extra Practice Copymaster 1.4, p. 4
 Reteaching Copymaster 1.4, p. 4
Special Populations
 Suggestions, Teacher's Edition, p. 1D

LESSON Notes

The opening investigation is a very important one. Students frequently ignore (and don't fully understand) the need to follow a prescribed order in computations. The investigation will alert them to the need for mathematical agreement in performing computations.

Example 1

A pair of equivalent expressions is any pair of expressions in which each expression can be transformed into the other by applying the properties and rules of algebra. Help students to see that a numerical expression in mathematics is like a phrase in English. Emphasize that when the numerical expressions $2+8\times3$ and 4×3^2 have been evaluated, the equals sign indicates that the expression before the equals sign is equivalent to the expression that follows the equal sign.

REASONING
In this lesson, and throughout the entire course, encourage students to *explain* why given pairs of expressions are equivalent by quoting the appropriate basic rules of operations.

┌ STARTER: Problem of the Day ┐

Fill in the blanks in this sequence in as many ways as you can. (From *Mathematics Teacher,* Mar. '94)

$1, \underline{\quad}, \underline{\quad}, \frac{1}{64}, \ldots$

Possible answers:
$1, \frac{1}{4}, \frac{1}{16}, \frac{1}{64}, \ldots, \frac{1}{4^n}$
$1, \frac{1}{8}, \frac{1}{27}, \frac{1}{64}, \ldots, \frac{1}{n^3}$
$1, \frac{43}{64}, \frac{22}{64}, \frac{1}{64}, \ldots,$ subtract $\frac{21}{64}$ to get the next term

Also available as a copymaster, page 2

┌ STARTER: Warm-Up Exercises ┐

Ask students to order the given steps for writing and posting a letter.
Answers may vary
a. address the envelope b. walk to the mailbox c. write the letter
d. date the letter e. seal the envelope
f. sign the letter g. place letter in mailbox h. place a stamp on the envelope i. write the return address on the envelope

Also available as a copymaster, page 2

You may wish to have students work in groups to create six examples of expressions that may or may not be equivalent. Each group should write answers on the back of their list. Lists can then be exchanged and checked, or can be collected for later review.

Example 2

Common-Error Alert!

Remind students to use their mnemonic for PEMDAS to determine which operations must be performed first. The left-to-right rule should be applied *after* their mnemonic has been used.

Addressing Misconceptions

Most students prioritize operations by performing them from left to right. After the investigation, emphasize that the highest priority is not, however, computing from left to right. For remembering the order of operations, students frequently find the following mnemonic useful:

Please **E**xcuse **M**y **D**ear **A**unt **S**ally.

The phrase indicates that the order of operations is **P**arentheses, **E**xponents, **M**ultiplication *and* **D**ivision, **A**ddition *and* **S**ubtraction. Make sure students understand the significance of using *and* in this summary of priority levels. Multiplication and division have the same priority level; addition and subtraction have the same priority level.

MATH JOURNAL

Have students write the mnemonic for PEMDAS into their math journals, or suggest that they compose their own mnemonic.

Need To Know

Stress that parentheses have the highest priority. Explain that numerical expressions such as 4(4) occur frequently in algebra when values are being assigned to variables. Many calculators that have parentheses use this priority. Have students experiment with available scientific calculators. They will probably find that 8/4(4) = 0.5, and that 8/4 * 4 = 8.

Operations having the same priority, such as multiplication and division *or* addition and subtraction, are performed from left to right. This is called the **Left-to-Right Rule.**

Example 2 | *Using the Left-to-Right Rule*

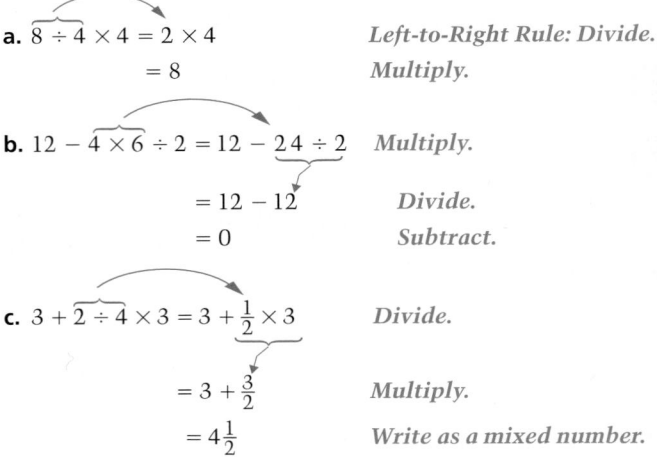

a. $8 \div 4 \times 4 = 2 \times 4$ *Left-to-Right Rule: Divide.*
$= 8$ *Multiply.*

b. $12 - 4 \times 6 \div 2 = 12 - 24 \div 2$ *Multiply.*
$= 12 - 12$ *Divide.*
$= 0$ *Subtract.*

c. $3 + 2 \div 4 \times 3 = 3 + \frac{1}{2} \times 3$ *Divide.*
$= 3 + \frac{3}{2}$ *Multiply.*
$= 4\frac{1}{2}$ *Write as a mixed number.* ∎

When you want to change the established order of operations *or* simply want to make an expression clearer, you should use parentheses or other **grouping symbols.** The most common grouping symbols are parentheses ( ) and brackets [ ]. Braces { } are also sometimes used as grouping symbols.

Expressions within grouping symbols must be evaluated first. Here is an example.

$(3 + 4) \times 2 = 7 \times 2$ *Add within parentheses.*
$= 14$ *Multiply.*

The established rules for order of operations are summarized below.

Order of Operations

To evaluate an expression involving more than one operation, use the following order.

1. First do operations that occur within grouping symbols.
2. Then evaluate powers.
3. Then do multiplications and divisions from left to right.
4. Finally do additions and subtractions from left to right.

Goal 2 Evaluating Expressions with a Calculator

Many calculators use the Order of Operations used in this book, but some do not. Try using your calculator to see whether it gives a result that is listed in the next example.

Technology
Using a Calculator

Example 3 — Order of Operations on a Calculator

When you enter 6 ⊞ 10 ⊟ 2 ⊟ 3 ⊟ on your calculator, does it display 8 or 5? Using the established order of operations, it should display 8.

$$6 + 10 \div 2 - 3 = 6 + 5 - 3 = 11 - 3 = 8$$

If it displays 5, it would have performed the operations as

$$[(6 + 10) \div 2] - 3 = [16 \div 2] - 3 = 8 - 3 = 5.$$

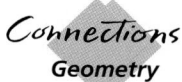
Connections
Geometry

Example 4 — Finding an Area of a Region

Write an expression that represents the area of the region at the left. Then evaluate the expression.

Solution The region at the left can be divided into two rectangles and one square.

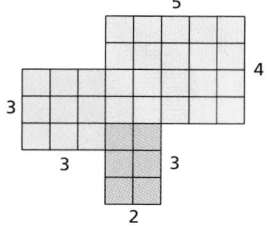

Verbal Model	Area of region	=	Area of rectangle	+	Area of rectangle	+	Area of square

$$\text{Area} = 2 \times 3 + 4 \times 5 + 3^2$$
$$= 6 + 20 + 9$$
$$= 35 \text{ square units} \quad ■$$

Communicating about MATHEMATICS

Cooperative Learning

▶ **SHARING IDEAS about the Lesson** See margin.

Using Multiplication Models Work with a partner. Copy the figure in Example 4 on graph or dot paper. Divide it to form a 2-by-7 rectangle, a 3-by-4 rectangle, and a 3-by-3 square. Then write an expression for the area and evaluate the expression. Do you obtain the same result as in Example 4? Repeat this process with other regions. What can you conclude?

Yes, order of operations is necessary to always get the same results.

P Portfolio Opportunity

Example 3

TECHNOLOGY

Use of calculators Some four-function calculators do not follow the order of operations. Tell students how to get correct answers with these calculators by using the parentheses keys (if they exist), by reordering the expression, or by using the memory. Here are possible keystrokes for Example 3. Remind students that whenever they use memory keys, it is important to clear memory before any new calculation.

6 ⊞ ⟮ 10 ⊟ 2 ⟯ ⊟ 3 ⊟
10 ⊟ 2 ⊞ 6 ⊟ 3 ⊟
6 M+ 10 ⊟ 2 ⊟ M+ 3 M− MRC

On some calculators data is entered in memory with a STO key and recalled with a RCL or MR key.

Assure students that if parentheses are included in their numerical expression, any calculator will provide the same result.

Example 4

CONNECTIONS TO GEOMETRY

Ask students whether any other partitions could be used to find the area of the region.

Yes, the partition associated with the numerical expression $3^2 + 2 \times 7 + 3 \times 4$ will work.

This example pinpoints the great importance of geometry in providing visual models or alternative representations of mathematical concepts. In this case, if the same area can be represented by two distinct numerical expressions, then these expressions must be equivalent.

See also the Enrichment note on TE page 21.

Communicating about MATHEMATICS

Challenge students to create other regions (on dot or graph paper) that would illustrate different priorities in the order of operations. See also the Enrichment note on page 21.

Writing Prompt

When performing calculations mentally, I feel . . . because . . .

Answer to Communicating

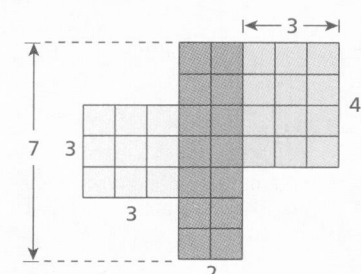

$$3^2 + 2 \times 7 + 3 \times 4 = 9 + 14 + 12$$
$$= 35 \text{ square units}$$

Extra Examples

Here are extra examples similar to some of those in the lesson.

1. Priority of operations

$4 + 6 \times 3 = 4 + 18$ 1st priority: multiplication
$\qquad\qquad = 22$ 2nd priority: addition

2. Left-to-Right Rule

$14 \div 2 \times 6 = 7 \times 6$ Left-to-Right Rule: Divide
$\qquad\qquad = 42$ Multiply

Technology

Learning About Your Calculator   **1.4**   Name _____

Exploration Using a Calculator

This activity has two parts. In Part I, you will learn whether your calculator uses the order of operations discussed in Lesson 1.4 of the textbook. (If your calculator does not use the correct order of operations, you should consider using one that does as this will help immensely with this course.) In Part II, you will learn how to evaluate numerical expressions with exponents and parentheses using your calculator.

Part I

Enter 32 ⊞ 8 ⊟ 2 ⊟ on your calculator. If your calculator uses the correct order of operations, the display will read 36. If the display reads 20, your calculator performed the operations as (32 + 8) ÷ 2 = 40 ÷ 2 = 20, which is incorrect. From this simple example, you can see how important it is that your calculator uses the correct order of operations.

Part II

The following example shows how you can use your calculator to evaluate numerical expressions involving exponents and parentheses.

EXAMPLE Using Exponents and Parentheses

Use a calculator to evaluate the following numerical expressions.
a. $(9 + 7) \div 2^2$ b. $(5 + 2)^3 - [2 \times (8 + 1)]^2$

SOLUTION
a. Enter the following keystrokes on your calculator.
⟮ 9 ⊞ 7 ⟯ ⊟ 2 x² ⊟
The display should show 4.
b. Enter the following keystrokes on your calculator.
⟮ 5 ⊞ 2 ⟯ yˣ 3 ⊟ ⟮ 2 x ⟮⟮ 8 ⊞ 1 ⟯⟯ x² ⟯ ⊟
The display should show 19.

EXERCISES

In Exercises 1–6, use your calculator to evaluate the numerical expression. List each keystroke.

1. $27 + 36 \div 9$ 2. $13 \times 7 - 54$ 3. $(41 - 29) \times 2.5$

4. $11^2 - 750 \div 10$ 5. $(21 + 9) \times 3^2 - 6^3$ 6. $2^4 - 4 + 2[(16 - 3^2)^2 - 10]$

7. Using *only* the numbers 1, 2, 3, 4, 5, 6, 7, 8, and 9 (each once) and the four number operations (each at least once), describe how you can use your calculator to obtain a final display of 22. (Do not use exponents or parentheses.)

© D.C. Heath and Company   *Technology: Using Calculators and Computers* **5**

1. 31; 27 ⊞ 36 ⊟ 9 ⊟

2. 37; 13 ⊠ 7 ⊟ 54 ⊟

3. 30; ⟮⟮ 41 ⊟ 29 ⟯⟯ ⊠ 2 ⊡ 5 ⊟

4. 46; 11 x² ⊟ 750 ⊟ 10 ⊟

5. 54; ⟮⟮ 21 ⊞ 9 ⟯⟯ ⊠ 3 x² ⊟ 6 yˣ 3 ⊟

6. 90; 2 yˣ 4 ⊟ 4 ⊞ 2 ⊠ ⟮⟮⟮ 16 ⊟ 3 x² ⟯ x² ⊟ 10 ⟯⟯ ⊟

7. Answers vary. See answers in back of supplement for one possible answer.

ASSIGNMENT GUIDE

Basic/Average:
Day 1: Ex. 5–17 odd, 19–25 odd, 27–33 odd
Day 2: Ex. 35–39, 41, 43, 44
Above Average: Ex. 15–25 odd, 27–33 odd, 35–40, 41, 42, 43–47
Advanced: Ex. 15–18, 23–26, 31–34, 37–41, 43–47
Selected Answers: Ex. 1–4, 5–41 odd

Guided Practice

▶ **Ex. 2** Have students make up their own examples of numerical expressions that would be ambiguous without an established order of operations.
▶ **Ex. 4** Point out that we use the Left-to-Right Rule when we have to decide between two operations of the same priority level.

Independent Practice

▶ **Ex. 5–18** As the problems become more involved, encourage students to write the intermediate steps as shown in Examples 1 and 2. Have students share the results at the board and have them explain their work to classmates. For students reluctant to go to the board, suggest that they work with partners, taking turns to explain their work to each other.
▶ **Ex. 29** Although parentheses are not needed, students may still insert them: $(6 \cdot 3) - (2 \cdot 5)$.
▶ **Ex. 30** Although only one set of parentheses is needed, students may insert a second set: $24 - [(12 - 4) \cdot 2]$
▶ **Ex. 32** Refer to the note for Ex. 29 above.
▶ **Ex. 33** Refer to the note for Ex. 30 above.

Answers

1. To always get the same results. Examples vary. Example: The total number of pencils in 3 boxes of 12 pencils each and 2 boxes of 10 pencils each is $3 \times 12 + 2 \times 10$ or 56, not 380.
2. Evaluating powers, multiplications and divisions, and additions and subtractions; to always get the same results.

20 Chapter 1

EXERCISES

Guided Practice

▶ **CHECK for Understanding** Exercises 1–2: See margin.

P **1.** Why is it important to learn to communicate mathematics? Give a real-life example of communicating mathematics.

P **2.** State the established order of operations. Why is it important to have an established order of operations?

3. Evaluate the expression.
   a. $18 - 4 \times 3$ 6
   b. $48 \div 6 \times 3$ 24
   c. $12 + 4^2 - 3 \times (5 - 2)$ 19

4. *Reasoning*   Insert parentheses in order to make the number sentence true.
   a. $3 \times (4 + 8) - 2 = 34$
   b. $(7 - 3) \div 2 \times (8 + 2) = 20$

Independent Practice

Computation Sense   **In Exercises 5–18, evaluate the expression without using a calculator.**

5. $7 + 12 \div 6$ 9
6. $12 - 3 \times 4$ 0
7. $5 \cdot 3 + 2^2$ 19
8. $5^2 - 8 \div 2$ 21
9. $11 + 4 \div 2 \times 9$ 29
10. $21 - 1 \cdot 2 \div 4$ $20\frac{1}{2}$
11. $8 + 14 - 2 + 4 \cdot 2^3$ 52
12. $30 - 3^3 + 8 \cdot 3 \div 12$ 5
13. $(9 + 7) \div 4 \times 2$ 8
14. $6 \div (17 - 11) \cdot 14$ 14
15. $4 \cdot (5)(5) + 13$ 113
16. $16 \div 4(2) \times 9$ 18
17. $3[16 - (3 + 7) \div 5]$ 42
18. $[1 + 3(9 + 12)] - 4^3$ 0

In Exercises 19–26, use a calculator to evaluate the expression.

19. $29 + 16 \div 8 \cdot 25$ 79
20. $36 + 16 - 50 \div 25$ 50
21. $18 \cdot 3 \div 3^3$ 2
22. $10 + 5^3 - 25$ 110
23. $149 - (2^8 - 40) \div 6$ 113
24. $20 - (3^5 \div 27) \cdot 2$ 2
25. $22 + (34 \cdot 2)^2 \div 8 + 59$ 659
26. $85 - (4 \cdot 2)^2 - 3 \cdot 7$ 0

Reasoning   **In Exercises 27–34, decide whether the number sentence is true or false according to the established order of operations. If it is false, insert parentheses to make it true.**

27. $(6 + 21) \div 3 = 9$ False
28. $(21 - 8) \cdot 2 = 26$ False
29. $6 \cdot 3 - 2 \cdot 5 = 8$ True
30. $24 - (12 - 4) \cdot 2 = 8$ False
31. $(6 + 3^2) \div 3 = 5$ False
32. $8^2 - 1 \cdot 3 - 5 = 56$ True
33. $7 + 7 \cdot (2 + 6) = 63$ False
34. $36 \div (9 - 6) \div 2 = 6$ False

20   *Chapter 1 ▪ Exploring Patterns*   P Portfolio Opportunity

---

Extra Practice

Extra Practice 1.4   Name _____

In Exercises 1–14, evaluate the expression without using a calculator.

1. $3 + 8 \div 2$ 7
2. $18 - 6 \div 2$ 15
3. $4 \cdot 3 + 4^2$ 28
4. $6^2 - 9 \cdot 4$ 0
5. $(3 + 2) \cdot 5 \cdot 2^3$ 8
6. $30 - 3^2 + 4 \cdot 5$ 41
7. $3[2^4 + 4 - 2]$ 6
8. $16 \div 8(2) \times 6$ 6
9. $24 + 4^2 \cdot 6$ 120
10. $64 \div (2)(8) + 12$ 16
11. $[2 + 3(2) + 3^2] - 4^2$ 1
12. $(4 + 6) \div 2 + 5^2$ 30
13. $24 + (3^2 \div 3) \cdot 11$ 57
14. $[(4^2 + 2) \div 2 + 10] - 2$ 17

In Exercises 15–22, use a calculator to evaluate the expression.

15. $36 + 3 \div 12 + 6$ 42.25
16. $12 - 3^2 + 9 \cdot 6$ 57
17. $100 \cdot 5 \div 5^3$ 4
18. $20 - (2^3 + 4^2) \cdot 6$ 8
19. $50 - (2 + 5^2) \cdot 100$ 42
20. $75 + 5^3 - 4^3 + 2^3$ 192
21. $24 + (2 \cdot 8)^2 + 4^2 - 6$ 34
22. $18 \cdot 2^3 - 5 \cdot 6 \div 2$ 129

In Exercises 23–30, decide whether the number sentence is true or false according to the established order of operations. If it is false, insert parentheses to make it true.

23. $4 + 24 \div 6 = 8$ True
24. $18 - 6 \div 2 = 6$ False, $(18 - 6) \div 2 = 6$
25. $6 \cdot 3 - 2 \cdot 3 = 18$ False, $6 \cdot (3 - 2) \cdot 3 = 18$
26. $24 - 3 \div 7 + 2 = 5$ 26. False,
27. $5 + 2^2 + 3 = 3$ False, $(5 + 2^2) \div 3 = 3$
28. $8^2 - 4 \div 2 + 2 = 64$ $(24 - 3) \div 7 + 2 = 5$
29. $24 + 4 + 2 - 2^2 = 0$
30. $4^2 - 3^2 \div 3 = 13$
False, $24 \div (4 + 2) - 2^2 = 0$ 28. True   30. True

In Exercises 31–34, write a numerical expression for the phrase. Then evaluate your expression.
$35 \div (9 + 3) \div 3$ $6 + (42 \div 21) = 8$
31. 36 divided by the sum of 9 and 3
32. 6 added to the quotient of 42 and 21
33. 42 divided the quotient of 14 and 2
34. 12 minus the product of 4 and 2
$42 \div (14 \div 2) = 6$ $12 - (4 \cdot 2) = 4$
35. You and three friends go to the movies. The group has $40 total. The cost per ticket is $5.25. Each one of the group wants a large soda for $1.25 each, and a box of candy for $1.15 each. Two of the four are willing to share a large buttered popcorn for $3.75 and the other two are going to share a medium unbuttered popcorn for $3.00. Write an expression that represents the total. How much money did the group spend? How much money remains? Total cost $= 4(5.25) + 4(1.25) + 4(1.15) + 3.75 + 3.00$. The total cost is $37.35. The amount of money remaining is $2.65.

4   *Order of Operations ▪ 1.4*   Windows

Reteaching

Reteach Chapter 1   Name _____

What you should learn:
1.4   How to use order of operations and how to use order of operations on a calculator.

Correlation to Pupil's Textbook:
Mid-Chapter Self-Test (p. 22)   Chapter Test (p. 47)
Exercises 14–18   Exercises 9–12

Examples   *Using the Order of Operations and Evaluating Expressions with a Calculator*

a. Use the Priority of Operations to evaluate the expression.
$16 \div 2^3 = 16 \div 8$ *First priority: exponent*
$= 2$ *Second priority: division*

b. Use the Left-to-Right Rule to evaluate the expression.
$24 \div 4 \times 2 = 6 \times 2$ *Left-to-Right Rule: divide*
$= 12$ *Multiply.*

c. Use a calculator to evaluate the expression.
$2 + 4^3 - 36$

If your calculator uses the Order of Operations used in the textbook, it should display 30.

Guidelines:
- A numerical expression is collection of numbers, operations, and grouping symbols.
- You are evaluating an expression when you perform the operations to obtain a single number.
- The Order of Operations is used to evaluate an expression involving more than one operation, using the order:
  1. First do operations that occur within grouping symbols.
  2. Then evaluate powers.
  3. Then do multiplications and divisions from left to right.
  4. Finally do additions and subtractions from left to right.

EXERCISES

In Exercises 1–6, evaluate the expression without using a calculator. Use a calculator to check your answer.

1. $18 - 5 + 3$ 16
2. $5 + 6 \div 3 \times 7$ 19
3. $4 \times 20 - 6^2$ 44
4. $12 \div (18 - 15) \cdot 2$ 8
5. $(9 + 13) \cdot 3 - 8$ 58
6. $5^2 + (9 - 5) \div 4$ 26

4   *Chapter 1 ▪ Exploring Patterns*   Windows

In Exercises 35–38, write a numerical expression for the phrase. Then evaluate your expression. **35.** $24 \div 8 + 9 = 12$ **37.** $36 \div (6 + 12) = 2$ **38.** $42 \div (1 \times 7) = 6$

35. 9 added to the quotient of 24 and 8

✪ **36.** 6 minus the difference of 18 and 15 $6 - (18 - 15)$

37. 36 divided by the sum of 6 and 12

✪ **38.** 42 divided by the product of 1 and 7 $= 3$

39. *School Clothes* You go to the mall to shop for school clothes. You purchase 2 pairs of jeans for $25 each, 3 shirts for $20 each, and 2 pairs of shoes for $25 each. Write an expression that represents your total cost. How much money did you spend? $2(\$25) + 3(\$20) + 2(\$25),$ $\$160$

40. *School Supplies* You go to your school supply store to buy school supplies. You have $40. You purchase 5 folders for $1 each, 3 notebooks for $1.20 each, 2 packs of pencils for $.80 each, and a calculator for $21.50. All prices include tax. Write an expression that represents the amount of money you have left. How much money do you have left?
$\$40 - 5(\$1) - 3(\$1.20) - 2(\$.80) - \$21.50, \$8.30$

Alberta, Canada **In 1993, the world's largest mall was the West Edmonton Mall in Alberta, Canada. It has 839 stores, including 11 major department stores.**

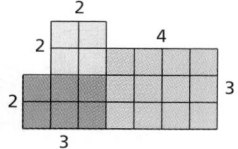

Making Connections within Mathematics

Geometry **In Exercises 41 and 42, write an expression that represents the area of the region. Then evaluate the expression.**

41.

$2 \times 3 + 2^2 + 3 \times 4$, 22 units²

42.

$3 \times 4 + 2 \times 4 + 2 \times 3$, 26 units²

Exploration and Extension

Twenty-Four Game **In Exercises 43–46, use the numbers to play a game of 24. The object of this game is to use the established order of operations to write an expression whose value is 24. You can reorder the numbers, but you cannot use grouping symbols. For instance, the numbers 3, 8, 9, and 9 can be written as 8 • 3 + 9 − 9 = 24.**

43. $8 \times 4 - 8 \times 1$
44. $9 \times 2 + 5 + 1$
45. $2 \times 3 \times 3 + 6$ or $2 \times 3 + 6$
46. $2^7 \div 8 + 8$

43. 1, 8, 4, 8 ✪ **44.** 1, 5, 9, 2 ✪ **45.** 3, 6, 2, 3 ✪ **46.** 2, 7, 8, 8

47. Play the Twenty-Four Game with a friend. Each person should create 4 sets of 4 numbers. (You must be able to get 24 with each set.) Then exchange sets, write the expressions, and check your results. Answers vary.

✪ More difficult exercises

Integrated Review

LOGICAL REASONING

Ask students to determine the perimeter of each figure. Pose the following question: If the area of one figure is smaller than the area of a second figure, will the perimeter also be smaller?

Exploration and Extension

This is a fun game that allows students to practice using the established order of operations.

Portfolio Opportunity: Math Log

Evaluate the expressions and explain why the results are different:
$8 \div 4 \times 2 + 6, 8 \div 4(2) + 6.$

Also available as a copymaster, page 5, Ex. 5

Alternative Assessment

Open-ended questions about the order of operations.

Available as a copymaster, page 16

Short Quiz

Covers Lessons 1.3 and 1.4

Available as a copymaster, page 2

▶ **Enrichment**

CONNECTIONS TO GEOMETRY
Have students explore the geometry connection mentioned in the Example 4 notes. This modeling of areas by means of numerical expressions (and vice versa) leads naturally to the use of algebra tiles in later chapters for modeling algebraic expressions. Have students find ways to partition the area shown here into two or more smaller areas, using horizontal and/or vertical lines. Have them then write at least three different expressions for the total area.

Be sure to notice any students who see the *difference of areas* solution. Not only does this represent a solid step forward in geometric thinking, but it also involves some sound problem-solving techniques.

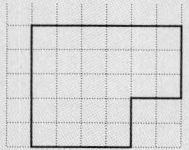

Mid-Chapter Self-Test

Resources

Color Transparencies
  Diagrams for Ex. 6, 7, p. 5

Students can take the Self-Test under test-like conditions and then check their answers with the Selected Answers section of the student text. The Mid-Chapter Self-Test includes a reference to the lesson in which each skill, strategy, or concept was presented. Students may use these references as a study aid if they are uncertain about how to do a given exercise in the Mid-Chapter Self-Test.

Answers

To get the next number:

2. Add 3 to the previous number.

3. Subtract 9 from the previous number.

4. Name next larger perfect square; or add 3, add 5, add 7, etc., to the previous number.

5. Add 1 to the denominator of the previous number.

6.

7.

8. The product of 12 and 4
9. The product of 176 and 12
10. The quotient of 15 and 3
11. The quotient of 369 and 41
12. 3 cubed
13. The square root of 256

Mid-Chapter SELF-TEST

Take this test as you would take a test in class. The answers to the exercises are given in the back of the book.

1. List several ways that numbers are used to describe objects in real life. **(1.1)** Answers vary. Height, weight, area

In Exercises 2–5, describe the pattern. Then list the next 3 numbers. (1.1) For patterns, see margin.

2. 3, 6, 9, [?], [?], [?] 12, 15, 18

3. 90, 81, 72, [?], [?], [?] 63, 54, 45

4. 1, 4, 9, [?], [?], [?] 16, 25, 36

5. $1, \frac{1}{2}, \frac{1}{3}, $ [?], [?], [?] $\frac{1}{4}, \frac{1}{5}, \frac{1}{6}$

In Exercises 6 and 7, draw the next three figures in the pattern. (1.1) See margin.

6.

7.

In Exercises 8–13, write a verbal description of the expression and evaluate the expression. (1.2, 1.3, 1.4) For descriptions, see margin.

8. 12×4 48

9. $(176)(12)$ 2112

10. $15 \div 3$ 5

11. $\frac{369}{41}$ 9

12. 3^3 27

13. $\sqrt{256}$ 16

In Exercises 14 and 15, imagine that you are in a music store and decide to buy 2 CDs and 3 cassettes. Each CD costs $14 and each cassette costs $8 including tax. (1.4)

14. How much money did you spend? $52

15. You brought $70 to the music store. After buying the CDs and cassettes and lending $6 to a friend, how much will you have left? $12

In Exercises 16–18, consider a square checkerboard that has an area of 400 square inches. (1.4)

16. What is the length of each side of the checkerboard? 20 in.

17. The checkerboard has 8 small squares on each side. What are the dimensions of each small square? $2\frac{1}{2}$ in. $\times 2\frac{1}{2}$ in.

18. How many small squares are on the checkerboard? What is the area of each? 64, $6\frac{1}{4}$ in.²

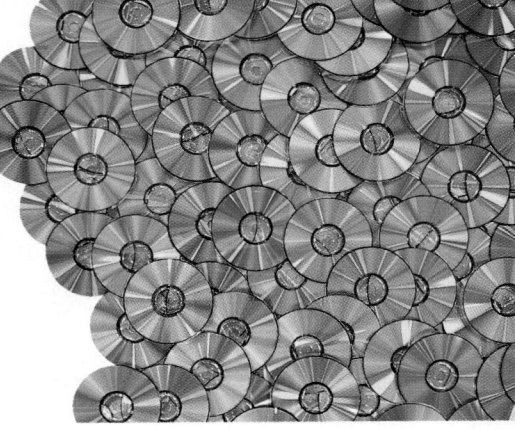

In 1991, consumers in the United States spent about $5.3 billion on CDs and about $4 billion on cassettes. (Source: Recording Industry Association of America)

Materials Needed: Pencil, graph paper, or dot paper

Example

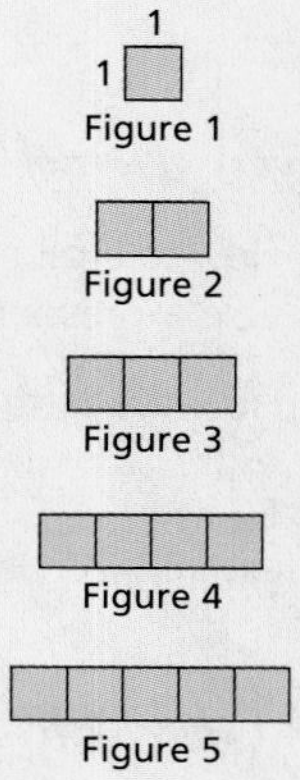

The 5 figures at the right form a pattern.

a. Find the perimeter of each figure.

b. Describe the 6th figure. Without drawing it, predict its perimeter. Then draw the figure to confirm your result.

c. What is the perimeter of the 41st figure?

d. Explain how the perimeter of each figure is related to its figure number.

1

1 □
Figure 1

□□
Figure 2

□□□
Figure 3

□□□□
Figure 4

□□□□□
Figure 5

Solution

a. The perimeters of the figures are as follows:

Figure	1	2	3	4	5
Perimeter	4	6	8	10	12
Pattern	2 + 2(1)	2 + 2(2)	2 + 2(3)	2 + 2(4)	2 + 2(5)

b. The sixth figure is a 1-by-6 rectangle. From the pattern in the table, its perimeter should be 2 + 2(6) or 14. The 6th figure is shown at the right. Notice that its perimeter is 1 + 6 + 1 + 6 or 14.

□□□□□□
Figure 6

c. From the pattern in the table, the perimeter of the 41st figure is 2 + 2(41) or 84.

d. To find the perimeter of any figure, multiply the figure number by 2 and add 2.

Exercises

In Exercises 1 and 2, repeat the steps described in the Example. See margin.

1.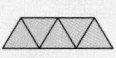

Figure 1   Figure 2   Figure 3   Figure 4   Figure 5

2.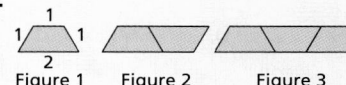

Figure 1   Figure 2   Figure 3   Figure 4   Figure 5

Materials
Teaching Tools
  Graph paper and dot paper, pp. T1–T3, C2–C4

The goal of this investigation is to have students describe patterns, and to use their observation to determine the solution to other problems.

ALTERNATE APPROACHES
In the solution to the example, the perimeter is found by finding the lengths of the top, bottom, and sides. Two alternate methods are provided here as examples of actual student work in author Boswell's classroom.

Erinn's Method
Each square had a perimeter of 4, and the figure number equals the number of squares. The squares share sides when put together, so subtract 2 for each "share." The number of shares is one less than the figure number. So, perimeter = 4 × figure number − 2 × (figure number − 1). For figure 41, perimeter = 4 × 41 − 2(41 − 1) = 164 − 80 = 84.

Brian's Method
All the squares except for those at the right and left end contribute 2 to the perimeter (top edge and bottom edge). These are called "middle squares," and there are always 2 less "middle squares" than the figure number. The right and left squares each contribute 3 (a top, bottom, and side edge) for a total of 6. So, perimeter = 2 × (figure number − 2) + 6. For figure 41, perimeter = 2 × (41 − 2) + 6 = 2 × 39 + 6 = 84.

Have students record their methods in their own words. Later, when students learn to simplify expressions, have them return to this activity to verify that the many methods suggested are indeed equivalent.

Below are other patterns to investigate, where two different shapes are used.

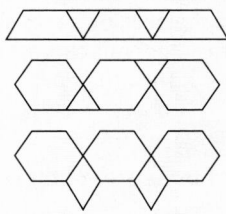

Answers
1. a. 3, 4, 5, 6, 7 **b.** A parallelogram made up of 6 equilateral triangles in a row, 8

c. 43 **d.** n = figure number, P = perimeter: $P = n + 2$

2. a. 5, 8, 11, 14, 17 **b.** A parallelogram made up of 6 isosceles trapezoids in a row, 20

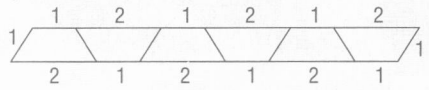

c. 125 **d.** n = figure number, P = perimeter: $P = 3n + 2$

▶ **PLANNING the Lesson**

Lesson Plan 1.5, p. 5

ORGANIZER

Starters (reproduced below)
 Problem of the Day 1.5, p. 2
 Warm-Up Exercises 1.5, p. 2
Lesson Resources
 Color Transparencies
  Picture for Ex. 27, p. 3
 Math Log, p. 5
 Answer Masters 1.5, p. 10
 Extra Practice Copymaster 1.5, p. 5
 Reteaching Copymaster 1.5, p. 5
Special Populations
 Suggestions, Teacher's Edition, p. 1D

LESSON Notes

Vocabulary Alert!

Identify "variable" and "substituting" as
key vocabulary for students to learn in
order to understand this lesson.

Remind students how the patterns in the
table on page 23 depend on the "figure number" of their respective columns. This becomes more apparent if rows 2 and 3 are
switched.

Figure	1	2	3	4	5
Pattern	2+2(1)	2+2(2)	2+2(3)	2+2(4)	2+2(5)
Perimeter	4	6	8	10	12

Explain that the pattern of the second row
could be written as 2+2(figure number). In
this context, "figure number" is a variable
that could be replaced by n or x, so that we
could write the algebraic expression $2+2n$ for
the perimeter of the nth figure.

Example 1

Ask students for the area of the rectangle. 37
units^2

Need To Know – Extension

Remind students of the order of operations, that the grouping symbol, "( )", is
used to hold the substitution, and that in
the expression $2+2(37)$, multiplication of
2 and 37 has the higher priority. Finally,
stress that in the expression $2x^2$, only the
x variable (or its substituted value) is
squared. The coefficient, 2, is not
squared.

1.5 Introduction to Algebra: Variables in Expressions

What you should learn:

Goal 1 How to evaluate variable expressions

Goal 2 How to use variable
expressions in formu-
las to model real-life
situations

Why you should learn it:

Learning to use variable expressions is a key part of learning
algebra. Variable expressions
allow you to model real-life
situations, such as finding the
distance traveled by a moon
rover.

Need to Know

When substituting a number
for a variable, you must
replace each occurrence of
the variable in the expression. For example, you can
evaluate $3x + 2x^2$ when
$x = 4$ as follows.

Expression
$3x + 2x^2$
↓
Substitute 4 for x.
$3(4) + 2(4^2)$
↓
Simplify.
$12 + 32 = 44$

Goal 1 **Evaluating Variable Expressions**

A **variable** is a letter that is used to represent one or more numbers. The numbers are the **values of the variable.** An **algebraic
expression** is a collection of numbers, variables, operations, and
grouping symbols. Here are some examples.

Algebraic Expression	Meaning
$5n$	5 times n
$4x^2$	4 times the square of x
$2a + bc$	2 times a, plus b times c

Replacing each variable in an algebraic expression by a number
is called **substituting** in the expression. The number obtained by
simplifying the expression is the **value of the expression.** To
evaluate an algebraic expression, use the following flowchart.

Write the algebraic expression	→	Substitute values for variables	→	Simplify the numerical expression

Parts of expressions have special names.

Sum: $4x$ and 5 are the **terms** of $4x + 5$.
Product: 7 and n are the **factors** of $7n$.
Quotient: $3a$ is the **numerator** and b is the **denominator** of $\frac{3a}{b}$.

Example 1 **Evaluating an Algebraic Expression**

The expression $2 + 2n$ represents the perimeter of a 1-by-n
rectangle. (See the Lesson Investigation on page 23.) Evaluate
this expression when $n = 37$. What does the result represent?

Solution To evaluate the expression, substitute 37 for n.

$2 + 2n$	*Write the expression.*
$= 2 + 2(37)$	*Substitute 37 for n.*
$= 2 + 74$	*Simplify 2(37).*
$= 76$	*Value of the expression*

The result represents the perimeter of a 1-by-37 rectangle.

STARTER: Problem of the Day

How many triangles will balance the
circle and square? 5

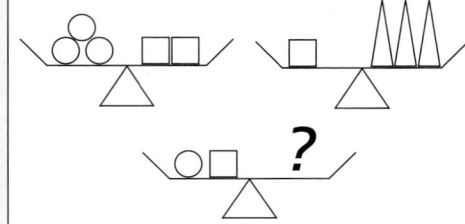

Also available as a copymaster, page 2

STARTER: Warm-Up Exercises

1. Describe or characterize a "substitute player" in games such as basketball
or football. What do you think a substitution in mathematics would be?
2. Without using words, write expressions for each of the following.
a. the product of 5 and 3 $5 \cdot 3$
b. the product of 5 and n $5 \times n, 5 \cdot n$, or
$5n$
c. 4 times the square of 3 4×3^2
d. 4 times the square of x $4 \times x^2$ or $4x^2$
e. the sum of 2 times 2 and 2 times 3
$2 \cdot 2 + 2 \cdot 3$
f. the sum of 2 times a and 2 times b
$2 \cdot a + 2 \cdot b$ or $2a + 2b$

Also available as a copymaster, page 2

Goal 2 Modeling Real-Life with Formulas

Algebraic expressions are often used to model real-life quantities. Here are two examples.

Quantity	Labels	Formula
Area of a Rectangle	A = area l = length w = width	$A = lw$
Distance	d = distance r = rate or speed t = time	$d = rt$

Each of these **formulas** (or algebraic models) can be written as a **verbal model.** For instance, $A = lw$ can be written as "the area of a rectangle is the product of its length and width."

Problem Solving
Verbal Model

Example 2 Finding a Distance

As an astronaut on the moon, you are driving your rover at a speed of 18 miles per hour. How far will you travel in 75 minutes?

Solution   Because the speed is stated in miles per *hour*, you should begin by writing 75 minutes as 1.25 hours.

Verbal Model   Distance = Rate · Time

Distance = d (miles)
Speed = r (miles per hour)
Time = t (hours)

$d = r \cdot t$ *Write algebraic model.*
$= (18)(1.25)$ *Substitute for r and t.*
$= 22.5$ *Simplify.*

In 75 minutes, you will travel 22.5 miles. ∎

Communicating *about* MATHEMATICS

▶ **SHARING IDEAS about the Lesson**

Extending the Example Repeat Example 2 for the following speeds and times. Describe the process you used. Descriptions vary.

A. 16 mph for 90 min.   **B.** 22 mph for 50 min. $18\frac{1}{3}$ mi
24 mi

1.5 • *Introduction to Algebra: Variables in Expressions*   **25**

Point out that formulas are simply algebraic models of real-life situations. Have students state (and write) the verbal model of $d = rt$.

Example 2

Ask students: Suppose your rover has a top speed of 21 miles per hour. How far would you travel in 90 minutes?   31.5 miles
For many students this example may be their first exposure to using three variables. Explain that this is frequently necessary in algebraic modeling.

Communicating *about* MATHEMATICS

EXTENSION
Ask students to use the verbal model in Example 2 to find the following.
a. The time taken to travel 150 miles at a speed of 55 miles per hour   ≈2 hours 44 minutes
b. The rate at which you need to travel in order to cover a distance of 85 miles in $1\frac{1}{2}$ hours.   ≈57 miles per hour

Writing Prompt
Describe the images that come to mind when you think about variables.

Lesson 1.5   **25**

ASSIGNMENT GUIDE

Basic/Average:
Day 1: Ex. 9, 13, 14, 21–27 odd, 37–40, 43
Day 2: Ex. 44, 45, 51–56
Above Average: Ex. 16–18, 29–32, 41, 42, 45, 46, 57–60
Advanced: Ex. 16–18, 29–32, 41, 42, 45, 46, 57–60
Selected Answers: Ex. 1–8, 9–53 odd

Guided Practice

▶ **Ex. 3–6**   These exercises are a valuable lead-in to algebraic modeling. Have students describe each of these words or phrases in their journals.

Independent Practice

▶ **Ex. 13, 14**

Common-Error Alert!

Students may incorrectly calculate $(3x)^2$ versus $3x^2$.

▶ **Ex. 20**   Check for the correct order of operations.
▶ **Ex. 33–36**   Explain to students that these exercises involve three variables, as in Example 3.
▶ **Ex. 41, 42**   These exercises are a preview of solving equations.

26   *Chapter 1*

EXERCISES

Guided Practice

▶ CHECK for Understanding

P 1. What is an algebraic expression? Give an example and state the expression in words.   See page 24.

  2. What does it mean to *evaluate* an expression?   Find its numerical value.

In Exercises 3–6, using 4 + *n* with n = 3, identify the following.

  3. The variable n

  4. The value of the variable   3

  5. The expression $4 + n$

  6. The value of the expression   7

In Exercises 7 and 8, evaluate the expression for a = 5 and b = 3.

  7. $3a + b$ 18

  8. $(2b^2 + 7) \div a$ 5

Independent Practice

In Exercises 9–20, evaluate the expression for *x* = 4.

  9. $5 + x$ 9
  10. $32 \div x$ 8
  11. $12x$ 48
  12. $x \cdot 3x$ 48
  13. $3x^2 + 9$ 57
  14. $2x^2 \cdot 3x$ 384
  15. $(x + 3)6$ 42
  16. $(x - 2) \div 4$ $\frac{1}{2}$
  17. $(9 - x)^2$ 25
  18. $(7 - x)^3$ 27
  19. $(8 - x + 8) \div x$ 3
  20. $x^2 - 3 \cdot x$ 4

In Exercises 21 –32, evaluate the expression for *a* = 2 and *b* = 7.

  21. $b - a$ 5
  22. ab 14
  23. $3b - a$ 19
  24. $5a + 2b$ 24
  25. $3a^2 \cdot b$ 84
  26. $(4b) \div (2a)$ 7
  27. $(24a - 6) \div b$ 6
  28. $b(9 - a)$ 49
  29. $(b - a)^3$ 125
  30. $(5 + b)^2 + a$ 146
  31. $(a + b) \div (b - 2a)$ 3
  32. $6(b - a) \div (3a)$ 5

In Exercises 33 –36, evaluate the expression for *x* = 5, *y* = 8, and *z* = 9.

  33. $x + y - z$ 4
  34. $x + (z - y)$ 6
  35. $z \div (y - x) + z$ 12
  36. $y(z - x) + x$ 37

In Exercises 37–40, match the algebraic expression with its verbal description.

  a. $a + 8$
  b. $x - 8$
  c. $n \div 8$
  d. $8y$

  37. The difference of a number and 8   b

  38. The product of a number and 8   d

  39. The quotient of a number and 8   c

  40. The sum of a number and 8   a

  41. *Reasoning*   If the expression $4x + 2$ has a value of 18, what is the value of x?   4

  42. *Reasoning*   If the expression $5n - 3$ has a value of 47, what is the value of n?   10

26   *Chapter 1 • Exploring Patterns*

P Portfolio Opportunity

Extra Practice

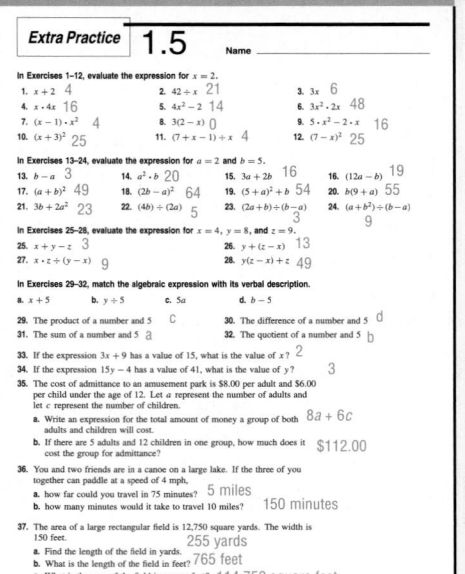

Extra Practice 1.5   Name ____

In Exercises 1–12, evaluate the expression for $x = 2$.
1. $x + 2$ 4
2. $42 \div x$ 21
3. $3x$ 6
4. $x \cdot 4x$ 16
5. $4x^2 - 2$ 14
6. $3x^2 \cdot 2x$ 48
7. $(x - 1) \cdot x^2$ 4
8. $3(2 - x)$ 0
9. $5 \cdot x^2 - 2 \cdot x$ 16
10. $(x + 3)^2$ 25
11. $(7 + x - 1) \div x$ 4
12. $(7 - x)^2$ 25

In Exercises 13–24, evaluate the expression for $a = 2$ and $b = 5$.
13. $b - a$ 3
14. $a^2 \cdot b$ 20
15. $3a + 2b$ 16
16. $(12a - b)$ 19
17. $(a + b)^2$ 49
18. $(2b - a)^2$ 64
19. $(5 + a)^2 + b$ 54
20. $b(9 + a)$ 55
21. $3b + 2a^2$ 23
22. $(4b) \div (2a)$ 5
23. $(2a + b) \div (b - a)$ 3
24. $(a + b^2) \div (b - a)$ 9

In Exercises 25–28, evaluate the expression for $x = 4$, $y = 8$, and $z = 9$.
25. $x + y - z$ 3
26. $x + (z - x)$ ____
27. $x \cdot z + (y - x)$ 9
28. $y(z - x) + z$ 49

In Exercises 29–32, match the algebraic expression with its verbal description.
a. $x + 5$
b. $y \div 5$
c. $5a$
d. $b - 5$
29. The product of a number and 5   c
30. The difference of a number and 5   d
31. The sum of a number and 5   a
32. The quotient of a number and 5   b

33. If the expression $3x + 9$ has a value of 15, what is the value of x? 2
34. If the expression $15y - 4$ has a value of 41, what is the value of y? 3
35. The cost of admittance to an amusement park is $8.00 per adult and $6.00 per child under the age of 12. Let a represent the number of adults and let c represent the number of children.
  a. Write an expression for the total amount of money a group of both adults and children will cost. $8a + 6c$
  b. If there are 5 adults and 12 children in one group, how much does it cost the group for admittance? $112.00
36. You and two friends are in a canoe on a large lake. If the three of you together can paddle at a speed of 4 mph,
  a. how far could you travel in 75 minutes?   5 miles
  b. how many minutes would it take to travel 10 miles?   150 minutes
37. The area of a large rectangular field is 12,750 square yards. The width is 150 feet.
  a. Find the length of the field in yards.   255 yards
  b. What is the length of the field in feet?   765 feet
  c. What is the area of the field in square feet?   114,750 square feet

Windows   *1.5 • Introduction to Algebra: Variables in Expressions* 5

Reteaching

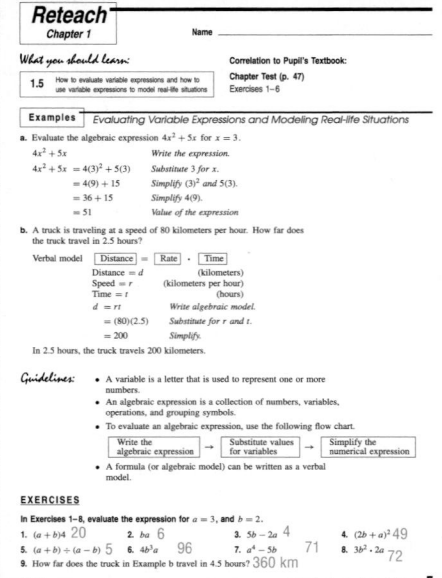

Reteach   Chapter 1   Name ____

What you should learn:
1.5   How to evaluate variable expressions and how to use variable expressions to model real-life situations

Correlation to Pupil's Textbook:
Chapter Test (p. 47)
Exercises 1–6

Examples   *Evaluating Variable Expressions and Modeling Real-life Situations*

a. Evaluate the algebraic expression $4x^2 + 5x$ for $x = 3$.
$4x^2 + 5x$ *Write the expression.*
$4x^2 + 5x = 4(3)^2 + 5(3)$ *Substitute 3 for x.*
$= 4(9) + 15$ *Simplify $(3)^2$ and $5(3)$.*
$= 36 + 15$ *Simplify 4(9).*
$= 51$ *Value of the expression*

b. A truck is traveling at a speed of 80 kilometers per hour. How far does the truck travel in 2.5 hours?

Verbal model   Distance = Rate · Time
  Distance = d (kilometers)
  Speed = r (kilometers per hour)
  Time = t (hours)
  $d = rt$ *Write algebraic model.*
  $= (80)(2.5)$ *Substitute for r and t.*
  $= 200$ *Simplify.*
In 2.5 hours, the truck travels 200 kilometers.

Guidelines:
• A variable is a letter that is used to represent one or more numbers.
• An algebraic expression is a collection of numbers, variables, operations, and grouping symbols.
• To evaluate an algebraic expression, use the following flow chart.

  Write the algebraic expression → Substitute values for variables → Simplify the numerical expression

• A formula (or algebraic model) can be written as a verbal model.

EXERCISES

In Exercises 1–8, evaluate the expression for $a = 3$, and $b = 2$.
1. $(a + b)4$ 20
2. ba 6
3. $5b - 2a$ 4
4. $(2b + a)^2$ 49
5. $(a + b) - (a - b)$ 5
6. $4b^3a$ 96
7. $a^4 - 5b$ 71
8. $3b^2 \cdot 2a$ 72
9. How far does the truck in Example b travel in 4.5 hours? 360 km

Windows   *Chapter 1 • Exploring Patterns* 5

43. *Pteranodon*   You are driving to Wild Animal Park, near San Diego, California. You see the sign shown below.   A flying distance, no; it is a distance along a straight line.

a. What does 22 miles represent? Does it mean that the driving distance to Wild Animal Park is 22 miles? Explain.

b. Suppose it takes a Pteranodon 120 minutes to reach Wild Animal Park. How fast would the Pteranodon be flying?   11 mph

Pteranodons, flying reptiles, became extinct millions of years ago. Most species of Pteranodons had wingspans that ranged from 36 to 40 feet.

Only 22 miles as the Pteranodon flies.
Wild Animal Park

Moon Rover   **In Exercises 44 and 45, imagine that you are an astronaut driving a moon rover.**

44. You travel at a speed of 20 miles per hour. How many minutes does it take you to travel 30 miles? 90

45. You travel at a speed of 25 miles per hour. How far will you travel in 105 minutes? $43\frac{3}{4}$ mi

46. *Going to a Movie*   You are treating some friends to a movie and popcorn. Tickets cost $6.00 per person. Popcorn costs $2.00 per bag. Let *f* represent the number of friends.

a. Write an expression for the total amount you will spend. $(6+2)(f+1)$ or $8f+8$

b. If $f = 2$, how much did it cost to treat you and your friends? $24

Integrated Review   *Making Connections within Mathematics*

Computation Sense   **In Exercises 47–54, evaluate the expression.**

47. $6(5-3)$ 12

48. $24 \div (8-4)$ 6

49. $(9+7)-3^2$ 7

50. $4^3-(8+9)$ 47

51. $1+11 \cdot 3^2$

52. $12-2^2 \cdot 3$ 0

53. $6(2 \div 4)$ 3

54. $8(6 \div 8)+5$ 11

Exploration and Extension

Guess, Check, and Revise   **In Exercises 55–60, find a value of the variable so that the values of the expressions are the same.**

55. $2x$ and $2+x$ 2

56. $4n+6$ and $6n$ 3

57. $8m-3$ and $6m+1$ 2

58. $x+4$ and $2x+1$ 3

59. $4n-8$ and $2n-4$ 2

60. $4y+3$ and $8y-9$ 3

❂ More difficult exercises   **1.5** • *Introduction to Algebra: Variables in Expressions*   **27**

▶ **Ex. 43**
EXTENSION
Have students research the speeds of different mammals, birds, and fishes. Then have students calculate the travel time for various distances.
▶ **Ex. 46**   Check to see that students included themselves in the cost!

Integrated Review
These exercises review the order of operations.

Exploration and Extension
▶ **Ex. 55–60**
GROUP ACTIVITY
Have students solve these problems with other members of their group. These exercises preview the solving of equations with the variable on both sides of the equation.

Portfolio Opportunity: Math Log
The formula $V = lwh$ is used to model the volume of a rectangular solid.
a. In this formula, what do V, l, w, and h represent? Why are these choices of variables convenient?
b. Would it be correct to use the formula $x = abc$ if $x = $ volume, $a = $ length, $b = $ width, and $c = $ height?
c. What does this tell you about the use of variables in formulas?

Also available as a copymaster, page 5, Ex. 6

PACING the Lesson

Suggested Number of Days

Basic/Average 2 **Above Average** 1

Advanced 1

PLANNING the Lesson

Lesson Plan 1.6, p. 6

ORGANIZER

Starters (reproduced below)
- Problem of the Day 1.6, p. 2
- Warm-Up Exercises 1.6, p. 2

Lesson Resources
- Color Transparencies
  - Graphs for Example 2 and Ex. 7–9, pp. 4, 5
- Teaching Tools
  - Graph paper, pp. T1, C2
- Math Log, p. 6
- Answer Masters 1.6, pp. 11–13
- Extra Practice Copymaster 1.6, p. 6
- Reteaching Copymaster 1.6, p. 6
- Enrichment Projects, pp. 2, 3

Special Populations
- Suggestions, Teacher's Edition, p. 1D

LESSON Notes

Students have already seen information presented in tables. Ask them why they think information is often organized in tables. Then have students describe the types of tables they have seen. Where are these tables usually found?

Example 1

In order to make students more aware of options, have them rearrange this table so that the rows of the table represent years and the columns represent scores.

1.6 Exploring Data: Tables and Graphs

What you should learn:

Goal 1 How to use tables to organize data

Goal 2 How to use graphs to model data visually

Why you should learn it:

You can use tables and graphs to help you see relationships among such data collections as survey results.

Goal 1 Using Tables to Organize Data

The word *data* is plural and it means facts or numbers that describe something. A collection of data is easier to understand when it is organized in a table or graph. There is no "best way" to organize data, but there are many good ways. One way to organize data is with a table. For instance, on page 23 the information about the perimeters of several rectangles was organized in a table. In that table, suppose you represent the figure number as n. Then the table could look like this.

Figure number, n	1	2	3	4	5
Perimeter, $2+2n$	4	6	8	10	12

Real Life **Football**

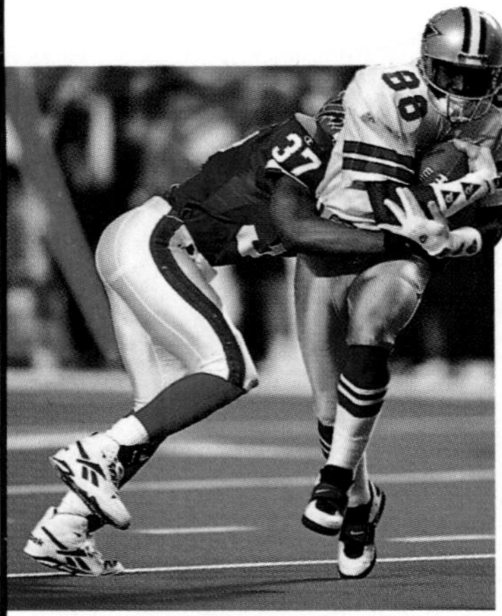

The Super Bowl is a football game between the winning teams of the NFC and AFC. The first Super Bowl was held in 1967.

Example 1 *Constructing a Table*

From 1985 through 1994, the winning and losing scores at the Super Bowl were as follows: *(Source: The Sporting News)*

38 to 16 (1985), 46 to 10 (1986), 39 to 20 (1987),
42 to 10 (1988), 20 to 16 (1989), 55 to 10 (1990),
20 to 19 (1991), 37 to 24 (1992), 52 to 17 (1993),
30 to 13 (1994)

Represent this data by a table.

Solution One way to represent the data by a table is shown below. Can you think of another way to represent the data?

Year	1985	1986	1987	1988	1989
Winning Score	38	46	39	42	20
Losing Score	16	10	20	10	16

Year	1990	1991	1992	1993	1994
Winning Score	55	20	37	52	30
Losing Score	10	19	24	17	13

Notice how the table helps to organize the data. ■

STARTER: Problem of the Day

What would Figure 13 look like? If each side of Figure 1 is 1 unit, what would be the perimeter of Figure 13?

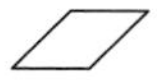

Fig. 1

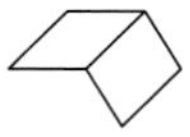

Fig. 2

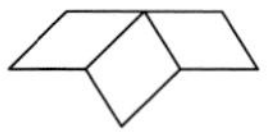

Fig. 3

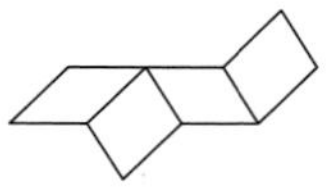

Fig. 4

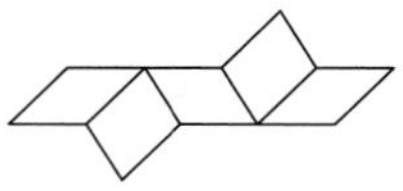

Fig. 5

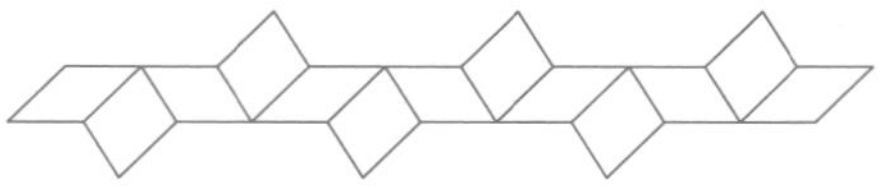

perimeter = 28

Also available as a copymaster, page 2

STARTER: Warm-Up Exercises

1. Find the average of the following numbers, rounding your result to the nearest whole number.
65, 72, 60, 83, 87, 78, 64 73
2. If the average of the following numbers is 42, what is the missing number?
38, 45, 60, ? 25
3. Order from shortest to tallest the following heights (in meters) of the world's ten highest dams.
245, 300, 243, 261, 335, 285, 245, 253, 272, 261
243, 245, 245, 253, 261, 261, 272, 285, 300, 335

Also available as a copymaster, page 2

Using Graphs to Organize Data

There are many ways to organize data graphically. Two types of graphs are shown in the next example.

Real Life
Football

Example 2 *Drawing Graphs*

Draw a bar graph and a line graph that represent the Super Bowl data given in Example 1.

Solution

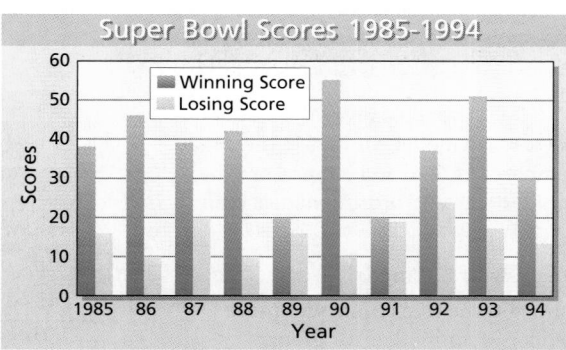

Graphs are pictures of data. Bar graphs and line graphs are commonly seen in magazines and newspapers. Encourage students to bring examples of graphs found in real-life settings.

Example 2

Point out that because we want to compare winning and losing scores over time, we place the units of time on the horizontal axis. The horizontal axis is then like a time line. Also, high and low scores become more visually apparent in this arrangement.

Explain to students that the inserts on the bar and line graphs are called "legends." Legends provide information that helps in understanding the data shown in the graph.

Ask students which representation of the Super Bowl scores they prefer. Which graph better illustrates the closeness of the games? Have them explain their reasons.

Communicating about MATHEMATICS

Have students draw a bar graph for Example 2 in which the bar is horizontal. Ask: Of the two bar graphs, which do you prefer?

Writing Prompt
I wonder . . .
(This is a very open-ended prompt, but over time students may become comfortable enough to share real issues that may or may not pertain to mathematics.)

Ⓟ

Communicating about MATHEMATICS

▶ **SHARING IDEAS about the Lesson**

Its Up to You Which Super Bowl in Example 2 do you think was the most exciting? Why? How are the two graphs similar? Different? Answers vary.

ost exciting:
swers vary,
obably that for
91; has the
sest score.

Here is an additional example similar to Example 2.
Drawing Graphs
From 1984 through 1992, the gold production (in millions of troy ounces) of the United States and of Canada, respectively, was as follows.
2.0 (U.S.A.), 2.6 (Canada), 1984; 2.4, 2.8, 1985; 3.7, 3.3, 1986; 4.9, 3.7, 1987; 6.4, 4.3, 1988; 8.5, 5.1, 1989; 9.4, 5.3, 1990; 9.5, 5.6, 1991; 10.5, 5.0, 1992
Draw a line graph that represents the data above.

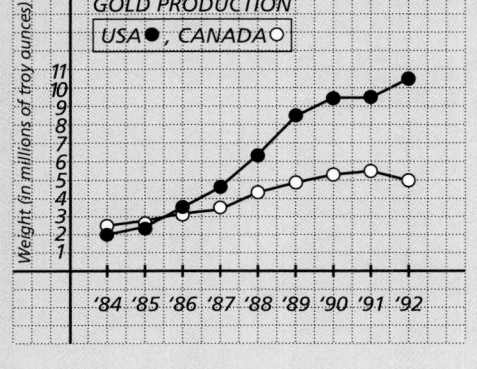

ASSIGNMENT GUIDE

Basic/Average:
Day 1: Ex. 3–10, 13, 16, 21–27
Day 2: Ex. 11, 12, 14, 15, 17
Above Average: Ex. 7–17, 24–28
Advanced: Ex. 7–17, 24–28
Selected Answers: Ex. 1, 2, 3–23 odd

Guided Practice

It may be necessary here to discuss some basic techniques for graphing, such as labeling axes in a meaningful way, choosing a scale, when to use a broken axis, and so on.

Independent Practice

▶ **Ex. 3–6, 7–9** Assign these problems as a group.
▶ **Ex. 12, 13** Remind students to plot the time on the horizontal axis.
▶ **Ex. 12**

Common-Error Alert!

Remind students to scale the vertical axis *before* plotting the points. Otherwise they may make the common error shown below.

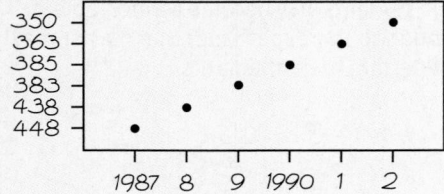

EXERCISES

Guided Practice

P ▶ **CHECK for Understanding**

1. Name some ways that you can organize data. Answers vary. Table, bar graph, line graph

2. How could you organize the following real-life data? Answers vary.
   a. The number of students eating school lunches each day last week
   b. The number of hours all students spent studying last night

Independent Practice

Olympic Medals **The table gives the medal count for the top five medal winners in the 1992 Summer Olympics. Let *G, S,* and *B* represent the number of gold, silver, and bronze medals won by a team.**

3. Which team won 112 medals? Unified Team

4. As a group, did the five teams win more gold medals, silver medals, or bronze medals? Gold

5. For which team is it true that $G - 5 = B$? Germany

6. For which team is it true that $B - 5 = S$? Cuba

P ▶ 7. Draw a bar graph or a line graph to represent the number of gold and silver medals won by each team. Which graph do you think is more appropriate? Explain. See Additional Answers.

1992 Summer Olympics

Country	Gold	Silver	Bronze
Unified Team	45	38	29
United States	37	34	37
Germany	33	21	28
China	16	22	16
Cuba	14	6	11

Javelin Throw **The bar graph shows the winning distances of the javelin throw in the Olympics.**

8. How far did the men's champion throw the javelin in 1980? 300 ft

9. In what year was the difference between the men's and women's throws the least? The greatest? 1988, 1976

10. Would a table better represent this data? Explain why or why not. Answers vary.

11. *Perimeter and Area* The side lengths of seven squares are 1, 2, 3, 4, 5, 6, and 7. Create a table that shows the perimeter and area of each square.

11., 12. See Additional Answers.

❂ 12. *Perimeter and Area* The widths and lengths of seven rectangles are n and $n + 2$, where n is equal to 1, 2, 3, 4, 5, 6, and 7. Create a table that shows the perimeter and area of each rectangle.

❂ More difficult exercises
P Portfolio Opportunity

Extra Practice

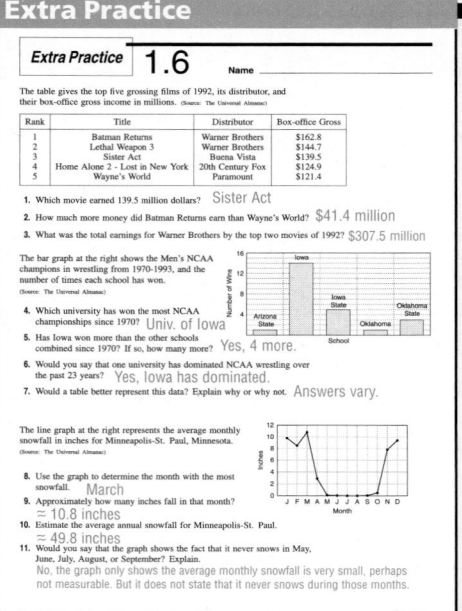

Reteaching

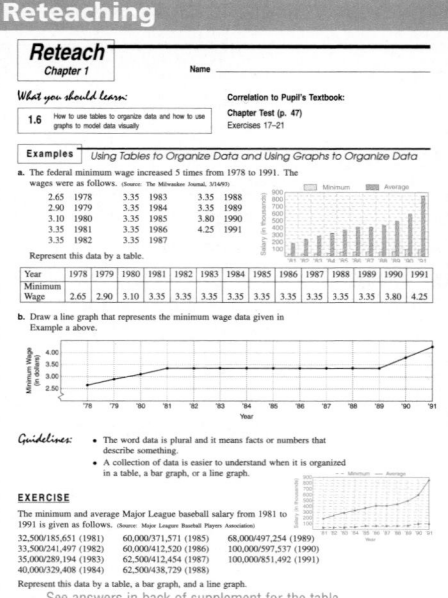

13. *Average Temperature* The average monthly temperatures (in degrees Fahrenheit) for Cleveland, Ohio, (*C*) and Seattle, Washington, (*S*) are listed in the table. Represent this data with a bar graph and a line graph. *(Source: U. S. National Oceanic and Atmospheric Administration)*
See Additional Answers.

Month	J	F	M	A	M	J
C	33°	35°	45°	58°	69°	78°
S	45°	50°	53°	58°	65°	69°

Month	J	A	S	O	N	D
C	82°	80°	74°	63°	49°	38°
S	75°	74°	69°	60°	51°	47°

14. *Estimation* Use the table in Exercise 13 to estimate the average annual temperature in Cleveland. Explain how you obtained your estimate. Answers vary.

15. *Estimation* Use the table in Exercise 13 to estimate the average annual temperature in Seattle. Explain how you obtained your estimate. Answers vary.

16. *It's Up to You* Explain what the line graph at the right could represent. Answers vary.

17. *Writing* Describe some advantages and disadvantages of organizing data with a table and with a graph. Answers vary.

The greatest recorded temperature variation in a 24-hour period occurred in Browning, Montana, in 1916. In January, the temperature fell 100°F from 44°F to −56°F.

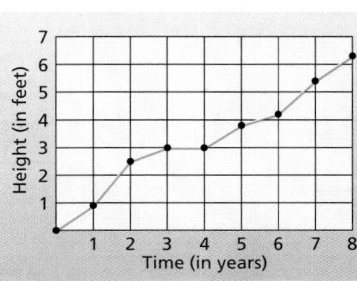

Integrated Review

Making Connections within Mathematics

Decimal Sense **In Exercises 18–23, find the difference.**

18. $107.2 - 84.3$ 22.9

19. $256.8 - 174.1$ 82.7

20. $4.28 - 3.69$ 0.59

21. $8.14 - 5.47$ 2.67

22. $14.823 - 11.602$ 3.221

23. $72.073 - 56.941$ 15.132

Exploration and Extension

24., 25. Check students' work.

24. *Research Project* Use your school's library or some other reference source to collect data on a topic. You can research any topic you want. After collecting your data, organize it in a table, bar graph, or line graph.

25. *Writing* Write a short paper discussing your research.

▶ **Ex. 16, 17**
Students could do these exercises in their journals.

Integrated Review
These exercises review operations with decimals and also substitution for a single variable in an algebraic expression.

Exploration and Extension
Assign this section as a group activity, and have groups report their results to the whole class. Encourage students to choose topics that interest them, or alternatively, to use existing research in another course such as social studies, science, and so on.

Portfolio Opportunity: Math Log
What could this graph represent? Explain your answer.

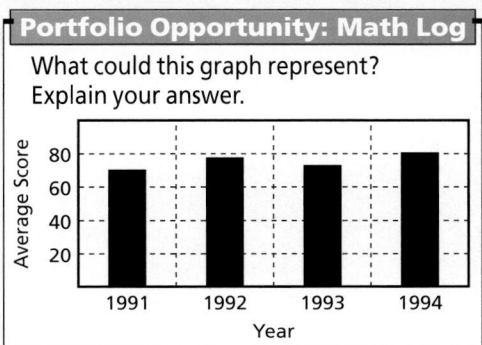

Also available as a copymaster, page 6, Ex. 7

Alternative Assessment
Suggestions for group oral presentations that evaluate students' understanding of the use of graphs in the organization of data.

Available as a copymaster, page 16

Short Quiz
Covers Lessons 1.5 and 1.6

Available as a copymaster, page 5

Mixed REVIEW

In Exercises 1–6, perform the operation. Round the result to two decimal places. (1.2, 1.3)

1. $6(14.2)$ 85.2

2. $8.45 \cdot 5$ 42.25

3. $13 \div 9$ 1.44

4. $19/2$ 9.5

5. $\dfrac{6.47}{5}$ 1.29

6. $\sqrt{155}$ 12.45

In Exercises 7–10, use the established order of operations to evaluate $72 - (8 + 4) \times 6$. (1.3)

7. Which operation is performed first? Addition

8. Which operation is performed second? Multiplication

9. Which operation is performed third? Subtraction

10. What is the value of the expression? 0

In Exercises 11–18, evaluate the expression for $x = 4$, $y = 5$, and $z = 2$. (1.4)

11. $2y$ 10

12. $4z - x$ 4

13. $(x + y)^2$ 81

14. $5x(x - 4)$ 0

15. $x + y \times z$ 14

16. $2x \div z^2$ 2

17. $(y - z)^2 - x$ 5

18. $(y - x) \div z$ $\frac{1}{2}$

Career Interview

Robotics Engineer

Larry Chao-Hsiung Li is a robotics engineer for NASA (the National Aeronautics and Space Administration). He works in a laboratory designing robots for use in current and future space missions.

Q: What led you into this career?

A: In the summer between my junior and senior years of college, I started working for NASA as part of a cooperative education program with the NASA Johnson Space Center in Houston, TX. After I graduated, I started working there full time and I have been there ever since.

Q: Do you use geometric reasoning in your work?

A: Yes, if we want a robot to move its arm to a certain spot, we have to change the x-, y-, and z-coordinates into angles of joint motor rotation and amounts of movement. This requires using sines, cosines, arctangents, and many other trig functions.

Q: What would you like to tell kids who are in school about math or geometry?

A: If you want to work in a really fun job you need to learn math! Math is really being used today!

Materials Needed: Square tiles or graph paper

Example   *Comparing Area and Perimeter*

How many different rectangular shapes can be formed with 12 square tiles? Form each rectangle and record its dimensions, area, and perimeter in a table.

Solution   In the figure at the right, you can see that there are only three different shapes of rectangles that can be formed. The dimensions, areas, and perimeters of these rectangles are shown in the following table.

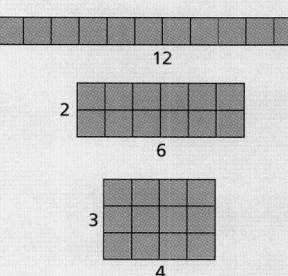

Dimensions	1-by-12	2-by-6	3-by-4
Area	12 square units	12 square units	12 square units
Perimeter	26 units	16 units	14 units

■

Exercises

In Exercises 1–6, decide how many different rectangular shapes can be formed with the tiles. Record the dimensions, area, and perimeter of each rectangle in a table. For tables, see margin.

1. 20 tiles 3   **2.** 24 tiles 4   **3.** 25 tiles 2

4. 18 tiles 3   **5.** 36 tiles 5   **6.** 37 tiles 1

7. If you double the number of tiles, do you double the number of rectangles that can be formed? Explain. No, not usually.

8. How should you arrange a given number of tiles to obtain the greatest perimeter? The least perimeter? **7., 8.** See margin.

In Exercises 9 and 10, write the number sentence that is suggested by the geometric model. For instance, the model shown below suggests the number sentence $4 \times (4 + 2) = 4 \times 4 + 4 \times 2$.

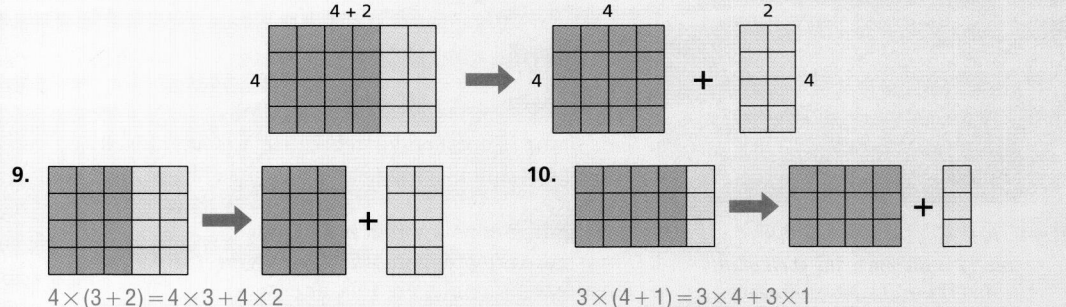

9. $4 \times (3 + 2) = 4 \times 3 + 4 \times 2$

10. $3 \times (4 + 1) = 3 \times 4 + 3 \times 1$

INVESTIGATION Notes

Materials
Overhead Manipulatives Kit
  Square tiles
Teaching Tools
  Graph paper, pp. T1, C2

This investigation should be done cooperatively in groups. Although some students may balk at using the tiles, having the tiles available reinforces the concept that area is *covering* and perimeter is *distance around*. Encourage students to actually put their fingers on the tiles in order to count area, and on the edges in order to calculate perimeter.

Students may observe some subtle patterns: Exercises 3 and 5 involve perfect squares, and therefore each will have a "rectangle" of equal dimensions; Ex. 6 involves a prime and has just one possible rectangle. Exercises 7 and 8 encourage students to try several cases and record observations. Exercise 9 and 10 preview the distributive property.

Answers

1.

Dimensions	1×20	2×10	4×5
Perimeter (units)	42	24	18
Area (units²)	20	20	20

2.

Dimensions	1×24	2×12	3×8	4×6
Perimeter (units)	50	28	22	20
Area (units²)	24	24	24	24

3.

Dimensions	1×25	5×5
Perimeter (units)	52	20
Area (units²)	25	25

4.

Dimensions	1×18	2×9	3×6
Perimeter (units)	38	22	18
Area (units²)	18	18	18

5.

Dimensions	1×36	2×18	3×12	4×9	6×6
Perimeter (units)	74	40	30	26	24
Area (units²)	36	36	36	36	36

6.

Dimensions	1×37
Perimeter (units)	76
Area (units²)	37

7. The number of rectangular shapes for 18 tiles (Exercise 4) is 3, and the number of rectangular shapes for 36 tiles (Exercise 5) is 5; $5 \neq 2(3)$.

8. In a row; as near to a square as possible

PACING the Lesson

Suggested Number of Days
Basic/Average 0   **Above Average** 1
Advanced 1

PLANNING the Lesson

Lesson Plan 1.7, p. 7

ORGANIZER

Starters (reproduced below)
Problem of the Day 1.7, p. 3
Warm-Up Exercises 1.7, p. 3
Lesson Resources
Color Transparencies
Diagrams for Example 1 and Ex. 21–24, pp. 5, 6
Math Log, p. 6
Technology, p. 6
Answer Masters 1.7, p. 14
Extra Practice Copymaster 1.7, p. 7
Reteaching Copymaster 1.7, p. 7
Enrichment Projects, pp. 4, 5
Special Populations
Suggestions, Teacher's Edition, p. 1D

▶ MEETING INDIVIDUAL NEEDS

For some students, this lesson may seem faster paced than the previous lessons. The change to geometry involves quite a number of new or vaguely remembered terms. These students may need to review terms such as *closed figure, line segment, endpoint,* and especially the meaning of *n-gon.* This term involves an abstraction, but it also offers an opportunity to reinforce the use of variables in algebra. In any case, be aware of these special difficulties.

Addressing Misconceptions

Point out to students that for a "closed figure" you can start at a vertex, trace all the sides, and end at the same vertex. Consequently, the following figures are not closed.

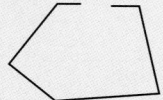 

Observe that the figure below is not a polygon because two sides intersect at a point other than at their endpoints.

1.7 Exploring Patterns in Geometry

What you should learn:

Goal 1 How to identify polygons and parts of polygons

Goal 2 How to discover properties of polygons

Why you should learn it:

Knowing the names of geometric figures, such as polygons, helps you communicate mathematical ideas.

Polygons occur frequently in nature. For instance, the shell of this desert tortoise has pentagons as part of its pattern.

Goal 1   Identifying Polygons

Geometry is the study of shapes and their measures. One of the most common geometric shapes is a polygon.

Polygons

A **polygon** is a closed figure that is made up of straight line segments that intersect at their endpoints. Each line segment is a **side** of the polygon, and each endpoint is a **vertex.** (The plural of vertex is *vertices.*) A polygon has the same number of vertices as it has sides. Polygons have special names, depending on their number of sides.

3 : Triangle	6 : Hexagon	9 : Nonagon
4 : Quadrilateral	7 : Heptagon	10 : Decagon
5 : Pentagon	8 : Octagon	*n* : *n*-gon

Example 1   *Identifying Polygons*

State whether the figure is a polygon. If it is, name it.

a.    b.   c.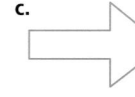

d.    e.    f.

Solution
a. This figure is not a polygon because it is not closed.
b. This figure is not a polygon because its sides are not all straight.
c. This figure is a polygon. It is a heptagon.
d. This figure is a polygon. It is a pentagon.
e. This figure is a polygon. It is a hexagon.
f. This figure is a polygon. It is a quadrilateral.

34   Chapter **1** ▪ Exploring Patterns

STARTER: **Problem of the Day**

If the area of the large rectangle is 147 units², what is the perimeter of the shaded rectangle?   36 units

Area: 48	Area: 15
	Area: 28

Also available as a copymaster, page 3

STARTER: **Warm-Up Exercises**

The following are polygons. How many can you name?

a.   b.

c. 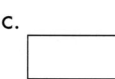   d.

e.    f.    g.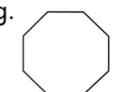

Answers may vary. **a.** triangle, **b.** square, **c.** rectangle, **d.** parallelogram, **e.** pentagon, **f.** hexagon, **g.** octagon

Also available as a copymaster, page 3

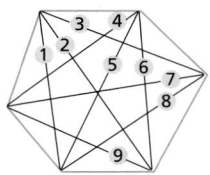

From each vertex of a hexagon you can draw 3 diagonals.

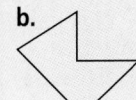

In a hexagon, you can draw a total of 9 different diagonals.

Goal 2 | Discovering Properties of Polygons

A segment that connects two vertices of a polygon and is not a side is a **diagonal** of the polygon.

LESSON INVESTIGATION

■ Investigating Diagonals of Polygons

Group Activity Determine the number of diagonals that can be drawn from each vertex of a triangle, a quadrilateral, and a pentagon. Then determine the total number of diagonals that can be drawn in each polygon. Record your results in a table. What patterns do you observe?

Type of Polygon	n	Diagonals from Each Vertex	Total Number of Diagonals
Triangle	3	0 ?	0 ?
Quadrilateral	4	1 ?	2 ?
Pentagon	5	2 ?	5 ?

Example 2 | *Problem Solving: Verbal and Algebraic Models*

In the investigation, you may have discovered the following.

Verbal Model

$$\boxed{\text{Total diagonals}} = \boxed{\text{Number of vertices}} \times \boxed{\begin{array}{c}\text{Diagonals from each vertex}\end{array}} \div 2$$

Total number of diagonals = T
Number of vertices = n

Algebraic Model

Number of diagonals from each vertex = $n - 3$

$$T = n \times (n - 3) \div 2 = \frac{n(n-3)}{2}$$ ■

Communicating about MATHEMATICS

▶ **SHARING IDEAS about the Lesson** 14, 20; Check students' work.

Using an Algebraic Model Use the algebraic model in Example 2 to find the total number of diagonals of a heptagon and an octagon. Confirm your results by drawing a diagram.

Example 1

Don't let students get overwhelmed by the terminology. The important part of this example is the actual recognition of similarities and differences in the figures, not the naming of them.

Lesson Investigation
Show diagonals of different polygons. Use colored pens to help distinguish among the drawn diagonals. Ask students how many diagonals are in a triangle.   None

Example 2

Be sure students understand the rationale of the verbal model. Observe that there are as many vertices as sides of a polygon. Point out that in counting diagonals drawn from each of n vertices, we exclude the vertex itself and also the two adjacent vertices, so only $n - 3$ diagonals can be drawn from each vertex, which suggests a total for the entire figure of $n(n - 3)$ diagonals. But since this expression counts each diagonal twice, we must divide by 2. Point out to students that this formula serves to model a geometric pattern relating the number of diagonals in a polygon to the number of vertices.

Communicating about MATHEMATICS

If students have understood the rationale of the algebraic model, they should have no problem in substituting the appropriate value for *n* in the formula. Point out that in confirming their results with a diagram, they are also checking the validity of the algebraic model itself.

Writing Prompt
If geometry were a song, what would it sound like?

Technology

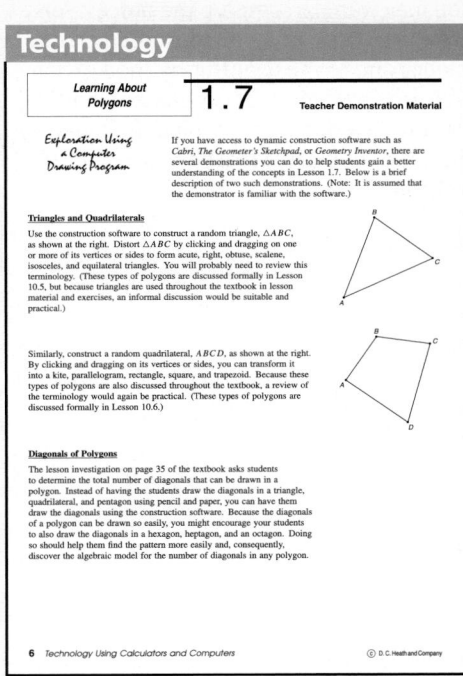

```
Learning About
Polygons          1.7        Teacher Demonstration Material

Exploration Using    If you have access to dynamic construction software such as
a Computer           Cabri, The Geometer's Sketchpad, or Geometry Inventor, there are
Drawing Program      several demonstrations you can do to help students gain a better
                     understanding of the concepts in Lesson 1.7. Below is a brief
                     description of two such demonstrations. (Note: It is assumed that
                     the demonstrator is familiar with the software.)

Triangles and Quadrilaterals
Use the construction software to construct a random triangle, △ABC,
as shown at the right. Distort △ABC by clicking and dragging on one
or more of its vertices or sides to form acute, right, obtuse, scalene,
isosceles, and equilateral triangles. You will probably need to review this
terminology. (These types of polygons are discussed formally in Lesson
10.5, but because triangles are used throughout the textbook in lesson
material and exercises, an informal discussion would be suitable and
practical.)

Similarly, construct a random quadrilateral, ABCD, as shown at the right.
By clicking and dragging on its vertices or sides, you can transform it
into a kite, parallelogram, rectangle, square, and trapezoid. Because these
types of polygons are also discussed throughout the textbook, a review of
the terminology would again be practical. (These types of polygons are
discussed formally in Lesson 10.6.)

Diagonals of Polygons
The lesson investigation on page 35 of the textbook asks students
to determine the total number of diagonals that can be drawn in a
polygon. Instead of having the students draw the diagonals in a triangle,
quadrilateral, and pentagon using pencil and paper, you can have them
draw the diagonals using the construction software. Because the diagonals
of a polygon can be drawn so easily, you might encourage your students
to also draw the diagonals in a hexagon, heptagon, and an octagon. Doing
so should help them find the pattern more easily and, consequently,
discover the algebraic model for the number of diagonals in any polygon.

6   Technology Using Calculators and Computers          © D.C. Heath and Company
```

OPTION: Extra Examples

Here are extra examples similar to those in the lesson.

1. Identifying Polygons
State whether the given figure is a polygon. If it is, name it.

a. 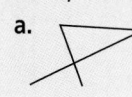   b.   c.

a. No; segments do not meet at the endpoints.
b. Yes; this figure is a pentagon.
c. Yes; this figure is a hexagon.

2. Writing Verbal and Algebraic Models
Use an algebraic model to find the number of diagonals in a nonagon.
Number of diagonals, $T = \frac{n(n-3)}{2}$
. For a nonagon, the number of vertices, n, is 9.
$T = \frac{9(9-3)}{2} = 27$.

ASSIGNMENT GUIDE

*Basic/Average:
Day 1: Ex. 5–13, 15–17
Day 2: Ex. 19–24, 25–35 odd

Above Average: Ex. 5–13, 15–20, 25–36

Advanced: Ex. 5–13, 15–20, 25–36

Selected Answers: Ex. 1–4, 5–31 odd

*You may wish to omit this lesson for these students.

Guided Practice

▶ **Ex. 1** This should be a closed book activity. A good definition may only emerge after several false starts; check for the three polygon "requirements": closed figure, straight sides, line segments meeting only at their endpoints.

Independent Practice

▶ **Ex. 15–18** Notice that the direction line includes the definition for a regular polygon. Also, make sure that students understand what *interior angle* means.

GROUP ACTIVITY
This set of exercises provides an excellent opportunity for students to work in groups as they investigate the pattern of interior angles in regular polygons. Note that the progression of exercises represents a neat blend of inductive and deductive reasoning (although students need not understand such terms at this stage). Having measured the interior angles of particular polygons, they check to see which of the four formulas is consistent with the pattern of results of their hands-on investigation and, finally, by extrapolating, they predict the interior angle measures of polygons not directly investigated.

CONNECTIONS TO SCIENCE
You may want to compare the process followed in Ex. 15–18 to lab sessions in physical science and to the scientific method in general — investigation or experiment, generalization via inductive reasoning, followed by the use of deductive reasoning to make predictions.

Answer

15.

Sides	3	4	5	6
Angle measure	60°	90°	108°	120°
Sum of angle measures	180°	360°	540°	720°

Guided Practice

▶ **CHECK for Understanding** Answers vary. (See page 34.)

P **1.** In your own words, state the definition of a polygon.

2. State the name of each polygon in GEOMETRY.

3. How many diagonals are there in the "O" of GEOMETRY? 2

4. *Problem Solving* Give an example of a verbal model and an algebraic model.
Answers vary.

2. G: nonagon, E: octagon, O: quadrilateral, M: decagon, E: heptagon, T: triangle, R: hexagon, Y: pentagon

Independent Practice

In Exercises 5–8, name the polygon.

5.
Quadrilateral

6.
Heptagon

7.
Hexagon

8.
Nonagon

In Exercises 9–12, decide whether the figure is a polygon. If it is, name it. If it is not, explain why. **9.** No, all sides not segments, **10.** No, not closed, **11.** Yes, octagon

9.

10.

11.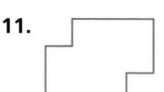

12.
See below.

13. Draw a hexagon with 2 sides equal in measure.

14. Draw an octagon with 4 sides equal to one length and the remaining 4 sides equal to a different length.
13., **14.** Check students' work.

Interior Angles **In Exercises 15–18, a polygon is regular if all its side lengths are equal and all its interior angle measures are equal. Each polygon shown at the right is regular.** For table, see margin.

15. Determine the sum of the measures of the interior angles of each regular polygon at the right. Record your results in a table.

16. One of the algebraic models below is a formula for determining the measure of an interior angle of a regular *n*-gon. Based on your results in Exercise 15, which one is it? c

a. $I = \dfrac{180°}{n}$ **b.** $I = \dfrac{360°}{n}$ **c.** $I = \dfrac{(n-2)(180°)}{n}$ **d.** $I = \dfrac{(n+1)(180°)}{12}$

✪ **17.** Use the formula found in Exercise 16 to find the measure of an interior angle of a regular decagon. 144°

✪ **18.** Use the formula found in Exercise 16 to find the measure of an interior angle of a regular octagon. 135°

12. No, different numbers of sides and vertices

Interior angle

60° 90°

108° 120°

36 *Chapter 1 • Exploring Patterns*

✪ More difficult exercises
P Portfolio Opportunity

Extra Practice

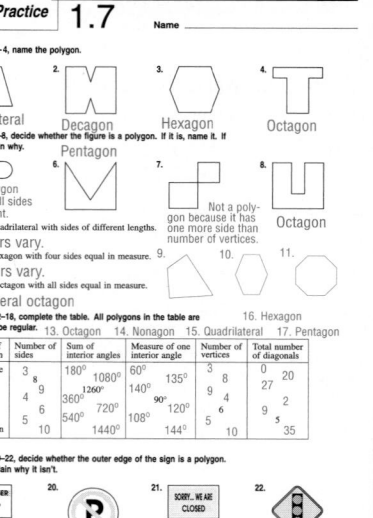

Reteaching

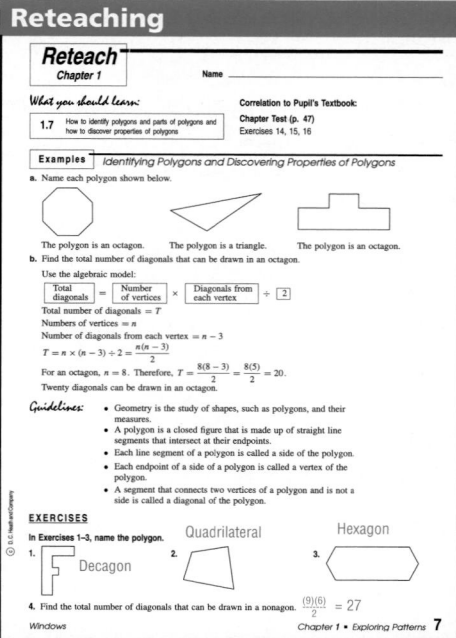

Area of a Triangle   The table below lists the base, height, and area of several triangles. Use the table to answer Exercises 19 and 20.

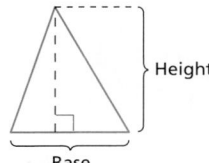
Height

Base

Triangle	Base	Height	(Base)(Height)	Area
1	6	4	24	12
2	3	2	6	3
3	10	5	50	25

19. Write a verbal model and an algebraic model for the area of a triangle. See margin.

20. Find the area of a triangle whose base is 16 inches and height is 8 inches. 64 in.²

Reasoning   **In Exercises 21–24, decide whether the outer edge of the sign is a polygon. If it is not, explain why it isn't.**

21.

Yes

22.

No, no segments

23.

No, all sides are not segments

24.

Yes

Integrated Review

Making Connections within Mathematics

Perimeter   **In Exercises 25 and 26, find the perimeter of the polygon when $a = 9$.**

25.

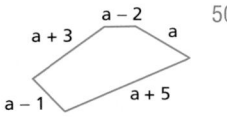
a – 2   50
a + 3   a
a – 1   a + 5

26.

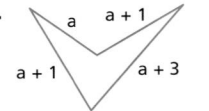
a   a + 1   41
a + 1   a + 3

Language Skills   **In Exercises 27–32, match each word with its definition.**

a. Government by 7 persons
b. Being between 90 and 100 years old
c. A period of 4 years
d. An athletic contest consisting of 5 events
e. Occurring every 8 years
f. A period of 10 years

27. Quadrennium c
28. Octennial e
29. Pentathlon d
30. Decade f
31. Heptarchy a
32. Nonagenarian b

Exploration and Extension

Convex or Nonconvex   **A polygon is convex if a segment joining any two interior points lies completely within the polygon. In Exercises 33–36, decide whether the polygon is convex.**

Interior points

Convex   Not convex

33.

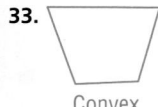
Convex

34.

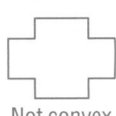
Not convex

35.

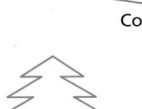
Not convex

36.

Convex

1.7 ▪ Exploring Patterns in Geometry   **37**

Enrichment

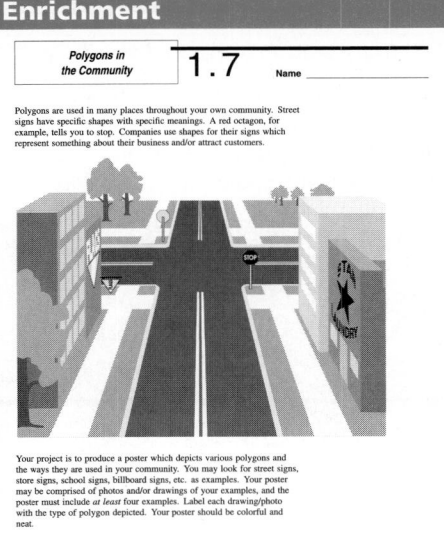

Polygons in the Community   **1.7**   Name _____

Polygons are used in many places throughout your own community. Street signs have specific shapes with specific meanings. A red octagon, for example, tells you to stop. Companies use shapes for their signs which represent something about their business and/or attract customers.

Your project is to produce a poster which depicts various polygons and the ways they are used in your community. You may look for street signs, store signs, school signs, billboard signs, etc. as examples. Your poster may be comprised of photos and/or drawings of your examples, and the poster must include *at least* four examples. Label each drawing/photo with the type of polygon depicted. Your poster should be colorful and neat.

© D.C. Heath and Company   Enrichment Projects **5**

▶ **Ex. 19, 20** These exercises continue the process described at the end of page 36.
Students may or may not remember the formula for the area of a triangle. The important thing here is that the table provides a pattern for students to investigate, so that a model emerges by which they can generalize and extrapolate.

Integrated Review

▶ **Ex. 27–32**
CONNECTIONS TO LANGUAGE ARTS
You may wish to alert a language arts teacher that mathematical prefixes are being studied and invite his/her suggestions.

Exploration and Extension

In these exercises, once again, students don't have to be burdened with terminology. It is more important that they have an opportunity to investigate a variety of figures and apply a rule of thumb to classify them. You may wish to have students use a toothpick or straw as a gauge. Apart from the label *convex*, this set of exercises helps establish several other geometric concepts—interior, exterior, the definition of segment, and so on.

Portfolio Opportunity: Math Log

1. The diagonals of a convex polygon lie in the polygon's interior. If the diagonals from one vertex of a convex *n*-gon are drawn, how many triangles are formed?
2. In your own words, define the term *closed figure*.

Also available as copymaster, page 6, Ex. 8, 9

Alternative Assessment

Chapter 1 Group Assessment
A problem-solving activity for 3 or 4 students that develops skills in writing an algebraic model.

Chapter 1 Individual Assessment
A similar follow-up activity for individual students. Adds incentive for the group activity and measures individual competence in the activity.

Available as copymasters, pages 59, 60

Answer
19. The area of a triangle is one half the product of the base and height, $A = \frac{1}{2}bh$.

ORGANIZER

Starters (reproduced below)
   Problem of the Day 1.8, p. 3
   Warm-Up Exercises 1.8, p. 3
Lesson Resources
   Math Log, p. 6
   Answer Masters 1.8, pp. 15–17
   Extra Practice Copymaster 1.8, p. 8
   Reteaching Copymaster 1.8, p. 8
   Enrichment Projects, pp. 6, 7
Special Populations
   Suggestions, Teacher's Edition, p. 1D

LESSON Notes

Recognizing number patterns is an important skill for understanding many real-life relationships. Students learn to recognize number patterns by starting with simple relationships and building upon them.

Example 1

Point out the use of tables in showing the algebraic relationships. You may want to combine Examples 1 and 2 into a mini-investigation to be conducted by students in small groups.

Example 2
Common-Error Alert!

Students may not recognize the repeating pattern of $\frac{1}{7}$ by looking at their calculators because too few decimal digits may appear in the display. It may be necessary that students use paper and pencil to observe the repeating pattern of $\frac{1}{7}$.

Students should have the opportunity to write repeating decimals using the "bar" notation. Ask them to write the following decimal numbers using that notation.
a. 0.0333… **b.** 0.030303…
c. 0.271271271…

1.8 Exploring Patterns with Technology

Goal 1 How to use a calculator to discover number patterns

Goal 2 How to use diagrams to discover number patterns in real-life situations

Many real-life situations, such as setting up a carnival game, have patterns that can be described with algebraic models. Knowing the patterns can help you understand the real-life situation.

Repeating and Terminating Decimals

The decimals for $\frac{1}{2}$ and $\frac{1}{4}$ terminate.
$\frac{1}{2} = 0.5$, $\frac{1}{4} = 0.25$
The decimals for $\frac{1}{3}$ and $\frac{1}{6}$ repeat.
$\frac{1}{3} = 0.333\ldots$, $\frac{1}{6} = 0.1666\ldots$
Repeating decimals are indicated by a bar, as in $\frac{1}{3} = 0.\overline{3}$.

Goal 1 — Discovering Number Patterns

In Lesson 1.7, you learned that polygons have special names, depending on their number of sides. Numbers also have special names, such as *whole numbers* (0, 1, 2, 3, …), *natural numbers* (1, 2, 3, 4, …), decimal numbers, and fractions.

Sequences of numbers often have patterns. Sometimes, a calculator or a computer can help you discover the pattern.

Example 1 — *Finding a Pattern for Products*

Use a calculator to calculate the product of 89 and the first nine natural numbers. Describe the pattern.

Solution You are asked to evaluate $89n$, when n is a natural number from 1 to 9. The results are shown in the table.

n	1	2	3	4	5	6	7	8	9
89n	89	178	267	356	445	534	623	712	801

From the table, you can see that the hundreds digit *increases* by 1, and the tens and the units digits *decrease* by 1.

Example 2 — *Finding a Pattern for Decimals*

Evaluate fractions of the form $\frac{1}{n}$ as a decimal for several values of n. Does the decimal repeat or terminate? What values of n produce terminating decimals?

Solution

Fraction	$\frac{1}{2}$	$\frac{1}{3}$	$\frac{1}{4}$	$\frac{1}{5}$	$\frac{1}{6}$	$\frac{1}{7}$	$\frac{1}{8}$
Decimal	0.5	$0.\overline{3}$	0.25	0.2	$0.1\overline{6}$	$0.\overline{142857}$	0.125

From the table, it appears that the fraction $\frac{1}{n}$ terminates if n is a product of 2's and 5's. For instance, $8 = 2 \cdot 2 \cdot 2$. This makes sense when you think that the decimal system is based on the number 10, which is the product of 2 and 5. ∎

Draw a diagram that shows the facts from the problem.

↓

Use the diagram to visualize the action of the problem.

↓

Use arithmetic or algebra to find a solution. Then check the solution against the facts.

A 3-row stack of wooden milk bottles has 6 bottles. How many bottles are in an n-row stack?

Goal 2 — Number Patterns in Real Life

Sometimes the facts of a problem are easier to understand when you picture them.

Example 3 — *Modeling Triangular Numbers*

Your school is having a carnival to raise money for band uniforms. You are in charge of a booth in which people try to knock over a stack of wooden bottles with a baseball. A "3-row" stack has 6 bottles. How many bottles does an "*n*-row" stack have?

Solution Begin by drawing some examples.

1   3   6   10   15   21

These numbers are called **triangular** numbers. To help discover their pattern, try simplifying the drawing. By doubling the number of squares in each "stack," you can see that the *n*th triangular number corresponds to half the area of an *n*-by-(*n* + 1) rectangle.

  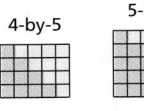 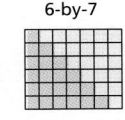
1-by-2   2-by-3   3-by-4   4-by-5   5-by-6   6-by-7

The algebraic model for triangular numbers is as follows.

Verbal Model

$$\text{nth triangular number} = \text{Width of rectangle} \times \text{Length of rectangle} \div 2$$

*n*th triangular number = T
Width of rectangle = n
Length of rectangle = $n + 1$

Algebraic Model

$$T = n \times (n + 1) \div 2 = \frac{n(n + 1)}{2}$$ ∎

▶ **SHARING IDEAS about the Lesson**

Using an Algebraic Model Use the algebraic model in Example 3 to find the 7th and 8th triangular numbers. Confirm your results by drawing diagrams.
28, 36; check students' work.

1.8 • *Exploring Patterns with Technology* **39**

Ask students: Does the 3-row stack of wooden milk bottles remind you of any other patterns? The pins in bowling have a similar pattern. Ask students to identify other real-life patterns they have noticed.

Example 3

You may wish to observe that triangular numbers represent the sum of consecutive natural numbers, as shown:

$1 = 1$
$3 = 1 + 2$
$6 = 1 + 2 + 3$
$10 = 1 + 2 + 3 + 4$

Students may find it helpful to have a concrete model of the relationship between triangular numbers and the rectangular array described in Example 3. Tag board or grids drawn on construction paper work well as physical models.

EXTENSION
Have students complete the table below in order to find the pattern for the area of the shaded Ls in the following sequence of figures. Explain that the expression in the bottom right corner of the table should be an algebraic model for finding any area in the sequence.

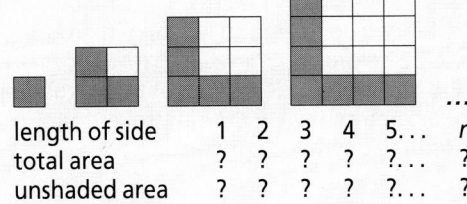

length of side	1	2	3	4	5...	*n*
total area	?	?	?	?	?...	?
unshaded area	?	?	?	?	?...	?
area of shaded Ls	?	?	?	?	?...	?

Bottom row of table: 1, 3, 5, 7, 9, ... $n^2 - (n - 1)^2$

Writing Prompt
Today I was confused when . . .
(Have students extend the writing to include whether or not the confusion was cleared up, and if so, how. If the students weren't confused, have them write a letter of explanation to a student who was absent, explaining the mathematical model for triangular numbers.)

OPTION: Extra Examples

Here is an additional example similar to Example 1.

Finding a pattern for products
Use a calculator to find the product of 9 and the first nine natural numbers. Describe the pattern.

Solution You are asked to evaluate 9*n*, when *n* is a natural number from 1 to 9. The results are shown in the table.

n	1	2	3	4	5	6	7	8	9
9*n*	9	18	27	36	45	54	63	72	81

One pattern you can see from the table is that the sum of the digits in each of the products is 9. Another pattern is that the tens digit increases by 1, while the ones digit decreases by 1.

ASSIGNMENT GUIDE

*Basic/Average:
Day 1: Ex. 3–9 odd, 13–15
Day 2: Ex. 19–24, 29, 30

Above Average:
Ex. 5–8, 11, 12, 15–20, 25–30

Advanced: Ex. 5–8, 11, 12, 15–20, 25–30

Selected Answers: Ex. 1, 2, 3–27 odd

*You may wish to omit this lesson for these students.

Guided Practice

This is a good opportunity to discuss briefly the number systems. You may wish to draw a simplified Venn diagram of the real numbers as shown below.

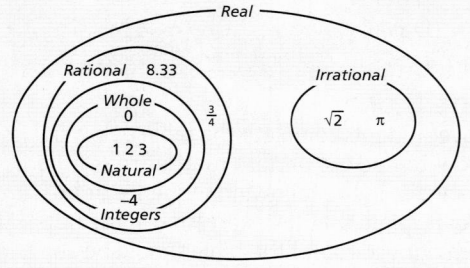

Independent Practice

▶ **Ex. 3–8** Students may need assistance in describing the patterns, so working in groups would be helpful.

▶ **Ex. 11, 12** If students are not using fraction calculators, review the keystrokes for performing operations on fractions.

Guided Practice

▶ **CHECK for Understanding**

1. What is the first whole number? What is the first natural number? 0, 1

2. Evaluate fractions of the form $\frac{n}{11}$ as a decimal for values of n from 1 through 4. Describe any patterns.
   $n = 1$: $0.\overline{09}$, $n = 2$: $0.\overline{18}$, $n = 3$: $0.\overline{27}$, $n = 4$: $0.\overline{36}$; the repeating decimal is $0.\overline{09}n$.

Independent Practice

In Exercises 3–8, create a table showing your calculations. See Additional Answers.

3. Calculate the quotient of 192 and each of the first 4 natural numbers.

4. Calculate the product of 75 and each of the first 9 whole numbers.

5. Evaluate fractions of the form $\frac{n}{3}$ as a decimal for the values of n from 1 through 9.

6. Evaluate fractions of the form $\frac{2}{n}$ as a decimal for the values of n from 1 through 9. What values of n produce repeating decimals?

7. Calculate $\frac{n^2}{2}$ for the first 7 whole numbers.

8. Calculate $\frac{n}{n+1}$ for the first 5 natural numbers.

In Exercises 9–12, use a calculator to evaluate the expressions. Then describe the pattern. For descriptions, see Additional Answers.

9.	10.	11.	12.
$8(2) + 2$ 18	$77(1443)$ 111111	$\frac{1}{5} + \frac{1}{8}(400)$ 50.2	$\frac{5}{6} + 9\left(\frac{1}{3}\right)$ $3.8\overline{3}$
$8(23) + 3$ 187	$154(1443)$ 222222	$\frac{2}{5} + \frac{1}{8}(400)$ 50.4	$\frac{5}{6} + 9\left(\frac{2}{3}\right)$ $6.8\overline{3}$
$8(234) + 4$ 1876	$231(1443)$ 333333	$\frac{3}{5} + \frac{1}{8}(400)$ 50.6	$\frac{5}{6} + 9\left(\frac{3}{3}\right)$ $9.8\overline{3}$
$8(2,345) + 5$ 18765	$308(1443)$ 444444	$\frac{4}{5} + \frac{1}{8}(400)$ 50.8	$\frac{5}{6} + 9\left(\frac{4}{3}\right)$ $12.8\overline{3}$
$8(23,456) + 6$ 187654	$385(1443)$ 555555	$\frac{5}{5} + \frac{1}{8}(400)$ 51	$\frac{5}{6} + 9\left(\frac{5}{3}\right)$ $15.8\overline{3}$
$8(234,567) + 7$ 1876543	$462(1443)$ 666666	$\frac{6}{5} + \frac{1}{8}(400)$ 51.2	$\frac{5}{6} + 9\left(\frac{6}{3}\right)$ $18.8\overline{3}$

Constant Function **In Exercises 13–18, write the keystrokes that will produce the sequence on your calculator. Then write the next four numbers in the sequence. For instance, the sequence 3, 5, 7, 9 can be produced on some calculators by these keystrokes.** 3 [+] 2 [=] [=] [=]

See Additional Answers.

✪ **13.** 1, 9, 17, 25, [?] [?] [?] [?]   ✪ **14.** 100, 87, 74, 61, [?] [?] [?] [?]

✪ **15.** 5, 15, 45, 135, [?] [?] [?] [?]   ✪ **16.** 1025, 205, 41, 8.2, [?] [?] [?] [?]

✪ **17.** 1008, 100.8, 10.08, [?] [?] [?] [?]   ✪ **18.** 12.3, 24.6, 49.2, [?] [?] [?] [?]

[?] This symbol indicates exercises where you should choose the appropriate method of calculations: mental math, paper and pencil, or calculator.

✪ More difficult exercises

Extra Practice

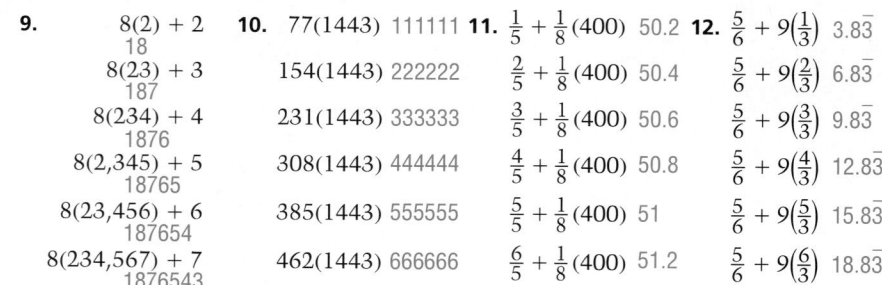

Reteaching

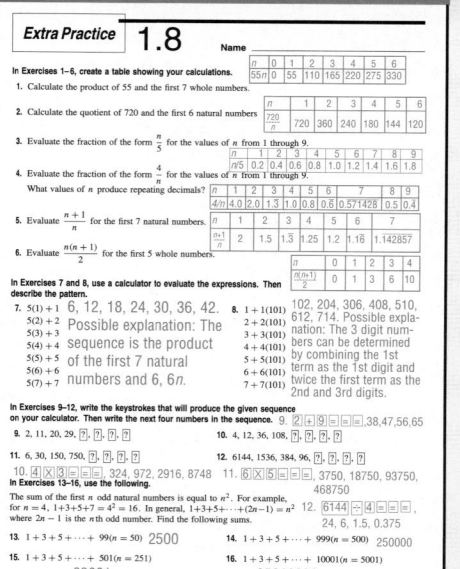

Modeling Cubic Numbers   The cubic numbers can be modeled as follows.

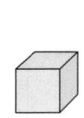 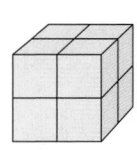 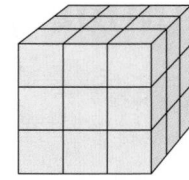

1 cubic unit   8 cubic units   27 cubic units   For model, see Additional Answers.

19. Draw a model for the next cubic number. What is the number? 64

20. Write a verbal and algebraic model that gives the cubic numbers.
   Raise each natural number to the 3rd power. n^3

Integrated Review
Making Connections within Mathematics

Sequences   In Exercises 21–28, find the next 4 numbers in the sequence.

21. 2, 5, 8, 11, ? ? ? ? 14, 17, 20, 23

22. 55, 50, 45, 40, ? ? ? ? 35, 30, 25, 20

23. 1, 2, 4, 8, ? ? ? ? 16, 32, 64, 128

24. 1, 4, 9, 16, ? ? ? ? 25, 36, 49, 64

25. $\frac{1}{2}, \frac{2}{3}, \frac{3}{4}, \frac{4}{5},$? ? ? ? $\frac{5}{6}, \frac{6}{7}, \frac{7}{8}, \frac{8}{9}$

26. $\frac{2}{3}, \frac{2}{4}, \frac{2}{5}, \frac{2}{6},$? ? ? ? $\frac{2}{7}, \frac{2}{8}, \frac{2}{9}, \frac{2}{10}$

27. 1, 5, 2, 6, ? ? ? ? 3, 7, 4, 8

28. 100, 81, 64, 49, ? ? ? ? 36, 25, 16, 9

Exploration and Extension

Fibonacci Sequence   The sequence 1, 1, 2, 3, 5, 8, 13, . . . is called a Fibonacci Sequence. It was developed by the Italian mathematician Leonardo Fibonacci (1175–1250).

29. Describe the pattern of the sequence. See below.

30. State the next three numbers in the sequence. 21, 34, 55

31. *Group Investigation*   In groups of four, you will investigate one of the many special proprieties of the Fibonacci Sequence. To begin, pick any two numbers such that the second is larger than the first. Each member of the group is to develop a Fibonacci-like sequence from the two numbers. Then, using the sequence, each member of the group is to compute the ratio of the consecutive terms and record the results in a table. For example, 12 and 20 would yield 12, 20, 32, 52, … . Describe the pattern.

Term	12	20	32	52
Quotient	$\frac{20}{12} = 1.6$	$\frac{32}{20} = 1.6$	$\frac{52}{32} = 1.625$	$\frac{84}{52} \approx 1.615$

Check students' work. The ratios get closer and closer to 1.61803 … .

29. Each number, except the first two, is the sum of the two preceding numbers.

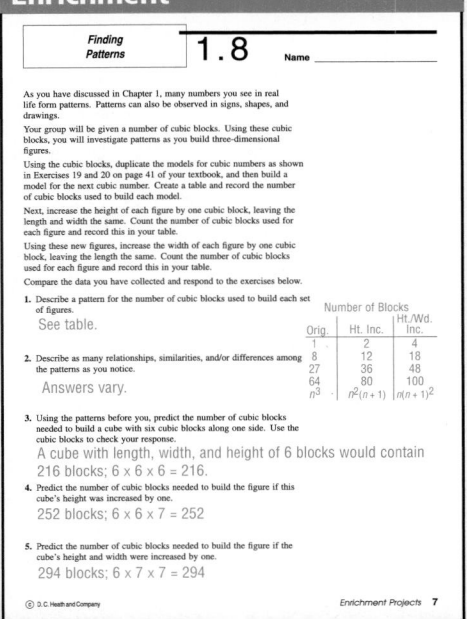

The numbers of overlapping clockwise and counterclockwise spirals in the heads of sunflowers are consecutive terms in the Fibonacci sequence like 34 and 55, or 55 and 89.

1.8 · *Exploring Patterns with Technology*   **41**

▶ **Ex. 13–18**

TECHNOLOGY
Some four-function calculators and most scientific calculators have a built in constant function. The general pattern for constant operations (including subtraction and division) on most four-function calculators is
Variable   Operation   Constant   = …
So, to generate the sequence 3, 5, 7, 9 you would enter 3 + 2 = = =. The constant function on most scientific calculators is not standardized, even among calculators of the same brand.
For example, for the TI-34, you would enter

Constant	Operation	Variable	
2	+	3	= = =

For TI calculators with a K key, such as the Challenger, enter

Constant	Operation	K	Variable=
2	+	K	3 = = =.

For Casio-like calculators, enter

Constant	Double Operation	Variable=
2	+ +	3 = = =.

Try to group students who have the same brand and type of calculator together.

Integrated Review
These exercises are a good opportunity for students to revive their pattern-finding skills.

Exploration and Extension
Have students do research on other Fibonacci patterns, the golden rectangle, and Fibonacci patterns in nature. Many resources are available including several from NCTM.

Portfolio Opportunity: Math Log
Complete the table of the sum of the first n natural numbers. Find an algebraic expression for these numbers.

n	1	2	3	4	5	6	7	8	9	10
Sum	1	3	6							

Also available as a copymaster, page 6, Ex. 10

Short Quiz
Covers Lessons 1.7 and 1.8

Available as a copymaster, page 6

Enrichment

Finding Patterns	**1.8**	Name _____

As you have discussed in Chapter 1, many numbers you see in real life form patterns. Patterns can also be observed in signs, shapes, and drawings.

Your group will be given a number of cubic blocks. Using these cubic blocks, you will investigate patterns as you build three-dimensional figures.

Using the cubic blocks, duplicate the models for cubic numbers as shown in Exercises 19 and 20 on page 41 of your textbook, and then build a model for the next cubic number. Create a table and record the number of cubic blocks used to build each model.

Next, increase the height of each figure by one cubic block, leaving the length and width the same. Count the number of cubic blocks used for each figure and record this in your table.

Using these new figures, increase the width of each figure by one cubic block, leaving the length the same. Count the number of cubic blocks used for each figure and record this in your table.

Compare the data you have collected and respond to the exercises below.

1. Describe a pattern for the number of cubic blocks used to build each set of figures.
   See table.

	Number of Blocks	
Orig.	Ht. Inc.	Ht./Wd. Inc.
1	2	4
8	12	18
27	36	48
64	80	100
n^3	$n^2(n+1)$	$n(n+1)^2$

2. Describe as many relationships, similarities, and/or differences among the patterns as you notice.
   Answers vary.

3. Using the patterns before you, predict the number of cubic blocks needed to build a cube with six cubic blocks along one side. Use the cubic blocks to check your response.
   A cube with length, width, and height of 6 blocks would contain 216 blocks; 6 × 6 × 6 = 216.

4. Predict the number of cubic blocks needed to build the figure if this cube's height was increased by one.
   252 blocks; 6 × 6 × 7 = 252

5. Predict the number of cubic blocks needed to build the figure if the cube's height and width were increased by one.
   294 blocks; 6 × 7 × 7 = 294

© D.C. Heath and Company   Enrichment Projects **7**

Chapter SUMMARY

Number patterns, whether in the abstract or as the language of real-life data, are the theme of this first chapter. Lesson 1.1 began with the observation of abstract number patterns or sequences, and the technique of identifying and describing them.
Lessons 1.2 and 1.3 reviewed basic rules for single-operation expressions and how such expressions are described verbally and with symbols. Lesson 1.4 presented the order of operations for multi-operation expressions. Since the concepts and skills of this course are taught in the context of real-life modeling, the fundamental concept that numerical expressions can be used as models was introduced as early as Lesson 1.2 (and developed further in Lessons 1.5 and 1.8). Lesson 1.5 made the giant step to the use of variables and the language of algebra. Once again, since this language is to be applied to analyzing, generalizing, and modeling real-life data, Lesson 1.6 presents methods of organizing data. Lessons 1.7 and 1.8 shows students how algebraic expressions can be used to model some simple number patterns and geometric patterns, and patterns in the visible world around us.

1 Chapter Summary

What did you learn?

Skills
1. Use numbers to identify and measure objects. **(1.1)**
2. Recognize and describe number patterns. **(1.1, 1.8)**
3. Use the four basic number operations. **(1.2)**
   ▪ Use multiplication models. **(1.2)**
4. Use powers and square roots. **(1.3)**
5. Use order of operations. **(1.4)**
   ▪ Use order of operations on a calculator. **(1.4)**
6. Use variables in expressions. **(1.5)**
   ▪ Evaluate algebraic expressions. **(1.5)**
7. Identify polygons and parts of polygons. **(1.7)**

Problem-Solving Strategies
8. Use verbal and algebraic models to solve real-life problems. **(1.5–1.8)**
9. Solve problems by using strategies such as guess, check, and revise and draw a diagram. **(1.8)**

Exploring Data
10. Organize and display data
    ▪ with a table. **(1.6–1.8)**
    ▪ with a graph. **(1.6)**

Why did you learn it?

Number patterns and geometric patterns occur frequently in real-life situations. Often these patterns can be modeled by using algebraic expressions or formulas. Being able to write and use models for real-life situations helps people succeed in their occupations. For instance, accountants use formulas to compute taxes. Medical technicians use formulas to analyze samples. Engineers use formulas to measure the strength of a structure. More importantly, whatever your work turns out to be, you will be able to perform more successfully if you can use formulas to model real life.

How does it fit into the bigger picture of mathematics?

Hundreds of years ago, mathematics was divided into two major branches: algebra and geometry. These branches used to have little overlap—equations and algebraic expressions belonged to algebra, and graphs, curves, and lines belonged to geometry. Today, however, algebra and geometry have a lot of overlap. For instance, you have seen that some geometrical patterns can be described by algebraic expressions.

In this course you will be preparing for future mathematical studies—not only studies in algebra and geometry, but also studies in statistics, probability, and trigonometry.

Number Patterns **In Exercises 1–6, describe the pattern. Then list the next 3 numbers. (1.1, 1.3)** For descriptions, see margin.

1. 15, 30, 45, 60   75, 90, 105   **2.** 100, 94, 88, 82   76, 70, 64   **3.** 2, 6, 12, 20   30, 42, 56

4. 3, 6, 18, 72   360; 2160; 15,120   **5.** 1, 8, 27, 64   125, 216, 343   **6.** 1, $\sqrt{3}$, $\sqrt{5}$, $\sqrt{7}$ 3, $\sqrt{11}$, $\sqrt{13}$

Sequences **In Exercises 7 and 8, write the first 6 numbers in the sequence. (1.1)**

7. The first number is 1. Each succeeding number is 9 more than the preceding number.   1, 10, 19, 28, 37, 46

8. The first two numbers are 1 and 2. Each succeeding number is the product of the two preceding numbers.   1, 2, 2, 4, 8, 32

Reasoning **In Exercises 9–12, without researching, match the state with its abbreviation. (1.1)**

a. AR   **b.** AL   **c.** AZ   **d.** AK

9. Alaska   d   **10.** Alabama   b   **11.** Arkansas   a   **12.** Arizona   c

13. Describe how you obtained your answers in Exercises 9–12. **(1.1)** Answers vary.

14. See margin.

14. Describe the pattern, $z1, y4, x7, w10, \ldots$.. **(1.1)**

15. *Migration*   Geese usually migrate south for the winter months. A flock of geese migrated 552 miles in 16 hours. How fast did the geese fly? **(1.1, 1.5)**   34.5 mph

16. *Migration*   Ducks, like geese, usually migrate south for the winter months. Ducks fly an average speed of 40 mph. If a flock of ducks migrates 18 hours in a day, how far will they travel? **(1.1, 1.5)**   720 mi

Snow geese can fly for many hours without stopping. Some flocks have flown 1700 miles in less than $2\frac{1}{2}$ days.

Computation Sense **In Exercises 17–24, evaluate the expression. (1.2)**

17. $21.86 + 53.09$ 74.95   **18.** 4.28×1.7 7.276   **19.** $542 - 291$ 251   **20.** $1146/6$ 191

21. $972 \div 18$ 54   **22.** $\frac{585}{15}$ 39   **23.** $(78)(64)$ 4992   **24.** $109 - 33$ 76

Number Sense **In Exercises 25 and 26, write a number sentence for the model. (1.2)**

$3 \times 5 = 15$ or $5 + 5 + 5 = 15$

$3 \times 4 = 12$ or $4 + 4 + 4 = 12$

25.

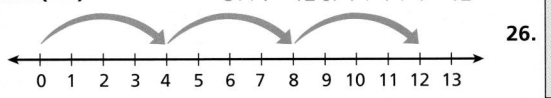

26.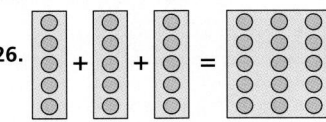

Computation Sense **In Exercises 27–32, write the expression as a power. Then evaluate. (1.3)**

27. 13×13 13^2, 169   **28.** $11 \times 11 \times 11 \times 11$ 11^4; 14, 641   **29.** $\left(\frac{1}{2}\right)\left(\frac{1}{2}\right)\left(\frac{1}{2}\right)$ $\left(\frac{1}{2}\right)^3$, $\frac{1}{8}$

30. $(3.2)(3.2)(3.2)(3.2)(3.2)$ 3.2^5, 335.54432   **31.** $\frac{5}{9} \cdot \frac{5}{9} \cdot \frac{5}{9}$ $\left(\frac{5}{9}\right)^3$, $\frac{125}{729}$ **32.** $1.01 \cdot 1.01 \cdot 1.01 \cdot 1.01$ 1.01^4, 1.04060401

This symbol indicates exercises where you should choose the appropriate method of calculation: mental math, paper and pencil, or calculator.

Have students begin this Review in class and complete it as a homework assignment.

ASSIGNMENT GUIDE

*Basic/Average: Ex. 4, 5, 7, 16, 25, 28, 29, 33, 34, 38, 39–47 odd, 71–76, 83–85

Above Average: Ex. 4, 5, 7, 16, 25, 28, 29, 33, 34, 38, 39–47 odd, 71–76, 83–85

Advanced: Ex. 5–8, 15, 16, 37–39, 41–47 odd, 63–66, 71–78, 83–85, 89–91

*For these students, you will need to limit assignments to cover only those lessons you chose to teach from this chapter.

Resources
Color Transparencies
   Graph for Ex. 67–70, p. 6
Answer Masters, pp. 18–20

Answers
To get the next number:
   1. Add 15 to the preceding number.
   2. Subtract 6 from the preceding number.
   3. Add 4, add 6, add 8, etc., to the preceding number.
   4. Multiply the preceding number by 2, by 3, by 4, etc.
   5. Name the next perfect cube.
   6. Name the square root of the next odd number.
   14. To get the next term, name the letter of the alphabet that precedes the letter in the preceding term and add 3 to the number in the preceding term.

In Exercises 33–36, use a calculator to evaluate the expression. Round to 2 decimal places. (1.3)

33. $\sqrt{289}$ 17   **34.** $\sqrt{729}$ 27   **35.** $\sqrt{2.07}$ 1.44   **36.** $\sqrt{5.63}$ 2.37

37. *Surveying*   A square plot of land contains 65,946 square feet. What are the lengths of the sides of the plot? **(1.3)** ≈ 256.8 ft

38. *Writing*   In your own words, write the Left-to-Right Rule. **(1.4)**   Check students' work.

39. *Writing*   In your own words, describe the established order of operations. **(1.4)**

Check students' work.

In Exercises 40–48, evaluate the expression. Verify your answer using a calculator. (1.3, 1.4)

40. $4 + 7 - 3$ 8   **41.** $21 - 13 + 8$ 16   **42.** $5 + 18 \div 6$ 8

43. $8 \cdot 4 - 2^3$ 24   **44.** $7^2 - 14 \times 3$ 7   **45.** $(8 - 2) \times 12 \div 3^2$ 8

46. $(2^3 + 1) \div (12 - 9)$ 3   **47.** $(5 - 3)[(8 - 2)^2 - 4^2]$ 40   **48.** $(3^3 + 15) \div \sqrt{49}$ 6

In Exercises 49–60, evaluate the expression for $m = 8$ and $n = 4$. (1.3, 1.4, 1.5)

49. $m + 5$ 13   **50.** $n - 1$ 3   **51.** $3n - 6$ 6   **52.** $2m + 7$ 23

53. $n \div m$ $\frac{1}{2}$ **54.** $m \div n$ 2   **55.** $2n - m$ 0   **56.** $\frac{1}{2}m + 3n$ 16

57. $n^2(m - n)$ 64   **58.** $m^2 + \sqrt{n}$ 66   **59.** $3m \div (2n^2 - m)$ 1   **60.** $n(m - n) + mn$ 48

Distance, Rate, Time   **In Exercises 61 and 62, use the formula $d = rt$. (1.5)**

61. Find d for $r = 35$ miles per hour and $t = 7$ hours.   245 mi

62. Find r for $d = 76$ miles and $t = 1.5$ hours. $50\frac{2}{3}$ mph

U. S. Patents   The number of patents (in thousands) granted by the United States for the years 1987 to 1991 is listed in the table. Use the table to answer Exercises 63–66. (*Source: U. S. Patent and Trademark Office*) **(1.6)**

Year	Total Number Granted	Individuals	Corporations	U.S. Government
1987	83.0	15.3	66.7	1.0
1988	77.9	14.3	62.9	0.7
1989	95.5	18.0	76.7	0.9
1990	90.4	17.3	72.1	1.0
1991	96.5	18.1	77.3	1.2

63. In what year were the most patents issued?   1991

64. How many individuals were granted a patent in 1989?   18,000

65. In 1990, how many more patents were issued to corporations than to individuals?   54,800

66. Represent this data with a bar graph or a line graph.   See margin.

See footnote on page 43.

Answers
66.

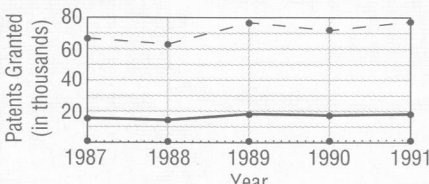

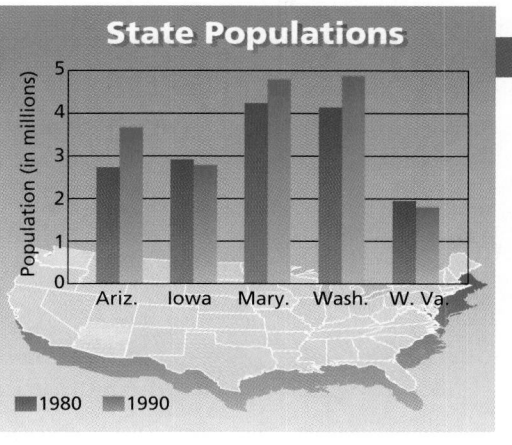

State Populations

Population **In Exercises 67–70, use the graph at the right. (1.6)**

67. In which states did the population increase between 1980 and 1990? Arizona, Maryland, Washington

68. Which state had the highest population in 1980? Maryland

69. Estimate the 1990 population of West Virginia. 1.8 million

70. Represent the data in the graph with a table. See margin.

Reasoning **In Exercises 71–76, decide whether the figure is a polygon. If it is, name it. If it is not, explain why. (1.7)**

No, not all sides are segments

71. 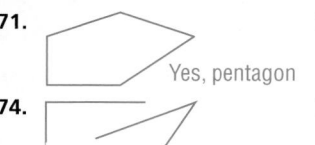 Yes, pentagon

72.  Yes, decagon

73.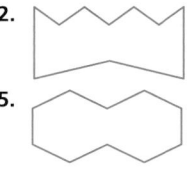

74.  No, not closed

75.  Yes, decagon

76. 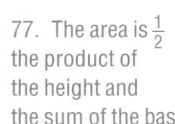 Yes, quadrilateral

Use the following information to answer Exercises 77 and 78. (1.4, 1.5, 1.6, 1.7)

Area of a Trapezoid A trapezoid is a quadrilateral that has exactly one pair of parallel sides. The table below lists the bases, b_1 and b_2, the height, and the area of several trapezoids. (The variable b_1 is read "b sub 1," and the variable b_2 is read "b sub 2.")

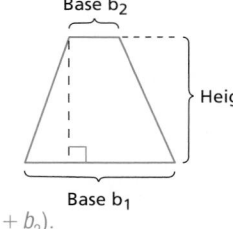

Base b_2

Height

Base b_1

Trapezoid	b_1	b_2	h	$h(b_1 + b_2)$	Area
1	8	6	6	84	42
2	4	2	3	18	9
3	10	5	4	60	30

77. The area is $\frac{1}{2}$ the product of the height and the sum of the bases; $A = \frac{1}{2}h(b_1 + b_2)$.

77. Write a verbal model and an algebraic model for the area of a trapezoid.

✪ **78.** Find the area of a trapezoid for which $b_1 = 12$, $b_2 = 8$, and $h = 7$. 70 units²

In Exercises 79 and 80, use a calculator to create a table. Describe the pattern. (1.1, 1.8) For tables, see margin.

Each number, after the first, is

79. The product of 105 and the first 9 natural numbers **79.** 105 more than the preceding number.

80. The sum of $9 + 9n$ using the first 9 natural numbers **80.** 9 more than the preceding number.

In Exercises 81 and 82, give the keystrokes for your calculator that produce the sequence. Then write the next three numbers. (1.8)

81. 15309, 5103, 1701, 567, ? ? ?
15309 ÷ 3 = = = = = = ; 189, 63, 21

82. 100, 90, 81, 72.9, ? ? ?
100 × 0.9 = = = = = = ;
65.61, 59.049, 53.1441

✪ More difficult exercises

Answers
70.

State	1980 Population (in millions)	1990 Population (in millions)
Arizona	2.7	3.7
Iowa	2.9	2.8
Maryland	4.2	4.8
Washington	4.1	4.9
West Virginia	1.9	1.8

79.

n	1	2	3	4	5	6	7	8	9
$105n$	105	210	315	420	525	630	735	840	945

80.

n	1	2	3	4	5	6	7	8	9
$9+9n$	18	27	36	45	54	63	72	81	90

Manufacturing Rovers   **In Exercises 83–85, use the following information.**

You own a business that makes rovers. Last month, your business spent $1 million to build 72 rovers. Each rover sold for $45,000.

⭐ **83.** A model for your profit is $P = I - E$

| Profit | = | Income | − | Expenses |

Use this verbal model to write an algebraic model for the profit. $2.24 million

⭐ **84.** What was your profit last month?

⭐ **85.** Which of the following would increase your profit?   All of them

  a. Reduce your expenses.

  b. Sell more rovers.

  c. Increase the price of a rover.

David R. Scott and James B. Irwin were the first astronauts to travel in a moon rover.

Driving Rovers   **In Exercises 86–88, imagine that you are an astronaut driving a moon rover. You are traveling at a speed of 22 miles per hour.**

86. How many minutes will it take you to travel 33 miles?   90

87. How far will you travel in 30 minutes?   11 miles

⭐ **88.** If the rover gets 13 miles per gallon, how many gallons of fuel will it take to travel 80 miles? $6\frac{2}{13}$

Transporting Rovers   **In Exercises 89–91, use the following information.**

On the highway you see a tractor-trailer transporting all-terrain rovers, as shown below. Each rover weighs 4,500 pounds. Without its cargo, the tractor-trailer weighs 33,000 pounds.

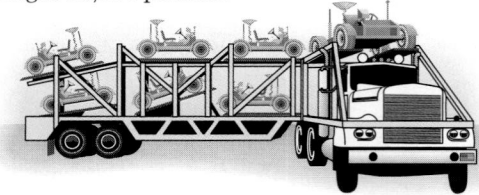

89. The weight is the sum of the trailer's weight and the product of 7 and a rover's weight.

⭐ **89.** Write a verbal model for the total weight of the tractor-trailer and the rovers.

⭐ **90.** Write an algebraic model that represents the total weight of the tractor-trailer and the rovers. $W = T + 7R$

⭐ **91.** What is the total weight?   64,500 lb

46   *Chapter 1 • Exploring Patterns*   ⭐ More difficult exercises

In Exercises 1–6, evaluate the expression for $a = 8$, $b = 3$, $c = 5$. (1.4, 1.5)

1. $a \cdot c$ 40

2. b^2 9

3. $\dfrac{a}{4}$ 2

4. $3c^3$ 375

5. $4(a + 1)^2$ 324

6. $\sqrt{(a+1)}$ 3

In Exercises 7 and 8, describe the pattern. Then list the next 3 numbers. (1.1)   For descriptions, see margin.

7. 1, 5, 9, 13, [?] [?] [?]   17, 21, 25

8. 1, 4, 9, 16, [?] [?] [?]   25, 36, 49

In Exercises 9–12, evaluate the expression. (1.4)

9. $3 + 5 \cdot 2 + 4$ 17

10. $10 - 5 \div 5 + 4$ 13

11. $(6 + 2) \cdot 2 + 3^2$ 25

12. $14 \div (9 - 7) + 2^3$ 10

13. Calculate the product of 321 and the first 7 whole numbers. Record the results in a table. Describe the pattern. (1.8)   For table, see margin.
Each number, after the first, is 321 more than the preceding number.

In Exercises 14 and 15, state whether the figure is a polygon. If it is, name it. (1.7)

14.

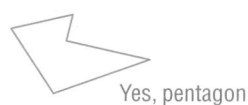

Yes, pentagon

15.

No

16. The side lengths of 5 squares are 1, 2, 3, 4, and 5. Complete the table by finding the perimeter and area of each square. (1.7)

Side Length	1	2	3	4	5
Perimeter	?	?	?	?	?
Area	?	?	?	?	?

4, 8, 12, 16, 20

1, 4, 9, 16, 25

In Exercises 17–20, use the bar graph at the right. *(Source: National Basketball Association)* (1.6)

17. About how many games did the Detroit Pistons win?   48

18. Which two teams had the same number of wins and losses?   Celtics and Knicks

19. Which team had the greatest difference between wins and losses?   Bulls

20. Represent this data with a table.   See margin.

21. *Gold Prices*   The average price of gold (in dollars per fine ounce) for the years 1987 through 1992 is listed in the table. Represent this data with a bar graph and a line graph. *(Source: U.S. Bureau of Mines)*   See margin.

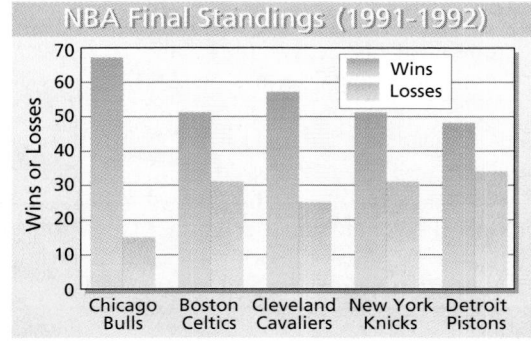
NBA Final Standings (1991-1992)

Year	1987	1988	1989	1990	1991	1992
Average Price	448	438	383	385	363	350

Answers

7. Each number, after the first, is 4 more than the preceding number.

8. Each number, after the first, is the next consecutive perfect square.

13.

n	0	1	2	3	4	5	6
321n	0	321	642	963	1284	1605	1926

20.

Team	Chicago Bulls	Boston Celtics	Cleveland Cavaliers	New York Knicks	Detroit Pistons
Wins	67	51	57	51	48
Losses	15	31	25	31	34

21.

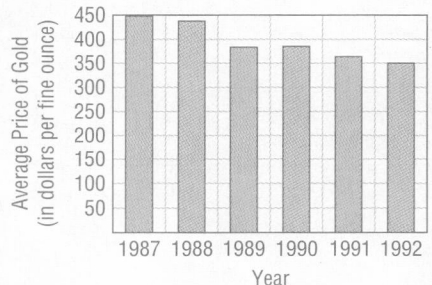

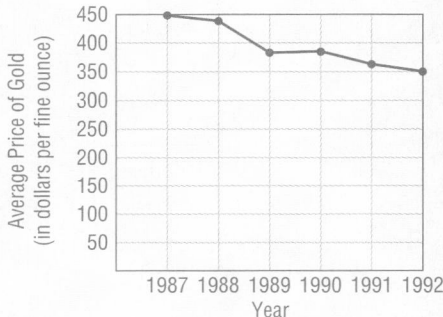

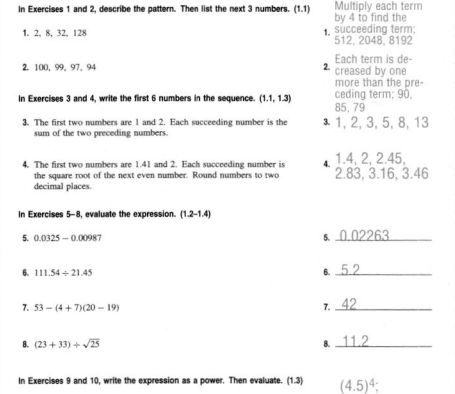

Chapter Test

Chapter **1** Test   Form C   Name _____
(Page 1 of 3 pages)   Date _____

In Exercises 1 and 2, describe the pattern. Then list the next 3 numbers. (1.1)

1. 2, 8, 32, 128

Multiply each term by 4 to find the
1. succeeding term; 512, 2048, 8192

2. 100, 99, 97, 94

Each term is decreased by one more than the preceding term; 90, 85, 79

In Exercises 3 and 4, write the first 6 numbers in the sequence. (1.1, 1.3)

3. The first two numbers are 1 and 2. Each succeeding number is the sum of the two preceding numbers.

3. 1, 2, 3, 5, 8, 13

4. The first two numbers are 1.41 and 2. Each succeeding number is the square root of the next even number. Round numbers to two decimal places.

4. 1.4, 2, 2.45, 2.83, 3.16, 3.46

In Exercises 5–8, evaluate the expression. (1.2–1.4)

5. 0.0325 − 0.00987   5. 0.02263

6. 111.54 ÷ 21.45   6. 5.2

7. 53 − (4 + 7)(20 − 19)   7. 42

8. $(23 + 33) \div \sqrt{25}$ 8. 11.2

In Exercises 9 and 10, write the expression as a power. Then evaluate. (1.3)

9. 4.5 · 4.5 · 4.5 · 4.5   9. $(4.5)^4$; 410.0625

10. $\frac{4}{5} \cdot \frac{4}{5} \cdot \frac{4}{5} \cdot \frac{4}{5}$ 10. $\left(\frac{4}{5}\right)^4$; $\frac{256}{625}$

11. A rectangular calendar has an area of 338 square inches. When folded in half, it forms a square. What is the length of the longer side? (1.4)   11. 26 inches

Windows   © D.C. Heath and Company   Chapter 1 • Exploring Patterns   **13**

◀ **FORMAL ASSESSMENT**

Three Chapter Tests   Form A is of average difficulty, Form B is of average difficulty in multiple choice format, and Form C is more challenging.

Available as copymasters, pp. 7–15

CHAPTER 2 ▪ OVERVIEW

Lesson	Pages	Goals	Meeting the NCTM Standards
Lesson Investigation 2.1	50	Algebraic Expressions	Algebra, Geometry, Measurement
2.1	51–54	1. Use the Distributive Property 2. Use the Distributive Property in real-life situations	Problem Solving, Communication, Reasoning, Connections, Computation and Estimation, Technology, Algebra, Geometry
2.2	55–58	1. Simplify expressions by adding like terms 2. Add like terms to simplify expressions in geometry	Problem Solving, Communication, Reasoning, Connections, Patterns and Functions, Algebra, Geometry
2.3	59–62	1. Check that a number is a solution of an equation 2. Use mental math to solve an equation	Problem Solving, Connections, Computation and Estimation, Algebra, Statistics, Geometry
Mixed Review	63	Review of arithmetic, algebra, and geometry	Computation and Estimation, Technology, Algebra
Milestones	63	The Changing Face of Money	Connections
Lesson Investigation 2.4	64	Solving Equations	Algebra, Geometry, Measurement
2.4	65–68	1. Use addition or subtraction to solve an equation 2. Use equations as algebraic models to solve real-life problems	Problem Solving, Communication, Reasoning, Connections, Technology, Algebra, Geometry, Measurement
Mid-Chapter Self-Test	69	Diagnose student weaknesses and remediate with correlated Reteaching Copymasters	Assessment
Lesson Investigation 2.5	70	Solving Equations	Algebra, Geometry, Measurement
2.5	71–74	1. Use multiplication or division to solve an equation 2. Use equations to solve real-life problems	Problem Solving, Communication, Connections, Technology, Algebra, Geometry, Measurement
Using a Spreadsheet	75	Make a table	Problem Solving, Technology, Statistics, Geometry, Measurement
2.6	76–80	1. Translate verbal phrases into algebraic expressions 2. Model real-life situations with algebraic expressions	Problem Solving, Communication, Connections, Patterns and Functions, Algebra, Statistics
Mixed Review	80	Review of arithmetic, algebra, and geometry	Algebra
2.7	81–84	1. Translate verbal sentences into algebraic equations 2. Model real-life situations with algebraic equations	Problem Solving, Communication, Connections, Algebra, Statistics, Geometry, Measurement
2.8	85-88	1. Use a systematic problem-solving plan 2. Use other problem-solving strategies such as "solving a simpler problem"	Problem Solving, Communication, Reasoning, Connections, Computation and Estimation, Algebra, Statistics, Geometry, Measurement
2.9	89–92	1. Solve simple inequalities. 2. Use inequalities as algebraic models	Problem Solving, Communication, Reasoning, Connections, Algebra, Statistics, Geometry
Chapter Summary	93	A restatement of what has been learned, why it has been learned, and how it fits into the structure of mathematics	Communication, Connections
Chapter Review	94–96	Review of concepts and skills learned in the chapter.	Problem Solving, Connections
Chapter Test	97	Diagnose student weaknesses and remediate with correlated Reteaching Copymasters	Assessment

48A

RESOURCES ORGANIZER

Lesson Pages	2.1 51–54	2.2 55–58	2.3 59–62	2.4 65–68	2.5 71–74	2.6 76–80	2.7 81–84	2.8 85–88	2.9 89–92
Lesson Plans	9	10	11	12	13	14	15	16	17
Problem of the Day	4	4	4	5	5	5	6	6	6
Warm-Up Exercises	4	4	4	5	5	5	6	6	6
Color Transparencies	—	7	7	—	—	8	9	—	10
Teaching Tools:									
Transparencies	—	T4	—	—	—	—	—	T5	—
Copymasters	—	C5	—	—	—	C6	—	C7	—
Math Log	7	7	7	8	8	8	9	9	9
Technology	8	—	—	—	9, 10	11	—	—	—
Answer Masters	22, 23	24, 25	26, 27	29, 30	31, 32	33, 34	36, 37	38	39, 40
Extra Practice Copymasters	9	10	11	12	13	14	15	16	17
Reteaching Copymasters	9	10	11	12	13	14	15	16	17
Enrichment Projects	8, 9	—	—	10, 11	—	—	—	—	—
Alternative Assessment:									
Projects	—	17	—	17, 18	—	18	—	—	—
Partner Quizzes	—	—	—	45	—	—	—	—	—
Group Assessment	—	—	—	—	—	—	—	—	61, 62
Formal Assessment									
Short Quizzes	—	16	—	17	—	20	—	21	—
Tests	—	—	—	18, 19	—	—	—	—	22–30
Overhead Manipulatives Kit	—	Algebra Tiles	Algebra Tiles	Algebra Tiles	Algebra Tiles	—	—	—	—
Complete Solutions Manual	Includes step-by-step solutions for all exercises in the student text								
Computerized Test Bank	Creates customized tests that include graphics								
Interactive CD-ROM Project	Provides an interactive and interdisciplinary chapter project								

STARTERS

Problem of the Day

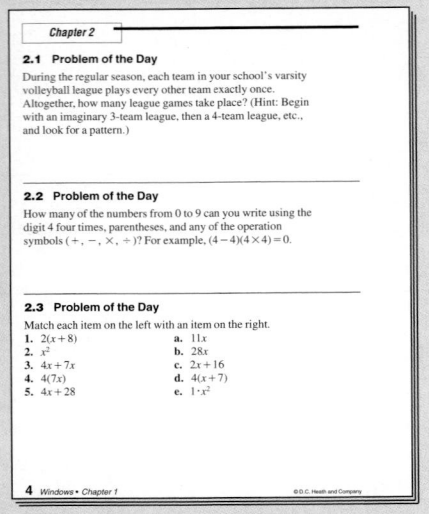

Warm-Up Exercises

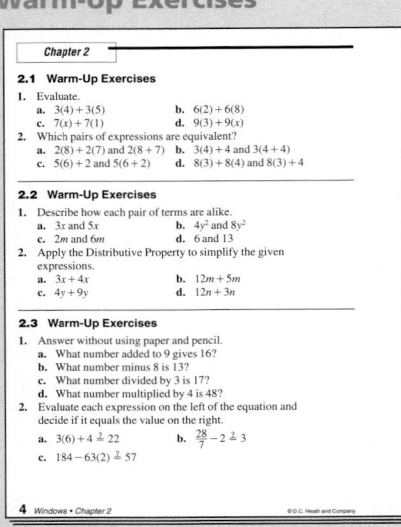

FOR TEACHERS

Answer Masters

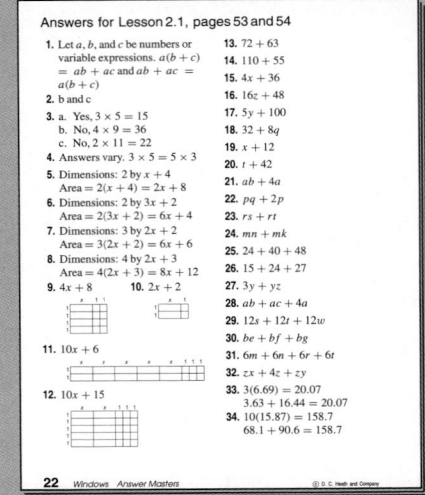

Lesson Plans

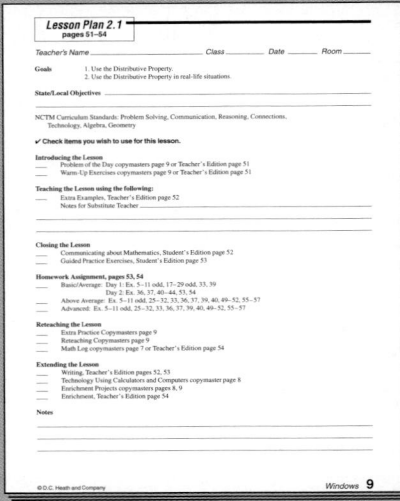

Teaching Tools

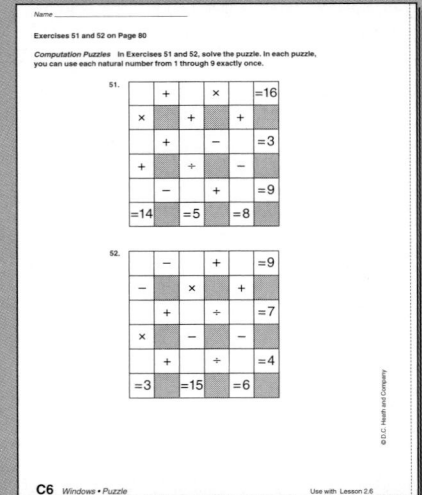

Teaching Tools includes:
Transparencies and Copymasters for classroom activities and study skills:

- Graph Paper
- Coordinate Planes
- Algebra Tiles
- Number Counters
- Fraction Strips
- Models

REAL LIFE
Color Transparencies for Real-Life Applications

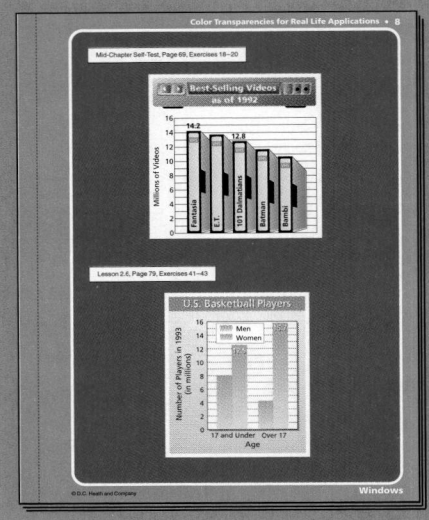

Technology: Using Calculators and Computers

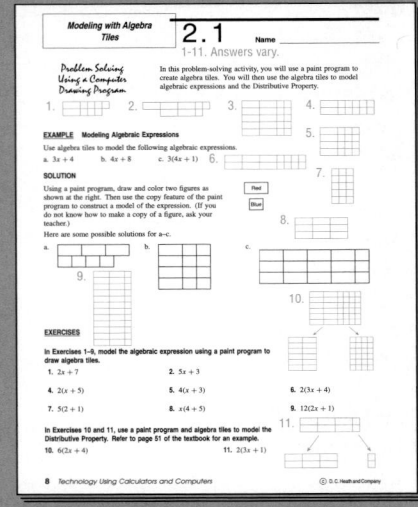

Also Available:

- Complete Solutions Manual
- Overhead Manipulatives Kit
- Computerized Testing Program

- **Interactive CD-ROM Projects**
  Interactive projects for solving real-world problems using multimedia

- **Interactions: Real Math–Real Careers**
  A videodisc–based resource that connects math to real careers and on-the-job problem solving

- **PACKETS® Performance Assessment for Middle School Mathematics**
  A program that links assessment and instruction in real-life settings

ASSESSMENT

Alternative Assessment

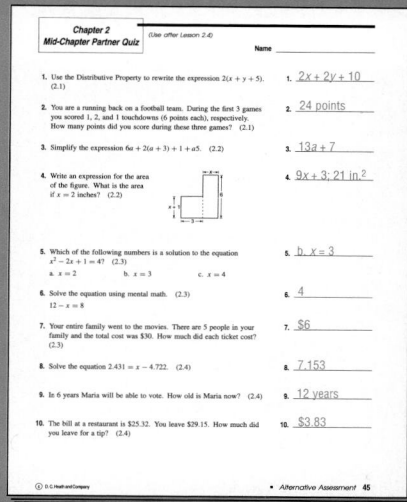

Alternative Assessment includes:
- Scoring Rubrics
- Portfolios
- Math Journals
- Projects
- Partner Quizzes
- Individual and Group Assessment

Formal Assessment

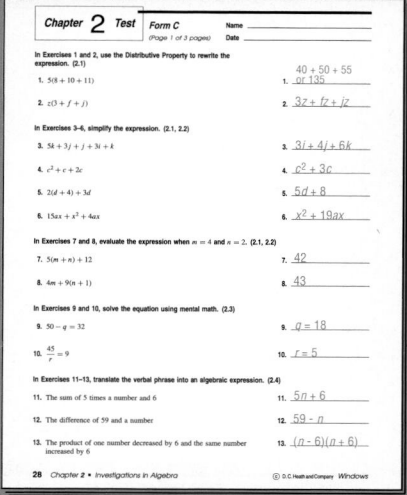

Formal Assessment includes:
- Short Quizzes (after every 2 lessons)
- Mid-Chapter Tests (2 forms)
- Chapter Tests (3 forms)
- Cumulative Tests (after every 3 Chapters)

MEETING INDIVIDUAL NEEDS

Extra Practice Copymasters

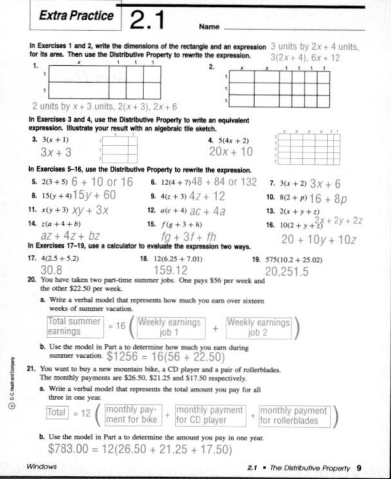

Reteaching Copymasters

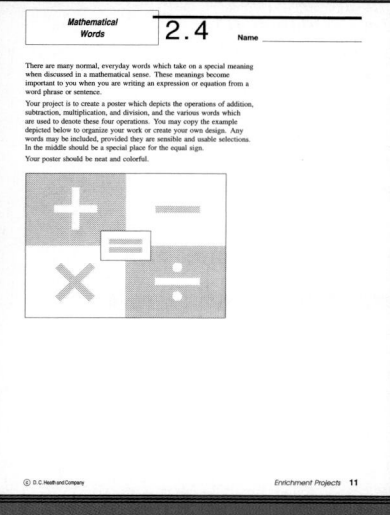

Enrichment Projects

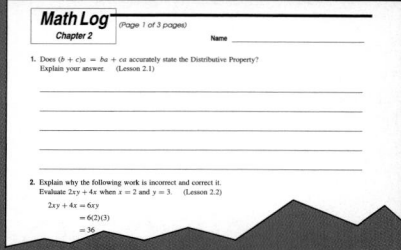

Math Log

Special Populations

Suggestions for providing equal access for:

Students Acquiring English Proficiency*

In Lesson 2.6, make sure that students know the verbal phrases associated with addition, subtraction, multiplication, and division as displayed on page 76.

Making a poster with this information can be helpful.

Lessons 2.7 and 2.8 require reading skills. Allow students with mixed reading skills to solve word problems in groups. Students may benefit from rewriting the problem-solving plan in Lesson 2.8 in their own words.

Students with Various Learning Styles*

Algebra tiles are used to model algebraic expressions in Lessons 2.1, 2.2, 2.4, and 2.5. Students who benefit from a **tactile** approach should be allowed to use the tiles with these lessons as long as they feel they are useful.

When reading word problems, students may also benefit from using highlighters or colored pencils to identify the pertinent information relating to the labels and the equation, as is done in the text.

For students with visual learning disabilities, it would be helpful to display a large poster that depicts the equal ($=$), less than ($<$), and greater than ($>$) signs with the label for each underneath, along with an example.

Underachieving Students*

These students may need encouragement in solving word problems. Allow them to work in groups of students who have mixed problem-solving abilities. Hand out copies of any lengthy class problems, and allow students to tape them into their notebooks followed by the solution.

*Gifted and Talented Students

Have students investigate the history of algebra. When was algebra first used and by whom? What did Ahmes, an Egyptian mathematician, have to do with algebra? Who is considered to be the "father" of algebra and why?

* See page T19 for descriptions of these special populations.

CHAPTER 2 OVERVIEW

PACING CHART

Lesson	Basic/ Average Course	Above Average Course	Advanced Course
2.1	2 days	1 day	1 day
2.2	2 days	1 day	1 day
2.3	2 days	1 day	1 day
2.4	2 days	1 day	1 day
2.5	2 days	1 day	1 day
2.6	2 days	1 day	1 day
2.7	2 days	1 day	1 day
2.8	2 days	1 day	1 day
2.9	0 days	1 day	1 day

About the Chapter

The concepts and skills of this course are taught in the context of real-life modeling. The students' ability to solve equations is, of course, central to this approach. This chapter lays early foundations for solving equations. After learning in Lessons 2.1 and 2.2 how the Distributive Property is used to help simplify and evaluate expressions, students will begin in Lesson 2.3 to solve the simplest equations with mental math and to check their solutions. In Lessons 2.4 and 2.5, students learn how the properties of equality are applied in order to maintain equivalent expressions on both sides of an equation. They see how this technique is applied in solving single-operation equations using addition, subtraction, multiplication, and division.

Meanwhile, Goal 2 of each of these lessons serves to remind students of the ongoing real-life context of these techniques. Algebraic modeling becomes the primary goal in Lessons 2.6 and 2.7, when students learn to translate verbal phrases into algebraic expressions and verbal sentences into equations. They learn to identify and label whatever numerical constants and variables are involved in such phrases and sentences. Lesson 2.8 introduces students to the technique of a systematic algebraic problem-solving plan that will be used throughout this course as a powerful tool in modeling real-life problems, from the simplest to the most complex. Lesson 2.9, alerting students to the fact that real-life situations often require an inequality model rather than an equation, offers students some practice in solving simple inequalities.

Investigations in Algebra

LESSONS

Apparel and accessory stores in the United States generate sales in excess of $95 million. However, each individual store must take in enough money to pay for the goods it is selling, to cover its operating costs (rent, insurance, advertising, salaries, etc.), and to pay off any outstanding debts or loans.

Real Life
The Fashion Business

Increases in Retail Prices

1990	$	$	$
1985	$	$	
1980	$	$	
1975	$	$	
1970	$	$	

Each $ represents the retail price of an item in 1960

The amount you pay for any item in a store is called the **retail price.** The graph at the left shows how clothing prices have changed over the years. The amount the store paid for the item is called the **wholesale price.** The **markup** is the amount the store adds to the wholesale price to get the retail price. So, in words,

retail price = wholesale price + markup.

In this chapter, you will learn how to assign variables and write verbal and algebraic models to describe real-life situations as part of a problem-solving plan.

LESSON INVESTIGATION 2.1
Algebraic Expressions

Materials

Teaching Tools
 Algebra tiles, pp. T4, C5
 Graph paper, pp. T1, C2
Overhead Manipulatives Kit

Take time to establish some ground rules for the use of tiles, especially for students who have had no previous practice with manipulatives. Give them plenty of two-way practice—identifying what a tile arrangement represents and, in turn, arranging their own representation. Be sure to give students the option of working with graph paper or with tiles used with an overhead projector.

The goal of this activity is to help students visualize the distributive property of multiplication over addition. Notice that just as the distributive property combines multiplication and addition, the rectangular display of tiles combines area (a model for multiplication) with putting together lengths (a model for addition).

Before students begin Exercises 1–8, be sure to check for students' understanding through several teacher-demonstrated models. This is an excellent activity/discussion for groups of three to four students.

EXTENSION

Ask student groups to design their own model of the distributive property using the tiles and then discuss two equivalent expressions of their model.

Materials Needed: algebra tiles or graph paper

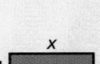

In this investigation you will use algebra tiles, like those at the right, to represent algebraic expressions. The smaller tile is a 1-by-1 square whose area is 1 square unit. It represents the number 1. The larger tile is a 1-by-x rectangle whose area is x square units. It represents the variable x.

Example   *Using Algebra Tiles*

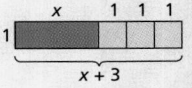

The expression $x + 3$ can be represented with algebra tiles as shown at the right. Use algebra tiles to represent the expression $2(x + 3)$. Then rearrange the tiles to represent an equivalent expression.

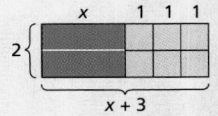

Solution   As shown at the right, you can represent the expression $2(x + 3)$ by doubling the number of tiles used to represent $x + 3$. These tiles can be rearranged to represent the expression $2x + 6$.

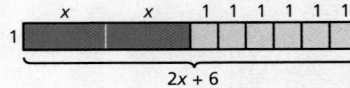

Thus, $2(x + 3)$ and $2x + 6$ are equivalent expressions.   ■

Exercises

In Exercises 1–4, model the expression with algebra tiles. Make a sketch of the model. See margin.

1. $x + 3$ **2.** $2x + 4$ **3.** $3x + 1$ **4.** $2x + 5$

In Exercises 5–8, match the algebra tiles with *two* of the expressions.

a. $2(3x + 1)$ **b.** $3(2x + 3)$ **c.** $4(x + 1)$ **d.** $2(2x + 1)$
e. $6x + 2$ **f.** $4x + 4$ **g.** $4x + 2$ **h.** $6x + 9$

5.
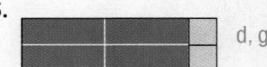
d, g

6.
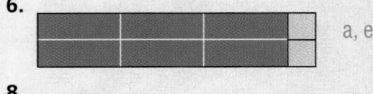
a, e

7.
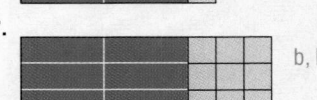
b, h

8.
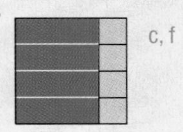
c, f

Answers

1.
x 1 1 1
1

2.
x x 1 1 1 1
1

3.
x x x 1
1

4.
x x 1 1 1 1 1
1

2.1

The Distributive Property

PACING the Lesson

Suggested Number of Days
Basic/Average 2   **Above Average** 1
Advanced 1

PLANNING the Lesson

Lesson Plan 2.1, p. 9

What you should learn:

Goal 1 How to use the Distributive Property

Goal 2 How to use the Distributive Property in real-life problems

Why you should learn it:

You can use the Distributive Property to model real-life situations, such as ordering clothes for a clothing retailer.

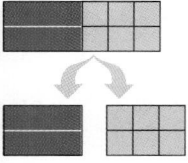
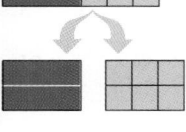

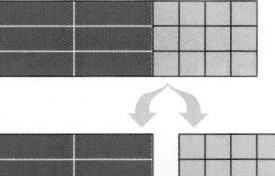
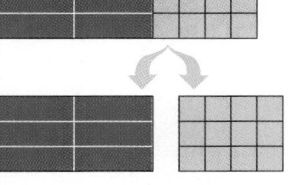

Algebra tiles can be used to model the Distributive Property. Which parts of Example 1 are illustrated by the algebra tiles shown above?

Goal 1 **Using the Distributive Property**

Two expressions that have one or more variables are **equivalent** if they have the same values when numbers are substituted for the variables. For instance, the expressions $2(3x)$ and $6x$ are equivalent.

$$2(3x) = 6x \qquad 2(3x) \text{ and } 6x \text{ are equivalent expressions.}$$

In the Lesson Investigation on page 50, you used algebra tiles to show that $2(x + 3)$ and $2x + 6$ are equivalent expressions. Another way to show these expressions are equivalent is with the **Distributive Property.**

> **The Distributive Property**
>
> Let *a, b,* and *c* be numbers or variable expressions.
> $$a(b + c) = ab + ac \quad \text{and} \quad ab + ac = a(b + c)$$

Example 1 *Using the Distributive Property*

a. $2(x + 3) = 2(x) + 2(3)$ *Apply Distributive Property.*

$ = 2x + 6$ *Simplify.*

b. $3(2x + 4) = 3(2x) + 3(4)$ *Apply Distributive Property.*

$ = 6x + 12$ *Simplify.*

c. $5(2) + 5(4) = 5(2 + 4)$ *Apply Distributive Property.*

$ = 5(6)$ *Simplify.*

$ = 30$ *Simplify.*

d. $x(x + 4) = x(x) + x(4)$ *Apply Distributive Property.*

$ = x^2 + 4x$ *Simplify.* ∎

In part **d,** notice that $x(4)$ is usually written as $4x$. This is a use of the **Commutative Property of Multiplication.**

ORGANIZER

Starters (reproduced below)
  Problem of the Day 2.1, p. 4
  Warm-Up Exercises 2.1, p. 4
Lesson Resources
  Math Log, p. 7
  Technology, p. 8
  Answer Masters 2.1, pp. 22, 23
  Extra Practice Copymaster 2.1, p. 9
  Reteaching Copymaster 2.1, p. 9
  Enrichment Projects, pp. 8, 9
Special Populations
  Suggestions, Teacher's Edition, p. 48D

LESSON Notes

"Equivalent expressions" is an important concept in algebra. One of the most common activities in algebra is the identification of equivalent expressions. Thus, before looking at the structure of the distributive property, make sure that students have an opportunity to make the definition of equivalent expressions meaningful to themselves.

Have students verify that the following expression pairs are equivalent by substituting several values of *x* into each expression pair.
a. $2(3x)$ and $6x$ **b.** $6(3x + 6)$ and $18x + 36$
c. $4(7x + 2)$ and $28x + 8$

Stress that the Distributive Property has two interpretations:
Expanding: $a(b + c) = ab + ac$ and
Factoring: $ab + ac = a(b + c)$.
Both are important in applications.

Example 1

Note the "change of direction" involved in **c.** The numbers in parentheses can be combined and multiplied by 5—one multiplication versus two! Ask students to model this operation using tiles or with a sketch.

STARTER: Problem of the Day

During the regular season, each team in your school's varsity volleyball league plays every other team exactly once. Altogether, how many league games take place? (Hint: Begin with an imaginary 3-team league, then a 4-team league, etc., and look for a pattern.)
$\frac{n(n-1)}{2}$, for an *n*-team league.

Also available as a copymaster, p. 4

STARTER: Warm-Up Exercises

1. Evaluate.
a. $3(4) + 3(5)$ **b.** $6(2) + 6(8)$
c. $7(x) + 7(1)$ **d.** $9(3) + 9(x)$
a. 27, **b.** 60, **c.** $7x + 7$, **d.** $27 + 9x$

2. Which pairs of expressions are equivalent?
a. $2(8) + 2(7)$ and $2(8 + 7)$
b. $3(4) + 4$ and $3(4 + 4)$
c. $5(6) + 2$ and $5(6 + 2)$
d. $8(3) + 8(4)$ and $8(3) + 4$
Only **a** has an equivalent pair.

Also available as a copymaster, p. 4

PROBLEM SOLVING

Example 2 is a first introduction for students to an algebraic problem-solving plan which will be developed gradually and systematically in later lessons. The plan will require students to create a verbal model for the problem to be solved, assign labels (constant values or variables), and write an algebraic model (an equation or a formula) for which a solution can be found.

Example 2

Work with students to help them express a verbal model of the situation described in this example. In particular, make sure they understand the role of the term "each" in the statement of the example. Point out that the first step in creating an algebraic model is the creation of an appropriate verbal model.

Communicating about MATHEMATICS

Discuss how the Distributive Property (and the Commutative Property of Addition) can be used to simplify $3(5) + 6(4) + 6(7) + 3(8) + 3(2)$.

Writing Prompt

Had we known about the Distributive Property before doing the first Warm-Up exercise of this lesson:

$$3(4) + 3(5)$$

we could have worked that exercise in the following way. . . .

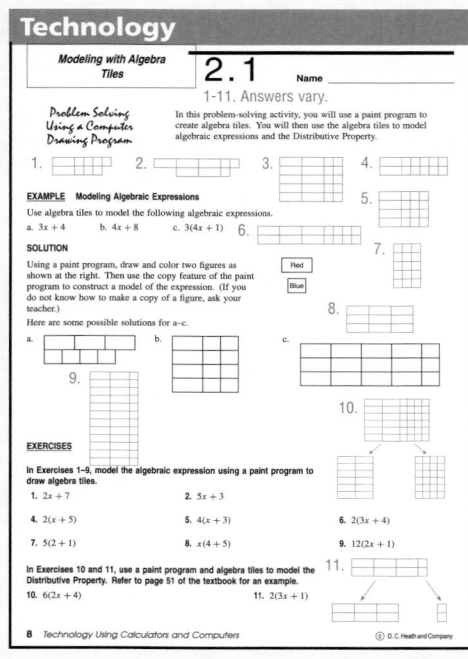

Goal 2 Solving Real-Life Problems

The Distributive Property is usually stated with a sum involving only two terms. However, it also applies to sums involving three or more terms.

$$a(b + c + d) = ab + ac + ad \qquad \textit{Sum with 3 terms}$$
$$a(b + c + d + e) = ab + ac + ad + ae \qquad \textit{Sum with 4 terms}$$

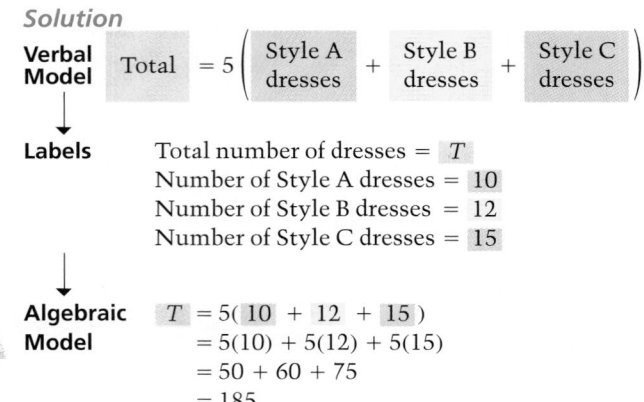

Real Life
Fashion Buying

Example 2 *Using the Distributive Property*

You are a fashion buyer for a clothing retailer that has 5 stores. You are attending a fashion show and decide to order 10 dresses of Style A, 12 dresses of Style B, and 15 dresses of Style C for *each* of the 5 stores. Use the Distributive Property to find the total number of dresses ordered.

Solution

Verbal Model   Total $= 5\left($ Style A dresses $+$ Style B dresses $+$ Style C dresses $\right)$

Labels
Total number of dresses $= T$
Number of Style A dresses $= 10$
Number of Style B dresses $= 12$
Number of Style C dresses $= 15$

Algebraic Model
$T = 5(10 + 12 + 15)$
$= 5(10) + 5(12) + 5(15)$
$= 50 + 60 + 75$
$= 185$

You are ordering 185 dresses. You can check this result by writing $5(10 + 12 + 15) = 5(37) = 185$. ∎

Communicating about MATHEMATICS

Cooperative Learning

▶ **SHARING IDEAS about the Lesson**

Using the Distributive Property Discuss with others in your group different ways to evaluate the expression $4(3x + 2)$ when $x = 5$. Which way do you prefer? Explain your reasoning.

$4(3x + 2) = 4(3 \cdot 5 + 2) = 68$, $4(3x + 2) = 12x + 8 = 12 \cdot 5 + 8 = 68$; preferences vary.

Study Tip...
Problem Solving One of your goals in this chapter is to learn how to organize your problem-solving solutions using a verbal model, labels, and an algebraic model. You will study this in more detail in Lesson 2.7.

◆ **OPTION: Extra Examples**
Here are some additional examples similar to Example 1 in the lesson.

Using the Distributive Property
a. $12(x + 4) = 12(x) + 12(4)$ Apply Distributive Property.
$ = 12x + 48$ Simplify.

b. $4(5 + 2x) = 4(5) + 4(2x)$ Apply Distributive Property.
$ = 20 + 8x$ Simplify.

c. $6(3) + 6(2) = 6(3 + 2)$ Apply Distributive Property.
$ = 6(5)$ Simplify.
$ = 30$ Simplify.

EXERCISES

Guided Practice

▶ **CHECK for Understanding**

1. State the Distributive Property. See page 51.

2. Which are correct applications of the Distributive Property? b and c

   a. $2(3 + 5) = 2(3) + 5$ **b.** $4(y + 7) = 4(y) + 4(7)$

   c. $16(x + 1) = 16x + 16$ **d.** $2(a + 6) = 2a + 6$

3. Decide whether the statement is true. Explain your reasoning. **a.** Yes, $3 \times 5 = 15$ **b.** No, $4 \times 9 = 36$

   a. $3(5x) \overset{?}{=} 15x$ **b.** $4(9x) \overset{?}{=} 13x$ **c.** $2(5 + 6) \overset{?}{=} 21$ No, $2 \times 11 = 22$

4. Give an example of the Commutative Property of Multiplication. Answers vary.
$3 \times 5 = 5 \times 3$

Independent Practice

Modeling Expressions   **In Exercises 5–8, write the dimensions of the rectangle and an expression for its area. Then use the Distributive Property to rewrite the expression.**

5.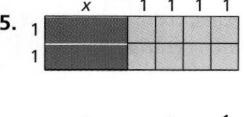
$2, x+4$;
$2(x+4)$;
$2x+8$

6. $2, 3x+2$;
$2(3x+2)$;
$6x+4$

7.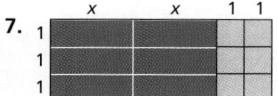
$3, 2x+2$;
$3(2x+2)$;
$6x+6$

8. $4, 2x+3$;
$4(2x+3)$;
$8x+12$

In Exercises 9–12, use the Distributive Property to write an equivalent expression. Illustrate your result with an algebra tile sketch.   For sketches, see Additional Answers.

9. $4(x + 2)$ $4x+8$ 10. $2(x + 1)$ $2x+2$ 11. $2(5x + 3)$ $10x+6$ 12. $5(2x + 3)$ $10x+15$

In Exercises 13–32, use the Distributive Property to rewrite the expression. 25., 26. See below.

13. $9(8 + 7)$ $72+63$ 14. $11(10 + 5)$ $110+55$ 15. $4(x + 9)$ $4x+36$ 16. $16(z + 3)$ $16z+48$

17. $5(y + 20)$ $5y+100$ 18. $8(4 + q)$ $32+8q$ 19. $1(x + 12)$ $x+12$ 20. $1(t + 42)$ $t+42$

21. $a(b + 4)$ $ab+4a$ 22. $p(q + 2)$ $pq+2p$ 23. $r(s + t)$ $rs+rt$ 24. $m(n + k)$ $mn+mk$

25. $4(6 + 10 + 12)$ 26. $3(5+8+9)$ 27. $y(3 + z)$ $3y+yz$ 28. $a(b + c + 4)$
$ab+ac+4a$

29. $12(s + t + w)$ 30. $b(e + f + g)$ 31. $6(m + n + r + t)$ 32. $z(x + 4 + y)$
$12s+12t+12w$ $be+bf+bg$ $6m+6n+6r+6t$ $zx+4z+zy$

It's Up to You   **In Exercises 33–35, use a calculator to evaluate the expression two ways. Which way do you prefer? Why?** Preferences and reasons vary.

33. $3(1.21 + 5.48)$
$3(6.69) = 20.07$
$3.63 + 16.44 = 20.07$

34. $10(6.81 + 9.06)$
$10(15.87) = 158.7$
$68.1 + 90.6 = 158.7$

35. $525(11.19 + 27.60)$
$525(38.79) = 20,364.75$
$5874.75 + 14,490 = 20,364.75$

25. $24 + 40 + 48$ 26. $15 + 24 + 27$

2.1 • *The Distributive Property*   **53**

Extra Practice

Extra Practice 2.1 Name _____

In Exercises 1 and 2, write the dimensions of the rectangle and an expression for its area. Then use the Distributive Property to rewrite the expression. 3 units by 2x + 4 units, 3(2x + 4), 6x + 12

1.

2.

2 units by x + 3 units, 2(x + 3), 2x + 6

In Exercises 3 and 4, use the Distributive Property to write an equivalent expression. Illustrate your result with an algebraic tile sketch.

3. $3(x + 1)$ $3x + 3$ 4. $5(4x + 2)$ $20x + 10$

In Exercises 5–16, use the Distributive Property to rewrite the expression.

5. $2(3 + 5)$ $6 + 10$ or 16 6. $12(4 + 7)$ $48 + 84$ or 132 7. $3(x + 2)$ $3x + 6$

8. $15(y + 4)$ $15y + 60$ 9. $4(z + 3)$ $4z + 12$ 10. $8(2 + p)$ $16 + 8p$

11. $x(y + 3)$ $xy + 3x$ 12. $a(c + 4)$ $ac + 4a$ 13. $2(x + y + z)$

14. $z(a + 4 + b)$ $az + 4z + bz$ 15. $f(g + 3 + h)$ $fg + 3f + fh$ 16. $10(2 + y + z)$ $20 + 10y + 10z$

In Exercises 17–19, use a calculator to evaluate the expression two ways.

17. $4(2.5 + 5.2)$ 30.8   18. $12(6.25 + 7.01)$ 159.12   19. $575(10.2 + 25.02)$ 20,251.5

20. You have taken two part-time summer jobs. One pays $56 per week and the other $22.50 per week.

   a. Write a verbal model that represents how much you earn over sixteen weeks of summer vacation.

   Total summer earnings = 16 (Weekly earnings job 1 + Weekly earnings job 2)

   b. Use the model in Part a to determine how much you earn during summer vacation. $1256 = 16(56 + 22.50)$

21. You want to buy a new mountain bike, a CD player and a pair of rollerblades. The monthly payments are $26.50, $21.25 and $17.50 respectively.

   a. Write a verbal model that represents the total amount you pay for all three in one year.

   Total = 12 (monthly payment for bike + monthly payment for CD player + monthly payment for rollerblades)

   b. Use the model in Part a to determine the amount you pay in one year. $783.00 = 12(26.50 + 21.25 + 17.50)$

Reteaching

Reteach Chapter 2   Name _____

What you should learn:

2.1 How to use the Distributive Property and how to use the Distributive Property in real-life problems

Correlation to Pupil's Textbook:
Mid-Chapter Self-Test (p. 69)   Chapter Test (p. 97)
Exercises 1–5, 11   Exercises 1, 2, 11

Examples Using the Distributive Property and Solving Real-Life Problems

a. Use the Distributive Property to rewrite each expression.

$6(n + 3) = 6(n) + 6(3)$ Apply Distributive Property.
$= 6n + 18$ Simplify.

$10(d + e + f) = 10(d) + 10(e) + 10(f)$ Apply Distributive Property.
$= 10d + 10e + 10f$ Simplify.

1.

b. You are helping your grandmother buy flowers for 3 planters. For each of the 3 planters, she selects 2 pansies and 4 impatiens and you select 3 petunias. Use the Distributive Property to find the total number of flowers.

Verbal Model   Total = 3 (pansies + impatiens + petunias)

2.

Labels   Total number of flowers = T
   Number of pansies = 2
   Number of impatiens = 4
   Number of petunias = 3

Algebraic Model $T = 3(2 + 4 + 3)$
   $= 3(2) + 3(4) + 3(3)$
   $= 6 + 12 + 9$
   $= 27$

3.

4.

You and your grandmother purchased 27 flowers. You can check this result by writing $3(2 + 4 + 3) = 3(9) = 27$.

Guidelines: • The Distributive Property: Let a, b, and c be numbers or variable expressions.
   $a(b + c) = ab + ac$ and $ab + ac = a(b + c)$

EXERCISES

In Exercises 1–4, use the Distributive Property to write an equivalent expression. Illustrate your result with an algebra tile sketch.

1. $3(x + 2)$ $3x + 6$ 2. $2(x + 1)$ $2x + 2$ 3. $4(2x + 3)$ $8x + 12$ 4. $5(x + 4)$ $5x + 20$

In Exercises 5–12, use the Distributive Property to rewrite the expression.

5. $8(11 + 7)$ $88 + 56$ 6. $10(r + 6)$ $10r + 60$ 7. $1(x + 9)$ $x + 9$ 8. $a(c + 3)$ $ac + 3a$

9. $x(y + z)$ $xy + xz$ 10. $5(d + e + 7)$ $5d + 5e + 35$ 11. $7(2 + e + 5)$ $14 + 7e + 35$ 12. $p(q + r + s)$ $pq + pr + ps$

Lesson 2.1 **53**

EXERCISE Notes

ASSIGNMENT GUIDE

Basic/Average:
Day 1: Ex. 5–11 odd, 17–29 odd, 33, 39
Day 2: Ex. 36, 37, 40–44, 53, 54

Above Average:
Ex. 5–11 odd, 25–32, 33, 36, 37, 39, 40, 49–52, 55–57

Advanced: Ex. 5–11 odd, 25–32, 33, 36, 37, 39, 40, 49–52, 55–57

Selected Answers: Ex. 1–4, 5–51 odd

Guided Practice

Throughout this course, be sure to make your expectations quite clear to students regarding any exercises that involve decision making, explanations, or descriptive answers.
▶ **Ex. 1–4** Allow students to work in groups for these exercises. The visual aspect of the arrows used in Example 1 may help point to the error in Exercise 2d.

WRITING
Ask students to write a justification for their answers to Exercises 2 and 3.

Independent Practice

At this stage of the process of simplifying algebraic expressions, you may have to remind some students of the "invisible 1," the unwritten multiplier that accompanies the expression "x."
▶ **Ex. 5–12** Note that these exercises are modeled in the Lesson Investigation and also in Example 1.
▶ **Ex. 13–23** Ask students to draw the arrows as shown in Example 1. This will help them distribute through to all terms.

MATH JOURNAL
Have students write the correct formula for perimeter in their journal.
► **Ex. 39, 40** Refer students to the model provided in Example 2.

GROUP ACTIVITY
Assign these problems in class as a teacher-led group activity. This will allow students to comfortably begin to use the verbal model for problem solving that is developed in this chapter.

Integrated Review

MENTAL MATH
This is a good opportunity to discuss the three methods for computation: mental math, paper and pencil, and calculator. Discuss which is the best method when collecting terms, and so on. Challenge students to an evaluation competition. One group should do all problems using mental math, one group should use paper and pencil, and one group should use calculators. Check for speed and accuracy.

Exploration and Extension

► **Ex. 52–55** The technique applied here can sometimes be a very useful one for a quick estimation.
► **Ex. 56** The writing prompt in this exercise is an excellent journal activity for closing the lesson.

Portfolio Opportunity: Math Log

Does $(b + c)a = ba + ca$ accurately state the Distributive Property? Explain your answer.

Also available as a copymaster, page 7, Ex. 1

Geometry **In Exercises 36 and 37, use the rectangle at the right.**

✪ **36.** Write an expression for the area of the rectangle. $3(x + 6)$

✪ **37.** Rewrite your expression using the Distributive Property. $3x + 18$

✪ **38.** *Geometry* Which of the following is a correct formula for the perimeter of a rectangle? Explain. b, perimeter = length + width +

  a. $P = 2 + (\text{length} \times \text{width})$ length + width =

  b. $P = 2(\text{length} + \text{width})$ 2 (length + width)

  c. $P = (\text{length} \times \text{width} \times 2)$

39. *Business* You own a small business that has 3 employees. You pay one employee \$1800 a month, the second \$1500 a month, and the third \$1300 a month.

  a. Write a verbal model that represents how much you pay all 3 employees in the year. See below.

  b. Use the model in Part **a** to determine how much you pay your employees in a year. \$55,200

  a. Total annual pay $= 12 \times$ Total monthly pay

Nearly two-thirds of all Americans get their first job in a small business. The fastest growing small businesses in 1993 were restaurants, computer and data services, and amusement and recreation services.

Integrated Review   *Making Connections within Mathematics*

Evaluating Expressions **In Exercises 40–51, evaluate the expression for $a = 2, b = 5, c = 8$, and $d = 10$.**

40. $2(a + 1)$ 6   **41.** $7(d + 6)$ 112   **42.** $a(b + 3)$ 16   **43.** $c(a + 9)$ 88

44. $3(a + c)$ 30   **45.** $12(b + d)$ 180   **46.** $a(c + d)$ 36   **47.** $b(c + a)$ 50

48. $3(a + b + c)$ 45   **49.** $8(b + c + d)$ 184   **50.** $a(b + c + d)$ 46   **51.** $d(c + b + a)$ 150

Exploration and Extension

Mental Math **In Exercises 52–55, use mental math with the Distributive Property to evaluate the product. For instance, 15(405) can be written as 15(400 + 5). Using mental math, the result is 6000 + 75 or 6075.**

✪ **52.** $3(522)$ 1566   ✪ **53.** $8(612)$ 4896   ✪ **54.** $11(409)$ 4499   ✪ **55.** $21(203)$ 4263

✪ **56.** *You Be the Teacher* Your friend applies the Distributive Property to multiplication and determines $2(3 \times 5) = 2(3) \times 2(5)$. Write a paragraph explaining how you would convince your friend that this is incorrect.

    $2(3 \times 5) \neq 2(3) \times 2(5)$
    $2(15) \neq 6 \times 10$
    $30 \neq 60$

✪ More difficult exercises
P Portfolio Opportunity

Enrichment

The distributive property of multiplication over addition can be modeled using areas of rectangles. Ask students to draw a picture of
$21(30) - 14(30) = (21 - 14)30 = 7(30)$,
an example of distributing multiplication over subtraction, by using areas of rectangles.

Sample solution:

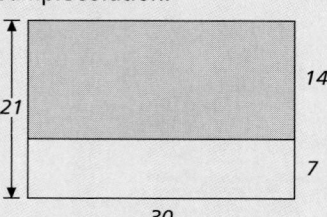

The area of the whole rectangle (21)(30) less the area of the gray rectangle (14)(30) is the area of the rectangle (7)(30).

2.2

Simplifying by Adding Like Terms

▶ **PACING the Lesson**

Suggested Number of Days
Basic/Average 2   **Above Average** 1
Advanced 1

▶ **PLANNING the Lesson**

Lesson Plan 2.2, p. 10

What you should learn:

oal 1 How to simplify expressions by adding like terms

oal 2 How to add like terms to simplify expressions in geometry

Why you should learn it:
valuating a simplified expression is usually easier than evaluating one that has not been implified.

Goal 1   Adding Like Terms

Two or more terms in an expression are **like terms** if they have the same variables, raised to the same powers.

Expression	Like Terms
$3x + x + 2$	$3x$ and x
$5y + 5 + 4$	5 and 4
$3y^2 + 4y + y^2 + y$	$3y^2$ and y^2, $4y$ and y

LESSON INVESTIGATION

■ Investigating Addition of Like Terms

Group Activity The expression $3x + 2x + 2$ can be modeled with algebra tiles, as shown at the left. After collecting like tiles, you can see that there are five x's and two 1's. This means that the expression $5x + 2$ is equivalent to $3x + 2x + 2$.

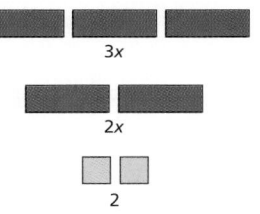
$3x$

$2x$

2

Model each of the following with algebra tiles, collect like tiles, and write the simplified expression.

$5x + 3$

a. $2x + 3 + 4x$ **b.** $x + 2x + 3x + 5$ **c.** $4x + 3 + x$

This procedure is called **adding like terms** (or **collecting like terms**). The rewritten algebraic expression is said to be **simplified**.

a. $6x + 3$ **b.** $6x + 5$

The Distributive Property can be used to add like terms.

Example 1   *Simplifying by Adding Like Terms*

a. $2x + 5x + 1 = (2 + 5)x + 1$ *Distributive Property*
$= 7x + 1$ *Simplify.*

b. $3b + 2 + 5b = 3b + 5b + 2$ *Commutative Property*
$= (3 + 5)b + 2$ *Distributive Property*
$= 8b + 2$ *Simplify.*   ■

Need to Know
In part **b** of Example 1, notice that you can reorder the terms of an expression. That is, $3b + 2 + 5b$ can be rewritten as $3b + 5b + 2$. This procedure is justified by the **Commutative Property of Addition.**

ORGANIZER

Starters (reproduced below)
   Problem of the Day 2.2, p. 4
   Warm-Up Exercises 2.2, p. 4
Lesson Resources
   Color Transparencies
      Graph for Example 2, p. 7
   Teaching Tools
      Algebra tiles, pp. T4, C5
   Math Log, p. 7
   Answer Masters 2.2, pp. 24, 25
   Extra Practice Copymaster 2.2, p. 10
   Reteaching Copymaster 2.2, p. 10
   Overhead Manipulatives Kit
      Algebra tiles
   Calculator
Special Populations
   Suggestions, Teacher's Edition, p. 48D

LESSON Notes

Point out that like terms may have different coefficients. Remind students of the "invisible 1" and that "$1y$" is equivalent to "y" (and vice versa). Also explain that it is customary to write the simplification of a variable expression in alphabetical order with constants written last. Ask students how the Commutative Property of Addition helps us reorder such expressions.

Lesson Investigation.
Ask students if $3x$ and $4y$ are like terms. Ask how these terms could be modeled using algebra tiles.
Different colors and sizes could be used to represent unlike terms.

Example 1

ALTERNATE APPROACH
You may want to point out that because the terms $2x$ and $5x$ are like terms, you can think of their sum as $2 + 5$ with the variable x attached later.

Study Tip Extension
Make sure students record the Distributive and Commutative Properties in their journals.

Many geometric relationships can be modeled using (like) algebraic terms. It is important to create such connections between algebra and geometry.

Example 2
Note that the given triangle is an isosceles triangle. Have students explain the use of the Distributive Property in this example.

Have students repeat this activity using an equilateral triangle, and then using a square.

Writing Prompt
I'm beginning to see why variables may become very useful, even in geometry, because . . .

Connections
Geometry

Perimeter of Triangle
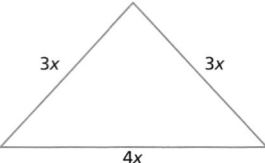

Example 2 *Simplifying before Evaluating*

Write an expression that represents the perimeter of the figure. Then evaluate the perimeter when x is 1, 2, 3, 4, and 5. Organize your results in a table and in a graph. Describe the pattern as the values of x increase by 1.

Solution To find an expression for the perimeter, add the lengths of the three sides.

$$\text{Perimeter} = 3x + 3x + 4x \quad \textit{Add the side lengths.}$$
$$= 10x \quad \textit{Add like terms.}$$

Next, evaluate the expression $10x$ when x is 1, 2, 3, 4, and 5. The results are shown in the table and in the bar graph.

x	1	2	3	4	5
Perimeter	10	20	30	40	50

From the table or the graph, you can see that the perimeter increases by 10 each time x increases by 1. ■

Communicating *about* MATHEMATICS

▶ **SHARING IDEAS about the Lesson**

A Perimeter Pattern Write an expression that represents the perimeter of the figure. Then evaluate the perimeter when x is 1, 2, 3, 4, and 5. Organize your results in a table or in a graph. Describe the pattern as the values of x increase by 1.

x	1	2	3	4	5
Perimeter, $13x$	13	26	39	52	65

Each perimeter, after the first, is 13 more than the preceding perimeter.

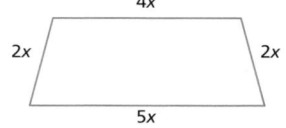

◆ **OPTION: Extra Examples**
Here are some additional examples similar to Example 1.
Simplifying by Adding Like Terms.
a. $4x + 13x + 3 = (4 + 13)x + 3$ Distributive Property
$= 17x + 3$ Simplify.

b. $3m + 7 + 9m = 3m + 9m + 7$ Commutative Property
$= (3 + 9)m + 7$ Distributive Property
$= 12m + 7$ Simplify.

EXERCISES

Guided Practice

▶ CHECK for Understanding **3.** Two numbers can be added in either order.

1. What is meant by like terms? State an example. See page 55.

2. State an example of adding like terms. Illustrate your result with an algebra tile sketch. Examples vary. $2x + 3x = 5x$ Check students' sketches.

3. Describe in your own words the Commutative Property of Addition.

4. When is it helpful to add like terms? When simplifying or evaluating an expression

In Exercises 5–8, decide whether the expression can be simplified. Explain.

5. $3x + x$ Yes, have like terms

6. $2a + 7$ No, no like terms

7. $2r + 5r^2$ No, no like terms

8. $5 + 2(x + 8)$ Yes, 5 and 2(8) are like terms.

Independent Practice

In Exercises 9–20, simplify the expression. **17.** $14r + 2s + 5$ **19.** $2x + 4y + 20z$

9. $2a + a$ $3a$

10. $5b + 7b$ $12b$

11. $3x + 6x + 9$ $9x + 9$

12. $8x + 4x + 12$ $12x + 12$

13. $9y + 10 + 3y$ $12y + 10$

14. $y + 5 + 13y$ $14y + 5$

15. $3a + 2b + 5a$ $8a + 2b$

16. $6x + x + 2y$ $7x + 2y$

17. $5 + r + 2s + 13r$

18. $p + 9q + 9 + 14p$ $15p + 9q + 9$

19. $2x + 4y + 3z + 17z$

20. $a + 2b + 2a + b + 2c$ $3a + 3b + 2c$

21. *Its Up to You* Write an expression that has four terms and simplifies to $16x + 5$. Answers vary. $8x + 2x + 5 + 6x$

22. *Reasoning* Explain the steps used to simplify $2x + 3 + 5x$. See margin.

In Exercises 23–34, simplify the expression.

23. $b + b^2 + 2b$ $b^2 + 3b$

24. $5x + 6x + x^3$ $x^3 + 11x$

25. $x^2 + x^2$ $2x^2$

26. $2a^3 + a^3$ $3a^3$

27. $3(x + 3) + 4x$ $7x + 9$

28. $8(y + 2) + y + 4$ $9y + 20$

29. $3(a + b) + 3(b + a)$ $6a + 6b$

30. $5(x + y) + 2(y + x)$ $7x + 7y$

31. $xy + 15xy$ $16xy$

32. $24rs + 12rs$ $36rs$

33. $x^2y + x^2y$ $2x^2y$

34. $6(r^2s + s^2) + r^2s$ $7r^2s + 6s^2$

In Exercises 35–40, simplify the expression. Then evaluate when $x = 2$ and $y = 5$.

35. $2x + 3x + y$ $5x + y$, 15

36. $y + 4y + 8x$ $8x + 5y$, 41

37. $4(x + y) + x$ $5x + 4y$, 30

38. $(x + y)4 + 7x$ $11x + 4y$, 42

39. $xy + x^2 + xy$ $x^2 + 2xy$, 24

40. $6xy + x^2 + x^2$ $2x^2 + 6xy$, 68

Geometry In Exercises 41 and 42, write an expression for the perimeter of each polygon. Are the expressions equivalent? Explain. See Additional Answers.

41.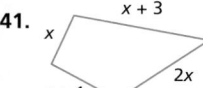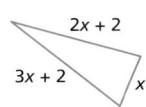

42.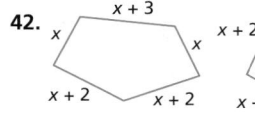

P Portfolio Opportunity

Extra Practice

Extra Practice 2.2 Name _____

In Exercises 1–9, simplify the expression.
1. $3x + x$ $4x$
2. $4y + 5y$ $9y$
3. $2z + 6z + 10$ $8z + 10$
4. $3a + 5b + 6a$ $9a + 5b$
5. $3z + 7 + 6z + 2$ $9z + 9$
6. $15z + 5 + 6z$ $21z + 5$
7. $3x + 2 + 8x + 4$ $11s + 2t + 4$
8. $12x + 3y + 4 + 6y$ $12x + 9y + 4$
9. $6x + 2 + 4x + 9$ $10x + 11$

In Exercises 10–18, simplify the expression.
10. $4a + 6a + 2a^2$ $2a^2 + 10a$
11. $5z + 2z + 6z^2$ $6z^2 + 7z$
12. $x^3 + 2x^2 + x^3$ $2x^3 + 2x^2$
13. $3(y + 2) + 6y$ $9y + 6$
14. $8(z + 1) + 2(z + 4)$ $10z + 16$
15. $5(st + 2) + 4st$ $10st + 12$
16. $3(x + z) + 4(z + 2)$ $3x + 7z + 8$
17. $4(x + 2) + 3(y + 6)$ $4x + 3y + 26$
18. $a(b + 2) + 3ab + 4$ $4ab + 2a + 4$

In Exercises 19–24, simplify the expression. Then evaluate when $x = 3$ and $y = 4$.
19. $3x + 2y + 6x$ $9x + 2y$, 35
20. $y + 2(y + 2)$ $3y + 4$, 16
21. $5(x + y) + 2x$ $7x + 5y$, 41
22. $(3 + x)y + x^2$ $x^2 + xy + 3y$, 33
23. $xy + x^2 + x^2$ $2x^2 + xy$, 30
24. $3(x + y) + 2(x + y)$ $5x + 5y$, 35

In Exercises 25 and 26, write an expression for the perimeter. Find the perimeter when x is 1, 2, 3, 4 and 5. Represent your results with a table. Then describe the pattern.

25. Perimeter = $8x$

x	1	2	3	4	5
Per.	8	16	24	32	40

Perimeter increases by 8 each time x increases by 1.

26. Perimeter = $12x$

x	1	2	3	4	5
Per.	12	24	36	48	60

Perimeter increases by 12 each time x increases by 1.

27. You and your family and your best friend and her family are planning a trip to an amusement park. There are two parents and three children in your friend's family, and there is one parent and two children in your family. The price of admission to the park is x dollars for adults and y dollars for youths.
  a. Write an expression for the cost of admission for your family. $x + 2y$
  b. Write an expression for the cost of admission for your friend's family. $2x + 3y$
  c. Write an expression for the total cost for both families combined. $3x + 5y$
  d. If the price of admission increases from x to $a + 1$ for adults and from y to $b + 2$ for youths, write a new expression for the cost for both families combined. Simplify this expression.
  $3(a + 1) + 5(b + 2) = 3a + 5b + 13$

Reteaching

Reteach Chapter 2 Name _____

What you should learn:
2.2 How to simplify expressions by adding like terms and how to add like terms to simplify expressions in geometry

Correlation to Pupil's Textbook:
Mid-Chapter Self-Test (p. 69) Chapter Test (p. 97)
Exercises 6–11   Exercises 10, 15, 16, 20, 21

Examples *Adding Like Terms and Simplifying Expressions in Geometry*

a. Identify the like terms in the expression.
  $4x^2 + 5x + x^2$ $4x^2$ and x^2 are like terms.

b. Simplify the expression by adding like terms.
  $2t + 7t^2 + 8t = 2t + 8t + 7t^2$ *Commutative Property*
  $= (2 + 8)t + 7t^2$ *Distributive Property*
  $= 10t + 7t^2$ *Simplify.*

c. Write an expression that represents the perimeter of the figure shown at the right. Then evaluate the perimeter when $x = \frac{1}{2}, 1, \frac{3}{2},$ and 2. Organize your results in a table and describe the pattern as the values of x increase by $\frac{1}{2}$.
  Perimeter $= 2x + 3x + 2x + 3x$ *Add the side lengths.*
  $= (2 + 3 + 2 + 3)x$ *Distributive Property*
  $= 10x$ *Simplify.*

Evaluate $10x$ when $x = \frac{1}{2}, 1, \frac{3}{2},$ and 2 and organize the results in a table.

x	$\frac{1}{2}$	1	$\frac{3}{2}$	2
Perimeter	5	10	15	20

The perimeter increases by 5 each time x increases by $\frac{1}{2}$.

Guidelines:
• Two or more terms in an expression are like terms if they have the same variables, raised to the same powers.
• When you add like terms (or collect like terms), the rewritten expression is said to be simplified.
• The Distributive Property can be used to add like terms.

EXERCISES

In Exercises 1–6, simplify the expression.
1. $y^2 + 2z + 3z$ $y^2 + 5z$
2. $a^2 + 2a^2$ $3a^2$
3. $4(c + d) + (c + d)$ $5(c + d) = 5c + 5d$
4. $(p + q) + 2(p + q)$ $3(p + q) = 3p + 3q$
5. $10xy + 3xy$ $13xy$
6. $7(x + 5) + 2x + 1$ $9x + 36$

ASSIGNMENT GUIDE

Basic/Average:
Day 1: Ex. 12–17, 23–28, 35, 36
Day 2: Ex. 41–43, 45, 47, 49

Above Average:
Ex. 15–20, 29–34, 39, 40, 41–43, 46, 48, 49

Advanced: Ex. 15–20, 29–34, 39, 40, 41–43, 46, 48, 49

Selected Answers: Ex. 1–8, 9–47 odd

Guided Practice

▶ **Ex. 1–4** Use these exercises as a small-group activity. For Exercise 2, the groups could use tiles.

▶ **Ex. 5–8** These exercises could be used as a journal entry for the day.

Independent Practice

▶ **Ex. 21** This is a good in-class activity. Be sure to reward creativity and variety.

▶ **Ex. 23, 24** These exercises alert students to the implied coefficient of 1 in expressions such as x, x^2, x^3, and so on.

Answer
22. $2x + 3 + 5x = 2x + 5x + 3$ Commutative Property
  $= (2 + 5)x + 3$ Distributive Property
  $= 7x + 3$ Simplify.

▶ **Ex. 43, 44** For these exercises, refer students to Example 2.

▶ **Ex. 45, 46** These should be assigned using a teacher-led discussion in class. This is a great opportunity to give students a gradual start in algebraic modeling.

Integrated Review

These exercises give students an opportunity to apply an algebraic expression in a modeling context.

Exploration and Extension

Use this as a closing 10-minute group activity. Ask each group to generate two questions from two lessons. Then use these questions to build a class quiz or test.

ALTERNATE APPROACH
Have students exchange tests, have them check that the criteria have been met, and then have them do the test.

Portfolio Opportunity: Math Log

Explain why the following work is incorrect and correct it.
Evaluate $2xy + 4x$ when $x = 2$ and $y = 3$.

$$2xy + 4x = 6xy$$
$$= 6(2)(3)$$
$$= 36$$

Also available as a copymaster, page 7, Ex. 2

Short Quiz

Covers Lessons 2.1 and 2.2.

Available as a copymaster, page 16

Alternative Assessment

A cooperative learning project that evaluates students' knowledge of the connection between real-world problems and algebra.

Available as a copymaster, page 17

Geometry **In Exercises 43 and 44, write an expression for the perimeter. Find the perimeter when x is 1, 2, 3, 4, and 5. Represent your results with a table or a bar graph. Then describe the pattern.** See Additional Answers.

43.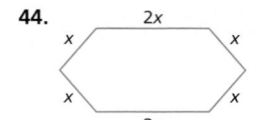

44.

✪ 45. *Baby-sitting* You have a baby-sitting job. You work after school for 3 hours on Wednesday, Thursday, and Friday, and 9 hours on Saturday. You earn x dollars an hour.

   a. Write an expression that represents your weekly earnings. $3(3x) + 9x$ or $18x$

   b. Suppose you earn \$3.25 an hour. How much money would you earn? \$58.50

✪ 46. *Arcade* While you are at the arcade, you play your favorite video games. You play 2 different video games; one that costs \$0.25 and the other that costs \$0.50. You play each video game x number of times.

   a. Write an expression for the total amount of money spent. $(0.25 + 0.50)x$ or $0.75x$

   b. If you play each game 5 times, how much do you spend? \$3.75

The circuit boards of arcade video games are made up of chips that operate by a tiny computer called a microprocessor.

Integrated Review

Making Connections within Mathematics

Modeling Perimeter **In Exercises 47 and 48, write a model for the perimeter. Then use your model to find the perimeter of the 10th and 15th figures in the sequence.** The perimeter, P, of the nth figure is

47. 1st   2nd   3rd   4th

$P = n + 2$; 12, 17

48. 1st   2nd   3rd   4th

$P = 4n$; 40, 60

Exploration and Extension

✪ 49. *You Be the Teacher* Imagine that you are teaching this class. You
P   decide to check your students on the material they have learned up to this point in the book. Write a test that you think covers the important concepts and skills. The test should have 20 questions with 2 questions from each lesson. Check students' work.

✪ More difficult exercises
P Portfolio Opportunity

▶ **Enrichment**

The equal sign in the equation
$4x + 5x = 9x$
is used to equate two equivalent expressions. Ask students to explain how this is different from the equal sign used in the equation $x + 8 = 10$. This should help to pave the way for the following lesson.

2.3

Solving Equations: Mental Math

What you should learn:

Goal 1 How to check that a number is a solution of an equation

Goal 2 How to use mental math to solve an equation

Why you should learn it:

Many real-life situations can be modeled with equations. Learning how to solve equations helps you solve real-life problems.

Goal 1 Checking Solutions

An **equation** states that two expressions are equivalent. Some equations, called **identities,** are true for all values of the variables they contain. Here are two examples.

$$3 + 2^2 = 7 \qquad \textit{Identity: Always true}$$

$$2(x + 3) = 2x + 6 \qquad \textit{Identity: True for all x}$$

Other equations, called **conditional equations,** are not true for all values of the variables they contain.

$$x + 1 = 4 \qquad \textit{Conditional equation: true only for x = 3}$$

$$3x = 12 \qquad \textit{Conditional equation: true only for x = 4}$$

Finding the values of a variable that make a conditional equation true is called **solving the equation,** and these values of the variable are **solutions** of the equation. Two equations are **equivalent** if they have the same solutions. You can check that a number is a solution by substituting in the original equation.

Example 1 *Checking Possible Solutions*

Which of the following numbers are solutions of the equation $4x - 3 = 5$?

a. $x = 2$ **b.** $x = 3$

Solution

a.
$4x - 3 = 5$	*Write original equation.*
$4(2) - 3 \overset{?}{=} 5$	*Substitute 2 for x.*
$8 - 3 \overset{?}{=} 5$	*Simplify.*
$5 = 5$	*x = 2 is a solution.* ✓

b.
$4x - 3 = 5$	*Write original equation.*
$4(3) - 3 \overset{?}{=} 5$	*Substitute 3 for x.*
$12 - 3 \overset{?}{=} 5$	*Simplify.*
$9 \neq 5$	*x = 3 is not a solution.* ⊗

Need to Know

Problem Solving

Checking a solution is an important part of solving equations. Throughout this course, you can learn to be a better problem solver if you develop the habit of always **checking your solutions.**

2.3 • *Solving Equations: Mental Math* **59**

In the Warm-Up Exercises, students were asked to answer the questions without use of paper and pencil. Tell them that they were using mental math. Using mental math means that we figure out a problem in our heads.

Example 2

MEETING INDIVIDUAL NEEDS
It is critical that students pose questions aloud or on paper when they first try using mental math. In so doing, they reinforce the essential problem-solving step —Understand the Problem. This is also the start of the process of translating from English to algebra and back again.

Even for students with stronger mental math abilities who would mentally solve these equations simply by "doing the same thing to both sides of the equation," this method of changing the equation into a statement can serve as a useful way of checking solutions.

Communicating
about MATHEMATICS

Have students create similar problems of increases and decreases for which they can write verbal and algebraic models, and then have students solve the resulting equations.

Writing Prompt
Describe the images that come to mind when you think about variables.

In 1991, Sidney Swartz, the chief executive officer of Timberland, asked his son Jeffrey to help restructure the shoe and boot manufacturing company. The company installed a team approach to manufacturing, and the company's sales increased dramatically. (Source: Timberland)

Goal 2   **Solving Equations with Mental Math**

As you study algebra, you will learn many techniques for solving equations. Some equations are simple enough that they can be solved mentally. For instance, to solve the equation

$$x + 2 = 8$$

you can think "what number can be added to 2 to produce 8?" The solution is $x = 6$. You can check this solution by writing $6 + 2 = 8$.

Example 2   *Solving Equations with Mental Math*

Solve the following equations.

a. $x + 4 = 10$ **b.** $x - 12 = 18$ **c.** $3x = 15$ **d.** $\frac{x}{4} = 5$

Solution

Equation	Stated as a Question	Solution
a. $x + 4 = 10$	*What number can be added to 4 to obtain 10?*	$x = 6$
b. $x - 12 = 18$	*What number can 12 be subtracted from to obtain 18?*	$x = 30$
c. $3x = 15$	*What number can be multiplied by 3 to obtain 15?*	$x = 5$
d. $\frac{x}{4} = 5$	*What number can be divided by 4 to obtain 5?*	$x = 20$

Communicating *about* MATHEMATICS

Real Life
Retail Sales

▶ **SHARING IDEAS about the Lesson**

Modeling a Real-Life Situation   In 1992, *Timberland* sold $290 million worth of shoes and boots. In 1993, the company sold $425 million worth of shoes and boots. How much more did the company sell in 1993 than in 1992?

1992 sales	+	Increase in sales	=	1993 sales	$290 + x = 425$
					$x = 135$

Answer: $135 million

Let x represent the increase in sales. Then rewrite the verbal model as an equation and solve the equation.

◤ **OPTION: Extra Examples**

Here are additional examples similar to some of those in the lesson.

1. Checking Possible Solutions
Which of the given numbers are solutions of the equation $3x - 5 = 19$?
a. $x = 8$ **b.** $x = 6$

Solution

a.	$3x - 5 = 19$	Write original equation.
	$3(8) - 5 \overset{?}{=} 19$	Substitute 8 for x.
	$24 - 5 \overset{?}{=} 19$	Simplify.
	$19 = 19$	$x = 8$ is a solution.
b.	$3x - 5 = 19$	Write original equation.
	$3(6) - 5 \overset{?}{=} 19$	Substitute 6 for x.
	$18 - 5 \overset{?}{=} 19$	Simplify.
	$13 \neq 19$	$x = 6$ is not a solution.

2. Solving Equations with Mental Math
Solve the following equations

a. $x - 2 = 7$ **b.** $\frac{x}{6} = 8$ **c.** $3x = 9$

Solution

Equation	Stated as Question	Solution
a. $x - 2 = 7$	What number can 2 be subtracted from to get 7?	$x = 9$
b. $\frac{x}{6} = 8$	What number divided by 6 gives 8?	$x = 48$
c. $3x = 9$	What number can be multiplied by 3 to get 9?	$x = 3$

EXERCISES

Guided Practice

▌CHECK for Understanding

1. Explain the difference between an identity and a conditional equation.   See page 59.
2. Write an example of an identity.   Examples vary. $4(x+2)=4x+8$
3. Write an example of a conditional equation.   Examples vary. $x+1=3$
4. Explain how to check a solution of an equation.   Substitute the number in the original equation, simplify, and see if you get an identity.

Independent Practice

Checking Solutions   **In Exercises 5–8, match the equation with a solution.**

a. 2   **b.** 3   **c.** 4   **d.** 5

5. $5x + 7 = 22$ b   **6.** $10 - 2y = 2$ c   **7.** $n^2 - 4 = 21$ d   **8.** $\dfrac{20}{x^2} = 5$ a

Mental Math   **In Exercises 9–12, write the equation as a question. Then solve it mentally.** For questions, see margin.

9. $z + 8 = 14$ 6   **10.** $7x = 42$ 6   **11.** $y - 18 = 16$ 34   **12.** $\dfrac{9}{x} = 3$ 3

Mental Math   **In Exercises 13–16, write the question as an equation. Then solve it mentally.**

13. What number can be subtracted from 33 to obtain 24? $33 - x = 24$, 9
14. What number can be added to 7 to obtain 19? $x + 7 = 19$, 12
15. What number can be multiplied by 8 to obtain 56? $8x = 56$, 7
16. What number can be divided by 9 to obtain 5? $\dfrac{x}{9} = 5$, 45

Mental Math   **In Exercises 17–20, decide whether $r = 4$ is a solution of the equation. If it isn't, use mental math to find the solution.**

17. $5r = 20$ Yes   **18.** $19 - r = 15$ Yes   **19.** $\dfrac{24}{r} = 8$ 3   **20.** $3r + r = 16$ Yes

Reasoning   **In Exercises 21–24, decide whether the equations have the same solutions. Explain why.**

21. a. $x - 15 = 8$ **22. a.** $x + 4 = 17$ **23. a.** $3x = 12$ **24. a.** $x \div 3 = 6$
 b. $15 - x = 8$ **b.** $4 + x = 17$ **b.** $\dfrac{x}{12} = 3$ **b.** $3 \div x = 6$
 No, $23 \neq 7$ Yes, $13 = 13$ No, $4 \neq 36$ No, $18 \neq \frac{1}{2}$

Mental Math   **In Exercises 25–36, solve the equation using mental math. Check your solution.**

25. $p + 7 = 18$ 11   **26.** $r + 11 = 14$ 3   **27.** $27 + n = 41$ 14   **28.** $x - 13 = 2$ 15

29. $y - 20 = 32$ 52   **30.** $81 - y = 76$ 5   **31.** $11x = 55$ 5   **32.** $2t = 18$ 9

33. $21 = 3m$ 7   **34.** $\dfrac{x}{4} = 9$ 36   **35.** $\dfrac{s}{12} = 4$ 48   **36.** $\dfrac{26}{y} = 2$ 13

P Portfolio Opportunity   **2.3** ▪ *Solving Equations: Mental Math*   **61**

ASSIGNMENT GUIDE

Basic/Average:
  Day 1: Ex. 5–24
  Day 2: Ex. 25–35 odd, 37, 38, 44, 45, 53–55, 57
Above Average: Ex. 5–24, 25–35 odd, 37, 38, 44, 45, 53–57
Advanced: Ex. 5–8, 9–39 odd, 46, 47, 49–55 odd, 57
Selected Answers: Ex. 1–4, 5–55 odd

EXERCISE Notes

Guided Practice

MATH JOURNAL
Use these exercises as a five-minute in-class journal writing activity in which students reflect on key terms of the lesson.

Independent Practice

▶ **Ex. 5–8** Assign these exercises as a group.
▶ **Ex. 25, 36** Encourage students to apply the method used in Example 2, at least for checking their solutions.

Answers
9. What number can be added to 8 to get 14?
10. What number can be multiplied by 7 to get 42?
11. What number can 18 be subtracted from to get 16?
12. What number can 9 be divided by to get 3?

Extra Practice

Extra Practice 2.3   Name _____

In Exercises 1–4, match the equation with a solution.
a. 2   b. 5   c. 3   d. 1
1. $3x - 4 = 11$ b   2. $y^2 + 4 = 13$ c   3. $8 - 3y = 5$ d   4. $16x^2 = 64$ a

In Exercises 5 and 6, write the equation as a question. Then solve it mentally.
5. $3x = 36$ What number can be multiplied by 3 to obtain 36?; 12
6. $z - 5 = 3$ 5 subtracted from what number is 3?; 8

In Exercises 7 and 8, write the question as an equation. Then solve it mentally.
7. What number can be added to 5 to obtain 19? $5 + x = 19$; 14
8. What number can be divided by 8 to obtain 7? $x/8 = 7$; 56

In Exercises 9–12, decide whether $x = 6$ is a solution of the equation. If it isn't, use mental math to find its solution.
9. $2x = 8$ No, $x = 4$ 10. $19 - x = 13$ Yes   11. $\frac{30}{x} = 5$ Yes   12. $3(x + 2) = 18$ No, $x = 4$

In Exercises 13 and 14, decide whether the equations have the same solutions. Explain your reasoning.
13. a. $3x = 12$ b. $\frac{12}{x} = 3$ Yes, $4 = 4$.
14. a. $12 - x = 8$ b. $x - 8 = 12$ No, $4 \neq 20$.

In Exercises 15–18, solve the equation using mental math. Check your solution.
15. $m + 6 = 11$ 5   16. $n - 6 = 7$ 13   17. $18 + p = 42$ 24   18. $q - 16 = 35$ 51

In Exercises 19 and 20, decide whether the equation is an identity or a conditional equation. Explain your reasoning.
19. $32 - x = 20$ Conditional equation, true for $x = 12$.
20. $9(x + 3) = 9x + 27$ Identity; true for all values of x.

In Exercises 21–23, use algebra to answer the question. Then use the graph at the right to check your answer. (Source: The Universal Almanac)
21. The number of farms in 1870 was 2.7 million. The number in 1910 was 3.7 million more than the number in 1870. How many farms were there in 1910? 6.4 million
22. The number in 1950 was two times the number in 1870. How many farms were there in 1950? 5.4 million
23. The number in 1930 divided by the number in 1990 is 3. The number in 1990 was 2.1 million. How many farms were there in 1930? 6.3 million

Farms in the U.S.

Reteaching

Reteach Chapter 2   Name _____

What you should learn:
2.3 How to check that a number is a solution of an equation and how to use mental math to solve an equation

Correlation to Pupil's Textbook:
Chapter Test (p. 97)
Exercises 12–14

Examples   Checking Solutions and Solving Equations with Mental Math

a. Decide whether $x = 3$ is a solution of the equation $5x - 10 = 4$.
   $5x - 10 = 4$ Write original equation.
   $5(3) - 10 \stackrel{?}{=} 4$ Substitute 3 for x.
   $15 - 10 \stackrel{?}{=} 4$ Simplify.
   $5 \neq 4$ $x = 3$ is not a solution. ⊗

b. Solve the equation with Mental Math.

Equation	Stated as a Question	Solution
$x - 9 = 11$	What number can 9 be subtracted from to obtain 11?	$x = 20$

c. Write the following question as an equation, then solve it mentally.
   What number can be multiplied by 12 to obtain 2?
   Let x be the number. The equation is $12x = 2$. The number $\frac{1}{6}$ can be multiplied by 12 to obtain 2.

Guidelines:
• An equation states that two expressions are equivalent.
• An identity is an equation that is true for all values of the variables that it contains.
• A conditional equation is not true for all values of the variables that it contains.
• The values that make a conditional equation true are called solutions of the equation.
• Two equations are equivalent if they have the same solutions.

EXERCISES

In Exercises 1–4, decide whether $x = 2$ is a solution of the equation. If it is not, use mental math to find the solution.
1. $16x = 48$ No, $x = 3$.   2. $18 - x = 16$ Yes   3. $\frac{8}{x} = \frac{1}{4}$ No, $x = 32$.   4. $5x + x = 12$ Yes

In Exercises 5–12, solve the equation using mental math. Check your solution.
5. $n + 4 = 15$ 11   6. $13 - a = 12$ 1   7. $3n = 18$ 6   8. $\frac{x}{7} = 2$ 14
9. $b - 4 = 5$ 9   10. $12y = 36$ 3   11. $\frac{24}{x} = 8$ 3   12. $19 + t = 26$ 7

Lesson 2.3 **61**

► **Ex. 40–43** These exercises can be used as an in-class small-group activity.

► **Ex. 47**

Common-Error Alert!

Students will commonly give 3 as the solution to Ex. 47. Encourage students to talk their way out of this by stating the equation as a question: What number divided by 12 gives 4?

Integrated Review

► **Ex. 48–50** Have students explain what order of operations they applied in arriving at their answers.

Exploration and Extension

This is quite a sophisticated problem, and can be a useful reinforcement of the terms used at the start of this lesson, especially the concepts of *identity* versus *conditional equation*. First explain to students that the subdivisions of the rectangles are not important. Have them start by writing an expression for the total area of the rectangle in **a**, in **b**, and in **c**. You may want to ask leading questions: If the area of the rectangle in **a** were equal to the area of the rectangle in **b**, what could you say about the two expressions that represent those areas? For what value of x would those expressions be equal? And so on.

Portfolio Opportunity: Math Log

A special type of conditional statement is called a contradiction. An example of a contradiction is $3x - 3x = 4$. In your own words define a contradiction.

Also available as a copymaster, page 7, Ex. 3

In Exercises 37–39, decide whether the equation is an identity or a conditional equation. Explain your reasoning. For explanations, see margin.

✪ **37.** $4(x + 7) = 4x + 28$
Identity

✪ **38.** $3 + x = 10$
Conditional equation

✪ **39.** $9x = 72$ Conditional equation

Growing Pumpkins In Exercises 40–43, use algebra to answer the question. Then, use the graph to check your answer. *(Source: World Pumpkin Confederation)*

40. The 1987 winner weighed 212 pounds less than the 1990 winner. How much did the 1990 winner weigh? 816.5 lb

41. The 1989 winner weighed $1\frac{1}{4}$ times as much as the 1987 winner. How much did the 1989 winner weigh? 755.625 lb

42. The 1992 winner weighed $10\frac{1}{2}$ pounds more than the 1990 winner. How much did the 1992 winner weigh? 827 lb

43. The 1988 winner's weight divided by the 1992 winner's weight is $\frac{3}{4}$. How much did the 1988 winner weigh? 620.25 lb

World Pumpkin Weigh-Off Winners
604.5
Weight (in pounds)

Mental Math In Exercises 44–47, solve the equation using mental math. Then write another equation that has the same solution. Equations vary.

✪ **44.** $x + 15 = 29$
14, $2x = 28$

✪ **45.** $7x = 70$
10, $x - 7 = 3$

✪ **46.** $31 - r = 24$
7, $\frac{r}{7} = 1$

✪ **47.** $\frac{t}{12} = 4$
48, $12 + t = 60$

Integrated Review *Making Connections within Mathematics*

Mental Math In Exercises 48–50, use mental math to evaluate the expression.

48. $7 \cdot 2 + 3 \cdot 6$ 32

49. $24 \div 3 - (2)(3)$ 2

50. $3[(7 - 4)^2 + 1]$ 30

Mental Math In Exercises 51–56, simplify the equation. Then solve it mentally.

51. $6x + 3x = 18$ $9x = 18, 2$

52. $4x + 8x = 24$ $12x = 24, 2$

53. $5x + 4x = 11 + 7$ $9x = 18, 2$

54. $17x = 9 + 25$ $17x = 34, 2$

55. $3x + 4x + 2x = 0$
$9x = 0, 0$

56. $8x + 7x + 3x = 9$ $18x = 9, \frac{1}{2}$

Exploration and Extension

✪ **57.** *Geometry* Which two rectangles have the same perimeter for all values of x? Explain your reasoning. a and c, $4x + 12 = 4x + 12$

a.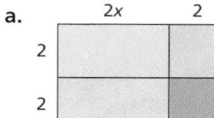

b.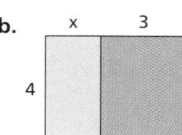

c.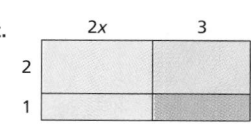

✪ More difficult exercise

Enrichment

Without using a calculator or paper or pencil, evaluate each expression.
1. $24 \cdot 2 + 24 \cdot 17 - 24 \cdot 19$
2. $16 \cdot 7 + 16 \cdot 2 + 16 \cdot 1$
3. $143 \cdot 41 - 43 \cdot 41$

Answers
37. True for all values of x
38. True only for $x = 7$
39. True only for $x = 8$

In Exercises 1–8, evaluate the expression when $x = 6$. (1.5)

1. $3x + 1$ 19
2. $\frac{x}{3} + 4$ 6
3. $x^2 - 8$ 28
4. $\frac{x}{2} - 3$ 0
5. $(x - 1) \cdot 2$ 10
6. $2 \cdot (x \div 3)$ 4
7. $\frac{1}{4} \cdot x^2$ 9
8. $(x^2 - 12) \div 4$ 6

In Exercises 9–14, simplify the expression and evaluate for $r = 4$ and $s = 5$. (1.5, 2.1, 2.2)

9. $16r + 2 - 12r$ $4r + 2, 18$
10. $2r^2 + r + r^2$ $3r^2 + r, 52$
11. $4s + 3r + 2s$ $3r + 6s, 42$
12. $3(r + s) - 2r$ $r + 3s, 19$
13. $2(r^2 + s) + r^2$ $3r^2 + 2s, 58$
14. $\frac{1}{5}r + s + 3s$ $\frac{1}{5}r + 4s, 20\frac{4}{5}$

In Exercises 15–20, use a calculator to evaluate the expression. (2.1)

15. $616(1.8 + 2.5)$ 2648.8
16. $412(2.02 - 1.64)$ 156.56
17. $951(8.25 \cdot 4)$ 31,383
18. $827(3.03 \div 3)$ 835.27
19. $\frac{1}{3}(3.14 \cdot 15)$ 15.7
20. $\frac{1}{5}(330 \div 3)$ 22

Milestones   THE CHANGING FACE OF MONEY

400 BC	100 BC	200 AD	500 AD	800 AD	1100 AD	1400 AD	1700 AD	2000 AD
er B.C.	Greek drachma 269 B.C.	Latin aureus 87 B.C.	Chinese paper money 600's		Banks, Italy 1200-1600		U.S Mint 1792	Universal Credit Card, 1950

In order to get the things you need you must find someone who has them and is willing to trade for things that you have. This process was made much easier in about 650 B.C., when a convenient item was created that was widely accepted in trade for anything, the coin. The first known metal coin, the *stater* (meaning standard) was made by King Croesus in Lydia, a kingdom on the western coast of modern Turkey. It was made of 0.3 ounces of gold and stamped with a lion's head. It had a standard size, weight, and purity. For centuries, the value of coins was based on the amount of precious metal in them. Between A.D. 700 and 900, the Chinese introduced paper money which had value only because people trusted that the issuer would take it back in return for its face value in coins. In the Middle Ages, banks (from the Italian word for bench) were established to help merchants establish credit to buy goods.

Tribes in the Pacific Northwest used fish-hooks as currency.

In our day world trading demands that the money of one country be exchanged for the money of another. Newspapers publish the rates of exchange between currencies daily.

- *Use the chart to determine how many English pounds you would get in exchange for 100 U.S. dollars.* 63.51

- *How many U.S. dollars could you get for 100 Japanese yen?* 0.99

EXCHANGE RATES (8/26/94)

Currency	In U.S. dollars	per U.S. dollars
British pound	1.5312	0.6531
Canadian dollar	0.7302	1.369
Greek drachma	0.0042	239.15
Japanese yen	0.0099	100.45
Mexican peso	0.2980	3.3554
Turkish lira	0.00003	32745.2

Milestones

Through historical anecdotes, Milestones highlight the development of mathematics, science, and invention over the centuries with time lines that show other important events of a period.

Theme: Coins and Currency

1. Use a newspaper to find the present exchange rates for the countries listed in the table. Answers vary.

2. Do you think that the dollar is stronger or weaker than it was in August, 1994? Answers vary.

Library Skills Have students use library resources to research some international monetary and trade associations.

INVESTIGATION Notes

Materials

Teaching Tools
  Algebra tiles, pp. T4, C5
Overhead Manipulatives Kit

The goal of this investigation is to use algebra tiles to help students visualize the use of subtraction to solve an equation. Be sure to identify the goal of *isolating* the tile that represents the variable *x*. Help students to observe the subtraction of the same number from both sides of an equation. Remind them that although mental math may seem more efficient, it is a limited technique. The techniques of Lessons 2.4, 2.5, and Chapter 4 will be needed to further the study of solving equations.

    This investigation interfaces well with the scale-balancing model provided in Lesson 2.4. For the exercises, be sure to give students the option of using sketches on graph paper. Note that in Ex. 2, the variable tile is on the right. For Ex. 7, you may wish to have students use the overhead projector for their explanations.

Materials Needed: algebra tiles

In this investigation, you will use algebra tiles to model and solve equations involving addition. Remember that each smaller tile represents the number 1 and each larger tile represents the variable *x*.

Example   *Using Algebra Tiles*

Model the equation $x + 3 = 6$ with algebra tiles. Then use the tiles to solve the equation. Finally, check your solution.

Solution

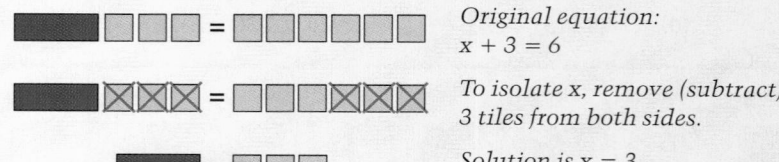

Original equation:
$x + 3 = 6$

To isolate x, remove (subtract) 3 tiles from both sides.

Solution is x = 3.

You can check that $x = 3$ is a solution as follows.

$$x + 3 = 6 \qquad \textit{Write original equation.}$$
$$3 + 3 \stackrel{?}{=} 6 \qquad \textit{Substitute 3 for x.}$$
$$6 = 6 \qquad \textit{x = 3 is a solution. ✔} \qquad ■$$

Exercises

In Exercises 1 and 2, an equation has been modeled and solved with algebra tiles. Write the equation and its solution. Then check the solution. See margin.

1.

2.

In Exercises 3–6, use algebra tiles to model and solve the equation.

P   **3.** $x + 4 = 7$ 3   **4.** $2 + x = 9$ 7   **5.** $6 = x + 4$ 2   **6.** $5 = 1 + x$ 4

7. *You Be the Teacher*   Suppose you are teaching a friend how to use algebra tiles to solve an equation. How would you explain the process to your friend? See margin.

Answers

1. $x + 2 = 4$
    $x = 2$

2. $6 = x + 1$
    $5 = x$

7. Model the equation with the algebra tiles. Remove one pair of unit tiles at a time, taking one from each side of the equal sign, until the *x* tile is alone on one side. The number of unit tiles left is the solution.

2.4 Solving Equations: Addition or Subtraction

PACING the Lesson

Suggested Number of Days
Basic/Average 2   Above Average 1
Advanced 1

PLANNING the Lesson

Lesson Plan 2.4, p. 12

What you should learn:

 Goal 1 How to use addition or subtraction to solve an equation

 Goal 2 How to use equations as algebraic models to solve real-life problems

Why you should learn it:

You can use addition or subtraction to solve equations that model real-life situations, such as buying a basketball.

Goal 1 Using Addition or Subtraction

The Lesson Investigation on page 64 shows how algebra tiles can be used to model and solve an equation. Another way to model an equation is to use a scale. Your goal is to find the value of x. Whatever you do to one side of the scale, you must also do to the other so that the scale remains in balance.

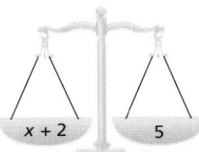 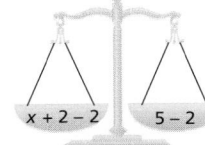 

Original equation: $x + 2 = 5$. | *Subtract 2 from both sides. Scale stays in balance.* | *Simplify both sides. Solution is $x = 3$.*

Addition and Subtraction Properties of Equality

Adding the same number to both sides of an equation or subtracting the same number from both sides of an equation produces an equivalent equation.

Study Tip...

Some people like to use a vertical format to show the steps of a solution. For instance, in part **a** of Example 1, you could write the following.

$$\begin{array}{r} x - 31 = 14 \\ +31 = +31 \\ \hline x = 45 \end{array}$$

Example 1 Solving Equations

Solve the equations **a.** $x - 31 = 14$ and **b.** $214 = y + 112$.

Solution Each equation that is part of a written solution is called a **step** of the solution.

a. $x - 31 = 14$ *Rewrite original equation.*
      $x - 31 + 31 = 14 + 31$ *Add 31 to both sides.*
           $x = 45$ *Simplify.*

The solution is 45. Check this in the original equation.

b. $214 = y + 112$ *Rewrite original equation.*
      $214 - 112 = y + 112 - 112$ *Subtract 112 from both sides.*
           $102 = y$ *Simplify.*

The solution is 102. Check this in the original equation. ■

ORGANIZER

Starters (reproduced below)
 Problem of the Day 2.4, p. 5
 Warm-Up Exercises 2.4, p. 5
Lesson Resources
 Math Log, p. 8
 Answer Masters 2.4, pp. 29, 30
 Extra Practice Copymaster 2.4, p. 12
 Reteaching Copymaster 2.4, p. 12
 Enrichment Projects, pp. 10, 11
 Calculator
Special Populations
 Suggestions, Teacher's Edition, p. 48D

LESSON Notes

MATH JOURNAL
Have students record the Addition and Subtraction Properties of Equality in their journals. These properties suggest the "Golden Rule" of equations, which states that "what you do to one side of an equation you must do to the other side."

Example 1
Encourage students to state (aloud) the steps they would follow to solve each equation. Putting their steps into words helps clarify the sequence of steps before trying to execute them.

▶ **MEETING INDIVIDUAL NEEDS**
Some students may still be uneasy with horizontal addition and subtraction. Be prepared to show the vertical representation, if necessary.

STARTER: Problem of the Day

Use the associative and distributive properties to simplify and evaluate the following.
a. $378 + 995 + 1005$ $378 + 2000 = 2378$
b. $672 \cdot 25 \cdot 4$ $672 \cdot 100 = 67200$
c. $452 \cdot 87 + 452 \cdot 13$
  $452(87 + 13) = 45200$
d. $74 \cdot 854 + 26 \cdot 854$
  $854(74 + 26) = 85400$

Also available as a copymaster, page 5

STARTER: Warm-Up Exercises

1. The perimeter of the triangle is 28. Find the value of x.   5

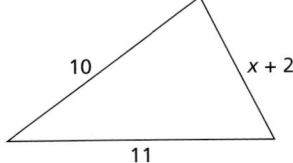

2. What are equivalent equations?
  Equations that have the same solutions.

3. Describe the process of checking the solution of an equation.
  Substitute the values for the variable in the original equation, and check that a true statement results.

Also available as a copymaster, page 5

Review the three main stages for translating a real-life situation into an algebraic relationship: verbal model, labels, and algebraic model. Students should have already recorded these stages in their journals. Encourage students to locate them in their journals.

Example 2

Ask students to redo the solution using the vertical format. Let students indicate which format they prefer. Stress the importance of copying the original equation at the beginning of each solution process.

Communicating about MATHEMATICS

Ask students to share their equations and then, as a class, examine the variety of relationships that were produced.

Writing Prompt

Suppose your math partner, reading the problem posed in Example 2 of this lesson, says: It's just dumb to use algebra for this simple stuff!" What would you say?

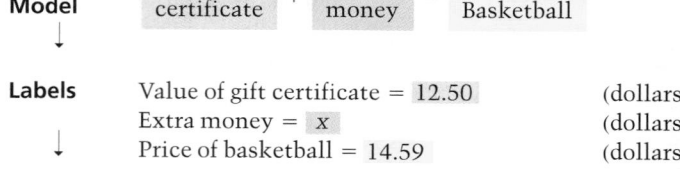
Real Life
Retail Sales

Study Tip...
Problem Solving *Even though you could use mental math to answer the question in Example 2, it is important to learn to use algebra to answer the question. Later, you will encounter problems that are too complicated to be solved with mental math. Then, your knowledge of algebra will really pay off!*

Goal 2 **Modeling Real Life with Equations**

Example 2 *Using an Equation as a Real-Life Model*

For your birthday, your grandmother sent you a $12.50 gift certificate for a sporting-goods store. You decide to use the certificate to buy a basketball that cost $14.59 (including tax). How much extra money do you need to pay?

Solution

Verbal Model	Gift certificate	$+$	Extra money	$=$	Price of Basketball

$\downarrow$

Labels Value of gift certificate $= 12.50$ (dollars)
$\downarrow$ Extra money $= x$ (dollars)
 Price of basketball $= 14.59$ (dollars)

Algebraic Model
$$12.50 + x = 14.59$$
$$12.50 + x - 12.50 = 14.59 - 12.50$$
$$x + 12.50 - 12.50 = 14.59 - 12.50$$
$$x = 2.09$$

You need an extra $2.09. You can check this result by noting that $12.50 + 2.09 = 14.59$. ∎

In the 3rd step of the solution, note that the terms 12.50 and x were reordered. This is justified by the **Commutative Property of Addition.** This and other properties of addition and multiplication are listed below.

Property

Commutative Property of Addition: $a + b = b + a$

Commutative Property of Multiplication: $ab = ba$

Associative Property of Addition: $a + (b + c) = (a + b) + c$

Associative Property of Multiplication: $a(bc) = (ab)c$

Communicating about MATHEMATICS

▶ **SHARING IDEAS about the Lesson**

Real-Life Modeling Think of a real-life situation that can be modeled with an equation. Then solve the equation.
Answers vary.

OPTION: Extra Examples
Here are additional examples similar to Example 1.
Solving Equations
Solve the equations
a. $x - 27 = 45$ b. $81 = m + 36$
Solution
a. $x - 27 = 45$ Rewrite original equation.
   $x - 27 + 27 = 45 + 27$ Add 27 to both sides.
         $x = 72$ Simplify.
b. $81 = m + 36$ Rewrite original equation.
   $81 - 36 = m + 36 - 36$ Subtract 36 from both sides.
         $45 = m$ Simplify.

EXERCISES

Guided Practice

▶ **CHECK for Understanding** Answers vary. $x = 4$, so $x + 3 = 4 + 3$ and $x + 3 = 7$

1. Give an example of the Addition Property of Equality.

2. Explain why the equations $x + 5 = 8$ and $x = 3$ are equivalent.
$x = 3$, so $x + 5 = 3 + 5$ and $x + 5 = 8$.

In Exercises 3–6, explain how to solve the equation. See margin.

3. $x + 24 = 38$ **4.** $y - 16 = 53$ **5.** $152 = r + 72$ **6.** $185 = s - 68$

In Exercises 7–10, state the property that is demonstrated.

7. $3 \cdot (8 \cdot 4) = (3 \cdot 8) \cdot 4$ **8.** $(3)(8) = (8)(3)$

9. $4 + 7 = 7 + 4$ **10.** $8 + (9 + 7) = (8 + 9) + 7$

7. Assoc. Prop. of Mult.   **8.** Comm. Prop. of Mult.   **9.** Comm. Prop. of Add.   **10.** Assoc. Prop. of Add.

Independent Practice

In Exercises 11–14, copy and complete the solution.

11.
$$x - 34 = 52$$
$$x - 34 + \boxed{?} = 52 + \boxed{?} \quad 34, 34$$
$$x = \boxed{?} \quad 86$$

12.
$$76 = y - 29$$
$$76 + \boxed{?} = y - 29 + \boxed{?} \quad 29, 29$$
$$\boxed{?} = y \quad 105$$

13.
$$r + 62 = 111$$
$$r + 62 - \boxed{?} = 111 - \boxed{?} \quad 62, 62$$
$$r = \boxed{?} \quad 49$$

14.
$$279 = t + 194$$
$$279 - \boxed{?} = t + 194 - \boxed{?} \quad 194, 194$$
$$\boxed{?} = t \quad 85$$

In Exercises 15–26, solve the equation. Then check your solution.

15. $n + 17 = 98$ 81   **16.** $m + 39 = 81$ 42   **17.** $x - 61 = 78$ 139

18. $z - 129 = 200$ 329   **19.** $356 = y - 219$ 575   **20.** $445 = t - 193$ 638

21. $736 = x + 598$ 138   **22.** $907 = s + 316$ 591   **23.** $n + 1.7 = 3.9$ 2.2

24. $11.31 = 5.31 + y$ 6   **25.** $7.49 = m - 5.86$ 13.35   **26.** $q - 12.42 = 9$ 21.42

27. Explain the steps you used to solve Exercise 20.   Added 193 to both sides, simplified.

28. Explain the steps you used to solve Exercise 21.   Subtracted 598 from both sides, simplified.

In Exercises 29–34, use a calculator to solve the equation.

29. $r + 217.46 = 598.07$ 380.61   **30.** $952.7 = s + 420.38$ 532.32   **31.** $1.397 = x - 1.973$ 3.370

32. $y - 4.85 = 13.01$ 17.86   **33.** $s + 1024 = 9785$ 8761   **34.** $5826 = r - 2290$ 8116

35. *Geometry*   Two angles are **supplementary** if the sum of their measures is 180°. An angle whose measure is 74° is supplementary to an angle whose measure is m. Find m.   106°

Extra Practice

Extra Practice 2.4   Name _____

In Exercises 1–4, copy and complete the solution.

1.
$$x + 21 = 65$$
$$x + 21 - \boxed{?} = 65 - \boxed{?} \quad 21$$
$$21 \quad x = \boxed{?} \quad 44$$

2.
$$32 \quad 58 = y - 32$$
$$58 + \boxed{?} = y - 32 + \boxed{?} \quad 32$$
$$90 \boxed{?} = y$$

3.
$$z - 28 = 101$$
$$z - 28 + \boxed{?} = 101 + \boxed{?} \quad 28$$
$$28 \quad z = \boxed{?} \quad 129$$

4.
$$217 \quad 312 = w + 217$$
$$312 - \boxed{?} = w + 217 - \boxed{?} \quad 217$$
$$95 \boxed{?} = w$$

In Exercises 5–13, solve the equation. Then check your solution.

5. $K + 25 = 48$ 23   **6.** $m + 17 = 71$ 54   **7.** $n - 23 = 43$ 66

8. $410 = s - 208$ 618   **9.** $617 + t = 694$ 77   **10.** $u - 3.7 = 11.2$ 14.9

11. $7.52 = v + 4.08$ 3.44   **12.** $w - 2.5 = 6.2$ 8.7   **13.** $x + 2.51 = 7$ 4.49

In Exercises 14–19, use a calculator to solve the equation.

14. $w - 12.31 = 49.69$ 62   **15.** $312.27 = x - 210.08$ 522.35   **16.** $3.218 = y - 7.011$ 10.229

17. $z + 2.08 = 13.01$ 10.93   **18.** $a + 4.21 = 101.23$ 97.02   **19.** $5386.01 = b - 32.07$ 5418.08

In Exercises 20–23, write an equation that represents the statement. Then solve the equation.

20. The difference of x and 7 is 28. $x - 7 = 28; 35$

21. The sum of y and 2.7 is 8.3. $y + 2.7 = 8.3; 5.6$

22. The sum of z and 3.1 is 15.2. $z + 3.1 = 15.2; 12.1$

23. The difference of a and 5.01 is 22.7. $a - 5.01 = 22.7; 27.71$

In Exercises 24–26, use the following information.
The 1992 NFL rushing leaders were Emmitt Smith, Barry Foster, Thurman Thomas and Barry Sanders, who rushed for 1352 yards.
(Source: The Universal Almanac)

24. The difference between Emmitt Smith's total and Barry Sanders' total was 361 yards. Find Emmitt Smith's total.   1713 yards

25. The sum of Thurman Thomas' total and Barry Sanders' total was 2839 yards. Find Thurman Thomas' total.   1487 yards

26. 23 yards was the difference of Emmitt Smith's total and Barry Foster's total. Find Barry Foster's total.   1690 yards

---

Reteaching

Reteach Chapter 2   Name _____

What you should learn:

	Correlation to Pupil's Textbook:
2.4 How to use addition or subtraction to solve an equation and how to use equations as algebraic models to solve real-life problems	Mid-Chapter Self-Test (p. 69) Chapter Test (p. 97)
	Exercises 15–20 Exercises 4, 5

Examples   *Using Addition or Subtraction and Modeling Real-Life with Equations*

a. Solve the equation showing each step of the solution.

$$n + 18 = 37 \quad \textit{Original equation}$$
$$n + 18 - 18 = 37 - 18 \quad \textit{Subtract 18 from both sides.}$$
$$n = 19 \quad \textit{Simplify.}$$

b. You want to purchase a compact disc for $15.79 (including sales tax), but you have only $11.75. How much money do you need to save before you can purchase the compact disc?

Verbal Model	Money you have	+	Money you must save	=	Price of compact disc

Labels   Money you have = 11.75   (dollars)
       Money you must save = x (dollars)
       Price of compact disc = 15.79   (dollars)

Algebraic Model
$$11.75 + x = 15.79$$
$$11.75 + x - 11.75 = 15.79 - 11.75$$
$$x + 11.75 - 11.75 = 15.79 - 11.75$$
$$x = 4.04$$

You need to save $4.04. You can check this result by noting that
$11.75 + 4.04 = 15.79.$

Guidelines: • Addition and Subtraction Properties of Equality: Adding the same number to both sides of an equation or subtracting the same number from both sides of an equation produces an equivalent equation.
• Properties of Addition and Multiplication:
   Commutative Property of Addition: $a + b = b + a$
   Commutative Property of Multiplication: $ab = ba$
   Associative Property of Addition: $a + (b + c) = (a + b) + c$
   Associative Property of Multiplication: $a(bc) = (ab)c$

EXERCISES

In Exercises 1–6, solve the equation and check your solution.

1. $f + 34 = 76$ 42   **2.** $h - 124 = 102$ 226   **3.** $457 = k + 79$ 378

4. $x - 3.4 = 15$ 18.4   **5.** $45.6 = z + 22.4$ 23.2   **6.** $86 = w - 25.8$ 111.8

EXERCISE Notes

ASSIGNMENT GUIDE
Basic/Average:
   Day 1: Ex. 11–14, 15–21 odd, 27, 29–31, 35–38
   Day 2: Ex. 39–42, 45, 46, 47–55 odd, 57, 58
Above Average:
   Ex. 15–25 odd, 27, 32–34, 35–41 odd, 45, 46, 51–55 odd, 57–59
Advanced: Ex. 15–25 odd, 27, 32–34, 35–41 odd, 45, 46, 51–55 odd, 57–59
Selected Answers: Ex. 1–10, 11–55 odd

Guided Practice

▶ **Ex. 3–6**
ALTERNATIVE ASSESSMENT
Students' explanations will vary considerably, and this is a good opportunity for alternative assessment.
▶ **Ex. 11–14** For help with these exercises, have students refer, if necessary, to Example 1.

Independent Practice

▶ **Ex. 15–26** In these exercises, the format of the solution is very important, and students must show their work. Encourage the students to vertically align the equal sign in each step.

Answers
3. Subtract 24 from both sides.
4. Add 16 to both sides.
5. Subtract 72 from both sides.
6. Add 68 to both sides.

Computation Sense **In Exercises 36–43, write an equation that represents the statement. Then solve the equation.** For equations, see margin.

36. The sum of x and 49 is 165. 116
37. The sum of r and 2.4 is 7.2. 4.8
38. The difference of y and 5.8 is 12.2. 18
39. The difference of n and 40 is 38. 78
40. 89 is the sum of a number and 37. 52
41. 173 is the sum of a number and 93. 80
42. 141 is the difference of a number and 503. 644
43. 317 is the difference of a number and 723. 1040

Downhill Skiing **In Exercises 44 and 45, use the information given in the caption of the photo.**

✪ **44.** How much higher is the summit than the base? 3250 ft

✪ **45.** You are skiing on a beginner trail. The head of the trail is 1530 feet higher than the base elevation. At what elevation does the beginner slope start? 9730 feet

✪ **46.** *Buying Skis* After purchasing a pair of used skis for $89.99 (including tax), you have $5.63 left. How much money did you have before buying the skis? $95.62

Vail, Colorado, is a popular Rocky Mountain ski resort. The base elevation of the resort is 8200 feet. The summit elevation is 11,450 feet.

Integrated Review   *Making Connections within Mathematics*

Measurement Sense **In Exercises 47–50, complete the statement using < , >, or = .**

47. 7 feet ? 82 inches >
48. 2.5 miles ? 13,200 feet =
49. 320 cm ? 3.2 m =
50. 6500 mm ? 65 m <

Mental Math **In Exercises 51–56, use mental math to solve the equation.**

51. $x + \frac{1}{2} = 1$ $\frac{1}{2}$
52. $y + \frac{3}{5} = 1$ $\frac{2}{5}$
53. $z - \frac{3}{4} = 1$ $1\frac{3}{4}$
54. $t - \frac{5}{2} = 1$ $3\frac{1}{2}$
55. $4 - s = 2.5$ 1.5
56. $3.3 - r = 2.6$ 0.7

P **Exploration and Extension**

57.–59. Examples vary.
✪ **57.** *Commutative Property?* Does subtraction have a commutative property? That is, does $a - b = b - a$? Explain. No, $5 - 3 \neq 3 - 5$

✪ **58.** *Associative Property?* Does subtraction have an associative property? That is, does $a - (b - c) = (a - b) - c$? Explain. No, $8 - (3 - 1) \neq (8 - 3) - 1$

✪ **59.** *It's Up to You* Decide whether the commutative and associative properties are true for division. Explain. No, $6 \div 2 \neq 2 \div 6$; no, $12 \div (6 \div 2) \neq (12 \div 6) \div 2$

✪ More difficult exercises
P Portfolio Opportunity

Take this test as you would take a test in class. The answers to the exercises are given in the back of the book.

In Exercises 1 and 2, simplify the expression. (2.1)

1. $5(x + 3)$ $5x + 15$

2. $2(a + 2b + 4)$ $2a + 4b + 8$

In Exercises 3 and 4, match the rectangle with its perimeter. (There may be more than one correct match.) (2.1)

a. $2x + 2y$ **e.** $2(x + 1)$

b. xy **f.** x

c. $x + y$ **g.** $2x + 2$

d. $2(x + y)$ **h.** $x + 1$

3.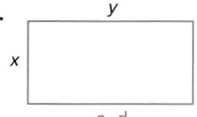
a, d

4.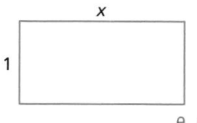
e, g

5. You are buying a $2.50 notebook and a $1.20 book cover for each of your 6 classes. What property allows you to compute your total cost as $6(2.50 + 1.20)$ or as $6(2.50) + 6(1.20)$? What is your total cost? **(2.1)** Distributive, $22.20

In Exercises 6–8, simplify the expression. (2.2)

6. $2a + 10a$ $12a$

7. $2x + 8 + x$ $3x + 8$

8. $7(x + 3) + 2x$ $9x + 21$

9. Simplify $2(3x + 4) + x$. Then evaluate the expression when $x = 4$. **(2.2)** $7x + 8$, 36

10. List all of the expressions that are equivalent to $3(2x + 1) + 3x$. **(2.2)**

  a. $6x + 3 + 3x$ a and c

  b. $5x + 3 + 3x$

  c. $9x + 3$

11. Write expressions for the perimeter and area of the rectangle. **(2.1, 2.2)**

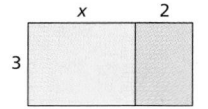

$2(3 + x + 2)$ or $2x + 10$, $3(x + 2)$ or $3x + 6$

In Exercises 12–14, use mental math to solve the equation. (2.3)

12. $3x = 39$ 13

13. $\frac{n}{4} = 20$ 80

14. $\frac{1}{2}x = 17$ 34

In Exercises 15–17, solve the equation. Show your work. (2.4)

15. $x + 13 = 28$ **16.** $19 = m - 4$ **17.** $7 + y = 11$

15.–17. See below.

In Exercises 18–20, use the bar graph at the right. (2.4)
(Source: Video Store)

18. *Fantasia* has sold 3.6 million more units than *Bambi*. How many million units did *Bambi* sell? 10.6

19. *101 Dalmatians* sold 0.9 million units less than *E.T.* How many million units did *E.T.* sell? 13.7

20. *101 Dalmatians* sold 1.2 million units more than *Batman*. How many million units did *Batman* sell? 11.6

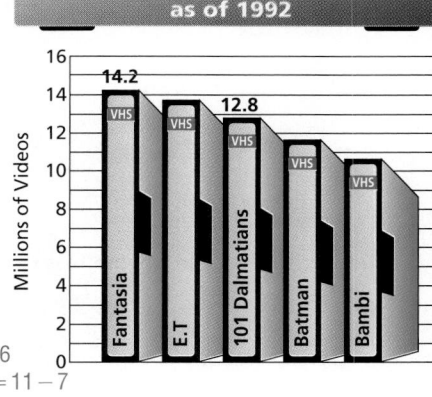

Best-Selling Videos as of 1992

15. $x + 13 - 13 = 28 - 13$
$x = 15$

16. $19 + 4 = m - 4 + 4$
$23 = m$

17. $7 + y - 7 = 11 - 7$
$y + 7 - 7 = 11 - 7$
$y = 4$

Partner Quiz

Chapter 2
Mid-Chapter Partner Quiz (Use after Lesson 2.4)
Name _____

1. Use the Distributive Property to rewrite the expression $2(x + y + 5)$. (2.1)
  1. $2x + 2y + 10$

2. You are a running back on a football team. During the first 3 games you scored 1, 2, and 1 touchdowns (6 points each), respectively. How many points did you score during these three games? (2.1)
  2. 24 points

3. Simplify the expression $6x + 2(a + 3) + 1 + a5$. (2.2)
  3. $13a + 7$

4. Write an expression for the area of the figure. What is the area if $x = 2$ inches? (2.2)
  4. $9x + 3$; 21 in.^{2}

5. Which of the following numbers is a solution to the equation $x^2 - 2x + 1 = 4$? (2.3)
  a. $x = 2$ b. $x = 3$ c. $x = 4$
  5. b. $x = 3$

6. Solve the equation using mental math. (2.3) $12 - x = 8$
  6. 4

7. Your entire family went to the movies. There are 5 people in your family and the total cost was $30. How much did each ticket cost? (2.3)
  7. $6

8. Solve the equation $2.431 = x - 4.722$. (2.4)
  8. 7.153

9. In 6 years Maria will be able to vote. How old is Maria now? (2.4)
  9. 12 years

10. The bill at a restaurant is $25.32. You leave $29.15. How much did you leave for a tip? (2.4)
  10. $3.83

© D.C. Heath and Company   • *Alternative Assessment* **45**

Mid-Chapter Test

Mid-Chapter **2** Test Form B
(Use after Lesson 2.4)
Name _____ Date _____

In Exercises 1–4, rewrite and/or simplify the expression. (2.1, 2.2)

1. $7(t + 5)$
  1. $7t + 35$

2. $3(i + 8 + 4j)$
  2. $3i + 24 + 12j$

3. $2u + 15 + 12u$
  3. $14u + 15$

4. $5(b + 9) + 2b$
  4. $7b + 45$

5. Evaluate the expression $7(8g + 4)$ for $g = 5$. (2.2)
  5. 308

In Exercises 6 and 7, use the rectangle below. (2.1, 2.2)

6. Write a simplified expression for the perimeter of the rectangle.
  6. $2y + 18$

7. Write a simplified expression for the area of the rectangle.
  7. $9y$

In Exercises 8–10, solve the equation. (2.3, 2.4)

8. $75 = 91 - a$
  8. $a = 16$

9. $56 + k = 80$
  9. $k = 24$

10. $5 + y = 42$
  10. $y = 37$

11. Draw and label a rectangle that has the same perimeter as the polygon at the right. (2.2–2.4)
  11. Answers will vary, but all responses should be a rectangle with a perimeter of $6x$.

Windows © D.C. Heath and Company   *Chapter 2 • Investigating in Algebra* **19**

◄ **ALTERNATIVE ASSESSMENT**

A **Partner Quiz** assesses students' achievement and provides them with an opportunity to communicate about mathematics.
Available as a copymaster, page 45

◄ **FORMAL ASSESSMENT**

Two **Mid-Chapter Tests** of average difficulty.
Available as copymasters, pages 18, 19

Materials
Teaching Tools
  Algebra tiles, pp. T4, C5
Overhead Manipulatives Kit

The goal of this investigation is to help students visualize the idea of dividing each side of an equation by the same nonzero number.

▶ MEETING INDIVIDUAL NEEDS
For some students, solving the equation $2x=6$ may be a mental math exercise. But for other students, the idea of grouping tiles may help them understand the concept of isolating the variable by using multiplication and division as modeled in Lesson 2.5. Note that the concept of removing tiles in order to divide is a reminder that division can be viewed as repeated subtraction.

Before assigning the exercises, be sure to demonstrate several examples of removing a group of tiles from each side. Remind students that the idea is to remove equal groups of tiles until only one variable tile remains.

EXTENSION
Ask students to create their own tile equation models.

Answers
1. $3x=6$
    $x=2$
2. $2x=8$
    $x=4$
3.

4.
    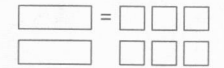
    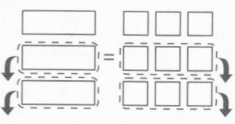
    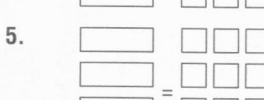
5.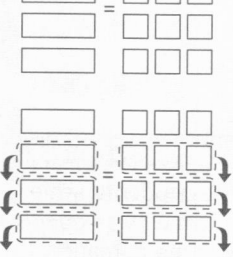

Materials Needed: algebra tiles

In this investigation, you will use algebra tiles to model and solve equations involving multiplication.

Example   *Using Algebra Tiles*

Model the equation $2x = 6$ with algebra tiles. Then use the tiles to solve the equation. Finally, check your solution.

Solution

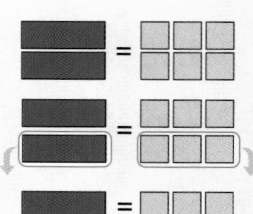

Original equation: $2x = 6$

To isolate x, divide each side into 2 groups and remove one group from each side.

Solution is $x = 3$.

You can check that $x = 3$ is a solution as follows.

$$2x = 6 \qquad \textit{Write original equation.}$$
$$2(3) \stackrel{?}{=} 6 \qquad \textit{Substitute 3 for x.}$$
$$6 = 6 \qquad \textit{x = 3 is a solution.} ✔ \qquad ■$$

Exercises

In Exercises 1 and 2, an equation has been modeled and solved with algebra tiles. Write the equation and its solution. Then check the solution. See margin.

1.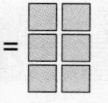
    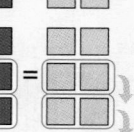

2.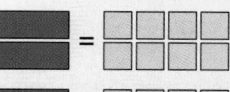
    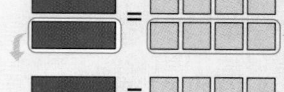

In Exercises 3–6, use algebra tiles to model and solve the equation. For models, see margin.

3. $2x = 10$ 5   **4.** $3n = 9$ 3   **5.** $4y = 12$ 3   **6.** $2b = 12$ 6

6.

2.5 Solving Equations: Multiplication or Division

▶ **PACING the Lesson**
Suggested Number of Days
Basic/Average 2   **Above Average** 1
Advanced 1

▶ **PLANNING the Lesson**
Lesson Plan 2.5, p. 13

 What you should learn:

 Why you should learn it:

Goal 1 How to use multiplication or division to solve an equation

Goal 2 How to use equations to solve real-life problems

You can use multiplication or division to solve equations that model real-life situations, such as finding the hourly rate for baby-sitting.

Goal 1 Using Multiplication or Division

In Lesson 2.4 you learned how to use addition or subtraction to solve an equation. In this lesson you will learn how to use multiplication or division to solve an equation.

Multiplication and Division Properties of Equality
Multiplying both sides of an equation by the same nonzero number or dividing both sides of an equation by the same nonzero number produces an equivalent equation.

Example 1 Solving Equations

Solve the equations **a.** $5x = 20$ and **b.** $12 = \frac{n}{4}$.

Solution

a. $5x = 20$ *Rewrite original equation.*

$\frac{5x}{5} = \frac{20}{5}$ *Divide both sides by 5.*

$x = 4$ *Simplify.*

The solution is 4. Check this in the original equation.

b. $12 = \frac{n}{4}$ *Rewrite original equation.*

$4 \cdot 12 = 4 \cdot \frac{n}{4}$ *Multiply both sides by 4.*

$48 = n$ *Simplify.*

The solution is 48. Check this in the original equation. ■

In Example 1, notice that you can simplify a fraction that has a **common** factor in its numerator and denominator. Here are two other examples.

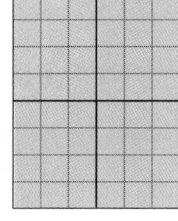

This is an area model for part b of Example 1. One-fourth of the area is 12. The entire area is 48.

Fraction	Factor	Divide	Simplify
$\frac{6}{4}$	$\frac{2 \cdot 3}{2 \cdot 2}$	$\frac{\cancel{2} \cdot 3}{\cancel{2} \cdot 2}$	$\frac{3}{2}$
$\frac{3x}{3}$	$\frac{3 \cdot x}{3}$	$\frac{\cancel{3} \cdot x}{\cancel{3}}$	$\frac{x}{1}$ or x

2.5 • *Solving Equations: Multiplication or Division*   **71**

ORGANIZER

Starters (reproduced below)
  Problem of the Day 2.5, p. 5
  Warm-Up Exercises 2.5, p. 5
Lesson Resources
  Math Log, p. 8
  Technology, pp. 9, 10
  Answer Masters 2.5, pp. 31, 32
  Extra Practice Copymaster 2.5, p. 13
  Reteaching Copymaster 2.5, p. 13
  Calculator
Special Populations
  Suggestions, Teacher's Edition, p. 48D

LESSON Notes

Point out how the Golden Rule of Equations applies here for multiplication and division. That is, if we multiply (or divide) one side of an equation by a number (a nonzero number for division), then an equivalent equation is produced when we multiply (or divide) the other side by the same number.

Example 1

In the Warm-Up Exercises, we used mental math to solve equations similar to these examples. Stress the importance of using algebra to solve simple equations now. Later, we will encounter more complex equations in which having equation-solving skills will really pay off. Also, note the use of the fraction bar to indicate division. Discuss the use of "—" versus "÷".

Make sure that students recognize that canceling works because:

$\frac{2 \cdot 3}{2 \cdot 2} = \frac{2}{2} \cdot \frac{3}{2} = 1 \cdot \frac{3}{2} = \frac{3}{2}$

Have students complete the following exercises and record their work in their journals using the same headings as found at the bottom of page 71.

a. $\frac{8}{6}$ **b.** $\frac{10}{4}$ **c.** $\frac{4x}{8}$

d. $\frac{16a}{4}$ **e.** $\frac{12y}{18}$ **f.** $\frac{14x}{8}$

STARTER: Problem of the Day

Write five equations in the form $x + a = c$ whose solution is 10.
Answers will vary.

Also available as a copymaster, page 5

STARTER: Warm-Up Exercises

1. Use mental math to solve each equation.
  a. $3 + x = 10$ **b.** $m - 5 = 16$
  c. $4y = 16$ **d.** $6x = 24$
  e. $\frac{y}{2} = 6$ **f.** $\frac{m}{8} = 4$
  a. 7, **b.** 21, **c.** 4, **d.** 4, **e.** 12, **f.** 32

2. Model each product using an area model for multiplication.
  a. $y = 5 \cdot 4$ **b.** $m = 4 \cdot 3$ **c.** $x = 3 \cdot 5$

Also available as copymasters

After completing Example 2, have students create models for the type of after-school work they may be aware of.

Real Life
Baby-Sitting

In 1991, 2000 eighth-grade students were surveyed about after-school work. The 4 most common types of work were lawn work, restaurant work, newspaper deliveries, and baby-sitting. (Source: Teacher Magazine, May/June 1991)

Goal 2 Modeling Real Life with Equations

Example 2 *Using an Equation as a Real-Life Model*

You are baby-sitting for a neighbor. You arrive at 3:30 P.M. and leave at 8:00 P.M. Your neighbor pays you $13.50. How much did you get paid per hour?

Solution From 3:30 to 8:00 is a total of 4.5 hours.

Verbal Model	Total time	·	Hourly rate	=	Total pay

Labels
Total time = 4.5   (hours)
Hourly rate = x   (dollars per hour)
Total pay = 13.5   (dollars)

Algebraic Model
$$4.5 \cdot x = 13.5$$
$$\frac{4.5x}{4.5} = \frac{13.5}{4.5}$$
$$x = 3$$

You got paid $3 per hour. You can check this by multiplying to see that 4.5(3) = 13.5.

Problem Solving: Checking Solutions Using Unit Analysis
When you are solving real-life problems that involve division, be sure to check that your units of measure make sense. For instance, you can check that the units of measure in Example 2 make sense as follows.

$$4.5 \text{ hours} \cdot \frac{3 \text{ dollars}}{\text{hour}} = 13.5 \text{ dollars}$$

Communicating about MATHEMATICS

▶ **SHARING IDEAS about the Lesson**

Unit Analysis Each of the following expressions was taken from a real-life situation. Simplify the expression, stating the units for the simplified result.

A. $\dfrac{50 \text{ miles}}{\text{hour}} \cdot 3 \text{ hours}$ 150 miles   **B.** $\dfrac{80 \text{ kilometers}}{\text{hour}} \cdot 2.5 \text{ hours}$ 200 kilometers

C. $\dfrac{2.5 \text{ dollars}}{\text{pound}} \cdot 4 \text{ pounds}$ 10 dollars   **D.** $\dfrac{28 \text{ miles}}{\text{gallon}} \cdot 10 \text{ gallons}$ 280 miles

For each of the above expressions, describe a real-life situation that the expression could represent. See margin.

EXERCISES

Guided Practice

▶ CHECK for Understanding

See page 71

P 1. In your own words, state the Multiplication and Division Properties of Equality.

See margin.

P 2. Give an example of how the Multiplication Property of Equality can be used.

P 3. Give an example of how the Division Property of Equality can be used. See margin.

In Exercises 4 and 5, state whether you would multiply or divide to solve the equation.

4. $6x = 54$ Divide by 6, or multiply by $\frac{1}{6}$

5. $\frac{x}{3} = 12$ Multiply by 3

6. Problem Solving Describe a real-life situation that can be modeled with an equation. Answers vary.

Independent Practice

In Exercises 7–10, write the equation as a verbal sentence. Then solve the equation. For verbal sentences, see margin.

7. $2x = 4$ 2

8. $3x = 21$ 7

9. $\frac{b}{2} = 3$ 6

10. $\frac{a}{3} = 3$ 9

In Exercises 11–34, solve the equation. Check your solution.

11. $4x = 16$ 4

12. $12y = 144$ 12

13. $56 = 7n$ 8

14. $6s = 48$ 8

15. $6 = \frac{x}{5}$ 30

16. $\frac{m}{2} = 2$ 4

17. $\frac{t}{8} = 9$ 72

18. $5y = 100$ 20

19. $2z = 50$ 25

20. $10a = 240$ 24

21. $\frac{b}{20} = 2$ 40

22. $16 = \frac{x}{4}$ 64

23. $\frac{n}{4} = 25$ 100

24. $\frac{m}{3} = 33$ 99

25. $5x = 625$ 125

26. $7s = 175$ 25

27. $6.3 = 3y$ 2.1

28. $5t = 6.5$ 1.3

29. $524 = \frac{a}{1}$ 524

30. $\frac{y}{6} = 345$ 2070

31. $\frac{z}{3.2} = 8$ 25.6

32. $\frac{t}{7.4} = 6$ 44.4

33. $4.8b = 36$ 7.5

34. $9.6x = 72$ 7.5

✪ 35. Sketch an area model for $\frac{x}{3} = 36$.

✪ 36. Sketch an area model for $\frac{n}{5} = 20$.

35., 36. See Additional Answers.

In Exercises 37–44, use a calculator to solve the equation.

37. $456x = 1368$ 3

38. $824x = 1648$ 2

39. $23x = 966$ 42

40. $55x = 3025$ 55

41. $\frac{x}{9} = 1025$ 9225

42. $\frac{x}{8} = 624$ 4992

43. $\frac{x}{136} = 17$ 2312

44. $\frac{x}{189} = 19$ 3591

Geometry **In Exercises 45–48, find the width of the rectangle.**

45.

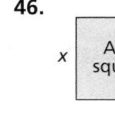

x | Area is 15 square units. | 5

3

46.

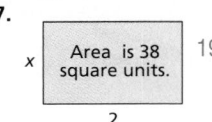

x | Area is 27 square units. | 3

9

47.

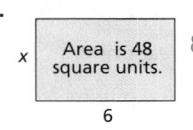

x | Area is 38 square units. | 19

2

48.

x | Area is 48 square units. | 8

6

✪ More difficult exercises
P Portfolio Opportunity

2.5 ▪ *Solving Equations: Multiplication or Division* **73**

Extra Practice

Extra Practice 2.5 Name _____

In Exercises 1 and 2, write the equation as a verbal sentence. Then solve the equation.

1. $5x = 10$ The product of 5 and a number is 10; $x = 2$.

2. $\frac{z}{2} = 11$ The quotient of a number and 2 is 11; $z = 22$.

In Exercises 3–18, solve the equation. Check your solution.

3. $3x = 15$ 5
4. $11y = 110$ 10
5. $81 = 9z$ 9
6. $35 = 7a$ 5
7. $8 = \frac{b}{9}$ 72
8. $\frac{c}{4} = 5$ 20
9. $\frac{d}{7} = 3$ 21
10. $\frac{m}{5} = 12$ 60
11. $6p = 132$ 22
12. $9q = 23.4$ 2.6
13. $7.5x = 337.5$ 45
14. $16t = 540$ 33.75
15. $\frac{v}{5.2} = 3$ 15.6
16. $5.5w = 247.5$ 45
17. $\frac{x}{3.2} = 16$ 51.2
18. $\frac{y}{15} = 3.2$ 48

In Exercises 19–26, use a calculator to solve the equation.

19. $523x = 2092$ 4
20. $489z = 1467$ 3
21. $34w = 306$ 9
22. $65t = 390$ 6
23. $\frac{x}{6} = 958$ 5748
24. $\frac{y}{8} = 605$ 4840
25. $\frac{z}{19} = 203$ 3857
26. $\frac{w}{621} = 31$ 19,251

In Exercises 27–30, solve for x.

27. x | Area is 28 square units 4

7

28. x | Area is 54 square units 6

9

29. 4 | Area is 68 square units | x 17

30. 7 | Area is 98 square units | x 14

In Exercises 31 and 32, write an equation that represents the sentence. Then solve the equation.

31. The number of motorcycles m times 5 equals 45 cycles. $5m = 45$, 9

32. The product of the number of compact discs c and 8 is 56 discs. $8c = 56$, 7

33. Walter Payton is the All-Time Pro Football rushing leader. He averaged approximately 4.368 yards per carry. Walter attempted 3838 carries over his 13 year career. (Source: *Universal Almanac*)

a. Write a verbal model that represents his total yards.

Total yards = Yards per carry ▪ Number of carries

b. Write an algebraic model that represents his total yards. Then solve the equation. $x = (4.368)(3838)$; $x = 16764.384$ yards

(NOTE: Actual total yards 16726.)

Windows 2.5 ▪ *Solving Equations: Multiplication or Division* **13**

Reteaching

Reteach Chapter 2 Name _____

What you should learn:

2.5 How to use multiplication or division to solve an equation and how to use equations to solve real-life problems

Correlation to Pupil's Textbook:
Chapter Test (p. 97)
Exercises 3, 6

Examples Using Multiplication or Division and Modeling Real-Life Situations

a. Solve the equation, using multiplication.

$\frac{k}{6} = 11$ Original equation

$6 \cdot \frac{k}{6} = 6 \cdot 11$ Multiply both sides by 6.

$k = 66$ Simplify.

b. You are ordering lunch at a fast-food restaurant. You order 4 burgers and the total price is $2.52 (including tax). What is the price of each burger?

Verbal Model: Number of burgers ▪ Price per burger = Total price

Labels: Number of burgers = 4
Price per burger = x (dollars)
Total price = 2.52 (dollars)

Algebraic Model: $4x = 2.52$ Original equation

$\frac{4x}{4} = \frac{2.52}{4}$ Divide both sides by 4.

$x = 0.63$ Simplify.

The price of each burger is $.63 (including tax). You can check this by multiplying to see that $4(0.63) = 2.52$.

Guidelines:
• Multiplication and Division Properties of Equality: Multiplying both sides of an equation by the same nonzero number or dividing both sides of an equation by the same nonzero number produces an equivalent equation.
• To simplify a fraction that has a common factor in its numerator and denominator, factor the numerator and denominator, divide each by the common factor, then simplify.
• When solving real-life problems that involve division, check to see that the units of measure make sense.

EXERCISES

In Exercises 1–8, solve the equation. Check your solution.

1. $8x = 96$ 12
2. $98 = 7n$ 14
3. $\frac{g}{3} = 34$ 102
4. $21 = \frac{k}{5}$ 105
5. $211.5 = 5a$ 42.3
6. $\frac{y}{2.7} = 6$ 16.2
7. $\frac{q}{1} = 55$ 55
8. $8.1z = 56.7$ 7

Windows Chapter 2 ▪ *Investigations in Algebra* **13**

EXERCISE Notes

ASSIGNMENT GUIDE

Basic/Average:
Day 1: Ex. 7–21 odd, 35–39 odd, 45, 46, 49–51
Day 2: Ex. 52–55, 58, 59–63 odd

Above Average:
Ex. 25–33 odd, 36, 40, 42, 47, 48, 55–58, 63

Advanced: Ex. 25–33 odd, 36, 40, 42, 47, 48, 55–58, 63

Selected Answers: Ex. 1–6, 7–61 odd

▶ **Ex. 1–6**
MATH JOURNAL
Use these exercises as a ten-minute journal activity at the end of the class period. Ask students to examine Example 2 for insight. For Exercises 2 and 3, students could create problems similar to Exercises 11–34.

Independent Practice

▶ **Ex. 7–10**
MENTAL MATH
Encourage students to try mental math for these exercises.

▶ **Ex. 11–34** For these exercises students should pay careful attention to the format of their solutions, following the format of Example 1. For exercises 30–34, encourage the use of a calculator.

▶ **Ex. 35, 36**
GROUP ACTIVITY
Assign these exercises as a two-minute in-class activity for small groups. A model is provided next to Example 1.

▶ **Ex. 37–44** Remind students that these exercises are marked with the calculator icon.

Answers
2. Answers vary. If $\frac{n}{3} = 6$, then $3 \cdot \frac{n}{3} = 3 \cdot 6$ and $n = 18$.
3. Answers vary. If $3n = 6$, then $\frac{3n}{3} = \frac{6}{3}$ and $n = 2$.
7. The product of 2 and x is 4.
8. The product of 3 and x is 21.
9. The quotient of b and 2 is 3.
10. The quotient of a and 3 is 3.

Lesson 2.5 **73**

Review of customary units of weight, length, capacity, and time is provided in the Student Handbook, page 681.

Exploration and Extension

Students will need help setting up the proper expressions for these exercises. They may find the placing of the appropriate conversion factors confusing.

Portfolio Opportunity: Math Log

What happens to an equation when both sides are multiplied by 0? Explain why you cannot divide both sides of an equation by 0.

Also available as a copymaster, page 8, Ex. 5

In Exercises 49–54, write an equation that represents the sentence. 52. $\frac{t}{6} = 10$, 60
Then solve the equation. 50. $4d = 100$, 25

49. The number of football players f times 4 equals 28 players. $4f = 28$, 7

50. The product of the number of dancers d and 4 is 100 dancers.

51. The number of bicycles b divided by 12 equals 2 bicycles. $\frac{b}{12} = 2$, 24

52. The quotient of the number of telephones t and 6 is 10 telephones.

53. 5 comic books times x dollars is $3.75. $5x = 3.75$, 0.75

54. The number of board games g times 20 dollars is 100 dollars. $20g = 100$, 5

✪ **55.** *Basketball Court*   The area of a basketball court is 4700 square feet. The width of a basketball court is 50 feet.

    a. Write an equation that represents the area of a basketball court. $4700 = 50L$

    b. Solve the equation to find the length of a basketball court. 94 ft

Basketball   **In Exercises 56 and 57, use the following**
information.   **56.** $24 \times 15.75 =$ Points scored this season

You play on your school's basketball team. This season your team played 24 games. You averaged 15.75 points per game.

✪ **56.** Use the number of games played and your points-per-game average to write a verbal model that represents the points you scored this season.

✪ **57.** Write an algebraic model that represents your total points scored this season. Then solve the equation to find your total. $24 \times 15.75 = t$, 378

✪ **58.** *Rollerblading*   You rollerblade 5 days a week. Each day you rollerblade the same distance in miles. How many miles a day do you rollerblade if you rollerblade a total of 20.5 miles in 5 days? 4.1

In the 1992–93 season, Shaquille O'Neal, a 7-foot-1-inch center for the Orlando Magic, finished among the top 10 in scoring for his first season. O'Neal scored 23.4 points per game, ranking eighth.

Integrated Review   *Making Connections within Mathematics*

Computing with Measures   **In Exercises 59–62, perform the indicated operation.**

59. 1 hr 50 min + 37 min   2 hr 27 min

60. 20 lb − (3 lb 4 oz + 1 lb 14 oz)   14 lb 14 oz

61. $3\frac{1}{2}$ yd ÷ 6 $\frac{7}{12}$ yd = 21 in. = 1 ft 9 in.

62. 126 gal ÷ 8 $15\frac{3}{4}$ gal = 15 gal 3 qt

Exploration and Extension

Measurement Sense   **In Exercises 63 and 64, perform the indicated conversion.**

✪ **63.** Convert 4.5 dollars per pound to cents per ounce. $\frac{28.125 \text{ cents}}{\text{ounce}}$

✪ **64.** Convert 55 miles per hour to feet per second. $\frac{80.6 \text{ feet}}{\text{second}}$

74   *Chapter 2* ▪ *Investigations in Algebra*   ✪ More difficult exercises

USING A SPREADSHEET
Make a Table

A **spreadsheet** is a computer program that creates tables. The following example shows how a spreadsheet can be used to help solve a real-life problem.

Example | *Creating a Wage Table*

Make a table that shows your total pay for working from 1 to 8 hours at hourly rates ranging from $2.00 per hour to $4.50 per hour.

Solution The table is shown below.

Hourly Rate

	$2.00	$2.50	$3.00	$3.50	$4.00	$4.50
1.0	$2.00	$2.50	$3.00	$3.50	$4.00	$4.50
1.5	$3.00	$3.75	$4.50	$5.25	$6.00	$6.75
2.0	$4.00	$5.00	$6.00	$7.00	$8.00	$9.00
2.5	$5.00	$6.25	$7.50	$8.75	$10.00	$11.25
3.0	$6.00	$7.50	$9.00	$10.50	$12.00	$13.50
3.5	$7.00	$8.75	$10.50	$12.25	$14.00	$15.75
4.0	$8.00	$10.00	$12.00	$14.00	$16.00	$18.00
4.5	$9.00	$11.25	$13.50	$15.75	$18.00	$20.25
5.0	$10.00	$12.50	$15.00	$17.50	$20.00	$22.50
5.5	$11.00	$13.75	$16.50	$19.25	$22.00	$24.75
6.0	$12.00	$15.00	$18.00	$21.00	$24.00	$27.00
6.5	$13.00	$16.25	$19.50	$22.75	$26.00	$29.25
7.0	$14.00	$17.50	$21.00	$24.50	$28.00	$31.50
7.5	$15.00	$18.75	$22.50	$26.25	$30.00	$33.75
8.0	$16.00	$20.00	$24.00	$28.00	$32.00	$36.00

Number of Hours Worked (row labels)

You can use the table to find your total pay. For instance, if you work 5.5 hours at $3.50 per hour, then your total pay is $19.25 ∎

Exercises

1. Make a table that shows the distance traveled for several different times and speeds.
Tables vary.

2. Make a table that shows the areas of several rectangles of different widths and heights.
Tables vary.

Materials
A spreadsheet computer program or a TI-82

The table shown for total pay can be demonstrated using a computer spreadsheet, or the TABLE feature on a TI-82 overhead graphing calculator.
On the TI-82, set
$Y_1 = 2X$,
$Y_2 = 2.5X$,
$Y_3 = 3X$,
$Y_4 = 3.5X$,
$Y_5 = 4X$, and
$Y_6 = 4.5X$.
Select TblSet, set TblMin = 1.0, ΔTbl = 0.5, and the other entries Auto.
Select TABLE to see parts of the wage table visually displayed.

For the exercises, help students to correctly format and label the table. Students will need help in getting started—choosing times and distances, and so on.

Have students discuss any previous connection to a similar spreadsheet table they might recall, for example, multiplication tables, IRS tax tables, banking interest rate tables, and so on.

You could verbally connect this type of table to a matrix, a concept that will be discussed later.

The *copy*, *fill down*, and/or *fill right* features of spreadsheet software enable you to create tables without having to enter each entry by hand. Familiarize yourself with the spreadsheet software before trying this activity with your students. After entering the formulas in the second row, show students how to use the *fill down* feature to create each column of the table. To create column B, highlight cells B2 through B16 and choose the *fill down* command from the edit menu.

	A	B	C	D
1		2	2.5	…
2	1	=2*A2	=2.5*A2	…
3	1.5	=2*A3	=2.5*A3	…
4	2	=2*A4	=2.5*A4	…

Ask students how they could adapt the spreadsheet so that it calculated the total pay for 1 to 8 hours at hourly rates from $5.00 to $8.00 per hour. Have students suggest other changes they could make to the spreadsheet.

Another spreadsheet application is available on page 11 of the Technology supplement to be used with Lesson 2.6.

PLANNING the Lesson

Lesson Plan 2.6, p. 14

ORGANIZER

Starters (reproduced below)
Problem of the Day 2.6, p. 5
Warm-Up Exercises 2.6, p. 5

Lesson Resources
Color Transparencies
    Graph for Ex. 41–43, p. 8
Teaching Tools
    Copymasters of Ex. 51, 52, p. C6
Math Log, p. 8
Technology, p. 11
Answer Masters 2.6, pp. 33, 34
Extra Practice Copymaster 2.6, p. 14
Reteaching Copymaster 2.6, p. 14
Calculator

Special Populations
Suggestions, Teacher's Edition, p. 48D

LESSON Notes

Make it quite clear to students that this is a key page —their principal reference source for the verbal phrases associated with the four basic operations. Have students close their texts and write the algebraic expression for each verbal phrase given in the opening section of the lesson. Then discuss the outcomes as a class.

Example 1

Common-Error Alert!

Encourage students to write each component phrase as it is read to avoid translation errors. Point out that the words "sum, difference, product," and "quotient" are followed by two number quantities. In the case of subtraction and division, these numbers or expressions must be combined *in the order in which they are read.* Give students plenty of practice in translating.

Study Tip Extension

Emphasize how each phrase can be read in parts. In Example **1a**, "three more than" is written as " +3" because it's more than some other quantity that will be indicated in another phrase of the sentence. The phrase "twice a number" is written as "2n." Thus, in combination, the complete phrase becomes "2x+3."

2.6 Modeling Verbal Expressions

What you should learn:

Goal 1 How to translate verbal phrases into algebraic expressions

Goal 2 How to model real-life situations with algebraic expressions

Why you should learn it:

To use algebra to solve real-life problems, you must translate verbal phrases into algebraic expressions.

Study Tip...

Problem Solving *When you are modeling a verbal phrase, you can usually choose any letter to represent the variable. Although common choices are x, y, and n, it is sometimes helpful to choose a letter that helps remind you what the variable represents. For instance, you might choose t to represent time or A to represent area.*

Goal 1 Translating Verbal Phrases

When you are translating verbal phrases into algebraic expressions, look for words that indicate a number operation.

	Verbal Phrase	Algebraic Expression
Addition:	The *sum* of 5 and a number	$5 + x$
	Nine *more than* a number	$n + 9$
	A number *plus* 2	$y + 2$
Subtraction	The *difference* of 8 and a number	$8 - n$
	Ten *less than* a number	$y - 10$
	Twelve *minus* a number	$12 - x$
Multiplication:	The *product* of 3 and a number	$3x$
	Seven *times* a number	$7y$
	A number *multiplied* by 4	$4n$
Division:	The *quotient* of a number and 3	$\frac{x}{3}$
	Four *divided* by a number	$\frac{4}{n}$

Order is important in subtraction and division, but not for addition and multiplication. For instance, "ten less than a number" is written as $y - 10$, not $10 - y$. On the other hand, "the sum of 5 and a number" can be written as $5 + x$ or $x + 5$.

Example 1 gives you some examples of phrases that contain two number operations.

Example 1 *Translating Verbal Phrases*

a. Three more than twice a number can be written as
$2x + 3$.   *Label: x represents a number.*

b. The sum of a number and 3 times another number can be written as
$n + 3m$.   *Labels: n is a number, m is another number.*

c. One number times the sum of 2 and another number can be written as
$x(2 + y)$.   *Labels: x is a number, y is another number.* ∎

STARTER: Problem of the Day

Suppose that you know these facts:
square + circle = 59
(square + triangle) + circle = 106
Evaluate these expressions.
a. square + (triangle + circle)   106
b. circle + square   59
c. triangle   47
d. square   Not enough information

Also available as a copymaster, page 5

STARTER: Warm-Up Exercises

1. What are the three steps of modeling real-life situations that we have used?
verbal models, labels, and algebraic models
2. What operations are indicated by the following words?
a. sum   **b.** difference
c. product   **d.** quotient
a. addition, b. subtraction,
c. multiplication, d. division
3. Evaluate each expression for $a=2$, $b=3$, $c=5$.
a. $2a+5$ **b.** $16-4b$ **c.** $a(c)-8$
d. $a(b)+c$ **e.** $bc-6a$ **f.** $\frac{2b}{a}$
a. 9, b. 4, c. 2, d. 11, e. 3, f. 3

Also available as a copymaster, page 5

Modeling Real-Life Phrases

Problem Solving When you are modeling a real-life situation, we suggest that you use three steps.

| Write a verbal model. | → | Assign labels to the model. | → | Write the algebraic model. |

Example 2 *Modeling a Real-Life Situation*

You are buying some cassettes and some compact discs. Each cassette costs $12 and each compact disc costs $15. Write an algebraic expression that represents your total cost. Then use the expression to find the cost of **a.** 3 cassettes and 2 compact discs and **b.** 2 cassettes and 3 compact discs.

Solution

| Verbal Model | Cost per cassette | · | Number of cassettes | + | Cost per disc | · | Number of discs |

Labels
Cost per cassette = 12   (dollars per cassette)
Number of cassettes = c (cassettes)
Cost per disc = 15   (dollars per disc)
Number of discs = d (discs)

Algebraic Model $12 \cdot c + 15 \cdot d$

a. The cost of 3 cassettes and 2 discs is as follows.
Total cost $= 12c + 15d$ *Algebraic expression*
$= 12(3) + 15(2)$ *Substitute 3 for c and 2 for d.*
$= \$66$ *Simplify.*

b. The cost of 2 cassettes and 3 discs is as follows.
Total cost $= 12c + 15d$ *Algebraic expression*
$= 12(2) + 15(3)$ *Substitute 2 for c and 3 for d.*
$= \$69$ *Simplify.* ■

Communicating *about* MATHEMATICS

▷ **SHARING IDEAS about the Lesson**

Guess, Check, and Revise In Example 2, suppose your total cost is $120. How many different combinations of cassettes and discs could you have purchased? Explain.

In 1974, long-playing albums were the most popular form of storing music. In 1984, cassettes were the most popular. In 1994, compact discs were the most popular. What form do you think will be most popular in the year 2004? (Source: Record Industry Association of America)

0 cassettes and
iscs, 0 cassettes
8 discs, 5
settes and 4
cs

Review the three steps of modeling real-life situations. Especially discuss with students the choice of labels. Students may need constant reminders that in this context a label is either a given (constant) value or it is a variable. Exercises 39 and 40 can be used as samples of how you can gradually ease students into the modeling mode, especially in the choice of labels.

Example 2
Give students ample time to agree that the verbal model of the total cost is as expressed in the example. Point out that labels "*c*" and "*d*" are more relevant to what they represent than, say, "*x*" and "*y*."

Communicating *about* MATHEMATICS

Have students discuss the variety of approaches or formats (tables, lists, guesses, etc.) that can be used to determine the combination of cassettes and disks that can be purchased. Ask students to assess which approaches seem to work best.

Writing Prompt
The word *model* has taken on a new meaning for me because now . . .

OPTION: Extra Examples

Here are additional examples similar to Example 1.

Translating Verbal Phrases
a. Two more than four times a number can be written as
$4x + 2$ Label: x represents a number.
b. The difference of 8 and a number can be written as
$8 - n$ Label: n represents a number.
c. Five times the sum of one number and three times another number can be written as
$5(p + 3q)$ Labels: p is a number, q is another number

Technology

| Analyzing the Indianapolis 500 | 2.6 | Name _____ |

Problem Solving Using a Spreadsheet

In this problem-solving activity, you will use a spreadsheet to analyze the race times and rates of speed of the top seven finishers in the 1994 Indianapolis 500.

1. ≈ 159.976 mph

EXAMPLE Creating a Spreadsheet
Use a spreadsheet to make a table listing the time, laps completed, distance traveled, and rate of speed of the top seven finishers in the 1994 Indianapolis 500. Create the table so that the average rate of speed of all seven drivers is given.

3. Change formula for average rate of speed to = SUM(F2:F5)/4.

SOLUTION
The spreadsheet should look similar to the one shown below. The race times are given in hours:minutes:seconds and the distance is given in miles (2.5 miles per lap × the number of laps). Notice that an extra column (Time in Hours) has been added and that the rates of speed are given in miles per hour. The formulas will be evaluated as you enter them into the spreadsheet.

4. See students' work.

	A	B	C	D	E	F
1	Driver	Time	Laps Completed	Distance	Time in Hours	Rate of Speed
2	Al Unser, Jr.	3:06:29	200	=2.5*C2	=3+6/60+29/3600	=D2/E2
3	Jacques Villeneuve	3:06:38	200	=2.5*C3	=3+6/60+38/3600	=D3/E3
4	Bobby Rahal	3:06:34	199	=2.5*C4	=3+6/60+34/3600	=D4/E4
5	Jimmy Vasser	3:06:36	199	=2.5*C5	=3+6/60+36/3600	=D5/E5
6	Robbie Gordon	3:06:38	199	=2.5*C6	=3+6/60+38/3600	=D6/E6
7	Michael Andretti	3:06:33	198	=2.5*C7	=3+6/60+33/3600	=D7/E7
8	Teo Fabi	3:06:40	198	=2.5*C8	=3+6/60+40/3600	=D8/E8
9					Avg. Rate of Speed	=SUM(F2:F8)/7

EXERCISES 2. The expressions in Column E, Time in Hours, are obtained by
1. Construct the spreadsheet in the example. List the average rate of speed of the drivers.
2. Explain how the expressions in Column E are obtained.
3. Modify the spreadsheet so that the average rate of speed of only the top *four* finishers is given.
4. Find the results of the most recent Indianapolis 500 race and analyze the rates of speed of the top seven finishers. Write a paragraph comparing your results to the results found in Exercise 1.

converting the minutes and seconds in Column B to hours and finding the sum of all 3 quantities (hours + minutes in hours + seconds in hours).

© D. C. Heath and Company   *Technology Using Calculators and Computers*   **11**

ASSIGNMENT GUIDE

Basic/Average:
Day 1: Ex. 7–12, 13–33 odd, 39
Day 2: Ex. 40–42, 44–47, 51

Above Average:
Ex. 13–33 odd, 39–43, 48–51

Advanced: Ex. 13–33 odd, 39–43, 48–51

Selected Answers: Ex. 1–6, 7–49 odd

Guided Practice

▶ **Ex. 5, 6**
MATH JOURNAL
Use these exercises as the journal entry for the day. This is an excellent opportunity for five minutes of small-group interaction.

Independent Practice

▶ **Ex. 7–12** Assign these exercises as a group.
▶ **Ex. 13–26** Students should write the original problem, underline the operation part of the verbal phrase (product, sum, difference, quotient, more than, and so on), then write the algebraic expression. If necessary, have students refer to the italicized words in the lesson introduction.
▶ **Ex. 30** and **37** At this stage, expect students to write the symbolic versions as $\frac{1}{2}m$ and $\frac{3}{4}a$, respectively. The alternatives, $\frac{m}{2}$ and $\frac{3a}{4}$, are more sophisticated.

Guided Practice

▶ **CHECK for Understanding**

In Exercises 1–4, write the phrase as an algebraic expression.

1. The temperature, decreased by 20° $t - 20°$
2. Five miles per hour more than the speed limit $s + 5$
3. \$0.25 per minute, plus \$1.40 $0.25m + 1.40$
4. Five dollars times the number of people, less \$15 $5n - 15$
P 5. **Problem Solving** Describe the steps for modeling a real-life situation.
P 6. **Problem Solving** Describe the two kinds of labels that are used to develop an algebraic model. Numbers and variables 5. Write a verbal model, assign labels to it, then write an algebraic model.

Independent Practice

In Exercises 7–12, match the verbal phrase with its algebraic expression.

a. $20y$ b. $20 + n$ c. $\frac{m}{8} - 4$ d. $2s + 8$ e. $x - 6$ f. $6 - x$

7. The sum of a number and 20 b   8. Eight more than twice a number d
9. The difference of 6 and a number f   10. 6 less than a number e
11. The product of a number and 20 a   12. 4 less than the quotient of a number and 8 c

In Exercises 13–26, translate the verbal phrase into an algebraic expression. Variables vary.

13. The difference of 32 and a number $32 - x$ 14. 72 plus a number $72 + x$
15. A number divided by 23 $\frac{x}{23}$ 16. The quotient of a number and 7 $\frac{x}{7}$
17. 9 more than 12 times a number $12x + 9$ 18. The sum of 1 and a number multiplied by 2 $1 + 2x$
19. 4 less than 3 times a number $3x - 4$ 20. 8 minus the product of 5 and a number $8 - 5x$
21. 18 times the product of a number and 5 $18(5x)$ 22. The sum of 3 and a number multiplied by 11 $3 + 11x$
23. The quotient of a number and 2 more than another number $\frac{x}{2 + y}$
24. The difference of 10, and one number divided by another number $10 - \frac{x}{y}$
25. The product of one number and the sum of another number and 13 $x(y + 13)$
26. The product of one number minus 4 and another number plus 4 $(x - 4)(y + 4)$

In Exercises 27–34, write as an algebraic expression. Variables vary.

27. Four more miles than yesterday $m + 4$ 28. Your salary plus \$572 $s + 572$
29. 3 times as much money as your sister $3m$ 30. Half as much money as your brother $\frac{1}{2}m$
31. 3 less runs than the Pirates scored $p - 3$ 32. 7 years younger than your cousin $a - 7$
33. Number of passengers times 3 $3p$ 34. Number of students divided by 3 $\frac{s}{3}$

Extra Practice

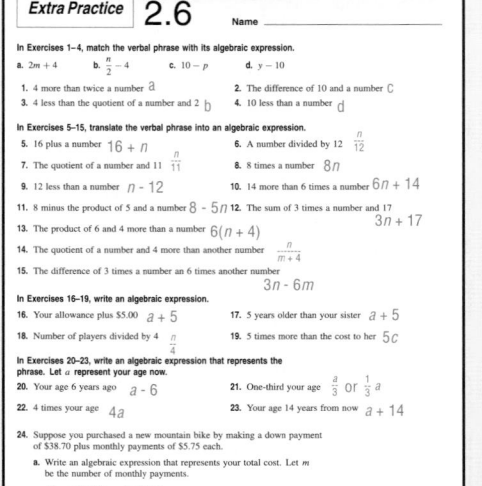

Reteaching

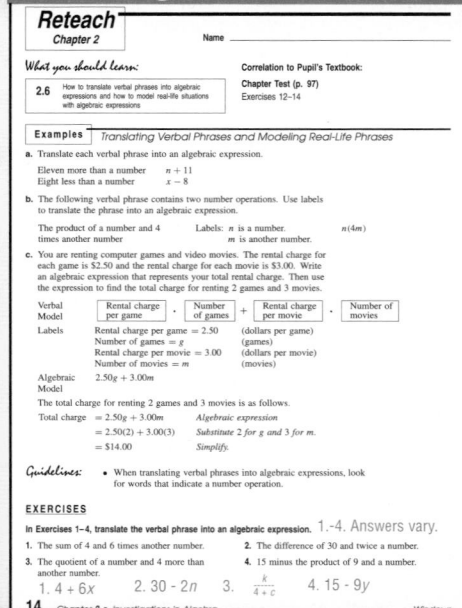

In Exercises 35–38, write an algebraic expression that represents the phrase. Let a represent your age now.

35. Your age eight years ago $a-8$

36. 10 times your age $10a$

37. Three-fourths your age $\frac{3}{4}a$

38. Your age 17 years from now $a+17$

39. *Collectors' Items* You are buying some comic books and baseball cards. Each comic book costs $1.50 and each pack of baseball cards costs $1.

   a. Write an algebraic expression that represents your total cost. Let c be the number of comics and b be the number of packs of baseball cards. $1.5c+b$

   b. Find the cost of 3 comic books and 4 packs of baseball cards. $8.50

   c. Find the cost of 4 comic books and 2 packs of baseball cards. $8

40. *Playing Pool* You and two friends are playing pool. The cost of renting the pool table is $7 for the first hour and $3 for each additional half hour.

   a. Write an algebraic expression that represents the total cost. Let h be the number of additional half hours. $7+3h$

   b. You and your friends are sharing the total cost equally. Write an expression that represents *your* cost. $(7+3h)\div 3$ or $\frac{7}{3}+h$

   c. You play for $2\frac{1}{2}$ hours. Find *your* cost. $5.33

Basketball **In Exercises 41–43, use the graph and algebra to answer the questions. Then use the graph to check your answer.** *(Source: American Basketball Council)*

41. Let m and w represent the numbers (in millions) of men and women (17 years old and younger) who played basketball. These two numbers are related by the equation $m-4.5=w$. How many women (17 years old and younger) played basketball? 8 million

42. Let M and W represent the numbers (in millions) of men and women (over 17) who played basketball. These two numbers are related by the equation $M-11.5=W$. How many women (over 17) played basketball? 4.2 million

43. What is the total number of players? 40.4 million

U.S. Basketball Players

44. *Currency Exchange* On February 7, 1994, the exchange rate between U. S. currency and Canadian currency was 1.25 Canadian dollars per 1 U. S. dollar. Use this information to complete the table.

U.S. Dollars	$1	$2	$5	$10	$x	?	?	?
Canadian Dollars	$1.25	$2.50	?	?	?	$7.50	$10	1.25x

$6.25 $1.25x $8 $x
$12.50 $6

○ More difficult exercises

2.6 ▪ *Modeling Verbal Expressions*   **79**

Integrated Review

▶ **Ex. 45–50** Ask students *why* they would want to simplify before evaluating.

Exploration and Extension

▶ **Ex. 51, 52** These are a lot of fun. You can use them as an end-of-class challenge. The right-hand puzzle is the easier one. Students need to be alert to the fact that the correct order of operations has to be followed. There is then only one correct solution. One suggested strategy is to think in terms of the constraints implied by the operations, given the particular result of that row or column. Then use guess-and-check, and so on. If students get completely blocked, offer them the following gifts—in Ex. 51, the position of the 2 (and, in dire straits, the 3) and in Ex. 52 the position of the 1.

Portfolio Opportunity: Math Log

Write a verbal phrase for the algebraic model $3 + 0.5x$. Make up a real-life situation in which this model could be used.

Also available as a copymaster, page 8, Ex. 6

Short Quiz

Covers Lessons 2.5 and 2.6

Available as a copymaster, page 20

Alternative Assessment

A cooperative learning project in which students write and use an algebraic model for a real-world application.

Available as a copymaster, page 18

Integrated Review   ***Making Connections within Mathematics***

Algebraic Expressions **In Exercises 45–50, simplify the expression. Then evaluate the expression when $a = 5$.**

45. $6a + 10a - 65$ $16a - 65, 15$ **46.** $7a + 4a + 3$ $11a + 3, 58$ **47.** $9a - 5a + 4a$ $8a, 40$

48. $20a - 13a - 2a$ $5a, 25$ **49.** $3(a + 2) + 8(a + 7)$ **50.** $10(a + 2) + 2(a + 1)$

                                                       $11a + 62, 117$ $12a + 22, 82$

Exploration and Extension

Computation Puzzles **In Exercises 51 and 52, solve the puzzle. In each puzzle, you can use each natural number from 1 through 9 exactly once.**

✪ **51.**

6	+	2	×	5	=16
×		+		+	
1	+	9	−	7	=3
+		÷		−	
8	−	3	+	4	=9
=14		=5		=8	

✪ **52.**

8	−	6	+	7	=9
−		×		+	
5	+	4	÷	2	=7
×		−		−	
1	+	9	÷	3	=4
=3		=15		=6	

Mixed REVIEW

2. Divide by 5 or multiply by $\frac{1}{5}$.

In Exercises 1–4, state an operation that can be used to solve the equation. (2.4, 2.5)

1. $c + 2 = 6$ **2.** $5b = 75$ **3.** $\frac{a}{3} = 2$ **4.** $d - 4 = 10$
Subtraction   Multiplication   Addition

In Exercises 5–12, solve the equation. (2.4, 2.5)

5. $8n = 32$ 4   **6.** $m - 12 = 20$ 32   **7.** $3n = 2$ $\frac{2}{3}$ **8.** $y + 6 = 10$ 4

9. $x - 4 = 6$ 10   **10.** $\frac{t}{8} = 2$ 16   **11.** $y + 2 = 2$ 0   **12.** $\frac{z}{12} = 3$ 36

In Exercises 13–20, simplify the equation. Then solve it mentally. (1.5, 2.3)

13. $2f + 3f = 10$ $5f = 10, 2$ **14.** $12r - 3r = 81$ $9r = 81, 9$

15. $6g = 10 + 2$ $6g = 12, 2$ **16.** $\frac{t}{2} = 4 + 1$ $\frac{t}{2} = 5, 10$

17. $2s + 3s + s = 18$ $6s = 18, 3$ **18.** $8p + 2p - p = 9$ $9p = 9, 1$

19. $4h - 3h + 2h = 9$ $3h = 9, 3$ **20.** $20q + 9q - 12q = 51$ $17q = 51, 3$

Enrichment

ALTERNATIVE ASSESSMENT
Groups of three or four students can create their own puzzle (with the solution) similar to exercises 51, 52. This can be a small-group assessment activity.

2.7

Real-Life Modeling with Equations

▶ PACING the Lesson

Suggested Number of Days
Basic/Average 2   **Above Average** 1
Advanced 1

▶ PLANNING the Lesson
Lesson Plan 2.7, p. 15

 Goal 1

How to translate verbal sentences into algebraic equations

 Goal 2

How to model real-life situations with algebraic equations

What you should learn:

Why you should learn it:

You can use algebraic equations to solve real-life problems, such as deciding how many pairs of jeans to order for a clothing store.

Problem Solving
Writing a Model

Goal 1   Translating Verbal Sentences

A phrase does not usually contain a verb, but a sentence must contain a verb. In Lesson 2.6, you learned that many phrases can be modeled as algebraic expressions. In this lesson, you will learn how to model sentences as algebraic equations. Here are examples of an expression and an equation.

Verbal Phrase	**Algebraic Expression**
The cost of several cassettes at $12 each	$12x$

Verbal Sentence	**Algebraic Equation**
The cost of several cassettes at $12 each is $60.	$12x = 60$

Notice that you can solve an equation, but you cannot solve an expression. For instance, the solution of the equation $12x = 60$ is $x = 5$, but it doesn't make sense to try to "solve" the expression $12x$.

Example 1   *Modeling and Solving a Word Problem*

The price of one television set is $283. It costs $147 less than another set. What is the price of the more expensive set?

Solution

Verbal Model	Smaller price	$=$	Larger price	$- 147$

Labels	Smaller price $= 283$	(dollars)
	Larger price $= x$	(dollars)

Algebraic Model
$$283 = x - 147 \qquad \textit{Algebraic equation}$$
$$283 + 147 = x - 147 + 147 \qquad \textit{Add 147 to each side.}$$
$$430 = x \qquad \textit{Simplify.}$$

The price of the more expensive set is $430. You can check this by observing that $283 is $147 less than $430. ∎

ORGANIZER

Starters (reproduced below)
    Problem of the Day 2.7, p. 6
    Warm-Up Exercises 2.7, p. 6
Lesson Resources
    Color Transparencies
        Graphs for Example 2 and Ex. 29, 30, p. 9
    Math Log, p. 9
    Answer Masters 2.7, pp. 36, 37
    Extra Practice Copymaster 2.7, p. 15
    Reteaching Copymaster 2.7, p. 15
    Calculator
Special Populations
    Suggestions, Teacher's Edition, p. 48D

LESSON Notes

Point out that verbal sentences have verbs or verbal phrases such as "is, is equal to, is the same as, equals" that translate into the algebraic relationship denoted by the equal sign. You may wish to have students compare this page with page 76, where *phrases* rather than complete sentences were used

Example 1

Remind students that the verbal model in the example is a translation of the opening sentence describing the situation.

Emphasize that many real-life situations require that we make comparisons based upon verbal or written statements or data contained in graphs or tables.

Communicating about MATHEMATICS

Let students compare their real-life problem situations. Discuss how they are alike and how they are different.

Write Prompt
Algebra is a kind of language because it uses . . . and . . .

Real Life
Retail Sales

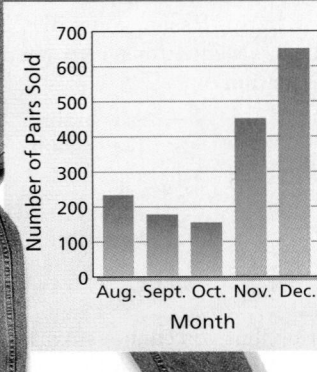

Monthly Jeans Sales

Number of Pairs Sold — Aug. Sept. Oct. Nov. Dec. — Month

Example 2   *Modeling a Real-Life Situation*

You work in a clothing store and are responsible for the jeans department. To earn a bonus in November–December, you need to sell at least 1.25 times as many pairs of jeans as you sold last November–December. The graph shows this year's sales, and you sold exactly as many pairs as was needed to make a bonus. How many pairs did you sell last November–December?

Solution   From the graph at the left, you can estimate that this November the store sold about 450 pairs of jeans, and this December the store sold about 650 pairs of jeans.

Verbal Model	$1.25 \cdot$	Number sold last year	$=$	Number sold this year	

Labels   Number sold last year $= n$ (pairs)
              Number sold this year $= 450 + 650 = 1100$ (pairs)

Algebraic Model $1.25 \cdot n = 1100$
$$\frac{1.25n}{1.25} = \frac{1100}{1.25}$$
$$n = 880$$

You sold 880 pairs of jeans last November–December.   ■

Communicating about MATHEMATICS

Cooperative Learning

▶ **SHARING IDEAS about the Lesson**

Modeling Real Life Work with a partner. Describe a real-life problem that fits the verbal model. Then assign labels to the model, write the equation, and solve the equation. Finally, explain how the solution of the equation helps you solve the real-life problem.

Answers vary.

A. | Miles driven this week | $+ 72 =$ | Miles driven last week |
|---|---|---|

B. | Number of tires | $\cdot$ | \$110 per tire | $=$ | Total cost |
|---|---|---|---|---|

EXERCISES

Guided Practice

▶ CHECK for Understanding

In Exercises 1–4, state whether the quantity is an expression or an equation. Solve or simplify.

1. $3 + x = 19$
Equation, 16

2. $5x - 3x + 6$
Expression, $2x + 6$

3. $2x = 18$
Equation, 9

4. $\frac{x}{3} = 7$
Equation, 21

In Exercises 5 and 6, write an algebraic equation that represents the verbal sentence. Then solve the equation.

5. The number of cars decreased by 21 is 84.
$c - 21 = 84$, 105

6. The cost of 10 T-shirts at x dollars each is $75.
$10x = 75$, 7.5

Independent Practice

In Exercises 7–12, match the sentence with an equation.

a. $7 = x + 5$ **b.** $\frac{x}{7} = 5$ **c.** $x - 7 = 5$ **d.** $7 = \frac{x}{5}$ **e.** $7x = 35$ **f.** $5x = 35$

7. The difference of x and 7 is 5. c

8. 5 times x equals 35. f

9. 7 is the sum of x and 5. a

10. 7 equals x divided by 5. d

11. The quotient of x and 7 is 5. b

12. The product of x and 7 is 35. e

In Exercises 13–18, write an algebraic equation that represents the verbal sentence. Then solve the equation. Variables vary.

13. The number of dogs increased by 9 is 20. $d + 9 = 20$, 11

14. 16 equals the number of tennis shoes decreased by 3. $16 = t - 3$, 19

15. The number of pencils divided by 12 is 4. $\frac{p}{12} = 4$, 48

16. The cost of 3 sweaters at x dollars each is $90.75. $3x = 90.75$, 30.25

17. y miles divided by 45 miles per hour equals 5 hours. $\frac{y}{45} = 5$, 225

18. 128 baseball cards is the sum of 65 baseball cards and x baseball cards. $128 = 65 + x$, 63

In Exercises 19–24, write a verbal sentence that represents the equation. See margin.

19. $f + 15 = 33$

20. $90 = s - 3$

21. $7c = 56$

22. $\frac{b}{9} = 8$

23. $11 + a = 23$

24. $21 = d - 18$

In Exercises 25 and 26, use a verbal model, labels, and an algebraic model to answer the question. See margin.

25. One number is 251 more than another number. The larger number is 420. What is the smaller number? 169

26. The product of a number and 38 is 912. Find the missing number. 24

Extra Practice

Reteaching

Answers

19. The sum of a number and 15 is 33.
20. 90 is the difference of a number and 3.
21. The product of 7 and a number is 56.
22. The quotient of a number and 9 is 8.
23. The sum of 11 and a number is 23.
24. 21 is the difference of a number and 18.
25. Larger number = smaller number + 251
Larger number: 420, smaller number: s
$420 = s + 251$
$169 = s$
Smaller number is 169.
26. A number × 38 = 912
A number: n
$n \cdot 38 = 912$
$n = 24$
Missing number is 24.

EXERCISE Notes

ASSIGNMENT GUIDE
Basic/Average:
Day 1: Ex. 7–12, 13–23 odd, 25, 26
Day 2: Ex. 27–34, 39–42
Above Average:
Ex. 13–23 odd, 25–30, 39–42
Advanced: Ex. 13–23 odd, 25–30, 39–42
Selected Answers: Ex. 1–6, 7–37 odd

Guided Practice
Use these exercises as a small-group check for students' readiness for the homework assignment.

Independent Practice
▶ **Ex. 7–12** Assign these exercises as a group.
▶ **Ex. 25, 26** Students will need your help with the format used in these exercises. Refer them to Example 2. This format is an integral part of the problem-solving plan outlined in Lesson 2.8. Give students plenty of practice with this kind of exercise.

► Ex. 29, 30

EXTENSION

Bring to class graphs of the type found in *USA-Today* that are in either bar graph or circle graph form and discuss the data from the graphs.

Integrated Review

Challenge the class to try mental math, or the format of Example 2, page 60, or using a calculator.

Exploration and Extension

Warn students that these exercises involve two operations.

Portfolio Opportunity: Math Log

In your own words, describe the difference between an algebraic expression and an algebraic equation.

Also available as a copymaster, page 9, Ex. 7

Geometry   In Exercises 27 and 28, use the verbal model to write an algebraic equation. Then use the guess, check, and revise method to solve the equation.

✪ **27.**   Perimeter $= 2 \left(\text{Width} + \text{Length} \right)$

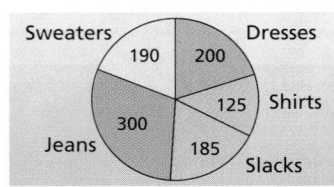
8

w | Perimeter is 25 inches.

$25 = 2(w + 8)$
$4.5 = w$

28.   Area $=$ Width $\cdot$ Length

w + 2

w | Area is 24 square units.

$24 = w(w + 2)$
$4 = w$

The Fashion Business   In Exercises 29 and 30, use the following information.

The company you work for designs a variety of clothes. Last week's sales (in units) are shown below. You expect the total sales for this week to be 500 units more than last week.

Sweaters 190 200 Dresses
125 Shirts
300
Jeans 185
Slacks

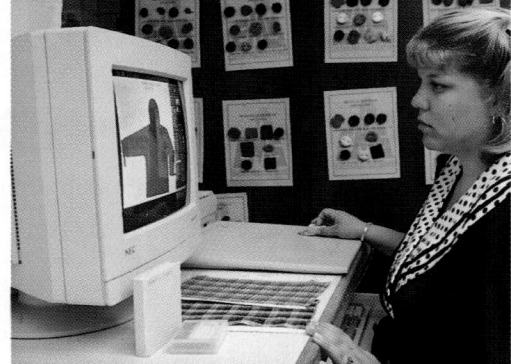

Many fashion designers use computers to design clothing.

✪ **29.**   In the following equation, what does n represent?   This week's sales
$n = (200 + 125 + 185 + 190 + 300) + 500$

✪ **30.**   How many of the 500 additional would you expect to be sweaters? Explain your reasoning.   95, $\dfrac{\text{Sweaters}}{\text{Last week's sales}} = \dfrac{190}{1000} = \dfrac{95}{500}$

Integrated Review   *Making Connections within Mathematics*

Equation Sense   In Exercises 31–38, solve the equation.

31. $x + 9 = 13$ 4   **32.** $x - 21 = 19$ 40   **33.** $12x = 48$ 4   **34.** $\frac{x}{8} = 10$ 80

35. $x + 3.4 = 6.6$ 3.2   **36.** $x - 5.5 = 6.6$ 12.1   **37.** $7.2x = 36$ 5   **38.** $\frac{x}{8.2} = 20$ 164

Exploration and Extension

Mental Math   In Exercises 39–42, write an algebraic equation that represents the verbal sentence. Use mental math to solve the equation.

$2x + 6 = 12, 3$ $7x - 6 = 8, 2$

✪ **39.** 2 times x, increased by 6, is 12.   ✪ **40.** The difference of 7 times x and 6 is 8.

✪ **41.** 5 times the sum of x and 4 is 25.   ✪ **42.** 8 times the difference of x and 2 is 8.

$5(x + 4) = 25, 1$ $8(x - 2) = 8, 3$

84   *Chapter 2 ▪ Investigations in Algebra*   ✪ More difficult exercises

2.8 A Problem-Solving Plan

► **PACING the Lesson**

Suggested Number of Days
Basic/Average 2   **Above Average** 1
Advanced 1

► **PLANNING the Lesson**

Lesson Plan 2.8, p. 16

What you should learn:

 Goal 1 How to use a systematic problem-solving plan

 Goal 2 How to use other problem-solving strategies such as "solving a simpler problem"

Why you should learn it:

Learning to be a systematic problem solver will help you in many real-life occupations, such as being a sales representative.

Real Life
Sales Bonus

Study Tip...
Problem Solving *An important part of your problem-solving plan is to be sure that you have actually **answered the question** posed in the real-life problem. For instance, in Example 1, the solution of the equation (x = 186,000) is not the answer to the question. The answer to the question is 456,000 + 186,000 or $642,000.*

Goal 1   **Using a Problem-Solving Plan**

In Lessons 2.6 and 2.7, you studied the three steps for algebraic modeling. These steps can be used as part of your **general problem-solving plan.**

> **A Problem-Solving Plan**
> 1. Ask yourself what you need to know to solve the problem. Then **write a verbal model** that will give you what you need to know.
> 2. **Assign labels** to each part of your verbal model.
> 3. Use the labels to **write an algebraic model** based on your verbal model.
> 4. **Solve** the algebraic model.
> 5. **Answer** the original question.
> 6. **Check** that your answer is reasonable.

Example 1   *Using a Problem-Solving Plan*

You are a sales representative for a publisher. You receive a salary plus a bonus, which is one-twentieth of the amount by which you exceed your previous year's sales. Last year your sales totaled $456,000. This year you earned a bonus of $9300. What were your sales this year?

Solution

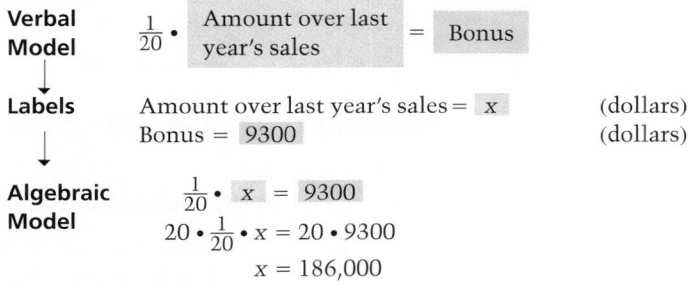

Verbal Model $\frac{1}{20} \cdot$ | Amount over last year's sales | $=$ | Bonus |

Labels   Amount over last year's sales $= x$ (dollars)
Bonus $= 9300$ (dollars)

Algebraic Model
$$\frac{1}{20} \cdot x = 9300$$
$$20 \cdot \frac{1}{20} \cdot x = 20 \cdot 9300$$
$$x = 186,000$$

You sold $186,000 more than last year. Thus, your sales for this year were 456,000 + 186,000 or $642,000. ∎

ORGANIZER

Starters (reproduced below)
Problem of the Day 2.8, p. 6
Warm-Up Exercises 2.8, p. 6
Lesson Resources
Teaching Tools
Problem-solving plan, pp. T5, C7
Math Log, p. 9
Answer Masters 2.8, p. 38
Extra Practice Copymaster 2.8, p. 16
Reteaching Copymaster 2.8, p. 16
Calculator
Special Populations
Suggestions, Teacher's Edition, p. 48D

LESSON Notes

Have students copy the problem-solving plan into their journals. Emphasize the importance of knowing the sequence of steps. You may wish to point out that the verbal model is basically a sentence, and the algebraic model is an equation.

Example 1

EXTENSION
Ask students: Suppose you sold $230,000 more than last year. What would your bonus be? What would be your sales this year?
bonus, $11,500; sales, $686,000

---

86 Chapter 2

PROBLEM SOLVING

Draw students' attention to the first paragraph. Example 2 applies the problem-solving strategy of "solve a simpler problem." Be sure to remind students of their nonalgebraic problem-solving options. The *algebraic modeling* plan presented in this lesson plays a major part in this course. But it is optional, and will prove more suitable to some real-life problems than to others. Not all students will necessarily find it helpful. Its great value lies in a very systematic, structured approach. However, be sure to allow students to solve problems from their own perspectives. Often, a teacher can gain insights into the ways students view mathematics by listening to their reasoning and helping them communicate their ideas.

Example 2

Remind students that the median income lies in the middle of all the incomes reported. You may want to explain that the four-year degree figure of $30,000 quoted in this example is based on the fees charged by several state colleges, but are not at all typical of private colleges.

Communicating about MATHEMATICS

Allow students to discuss the added benefits of obtaining other advanced degrees. Remind them that they must make estimates of the cost of securing additional education. Discuss how many years each degree might take. For example, an associate degree would require two years after high school, a bachelor degree four years after high school, etc.

Writing Prompt
Today's lesson was . . . because . . .

Real Life
Planning a Career

Eight years after working with only a high school diploma, Deloris McClam went back to school. She earned her bachelor's degree in 1987. By 1993, her salary was over $60,000. She maintains that her degree has made a significant difference in her career.
(Source: Black Enterprise)

Goal **2** **Using Other Problem-Solving Strategie**

In this (and every) lesson, don't be afraid to try a variety of problem-solving strategies. For instance, you might try "guess, check, and revise" or "solving a simpler problem."

Example **2** *Decision Making*

It is 1990, and you have just graduated from high school. Explain how to use the table to decide whether a college degree is a good financial investment. *(Source: U.S. Bureau of Census)*

Education	Median Income (1990)
9th to 12th Grade, No Diploma	$5,904
High school graduate	$12,924
Some College, No Degree	$15,360
Associate Degree	$20,064
Bachelor's Degree	$25,392
Master's Degree	$33,864
Doctorate Degree	$46,260
Professional Degree	$59,532

Solution **Simplify the Problem.** This is a complicated question, with many unknowns, such as the cost of college, the rate of inflation, and the actual salaries you will receive. However, to obtain a general sense of the answer, assume that a 4-year degree will cost $30,000. Assume that you work for 45 years with a high school degree or work for 41 years with a college degree.

High School Degree $45 (\$12,924) = \$581,580$
College Degree $41 (\$25,392) - \$30,000 = \$1,011,072$

Although this analysis is overly simple, it still appears clear that a college degree is a good financial investment. ∎

P *Communicating* about **MATHEMATICS**

▶ **SHARING IDEAS about the Lesson**   Answers vary.

It's Up to You Suppose you have just obtained a bachelor's degree. Use the above table to decide whether a master's degree (requiring 2 years) is a good financial investment.

◆ **OPTION: Extra Examples**

Here is an extra example similar to Example 1.

Using a Problem-Solving Plan
You are a sales representative. You receive a bonus that is one-fifteenth of the amount by which you exceed your last year's sales. This year your sales totaled $477,500. If this year's bonus was $8,500, what were your total sales last year?

Verbal Model
$\frac{1}{15}$ • Amount over last year's sales $=$ bonus

Labels
Amount over last year's sales $= x$ (dollars)
Bonus $= 8500$ (dollars)

Algebraic Model
$\frac{1}{15} \cdot x = 8500$

$15 \cdot \frac{1}{15} \cdot x = 15 \cdot 8500$

$x = 127,500$

You sold $127,500 more than last year. Thus, your sales last year were $477,500 - 127,500$ or $350,000$.

EXERCISES

Guided Practice

CHECK for Understanding

1. Order the steps for a general problem-solving plan. d, a, f, c, b, e
   - **a.** Assign labels.
   - **b.** Answer the original question.
   - **c.** Solve the algebraic model.
   - **d.** Write a verbal model.
   - **e.** Check your solution.
   - **f.** Write an algebraic model.

2. When using the problem-solving plan, why is it important to *answer the original question*?
   The solution of the equation may not be the answer to the question.

Independent Practice

Getting an A   **In Exercises 3–7, consider the following question.**

Your history grade is based on five 100-point tests. To earn an *A*, you need a total of 460 points. Your first four test scores are 89, 85, 92, and 97. What is the minimum score you need to earn an *A*?

3. Write a verbal model that relates the total points needed, the number of points obtained, and the final test score. Points needed = Points obtained + Final score

4. Assign labels to the three parts of your model. Respectively: 460, 89 + 85 + 92 + 97, x (points)

5. Use the labels to translate your verbal model into an algebraic model. 460 = (89 + 85 + 92 + 97) + x

6. Solve the algebraic model. 97

7. Your final test score is 98 points. Did you get an *A*?
   Yes

Taking a Hike   **In Exercises 8–12, consider the following question.**

You are taking a three-day hiking and camping trip. The trail is 29 miles long. On the first day you hike 8 miles. On the second day you hike 11 miles. How much farther do you need to go?

8. Write a verbal model that relates the trail length, the number of miles traveled, and the distance left to hike. See below.

9. Assign labels to the three parts of your model. Respectively: 29, 8 + 11, x (miles)

10. Use the labels to translate your verbal model into an algebraic model. 29 = (8 + 11) + x

11. Solve the algebraic model. 10

12. Explain why your solution is reasonable.
    It is between 0 and 29.

. Trail length = Miles traveled + Distance left

The Appalachian National Scenic Trail extends about 2000 miles from Mt. Katahdin in Maine to Springer Mountain in Georgia.

2.8 ▪ *A Problem-Solving Plan*   **87**

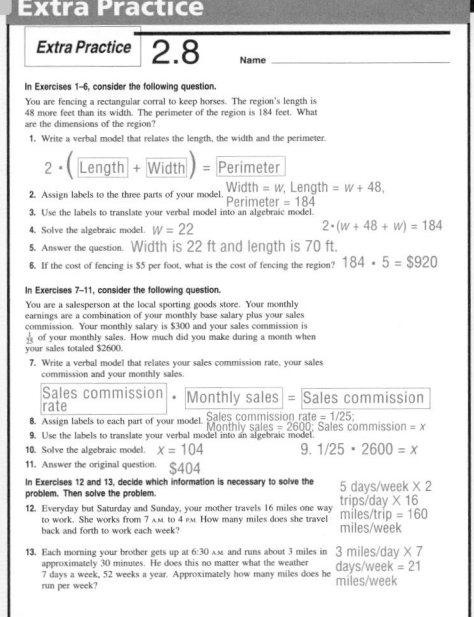
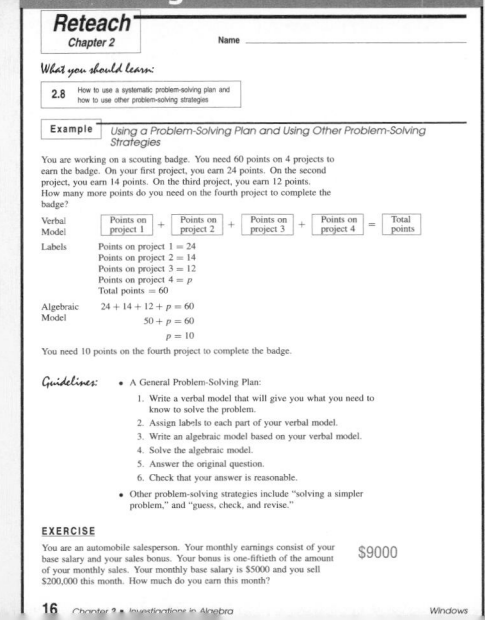
Lesson 2.8   **87**

88 Chapter 2

▶ **Ex. 13–17** Once again, emphasize the need for an appropriate solution format for these problems.
▶ **Ex. 18, 19** Ask students to write down the information that was not needed to solve the problem.

Integrated Review

▶ **Ex. 24–27** Make sure students know the formula for the area of a square. Then encourage them to use the square-root key on their calculators.

EXTENSION
Have students find the perimeter of each square.

Exploration and Extension

Assign these exercises as an in-class five-minute small-group activity. This could also be an opportunity for a group project on finding needed information.

PROBLEM SOLVING
Reasonableness of Answers Students could also be encouraged to write their own type of "reasonable answer" problem. This is a most important problem-solving step, especially now that calculators are being widely used.

Portfolio Opportunity: Math Log

A problem asks you to find the total number of hours that a mechanic worked on your car. You arrive at an answer of 536 hours. This answer does not make sense. Name some reasons why you may have arrived at this unreasonable answer.

Also available as a copymaster, page 9, Ex. 8

Short Quiz

Covers Lessons 2.7 and 2.8

Available as a copymaster, page 21

Earning a Commission **In Exercises 13–17, consider the following question.**

You are an assistant manager at a computer software store. Your annual earnings consist of your base salary and your sales commission. Your commission is one-twentieth of the amount of your annual sales. Your base salary is $16,500 and you sell $150,000 of merchandise this year. How much money did you make?

13. Write a verbal model that relates your sale commission, your commission rate, and your annual sales. **13., 14.** See Additional An
14. Assign labels to each part of your model.
15. Use the labels to translate your verbal model into an algebraic model. $x = \frac{1}{20} \cdot 150$
16. Solve the algebraic model. **7500**
17. Answer the original question and check your answer. $24,000

Necessary Information **In Exercises 18 and 19, decide which information is necessary to solve the problem. Then solve the problem.**

18. Every morning, except Sunday, your sister gets up at 5:30 A.M. and travels 7 miles to the skating rink to practice. Each practice lasts $2\frac{1}{2}$ hours. How many miles does she travel each week in order to practice? **84**

19. Your Spanish club is selling T-shirts. Each shirt sells for $9.50. The club needs to rais $2,000 for a trip. You sell 17 T-shirts and have 3 left to sell. How much money have you raised? **$161.50**

Integrated Review *Making Connections within Mathematics*

Mental Math **In Exercises 20–23, evaluate the expression.**

20. $\frac{1}{3}(84)$ **28**
21. $\frac{1}{5}(375)$ **75**
22. $\frac{1}{20}(72,000)$ **3600**
23. $\frac{1}{15}(81,000)$ **5400**

Geometry **In Exercises 24–27, find the length of each side of the square.**

24.

Area is 225 square inches.

15 in.

25.

Area is 441 square centimeters.

21 cm

26.

Area is 96.43 square meters.

≈9.82 m

27.

Area is 51.98 square feet.

≈7.21 ft

Exploration and Extension

P *Is Your Answer Reasonable?* **In Exercises 28–30, decide if the answer seems reasonable. Explain your reasoning.** **28., 29.** See margin.

✪ 28. A problem asks you to find the time it takes to drive a car from Washington, D.C., to Portland, Oregon, and your answer is 12 hours.
✪ 29. A problem asks you to find the area of your bedroom, and your answer is 650 square feet.
✪ 30. A problem asks you to find the average age of the students in your class, and your answer is 13.46. Answers vary.

✪ More difficult exercise
P Portfolio Opportunit

▶ **Enrichment**

Have students write a song (possibly rap) or a poem (rhyme) or a comedic presentation about a creative word problem (together with the appropriate solution) such as that used in Ex. 13–17. Student groups should be prepared to perform their work for the class.

Answers
28. No, the distance is too far (over 2000 miles) to be driven in 12 hours.
29. No, the area is too big (more than the area of a 25-foot square) to be a reasonably sized bedroom.

2.9

Exploring Variables and Inequalities

What you should learn:

Goal 1 How to solve simple inequalities

Goal 2 How to use inequalities as algebraic models to solve real-life problems

Why you should learn it:

You can use inequalities to solve real-life problems, such as describing the number of yards needed for a first down.

Goal 1 **Solving Simple Inequalities**

Some sentences are better modeled with **inequalities** instead of equations. An inequality is formed when an **inequality symbol** is placed between two expressions. Here are four kinds of inequality symbols.

Inequality Symbol	**Meaning**
$<$	is less than
$\leq$	is less than or equal to
$>$	is greater than
$\geq$	is greater than or equal to

A **solution** of an inequality is a number that produces a true statement when it is substituted for the variable in the inequality. For instance, 2 is one of the many solutions of $x < 5$ because $2 < 5$ is a true statement.

Finding all solutions of an inequality is called **solving the inequality.** You can do this in much the same way you solve an equation. That is, you can add or subtract the same number from each side, or you can multiply or divide both sides by the same positive number.

Reading Inequalities

The inequality in part c is read as "16 is greater than x." This inequality can also be written as $x < 16$, which is read as "x is less than 16."

Example 1 *Solving Inequalities*

a.
$x + 4 \leq 6$	*Original inequality*
$x + 4 - 4 \leq 6 - 4$	*Subtract 4 from each side.*
$x \leq 2$	*Solution of inequality*

b.
$3x \geq 12$	*Original inequality*
$\frac{3x}{3} \geq \frac{12}{3}$	*Divide both sides by 3.*
$x \geq 4$	*Solution of inequality*

c.
$14 > x - 2$	*Original inequality*
$14 + 2 > x - 2 + 2$	*Add 2 to each side.*
$16 > x$	*Solution of inequality*

2.9 • Exploring Variables and Inequalities **89**

PACING the Lesson
Suggested Number of Days
Basic/Average 0 **Above Average** 1
Advanced 1

PLANNING the Lesson
Lesson Plan 2.9, p. 17

ORGANIZER

Starters (reproduced below)
  Problem of the Day 2.9, p. 6
  Warm-Up Exercises 2.9, p. 6
Lesson Resources
  Color Transparencies
    Diagram for Example 2 and Ex. 80, 81, p. 10
  Math Log, p. 9
  Answer Masters 2.9, p. 39
  Extra Practice Copymaster 2.9, p. 17
  Reteaching Copymaster 2.9, p. 17
  Calculator
Special Populations
  Suggestions, Teacher's Edition, p. **48**D

LESSON Notes

Remind students of the Golden Rule of Equations—what you do to one side of an equation you must do to the other side. Explain to them that the same rule applies to inequalities, with the exception of multiplication or division by a negative number.

Motivate the use of inequalities by posing appropriate questions: "If a model plane costs $5.49 (including tax) and you have $3, for what amount should you sell another one of your models in order to make the purchase?" At least $2.49

Examples involving future performance on exams is another situation involving inequalities that students will easily understand.

Example 1

Addressing Misconceptions

Emphasize that an inequality may have infinitely many solutions. Have students list some solutions to such inequalities as $x < 8$ to verify their understanding of solution in this context. In particular, not only are the values, 7, 6, 5, 4, etc., solutions, but values such as $7\frac{1}{4}$, 6.23, and $\sqrt{5}$ are, too.

Have students graph several solutions of Example **1a** on a number line. Ask them on which side of $x = 2$ the solutions occur. Have students repeat the process for Examples **1b** and **1c**. Ask them to compare the graphs' relationships. "Less than" solutions are on the left; "greater than" solutions are on the right

---

Ask students to identify situations which can be described with inequalities.

Example 2

Although many students may be able to solve the equations using mental math, encourage them to use algebra in order to develop skills for later use in more complex situations. For this example, you may need to have a student briefly explain the appropriate rules of football.

Communicating about MATHEMATICS

Inform students that a "theorem" in mathematics is a statement that can be shown to be true, usually using proof or other deductive reasoning.

Writing Prompt

Daily temperature ranges are better modeled by inequalities than by equations. Can you think of some other real-life situations which are best modeled by inequalities?

Real Life
Football

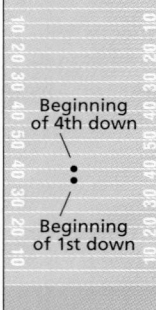

Beginning
of 4th down

Beginning
of 1st down

Goal **2** **Modeling Real Life with Inequalities**

Example **2** *Modeling a Real-Life Situation*

Your team begins its first down on its own 36th yard line. By the fourth down, the team is beginning on its own 40th yard line. How many additional yards must the team gain to be awarded a new first down?

Solution Going into its fourth down, the team has gained 4 yards. By the end of the fourth down, the team needs to have gained at least 10 yards to be awarded a new first down.

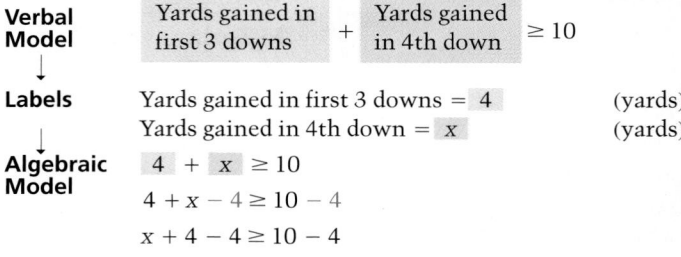

Verbal Model | Yards gained in first 3 downs | + | Yards gained in 4th down | ≥ 10

Labels Yards gained in first 3 downs = 4   (yards)
Yards gained in 4th down = x (yards)

Algebraic Model $4 + x \geq 10$
$4 + x - 4 \geq 10 - 4$
$x + 4 - 4 \geq 10 - 4$
$x \geq 6$

The team must gain at least 6 yards in its fourth down. ∎

Communicating about MATHEMATICS

▶ **SHARING IDEAS about the Lesson**

The Triangle Inequality A theorem in geometry states the sum of the lengths of any two sides of a triangle must be greater than the length of the third side of the triangle. For instance, in the triangle at the left, you can write the inequalities

$$a + b > c, \quad a + c > b, \quad \text{and} \quad b + c > a.$$

In the following triangles, what does the Triangle Inequality allow you to say about the value of x?

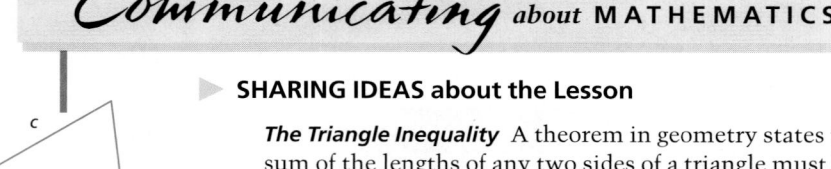

A. $11 > x > 1$ **B.** $8 > x > 2$

◤ **OPTION: Extra Examples**

Here are additional examples similar to Example 1.

Solving Inequalities

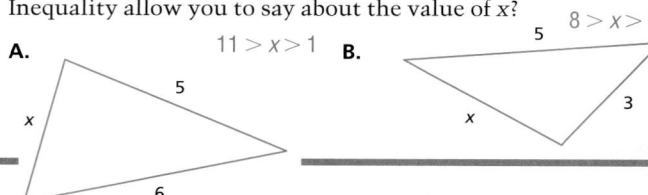

a. $x + 8 \geq 14$ Original inequality
$x + 8 - 8 \geq 14 - 8$ Subtract 8 from each side.
$x \geq 6$ Solution of inequality

b. $3m \leq 48$ Original inequality
$\frac{3m}{3} \leq \frac{48}{3}$ Divide each side by 3.
$m \leq 16$ Solution of inequality

c. $32 \geq k + 5$ Original inequality
$32 - 5 \geq k + 5 - 5$ Subtract 5 from each side.
$27 \geq k$ Solution of inequality

EXERCISES

Guided Practice

▶ CHECK for Understanding

P **1.** Write the four kinds of inequality symbols and their meanings. See page 89.

P **2.** *True or False?*   An inequality can have many solutions. True

In Exercises 3–6, state whether the number is a solution of the inequality
$x - 5 < 11$.

3. 11 Yes   **4.** 16 No   **5.** 15 Yes   **6.** 30 No

In Exercises 7–9, solve the inequality.

7. $x + 4 \leq 7$ $x \leq 3$ **8.** $3x \geq 10$ $x \geq 3\frac{1}{3}$ **9.** $9 < x - 5$ $x > 14$

P **10. Problem Solving**   State an example of an inequality used in a real-life situation.
Answers vary. No more than 10 people are allowed on the elevator.

Independent Practice

In Exercises 11–16, state two solutions of the inequality. Answers vary.

11. $x < 4$ $1, 3\frac{1}{2}$ **12.** $y \geq 12.3$ 12.35, 20   **13.** $45 < x$ 46, 1000

14. $100 \geq a$ 100, 6   **15.** $t < 2\frac{1}{2}$ $2\frac{1}{4}, 2$ **16.** $y \geq 0$ 0, 7

In Exercises 17–34, solve the inequality.

17. $x + 5 < 11$ $x < 6$ **18.** $s - 4 > 9$ $s > 13$ **19.** $7y \leq 42$ $y \leq 6$

20. $\frac{x}{8} \geq 11$ $x \geq 88$ **21.** $22 \leq b + 22$ $b \geq 0$ **22.** $16 \geq s - 3$ $s \leq 19$

23. $56 < 14t$ $t > 4$ **24.** $45 > 5m$ $m < 9$ **25.** $x + 25 \geq 26$ $x \geq 1$

26. $n - 34 \leq 16$ $n \leq 50$ **27.** $17y \geq 68$ $y \geq 4$ **28.** $\frac{x}{2} \leq 52$ $x \leq 104$

29. $x + 3.4 > 5.8$ $x > 2.4$ **30.** $y - 13.7 < 5.4$ $y < 19.1$ **31.** $8.9k \geq 17.8$ $k \geq 2$

32. $\frac{a}{2.5} \leq 4.2$ $a \leq 10.5$ **33.** $3.8 < \frac{x}{5.5}$ $x > 20.9$ **34.** $138.6 > 5.5y$ $y < 25.2$

In Exercises 35–40, write an inequality that represents the sentence. Then solve the inequality.

35. c plus 5 is greater than or equal to 19.36. $c + 5 \geq 19.36, c \geq 14.36$

36. The difference of b and 7 is less than 24. $b - 7 < 24, b < 31$

37. x times 2 is less than 42. $2x < 42, x < 21$

38. The product of y and 3 is greater than 39. $3y > 39, y > 13$

39. 20 is greater than or equal to m divided by 6. $20 \geq \frac{m}{6}, 120 \geq m$

40. 15 is less than or equal to the quotient of x and 5. $15 \leq \frac{x}{5}, 75 \leq x$

P Portfolio Opportunity   **2.9 ▪** *Exploring Variables and Inequalities*   **91**

Lesson 2.9   **91**

▶ **Ex. 55** Assign this exercise as a five-minute practice problem in class for small groups. You may need to review the formula $d = rt$ with the students.

Integrated Review

Assign these exercises as a group. This provides an inequality connection to previous lessons in this chapter.

Exploration and Extension

These exercises connect to the Communicating about Mathematics feature in this lesson. Be sure to review this feature in class before assigning these exercises. Ask students to write a numerical "test" for deciding whether or not the lengths could be side-lengths for a triangle.

Portfolio Opportunity: Math Log

In Chapter 2, the conditional equations you have solved have had one solution. How are the solutions of inequalities different?

Also available as a copymaster, page 9, Ex. 9

Alternative Assessment

Chapter 2 Group Assessment
A problem-solving activity for 3 or 4 students that uses inequalities to model a real-life situation.

Chapter 2 Individual Assessment
A similar follow-up activity for individual students. Adds incentive for the group activity and measures individual competence in the activity.

Available as copymasters, pages 61, 62

In Exercises 41–46, write a sentence that represents the inequality. See margin.

✪ 41. $d + 11 < 52$ ✪ 42. $f - 5 \geq 29$ ✪ 43. $3h \leq 60$

✪ 44. $\frac{p}{36} > 2$ ✪ 45. $17 > c - 31$ ✪ 46. $23 \leq e + 9$

Number Sense   **In Exercises 47–54, state whether the inequality $x \leq 5.6$ is true for the value of x.**

47. 5 Yes   48. 5.65 No   49. 5.61 No   50. 5.60 Yes

51. 5.59 Yes   52. 5.7 No   53. 5.06 Yes   54. 0.56 Yes

✪ 55. *Bike Racing*   You are a member of the "Hot Wheelers" bicycling team. Your team competes in a relay race with 4 other teams. The race consists of 20 miles of semi-rugged terrain. The table at the right shows the times that each team took to finish.

Team Name	Time
Hot Wheelers	69 minutes
Bikin' Buddies	85 minutes
Cruisin' Kids	76 minutes
Brave Bikers	71 minutes
Flyin' Friends	81 minutes

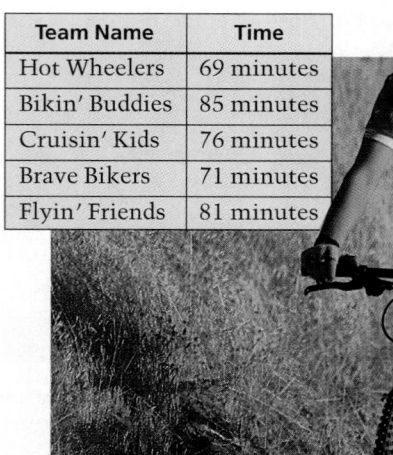

a. Who was the first place team? Hot Wheelers

b. Convert the first place team's time from minutes to hours. 1.15 hours

c. Write verbal and algebraic models to show how many fewer minutes the last place team would need to place first.

d. Write verbal and algebraic models to show how many fewer minutes the Cruisin' Kids would need to tie or beat the Brave Bikers.

e. Using the formula $D = r \cdot t$, find the average speed of the Hot Wheelers. ≈ 17.4 mph

55. **c., d.** See Additional Answers.

Integrated Review   *Making Connections within Mathematics*

Reasoning   **In Exercises 56–61, complete the statement with $<$, $>$, or $=$.**

56. $6 \cdot 9$? $13 \cdot 4$ $>$ 57. $124 - 14$? $50 \cdot 2$ $>$ 58. $\frac{120}{6}$? $\frac{342}{18}$ $>$

59. $3(x)$? $3(x + 1)$ $<$ 60. $4x + 4x$? $5x + 3x + 2$ $<$ 61. $6(x + 2)$? $6x + 2$ $>$

Exploration and Extension

Triangle Inequality   **In Exercises 62–65, decide whether the numbers could be lengths of the sides of a triangle. The *Triangle Inequality* states that the sum of the lengths of *any* two sides must be greater than the length of the third side.**

✪ 62. $4, 5, 6$ Yes   ✪ 63. $2, 3, 6$ No   ✪ 64. $4, 6, 12$ No   ✪ 65. $8, 9, 11$ Yes

▶ **Enrichment**

Give students scissors, straws, and rulers. Have them work in small groups to cut lengths of 2, 3, and 6 inches as in Exercise 63. Ask them to see whether the straw model verifies their answers to Exercises 62 and 65.

Answers
41. The sum of d and 11 is less than 52.
42. The difference of f and 5 is greater than or equal to 29.
43. The product of 3 and h is less than or equal to 60.
44. The quotient of p and 36 is greater than 2.
45. 17 is greater than the difference of c and 31.
46. 23 is less than or equal to the sum of e and 9.

2

Chapter Summary

What did you learn?

Skills

1. Use the Distributive Property to simplify expressions. **(2.1)**
2. Simplify expressions by adding like terms. **(2.2)**
3. Use substitution to check a solution of an equation. **(2.3)**
4. Solve equations
   - using mental math. **(2.3)**
   - using addition or subtraction. **(2.4)**
   - using multiplication or division. **(2.5)**
5. Write algebraic models.
   - Translate verbal phrases as algebraic expressions. **(2.6)**
   - Translate verbal sentences as algebraic equations. **(2.7)**
   - Translate verbal sentences as algebraic inequalities. **(2.9)**
6. Solve inequalities.

Problem-Solving Strategies

7. Write equations or inequalities as algebraic models of real-life situations. **(2.4–2.9)**
8. Use other problem-solving strategies such as guess, check, and revise and solve a simpler problem. **(2.1–2.9)**

Exploring Data

9. Use a general problem-solving plan to solve real-life problems. **(2.8–2.9)**
10. Use tables and graphs to interpret and organize data. **(2.2, 2.7–2.9)**

Why did you learn it?

In this chapter, you saw how companies can use mathematics to help plan for future sales or order merchandise. You also saw how a sales representative can use mathematics to determine his or her bonus, how you can use mathematics to help determine the financial value of further education, and how a football team can use mathematics to determine the number of yards needed to make a first down. As you continue studying this book, you will see many other examples that point out that algebra and geometry are not just useful to engineers and scientists. They can be useful to anyone—in a wide variety of real-life situations.

How does it fit into the bigger picture of mathematics?

In this chapter, you studied the three basic building blocks of algebra: expressions, equations, and inequalities. You were also introduced to techniques that can be used to solve simple equations and inequalities. Most of the equations and inequalities in this chapter can be solved with mental math. In addition to using mental math, be sure that you can also solve equations and inequalities using systematic techniques, such as adding the same number to both sides. The value of these techniques will become clear in later chapters when you study more difficult equations.

COOPERATIVE LEARNING
Encourage students to study together. Emphasize the importance of teaching a classmate how to perform a skill or how to recall a procedure. When students work together, everyone wins. The students receiving help get additional instruction, and the students giving help gain a deeper understanding of the skills and concepts involved.

Chapter SUMMARY

This chapter laid the foundations for algebraic modeling. A major element in this foundation is a student's ability to solve simple equations, using either mental math or the more systematic technique of isolating the variable by generating equivalent equations. To this end, students were shown how to use the Distributive Property and the properties of equality to write equivalent expressions, ensuring that the "Golden Rule" of equations is obeyed—that whatever is done to one side of an equation must be done to the other. With this technique, students were empowered to deal with simple single-operation equations. Another major element in the foundation for algebraic modeling is the ability to translate from the verbal to the symbolic. Students were given practice in this technique before being introduced to the writing of simple algebraic models, both equations and inequalities. They were shown how to identify and label elements of the verbal model and proceed to the writing of a simple equation. This technique was offered them as a powerful and systematic tool in real-life problem solving.

Have students begin this Review in class and complete it as a homework assignment.

ASSIGNMENT GUIDE

Basic/Average:
Ex. 11–19 odd, 23–27 odd, 33–43 odd, 59–65 odd, 45–53 odd, 68–72, 80, 81

Above Average:
Ex. 11–19 odd, 23–27 odd, 33–43 odd, 59–65 odd, Ex. 45–53 odd, 68–72, 80, 81

Advanced:
Ex. 13–19 odd, 30–32, 33–43 odd, 59–63 odd, Ex. 45–53 odd, 73–78, 80, 81

Resources

Color Transparencies
  Diagrams for Ex. 80, 81, p. 10
Answer Masters, pp. 41, 42

In Exercises 1–4, use the Distributive Property to rewrite the expression. (2.1)

1. $3(9 + 10)$ $27 + 30$ **2.** $7(5 + 8)$ $35 + 56$ **3.** $4(x + 6)$ $4x + 24$ **4.** $2(y + 12)$ $2y + 24$

In Exercises 5–16, simplify the expression. (2.1, 2.2)

5. $3m + 8m$ $11m$

6. $12x + 5x$ $17x$

7. $18x^2 + 12x + 12x^2$ $30x^2 + 12x$

8. $5r^2 + 2r + r^2 + 9r^2$ $15r^2 + 2r$

9. $x^2 + x + 3x + 7x^2$ $8x^2 + 4x$

10. $2m + 4m + 7m + 9m^2$ $9m^2 + 13m$

11. $16w + 10 + 4w + 12$ $20w + 22$

12. $9 + r + 47 + 39r$ $40r + 56$

13. $3(a + 4b) + 4(3a + b)$ $15a + 16b$

14. $9(x + 2y) + 2(9x + y)$ $27x + 20y$

15. $3(x + y) + 2x + y$ $5x + 4y$

16. $4(s + t) + 5s$ $9s + 4t$

Mental Math **In Exercises 17–20, decide whether the given value is a solution. (2.3, 2.9)**

17. $4x + 7 = 43; x = 9$ Yes

18. $12m - 16 = 36; m = 4$ No

19. $\frac{s}{2} - 24 < 8; s = 64$ No

20. $\frac{36}{t} + 10 \geq 16; t = 6$ Yes

In Exercises 21–29, use mental math to solve the equation. (2.3)

21. $17 + p = 25$ 8

22. $q + 11 = 35$ 24

23. $y - 17 = 34$ 51

24. $16 - z = 9$ 7

25. $7m = 63$ 9

26. $64 = 16m$ 4

27. $\frac{x}{8} = 7$ 56

28. $\frac{n}{5} = 6$ 30

29. $\frac{72}{r} = 18$ 4

Raising the Vasa **In Exercises 30–32, use the following information. (2.3, 2.4)**

The *Vasa*, a Swedish war vessel, was one of the largest warships of its time. However, in 1628, the *Vasa* sank on its maiden voyage. It never fought a battle. In 1961, restoration crews raised it from the bottom of the Stockholm Harbor. It took 18 years to completely restore the hull of the vessel.

30. How many years was the *Vasa* underwater? 333

31. How long ago did the *Vasa* sink? Answers vary.

32. In what year was the restoration on the hull of the vessel completed? 1979

A Swedish Warship **This model of the Vasa is one-tenth the original size. It took four years to build.**

In Exercises 33–40, write an algebraic model for the phrase or sentence. (2.6, 2.7, 2.9) Variables vary.

33. The sum of a number and 71 $n + 71$

34. The difference of 15 and a number $15 - n$

35. Eight students receive an equal share. $\frac{n}{8}$

36. Three times more than your friend has $3n$

37. The difference of a number and 16 is 19.

38. Twelve plus another number is 51. $12 + n$

39. The product of a number and 7 is 84.

40. The quotient of 35 and a number is 7. $\frac{35}{n} = $

37. $n - 16 = 19$ **39.** $7n = 84$

In Exercises 41–44, write an algebraic equation or inequality for the verbal sentence. Then solve. (2.7, 2.9)

41. The quotient of a number and 6 is equal to 3. $\frac{n}{6} = 3$, 18

42. The product of a number and 8 is equal to 72. $8n = 72$, 9

43. The difference of a number and 15 is less than or equal to 3. $n - 15 \leq 3$, $n \leq 18$

44. The product of a number and the sum of 7 and 8 is greater than 45. $n(7 + 8) > 45$, $n > 3$

In Exercises 45–56, solve the equation. Then check your solution. (2.3, 2.4, 2.5)

45. $x + 34 = 82$ 48

46. $m + 92 = 131$ 39

47. $37 = y - 15$ 52

48. $z - 39 = 61$ 100

49. $14.2 + t = 29.1$ 14.9

50. $19.68 = s - 14.58$ 34.26

51. $20x = 420$ 21

52. $18x = 711$ 39.5

53. $\frac{r}{12} = 12$ 144

54. $\frac{x}{1} = 1$ 1

55. $\frac{n}{2.2} = 3.3$ 7.26

56. $5.5m = 100.1$ 18.2

In Exercises 57–65, solve the inequality. (2.9)

57. $x + 5 > 14$ $x > 9$

58. $71 \leq x + 49$ $x \geq 22$

59. $y - 23 < 14.4$ $y < 37.4$

60. $r - 1.1 \geq 3.02$ $r \geq 4.12$

61. $3x > 18$ $x > 6$

62. $12x \leq 144$ $x \leq 12$

63. $\frac{x}{8} < 5$ $x < 40$

64. $\frac{x}{2} \geq 54$ $x \geq 108$

65. $\frac{x}{4.4} > 12.5$ $x > 55$

Geometry **In Exercises 66 and 67, write simplified expressions for the perimeter and area of the region. (2.1, 2.2)**

66.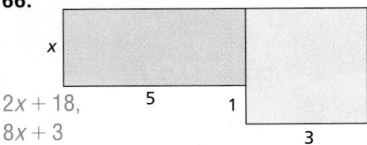
$2x + 18$,
$8x + 3$

67.
$2x + 26$,
$11x + 8$

Savings Plan **In Exercises 68–72, consider the following question. (2.8)**

You are saving your money to buy a portable CD player. You have a paper route and you earn $14.50 a week. The portable CD player costs $135 including tax. You spend $5 a week and save the rest of your money. In how many weeks will you have enough money to buy the CD player? **68., 69.** See margin.

68. Write a verbal model that relates the price of the portable CD player, the amount you save each week, and the number of weeks you need to save your money.

69. Assign labels to each part of your model. $135 \leq (14.50 - 5)n$

70. Use the verbal model to write an algebraic model.

71. Solve the algebraic model. $n \geq \approx 14.2$

72. Answer the question and check your answer.   15

✪ More difficult exercises

Fashion Sales   **In Exercises 73–78, use the following information.**

The Gap is a popular retail clothing company. It specializes in jeans, sweatsuits, shirts, sweaters, and other casual apparel. The table gives information about *The Gap*. *(Source: The Gap, Inc.)*

74. $P = S - C$

75. $1789.5 million,
$2289.1 million,
$2749.3 million,
$3057 million,
$3518 million

Year	1990	1991	1992	1993	1994
Sales (millions)	$1,934	$2,519	$2,960	$3,300	$3,800
Number of Stores	1,092	1,216	1,307	1,420	1,570
Profit (millions)	$144.5	$229.9	$210.7	$243	$282

✪ **73.** What was the total profit for 1990 through 1994? $1110.1 million

✪ **74.** Profit is the difference between sales and cost. Write an algebraic model for this statement.

✪ **75.** Use the algebraic model to find *The Gap's* cost for each year given in the table.

✪ **76.** Let *S* represent the number of stores in 1990 and let *R* represent the number of stores in 1994. Write an equation that relates *S* and *R*. $S + 478 = R$

✪ **77.** Let *P* represent the profit (in millions of dollars). During which years did the profit satisfy the inequality $P \geq 210$?   1991, 1992, 1993, 1994

✪ **78.** Let *P* represent the profit (in millions of dollars) and let *S* represent the number of stores. The expression $\frac{P}{S}$ represents the average profit per store. For which year was this average profit greatest? 1991

✪ **79.** *Research Project*   Research a career in the field of fashion or sports uniform design. Answers vary.

   a. Write your results. Include the name of the profession, job requirements, and the environment of the job.

   b. List several ways that mathematics is used in the profession.

   c. If you know a person who has the profession you have researched, interview the person and write about the results.

Clothing Patterns   **In Exercises 80 and 81, estimate the area of the pattern piece. Each square is 6 inches by 6 inches.** Answers vary.

✪ **80.**

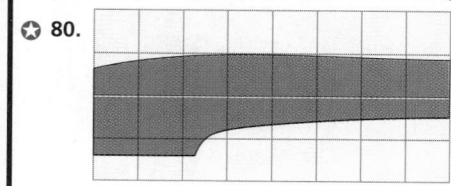

✪ **81.**

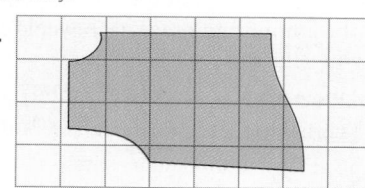

$14 \times 36 = 504$ in.²

$13 \times 36 = 468$ in.²

✪ More difficult exercises

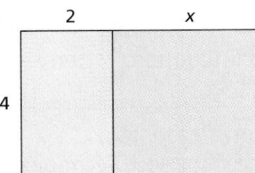

Chapter TEST

In Exercises 1 and 2, apply the Distributive Property. (2.1)

1. $7(a + 2)$ $7a + 14$

2. $3(b + 2c + 3)$ $3b + 6c + 9$

In Exercises 3–6, solve the equation. Show your work. (2.3–2.5) Check students' work

3. $3x = 15$ 5

4. $y - 6 = 0$ 6

5. $p + 2 = 9$ 7

6. $\frac{1}{4}q = 3$ 12

In Exercises 7–9, solve the inequality. Show your work. (2.9) Check students' work

7. $x - 2 > 4$ $x > 6$

8. $10 \geq 3 + y$ $y \leq 7$

9. $7 + z < 14$ $z < 7$

10. Write simplified expressions for the perimeter and area of the rectangle. (2.2)

$2x + 12$, $4x + 8$

11a. See margin.

11. *Business* You are the manager of two sporting goods stores. The weekly cost to operate Store 1 is \$3500 and the weekly cost to operate Store 2 is \$5600. (2.1)

  a. Write a verbal model that represents the yearly costs of operating the two stores.

  b. Use the model in Part **a** to determine the yearly cost of operating both stores.
$473,200

In Exercises 12–14, you buy *n* juice boxes. Each juice box costs \$0.50. (2.7, 2.8)

12. Write an algebraic expression for the total amount you spent. $0.50n$

13. You spent \$3.00. Write an equation that can be solved to find the number of juice boxes you bought. $0.50n = 3.00$

14. Solve the equation to find the number of juice boxes. 6

In Exercises 15 and 16, simplify by adding like terms. (2.2)

15. $3a + 6b + 2a$ $5a + 6b$

16. $12p + 4q + 2q + 3p$ $15p + 6q$

In Exercises 17–19, write an algebraic equation or inequality that represents the verbal sentence. Then solve. (2.6, 2.7, 2.9)

17. A number decreased by 14 is at least 36. $n - 14 \geq 36$, $n \geq 50$

18. The product of a number and 12 equals 60. $12n = 60$, 5

19. A number divided by 21 is 15. $\frac{n}{21} = 15$, 315

In Exercises 20 and 21, write an expression for the perimeter. Find the perimeter when *x* is 1, 2, 3, and 4. Represent your results in a table. (2.2) For tables, see margin.

20.

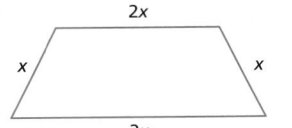

21.

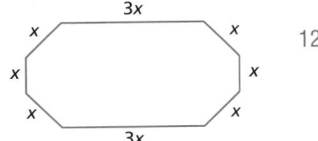

Chapter Test

Chapter **2** Test	Form C

(Page 1 of 3 pages)   Name _____ Date _____

In Exercises 1 and 2, use the Distributive Property to rewrite the expression. (2.1)

1. $5(8 + 10 + 11)$ — $40 + 50 + 55$ or 135

2. $z(3 + f + j)$ — $3z + fz + jz$

In Exercises 3–6, simplify the expression. (2.1, 2.2)

3. $5k + 3j + j + 3i + k$ — $3i + 4j + 6k$

4. $c^2 + c + 2c$ — $c^2 + 3c$

5. $2(d + 4) + 3d$ — $5d + 8$

6. $15ax + x^2 + 4ax$ — $x^2 + 19ax$

In Exercises 7 and 8, evaluate the expression when $m = 4$ and $n = 2$. (2.1, 2.2)

7. $5(m + n) + 12$ — 42

8. $4m + 9(n + 1)$ — 43

In Exercises 9 and 10, solve the equation using mental math. (2.3)

9. $50 - q = 32$ — $q = 18$

10. $\frac{45}{r} = 9$ — $r = 5$

In Exercises 11–13, translate the verbal phrase into an algebraic expression. (2.4)

11. The sum of 5 times a number and 6 — $5n + 6$

12. The difference of 59 and a number — $59 - n$

13. The product of one number decreased by 6 and the same number increased by 6 — $(n - 6)(n + 6)$

28 *Chapter 2 • Investigations in Algebra* © D.C. Heath and Company *Windows*

Answers

11. a. Yearly cost to operate both stores $= 52 \times$ (Weekly cost to operate Store 1 + Weekly cost to operate Store 2)

20.

x	1	2	3	4
Perimeter $(7x)$	7	14	21	28

21.

x	1	2	3	4
Perimeter $(12x)$	12	24	36	48

◀ FORMAL ASSESSMENT

Three **Chapter Tests.** Form A is of average difficulty, Form B is of average difficulty in multiple choice format, and Form C is more challenging.

Available as copymasters, pages 22–30

CHAPTER 3 GOALS

CHAPTER 3 ■ OVERVIEW

RESOURCES ORGANIZER

Lesson Pages	3.1 100–103	3.2 105–108	3.3 109–112	3.4 115–118	3.5 122–125	3.6 126–130	3.7 131–134	3.8 135–138
Lesson Plan	18	19	20	21	22	23	24	25
Problem of the Day	7	7	7	8	8	8	9	9
Warm-Up Exercises	7	7	7	8	8	8	9	9
Color Transparencies	11	12	13, 14	113	—	—	14	—
Teaching Tools: Transparencies	T6	T6	—	T6	—	—	—	T8, T9
Copymasters	C8	C8	—	C8	—	—	—	C10, C11
Math Log	10	10	11	11	11	12	12	12
Technology	—	—	13	—	14	—	—	15
Answer Masters	44, 45	46, 47	48, 49	51, 52	53, 54	55, 56	58, 59	60–62
Extra Practice Copymasters	18	19	20	21	22	23	24	25
Reteaching Copymasters	18	19	20	21	22	23	24	25
Enrichment Projects	—	—	—	12, 13	—	14, 15	—	16, 17
Alternative Assessment: Projects	—	—	—	19	—	19	20	20
Partner Quizzes	—	—	—	46	—	—	—	—
Group Assessment	—	—	—	—	—	—	—	63, 64
Formal Assessment Short Quizzes	—	31	—	32	—	35	—	36
Tests	—	—	—	33, 34	—	—	—	37–45
Overhead Manipulatives Kit	—	Number Counters	—	Number Counters	Number Counters	—	—	—
Complete Solutions Manual	Includes step-by-step solutions for all exercises in the student text							
Computerized Test Bank	Creates customized tests that include graphics							
Interactive CD-ROM Project	Provides an interactive and interdisciplinary chapter project							

STARTERS

Problem of the Day

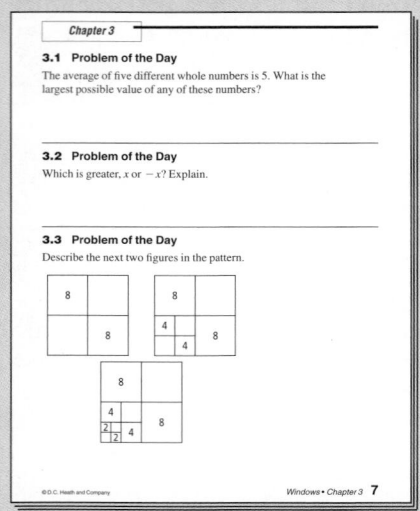

Chapter 3

3.1 Problem of the Day
The average of five different whole numbers is 5. What is the largest possible value of any of these numbers?

3.2 Problem of the Day
Which is greater, x or $-x$? Explain.

3.3 Problem of the Day
Describe the next two figures in the pattern.

© D.C. Heath and Company   Windows • Chapter 3 **7**

Warm-Up Exercises

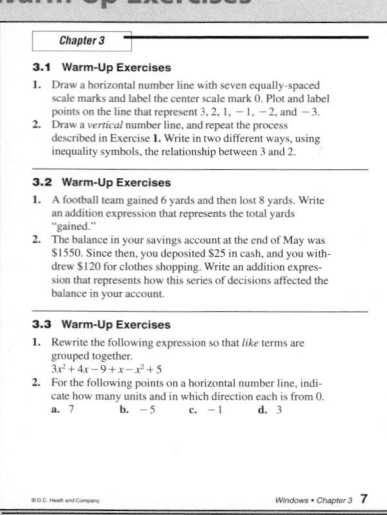

Chapter 3

3.1 Warm-Up Exercises
1. Draw a horizontal number line with seven equally-spaced scale marks and label the center scale mark 0. Plot and label points on the line that represent 3, 2, 1, -1, -2, and -3.
2. Draw a *vertical* number line, and repeat the process described in Exercise 1. Write in two different ways, using inequality symbols, the relationship between 3 and 2.

3.2 Warm-Up Exercises
1. A football team gained 6 yards and then lost 8 yards. Write an addition expression that represents the total yards "gained."
2. The balance in your savings account at the end of May was $1550. Since then, you deposited $25 in cash, and you withdrew $120 for clothes shopping. Write an addition expression that represents how this series of decisions affected the balance in your account.

3.3 Warm-Up Exercises
1. Rewrite the following expression so that *like* terms are grouped together.
$3x^2 + 4x - 9 + x - x^2 + 5$
2. For the following points on a horizontal number line, indicate how many units and in which direction each is from 0.
a. 7   b. -5 c. -1 d. 3

© D.C. Heath and Company   Windows • Chapter 3 **7**

FOR TEACHERS

Answer Masters

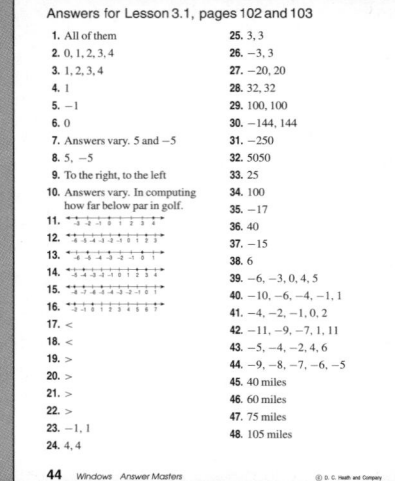

Answers for Lesson 3.1, pages 102 and 103

1. All of them
2. 0, 1, 2, 3, 4
3. 1, 2, 3, 4
4. 1
5. -1
6. 0
7. Answers vary. 5 and -5
8. 5, -5
9. To the right, to the left
10. Answers vary. In computing how far below par in golf.
17. <
18. <
19. >
20. >
21. >
22. >
23. -1, 1
24. 4, 4
25. 3, 3
26. -3, 3
27. -20, 20
28. 32, 32
29. 100, 100
30. -144, 144
31. -250
32. 5050
33. 25
34. 100
35. -17
36. 40
37. -15
38. 6
39. -6, -3, 0, 4, 5
40. -10, -6, -4, -1, 1
41. -4, -2, -1, 0, 2
42. -11, -9, -7, 1, 11
43. -5, -4, -2, 4, 6
44. -9, -8, -7, -6, -5
45. 40 miles
46. 60 miles
47. 75 miles
48. 105 miles

44 Windows   Answer Masters   © D.C. Heath and Company

Lesson Plans

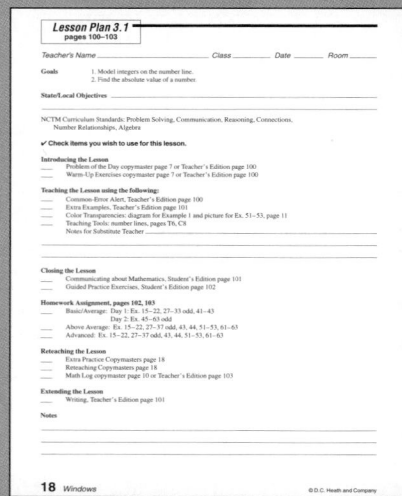

Lesson Plan 3.1
pages 100–103

Teacher's Name _____ Class _____ Date _____ Room _____

Goals
1. Model integers on the number line.
2. Find the absolute value of a number.

State/Local Objectives

NCTM Curriculum Standards: Problem Solving, Communication, Reasoning, Connections, Number Relationships, Algebra

✓ Check items you wish to use for this lesson.

Introducing the Lesson
____ Problem of the Day copymaster page 7 or Teacher's Edition page 100
____ Warm-Up Exercises copymaster page 7 or Teacher's Edition page 100

Teaching the Lesson using the following:
____ Common-Error Alert, Teacher's Edition page 100
____ Extra Examples, Teacher's Edition page 101
____ Color Transparencies: diagram for Example 1 and picture for Ex. 51–53, page 11
____ Teaching Tools: number lines, pages T6, C8
____ Notes for Substitute Teacher

Closing the Lesson
____ Communicating about Mathematics, Student's Edition page 101
____ Guided Practice Exercises, Student's Edition page 102

Homework Assignment, pages 102, 103
Basic/Average: Day 1: Ex. 15–22, 27–33 odd, 41–43
Day 2: Ex. 45–63 odd
Above Average: Ex. 15–22, 27–37 odd, 43, 44, 51–53, 61–63
Advanced: Ex. 15–22, 27–37 odd, 43, 44, 51–53, 61–63

Reteaching the Lesson
____ Extra Practice Copymasters page 18
____ Reteaching Copymasters page 18
____ Math Log copymaster page 10 or Teacher's Edition page 103

Extending the Lesson
____ Writing, Teacher's Edition page 101

Notes

18 Windows   © D.C. Heath and Company

Teaching Tools

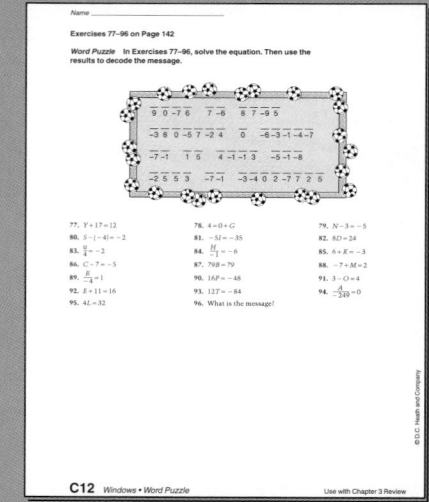

Name _____

Exercises 77–96 on Page 142

Word Puzzle In Exercises 77–96, solve the equation. Then use the results to decode the message.

77. $Y + 17 = 12$
78. $4 = 0 + G$
79. $N - 3 = -5$
80. $5 - |-4| = -2$
81. $-5I = -35$
82. $8O = 24$
83. $\frac{S}{4} = -2$
84. $\frac{H}{4} = -6$
85. $6 + E = -3$
86. $C - 7 = -5$
87. $7 9 B = 79$
88. $-7 + M = 4$
89. $\frac{R}{5} = 1$
90. $16P = -48$
91. $7 + A = 0$
92. $E + 11 = 16$
93. $12T = -84$
94. $\frac{A}{-248} = 0$
95. $4L = 32$
96. What is the message?

C12 Windows • Word Puzzle   Use with Chapter 3 Review

Teaching Tools includes:
Transparencies and Copymasters for classroom activities and study skills:
- Graph Paper
- Dot Paper (Geoboards)
- Algebra Tiles
- Number Counters
- Fraction Strips
- Models

REAL LIFE

Color Transparencies for Real-Life Applications

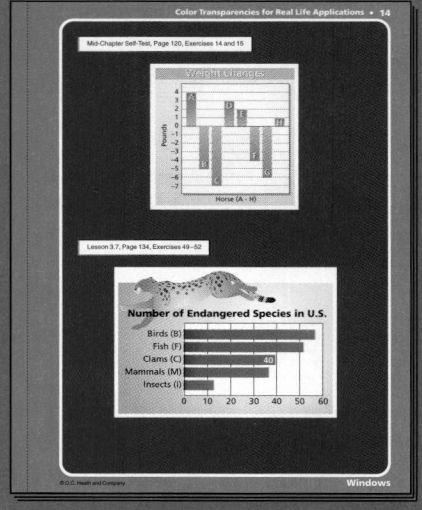

Color Transparencies for Real Life Applications • 14

Mid-Chapter Self-Test, Page 120, Exercises 14 and 15

WEIGHT CHANGES

Lesson 3.7, Page 134, Exercises 49–52

Number of Endangered Species in U.S.

Windows

Technology: Using Calculators and Computers

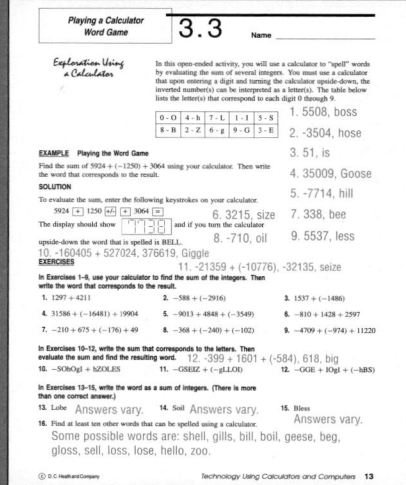

Playing a Calculator Word Game   **3.3**   Name _____

Exploration Using a Calculator

In this open-ended activity, you will use a calculator to "spell" words by evaluating the sum of several integers. You must use a calculator that upon entering a digit and turning the calculator upside-down, the inverted number(s) can be interpreted as a letter(s). The table below lists the letter(s) that correspond to each digit 0 through 9.

| 0 - O | 4 - h | 7 - L | 1 - 1 | 5 - S |
| 8 - B | 2 - Z | 6 - g | 9 - G | 3 - E |

EXAMPLE Playing the Word Game
Find the sum of $5924 + (-1250) + 3064$ using your calculator. Then write the word that corresponds to the result.

SOLUTION
To evaluate the sum, enter the following keystrokes on your calculator:
$5924 \; [+] \; 1250 \; [-] \; 3064 \; [=]$
The display should show ⬚⬚⬚⬚ and if you turn the calculator upside-down the word that is spelled is BELL.

EXERCISES
In Exercises 1–9, use your calculator to find the sum of the integers. Then write the word that corresponds to the result.
1. $1297 + 4211$
2. $-588 + (-2916)$
3. $1537 + (-1486)$
4. $31586 + (-16481) + 19904$
5. $-9013 + 4848 + (-3549)$
6. $-810 + 1428 + 2597$
7. $-210 + 675 + (-176) + 49$
8. $-368 + (-240) + (-102)$
9. $-4709 + (-974) + 11220$

In Exercises 10–12, write the sum that corresponds to the letters. Then evaluate the sum and find the resulting word.
10. $-SObOgl + bZOLES$
11. $-GSEbZ + (-gLLOl)$
12. $-GGE + lOgl + (-hBS)$

In Exercises 13–15, write the word as a sum of integers. (There is more than one correct answer.)
13. Lobe Answers vary.
14. Soil Answers vary.
15. Bless Answers vary.
16. Find at least ten other words that can be spelled using a calculator.
Some possible words are: shell, gills, bill, boil, geese, beg, gloss, sell, loss, lose, hello, zoo.

1. 5508, boss
2. -3504, hose
3. 51, is
4. 35009, Goose
5. -7714, hill
6. 3215, size
7. 338, bee
8. -710, oil
9. 5537, less
10. -160405 + 527024, 376619, Giggle
11. -21359 + (-10776), -32135, seize
12. -399 + 1601 + (-584), 618, big

© D.C. Heath and Company   Technology Using Calculators and Computers **13**

Also Available:

- Complete Solutions Manual
- Overhead Manipulatives Kit
- Computerized Testing Program

- **Interactive CD-ROM Projects**
Interactive projects for solving real-world problems using multimedia

- **Interactions: Real Math–Real Careers**
A videodisc–based resource that connects math to real careers and on-the-job problem solving

- **PACKETS® Performance Assessment for Middle School Mathematics**
A program that links assessment and instruction

ASSESSMENT

Alternative Assessment

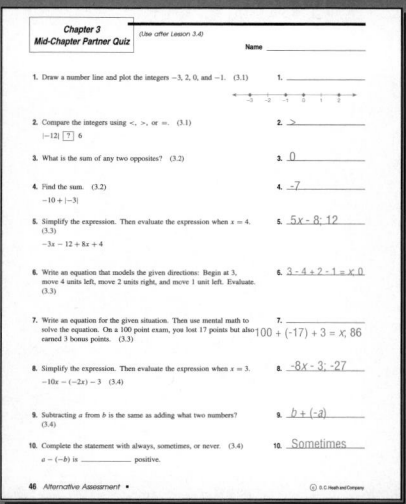

Alternative Assessment includes:
- Scoring Rubrics
- Portfolios
- Math Journals
- Projects
- Partner Quizzes
- Individual and Group Assessment

Formal Assessment

Formal Assessment includes:
- Short Quizzes (after every 2 lessons)
- Mid-Chapter Tests (2 forms)
- Chapter Tests (3 forms)
- Cumulative Tests (after every 3 Chapters)

MEETING INDIVIDUAL NEEDS

Extra Practice Copymasters

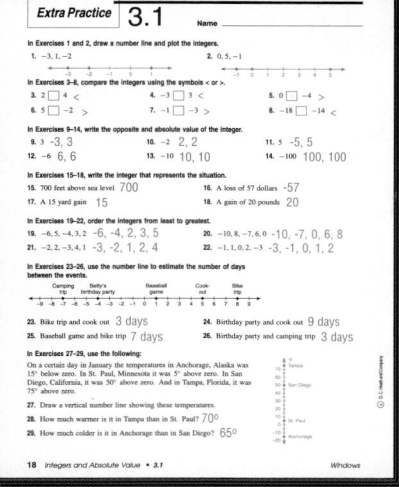

Reteaching Copymasters

Enrichment Projects

Math Log

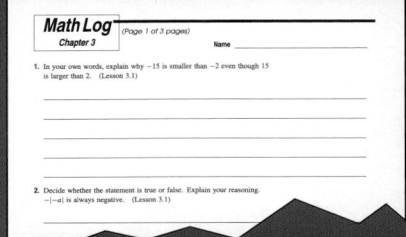

Special Populations

Suggestions for providing equal access for:

Students Acquiring English Proficiency*

Students need help understanding the concept of positive and negative numbers as well as reading these numbers correctly. Students will need opportunities to apply these skills in practical situations. Have students keep a mock checkbook or a record of temperatures to help them understand the practical applications of adding and subtracting integers.

Students with Various Learning Styles*

Allow some students to use number lines and number counters as visual aids in working problems involving negative numbers until they are ready to think more abstractly.

Underachieving Students*

An activity that reinforces addition and subtraction of integers is "walking" the number line. Use masking tape to make a number line on the floor and have students act as the points on the line. By walking forward and backward, students can demonstrate addition and subtraction. Following a stock in a popular company will help students see the practical application for the use of positive and negative numbers.

Gifted and Talented Students*

Ask students to interview someone who owns a business. Have them ask how positive and negative numbers are used in the business.

Have students create a time line similar to the one given in the Exploration and Extension of Lesson 3.2 on a subject of their choice. Have students mark the time line with integers that indicate how long ago specific events occurred.

* See page T19 for descriptions of these special populations.

CHAPTER 3 OVERVIEW

PACING CHART

About the Chapter

As is evident in the second goal of most of the lessons in this text, the underlying purpose of building students' algebraic skills is the ability to model and solve real-life problems by writing and solving algebraic equations. Operations with integers are central to that ability, and are presented in Lessons 3.2–3.7. Three investigations in this chapter offer hands-on representations of adding, subtracting, and multiplying integers with colored counters. Note that the investigations are only loosely associated with the lessons that follow them. The teaching notes for Investigation 3.4 suggest how the investigation can be used to "discover" the rule for subtraction which is formally presented in Lesson 3.4. Before using the investigation for 3.5 on modeling multiplication, you may wish to familiarize yourself with the interpretation of multiplication that is assumed in the investigation. You will find this in the teacher notes. The final lesson of this chapter brings students to a further stage in understanding equations, to *graphing* equations in the coordinate plane

CHAPTER 3

Modeling Integers

Sports medicine has helped today's coaches learn how to protect their athletes from permanent damage and from injuries from sprains and breaks. Of all athletes, dancers have been proven to be the most fit and the most flexible. So, many athletic coaches have their teams trained in dance movements to improve their endurance and flexibility.

Real Life
Coaching an Athlete

To test your own flexibility, mark a line on the floor and place a yardstick across the line as shown. Sit with your feet about 5 inches apart, heels on the line. With your knees straight, *slowly* bend forward from your waist as far as you can. Mark the point at which you touch the stick. Measure the distance from this point to the line. Use this chart to determine your score.

Distance from Line			
< –7″ Needs help	–7″ to 2″ Fair	2″ to 7″ Good	> 7″ Excellent

In this test, the yardstick is used as a kind of number line. The number line is just one of the models for positive and negative numbers that are used to explore integers in this chapter.

Using the Page

The measuring stick should be placed so that the line is even with an inch mark. To determine their scores, have students count the number of inches away from the line they marked their reaches. If they marked past the line, their scores are positive. If they marked before the line, their scores are negative.

Familiarize students with number lines by having them draw a big number line on which they can record their results. What conclusions can they draw from the number line about the class' flexibility?

Multimedia Resources

Interactive CD-ROM Projects A project for this chapter combines print, animation, sound and video presentations to capture students' interest in Temperature. This interactive approach shows students how the math concepts and problem-solving strategies they are learning will be used in the future in dealing with important personal, national, and world issues.
The theme of Temperature correlates to exercises and examples on pages 100, 106, 123, and 125.

Interactions: Real Math—Real Life The theme of this chapter, Coaching an Athlete, correlates with an episode of **Interactions** which is a videodisc-based multimedia resource that connects middle school math topics with real-life careers. In each of the twelve episodes, students go on-site with a variety of professionals to witness real-life applications of the math they are studying. Students see math concepts and problem-solving strategies in a context that helps them connect what they are studying to the world outside the classroom. **Interactions** was developed by the Foundation for Advancements in Science and Education (FASE) and is published by D.C. Heath and Company.
The theme of Coaching an Athlete is continued throughout the chapter on pages 113, 127, 129, and 142.

Performance Assessment Resource The PACKETS® Program: Performance Assessment for Middle School Mathematics was developed by Educational Testing Service and is published by D.C. Heath. **PACKETS** helps you assess your students' performances as they learn. You can use a wide variety of **PACKETS** Activity Units with this chapter because, in every activity, students will use ideas from all topic areas of mathematics. However, you can use the chart on page T16 to help you choose the **PACKETS** Activity Unit(s) that may fit best with this chapter.

▶ **PLANNING** the Lesson

Lesson Plan 3.1, p. 18

ORGANIZER

Starters (reproduced below)
Problem of the Day 3.1, p. 7
Warm-Up Exercises 3.1, p. 7
Lesson Resources
Color Transparencies,
Diagram for Example 1, p. 11
Picture for Ex. 51–53, p. 11
Teaching Tools
Number lines, pp. T6, C8
Math Log, p. 10
Answer Masters 3.1, pp. 44, 45
Extra Practice Copymaster 3.1, p. 18
Reteaching Copymaster 3.1, p. 18
Special Populations
Suggestions, Teacher's Edition, p. 98D

LESSON Notes

Review the different types of numbers that students have already seen: natural (counting) numbers, whole numbers, integers, and fractions (or rationals). You may wish to refer to the diagram in the teaching notes on page 40. Point out that zero is neither positive nor negative. Motivate the need for negative integers using examples involving sub-zero temperatures, debits in a checking account, or losses on a football field. Emphasize that –5 is a number, not an indication to perform a subtraction operation. Have students sketch in their journals a number line that shows integers.

Ask students: Are integers the only numbers that can be represented on a number line? No, all real numbers can be shown on a number line.

After introducing *opposites* (following Example 2), you may wish to point out to students that integers are composed of all the whole numbers and their opposites. Remind students that the ellipsis symbol, " . . .", is used to indicate that a pattern continues.

Example 1

Carefully monitor how students draw their number lines. Stress that the scale marks should be equally spaced and labeled. Points should be plotted *on* the line, not above it.

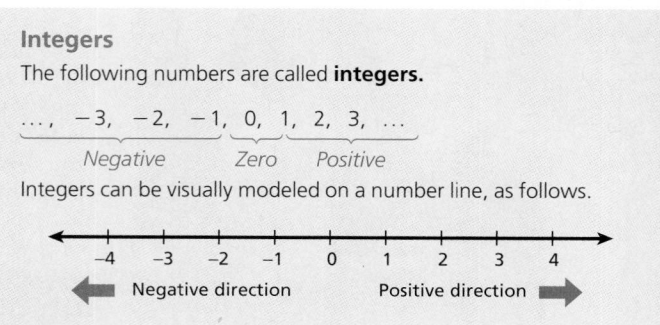

3.1 Integers and Absolute Value

What you should learn:

Goal 1 How to model integers on a number line

Goal 2 How to find the absolute value of a number

Why you should learn it:

You can use integers to model real-life situations, such as temperatures that are below zero.

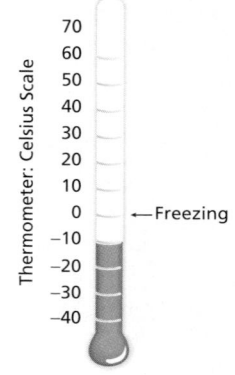

This thermometer shows a temperature of −10°C. This is read as "negative 10 degrees Celsius" or "10 degrees below zero Celsius." On a vertical number line such as this the negative direction is downward and the positive direction is upward.

Goal 1 Integers and the Number Line

Many real-life situations can be modeled with whole numbers. Some situations, such as temperatures, are more easily modeled with an expanded set of numbers called *integers*.

> **Integers**
> The following numbers are called **integers.**
>
> $$\dots,\ -3,\ -2,\ -1,\ 0,\ 1,\ 2,\ 3,\ \dots$$
>
> $\underbrace{\quad\quad}_{Negative}\ \underbrace{\ }_{Zero}\ \underbrace{\quad}_{Positive}$
>
> Integers can be visually modeled on a number line, as follows.
>
> $\xleftarrow{\quad\quad} \overset{-4\ \ -3\ \ -2\ \ -1\ \ \ 0\ \ \ 1\ \ \ 2\ \ \ 3\ \ \ 4}{\rule{6cm}{0.4pt}} \xrightarrow{\quad\quad}$
>
> ◀ Negative direction   Positive direction ▶

Here are some things you need to know about integers.

1. A negative integer such as -5 is read as "negative 5." Although the negative sign " $-$ " is the same sign that is used for subtraction, it does not mean the same thing.

2. A positive integer such as 12 can be written with a positive sign as $+12$. It is more common, however, to omit the positive sign.

3. If a and b are integers, then the inequality $a < b$ means that a lies *to the left* of b on the number line.

Example 1 *Plotting Integers on the Number Line*

Draw a number line and plot the integers -6, -2, and 3.

Solution To *plot* the integer on the number line, draw a dot at the point that represents the integer. Note that -6 is to the left of -2, which means that $-6 < -2$.

$\xleftarrow{\qquad} \overset{-7\ \ -6\ \ -5\ \ -4\ \ -3\ \ -2\ \ -1\ \ \ 0\ \ \ 1\ \ \ 2\ \ \ 3\ \ \ 4}{\rule{7cm}{0.4pt}} \xrightarrow{\qquad}$

Elevations are measured in distances above or below sea level. The lowest elevation in the United States is Death Valley. Its elevation is −282 feet. Because |−282| = 282, this can also be described as 282 feet below sea level.

Goal 2 Finding the Absolute Value of a Number

The **absolute value** of a number is the distance between the number and 0. Absolute values are written with two vertical rules, | |, called **absolute value signs**. Because distance cannot be negative, it follows that the absolute value of a number cannot be negative.

Example 2 *Finding Absolute Values*

Find the absolute value of **a**. −4 and **b**. 3.

Solution

a. On a number line, the distance between −4 and 0 is 4. This means that |−4| = 4.

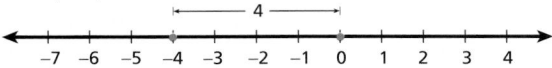

b. On a number line, the distance between 3 and 0 is 3. This means that |3| = 3.

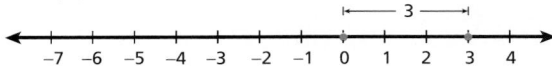

Two numbers that have the same absolute value but opposite signs are called **opposites.** For instance, −4 and 4 are opposites. Zero is its own opposite.

Communicating about MATHEMATICS

Cooperative Learning

▶ **SHARING IDEAS about the Lesson**

Reasoning Work with a partner. Decide whether the statement is true or false. In each case, explain your reasoning.
See margin.

A. The absolute value of a negative integer is a positive integer.

B. The absolute value of any integer is positive.

C. The absolute value of −6 is greater than the absolute value of −4.

D. −6 is greater than −4.

E. Zero is the only integer that is its own opposite.

F. If $a \leq b$, then $|a| \leq |b|$.

When graphing points on a number line, many students will simply label the appropriate scale marks and feel that they have answered the question without actually plotting any points.

Be sure students understand that the absolute value of a number cannot be negative. Point out that the concept of absolute value is needed to perform computations with integers.

Example 2

Explain to students that in stating distance from 0 we count steps to either side of 0. The first step away from 0 is counted as 1, and so on.

Communicating about MATHEMATICS

Encourage students to use a number line to support their reasoning. In general, students' written explanations for a false response should include a counterexample.

Part **F** provides an opportunity for a discussion of the expression |−x|. Explain that, although |−3| = 3, we cannot write |−x| = x if x is a negative number. Have them go through the substitution process for some negative value of x. Students will need to remember this when working Ex. 39, 40 in the Cumulative Review, page 144.

Writing Prompt
Refer back to the Problem of the Day. Ask students if their solution to that problem would be different if integers were considered instead of whole numbers and, if so, why.

OPTION: Extra Examples

Here are additional examples similar to those of the lesson.

1. Plotting Integers on the Number Line
Draw a number line and plot the integers 0, 6, and −1.
Solution
To plot the integer on the number line, draw a dot at the point that represents the integer.

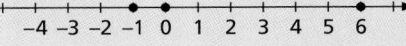

2. Finding Absolute Values
Find the absolute value of **(a)** −3 and **(b)** 4.
Solution
a. On a number line, the distance between −3 and 0 is 3. This means that |−3| is 3.

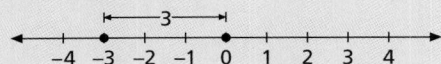

b. On a number line, the distance between 4 and 0 is 4. This means that |4| is 4.

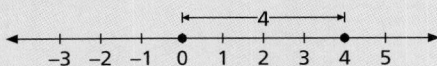

Answers to Communicating
A. True, distance cannot be negative.
B. False, 0 is a counterexample.
C. True, 6 > 4
D. False, −6 lies to the left of −4 on the number line.
E. True, 0 is neither positive nor negative.
F. False, −6 ≤ −4 but 6 ≥ 4

ASSIGNMENT GUIDE

Basic/Average:
Day 1: Ex. 15–22, 27–37 odd, 41–43
Day 2: Ex. 45–63 odd

Above Average: Ex. 15–22, 27–37 odd, 43, 44, 51–53, 61–63

Advanced: Ex. 15–22, 27–37 odd, 43, 44, 51–53, 61–63

Selected Answers: Ex. 1–10, 11–61 odd

Guided Practice

In their journals have students define the absolute value of a number in their own words.
▶ **Ex. 1–10** Have students work with a partner or in groups to answer these questions.

Independent Practice

▶ **Ex. 31–38** Have students think of other situations that can be represented by an integer.

EXERCISES

Guided Practice

▶CHECK **for Understanding**

In Exercises 1–6, use the following set of numbers.

$$-4, -3, -2, -1, 0, 1, 2, 3, 4$$

1. Which are integers? All of them

2. Which are whole numbers? 0, 1, 2, 3, 4

3. Which are natural numbers? 1, 2, 3, 4

4. Which is the smallest positive integer? 1

5. Which is the greatest negative integer? -1

6. Which is neither positive nor negative? 0

7. Give an example of two numbers that are opposites. Answers vary. 5 and -5

8. State two values of x that make $|x| = 5$ true. 5, -5

9. On a number line, which direction is positive? Which is negative? To the right, to the left

10. *Problem Solving*   Describe an example (other than temperature) of how negative integers are used in real life. Answers vary. In computing how far below par in golf.

Independent Practice

In Exercises 11–16, draw a number line and plot the integers. See margin.

11. 0, 4, -3 **12.** $-1, 2, -6$ **13.** $-5, -3, 0$ **14.** $-4, 2, 3$ **15.** $-7, -8, -5$ **16.** 0, $-2, 7$

In Exercises 17–22, compare the integers using the symbols $<$ or $>$.

17. 0 [?] 4 $<$ **18.** -2 [?] 1 $<$ **19.** 0 [?] -3 $>$

20. 4 [?] -6 $>$ **21.** $|-1|$ [?] -2 $>$ **22.** $|-14|$ [?] $|-13|$ $>$

In Exercises 23–30, write the opposite and the absolute value of the integer.

23. 1 $-1, 1$ **24.** -4 4, 4   **25.** -3 3, 3   **26.** 3 $-3, 3$

27. 20 $-20, 20$ **28.** -32 32, 32   **29.** -100 100, 100   **30.** 144 $-144, 144$

Number Sense   **In Exercises 31–38, write the integer that represents the situation.**

31. 250 feet below sea level -250 **32.** An elevation of 5050 feet 5050

33. A gain of 25 yards 25   **34.** $100 deposit in a checking account 100

35. 17 degrees below zero -17 **36.** A profit of $40 40

37. A loss of 15 pounds -15 **38.** A gain of 6 hours 6

In Exercises 39–44, order the integers from least to greatest.   **40.** $-10, -6, -4, -1, 1$ **41.** $-4, -2, 0, 2$

39. 0, $-6, 5, -3, 4$ **40.** $-1, -10, 1, -4, -6$ **41.** $-1, 2, -2, 0, -4$

42. $-9, -11, 11, 1, -7$ **43.** 6, 4, $-4, -5, -2$ **44.** $-7, -8, -9, -6, -5$

39. $-6, -3, 0, 4, 5$ **42.** $-11, -9, -7, 1, 11$ **43.** $-5, -4, -2, 4, 6$ **44.** $-9, -8, -7, -6, -5$

Answers

11.
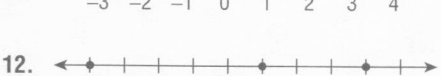
$-3 \quad -2 \quad -1 \quad 0 \quad 1 \quad 2 \quad 3 \quad 4$

12.
$-6 \quad -5 \quad -4 \quad -3 \quad -2 \quad -1 \quad 0 \quad 1 \quad 2 \quad 3$

13.
$-6 \quad -5 \quad -4 \quad -3 \quad -2 \quad -1 \quad 0 \quad 1$

14.
$-5 \quad -4 \quad -3 \quad -2 \quad -1 \quad 0 \quad 1 \quad 2 \quad 3 \quad 4$

15.
$-8 \quad -7 \quad -6 \quad -5 \quad -4 \quad -3 \quad -2 \quad -1 \quad 0 \quad 1$

16.
$-2 \quad -1 \quad 0 \quad 1 \quad 2 \quad 3 \quad 4 \quad 5 \quad 6 \quad 7$

Cities in Illinois In Exercises 45–50, use the number line to estimate the distance in miles between the two cities.

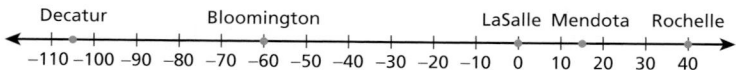

Decatur   Bloomington   LaSalle Mendota Rochelle

-110 -100 -90 -80 -70 -60 -50 -40 -30 -20 -10 0 10 20 30 40

45. LaSalle and Rochelle   40 miles

46. LaSalle and Bloomington   60 miles

47. Mendota and Bloomington   75 miles

48. Decatur and LaSalle   105 miles

49. Bloomington and Decatur   45 miles

50. Rochelle and Decatur   145 miles

Swimming In Exercises 51–53, use the following information.

You are at a swimming pool that is 3 feet deep at the shallow end and 14 feet deep at the deep end. There are three diving boards: a low diving board (3 feet above the water), a middle diving board (10 feet above the water), and a high diving board (16 feet above the water).

51. Draw a vertical number line showing the heights and depths in feet.   See margin.

52. You dive off the middle diving board to a depth of 9 feet below the surface. How far did you dive vertically?   19 ft

53. You dive off the high diving board and touch the bottom of the deep end. How far did you dive vertically?   30 ft

Diving platforms used in competitions can be as high as 10 meters (33 feet) above the water.

Integrated Review

Making Connections within Mathematics

Mental Math In Exercises 54–62, solve the equation.

54. $x + 13 = 20$ 7

55. $m - 15 = 6$ 21

56. $3x = 36$ 12

57. $\frac{x}{12} = 5$ 60

58. $n - 17 = 9$ 26

59. $12y = 96$ 8

60. $14 = x - 4$ 18

61. $17 = 6 + b$ 11

62. $34 = 2x$ 17

Exploration and Extension

63. *Logical Reasoning* Find and plot on a number line four different integers a, b, c, and d such that   See margin.

- d is neither negative nor positive,
- a and b are the same distance from d,
- c is the least positive integer and three units to the left of b.

✪ More difficult exercises

P Portfolio Opportunity

3.1 • *Integers and Absolute Value*   **103**

▶ **Ex. 45–50** These questions preview operations on integers.

EXTENSION
Ask students: If Bloomington were midway between Decatur and another city on the number line, where would the other city be located?

▶ **Ex. 51–53** Students unfamiliar with swimming pools may need help visualizing the situation described here. You may wish to suggest that they represent the water level by 0.

Integrated Review

Encourage students to solve these equations using mental math.

Exploration and Extension

Have students write clues similar to those in the problem in order to challenge their classmates.

Portfolio Opportunity: Math Log

1. In your own words, explain why -15 is smaller than -2 even though 15 is larger than 2.
2. Decide whether the statement is true or false. Explain your reasoning.
   $-|-a|$ is always negative.

Also available as a copymaster, page 10, Ex. 1, 2

Answers

51.

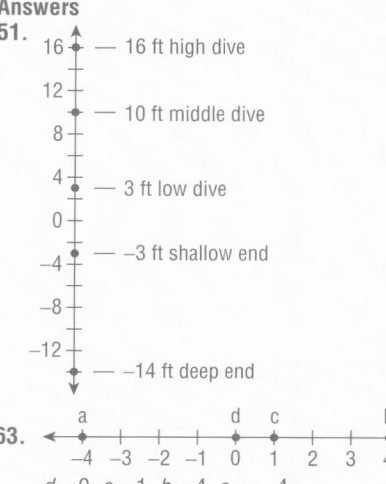

16 — 16 ft high dive

12

— 10 ft middle dive

8

4 — 3 ft low dive

0

-4 — -3 ft shallow end

-8

-12 — -14 ft deep end

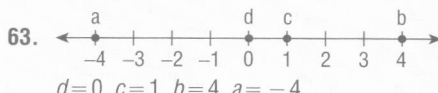

63.

a   d   c   b

-4 -3 -2 -1 0 1 2 3 4

$d = 0$, $c = 1$, $b = 4$, $a = -4$

Materials

Teaching Tools
  Number counters, pp. T7, C9

Using manipulatives to introduce integer operations provides a concrete model for students as they build a conceptual understanding of integers. Any type of chips or counters can be used, provided that two colors, such as red and black, are available. In these investigations, +1 is modeled with a *black* counter, while –1 is modeled with a *red* counter. Use a sheet of paper as a mat. Students may find it helpful to recall the phrase "in the red" to describe a debit balance.

In Addition, each addend is modeled with the appropriate number of counters. Then both integer models are added by being placed together on the mat and *regrouped*. The result of the operation (addition) is the *new group* which is formed. Counters of opposite colors (positive and negative) can be paired to produce a zero result. You may wish to compare a zero-pair to a neutral particle in chemistry, or to using $1 to clear a debt of $1 leaving a result of 0 (no money, no debt). Further notes on the application of zero-pairs in these chapter investigations are provided where needed.

Make sure that students understand the basic steps involved in these investigations:

Model the integers →Regroup counters on mat→Identify resulting group

MATH JOURNAL
Have students work Ex. 13–16 in their journals or portfolios.

Materials Needed: number counters, mat, pencil, paper

In this investigation, you will use number counters to model integer addition.

Sample 1: Finding the Sum of Two Positive Integers

Choose 3 black counters to represent positive 3 and 2 black counters to represent positive 2.

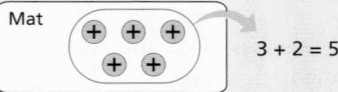

$3 + 2 = 5$

Place the counters on the mat and count the total number of black counters.

Sample 2: Finding the Sum of Two Negative Integers

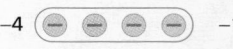

Choose 4 red counters to represent negative 4 and 1 red counter to represent negative 1.

$-4 + (-1) = -5$

Place the counters on the mat and count the total number of red counters.

Sample 3: Finding the Sum of Positive and Negative Integers

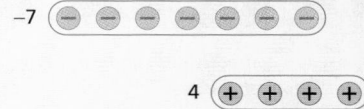

Choose 7 red counters to represent negative 7 and 4 black counters to represent positive 4.

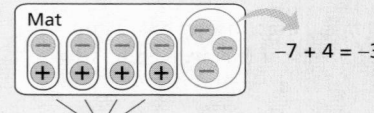

$-7 + 4 = -3$

Add to zero.

Place the counters on the mat and group pairs of black and red counters. Each pair has a sum of zero. The remaining counters represent the sum.

Exercises

In Exercises 1–12, use number counters to find the sum. Check students' models.

1. $3 + 4$ 7
2. $-1 + (-3)$ -4
3. $-2 + (-5)$ -7
4. $-4 + 4$ 0
5. $3 + (-3)$ 0
6. $6 + (-4)$ 2
7. $-7 + 2$ -5
8. $-5 + 8$ 3
9. $6 + (-3)$ 3
10. $5 + (-7)$ -2
11. $8 + (-8)$ 0
12. $4 + (-9)$ -5

P **13.** Write a general statement about the sum of two positive integers.   13.–16. See margin.

P **14.** Write a general statement about the sum of two negative integers.

P **15.** Can the sum of a positive integer and a negative integer be positive? Can it be negative? How can you predict when a sum will be positive or negative?

P **16.** Can the sum of two integers be zero? What can you say about such integers?

Answers
13. The sum of two positive integers is always positive.
14. The sum of two negative integers is always negative.
15. Yes, yes, the sign of a sum will be the same as the sign of the integer with the greater absolute value.
16. Yes, they are opposites.

3.2

Adding Two Integers

PACING the Lesson

Suggested Number of Days
Basic/Average 2 **Above Average** 1
Advanced 1

PLANNING the Lesson

Lesson Plan 3.2, p. 19

What you should learn:

 How to use absolute values to add two integers

 How to use integer addition to solve real-life problems

Why you should learn it:

You can use integer addition to solve real-life problems, such as finding the temperature.

Goal 1   Adding Two Integers

The *Investigation* on page 104 shows how number counters can be used to add two integers. In this lesson, you will learn rules that can be used to add two integers.

Adding Two Integers

Rule	Examples
1. To add two integers with the *same sign*, add their absolute values and write the common sign.	$3 + 4 = 7$ $-2 + (-6) = -8$
2. To add two integers with *opposite signs*, subtract the smaller absolute value from the larger absolute value and write the sign of the integer with the greater absolute value.	$-2 + 5 = 3$ $1 + (-7) = -6$

Example 1   *Adding Integers with the Same Sign*

a. The sum of two positive integers is positive.

$4 + 5 = 9$

b. The sum of two negative integers is negative.

$-12 + (-3) = -15$ ■

Example 2   *Adding Integers with Opposite Signs*

a. The sum of 5 and -8 is negative because -8 has a greater absolute value than 5.

     Write sign of -8.   *Subtract 5 from 8.*

$$5 + (-8) = -3$$

b. The Sum of Opposites The sum of 6 and -6 is zero because both integers have the same absolute value.

$6 + (-6) = 6 - 6$ *Subtract 6 from 6.*

$= 0$ *The sum is zero.*

The sum of any two opposites is zero. ■

Zero Property of Addition

When zero is added to an integer, the sum is the same integer. Here are two examples of this property.

$3 + 0 = 3$

$0 + (-5) = -5$

3.2 • Adding Two Integers   **105**

ORGANIZER

Starters (reproduced below)
   Problem of the Day 3.2, p. 7
   Warm-Up Exercises 3.2, p. 7
Lesson Resources
   Color Transparencies
     Diagram for Ex. 55–57, p. 12
   Teaching Tools
     Number lines, pp. T6, C8
   Math Log, p. 10
   Answer Masters 3.2, pp. 46, 47
   Extra Practice Copymaster 3.2, p. 19
   Reteaching Copymaster 3.2, p. 19
Special Populations
   Suggestions, Teacher's Edition, p. 98D

LESSON Notes

ALTERNATE APPROACH
Using manipulatives This lesson begins by stating the rules for adding integers. However, many students may still find the use of colored counters easier to understand than the concept of absolute value. For example, in adding a positive integer to a negative integer (see Sample 3 in the investigation on page 104), encourage students to shortcut the regrouping process by simply recognizing the color of the larger group of counters, then removing *from this group* a number of counters equal to the number in the smaller group. The remaining counters in the larger group now represent both the magnitude *and sign* of the result.

Example 1

Emphasize that adding integers with like signs (or counters of the same color) is really no different than the usual addition of like objects.

Example 2

Make sure that *all* students understand the importance of the Sum of Opposites property presented here.

MATH JOURNAL
Have students record the Zero Property of Addition in their journals.

In real-life situations, math-related words are used to indicate negative integers instead of the term "negative", for example, a "loss" of 3 yards in football, a temperature "drop" of 8 degrees, or a "debit" of $30 in a checking account.

Example 3 ———————

A degree Celsius (°C) is a metric unit of temperature. At sea level, water boils at 100°C and freezes at 0°C.

Communicating about MATHEMATICS

Ask students to identify real-life situations in which negative integers are used. Have them write an algebraic model for one such situation.

Writing Prompt
Write an explanation for your partner of how you can predict whether the sum of a positive integer and a negative integer will be positive or negative.

Real Life
Meteorology

In northern cities like Chicago, the temperature can change rapidly. For instance, in an hour, the temperature can drop from 20°C (68°F) to 10°C (50°F).

Goal 2 **Solving Real-Life Problems**

Example 3 *Finding a Temperature*

The thermometers at the right show the temperatures (in degrees Celsius) at 1 P.M., 2 P.M., and 3 P.M.

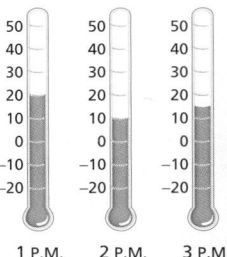

1 P.M. 2 P.M. 3 P.M.

a. Use the thermometers to approximate the temperatures.

b. Write an addition equation that relates the temperatures at 1 P.M. and 2 P.M.

c. Write an equation that relates the temperatures at 2 P.M. and 3 P.M.

Solution

a. At 1 P.M. the temperature is 20°C. At 2 P.M. the temperature is 10°C. At 3 P.M. the temperature is 15°C.

b. From 1 P.M. to 2 P.M. the temperature *dropped* 10 degrees. This can be represented by adding -10 degrees to the 1 P.M. temperature.

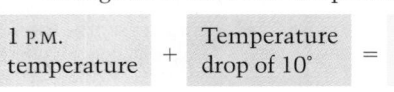

| 1 P.M. temperature | + | Temperature drop of 10° | = | 2 P.M. temperature |

$$20 + (-10) = 10$$

c. From 2 P.M. to 3 P.M. the temperature *rose* 5 degrees. This can be represented by adding 5 degrees to the 2 P.M. temperature.

| 2 P.M. temperature | + | Temperature rise of 5° | = | 3 P.M. temperature |

$$10 + 5 = 15$$ ∎

Communicating about MATHEMATICS

▶ **SHARING IDEAS about the Lesson**

Problem Solving Explain how each real-life situation can be modeled by integer addition.

A. You owe your uncle $25. You pay back $15. $-25 + 15 = -10$

B. You owe your sister $15. You borrow another $10.

C. You owe your mom $40. You pay all of it back. $-40 + 40 = 0$

B. $-15 + (-10) = -2$

OPTION: Extra Examples

Here is an additional example similar to Example 2.

Adding Integers with Opposite Signs
Add.   **a.** 18 and -26 **b.** 7 and -7
Solution
a. The sum of 18 and -26 is negative because -26 has a greater absolute value than 18.

Write sign of -26. Subtract 18 from 26.

$$18 + (-26) = -8$$

b. The sum of 7 and -7 is zero because both integers have the same absolute value.

EXERCISES

Guided Practice

▶ **CHECK for Understanding**

5. $5 + (-2) = 3$ **6.** $1 + (-6) = -5$
7. $4 + (-4) = 0$ **8.** $-3 + (-5) = -8$

In Exercises 1–4, find the sum. Write your conclusion as an equation.

1. $4 + 3$
$4 + 3 = 7$

2. $2 + (-2)$
$2 + (-2) = 0$

3. $7 + (-5)$
$7 + (-5) = 2$

4. $-7 + (-5)$
$-7 + (-5) = -12$

In Exercises 5–8, write the equation modeled by the number counters. See above.

5.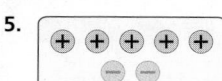

6.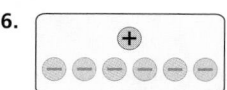

7.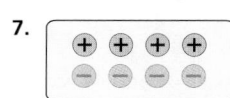

8.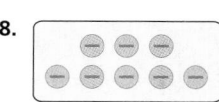

9. Discuss the two rules used in this lesson to add integers. Which rule should be used to find the sum of 8 and -11? Explain. See margin.

10. *Computation Sense*   From the number line below, state whether $a + b$ is negative, zero, or positive. Explain.

Positive, $|b| > |a|$

Independent Practice

For equations, see Additional Answers.

Mental Math   **In Exercises 11–26, find the sum. Write your conclusion as an equation.**

11. $11 + 15$ 26
12. $-8 + (-2)$ -10
13. $-13 + (-13)$ -26
14. $10 + 24$ 34

15. $10 + (-10)$ 0
16. $-8 + 8$ 0
17. $-13 + 13$ 0
18. $24 + (-24)$ 0

19. $13 + 0$ 13
20. $-7 + 0$ -7
21. $0 + 15$ 15
22. $0 + (-33)$ -33

23. $2 + (-9)$ -7
24. $39 + (-21)$ 18
25. $-16 + 12$ -4
26. $-17 + 13$ -4

Addition Patterns   **In Exercises 27-30, complete the statements. Then describe the pattern.**

Sums decrease by 1.

27.
$4 + 3 = \boxed{?}$ 7
$4 + 2 = \boxed{?}$ 6
$4 + 1 = \boxed{?}$ 5
$4 + 0 = \boxed{?}$ 4
$4 + (-1) = \boxed{?}$ 3
Sums decrease by 1.

28.
$-2 + (-3) = \boxed{?}$ -5
$-2 + (-2) = \boxed{?}$ -4
$-2 + (-1) = \boxed{?}$ -3
$-2 + 0 = \boxed{?}$ -2
$-2 + 1 = \boxed{?}$ -1
Sums increase by 1.

29.
$3 + (-7) = \boxed{?}$ -4
$3 + (-5) = \boxed{?}$ -2
$3 + (-3) = \boxed{?}$ 0
$3 + (-1) = \boxed{?}$ 2
$3 + 1 = \boxed{?}$ 4
Sums increase by 2.

30.
$-6 + (-4) = \boxed{?}$ -10
$-6 + (-5) = \boxed{?}$ -11
$-6 + (-6) = \boxed{?}$ -12
$-6 + (-7) = \boxed{?}$ -13
$-6 + (-8) = \boxed{?}$ -14

Equation Sense   **In Exercises 31–34, find three sets of values of x and y that make the equation true. (There are many correct answers.)** Answers vary.

31. $x + y = 7$
32. $x + y = -2$
33. $x + y = -8$
34. $x + y = 10$

Mental Math   **In Exercises 35–38, use mental math to solve the equation.**

35. $4 + x = 7$ 3
36. $6 + n = 5$ -1
37. $-2 + m = -5$ -3
38. $-3 + y = 0$ 3

ASSIGNMENT GUIDE

Basic/Average:
   Day 1: Ex. 11–33, 35–38, 39, 40
   Day 2: Ex. 41–44, 45–53 odd, 55–57
Above Average: Ex. 19–45, 52–57
Advanced: Ex. 19–45, 52–57
Selected Answers: Ex. 1–10, 11–53 odd

Guided Practice

▶ **Ex. 10** This exercise provides a visual context for integer addition.

EXTENSION
You may wish to have students check the effect of changing the locations of a and b.

Independent Practice

▶ **Ex. 11–26** Encourage students to compute these sums mentally.
▶ **Ex. 27–30** In this context, answers such as "the sum is increasing by 1" are acceptable.
▶ **Ex. 31–34** Encourage students to state each of these equations as a question, as suggested on page 60.

GROUP ACTIVITY

Geometry Connection If students are familiar with graphing, place a coordinate grid on the overhead projector (or chalkboard) and have all groups plot their answers to Ex. 31 on this plane. Then join the points. Repeat this for each of the other exercises in this set, using a new grid for each exercise.

Extra Practice

Extra Practice **3.2**   Name _____

In Exercises 1–12, find the sum. Write your conclusion as an equation. $-12 + (-12) = -24$
1. $3 + 12$ $3 + 12 = 15$
2. $-6 + (-3)$ $-6 + (-3) = -9$
3. $-12 + (-12)$
4. $6 + 16$ $6 + 16 = 22$
5. $-5 + 5$ $-5 + 5 = 0$
6. $12 + (-18)$
7. $-19 + 12$ $-19 + 12 = -7$
8. $26 + (-26)$ $26 + (-26) = 0$
9. $4 + 0$ $12 + (-18) = -6$
   $4 + 0 = 4$
10. $0 + (-11)$ $0 + (-11) = -11$
11. $15 + (-2)$ $15 + (-2) = 13$
12. $-12 + 0$
   $-12 + 0 = -12$

In Exercises 13–15, complete the statement. Then describe the pattern.
13. $5 + (-3) = \square$ 2,3,4,5,6
   $5 + (-2) = \square$ Increase
   $5 + (-1) = \square$ by 1
   $5 + 0 = \square$
   $5 + 1 = \square$
14. $-3 + 3 = \square$ 0,-1,-2,
   $-3 + 2 = \square$ -3,-4
   $-3 + 1 = \square$ Decrease
   $-3 + 0 = \square$ by 1
   $-3 + (-1) = \square$
15. $2 + (-6) = \square$
   $2 + (-4) = \square$
   $2 + (-2) = \square$
   $2 + 0 = \square$
   $2 + 2 = \square$
   $-4, -2, 0, 2, 4$
   Increase by 2

In Exercises 16–18, find three sets of values of x and y that make the equation true. (There are many correct answers.)
16. $x + y = 6$
   Answers vary.
17. $x + y = -4$
   Answers vary.
18. $x + y = -10$
   Answers vary.

In Exercises 19–21, use mental math to solve the equation.
19. $3 + x = -6$
   $x = -9$
20. $-4 + z = -2$
   $z = 2$
21. $-3 + m = 10$
   $m = 13$

In Exercises 22 and 23, match the equation with the real life situation. Then solve the equation for x and explain what x represents in the problem.
a. You have 100 dollars in a savings account and you withdraw 30 dollars.
b. A submarine is 100 feet below sea level. It ascends 30 feet.
22. $-100 + 30 = x$
   b, $x = -70$, 70 ft below sea level
23. $100 - 30 = x$
   a, $x = 70$, $70 in the account

In Exercises 24 and 25, write a real life situation that can be represented by the equation.
24. $10 + (-5) = x$
   Answers vary.
25. $-25 + 10 = x$
   Answers vary.

In Exercises 26 and 27, find a pair of integers whose sum is -2. (Use the integers labeled $a, b, c,$ and d.)
26.
b, c
27.
a, c

Reteaching

Reteach
Chapter 3   Name _____

What you should learn:

| 3.2 | How to add two integers and how to use integer addition to solve real-life problems |

Correlation to Pupil's Textbook:
Mid-Chapter Self-Test (p. 120)   Chapter Test (p. 143)
Exercises 7–10, 12   Exercise 7

Examples *Adding Two Integers and Solving Real-Life Problems*

a. To add two integers with the same sign, add their absolute values and write the common sign.

Add -12 and -4. $-12 + (-4) = -16$ The sum of two negative integers is negative.

Add 7 and 8. $7 + 8 = 15$ The sum of two positive integers is positive.

b. To add two integers with opposite signs, subtract the smaller absolute value from the larger absolute value and write the sign of the integer with the greater absolute value.

Add -5 and 3.   Subtract 3 from -5 and write $(-5) + 3 = -2$
the sign of -5.

c. The price of gasoline was $1.03 per gallon in March. In April, the price was $1.01 per gallon. Write an addition equation that relates the gasoline prices in March and April.

From March to April, the price dropped $0.02. This can be represented by adding (-0.02) to the March price.

| March price | + | Price drop of (-0.02) | = | April price |

$1.03 + (-0.02) = 1.01$

Guidelines:
• The sum of two positive integers is positive.
• The sum of two negative integers is negative.
• The sum of any two opposites is zero.

1. $-9 + 12 = 3$

EXERCISES
   2. $5 + (-14) = -9$ **3.** $7 + 11 = 18$
In Exercises 1–8, find the sum. Write your conclusion as an equation.   **4.** $0 + (-17) = -17$
1. $-9 + 12$
2. $5 + (-14)$
3. $7 + 11$
4. $0 + (-17)$
5. $-23 + 4$
6. $-11 + (-13)$
7. $6 + 0$
8. $8 + (-8)$
$-23 + 4 = -19$ $-11 + (-13) = -24$ $6 + 0 = 6$ $8 + (-8) = 0$

Answer
9. One rule is for integers with the same sign, and a second rule is for integers with different signs. Since 8 and -11 have different signs, the second rule should be used to add them.

Modeling Real Life **In Exercises 39–42, match the equation with the real-life situation. Then solve the equation for x and explain what x represents in the problem.**

a. *Elevator Ride* You enter an elevator on the 5th floor. The elevator goes down 3 floors.

b. *Football* Your team is on its own 35-yard line. The running back rushes for a 10-yard gain.

c. *Temperature* The temperature is 35°F. The temperature drops 10 degrees.

d. *Borrowed Money* Your sister owes you $5. She pays $3 of it back to you.

39. $-5 + 3 = x$ d, -2, $2 debt

40. $5 - 3 = x$ a, 2, 2nd floor

41. $35 + 10 = x$ b, 45, 45-yard line

42. $35 + (-10) = x$ c, 25, 25°F

Emmitt Smith won the National Football League rushing title several times. In 1992, he rushed for 1713 yards.

Problem Solving **In Exercises 43 and 44, write a real-life situation that can be represented by the equation.** Answers vary.

⊕ **43.** $12 + (-15) = x$

✪ **44.** $-15 + 40 = x$

Number Line Model **In Exercises 45 and 46, find a pair of integers whose sum is -1. (Use the integers labeled a, b, c, and d.)** a and d, b and c

45. 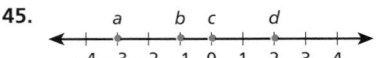 a and d, b and c

46.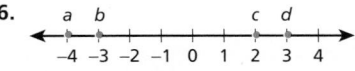

Integrated Review

Making Connections within Mathematics

Computation Sense **In Exercises 47–54, simplify the expression.**

47. $|9 + 7|$ 16

48. $|15 + 6|$ 21

49. $|11 + (-2)|$ 9

50. $|5 + (-8)|$ 3

51. $|-7 + 4|$ 3

52. $|-3 + 10|$ 7

53. $|-2 + (-6)|$ 8

54. $|-10 + (-1)|$ 11

Exploration and Extension

Dinosaurs **In Exercises 55–57, find the period in which the dinosaur lived.**

⊕ **55.** *Stegasaurus:* 122 million years before the end of the Cretaceous Period Jurassic

⊕ **56.** *Torosaurus:* 117 million years after the beginning of the Jurassic Period Cretaceous

⊕ **57.** *Plateosaurus:* 72 million years before the end of the Jurassic Period Triassic

3.3

Adding Three or More Integers

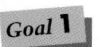

What you should learn:

Goal 1 How to add three or more integers

Goal 2 How to simplify expressions by adding like terms

Why you should learn it:

You can use integer addition to solve real-life problems, such as finding the total number of yards gained in football.

Technology
Using a Calculator

Real Life
Football

Goal 1 **Adding Three or More Integers**

One way to model the sum of three or more integers is with a number line. On the number line, adding a positive number is represented by *movement to the right* and adding a negative number is represented by *movement to the left.*

Example 1   *Modeling Addition with a Number Line*

The sum of 3, -5, and 4 can be modeled as shown below.

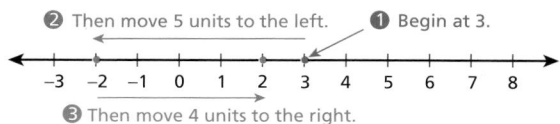

❷ Then move 5 units to the left.   ❶ Begin at 3.

❸ Then move 4 units to the right.

Begin at 3, then move 5 units to the left, then move 4 units to the right. Because you end at 2, you can conclude that $3 + (-5) + 4 = 2$. ∎

Example 2   *Using a Calculator to Add Integers*

Use a calculator to find $-6 + 5 + (-7) + 1$.

Solution

Calculator Steps	Display	Conclusion
6 +/- + 5 + 7 +/- + 1 =	-7	The sum is -7. ∎

Example 3   *Finding the Number of Yards Gained*

On its first down, your team gained 7 yards. On its second down, it lost 13 yards. On its third down, it gained 14 yards. On its fourth down, it gained 1 yard. Did your team gain 10 yards and thus earn a first down?

Solution The total number of yards gained is
$7 + (-13) + 14 + 1$ or 9.
Thus, the team did not earn a first down. ∎

3.3 • Adding Three or More Integers **109**

LESSON Notes

ALTERNATE APPROACH
Using manipulatives For the first part of this lesson, you may wish to make a long number line out of string or yarn on the floor of your classroom. Increment the number line using spaces equal to a small footstep. Have different students perform addition of integers by stepping forward and backward along the number line to compute sums such as $5 + -7 = -2$. Do several examples. In some examples have students discover that the order doesn't matter. For example, $5 + -4 + 8$ yields the same answer as $5 + 8 + -4$. This gives students insight to the commutative property of addition, as well as demonstrating the strategy that adding the addends with the same sign is more efficient than doing the addition in order.

Example 1

Make sure students intuit the significance of beginning at 3 rather than at zero. This may well stimulate discussion of other options, such as beginning at -5! Such a discussion is even more likely to arise if the approach described above is used.

Example 2

Make sure that students realize the difference between the minus sign in a negative number and the minus sign in a subtraction operation.

Example 3

Have students explain first downs in football for those who are not familiar with the rules.

Goal 2   Adding Like Terms

In the expression $-5x + 2$, the number -5 is the **coefficient** of x. When you add like terms, you can add the coefficients. Here are two examples.

Expression	Apply Distributive Property.	Simplify.
$4n + (-6n) + 3$	$[4 + (-6)]n + 3$	$-2n + 3$
$-5x + 7x + (-3x)$	$[-5 + 7 + (-3)]x$	$-x$

Example 4   *Evaluating an Expression*

Simplify the expression $-15x + 40x + (-16x)$. Then evaluate the expression when **a.** $x = 2$ and **b.** $x = 4$.

Solution

$$-15x + 40x + (-16x) = [-15 + 40 + (-16)]x$$
$$= 9x \quad \textit{Simplify.}$$

a. When $x = 2$, the value of the expression is
$9x = 9(2) = 18$.

b. When $x = 4$, the value of the expression is
$9x = 9(4) = 36$.

Need to Know

Coefficients of -1 and 1 are usually implied (rather than written). For instance, the coefficent of x is 1 and the coefficient of $-x$ is -1.

Communicating about MATHEMATICS

Real Life
Business

▶ **SHARING IDEAS about the Lesson**

Profit or Loss? You own an art business whose monthly profits and losses are shown in the graph. Did your business have an overall profit or an overall loss for the year? Explain.

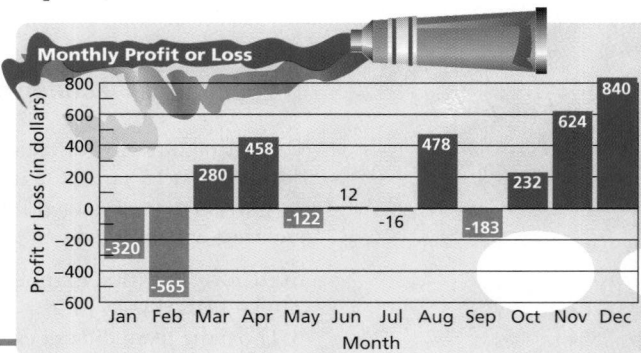

Monthly Profit or Loss

Month	Value
Jan	-320
Feb	-565
Mar	280
Apr	458
May	-122
Jun	12
Jul	-16
Aug	478
Sep	-183
Oct	232
Nov	624
Dec	840

An overall profit; the graph shows more profit above the line for zero than below it, so the sum of the profits and losses will be positive.

Technology

Playing a Calculator Word Game   **3.3**   Name _____

Exploration Using a Calculator

In this open-ended activity, you will use a calculator to "spell" words by evaluating the sum of several integers. You must use a calculator that upon entering a digit and turning the calculator upside-down, the inverted number(s) can be interpreted as a letter(s). The table below lists the letter(s) that correspond to each digit 0 through 9.

0 - O	4 - h	7 - L	1 - I	5 - S
8 - B	2 - Z	6 - g	9 - G	3 - E

EXAMPLE Playing the Word Game

Find the sum of $5924 + (-1250) + 3064$ using your calculator. Then write the word that corresponds to the result.

SOLUTION

To evaluate the sum, enter the following keystrokes on your calculator.

5924 ⊞ 1250 ⊬ ⊞ 3064 ⊟

The display should show ⟦7738⟧ and if you turn the calculator upside-down the word that is spelled is BELL.

EXERCISES

In Exercises 1–9, use your calculator to find the sum of the integers. Then write the word that corresponds to the result.

1. $1297 + 4211$
2. $-588 + (-2916)$
3. $1537 + (-1486)$
4. $31586 + (-16481) + 19904$
5. $-9013 + 4848 + (-3549)$
6. $-810 + 1428 + 2597$
7. $-210 + 675 + (-176) + 49$
8. $-368 + (-240) + (-102)$
9. $-4709 + (-974) + 11220$

In Exercises 10–12, write the sum that corresponds to the letters. Then evaluate the sum and find the resulting word.

10. $-\text{SObOgl} + \text{hZOLES}$
11. $-\text{GSEIZ} + (-\text{gLLOI})$
12. $-\text{GGE} + \text{IOgI} + (-\text{hBS})$

In Exercises 13–15, write the word as a sum of integers. (There is more than one correct answer.)

13. Lobe   Answers vary.
14. Soil   Answers vary.
15. Bless   Answers vary.

16. Find at least ten other words that can be spelled using a calculator.
Some possible words are: shell, gills, bill, boil, geese, beg, gloss, sell, loss, lose, hello, zoo.

1. 5508, boss
2. -3504, hose
3. 51, is
4. 35009, Goose
5. -7714, hill
6. 3215, size
7. 338, bee
8. -710, oil
9. 5537, less
10. -160405 + 527024, 376619, Giggle
11. -21359 + (-10776), -32135, seize
12. -399 + 1601 + (-584), 618, big

© D.C. Heath and Company   Technology Using Calculators and Computers 13

EXERCISES

Guided Practice

▶ **CHECK for Understanding**

In Exercises 1 and 2, use a number line to illustrate the movement. Then write your conclusion as an equation. See margin.

1. Begin at 4. Then move 2 units to the right. Then move 6 units to the left.

2. Begin at 2. Then move 5 units to the left. Then move 8 units to the right.

3. What are the terms in $-3x + 5x + 7$? Simplify the expression. $-3x, 5x, 7; 2x + 7$

4. *Computation Sense* From the number line, state whether $a + b + c$ is negative, positive, or zero. Explain. Positive; $a + c$ is positive because $|c| > |a|$, and b is positive.

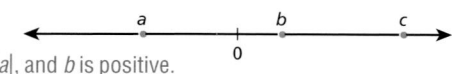

Independent Practice

In Exercises 5–16, find the sum. Write your conclusion as an equation. For equations, see Additional Answers.

5. $4 + (-5) + 6$ 5

6. $3 + (-9) + 13$ 7

7. $-7 + 1 + (-8)$ -14

8. $-6 + 2 + (-15)$ -19

9. $-8 + 12 + (-1)$ 3

10. $-10 + 16 + (-4)$ 2

11. $-12 + (-4) + (-8)$ -24

12. $-11 + (-7) + (-3)$ -21

13. $5 + (-6) + (-13)$ -14

14. $4 + (-8) + 9 + (-2)$ 3

15. $-7 + (-6) + 2 + (-7)$ -18

16. $-12 + (-4) + 20$ 4

In Exercises 17–22, use a calculator to find the sum.

17. $-36 + 49 + (-2) + 15$ 26

18. $-23 + 112 + (-9) + 13$ 93

19. $19 + (-39) + (-51)$ -71

20. $92 + (-20) + (-101)$ -29

21. $84 + (-89) + (-40)$ -45

22. $111 + 105 + (-99)$ 117

Reasoning **In Exercises 23 and 24, decide whether the sum is positive or negative. Explain how you can make your decision *without* actually finding the sum.**

23. $-237 + 122 + 69$ Negative, $|-237| > |122 + 69|$

24. $-142 + 127 + 89$ Positive, $|-142| < |127 + 89|$

In Exercises 25–36, simplify the expression. Then evaluate it when $x = 2$.

25. $-2x + 5x + 9$ $3x + 9, 15$

26. $8x + (-6x) + 3$ $2x + 3, 7$

27. $-2x + 10x + (-7x)$ $x, 2$

28. $9x + 13x + (-10x)$ $12x, 24$

29. $13x + (-11x) + x$ $3x, 6$

30. $2x + (-9x) + x$ $-6x, -12$

31. $-3x + 2x + 26x$ $25x, 50$

32. $-4x + 9x + 6x$ $11x, 22$

33. $-7x + 8 + 17x$ $10x + 8, 28$

34. $-8x + 10 + 12x$ $4x + 10, 18$

35. $5x + 3 + (-8) + (-3x)$ $2x + (-5), -1$

36. $9x + 6 + (-18) + (-6x)$ $3x + (-12), -6$

In Exercises 37–42, complete the statement using $>$, $<$, or $=$.

37. $-4 \boxed{?} 6 + (-2)$ $<$

38. $3 + (-4) \boxed{?} 6 + (-9)$ $>$

39. $-5 + 5 \boxed{?} -5 + (-5)$ $>$

40. $-5 + (-3) \boxed{?} -9$ $>$

41. $-9 \boxed{?} -7 + 16$ $<$

42. $4 + (-2) \boxed{?} -6 + 8$ $=$

Extra Practice

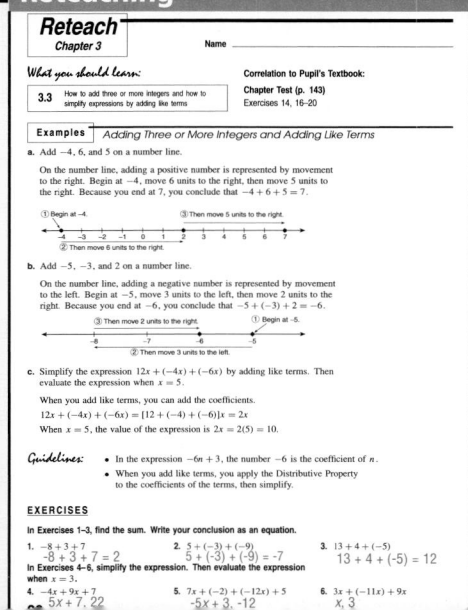

Reteaching

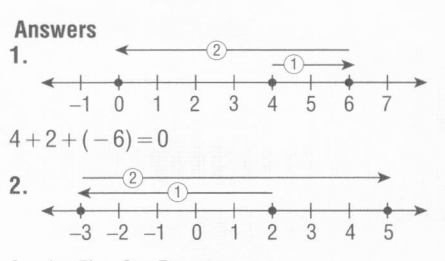

EXERCISE Notes

ASSIGNMENT GUIDE

Basic/Average:
Day 1: Ex. 11–29 odd, 37–41 odd, 43, 44
Day 2: Ex. 45–52

Above Average: Ex. 11–23 odd, 31–45 odd, 48–52

Advanced: Ex. 11–23 odd, 31–45 odd, 48–52

Selected Answers: Ex. 1–4, 5–51 odd

Guided Practice

▶ **Ex. 4** This exercise offers a visual context for integer addition.

EXTENSION
You may wish to have students change the locations of a, b, and c to yield different solutions.

Independent Practice

▶ **Ex. 5–16** Encourage students to compute these sums mentally.

▶ **Ex. 29, 30**

Common-Error Alert!

Students may forget to include the coefficient 1 that is implied in each of these exercises.

Answers

1.

$$4 + 2 + (-6) = 0$$

2.

$$2 + (-5) + 8 = 5$$

First Downs   **In Exercises 43 and 44, decide whether the football team earns a first down. Explain your reasoning.**

43. On its first down, the team gains 6 yards. On its second down, it loses 3 yards. On its third down, it loses 4 yards. On its fourth down, it gains 8 yards.
No, $6 + (-3) + (-4) + 8 < 10$

✪ 44. On its first down, the team gains 8 yards. On its second down, it gains 1 yard. On its third down, it loses 5 yards. On its fourth down, it gains 7 yards.
Yes, $8 + 1 + (-5) + 7 \geq 10$

Flying a Plane   **In Exercises 45–47, imagine that you are flying a Boeing 747 jet airliner. You are instructed by air traffic control to change your elevation, then change it again. What is your final elevation? In which exercise must the airplane have changed directions? Explain.**   Exercise 47, because 35 is odd and 34 is even

✪ 45. You are flying at an altitude of 31,000 feet. You lower the airplane 2,000 feet, then raise the airplane 4,000 feet. 33,000 ft

✪ 46. You are flying at an altitude of 40,000 feet. You raise the airplane 4,000 feet. Then you lower the airplane 6,000 feet. 38,000 ft

✪ 47. You are flying at an altitude of 35,000 feet. You raise the airplane 5,000 feet. Then you lower the airplane 6,000 feet. 34,000 ft

Commercial airplanes whose direction is north or east must fly at "odd" altitudes. Those whose direction is south or west must fly at "even" altitudes.

Integrated Review

Making Connections within Mathematics

Number Sense   **In Exercises 48–51, complete the statement using >, <, or =.**

48. $|3 + (-2)|$ [?] $|3| + |-2|$ <

49. $|-4 + (-5)|$ [?] $|-4| + |-5|$ =

50. $|-4 + 7|$ [?] $|-4| + |7|$ <

51. $|-5 + 3|$ [?] $|-5| + |3|$ <

Exploration and Extension

✪ 52. *Finding an Exam Average*   You have the following exam scores in math.

84, 91, 82, 89, 93, 84, 87, 94

Here is one way to find your average without using a calculator. Begin by guessing the average, say 85. Then, determine the amounts by which your scores are above or below 85, as shown at the right. Find the average of these amounts. Add that average to 85 to determine your actual average. 3, 88

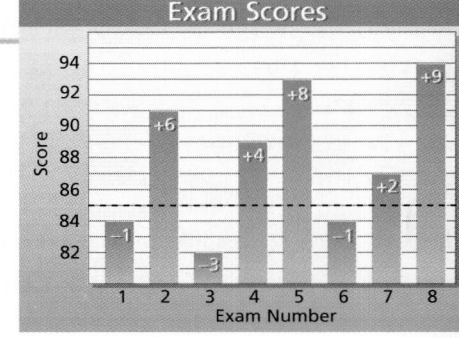

Exam Scores

Score vs *Exam Number*

(Bar graph showing: Exam 1: −1, Exam 2: +6, Exam 3: −3, Exam 4: +4, Exam 5: +8, Exam 6: +2, Exam 7: −1, Exam 8: +9)

Mixed REVIEW

In Exercises 1–8, evaluate the expression when $n = 3$. (1.3–1.5)

1. $6n - 12$ 6
2. $n^2 - 4$ 5
3. $13n + 16$ 55
4. $1.2n + 1.5$ 5.1

5. $6 \times (n - 1)$ 12
6. $\frac{1}{4}(n \times 8)$ 6
7. $n^2 \div 3$ 3
8. $14 \times (n + 2) - 15$
                                    55

In Exercises 9–11, complete the statement using $>$, $<$, or $=$. (3.1)

9. $\frac{1}{8}(32)$? $\frac{1}{4}(16)$ $=$
10. $16 + (-8)$? $10 + (-3)$ $>$
11. $-12 + (-2)$? $-17 + 5$
                                                       $<$

12. Are the equations $x - 12 = 4$ and $x = 17$ equivalent? Explain. **(2.4)** No, the solutions are different.

In Exercises 13–20, solve the equation. Check your solution. (2.4)
                                                                                            33
13. $x - 2 = 14$ 16
14. $y + 5 = 6$ 1
15. $14 + z = 34$ 20
16. $a - 11 = 22$

17. $3b = 6$ 2
18. $16c = 32$ 2
19. $\frac{1}{2}p = 5$ 10
20. $10q = \frac{1}{2}$ $\frac{1}{20}$

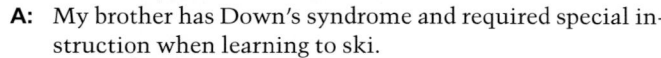

Career Interview

Downhill Ski Coach

Catherine Smith, certified by the Vermont Handicapped Ski and Sports Association, is the head downhill ski coach for the Vermont Special Olympics.

Q: *What led you into this career?*
A: My brother has Down's syndrome and required special instruction when learning to ski.

Q: *What is your favorite part of your job?*
A: Working with the athletes. Our athletes have a unique perspective—they care as much about the success of their peers as they do about their own success.

Q: *What math do you use in your job?*
A: To maintain balance and stability, skiers have to learn how to position their skis at different angles in order to turn, speed, and stop. I draw a diagram in the snow of a clock and use the hand positions on the clock to describe the position of the skis.

Q: *What would you like to tell kids who are in school about math?*
A: Don't get uptight about math. It's easy when you relate it to things you know and it is fun! There are a lot of uses for it and math is one of the most important skills you'll use when you get any type of job.

Materials

Teaching Tools
  Number counters, pp. T7, C9

Be aware that this investigation for subtracting integers does not assume the Subtracting Integers rule presented on page 116. For this reason, in addition to the steps described in the investigation on page 104, two further techniques must be used.

- To model subtraction, counters must be *removed* from the mat during regrouping.
- When the number of counters to be removed exceeds the number of counters on the mat, we keep placing zero-pairs on the mat until there are enough counters to be removed.

  In Sample 2, we need to remove 7 black counters. There are only 4 black counters on the mat. So we place 3 zero-pairs on the mat. We can then remove 7 black counters, leaving 3 *red* counters that represent the result of the operation.

  Similarly, in Sample 4, we need to remove 4 red counters. There are no red counters on the mat. So we place 4 zero-pairs on the mat. We can then remove 4 red counters, leaving 5 *black* counters that represent the result of the operation.

MATH JOURNAL

Have students work Ex. 9 in their journals or portfolios.

EXTENSION

You may wish to have students discover the Subtracting Integers rule presented on page 116. Have them model $4 + (-7)$ and compare the process and result with Sample 2. Similarly have them compare $-5 + 3$ with Sample 3 and $1 + 4$ with Sample 4.

LESSON INVESTIGATION 3.4
Modeling Subtraction

Materials Needed: number counters, mat, pencil, paper

In this investigation, you will use number counters to model integer subtraction.

Sample 1: Finding the Difference of Two Positive Integers

The difference $5 - 3 = 2$ can be modeled as follows.

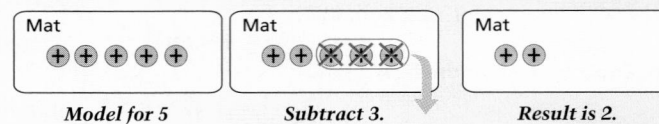

Model for 5   *Subtract 3.*   *Result is 2.*

Sample 2: Finding the Difference of Two Positive Integers

The difference $4 - 7 = -3$ can be modeled as follows.

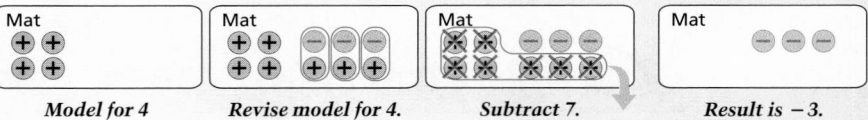

Model for 4.   *Revise model for 4.*   *Subtract 7.*   *Result is −3.*

Sample 3: Finding the Difference of Two Negative Integers

The difference $-5 - (-3) = -2$ can be modeled as follows:

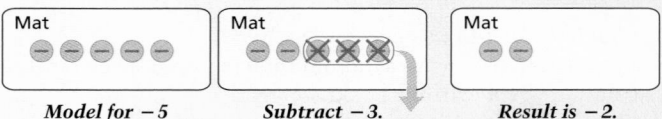

Model for −5   *Subtract −3.*   *Result is −2.*

Sample 4: Finding the Difference of a Positive and a Negative Integer

The difference $1 - (-4) = 5$ can be modeled as follows.

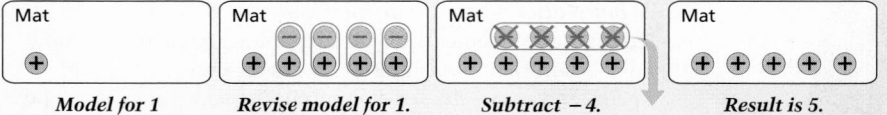

Model for 1   *Revise model for 1.*   *Subtract −4.*   *Result is 5.*

Exercises

In Exercises 1–8, use number counters to find the difference.   Check students' work.

1. $6 - 4$ 2   **2.** $3 - 2$ 1   **3.** $4 - 6$ −2   **4.** $5 - 8$ −3

5. $-2 - (-4)$ 2   **6.** $-1 - (-2)$ 1   **7.** $1 - (-5)$ 6   **8.** $-6 - 2$ −8

P **9.** *Think About It*   Can the difference of a positive integer and a negative integer be positive? Can it be negative? Explain.
Yes, no; subtracting a negative integer gives the same result as adding its opposite.

114   *Chapter 3* ▪ *Modeling Integers*   **P** Portfolio Opportunity

---

3.4

Subtracting Integers

What you should learn:

Goal 1 How to use opposites to subtract integers

Goal 2 How to simplify expressions involving subtraction

Why you should learn it:

You can use integer subtraction to simplify algebraic expressions, such as $5x - (-4x) + 3$.

Goal 1 Subtracting Integers

The *Investigation* on page 114 shows how counters can be used to subtract integers. In this lesson, you will use opposites to subtract integers. The number you obtain from subtracting one integer from another is the **difference** of the integers.

LESSON INVESTIGATION

■ Investigating Integer Subtraction

Group Activity Complete the following. Compare your results with others in your group. How do the results of the two columns compare? Use your results to describe a rule for subtracting integers.

$5 - 3 = \boxed{?}$ 2		$5 + (-3) = \boxed{?}$ 2
$5 - 4 = \boxed{?}$ 1		$5 + (-4) = \boxed{?}$ 1
$5 - 5 = \boxed{?}$ 0		$5 + (-5) = \boxed{?}$ 0
$5 - 6 = \boxed{?}$ −1		$5 + (-6) = \boxed{?}$ −1
$5 - 7 = \boxed{?}$ −2		$5 + (-7) = \boxed{?}$ −2

Need to Know

If an integer b is positive, then its opposite $-b$ is negative. For instance, the opposite of 17 is -17.

If an integer b is negative, then its opposite $-b$ is positive. For instance, the opposite of -5 is 5.

Notice that the integer $-b$ is *not necessarily negative*. If b is itself negative, then $-b$ is positive.

Subtracting Integers

To subtract an integer b from an integer a, add the opposite of b to a.

$$a - b = a + (-b)$$

Example **1** *Subtracting Integers*

a. $5 - 7 = 5 + (-7) = -2$ *Opposite of 7 is -7.*

b. $-6 - 8 = -6 + (-8) = -14$ *Opposite of 8 is -8.*

c. $-9 - (-9) = -9 + (9) = 0$ *Opposite of -9 is 9.*

d. $-5 - (-1) = -5 + 1 = -4$ *Opposite of -1 is 1.*

e. $13 - 12 = 13 + (-12) = 1$ *Opposite of 12 is -12.* ■

3.4 • Subtracting Integers   115

ORGANIZER

Starters (reproduced below)
  Problem of the Day 3.4, p. 8
  Warm-Up Exercises 3.4, p. 8
Lesson Resources
  Color Transparencies
    Picture for Ex. 56–58, p. 13
  Teaching Tools
    Number lines, pp. T6, C8
  Math Log, p. 11
  Answer Masters 3.4, pp. 51, 52
  Extra Practice Copymaster 3.4, p. 21
  Reteaching Copymaster 3.4, p. 21
  Enrichment Projects, pp. 12, 13
Special Populations
  Suggestions, Teacher's Edition, p. 98D

LESSON Notes

The teacher notes for the investigation on page 115 included an Extension, in which it was explained how students could be encouraged to discover the rule for subtracting integers. Instead of subtracting 7 in Sample 2 by removing 7 black counters from the mat, students were asked to add 7 red counters. This technique was found to produce the same result. In other words, subtracting an integer is equivalent to adding its opposite.

Common-Error Alert!

Be sure to emphasize the third paragraph in the Need to Know box. Warm-Up Exercise 3 also referred to this concept. Some students have difficulty in recognizing that $-b$ does not imply a negative number. You can help them over this difficulty by reinforcing the concept of *variable* as a kind of placeholder for values that may turn out to be either positive or negative. Ask students for examples where $-b$ is not a negative number.

Example 1

Emphasize that the process of subtracting integers involves writing an equivalent statement of addition. You may wish to verbalize the intermediate step in each part of the example. For example, "instead of subtracting 7, add negative 7 . . . instead of subtracting negative 9, add 9, etc."

The average of Sarah's ten test scores is 87. However, her teacher has a new method for computing averages that involves throwing out the top and bottom scores and averaging what remains. Sarah's top score is 95 and her low score is 55. Should Sarah complain about this new averaging method? No! Sarah's total score was 870. After subtracting 95 and 55, her remaining score is 720 and her new average is 90.

Also available as a copymaster, page 8

1. Add these integers.
   a. $-6 + (-8)$
   b. $13 + (-15)$
   c. $11 + (-7) + 3$
   a. -14, b. -2, c. 7
2. Find the absolute value as indicated.
   a. $|5|$ **b.** $|-6|$ **c.** $|-3|$ **d.** $|0|$
   a. 5, b. 6, c. 3, d. 0
3. Which of the following is a negative number when $x = -1$?
   a. $3x$ **b.** $-3x$ a.

Also available as a copymaster, page 8

Goal 2 Simplifying Expressions

The *terms* of an algebraic expression are separated by addition, not subtraction. To recognize the terms of an expression involving subtraction, you can rewrite the expression as a sum. Here are two examples.

Expression	Rewrite as Sum	Terms
$2x - 4$	$2x + (-4)$	$2x$ and -4
$-3x - 2x + 5$	$-3x + (-2x) + 5$	$-3x$, $-2x$, and 5

The *Distributive Property*, $a(b + c) = ab + ac$, also applies to subtraction. The "subtraction form" of the property is

$a(b - c) = ab - ac$.   *Distributive Property*

The next example shows how this property can be used.

Example 2 *Simplifying Expressions*

Simplify the expression $11x - 2x + 3$. Then evaluate the expression when **a.** $x = 5$ and **b.** $x = 8$.

Solution

$$11x - 2x + 3 = (11 - 2)x + 3 \quad \textit{Distributive Property}$$
$$= 9x + 3 \quad \textit{Simplify.}$$

a. When $x = 5$ the value of the expression is
$$9x + 3 = 9(5) + 3 = 48.$$

b. When $x = 8$ the value of the expression is
$$9x + 3 = 9(8) + 3 = 75.$$

"There isn't no way" means "there is a way." Two negative conditions applied to a noun and two negative conditions applied to a number both result in a positive condition.

Communicating about MATHEMATICS

▶ **SHARING IDEAS about the Lesson** See above.

Connections
English

Comparing Mathematics and English A friend of yours says "There isn't no way I will finish on time." Your friend meant to say that he will not be able to finish on time, but what does his statement really mean?

Your friend's statement contains a *double negative*. How is his statement related to the mathematical equation $3 - (-4) = 7$?

EXERCISES

Guided Practice

▶ **CHECK for Understanding**

1. Explain how to evaluate $5 - (-2)$.
  $5 - (-2) = 5 + 2 = 7$

2. Apply the Distributive Property to $r(s - t)$.
  $rs - rt$

Reasoning **In Exercises 3–6, decide whether the statement is true for all values of x, some values of x, or no values of x. Explain.** For explanations, see margin.

3. $5x - 2x - 12 = 5x + (-2x) + (-12)$ All

4. The opposite of x is 0. Some

5. $3(x - 4) = 3x - (-12)$. No

6. The opposite of x is negative. Some

Independent Practice

In Exercises 7–22, find the difference. Write your conclusion as an equation.
11.–18. For equations, see Additional Answers.

7. $11 - 6$ $11 - 6 = 5$

8. $19 - 17$ $19 - 17 = 2$

9. $13 - 18$ $13 - 18 = -5$

10. $5 - 9$ $5 - 9 = -4$

11. $23 - (-8)$ 31

12. $2 - (-4)$ 6

13. $-10 - 7$ -17

14. $-3 - 3$ -6

15. $-5 - (-5)$ 0

16. $-16 - (-8)$ -8

17. $-5 - 5$ -10

18. $-16 - 8$ -24

19. $0 - 27$ $0 - 27 = -27$

20. $0 - 13$ $0 - 13 = -13$

21. $0 - (-61)$
  $0 - (-61) = 61$

22. $0 - (-43)$
  $0 - (-43) = 43$

In Exercises 23–28, evaluate the expression when $a = 5$ and when $a = -5$.

23. $a - 1$ $4, -6$

24. $1 - a$ $-4, 6$

25. $a - 6$ $-1, -11$

26. $6 - a$ $1, 11$

27. $a - a$ $0, 0$

28. $a + a$ $10, -10$

In Exercises 29–32, rewrite the expression as a sum. Then identify the terms of the expression. See margin.

29. $3x - 2x + 16$

30. $7x - 9x - 5$

31. $7a - 5b$

32. $4 - 2n + 4m$

In Exercises 33–44, simplify the expression.

33. $9x - 6x - 17$ $3x - 17$

34. $18n - 12n + 4$ $6n + 4$

35. $-11y - (-15y) - 2$ $4y - 2$

36. $-20x - (-30x) + 10$ $10x + 10$

37. $b - (-2b)$ $3b$

38. $3x - (-3x)$ $6x$

39. $-2a - 3a - 4$ $-5a - 4$

40. $-13x - 13x - 13$ $-26x - 13$

41. $4m - 6m + 8$ $-2m + 8$

42. $16y - 20y + 24$ $-4y + 24$

43. $-14x - (-10x)$ $-4x$

44. $-30x - (-19x)$ $-11x$

In Exercises 45–50, use a calculator to evaluate the expression.

45. $-8 - 8 - (-8)$ -8

46. $8 - (-8) - 8$ 8

47. $21 - (-62) - 43$ 40

48. $43 - (-21) - 62$ 2

49. $-84 - 72 - (-100)$ -56

50. $-69 - (-96) - 56$ -29

51. *Technology* Explain the difference between the $\boxed{+/-}$ key and the $\boxed{-}$ key on a calculator. See margin.

P Portfolio Opportunity

ASSIGNMENT GUIDE

Basic/Average:
  Day 1: Ex. 7–13 odd, 26–28, 31, 32, 33–37 odd
  Day 2: Ex. 48–50, 54–57, 59–65 odd, 71

Above Average:
  Ex. 15–21 odd, 26–28, 39–43 odd, 48–50, 53–55 odd, 57, 58, 71

Advanced: Ex. 15–21 odd, 26–28, 39–43 odd, 48–50, 53–55 odd, 57, 58, 71

Selected Answers: Ex. 1–6, 7–65 odd

Guided Practice

▶ **Ex. 6** It may be necessary to work through several examples. Stress that the sign of x is unknown until x is replaced with a specific value.

Independent Practice

▶ **Ex. 23–28** Assign these exercises as a group. Point out that subtraction is not commutative.

▶ **Ex. 33, 34**
These exercises give students plenty of practice in distinguishing subtraction operations from negative signs.

▶ **Ex. 51**
MATH JOURNAL
The focus of this exercise is again the distinction between a subtraction operation and a negative sign. Have students write an explanation in their journals or portfolios.

Extra Practice

Extra Practice 3.4 Name _____

In Exercises 1–9, find the difference. Write your conclusion as an equation.
1. $3 - 7$ $3 - 7 = -4$
2. $-4 - (-3)$ $-4 - (-3) = -1$
3. $6 - (-8)$ $6 - (-8) = 14$
4. $10 - (-2)$ $10 - (-2) = 12$
5. $-23 - 2$ $-23 - 2 = -25$
6. $12 - (-8)$ $12 - (-8) = 20$
7. $14 - (-3)$ $14 - (-3) = 17$
8. $16 - (-16)$ $16 - (-16) = 32$
9. $-16 - 16$ $-16 - 16 = -32$

In Exercises 10–15, evaluate the expression when $a = 2$ and when $a = -2$.
10. $a - 3$ $-1, -5$
11. $3 - a$ $1, 5$
12. $a - 2$ $0, -4$
13. $6 - a$ $4, 8$
14. $a - a$ $0, 0$
15. $a + a$ $4, -4$

In Exercises 16 and 17, rewrite the expression as a sum. Then identify the terms of the expression.
16. $-4x - 2x + 8$ $4x + (-2x) + 8;$ $4x, -2x, 8$
17. $10x - 12 - 5$ $10x + (-12) + (-5);$ $10x, -12, -5$

In Exercises 18–23, simplify the expression.
18. $2x - 8x - 7$ $-6x - 7$
19. $11m - 2m + 2$ $9m + 2$
20. $-12y - (-3y) - 3$ $-9y - 3$
21. $-30x - 25x - 3x$ $-58x$
22. $-4z - (-16z)$ $12z$
23. $6 - (-2m) - 3m$ $6 - m$ or $-m + 6$

In Exercises 24–27, use a calculator to evaluate the expression.
24. $-20 - 37 - (-81)$ 24
25. $116 - 231 - (-324)$ 209
26. $6 - 6 - (-6)$ 6
27. $-6 - (-6) - 6$ -6

In Exercises 28 and 29, find values for a and b so that the statement is true. (There are many correct answers.)
28. a is positive, b is positive, and $b - a$ is negative. Answers vary.
29. a is negative, b is negative, and $b - a$ is positive. Answers vary.

In Exercises 30–32, use the table which shows the highest and lowest elevations on the continents. Positive numbers are elevations in feet above sea level and negative numbers are elevations in feet below sea level.

Asia, 30,340 ft;
North America, 20,602 ft;
Africa, 19,852 ft;
Europe, 18,602 ft

Continent	Highest point	Feet above sea level	Lowest point	Feet below sea level
Asia	Mt. Everest	29,028	Dead Sea	-1312
North America	Mt. McKinley	20,320	Death Valley	-282
Africa	Mt. Kilimanjaro	19,340	Lake Assal	-512
Europe	Mt. Elbrus	18,510	Caspian Sea	-92

30. Find the difference between the highest point and lowest point on each continent.
31. Find the difference between the lowest points in Asia and North America. -1030 ft
32. Find the difference between the highest points in Africa and Europe. 830 ft

---

Reteaching

Reteach Chapter 3 Name _____

What you should learn:

| 3.4 | How to use opposites to subtract integers and how to simplify expressions involving subtraction |

Correlation to Pupil's Textbook:
Mid-Chapter Self-Test (p. 120) Chapter Test (p. 143)
Exercises 11, 13 Exercise 8

Examples *Subtracting Integers and Simplifying Expressions*

a. To subtract an integer b from an integer a, add its opposite.
  $4 - 9 = 4 + (-9) = -5$ Opposite of 9 is -9.
  $-8 - (-5) = -8 + 5 = -3$ Opposite of -5 is 5.
  $15 - 6 = 15 + (-6) = 9$ Opposite of 6 is -6.
  $-10 - 5 = -10 + (-5) = -15$ Opposite of 5 is -5.

b. To recognize the terms of an expression involving subtraction, you can rewrite the expression as a sum.
  Rewrite $5x - x - 3$ as a sum. $5x - x - 3 = 5x + (-1x) + (-3)$
  Identify the terms of the expression. The terms are $5x$, $-1x$, and -3.

c. The "subtraction form" of the Distributive Property is $a(b - c) = ab - ac$.
  Use the Distributive Property to simplify the expression $9x - 4x - 5$. Then evaluate the expression when $x = 4$.
  $9x - 4x - 5 = (9 - 4)x - 5$ Distributive Property
  $\qquad = 5x - 5$ Simplify.
  When $x = 4$, the value of the expression is $5x - 5 = 5(4) - 5 = 15$.

Guidelines:
  • The number you obtain from subtracting one integer from another is the difference of the integers.
  • If b is positive, then its opposite $-b$ is negative.
  • If b is negative, then its opposite $-b$ is positive.
  • The terms of an algebraic expression are separated by addition, not subtraction.

EXERCISES
1. $11 - 16 = -5$
2. $24 - (-3) = 27$
3. $-18 - 9 = -27$

In Exercises 1–8, find the difference. Write your conclusion as an equation.
1. $11 - 16$
2. $24 - (-3)$
3. $-18 - 9$
4. $-15 - (-4) = -11$
5. $0 - 33$ $0 - 33 = -33$
6. $35 - 6$ $35 - 6 = 29$
7. $0 - (-13)$
  $7, 0$ $0 - (-13) = 13$
8. $-5 - 5$

In Exercises 9–11, rewrite the expression as a sum. Then identify the terms of the expression.
9. $3n + (-5n) + m$; $3n, -5n, m$
10. $8x + (-3x) + (-4)$; $8x, -3x, -4$
11. $7a - 9b - 6$
  $7a + (-9b) + (-6)$; $7a, -9b, -6$

In Exercises 12–14, simplify the expression. Then evaluate the expression when $x = 2$.
12. $-16x - (-5x) + 8$ $-11x + 8, -14$
13. $-12x - 7x + 10$ $-19x + 10, -28$
14. $2x - (-2x)$ $4x, 8$

Answers

3. Subtracting a quantity gives the same result as adding its opposite.

4. x can only equal 0.

5. The equation simplifies to $3x + 12 = 3x - 12$, which cannot be true for any value of x.

6. The statement is false when $x \le 0$.

29. $3x + (-2x) + 16; 3x, -2x, 16$

30. $7x + (-9x) + (-5); 7x, -9x, -5$

31. $7a + (-5b); 7a, -5b$

32. $4 + (-2n) + 4m; 4, -2n, 4m$

51. The $\boxed{+/-}$ key refers to the sign of a number, usually negative; the $\boxed{-}$ key refers to the operation of subtraction and is used between two numbers.

Ex. 52–55

COOPERATIVE LEARNING

These exercises offer a fine opportunity for working cooperatively. Have students discuss the problems in small groups and later report results to the whole class. Results could also be posted on the bulletin board.

▶ Ex. 56–58

EXTENSION

Have students research the high and low temperatures for the remaining planets.

Integrated Review

▶ **Ex. 59–62** Have students label the points they plot with "–a". This will help to reinforce the concept that –a can be a positive number.

Exploration and Extension

▶ **Ex. 67–71** Assign these exercises as a group. Students should conclude that subtraction is not commutative.

EXTENSION

Ask students to find the absolute value of each answer to Ex. 67–70, and then have them make a conjecture. Students should conclude that $|a - b| = |b - a|$.

Portfolio Opportunity: Math Log

Can the sign of $a - b$ be determined by knowing only the signs of a and b? Provide an explanation or counterexample for each case.

Also available as a copymaster, page 11, Ex. 5

Short Quiz

Covers Lessons 3.3 and 3.4

Available as a copymaster, page 32

Alternative Assessment

A cooperative learning project that develops students' ability to use integer operations.

Available as a copymaster, page 19

Computation Sense **In Exercises 52–55, find values for x and y so that the statement is true. (There are many correct answers.)** Answers vary. **52.** $x=3, y=2$ **53.** $x=2, y=3$

✪ **52.** x is positive, y is positive, and $x - y$ is positive.

✪ **53.** x is positive, y is positive, and $x - y$ is negative.

✪ **54.** x is negative, y is negative, and $x - y$ is negative.

✪ **55.** x is negative, y is negative, and $x - y$ is positive.
  54. $x = -3, y = -2$ **55.** $x = -2, y = -3$

Science **In Exercises 56–58, use the table, which gives the low and high surface temperatures of four planets in degrees Fahrenheit.**

Of the other eight planets in our solar system, Mars has a temperature range that is most similar to the range on Earth.

	1080	265	288	18
Planet	Mercury	Earth	Mars	Pluto
Low	−279	−129	−225	−387
High	801	136	63	−369

56. Find the difference between the high temperature and the low temperature of each planet. See above.

57. Find the difference between the low temperatures of Earth and Pluto. 258°

58. Find the difference between the high temperatures of Mercury and Mars. 738°

Integrated Review *Making Connections within Mathematics*

Opposites **In Exercises 59–62, copy the number line and plot the opposite of a.** Check students' work.

59.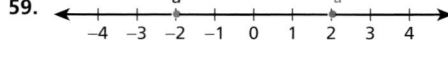

60.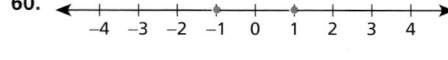

61.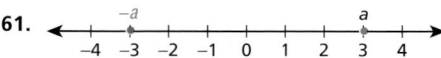

62.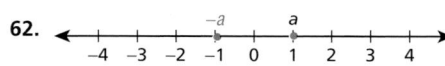

Equation Sense **In Exercises 63–66, solve the equation. Check your solution.**

63. $t + 34 = 71$ 37   **64.** $r - 85 = 97$ 182   **65.** $36n = 324$ 9   **66.** $\frac{s}{28} = 5$ 140

Exploration and Extension

In Exercises 67–70, evaluate the expression.

67. $5 - 3$ 2   **68.** $3 - 5$ −2   **69.** $-7 - 12$ −19   **70.** $12 - (-7)$ 19

✪ **71.** *Making a Conjecture* Use the results of Exercises 67–70 to make a conjecture about the values of $a - b$ and $b - a$. Test your conjecture with several values of a and b. $a - b$ and $b - a$ are opposites.

✪ More difficult exercises

Enrichment

| Temperature Changes | 3.4 | Name _____ |

Below is the game board to "The Integer Game," designed to help you add and subtract integers. Your teacher will provide you with markers, dice and a coin. One die represents positive numbers and the other represents negative numbers. One side of the coin represents addition; the other side represents subtraction.

When it is your turn, roll the dice and flip the coin. Create an expression using the two integers on the dice and the operation indicated by the coin and calculate the answer. If the answer is positive, move forward that many spaces. If it is negative, move backward. Take turns until someone in your group has reached 100 points. Good luck!!

Add −15 to your score	Lose a turn!	Go ahead 3 spaces
Take another turn!		Subtract −5 from your score
	THE INTEGER GAME	
Go back 2 spaces		Add the next player's score to yours!
You lose 10 points	You earn 9 points	START ←

USING A CALCULATOR
Negative Numbers

Technology
Using a Calculator

All scientific and graphing calculators have a key that allows you to enter a negative number. For example, to enter −9 on a scientific or graphing calculator, use the following keystrokes.

	Keystrokes	Display
Scientific calculator:	9 [+/−]	−9
Graphing calculator:	[(−)] 9	−9

Make sure you do not confuse these keys with the subtraction key. They are not the same!

Example   *Adding and Subtracting Integers*

Use a scientific or graphing calculator to evaluate the following expressions.

a. −9 + 4 + (−11)   **b.** 7 + (−10) − (−5)

Solution

Use the keystrokes that correspond to your calculator.

Scientific calculator
a. Keystrokes:

     9 [+/−] [+] 4 [+] 11 [+/−] [=]
     The display should show −16.

b. Keystrokes:

     7 [+] 10 [+/−] [−] 5 [+/−] [=]
     The display should show 2.

Graphing calculator
a. Keystrokes:

     [(−)] 9 [+] 4 [+] [(−)] 11 [ENTER]
     The display should show −16.

b. Keystrokes:

     7 [+] [(−)] 10 [−] [(−)] 5 [ENTER]
     The display should show 2.

Exercises

In Exercises 1–6, use a scientific or graphing calculator to evaluate the expression.

1. −12 + 16 + (−6)   −2   **2.** 8 − (−17) − 30   −5   **3.** 37 + 16 + (−53)   0

4. 83 + (−62) − 31   −10   **5.** 154 − 23 + (−76) − (−2)   57   **6.** 148 − (−16) + (−121)   43

7. Using your calculator, evaluate 31 + 14 and 31 − (−14). What is the result of each expression? Is $a + b$ always equal to $a − (−b)$ when a and b are integers? Investigate.   45, yes

One common mistake students make when using a scientific calculator is to press the [+/−] key before they enter the number. Students can become further confused because, on the graphing calculator, the [(−)] key *is* entered before the number.

To emphasize that the [−] key and the [+/−] key have different functions, have students enter Example **b** using only the [−] key and discuss their results.

Mid-Chapter SELF-TEST

Take this test as you would take a test in class. The answers to the exercises are given in the back of the book.

In Exercises 1–3, draw a number line and plot the numbers. (3.1) See margin.

1. $-2, 1, -4$ **2.** $4, -1, 0$ **3.** $2, -2, 0$

4. Write the opposite and absolute value of 7. **(3.1)** $-7, 7$

5. Write the opposite and absolute value of -5. **(3.1)** $5, 5$

6. Order the integers $-2, 4, 3,$ and -3 from least to greatest. **(3.1)** $-3, -2, 3, 4$

In Exercises 7–9, use mental math to solve the equation. (3.2)

7. $2 + a = 10$ 8 **8.** $-5 + b = 5$ 10 **9.** $3 + c = -2$ -5

In Exercises 10–13, evaluate the expression when $a = -2$ and $b = -8$. (3.2)

10. $|a| + |b|$ 10 **11.** $|b| - |a|$ 6 **12.** $|a + b|$ 10 **13.** $|a - b|$ 6

In Exercises 14 and 15, use the bar graph at the right. The graph shows the changes in weights (in pounds) of eight racehorses during a ten-week training program. (3.3)

14. Find the sum of the changes in weights of the eight horses. -12 lb

15. Which horse's weight changed the most? Explain your reasoning. C's, $|-7|$ or 7 is the biggest change.

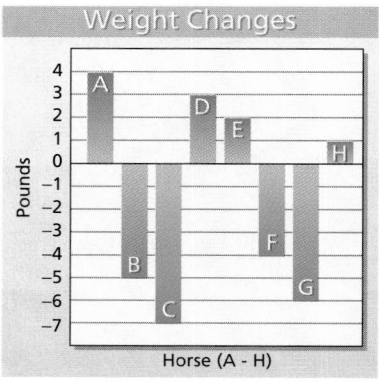
Weight Changes

In Exercises 16 and 17, simplify the expression. Then evaluate the expression when $a = 6$ and $b = 2$. (3.3)

16. $4a + 2a - 6b$
$6a - 6b, 24$

17. $7a - 2b - 3a$
$4a - 2b, 20$

In Exercises 18–20, consider the following. (3.3)

You are a golfer in the PGA tour. Each tournament consists of 4 rounds of 18 holes. You have completed 2 tournaments with the indicated scores. (Each score lists your strokes above or below par.) To find your final score, add the scores for the 4 rounds.

First Tournament: $-2, 1, 2, -2$
Second Tournament: $3, -2, -2, 1$

18. Find the final score for your first tournament. -1

19. Find the final score for your second tournament. 0

20. Your opponent scored $3, -2, -2,$ and 1 in the first tournament. Whose score was better? Your score

In 1991, about 1.7 million teenagers played golf in the United States. (Source: National Sporting Goods Association)

Answers

1.
$-4 \ -3 \ -2 \ -1 \ 0 \ 1 \ 2$

2.
$-2 \ -1 \ 0 \ 1 \ 2 \ 3 \ 4$

3.
$-3 \ -2 \ -1 \ 0 \ 1 \ 2 \ 3$

Alternative Assessment ▶

A **Partner Quiz** assesses students' achievement and provides them with an opportunity to communicate about mathematics.
Available as a copymaster, page 46

Formal Assessment ▶

Two **Mid-Chapter Tests** of average difficulty.
Available as copymasters, pages 33, 34

Partner Quiz

| Chapter 3 | (Use after Lesson 3.4) |
| Mid-Chapter Partner Quiz | |
Name _____

1. Draw a number line and plot the integers $-3, 2, 0,$ and -1. (3.1) 1. _____
$-3 \ -2 \ -1 \ 0 \ 1 \ 2$

2. Compare the integers using $<$, $>$, or $=$. (3.1) 2. $>$
$|-12| \boxed{?} 6$

3. What is the sum of any two opposites? (3.2) 3. 0

4. Find the sum. (3.2) 4. -7
$-10 + |-3|$

5. Simplify the expression. Then evaluate the expression when $x = 4$. (3.3) 5. $5x - 8$; 12
$-3x - 12 + 8x + 4$

6. Write an equation that models the given directions: Begin at 3, move 4 units left, move 2 units right, and move 1 unit left. Evaluate. (3.3) 6. $3 - 4 + 2 - 1 = x$, 0

7. Write an equation for the given situation. Then use mental math to solve the equation. On a 100 point exam, you lost 17 points but also earned 3 bonus points. (3.3) 7. $100 + (-17) + 3 = x$; 86

8. Simplify the expression. Then evaluate the expression when $x = 3$. (3.4) 8. $-8x - 3$; -27
$-10x - (-2x) - 3$

9. Subtracting a from b is the same as adding what two numbers? (3.4) 9. $b + (-a)$

10. Complete the statement with always, sometimes, or never. (3.4) 10. Sometimes
$a - (-b)$ is _____ positive.

Mid-Chapter Test

| Mid-Chapter **3** | Test | Form B | Name _____ |
| | (Use after Lesson 3.4) | | Date _____ |

In Exercises 1 and 2, order the numbers from least to greatest. (3.1)

1. $5, -6, 3, |4|$ 1. $-6, 3, 4, 5$

2. $-2, 7, 0, |-5|$ 2. $-2, 0, 5, 7$

3. Write the opposite and absolute value of -8. 3. $+8, +8$

4. Choose four numbers between -4 and $+4$. Draw them on a number line. 4. Answers vary.

In Exercises 5 and 6, solve the equation. (3.2)

5. $4 + t = -7$ 5. $t = -11$

6. $-3 + g = -5$ 6. $g = -2$

In Exercises 7 and 8, evaluate the expression when $m = 5$ and $n = 7$. (3.1, 3.4)

7. $|m| - n$ 7. -2

8. $n - |m|$ 8. 2

9. Simplify the expression $12c + (-7c) - 2d$ when $c = 2$ and $d = 4$. (3.4) 9. 2

In Exercises 10 and 11, use the bar graph showing the change in Jeremy's 50-meter freestyle swim times from his average time for one week. His average time is 35.00 (35 seconds). (3.1, 3.3)

Jeremy's 50-m Freestyle Times

10. On what day did Jeremy's time change the most? Explain your reasoning. Saturday; a change of 0.08 seconds. 10.

11. On which day was Jeremy's time the fastest? What was it? 11. Saturday; 34.52

Materials Needed: number counters, mat, pencil, paper

In this investigation, you will use number counters to model integer multiplication.

Sample 1: Finding the Product of a Positive and a Negative Integer

To model the product $3 \times (-2)$, you can *put in* 2 red counters, 3 times. The result shows that $3 \times (-2) = -6$.

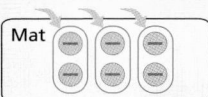 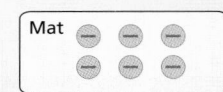

Put in −2, 3 times.   *Result is −6.*

Sample 2: Finding the Product of a Negative and a Positive Integer

To model the product -3×2, you can *take out* 2 black counters, 3 times. Because there are no black counters to take out, begin by modeling 0 with 6 pairs of red and black counters. The result shows that $-3 \times 2 = -6$.

 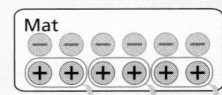 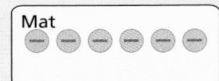

Model for 0   *Take out 2, 3 times.*   *Result is −6.*

Sample 3: Finding the Product of Two Negative Integers

To model the product $-3 \times (-2)$, you can *take out* 2 red counters, 3 times. Because there are no red counters to take out, begin by modeling 0 with 6 pairs of red and black counters. The result shows that $-3 \times (-2) = 6$.

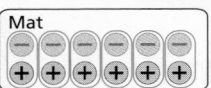 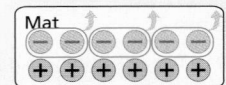 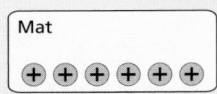

Model for 0   *Take out −2, 3 times.*   *Result is 6.*

Exercises

In Exercises 1–8, use number counters to find the product. Check students' work.

1. 2×4 8   **2.** 3×2 6   **3.** $2 \times (-5)$ −10   **4.** $4 \times (-3)$ −12

5. -3×3 −9   **6.** -2×2 −4   **7.** $-2 \times (-4)$ 8   **8.** $-3 \times (-4)$ 12

 **9.** What can you say about the product of a negative integer and a positive integer? Can the result be positive? It is always negative, no.

10. Write a general statement about the product of two negative integers. The product of two negative integers is always positive.

Materials
Teaching Tools
   Number counters, pp. T7, C9

The basic principle of multiplication applied in this investigation is as follows:
In the expression $a \times b$, if a is positive, b is added a times. If a is negative, b is subtracted a times.

For example, the expression 3×2 represents the *adding* of 2, *3 times*.

On the other hand, -3×2 represents the *subtracting* of 2, *3 times*.

In terms of modeling $a \times b$, if a is positive, you *add* b tiles a times; if a is negative, you *remove* b tiles a times.

If the number of tiles to be removed exceeds the number of tiles on the mat, keep placing zero-pairs on the mat until there are enough counters to be removed. For instance, in Sample 2, the convention requires that we remove 6 black counters from the mat (2 black counters, 3 times). There are no black counters on the mat, so we place 6 zero-pairs on the mat, remove 6 black counters, resulting in a set of 6 red counters that represent the result of the operation.

MATH JOURNAL
Have students work Ex. 9, 10 in their journals or portfolios.

▶ **PACING the Lesson**

Suggested Number of Days
Basic/Average 2 **Above Average** 1
Advanced 1

▶ **PLANNING the Lesson**

Lesson Plan 3.5, p. 22

ORGANIZER

Starters (reproduced below)
　Problem of the Day 3.5, p. 8
　Warm-Up Exercises 3.5, p. 8
Lesson Resources
　Math Log, p. 11
　Technology, p. 14
　Answer Masters 3.5, pp. 53, 54
　Extra Practice Copymaster 3.5, p. 22
　Reteaching Copymaster 3.5, p. 22
Special Populations
　Suggestions, Teacher's Edition, p. 98D

LESSON Notes

MATH JOURNAL
Be sure students record the rules for multiplying integers in their journals.

ALTERNATE APPROACH
Using a videotape model Patterns are useful in developing the rule for multiplying
integers. One technique is to use a videotape
of somebody walking forwards and backwards on a sidewalk. If forward motion is
interpreted as positive, the direction of walking and the direction of the videotape can
then be combined in four possible ways.

Direction of walking	Direction of tape	Apparent motion	Rule
forward	forward	forward	$+ \times + = +$
forward	reverse	reverse	$+ \times - = -$
reverse	forward	reverse	$- \times + = -$
reverse	reverse	forward	$- \times - = +$

Example 1

Have students repeat these computations
using calculators. Then, ask them to use their
calculators to perform the computations in
the Need to Know box. Discuss the results
as a class and resolve differences among
calculators.

3.5 Multiplying Integers

What you should learn:

Goal 1 How to multiply integers

Goal 2 How to use integer multiplication to model real-life problems

Why you should learn it:

You can use integer multiplication to solve real-life problems,
such as finding the wind-chill
factor.

Goal 1 **Multiplying Integers**

In this lesson, you will learn how to find products of one or
more negative factors. Here is an example.

$$3(-3) = (-3) + (-3) + (-3) = -9$$

LESSON INVESTIGATION

■ Investigating Integer Multiplication
Group Activity Complete the following. What patterns
can you observe?

$(3)(3) = \boxed{?}$ 9		$(3)(-2) = \boxed{?}$ -6
$(2)(3) = \boxed{?}$ 6		$(2)(-2) = \boxed{?}$ -4
$(1)(3) = \boxed{?}$ 3		$(1)(-2) = \boxed{?}$ -2
$(0)(3) = \boxed{?}$ 0		$(0)(-2) = \boxed{?}$ 0
$(-1)(3) = \boxed{?}$ -3		$(-1)(-2) = \boxed{?}$ 2
$(-2)(3) = \boxed{?}$ -6		$(-2)(-2) = \boxed{?}$ 4
$(-3)(3) = \boxed{?}$ -9		$(-3)(-2) = \boxed{?}$ 6

> **Need to Know**
>
> When there are no grouping
> symbols, the order of opera-
> tions for powers and for
> negative signs is that the
> power is evaluated *before*
> the negative sign.
>
> **a.** $-3^2 = -(3)(3) = -9$
> **b.** $(-3)^2 = (-3)(-3) = 9$
>
> This order of operations also
> applies to expressions that
> have variables. For instance,
> the value of $-x^2$ when
> $x = -4$ is
>
> $-(-4)(-4) = -16.$

Multiplying Integers
1. The product of two positive numbers is positive.
2. The product of two negative numbers is positive.
3. The product of a positive and a negative number is negative.

Example 1 *Multiplying Integers*

a. $4(3) = 12$ 　　*Product is positive.*
b. $5(-2) = -10$ 　*Product is negative.*
c. $(-4)(6) = -24$ 　*Product is negative.*
d. $(-3)(-11) = 33$ 　*Product is positive.*

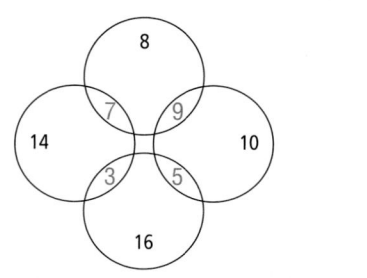

STARTER: Problem of the Day

Put a different odd number in each of
the four circle overlaps so that the sum
of the three numbers in each circle is 24.

8
7　9
14　10
3　5
16

Also available as a copymaster, page 8

STARTER: Warm-Up Exercises

1. State the three steps for modeling
real-life problems. Refer to your journals
if necessary.
　1. write a verbal model, **2.** assign labels,
　and **3.** write an algebraic model
2. Evaluate each expression when
$m = 15$ and $m = -12$.
　a. $3m + 21$ 　　**b.** $4m - 6$
　a. 66, -15, **b.** 54, -54

Also available as a copymaster, page 8

The rules for multiplying positive and negative integers also apply to fractions and decimals. For example, $\frac{1}{2} \cdot (-4) = -2$.

Example 2   *Writing and Using a Model*

Real Life
Temperature

To convert from a Celsius temperature to a Fahrenheit temperature, multiply the Celsius temperature by $\frac{9}{5}$ and add 32. Write an algebraic model for this relationship. Then use the model to find the Fahrenheit temperature that corresponds to **a.** $-20°$C and **b.** $-30°$C.

Solution

Verbal Model

$$\boxed{\text{Fahrenheit temperature}} = \frac{9}{5} \cdot \boxed{\text{Celsius temperature}} + 32$$

Labels

Fahrenheit temperature = F (degrees F)
Celsius temperature = C (degrees C)

Algebraic Model

$$F = \frac{9}{5} \cdot C + 32$$

a. The Fahrenheit temperature corresponding to $-20°$C is

$F = \frac{9}{5}C + 32$ *Write model.*
$= \frac{9}{5}(-20) + 32$ *Substitute −20 for C.*
$= -36 + 32$ *Simplify.*
$= -4°$F.   *Simplify.*

b. The Fahrenheit temperature corresponding to $-30°$C is

$F = \frac{9}{5}C + 32$ *Write model.*
$= \frac{9}{5}(-30) + 32$ *Substitute −30 for C.*
$= -54 + 32$ *Simplify.*
$= -22°$F.   *Simplify.* ∎

Wind-Chill Factor

Wind Speed (miles per hour)	Actual Air Temperature (°F)					
	30	20	10	0	−10	−20
5	27	16	7	−5	−15	−26
10	16	3	−9	−22	−34	−46
15	9	−5	−18	−31	−45	−58
20	4	−10	−24	−39	−53	−67
25	1	−15	−29	−44	−59	−74
30	−2	−18	−33	−49	−64	−79
35	−4	−20	−35	−52	−67	−82
40	−5	−21	−37	−53	−69	−84
45	−6	−22	−38	−54	−70	−85

Apparent Temperature (°F)

When the wind is blowing, you feel colder than the actual temperature given by a thermometer. The temperature that you feel is called the wind-chill factor.

Communicating about MATHEMATICS

▶ **SHARING IDEAS about the Lesson**

Finding the Wind-Chill Factor The temperature is $-10°$C. The wind speed is 40 miles per hour. How cold does it feel on the Fahrenheit scale? Refer to the table above. About $-31°$F

You may want to show students examples of multiplying positive and negative fractions and decimals, similar to these:

$\left(\frac{1}{2}\right)\left(\frac{1}{3}\right) = \frac{1}{6}$ $\left(-\frac{1}{2}\right)\left(\frac{1}{3}\right) = -\frac{1}{6}$

$\left(\frac{1}{2}\right)\left(-\frac{1}{3}\right) = -\frac{1}{6}$ $\left(-\frac{1}{2}\right)\left(-\frac{1}{3}\right) = \frac{1}{6}$

Example 2

Most students will recall that the (sea level) boiling point and freezing point of water on the Celsius scale is 100°C and 0°C respectively. Have students use the model to compute the corresponding Fahrenheit temperatures.
212°F, 32°F

Communicating about MATHEMATICS

Suppose the temperature is 20°F and the wind speed is 35 miles per hour. How cold does it feel on the Fahrenheit scale?
−20°F

How can we express the wind-chill factor table in Celsius degrees?

Use $C = \frac{5}{9}(F - 32)$ to convert degrees Fahrenheit into degrees Celsius.

Writing Prompt
What were your first thoughts about multiplication of integers?

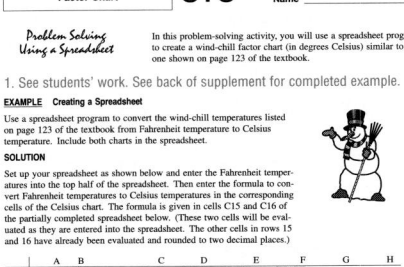

Technology

Creating a Wind-Chill Factor Chart   **3.5**   Name _____

Problem Solving Using a Spreadsheet   In this problem-solving activity, you will use a spreadsheet program to create a wind-chill factor chart (in degrees Celsius) similar to the one shown on page 123 of the textbook.

1. See students' work. See back of supplement for completed example.

EXAMPLE Creating a Spreadsheet

Use a spreadsheet program to convert the wind-chill temperatures listed on page 123 of the textbook from Fahrenheit temperature to Celsius temperature. Include both charts in the spreadsheet.

SOLUTION

Set up your spreadsheet as shown below and enter the Fahrenheit temperatures into the top half of the spreadsheet. Then enter the formula to convert Fahrenheit temperatures to Celsius temperatures in the corresponding cells of the Celsius chart. The formula is given in cells C15 and C16 of the partially completed spreadsheet below. (These two cells will be evaluated as they are entered into the spreadsheet. The other cells in rows 15 and 16 have already been evaluated and rounded to two decimal places.)

	A	B	C	D	E	F	G	H
1			WIND	CHILL	FACTOR	CHART		
2	Wind			Air	Temp	(F°)		
3	Speed	0	30	20	10	0	−10	−20
4		5	27	16	7	−5	−15	−26
5		10	16	3	−9	−22	−34	−46
6		15	9	−5	−18	−31	−45	−58
7		20	4	−10	−24	−39	−53	−67
8		25	1	−15	−29	−44	−59	−74
9		30	−2	−18	−33	−49	−64	−79
10		35	−4	−20	−35	−52	−67	−82
11		40	−5	−21	−37	−53	−69	−84
12		45	−6	−22	−38	−54	−70	−85
13								
14	Wind			Air	Temp	(C°)		
15	Speed	0	=(C3−32)*(5/9)	−6.67	−12.22	−17.78	−23.33	−28.89
16		5	=(C4−32)*(5/9)	−8.99	−13.89	−20.56	−26.11	−32.22

EXERCISES

1. Use a spreadsheet program to complete the example. (Hint: Use the copy feature of the spreadsheet program as much as possible.)
2. To convert from Fahrenheit to Celsius, use the formula $(F - 32) \times 5/9$, where F is the Fahrenheit temperature. Integers: -20, -30, -45, -50, -55 and -65

2. Write a paragraph explaining how to convert from Fahrenheit temperature to Celsius temperature. Then list all the integers that occur in the Celsius scale you created.

14   *Technology Using Calculators and Computers*   © D.C. Heath and Company

EXERCISE Notes

ASSIGNMENT GUIDE

Basic/Average:
   Day 1: Ex. 7–47 odd
   Day 2: Ex. 49–53, 54, 55, 56, 58

Above Average: Ex. 13–45 odd, 49–57 odd

Advanced: Ex. 13–45 odd, 49–57 odd

Selected Answers: Ex. 1–6, 7–55 odd

Guided Practice

▶ **Ex. 4** This exercise provides a visual interpretation for signed-number multiplication.

EXTENSION
Have students change the location of *a*, *b*, and *c* to yield different solutions.

▶ **Ex. 5, 6**

MATH JOURNAL
These are good exercises for students to include in their journals or portfolios.

Independent Practice

▶ **Ex. 19–22** These exercises review the different ways in which multiplication can be represented.

▶ **Ex. 24, 26**

Common-Error Alert!

Because of the exponent, many students may need guidance as to what quantity is to be squared. Refer them to the Need to Know box on page 122.

▶ **Ex. 27, 30** These exercises introduce a third integer in the multiplication.

EXTENSION
To show that the multiplication of integers is associative, you may wish to have students work these exercises in steps, starting from opposite sides of the 3-factor expression. Have them show that 6 (10)(−2) is equivalent to either 60(−2) or 6(−20).

Answers
9. $-4 \cdot (-6) = 24$
10. $-10 \cdot (-2) = 20$
11. $5 \cdot (-11) = -55$
12. $-8 \cdot 6 = -48$
13. $(-7)(-9) = 63$
14. $(-4)(-12) = 48$

124 *Chapter 3*

EXERCISES

Guided Practice

▶ **CHECK for Understanding**

In Exercises 1–3, write the sum as a product. Then simplify.

1. $(-4) + (-4) + (-4)$ $3(-4), -12$

2. $(-x) + (-x) + (-x)$ $3(-x), -3x$

3. $(-8) + (-8) + (-8) + (-8)$ $4(-8), -32$

4. *Computation Sense* Use the number line to decide whether *ab*, *ac*, and *bc* are positive or negative. Positive, negative, negative

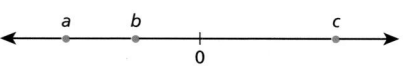

P 5. *Logical Reasoning* If *x* is not zero, which expression must be positive: x^2, $2x$, $-4x$. x^2

P 6. Which expression is equal to $(-4)(-4)$: -4^2 or $(-4)^2$? $(-4)^2$

Independent Practice

In Exercises 7–18, find the product. Write your conclusion as an equation.   9.–14. See margin.

7. $3 \cdot 9$ $3 \cdot 9 = 27$
8. $7(8)$ $7(8) = 56$
9. $-4 \cdot (-6)$
10. $-10 \cdot (-2)$

11. $5 \cdot (-11)$
12. $-8 \cdot 6$
13. $(-7)(-9)$
14. $(-4)(-12)$

15. $(-10)(3)$ $(-10)(3) = -30$
16. $(-1)(54)$ $(-1)(54) = -54$
17. $(-20)(0)$ $(-20)(0) = 0$
18. $0 \cdot (-4)$ $0 \cdot (-4) = 0$

In Exercises 19–22, simplify the expression.

19. $-7 \cdot x$ $-7x$
20. $6 \cdot (-y)$ $-6y$
21. $(-14)(-a)$ $14a$
22. $(-b)(-25)$ $25b$

In Exercises 23–26, evaluate the expression when $a = 8$ and $b = -2$.

23. ab -16
24. ab^2 32
25. $-b$ 2
26. $-a^2$ -64

In Exercises 27–30, find the product. Sample: $-3 \cdot (-2) \cdot (-4) = -24$

27. $1 \cdot (-9) \cdot 3$ -27
28. $6(10)(-2)$ -120
29. $4 \cdot (-2) \cdot (-8)$ 64
30. $11(-3)(-3)$ 99

P 31. Is the product of three negative numbers positive or negative? Negative

P 32. Is the product of four negative numbers positive or negative? Positive

In Exercises 33–40, use a calculator to find the product.

33. $-1.4 \cdot (-6)$ 8.4
34. $-8 \cdot (-1.5)$ 12
35. $\frac{7}{8}(-24)$ -21
36. $\frac{5}{6}(-42)$ -35

37. $(-542)(-15)$ 8130
38. $(-712)(-21)$ $14,952$
39. $(43)(-2)(-4)$ 344
40. $(-36)(7)(-4)$ 1008

Mental Math   **In Exercises 41–48, use mental math to solve the equation.**

41. $2x = -4$ -2
42. $3m = -9$ -3
43. $-6b = 12$ -2
44. $-8n = 24$ -3

45. $-3a = 27$ -9
46. $-7y = 42$ -6
47. $1.5m = -3$ -2
48. $-2x = -3.2$ 1.6

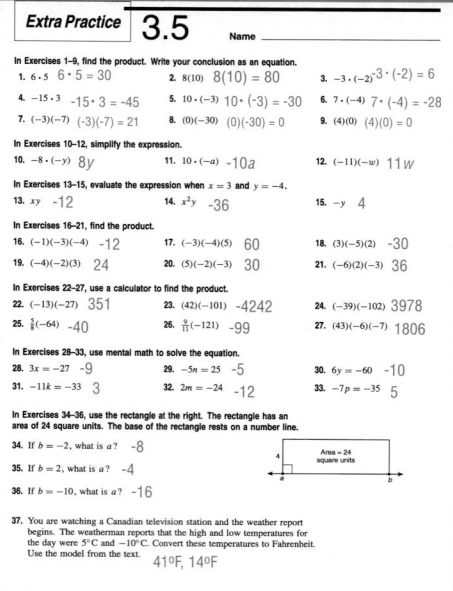

Extra Practice

Extra Practice   3.5   Name _____

In Exercises 1–9, find the product. Write your conclusion as an equation.
1. $6 \cdot 5$ $6 \cdot 5 = 30$
2. $8(10)$ $8(10) = 80$
3. $-3 \cdot (-2)$ $-3 \cdot (-2) = 6$
4. $-15 \cdot 3$ $-15 \cdot 3 = -45$
5. $10 \cdot (-3)$ $10 \cdot (-3) = -30$
6. $7 \cdot (-4)$ $7 \cdot (-4) = -28$
7. $(-3)(-7)$ $(-3)(-7) = 21$
8. $(0)(-30)$ $(0)(-30) = 0$
9. $(4)(0)$ $(4)(0) = 0$

In Exercises 10–12, simplify the expression.
10. $-8 \cdot (-y)$ $8y$
11. $10 \cdot (-a)$ $-10a$
12. $(-11)(-w)$ $11w$

In Exercises 13–15, evaluate the expression when $x = 3$ and $y = -4$.
13. xy -12
14. x^2y -36
15. $-y$ 4

In Exercises 16–21, find the product.
16. $(-1)(-3)(-4)$ -12
17. $(-3)(-4)(5)$ 60
18. $(3)(-5)(2)$ -30
19. $(-4)(-2)(3)$ 24
20. $(5)(-2)(-3)$ 30
21. $(-6)(2)(-3)$ 36

In Exercises 22–27, use a calculator to find the product.
22. $(-13)(-27)$ 351
23. $(42)(-101)$ -4242
24. $(-39)(-102)$ 3978
25. $\frac{5}{8}(-64)$ -40
26. $\frac{9}{11}(-121)$ -99
27. $(43)(-6)(-7)$ 1806

In Exercises 28–33, use mental math to solve the equation.
28. $3x = -27$ -9
29. $-5n = 25$ -5
30. $6y = -60$ -10
31. $-11k = -33$ 3
32. $2m = -24$ -12
33. $-7p = -35$ 5

In Exercises 34–36, use the rectangle at the right. The rectangle has an area of 24 square units. The base of the rectangle rests on a number line.
34. If $b = -2$, what is a? -8
35. If $b = 2$, what is a? -4
36. If $b = -10$, what is a? -16

Area = 24 square units

37. You are watching a Canadian television station and the weather report begins. The weatherman reports that the high and low temperatures for the day were 5°C and −10°C. Convert these temperatures to Fahrenheit. Use the model from the text.   41°F, 14°F

22 *Multiplying integers • 3.5*   Windows

Reteaching

Reteach   Chapter 3   Name _____

What you should learn:

| 3.5 | How to multiply integers and how to use integer multiplication to model real-life problems |

Correlation to Pupil's Textbook:
Chapter Test (p. 143)
Exercises 9, 10

Examples   *Multiplying Integers and Modeling Real-Life Situations*

a. Multiply 6 and 3. $6(3) = 18$ The product of two positive numbers is positive.
   Multiply −5 and −7. $(-5)(-7) = 35$ The product of two negative numbers is positive.
   Multiply 4 and −11. $4(-11) = -44$ The product of a positive and a negative number is negative.

b. Evaluate $-x^2$ when $x = 5$.
   The order of operations for powers and for negative signs is that the power is evaluated before the negative sign.
$$-x^2 = -(x)(x) = -(5)(5) = -25$$

c. To convert from a Fahrenheit temperature to a Celsius temperature, subtract 32 from the Fahrenheit temperature and multiply by $\frac{5}{9}$. Write an algebraic model for this relationship. Then use the model to find the Celsius temperature that corresponds to −13° F.

| Verbal Model | $\left(\begin{array}{c}\text{Celsius}\\\text{temperature}\end{array}\right) = \left(\left(\begin{array}{c}\text{Fahrenheit}\\\text{temperature}\end{array}\right) - 32\right)\frac{5}{9}$ |

Labels   Celsius temperature = C (degrees C)
    Fahrenheit temperature = F (degrees F)

Algebraic Model $C = (F - 32)\frac{5}{9}$

The Celsius temperature that corresponds to −13° F is
$C = (F - 32)\frac{5}{9}$ *Write model.*
$= (-13 - 32)\frac{5}{9}$ *Substitute −13 for F.*
$= (-45)\frac{5}{9}$ *Simplify.*
$= -25°C.$ *Simplify.*

Guidelines: • The order of operations for powers and for negative signs applies to expressions that have variables (the power of a variable is evaluated before the negative sign).

EXERCISES
In Exercises 1–4, find the product. Write your conclusion as an equation.
1. $4(-5)$ $4(-5) = -20$
2. $(-9)(-8)$ $(-9)(-8) = 72$
3. $-10 \cdot 2$ $-10 \cdot 2 = -20$
4. $15(1)$ $15(1) = 15$

In Exercises 5–8, evaluate the expression when $x = -2$ and $y = -3$.
5. xy 6
6. $x^2(y)$ -12
7. xy^2 -18
8. $-x^2$ -4

22 *Chapter 3 ▪ Modeling Integers*   Windows

Geometry In Exercises 49–51, use the rectangle at the right. The rectangle has an area of 15 square units. The base of the rectangle rests on a number line.

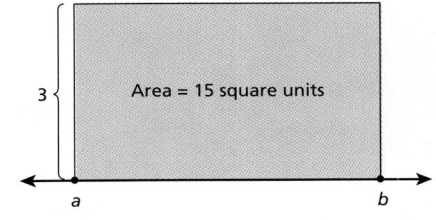

Area = 15 square units

49. If $a = -4$, what is b? 1

50. If $b = -6$, what is a? -11

51. If $b = 3$, what is a? -2

Temperature Scales In Exercises 52 and 53, use the following.

Temperatures are sometimes measured on the Kelvin scale.

- To convert from Fahrenheit to Celsius, subtract 32 from the Fahrenheit temperature and multiply by $\frac{5}{9}$.
- To convert from Celsius to Kelvin, add 273.15 to the Celsius temperature. $C = \frac{5}{9}(F - 32)$, $K = C + 273.15$

52. Write algebraic models for converting from Fahrenheit to Celsius and from Celsius to Kelvin. (See page 123 for a model for converting from Celsius to Fahrenheit.)

53. Copy and complete the table.

Scale	Fahrenheit	Celsius	Kelvin
Temperature	212°F	?	373.15K	100°C
Temperature	32°F	0°C	?	273.15K
Temperature	−40°F	?	?
Temperature	14°F	?	?

−40°C, 233.15K; −10°C, 263.15K

Helsinki University of Technology
The lowest temperature ever reached is two billionths of a degree above absolute zero. It was achieved at the Low Temperature Laboratory at the Helsinki University of Technology in Finland.

Integrated Review

Making Connections within Mathematics

Number Sense In Exercises 54 and 55, choose values of a and b so that both statements are true. Values vary.

54. ab is positive and $a + b$ is negative.
Either is -5, other is -6.

55. ab is negative and $a + b$ is positive.
Either is -5, other is 6.

Exploration and Extension

Matrices In Exercises 56–58, multiply using the following information.

$$\begin{bmatrix} 3 & -2 \\ -1 & 4 \end{bmatrix}$$

The array at the right is a **matrix**. To multiply a matrix by a number, multiply each element of the matrix by the number.

$$-2\begin{bmatrix} 3 & -2 \\ -1 & 4 \end{bmatrix} = \begin{bmatrix} (-2)(3) & (-2)(-2) \\ (-2)(-1) & (-2)(4) \end{bmatrix} = \begin{bmatrix} -6 & 4 \\ 2 & -8 \end{bmatrix}$$

56. $-1\begin{bmatrix} 1 & -3 \\ 0 & -1 \end{bmatrix}$ $\begin{bmatrix} -1 & 3 \\ 0 & 1 \end{bmatrix}$

✪ 57. $-3\begin{bmatrix} 1 & -5 \\ 4 & -2 \end{bmatrix}$ $\begin{bmatrix} -3 & 15 \\ -12 & 6 \end{bmatrix}$

✪ 58. $2\begin{bmatrix} 8 & 6 \\ -7 & -4 \end{bmatrix}$ $\begin{bmatrix} 16 & 12 \\ -14 & -8 \end{bmatrix}$

✪ More difficult exercises

3.5 ▪ *Multiplying Integers* **125**

▶ **Ex. 31, 32**
MATH JOURNAL
As an extension of these exercises, ask students to answer the following question in their journals. In general, how do you determine if the product of n factors will be positive or negative?

▶ **Ex. 49–51** Assign these exercises as a group.

▶ **Ex. 52, 53**
GROUP ACTIVITY
Have students work these exercises in groups to help insure that a model is developed that can be used to complete the table. You may wish to explain that the Kelvin temperature scale is used mainly in the context of gases in the physical sciences. Temperatures on the Kelvin scale are written without a degree symbol.

Integrated Review

Have students share the various answers that result from these problems. Have them summarize the solutions.

Exploration and Extension

You may wish to comment that an array is a visual way to organize data. Have students give additional examples of where they have seen a matrix (box scores, attendance records, wind-chill chart, etc.).

Portfolio Opportunity: Math Log

Explain why $(-2)^n$ is positive if n is even and negative if n is odd.

Also available as a copymaster, page 11, Ex. 6

▶ **PACING** the Lesson

Suggested Number of Days
Basic/Average 2   **Above Average** 1
Advanced 1

▶ **PLANNING** the Lesson

Lesson Plan 3.6, p. 23

ORGANIZER

Starters (reproduced below)
   Problem of the Day 3.6, p. 8
   Warm-Up Exercises 3.6, p. 8
Lesson Resources
   Math Log, p. 12
   Answer Masters 3.6, pp. 55, 56
   Extra Practice Copymaster 3.6, p. 23
   Reteaching Copymaster 3.6, p. 23
   Enrichment Projects, pp. 14, 15
Special Populations
   Suggestions, Teacher's Edition, p. 98D

LESSON Notes

Lesson Investigation
Stress the connection between multiplication and division. Patterns relating multiplication and division can be used to arrive at the rules for the sign of the quotient when dividing integers as follows.

Multiplication Statement	Corresponding Division Statement
$-3 \times 3 = -9$ →	$-9 \div -3 = 3$
$-3 \times 2 = -6$ →	$-6 \div -3 = 2$
$-3 \times 1 = -3$ →	$-3 \div -3 = 1$
$-3 \times 0 = 0$ →	$0 \div -3 = 0$
$-3 \times -1 = 3$ →	$3 \div -3 = -1$
$-3 \times -2 = 6$ →	$6 \div -3 = -2$
$-3 \times -3 = 9$ →	$9 \div -3 = -3$

MATH JOURNAL
Have students record the rules for dividing integers in their journals.

Zero in Division

EXTENSION
The special rules for 0 should be explained to students. Division by 0 is meaningless because of the inverse relationship of multiplication and division. If $\frac{4}{0} = m$ then $0 \cdot m = 4$. But this isn't true, no matter what the value of m. So division by 0 is not defined. However, $\frac{0}{4}$ is meaningful. For, if $\frac{0}{4} = m$, then $4 \cdot m = 0$, which is true provided $m = 0$.

Example 1

Have students check each division statement using the corresponding multiplication statement.

3.6 Dividing Integers

What you should learn:

Goal 1 How to divide integers

Goal 2 How to use integer division to model real-life problems

Why you should learn it:

You can use integer division to solve real-life problems involving averages, such as finding the average weight loss of a wrestling team.

Goal 1 **Dividing Integers**

To perform division by hand, use **long division** as shown below. Notice that you can check your result by multiplying.

```
   Divisor        Quotient
            14   ← 
        26)364   ← Dividend
        26        Multiply: (1)(26)
        104       Subtract
        104       Multiply: (4)(26)
          0       Subtract
```

Check:
```
      26
   ×  14
     104
      26
     364
```

LESSON INVESTIGATION

■ **Investigating Integer Division**

Group Activity Solve the following division problems. Explain how to use the multiplication check illustrated above to determine the sign of the quotient.

a. $24 \div (-6)$ -4 **b.** $-24 \div (-6)$ 4 **c.** $(-24) \div 6$ -4

Discuss the results with members of your group. What can you conclude about the rules for division of integers?

Zero in Division

The number 0 has special rules regarding division.

1. You cannot divide a number by 0. Expressions with 0 divisors, such as $4 \div 0$, are meaningless.

2. When 0 is divided by a nonzero number, the result is 0. For instance, $0 \div (-4) = 0$.

Dividing Integers

1. The quotient of two positive numbers is positive.
2. The quotient of two negative numbers is positive.
3. The quotient of a positive and a negative number is negative.

Example 1 *Dividing Integers*

a. $\frac{12}{-2} = -6$ *Quotient is negative.*

b. $\frac{-20}{4} = -5$ *Quotient is negative.*

c. $\frac{-36}{-6} = 6$ *Quotient is positive.*

■

126   *Chapter 3 ▪ Modeling Integers*

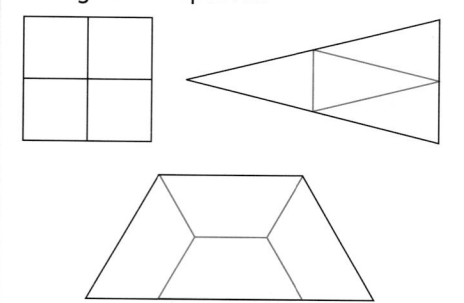

┌─ **STARTER: Problem of the Day** ─┐
The square has been divided into four smaller pieces that are the same *shape* as the original. Do the same for the triangle and trapezoid.

┌─ **STARTER: Warm-Up Exercises** ─┐
1. How are the operations of multiplication and division related? opposite or inverse operations
2. Compute.
   a. $\frac{12}{2}$ **b.** $\frac{20}{4}$
   c. $\frac{36}{6}$ **d.** $\frac{45}{15}$
   a. 6, **b.** 5, **c.** 6, **d.** 3
3. Use the quotient and divisor to write the appropriate multiplication statement for each expression in Exercise 2 above.
   a. $2 \cdot 6 = 12$, **b.** $4 \cdot 5 = 20$, **c.** $6 \cdot 6 = 36$
   d. $15 \cdot 3 = 45$

Also available as a copymaster, page 8

Also available as a copymaster, page 8

Goal 2 — Modeling Real-Life Problems

To find the average (or **mean**) of n numbers, add the numbers and divide the result by n. For instance, the average of 24, 37, 21, and 42 is

$$\text{Average} = \frac{24 + 37 + 21 + 42}{4}$$
$$= \frac{124}{4}$$
$$= 31.$$

Example 2 — Finding an Average Weight Change

You are coaching your school's wrestling team. During the months of December and January, the 15 members of the team recorded the following weight gains or losses (in pounds).

$$-5, 0, -7, -3, 2, -4, -6, -1, 0, -3, -4, -4, -2, -5, -3$$

What was the average weight gain or loss per team member?

Solution

Verbal Model	$\dfrac{\text{Average}}{\text{gain or loss}} = \dfrac{\text{Sum of gains and losses}}{15}$	
Labels	Average gain or loss = A	(pounds)
	Sum of gains and losses = -45	(pounds)
Algebraic Model	$A = \dfrac{-45}{15}$	
	$= -3$	

The average was a loss of 3 pounds per team member. ∎

There are 13 weight classes in high school wrestling. The classes range from 103 pounds to a heavy-weight class of no more than 275 pounds.

P *Communicating* about MATHEMATICS

Cooperative Learning

▶ **SHARING IDEAS about the Lesson**

It's Up to You Work with a partner to create a single list of weight changes that satisfies all of the following.

- 10 people are on the wrestling team.
- 4 people gained, 5 lost, and 1 stayed the same.
- The average weight change was a loss of 3 pounds.

Lists vary. 0, 1, 2, 3, 4, -4, -6, -8, -10, -12

P Portfolio Opportunity

3.6 • *Dividing Integers*   **127**

The mean is one type of average. The *mode* and *median* are two other types of "averages" (or measures of central tendency) that you may want to tell students about. The mode is the number that occurs most frequently in a collection of numbers; the median is the middle number of a collection of numbers (or the average of the two middle numbers if the number of data entries is even). These concepts are presented in detail in Lesson 14.1.

Example 2

Weight gains and losses are another real-life context that involves operations with negative integers. You may wish to assure students that finding the average of these numbers doesn't require the algebraic model shown here. The model is presented as a reminder of the general problem-solving plan that is available if needed.

EXTENSION

If you have mentioned the median and mode as other kinds of average, have students order the set of weight gains and losses and then find the median and mode of the set.
Median: -3, Mode: (two) -3 and -4

Communicating about MATHEMATICS

Make sure that students understand that the first and third pieces of information together mean that there was a total loss of 30 pounds. One entry must be zero. Of the others, four entries must be positive; the other five must be negative.

EXTENSION

Have students create a similar list of weight changes that satisfies all of the following:
- 15 people on the wrestling team
- 6 people gained, 7 people lost, 2 stayed the same
- Average weight change was a gain of 2 pounds   Answers will vary.

Writing Prompt

Right now I think division of integers is . . . because . . .

OPTION: Extra Examples

Here is an additional example similar to Example 1.

Dividing Integers

a. $\dfrac{48}{-4} = -12$ *Quotient is negative.*

b. $\dfrac{-54}{6} = -9$ *Quotient is negative.*

c. $\dfrac{-121}{-11} = 11$ *Quotient is positive.*

ASSIGNMENT GUIDE

Basic/Average:
Day 1: Ex. 17–43 odd
Day 2: Ex. 47, 48, 51–73 odd

Above Average: Ex. 21–31 odd, 37–43 odd, 47–49, 57–67 odd, 73, 74

Advanced: Ex. 21–31 odd, 37–43 odd, 47–49, 57–67 odd, 73, 74

Selected Answers: Ex. 1–8, 9–67 odd

Guided Practice

▶ **Ex. 1–4** These exercises summarize the four possibilities in the division of integers.
▶ **Ex. 6–8** These exercises provide a visual context for integer division.

EXERCISES

Guided Practice

▶ **CHECK for Understanding**

In Exercises 1–4, state whether the quotient is negative or positive.

1. $216 \div 9$ Positive   **2.** $-28 \div 4$ Negative   **3.** $\frac{48}{-6}$ Negative   **4.** $\frac{-522}{-9}$ Positive

5. Explain how to check that $\frac{-6}{-2} = 3$. Multiply 3 by -2 to see if you get -6.

Computation Sense **In Exercises 6–8, decide whether $\frac{a}{b}$ is positive or negative.**

6.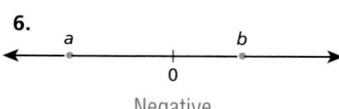

Negative

7.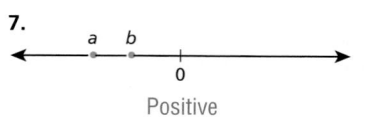

Positive

8.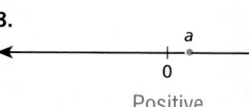

Positive

Independent Practice

Computation Sense **In Exercises 9–24, evaluate the expression. Check your result by multiplying.**

9. $\frac{54}{2}$ 27   **10.** $\frac{100}{5}$ 20   **11.** $\frac{-90}{15}$ -6 **12.** $\frac{-130}{26}$ -5

13. $384 \div (-12)$ -32 **14.** $376 \div (-8)$ -47 **15.** $-954 \div (-18)$ 53   **16.** $-1058 \div (-46)$ 23

17. $\frac{0}{-75}$ 0   **18.** $\frac{0}{1000}$ 0   **19.** $-1020 \div 30$ -34 **20.** $-300 \div 12$ -25

21. $1568 / (-16)$ -98 **22.** $242 / (-11)$ -22 **23.** $-1659 / (-21)$ 79   **24.** $-3621 / (-71)$ 51

Division Patterns **In Exercises 25–28, complete the statements. Then describe the pattern.** For descriptions, see margin.

25. $-2 \div 2 = \boxed{?}$ -1
$-4 \div 2 = \boxed{?}$ -2
$-6 \div 2 = \boxed{?}$ -3
$-8 \div 2 = \boxed{?}$ -4
$-10 \div 2 = \boxed{?}$ -5

26. $-1 \div (-1) = \boxed{?}$ 1
$-2 \div (-2) = \boxed{?}$ 1
$-3 \div (-3) = \boxed{?}$ 1
$-4 \div (-4) = \boxed{?}$ 1
$-5 \div (-5) = \boxed{?}$ 1

27. $0 \div (-1) = \boxed{?}$ 0
$0 \div (-2) = \boxed{?}$ 0
$0 \div (-3) = \boxed{?}$ 0
$0 \div (-4) = \boxed{?}$ 0
$0 \div (-5) = \boxed{?}$ 0

28. $64 \div (-32) = \boxed{?}$
$32 \div (-16) = \boxed{?}$
$16 \div (-8) = \boxed{?}$
$8 \div (-4) = \boxed{?}$
$4 \div (-2) = \boxed{?}$

In Exercises 29–32, evaluate the expression when $x = -2$, $y = 3$, and $z = -4$.

29. $\frac{-2x}{4}$ 1   **30.** $\frac{xz}{2}$ 4   **31.** $\frac{xy}{z}$ $1\frac{1}{2}$ **32.** $\frac{-yz}{x}$ -6

Mental Math **In Exercises 33–40, use mental math to solve the equation.**

33. $\frac{b}{7} = -7$ -49 **34.** $\frac{a}{4} = -5$ -20 **35.** $\frac{x}{-4} = 6$ -24 **36.** $\frac{z}{-8} = 5$ -40

37. $\frac{m}{-2} = -24$ 48   **38.** $\frac{n}{-3} = -13$ 39   **39.** $\frac{63}{n} = -7$ -9 **40.** $\frac{81}{p} = -3$ -27

Extra Practice

Extra Practice **3.6**   Name _____

In Exercises 1–9, evaluate the expression. Check your results by multiplying.

1. $\frac{96}{3}$ 32   2. $\frac{180}{4}$ 45   3. $\frac{-512}{16}$ -32
4. $-208 \div (-8)$ 26   5. $288 \div (-16)$ -18 6. $\frac{0}{-36}$ 0
7. $0 \div 327$ 0   8. $-1008 \div (-21)$ 48   9. $2730 \div (-65)$ -42

In Exercises 10 and 11, complete the statement. Then describe the pattern.

10. $-36 \div 2 = \square$ $-18, -17, -16,$
$-34 \div 2 = \square$ $-15, -14$
$-32 \div 2 = \square$ Increase by 1
$-30 \div 2 = \square$
$-28 \div 2 = \square$

11. $-2 \div (-1) = \square$ 2, 3, 4, 5, 6
$-3 \div (-1) = \square$ Increase by 1
$-4 \div (-1) = \square$
$-5 \div (-1) = \square$
$-6 \div (-1) = \square$

In Exercises 12–14, evaluate when $x = -3$, $y = 2$ and $z = -4$.

12. xz 12   13. $\frac{-6y}{x}$ 4   14. $\frac{xz}{y}$ 6

In Exercises 15–20, use mental math to solve the equation.

15. $\frac{a}{8} = -2$ -16 16. $\frac{c}{-5} = -4$ 20   17. $\frac{z}{3} = -6$ -18
18. $\frac{w}{-2} = 11$ -22 19. $\frac{m}{-6} = 5$ -30 20. $\frac{n}{3} = -10$ -30

In Exercises 21 and 22, find the average of the numbers.

21. 18, 11, 15, 17, 13, 16 15   22. $-8, -6, -5, -8, -7, -2$ -6

In Exercises 23 and 24, use the table which shows the gold medal winners and their times in the women's 100-meter freestyle during the Olympic Games from 1972 through 1992.

Year	Winner	Country	Time in Seconds
1972	Sandra Neilson	United States	58.59
1976	Kornelia Ender	East Germany	55.65
1980	Barbara Krause	East Germany	54.79
1984	Nancy Hogshead	United States	55.92
1988	Kristin Otto	East Germany	54.93
1992	Zhuang Yong	China	54.65

23. Find the average winning time for the last six Summer Olympics. 55.755 seconds

24. Predict whether the average winning time for the next six Olympic Games will be more or less than your result in Exercise 23. Explain your predictions. Less than result in Exercise 23. If trend of faster times continues, then the average of the next six Olympic games will be faster.

Windows   3.6 ▪ Dividing Integers **23**

Reteaching

Reteach Chapter 3   Name _____

What you should learn:
3.6 How to divide integers and how to use integer division to model real-life problems

Correlation to Pupil's Textbook:
Chapter Test (p. 143)
Exercises 6, 11, 12, 19–21

Examples Dividing Integers and Modeling Real-Life Problems

a. Divide 15 by 5. $\frac{15}{5} = 3$ The quotient of two positive numbers is positive.

Divide -28 by -7. $\frac{-28}{-7} = 4$ The quotient of two negative numbers is positive.

Divide 18 by -9. $\frac{18}{-9} = -2$ The quotient of a positive and a negative number is negative.

b. The local weather station recorded the following daily low temperatures (in degrees Fahrenheit) over a 12-day period during the month of January.
$-4, -2, -5, 0, 2, -7, -6, 4, 5, 7, -1, -5$

What was the average daily low temperature (in degrees Fahrenheit) for the 12-day period?

Verbal Model	Average daily low temperature	=	Sum of temperatures above and below zero
			12

Labels Average daily low temperature $= A$ (degrees Fahrenheit)
Sum of temperatures above and below zero $= -12$ (degrees Fahrenheit)

Algebraic
Model
$A = \frac{-4 + (-2) + (-5) + 0 + 2 + (-7) + (-6) + 4 + 5 + 7 + (-1) + (-5)}{12}$
$= \frac{-12}{12} = -1$

The average daily low temperature was $-1°$F.

Guidelines: • You cannot divide a number by 0.
• When 0 is divided by a nonzero number, the result is 0.
• To find the average (or mean) of n numbers, add the numbers and divide the result by n.

EXERCISES

In Exercises 1–8, evaluate the expression. Check your result by multiplying.

1. $\frac{66}{3}$ 22   2. $\frac{120}{-8}$ -15 3. $\frac{-144}{9}$ -16 4. $\frac{-170}{-34}$ 5
5. $0/-26$ 0   6. $297 \div 27$ 11   7. $-525 \div (-35)$ 15   8. $338/(-13)$ -26

In Exercises 9–10, find the average of the numbers.

9. $-8, -5, 4, 13, -12, -4$ -2 10. $-15, -6, -23, 0, -11$ -11

Windows   Chapter 3 ▪ Modeling Integers **23**

Answers

25. Quotients decrease by 1.
26. Quotients are always 1.
27. Quotients are always 0.
28. Quotients are always -2.

In Exercises 41–46, find the average of the numbers.

41. 35, 38, 34, 39, 32, 38 36

42. 22, 19, 21, 20, 18, 22, 25 21

43. −4, −2, 0, 1, −3, 1, 2, −5, 3, −3 −1

44. 3, 3, −4, 6, 2, 1, −2, −1, 2, −4, 5 1

45. −6, −9, −4, −2, −7, −6, −8 −6

46. −20, −16, −12, −17, −10 −15

Coaching a Speed Skater   **In Exercises 47–49, use the following information.**

In five trial runs on a 500 m track, your skater has times of 44.21 seconds, 45.02 seconds, 44.78 seconds, 45.10 seconds, and 44.13 seconds.

47. Find the average trial time of the skater. 44.648 seconds

48. Another skater, after five trial runs, had an average trial time of 45.07 seconds. What could her trial times have been? See margin.

49. Is it possible that the second skater had a faster trial time than the first? Explain. See margin.

By 1994, Bonnie Blair had won 5 Olympic gold medals.

Integrated Review

Making Connections within Mathematics

Logical Reasoning   **In Exercises 50–53, decide whether the statement is** *always,* *sometimes,* **or** *never* **true.**

50. The sum of a positive number and a negative number is positive. Sometimes

51. The difference of a negative number and a positive number is negative. Always

52. The product of a positive number and a negative number is positive. Never

53. The quotient of a positive number and a negative number is equal to −1. Sometimes

Computation Sense   **In Exercises 54–56, evaluate the expression.**

54. $(24 - 16) \div 2$ 4   **55.** $(36 + 18) \div (-6)$ −9   **56.** $(10 - 24) \div (-5 - 2)$ 2

Equation Sense   **In Exercises 57–64, solve the equation.**

57. $m + 21 = 44$ 23   **58.** $p + 16 = 57$ 41   **59.** $r - 76 = 12$ 88   **60.** $47 = t - 19$ 66

61. $12m = 60$ 5   **62.** $8s = 72$ 9   **63.** $\frac{x}{6} = 12$ 72   **64.** $\frac{y}{10} = 80$ 800

Geometry   **In Exercises 65–68, write an expression that does not contain parentheses for the area of the rectangle.**   **65.** $3x - 12$ **66.** $10x - 30$ **67.** $-4x + 12$ **68.** $8x - 40$

65. $x - 4$
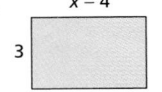
3

66. $2x - 6$
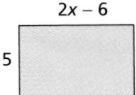
5

67. $-x + 3$
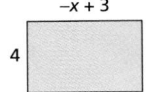
4

68. $x - 5$
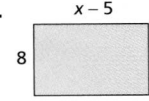
8

✪ More difficult exercises

3.6 ▪ *Dividing Integers*   **129**

▶ **Independent Practice**

▶ **Ex. 47–49**   Assign these exercises as a group. Have groups share their result for Ex. 48 with the whole class.

Integrated Review

▶ **Ex. 50–53**
These are good group discussion questions involving plenty of critical thinking.
▶ **Ex. 65–68**

Common-Error Alert!

Students may forget to use parentheses when writing the expression for the area of each rectangle.

Answers
48. Answers vary. Example: 44.03, 45.33, 45.33, 45.33, and 45.33.
49. Yes, see example for Exercise 48.

Exploration and Extension

▶ **Ex. 69–73** This may be students' first exposure to the concept of reciprocal. Explain to students that the minus sign in the reciprocal of a negative integer is usually written in front of the fraction.

Note that the answer to Ex. 73 represents an effective *definition* of reciprocal: For all real numbers a and b (except 0), if $ab = 1$, then a and b are reciprocals. In later work, by using this definition students will be better prepared to write the reciprocal of, say, $\frac{2}{3}$ as $\frac{3}{2}$ rather than $\frac{1}{\frac{3}{2}}$!

Portfolio Opportunity: Math Log

Is the answer to $\frac{0}{0}$ meaningless or is it 0? Explain your answer.

Also available as a copymaster, page 12, Ex. 7

Short Quiz

Covers Lessons 3.5 and 3.6

Available as a copymaster, page 35

Alternative Assessment

A problem-solving project that develops logical thinking.

Available as a copymaster, page 19

Exploration and Extension

Finding Reciprocals   In Exercises 69–72, find the reciprocal of the number. The reciprocal of a nonzero number a is $\frac{1}{a}$. For instance, the reciprocal of -2 is $\frac{1}{-2}$ or $-\frac{1}{2}$.

69. -4 $-\frac{1}{4}$ **70.** $5\frac{1}{5}$ **71.** $7\frac{1}{7}$ **72.** -3 $-\frac{1}{3}$

73. *Writing a Conjecture*   Multiply several numbers by their reciprocals. Then write a conjecture about the product of a number and its reciprocal.   The product of a number and its reciprocal is always 1.

Reasoning   In Exercises 74 and 75, solve the puzzle by replacing each ? with a single digit.

74.

```
        2 ? 4
1 ? 5 ) 3 ? 0 6
      - ? ?      3, 0
        ? 0 6
      - 6 0
          0
```

75.

```
      6   ? ? 1, 9
3 ? ) ? ? ? ?  6, 8, 4
    - ? 6        3
      ? 2 ? 3, 4
    - 3 ? ?  2, 4
          0
```

Mixed REVIEW

In Exercises 1–8, evaluate the expression. (3.2–3.6)

1. $9 + 3$ 12
2. $4 - 2$ 2
3. $6 + (-3)$ 3
4. $8 - (-2)$ 10
5. $8 \times (-4)$ -32
6. $(-3) \times (-5)$ 15
7. $-84 \div 4$ -21
8. $(-7)^2$ 49

In Exercises 9 and 10, translate the verbal sentence into an algebraic equation. (2.7)

9. The cost of 3 burritos is \$4.20 $3b = 4.2$
10. The depth of 4 fathoms is 24 feet. $4f = 24$

In Exercises 11–14, describe the pattern and list the next three numbers in the sequence. (1.1, 3.5, 3.6)   For descriptions, see Additional Answers.

11. $2, -4, 8, -16,$? ? ? $32, -64, 128$
12. $-1, 3, -9, 27,$? ? ? $-81, 243, -729$
13. $-2, 1, -\frac{1}{2}, \frac{1}{4},$? ? ? $-\frac{1}{8}, \frac{1}{16}, -\frac{1}{32}$
14. $-78125, 15625, -3125, 625,$? ? ? $-125, 25, -5$

In Exercises 15–20, evaluate the expression. (1.4, 3.2–3.6)

15. $3 + (-6) \times (-4)$ 27
16. $-4 \times 6 \div 3$ -8
17. $(3 - 6)^2$ 9
18. $8 - (-2) \times 4$ 16
19. $15 \times \left(\frac{3}{5} - \frac{2}{5}\right)$ 3
20. $6.2 - 4.5 \div 1.5$ 3.2

---

130   *Chapter 3* ▪ *Modeling Integers*   ✪ More difficult exercises

Enrichment

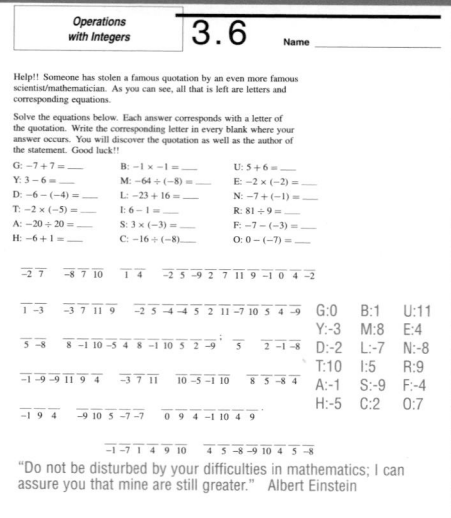

| Operations with Integers | 3.6 | Name _____ |

Help!! Someone has stolen a famous quotation by an even more famous scientist/mathematician. As you can see, all that is left are letters and corresponding equations.

Solve the equations below. Each answer corresponds with a letter of the quotation. Write the corresponding letter in every blank where your answer occurs. You will discover the quotation as well as the author of the statement. Good luck!!

G: $-7 + 7 =$ ___   B: $-1 \times -1 =$ ___   U: $5 + 6 =$ ___
Y: $3 - 6 =$ ___   M: $-64 \div (-8) =$ ___   E: $-2 \times (-2) =$ ___
D: $-6 - (-4) =$ ___   L: $-23 + 16 =$ ___   N: $-7 + (-1) =$ ___
T: $-2 \times (-5) =$ ___   I: $6 - 1 =$ ___   R: $81 \div 9 =$ ___
A: $-20 \div 20 =$ ___   S: $3 \times (-3) =$ ___   F: $-7 - (-3) =$ ___
H: $-6 + 1 =$ ___   C: $-16 \div (-8) =$ ___   O: $0 - (-7) =$ ___

G:0   B:1   U:11
Y:-3   M:8   E:4
D:-2   L:-7   N:-8
T:10   I:5   R:9
A:-1   S:-9   F:-4
H:-5   C:2   O:7

"Do not be disturbed by your difficulties in mathematics; I can assure you that mine are still greater."   Albert Einstein

3.7 Problem Solving Using Integers

What you should learn:

 Goal 1 How to use properties of equality to solve equations involving integers

 Goal 2 How to use integer operations to model real-life problems

Why you should learn it:

You can use integer operations to solve real-life problems, such as finding the profit or loss from a dance.

Inverse Operations

To help you decide which operation to perform to solve an equation, remember that addition and subtraction are **inverse operations** and multiplication and division are inverse operations. For instance, in the equation $-12 = n + 3$, notice that the side of the equation with n involves addition. To isolate n, you should perform the inverse (or opposite) operation. That is, you should subtract 3 from each side.

Goal 1 Solving Equations

In Lessons 2.4 and 2.5, you learned how to use properties of equality to solve equations. These properties also apply to negative and positive integers. For instance, to solve the equation $x - 5 = -7$, you can add 5 to each side of the equation.

Example 1 Using Addition or Subtraction

Solve the equations **a.** $x - 5 = -7$ and **b.** $-12 = n + 3$.

Solution

a.
$$x - 5 = -7 \qquad \textit{Rewrite original equation.}$$
$$x - 5 + 5 = -7 + 5 \qquad \textit{Add 5 to each side.}$$
$$x = -2 \qquad \textit{Simplify.}$$

The solution is -2. Check this in the original equation.

b.
$$-12 = n + 3 \qquad \textit{Rewrite original equation.}$$
$$-12 - 3 = n + 3 - 3 \qquad \textit{Subtract 3 from each side.}$$
$$-15 = n \qquad \textit{Simplify.}$$

The solution is -15. Check this in the original equation. ■

Example 2 Using Multiplication or Division

Solve the equations **a.** $3y = -18$ and **b.** $\frac{m}{-2} = 15$.

Solution

a.
$$3y = -18 \qquad \textit{Rewrite original equation.}$$
$$\frac{3y}{3} = \frac{-18}{3} \qquad \textit{Divide each side by 3.}$$
$$y = -6 \qquad \textit{Simplify.}$$

The solution is -6. Check this in the original equation.

b.
$$\frac{m}{-2} = 15 \qquad \textit{Rewrite original equation.}$$
$$-2 \cdot \frac{m}{-2} = -2 \cdot 15 \qquad \textit{Multiply each side by } -2.$$
$$m = -30 \qquad \textit{Simplify.}$$

The solution is -30. Check this in the original equation. ■

3.7 • *Problem Solving Using Integers* **131**

LESSON Notes

Remind students of the general technique for solving equations that was introduced in Chapter 2—isolate the variable by generating equivalent expressions at each side of the equation, making sure that whatever you do to one side of the equation is also done to the other side. Refer students to their journal entries if necessary.

　The concept of inverse operations presented on this page is essential to the process of isolating the variable, and the application of the concept will get more complex as students later meet more complex expressions.

Example 1

Encourage students to verbalize the process of isolating x (or n)—"If x has been decreased by 5, I can isolate x by *adding* 5" or "if n has been increased by 3, I can isolate n by *subtracting* 3." Encourage students to use their calculators to check solutions. In Example 1, some students may wish to use the vertical format for solving the equation.

Example 2

Verbalize the process—"If y has been multiplied by 3, I can isolate y by dividing by 3" or "if m has been divided by -2, I can isolate m by multiplying by -2."

STARTER: Problem of the Day

Use three of the five numbers in the set $\{-2, -4, -6, -8, -10\}$ to make a true statement below.

$$\left(-2\right) + \left(-4\right) - \left(-8\right) = 2$$
$$\left(-6\right) + \left(-4\right) - \left(-2\right) = -8$$
$$\left(-2\right) \times \left(-4\right) - \left(-6\right) = 2$$
$$\left(-4\right) \div \left(-2\right) + \left(-10\right) = -8$$

Also available as a copymaster, page 9

STARTER: Warm-Up Exercises

1. In each case state the opposite operation.
a. Addition　　**b.** Multiplication.
a. subtraction, **b.** division
2. Solve.
a. $x + 5 = 7$　　**b.** $12 = n + 3$
c. $3y = 18$　　**d.** $\frac{m}{2} = 15$
a. $x = 2$, **b.** $n = 9$, **c.** $y = 6$, **d.** $m = 30$

Also available as a copymaster, page 9

Integers are useful in describing financial credits and debits.

Example 3

This is a real context in which the full algebraic model is appropriate. Make sure to "walk" students through the steps from verbal model to algebraic model, discuss the labels, etc. Here is a good opportunity to explore the whole purpose of making a model and of using it to plan, predict, make conjectures, and so on.

For example, ask students: What is the smallest number of people who must attend the dance to avoid any loss?   145 people

Communicating about MATHEMATICS

Be prepared to help students identify the labels that are involved in this model, so that they can make the leap from verbal model to algebraic model. Be sure to encourage them to think up other conjectures or questions about the yearbook project that can be answered by using their model.

Writing Prompt
I think solving equations is . . . because . . .

Real Life
Budgeting

Many current songs are accompanied by videos. The first commercially successful home video recorder was introduced in 1975.

Example 3   *Planning a Dance*

Your class is sponsoring a school video dance. Your expenses will be $750 for a disc jockey, $75 for security, and $40 for advertisements. You will charge $6 per person. Will your class make a profit if 125 people attend? If 250 people attend?

Solution   The profit is the difference between your total income (from ticket sales) and your total expenses.

Verbal Model	Profit	=	Ticket price	·	Number of people	−	Expenses

Labels
Profit = P (dollars)
Ticket price = 6   (dollars per person)
Number of people attending = n (people)
Expenses = 750 + 75 + 40 = 865   (dollars)

Algebraic Model $P = 6 \cdot n - 865$

If 125 people attend, then the profit is

$$P = 6(125) - 865 = -115$$

which means that your class had a loss of $115.

If 250 people attend, then the profit is

$$P = 6(250) - 865 = 635$$

which means that your class had a profit of $635.   ∎

Communicating about MATHEMATICS

▶ **SHARING IDEAS about the Lesson**

Real Life
Budgeting

Work Backward   You are on the school yearbook staff. The printing company that is producing the yearbooks will charge $2400, plus $6 per book. You expect to sell 300 yearbooks. Use the following verbal model to decide how much you can reasonably charge for each yearbook. (Your answer depends on the amount of profit you want to make.)

Profit	=	Number of books	·	Price per book	−	(2400 + 6 ·	Number of books)

Answers vary.

OPTION: Extra Examples

Here are additional examples similar to some of those in the lesson.

1. Using Addition or Subtraction
Solve the equations
(a) $n - 10 = 6$ **(b)** $4 = y + 10$.
Solution
a. $n - 10 = 6$ *Original equation.*
   $n - 10 + 10 = 6 + 10$ *Add 10 to each side.*
      $n = 16$ *Simplify.*
The solution is 16. Check by substitution.
b. $4 = y + 10$ *Original equation.*
   $4 - 10 = y + 10 - 10$ *Subtract 10 from each side.*
   $-6 = y$ *Simplify.*
The solution is −6. Check by substitution.

2. Using Multiplication or Division
Solve the equations
(a) $-6x = 18$ **(b)** $-3 = \frac{n}{-3}$.
Solution
a. $-6x = 18$ *Original equation.*
   $\frac{-6x}{-6} = \frac{18}{-6}$ *Divide each side by −6.*
      $x = -3$ *Simplify.*
The solution is −3. Check by substitution.
b. $-3 = \frac{n}{-3}$ *Original equation.*
   $-3 \cdot -3 = -3 \cdot \frac{n}{-3}$ *Multiply each side by −3.*
   $9 = n$ *Simplify.*
The solution is 9. Check by substitution.

EXERCISES

Guided Practice

▶ **CHECK for Understanding**

1. *Writing*   In your own words, state the four properties of equality.   See pages 65 and 71.

In Exercises 2–5, state the property of equality that can be used to solve the equation. Then solve the equation.   For properties, see margin.

2. $x - 4 = -8$ -4 **3.** $-6 = y + 8$ -14 **4.** $\frac{a}{-5} = 7$ -35 **5.** $-5b = 35$ -7

6. *Problem Solving*   Describe a real-life situation in which you can use integer operations.
   Answers vary. In computing how far above or below par in golf.

Independent Practice

In Exercises 7–12, decide whether the value of the variable is a solution of the equation. If not, find the solution.

7. $x - 7 = 3; x = 10$ Yes   **8.** $t + 7 = -10; t = -17$ Yes   **9.** $9 = s + 5; s = 14$ No, $s=4$

10. $-42 = -14b; b = 3$ Yes   **11.** $\frac{m}{-2} = 12; m = -24$ Yes   **12.** $\frac{n}{-6} = -8; n = -48$ No, $n=48$

In Exercises 13–28, solve the equation. Check your solution.

13. $x + 2 = -11$ -13 **14.** $y + 1 = 5$ 4   **15.** $x - 9 = 15$ 24   **16.** $-17 = p - 13$ -4

17. $q + 12 = 3$ -9 **18.** $r - 6 = -2$ 4   **19.** $72 = -6x$ -12 **20.** $-15t = -60$ 4

21. $\frac{y}{-7} = 9$ -63 **22.** $-5 = \frac{s}{-11}$ 55   **23.** $2x = -34$ -17 **24.** $\frac{a}{20} = -4$ -80

25. $b + 5.6 = -8.4$ -14 **26.** $y - 3.8 = 5.2$ 9   **27.** $2 = -4z$ $-\frac{1}{2}$ **28.** $\frac{c}{-6.1} = -9$ 54.9

In Exercises 29–32, write an algebraic equation for the sentence. Then solve the equation and write your conclusion as a sentence.   See margin.

29. The difference of x and 20 is -4.   **30.** -10 is the sum of y and 25.

31. 51 is the product of a and -3.   **32.** The quotient of t and -6 is -14.

In Exercises 33–38, use a calculator to solve the equation. Then check the solution.

33. $-1088 = y + 129$ -1217 **34.** $m - 364 = -1980$ -1616 **35.** $-486s = 7776$ -16

36. $-555t = -8325$ 15   **37.** $-56 = \frac{p}{-23}$ 1288   **38.** $\frac{q}{67} = -31$ -2077

In Exercises 39–44, match the equation with its solution.

a. 9   **b.** -13 **c.** -8 **d.** 7   **e.** -12 **f.** -16

39. $a - 4 + 9 = -8$ b   **40.** $t - 12 + 3 = -2$ d   **41.** $x + 6 - 7 = -13$ e

42. $-27 = 4x - 7x$ a   **43.** $y + 3y = -32$ c   **44.** $\frac{p}{2} = 13 - 21$ f

P Portfolio Opportunity

3.7 ▪ Problem Solving Using Integers   **133**

EXERCISE Notes

ASSIGNMENT GUIDE
Basic/Average:
   Day 1: Ex. 7–43 odd
   Day 2: Ex. 45–47 odd, 49–51 odd

Above Average: Ex. 7–19 odd, 33–43 odd, 47, 48, 49–51 odd

Advanced: Ex. 7–19 odd, 33–43 odd, 47, 48, 49–51 odd

Selected Answers: Ex. 1–6, 7–51 odd

Guided Practice

▶ **Ex. 1**   Note that the annotation for this exercise references the pupil pages where students can find the required statements.

Independent Practice

▶ **Ex. 7–12**   Have students describe a method for using a calculator to answer these questions.

▶ **Ex. 13–28**   Have students work these exercises in groups. Encourage them to think of each equation in terms of opposite operations. Solutions can be shared at the chalkboard or on the overhead projector. Encourage students to check their solutions.

▶ **Ex. 39–44**   Remind students to combine integers and like terms first.

Answers
2. Addition
3. Addition (of -8) or Subtraction (of 8)
4. Multiplication
5. Multiplication (of $-\frac{1}{5}$) or Division (by -5)

29. $x - 20 = -4$, 16, the difference of 16 and 20 is -4.
30. $-10 = y + 25$, -35, -10 is the sum of -35 and 25.
31. $51 = -3a$, -17, 51 is the product of -17 and -3.
32. $\frac{t}{-6} = -14$, 84, the quotient of 84 and -6 is -14.

Lesson 3.7   **133**

▶ Ex. 47, 48
These exercises serve as useful "maintenance" of the basic problem-solving plan.

EXTENSION
Ask students: In order to make a profit, how many students need to attend if the ticket price is **(a)** raised to $6 per person? **(b)** lowered to $4 per person?
a. At least 182, b. At least 373

Integrated Review

Note that students may *estimate* answers to these exercises by reading the bar graph, but they need the precise value of C (given on the bar graph) and the series of linear equations in order to give precise answers.

Exploration and Extension

This project offers students an opportunity to investigate areas of interest to them.

Portfolio Opportunity: Math Log

Which two of the following equations correctly model the given problem. Explain why two models are correct.

Chris' father's age is 6 years less than four times Chris' age. If his father is 46, how old is Chris?
a. $6 - 4x = 46$ **b.** $4x - 46 = 6$
c. $4x - 6 = 46$ **d.** $46 - 4x = 6$

Also available as a copymaster, page 12, Ex. 8

Alternative Assessment

A journal entry project that develops modeling and writing skills.

Available as a copymaster, page 20

Hot-Air Balloon Ride **In Exercises 45 and 46, imagine that you are taking a hot-air balloon ride.**

✪ **45.** You are flying at an altitude of x feet. You descend 6,891 feet to an altitude of 18,479 feet. Which of the following models will correctly determine your original altitude? Solve the correct model and use the result to determine your original altitude.

  a. $\boxed{x} - 6,891 = 18,479$ a; 25,370; 25,370 ft

  b. $18,479 - \boxed{x} = 6,891$

✪ **46.** You are flying at an altitude of 19,653 feet. You descend 8,905 feet, rise 9,842 feet, descend 14,450 feet, and descend another 6,140 feet. Write an algebraic model that represents your final altitude. What is your final altitude? 0 ft For model, see margin.

The altitude record in a hot-air balloon is 64,996 feet over Laredo, Texas, achieved by Per Lindstrand in 1988.

Rock-N-Roll **In Exercises 47 and 48, use the following information.**

Your school is sponsoring a rock-n-roll concert. The expenses include $800 for the band, $20 for posters, $200 for refreshments, and $70 for security. The tickets cost $5 per person. $P = 5n - (800 + 20 + 200 + 70)$

✪ **47.** Use the verbal model $\boxed{\text{Profit}} = \boxed{\text{Income}} - \boxed{\text{Expenses}}$ to write an algebraic model for the profit. Let P represent the profit and let n represent the number of tickets sold.

✪ **48.** How many people must attend to make a profit of $250? 268

Integrated Review   *Making Connections within Mathematics*

Endangered Species **In Exercises 49–52, use the following equations and the information at the right.**
(Source: U.S. Fish and Wildlife Service)

$$C + 17 = B \qquad F - B = -5$$
$$B - M = \tfrac{1}{2}C \qquad I + M = C + 10$$

49. How many species of birds are endangered? 57
50. How many species of fish are endangered? 52
51. How many species of mammals are endangered? 37
52. How many species of insects are endangered? 13

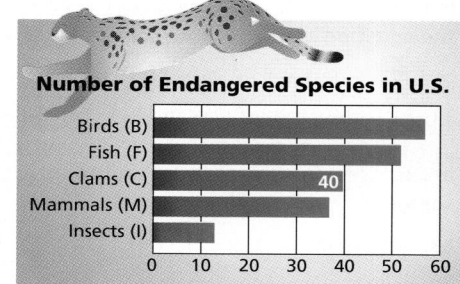

Number of Endangered Species in U.S.

Birds (B)	
Fish (F)	
Clams (C)	40
Mammals (M)	
Insects (I)	

0 10 20 30 40 50 60

Exploration and Extension

✪ **53.** **Research Project**   Use some reference source to find information
P   about a world record. Use your findings to write a story problem.   Answers vary.

✪ More difficult exercises
P Portfolio Opportunity

Answer
46. $a = 19,653 - 8905 + 9842 - 14,450 - 6140$

3.8

Exploring Patterns in the Coordinate Plane

PACING the Lesson

Suggested Number of Days
Basic/Average 2 **Above Average** 2
Advanced 1

PLANNING the Lesson

Lesson Plan 3.8, p. 25

What you should learn:

 Goal 1 How to plot points in a coordinate plane

 Goal 2 How to use a coordinate plane to represent data graphically

Why you should learn it:

Representing data in a coordinate plane helps you discover relationships and patterns between two variables.

Goal 1 **Points in a Coordinate Plane**

A **coordinate plane** has two number lines that intersect at a right angle. The point of intersection is the **origin.** The horizontal number line is usually called the **x-axis,** and the vertical number line is usually called the **y-axis.** (The plural of axis is *axes.*)

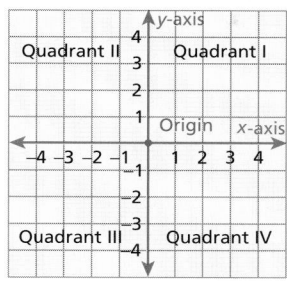

The two axes divide the coordinate plane into four parts called **quadrants.**

Each point in a coordinate plane can be represented by an **ordered pair** of numbers, (x, y). The first number is the **x-coordinate,** and it gives the position of the point relative to the x-axis. The second number is the **y-coordinate,** and it gives the position of the point relative to the y-axis.

$$(x, y)$$
x-coordinate —   — y-coordinate

Locating the point in the coordinate plane that corresponds to an ordered pair is called **plotting the point.**

Example 1 *Plotting Points in a Coordinate Plane*

Plot the points $A(4, 3)$, $B(4, -2)$, $C(-4, -2)$, and $D(-4, 3)$. Then find the perimeter and area of rectangle $ABCD$.

Solution The points are plotted in the coordinate plane at the left. The sides of the rectangle are denoted by the line segments

$\overline{AB}$, $\overline{BC}$, $\overline{CD}$, and $\overline{AD}$. *Sides of rectangle ABCD*

The lengths of the sides are

$AB = 5$, $BC = 8$, $CD = 5$, and $AD = 8$. *Lengths*

The rectangle has a perimeter of $5 + 8 + 5 + 8$ or 26 units, and an area of $5(8)$ or 40 square units. ∎

3.8 • *Exploring Patterns in the Coordinate Plane* **135**

ORGANIZER

Starters (reproduced below)
Problem of the Day 3.8, p. 9
Warm-Up Exercises 3.8, p. 9
Lesson Resources
Teaching Tools
Coordinate plane, pp. T8, C10
Coordinate planes, pp. T9, C11
Math Log, p. 12
Technology, p. 15
Answer Masters 3.8, pp. 60–62
Extra Practice Copymaster 3.8, p. 25
Reteaching Copymaster 3.8, p. 25
Enrichment Projects, pp. 16, 17
Special Populations
Suggestions, Teacher's Edition, p. 98D

LESSON Notes

MATH JOURNAL
Students should record the definitions of all the boldface terms of this lesson in their journals. Have them include a sketch of a coordinate plane with labels.

Many students may be familiar with the grid of the game Battleship. Other students are used to looking at city street maps, or have often heard identifying phrases such as "Myrtle Avenue and 83rd Street." Point out that the coordinate plane is designed to allow every point in the plane to be uniquely located. You may wish to emphasize this by coordinatizing your classroom.

Addressing Misconceptions

Point out that, in general, the ordered pair (a, b) is not the same as (b, a). Illustrate the distinction by plotting such points as $(2, -3)$ and $(-3, 2)$. You may wish also to show that evaluating the expression $x + 2y$ for the ordered pair $(2, -3)$ results in $2 + 2(-3) = -4$, but evaluating the expression for $(-3, 2)$ results in $-3 + 2(2) = 1$.

Example 1

Make sure that students understand how the lengths of the sides of the rectangle are determined.

| STARTER: Problem of the Day |

For the triangle on the left, arrange the numbers $-3, -2, -1, 1, 2, 3$ in the circles, so that the sum of the numbers on each side of the triangle is 2. For the triangle on the right, arrange the numbers $-4, -3, -2, -1, 0, 1$ in the circles, so that the same sum results on each side of the triangle.

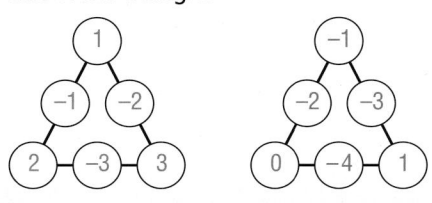

| STARTER: Warm-Up Exercises |

1. Locate the following points on a number line.
a. -6 **b.** 4 **c.** 0
d. 10 **e.** -2

2. Find the perimeter and area of the following figures.

a. 7 (width 3)   **b.** 2 (width), 6 (height)

a. perimeter = 20 units, area = 21 sq. units;
b. perimeter = 16 units, area = 12 sq. units

Also available as a copymaster, page 9

Also available as a copymaster, page 9

MATH JOURNAL

Students should be encouraged to write the first sentence of this page into their journals, and to entitle it "Solution of an equation having 2 variables." Ask students: How should the sentence be reworded to refer to an equation having 1 variable?"

Answers will vary: a number is a solution of an equation involving *x* if the equation is true when that number is substituted into the equation.

Example 2

Tables and graphs are two effective ways of representing data. Ask students which of these two forms of display conveys more information.

Communicating about MATHEMATICS

Have students investigate whether any equation of the form $x + y = k$, where k is a constant, is *always* a straight line.   Yes, it is.

Writing Prompt

Explain what is most important to understand about plotting points in the coordinate plane.

Technology

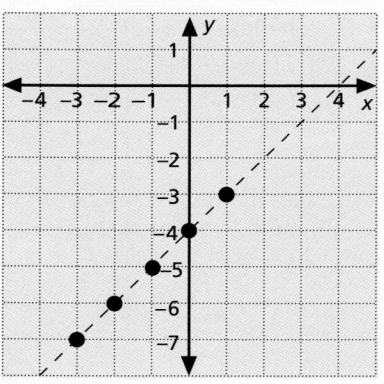

An ordered pair (x, y) is a **solution** of an equation involving x and y if the equation is true when the values of x and y are substituted into the equation. Most equations in two variables have many solutions. For instance, 3 solutions of $x + y = 4$ are shown below.

Equation	Solution	Check
$x + y = 4$	$(1, 3)$	$1 + 3 = 4$
$x + y = 4$	$(-3, 7)$	$-3 + 7 = 4$
$x + y = 4$	$(0, 4)$	$0 + 4 = 4$

Example 2   *Representing Data*

Construct a table that shows several solutions of the equation $2 + x = y$. Then plot the corresponding points and describe the graphical pattern.

Solution   Begin by choosing an x-value, such as $x = -3$. Substitute -3 for x in the equation to obtain

$$2 + (-3) = y \quad \text{or} \quad y = -1.$$

This implies that $(-3, -1)$ is a solution of the equation. Other solutions are shown in the table.

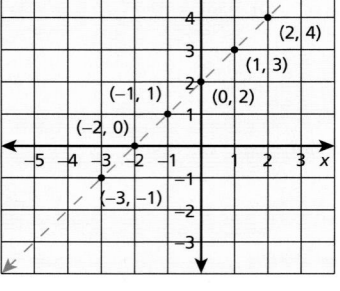

x	-3	-2	-1	0	1	2
y	-1	0	1	2	3	4
(x, y)	$(-3, -1)$	$(-2, 0)$	$(-1, 1)$	$(0, 2)$	$(1, 3)$	$(2, 4)$

After plotting the points in a coordinate plane, you can see that all 6 points lie on a line. If you try finding other solution points of the equation, you will discover that they lie on the same line.

Communicating about MATHEMATICS

▶ **SHARING IDEAS about the Lesson**

Extending the Example Construct a table that shows several solutions of the equation. Then plot the corresponding points and describe the graphical pattern.

$x + y = 3$ The graph is a straight line containing points $(0, 3)$ and $(3, 0)$. See Additional Answers.

Here is an additional example similar to Example 2.

Representing Data

Construct a table that shows several solutions of the equation, $-4 + x = y$. Then plot the corresponding points and describe the graphical pattern.

x	-3	-2	-1	0	1
y	-7	-6	-5	-4	-3
(x, y)	$(-3, -7)$	$(-2, -6)$	$(-1, -5)$	$(0, -4)$	$(1, -3)$

Solution

Begin by choosing an x-value, such as $x = -3$. Substitute -3 for x in the equation to obtain

$$-4 + (-3) = y \quad \text{or} \quad y = -7.$$

This implies that $(-3, -7)$ is a solution of the equation. Other solutions are shown in the table.

After plotting the points in a coordinate plane, you can see that all 5 points lie on a line.

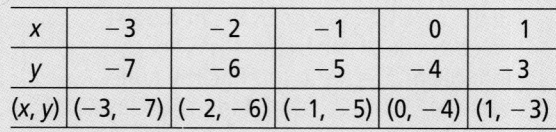

EXERCISES

Guided Practice

▶ **CHECK for Understanding**   **1., 2.** See margin.

1. Explain how to construct and label a coordinate plane.

2. Explain how to decide whether an ordered pair (x, y) is a solution of an equation.

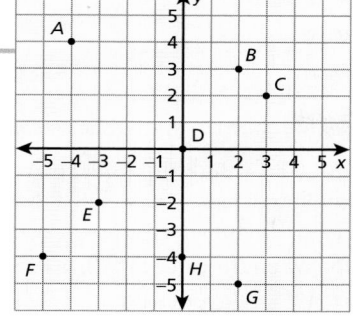

In Exercises 3–10, use the coordinate plane at the right to state the x- and y-coordinate of the point. Then state the quadrant in which the point lies.

3. A $(-4, 4)$, II

4. B $(2, 3)$, I

5. C $(3, 2)$, I

6. D $(0, 0)$, none

7. E $(-3, -2)$, III

8. F $(-5, -4)$, III

9. G $(2, -5)$, IV

10. H $(0, -4)$, none

Independent Practice

In Exercises 11–16, match the ordered pair with its corresponding point in the coordinate plane. Identify the quadrant in which the point lies.

11. $(1, -2)$ J, IV

12. $(-2, 1)$ M, II

13. $(3, 4)$ I, I

14. $(-3, 2)$ N, II

15. $(-1, -4)$ L, III

16. $(4, -3)$ K, IV

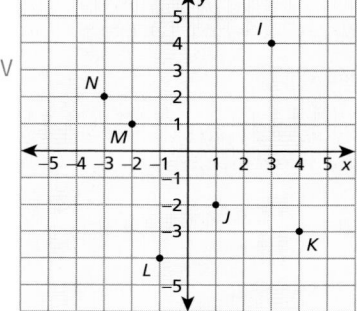

In Exercises 17–24, plot the points on a single coordinate plane. Determine the quadrant in which each point lies.

17. $A(-6, -2)$ III

18. $B(-1, -5)$ III   For graphs,

19. $C(3, 7)$ I

20. $D(7, 3)$ I   see margin.

21. $E(-1, 0)$ none

22. $F(0, 4)$ none

23. $G(-4, 5)$ II

24. $H(2, -6)$ IV

In Exercises 25–28, determine the quadrant in which (x, y) lies.

25. $x < 0$ and $x = y$ III

26. $x > 0$ and $y = -x$ IV

27. $y > 0$ and $y = -x$ II

28. $y > 0$ and $x = y$ I

Coordinate Geometry   **In Exercises 29 and 30, plot the points to form the vertices of a rectangle. Find the area and perimeter of the rectangle.** For graphs, see Additional Answers.

29. $A(1, 3)$, $B(-2, 3)$, $C(1, -4)$, $D(-2, -4)$
21 units², 20 units

30. $A(-4, 4)$, $B(1, 4)$, $C(1, -1)$, $D(-4, -1)$
25 units², 20 units

Equation Sense   **In Exercises 31–33, show that the ordered pair is a solution of the equation. Then find three other solutions.** Solutions vary.

31. $3 + x = y$; $(7, 10)$
$3 + 7 = 10$; $(1, 4), (2, 5), (3, 6)$

32. $y - 5 = x$; $(-8, -3)$
$-3 - 5 = -8$; $(1, 6), (2, 7), (3, 8)$

33. $x + y = 6$; $(8, -2)$
$8 + (-2) = 6$; $(1, 5), (2, 4), (3, 3)$

3.8 ▪ Exploring Patterns in the Coordinate Plane   **137**

EXERCISE Notes

ASSIGNMENT GUIDE

Basic/Average:
Day 1: Ex. 11–15, 21–37 odd
Day 2: Ex. 40–43, 45–51 odd

Above Average:
Day 1: Ex. 11–15, 21–37 odd
Day 2: Ex. 40–43, 45–51 odd

Advanced: Ex. 11–15, 21–37 odd, 41–51 odd

Selected Answers: Ex. 1–10, 11–49 odd

Guided Practice

Have students work these exercises in their groups.

Independent Practice

▶ **Ex. 25–28** Assign these exercises as a group.

▶ **Ex. 29, 30** Explain to students that the lengths of the sides of these rectangles are determined by counting.

Answers

1. Draw two lines that intersect at a right angle. Label the vertical line with a letter, usually y, and label the horizontal line with another letter, usually x. Label points to the right of and up from their intersection with positive numbers, and label points to the left of and down from their intersection with negative numbers.

2. Substitute the values of x and y into the equation and see if the resulting equation consists of the same value on each side of the equal sign. If this occurs, then the ordered pair is a solution.

17–24.

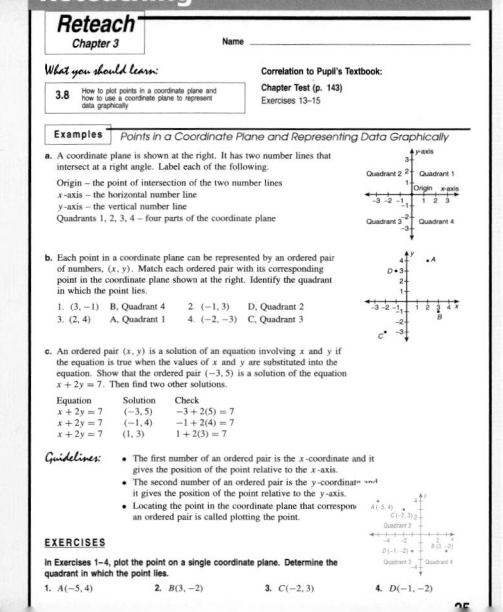

PROBLEM SOLVING

Suggest to students that, in making this table, they select *small* values of *x* in order to minimize the computations, for example, 0, 1, 2. Also suggest that, in Ex. 37, it makes sense to select a multiple of 2 as an *x*-value in this exercise.

At this point, since students are regularly finding linear patterns, you may want to point out that many other patterns exist in algebraic relationships.

▶ **Ex. 40–43** These exercises provide practice in reading and interpreting a graph.

Integrated Review

▶ **Ex. 48–50** For these exercises, students need to remember the Distributive Property.

Exploration and Extension

You may wish to point out to students that the sequences produced in these exercises are sequences of ordered pairs. In each exercise, the pattern formed by these pairs on the coordinate plane is a linear one.

Portfolio Opportunity: Math Log

What can be determined about the signs of *x* and *y* if (*x*, *y*) lies
a. in the first quadrant.
b. in the second quadrant.
c. in the third quadrant.
d. in the fourth quadrant.
e. on the x-axis.
f. on the y-axis.

Also available as a copymaster, page 12, Ex. 9

Short Quiz

Covers Lessons 3.7 and 3.8

Available as a copymaster, page 36

Alternative Assessment

Chapter 3 Group Assessment
A graphing activity for 3 or 4 students.

Chapter 3 Individual Assessment
A similar follow-up activity for individual students. Adds incentive for the group activity and measures individual competence in the activity.

Available as copymasters, pages 63, 64

Alternative Assessment

A cooperative learning activity that develops data organizing skills and graph analysis skills.

Available as a copymaster, page 20

Visualizing Patterns **In Exercises 34–39, construct a table that lists several solutions of the equation. Then plot the points and describe the pattern.** See Additional Answers.

34. $y = 4 - x$
35. $-5x = y$
36. $2x - y = 1$
37. $\frac{1}{2}x + 3 = y$
38. $x + y = -2$
39. $3x - 2 = y$

Selling Jeans **In Exercises 40–43, use the following.**

You own a clothing store. You pay $20 for a pair of jeans. The number of pairs you sell in a month depends on the price you charge customers, as shown in the graph.

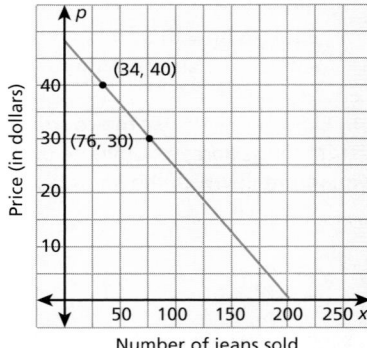

✪ **40.** When the price is $30, how many pairs will you sell? 76
✪ **41.** When the price is $40, how many pairs will you sell? 34
✪ **42.** Your profit is given by

$$\text{Profit} = px - 20x \,.$$
$760 \qquad $680

What is your profit when $p = 30? When $p = 40?

✪ **43.** *It's Up to You* Can stores always make a greater profit by charging more? Explain your reasoning.
No; when prices go up, sales will usually go down.

Integrated Review   *Making Connections within Mathematics*

Equation Sense **In Exercises 44–47, solve the equation.**

44. $x + 15 = -3$ -18
45. $n - 5 = -12$ -7
46. $10m = -1$ $-\frac{1}{10}$
47. $\frac{p}{-1} = 5$ -5

Geometry **In Exercises 48–50, write an expression for the area of the blue region.**

48.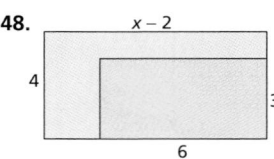
$4x - 26$

49.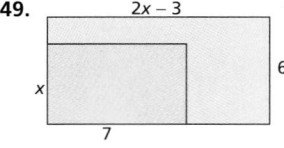
$5x - 18$

50.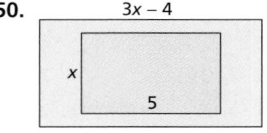
$7x - 16$

Exploration and Extension

A Coordinate Sequence **You are given a point on the coordinate plane and a procedure that produces a sequence. In Exercises 51 and 52,**
a. **find the sequence,**
b. **plot the points on a coordinate plane, and**
c. **describe the results.** See Additional Answers.

✪ **51.** (0, 0); add 1 to the *x*-coordinate and add 1 to the *y*-coordinate.
✪ **52.** (3, 1); subtract 3 from the *x*-coordinate and add 2 to the *y*-coordinate.

138   *Chapter 3* • *Modeling Integers*   ✪ More difficult exercises

Enrichment

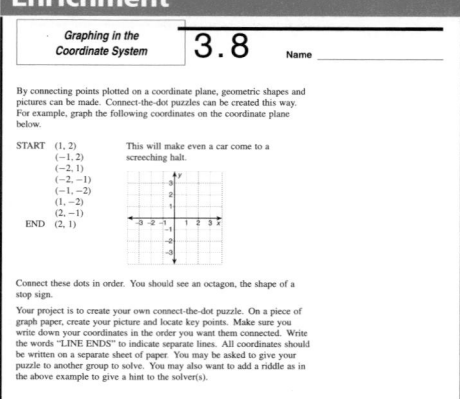

3

Chapter Summary

What did you learn?

Why did you learn it?

In prehistoric times, humans led simple lives. They could solve most of their real-life problems with counting numbers, such as 1, 2, 3, and so on. As life became more and more complex, humans found that they needed other types of numbers. In this chapter, you have seen that many real-life quantities can be modeled with negative numbers. For instance, a weight change of -4 pounds means that you have lost 4 pounds. A "profit" of $-\$260$ means that you had a loss of $260. A temperature of $-25°F$ means that the temperature is 25 degrees below zero.

How does it fit into the bigger picture of mathematics?

Some people think that mathematics consists of dozens of unrelated rules that have to be memorized. With that outlook, mathematics is much more difficult than it has to be. Throughout this course, we hope that you will look for connections between different parts of mathematics. For instance, in this chapter you learned that the equation-solving techniques you studied in Chapter 2 can also be applied to equations involving integers. Later, you will learn that the same techniques can be applied to equations with variables on both sides and to equations that contain fractions or decimals. Rather than remembering dozens of rules for solving equations, you will learn that you only need one basic rule: *performing the same operation to both sides of an equation produces an equivalent equation.*

Chapter Summary **139**

SUMMARY and REVIEW

COOPERATIVE LEARNING
Encourage students to study together. Emphasize the importance of teaching a classmate how to perform a skill or how to recall a procedure. When students work together, everyone wins. The students receiving help get additional instruction, and the students giving help gain a deeper understanding of the skills and concepts involved.

Chapter SUMMARY

An important part of students' readiness to use algebra to model real-life problems is the ability to perform operations with integers. In this chapter, students learned the rules for adding, subtracting, multiplying, and dividing integers. Several investigations were devoted to an alternative representation of these operations through modeling with colored counters. Students also learned to identify the various elements that constitute an algebraic expression—terms, variables, and coefficients (including the unwritten coefficients of 1 and -1). Meanwhile, in the frequent real-life modeling examples, students were systematically reminded of the underlying purpose of building algebra skills—the ability to write and solve equations. In the final lesson of this chapter, students were introduced to the relation between an equation and its visual representation in the coordinate plane—its graph.

Chapter REVIEW

Have students begin this Review in class and complete it as a homework assignment.

ASSIGNMENT GUIDE

Basic/Average:
Ex. 7–15 odd, 23–29 odd, 44, 47–73 odd

Above Average:
Ex. 21–43 odd, 45, 46, 49–75 odd

Advanced:
Ex. 21–43 odd, 45, 46, 49–75 odd

Resources
Color Transparency
  Picture for Ex. 75, 76, p. 15
Answer Masters, pp. 63–65

Chapter **REVIEW**

In Exercises 1–4, plot the integers on a number line. (3.1) See margin.

1. $1, -4, 0, -7$ **2.** $2, 3, -2, -6$ **3.** $0, -1, -2, 5$ **4.** $-4, -3, 3, 4$

In Exercises 5 and 6, order the integers from least to greatest. (3.1)

5. $5, -7, 8, -3, 0$ $-7, -3, 0, 5, 8$ **6.** $0, -1, 12, -5, -13$ $-13, -5, -1, 0, 12$

Number Sense **In Exercises 7–10, write the integer associated with the phrase. (3.1)**

7. A loss of $365 -365 **8.** 5 units to the left -5

9. Up 17 units 17 **10.** 875 feet above sea level 875

In Exercises 11–19, evaluate the expression. (3.2, 3.3, 3.4)

11. $17 + (-16)$ 1 **12.** $25 + (-35)$ -10 **13.** $-27 + (-15)$ -42

14. $-63 + 12$ -51 **15.** $-10 - 31$ -41 **16.** $-5 - |-11|$ -16

17. $49 - |-51|$ -2 **18.** $-10 - (-11) + (-12)$ -11 **19.** $10 + 11 - (-12)$ 33

In Exercises 20–28, simplify the expression. (3.3, 3.4)

20. $3x + (-x) + 10$ $2x+10$ **21.** $5x + (-2x) - 6$ $3x-6$ **22.** $-7x + (-8x) + 15$ $-15x+$

23. $-12x + 16x + (-8)$ $4x-8$ **24.** $-3x - (-12x) + 2$ $9x+2$ **25.** $-4x - (-9x) - 6$ $5x-6$

26. $-6x - 6x - 6$ $-12x-6$ **27.** $12x - (-12x) + 12$ $24x+12$ **28.** $8x - (-10x) + (-7x)$ $11x$

An Investment **In Exercises 29–31, use the following information. (3.3)**

You have two $250 investments. At the end of each quarter you receive a statement that shows the change in your balance for that quarter.

Time (in months)	3	6	9	12
Investment 1	$18	−$15	$7	$20
Investment 2	$4	$4	$4	$4

⭐ 29. Which investment earned more after 6 months?

⭐ 30. Which investment earned more after 12 months?

                        29. 2   **30.** 1

⭐ 31. One of these investments is a stock purchase and one is a bank savings account. Which is which? Explain your reasoning. See margin.

Computation Sense **In Exercises 32–35, *a* is positive and *b* is negative. Decide whether the expression is positive or negative. (3.1, 3.5, 3.6)**

32. ab Negative   **33.** $-\dfrac{a}{b}$ Positive   **34.** $-5ab$ Positive   **35.** $\dfrac{6a}{-2b}$ Positive

In Exercises 36–43, evaluate the expression. (3.5, 3.6)

36. $9(8)$ 72 **37.** $(-3)(7)$ -21 **38.** $5(-9)$ -45 **39.** $(-6)(-4)$ 24

40. $14 \div (-2)$ -7 **41.** $-52 \div 13$ -4 **42.** $\dfrac{-96}{-12}$ 8 **43.** $\dfrac{-144}{4}$ -36

44. *Averages*   Find the average of the numbers. **(3.6)**

$-274, -266, -290, -281, -275, -300, -259, -262, -270, -283$ -276

Answers

1.

2.

3.
<-3 -2 -1 0 1 2 3 4 5 6>

4.
<-4 -3 -2 -1 0 1 2 3 4 5>

31. Investment 1 is the stock purchase because a bank savings account does not lose money as Investment 1 did at 6 months; so Investment 2 is the bank savings account.

Batting Average   **In Exercises 45 and 46, use the information given in the caption of the photo. (3.3)**

45. During a baseball season, you had 28 hits in 56 times at bat. What is your batting average? 0.5

46. During a baseball season, you played 16 games. Your hit totals in each game were

1, 4, 0, 2, 2, 1, 3, 0, 0, 2, 4, 3, 1, 1, 0, 4.

What was your average number of hits per game? 1.75

In Exercises 47–50, write an algebraic model for the statement. Then solve the model. (3.7)

47. The difference of a number and -8 is 7. $x-(-8)=7, -1$

48. The sum of a number and -9 is -21. $x+(-9)=-21, -12$

49. The product of a number and 4 is -28. $4x=-28, -7$

50. The quotient of a number and -15 is 3. $\frac{x}{-15}=3, -45$

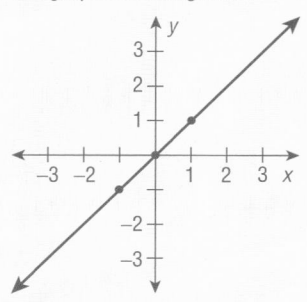

A baseball player's batting average is found by dividing the number of hits by the number of times at bat.

In Exercises 51–58, solve the equation. Check your solution. (3.3, 3.4, 3.7)

51. $x + 9 = -6$ -15 **52.** $y + 15 = 8$ -7 **53.** $m - 8 = 6$ 14   **54.** $-14 = n - 27$ 13

55. $-14s = 42$ -3 **56.** $10t = -80$ -8 **57.** $\frac{r}{-7} = -8$ 56   **58.** $\frac{p}{5} = 11$ 55

In Exercises 59–62, plot the point and name its quadrant. (3.8)   For graphs, see margin.

59. $(-5, 1)$ II   **60.** $(-1, -6)$ III   **61.** $(4, 5)$ I   **62.** $(6, -3)$ IV

63. *Coordinate Geometry*   In a coordinate plane, plot the points   For graph, see margin.
$A(7, 1), B(7, -5), C(-1, -5),$ and $D(-1, 1)$. What type of figure is $ABCD$? Find its perimeter and area. **(3.8)**   Rectangle; 28 units, 48 units²

Equation Sense   **In Exercises 64–66, determine whether the ordered pair is a solution of the equation. (3.8)**

64. $x - y = -2; (-3, 1)$ No   **65.** $x + 7 = y; (-4, -3)$ No   **66.** $y = -4x; (3, -12)$ Yes

Equation Sense   **In Exercises 67–70, construct a table that lists several solutions of the equation. Then plot the points and describe the pattern. (3.8)** See margin.

67. $x + 1 = y$ **68.** $y = x$ **69.** $y = -2x$ **70.** $x + y = 1$

Logical Reasoning   **In Exercises 71–74, decide whether the statement is sometimes, always, or never true. Explain. (3.4)**   For explanations, see margin.

71. The opposite of n is $-n$. Always   ✪ **72.** The opposite of n is negative. Sometimes

73. The absolute value of $-n$ is n. Sometimes   ✪ **74.** $x(y - z) = xy + (-xz)$ Always

✪ More difficult exercises

Chapter Review   **141**

68.

x	-1	0	1
y	-1	0	1
(x, y)	$(-1, -1)$	$(0, 0)$	$(1, 1)$

The graph is a straight line.

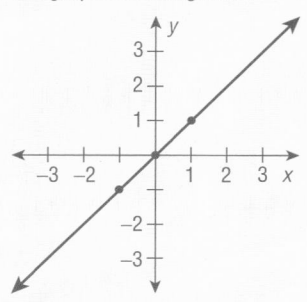

69.

x	-1	0	1
y	2	0	-2
(x, y)	$(-1, 2)$	$(0, 0)$	$(1, -2)$

The graph is a straight line.

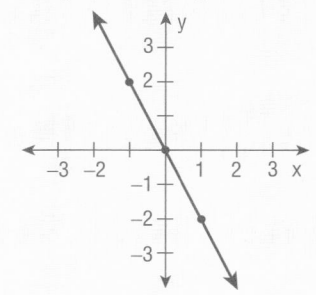

70.

x	-1	0	1
y	2	1	0
(x, y)	$(-1, 2)$	$(0, 1)$	$(1, 0)$

The graph is a straight line.

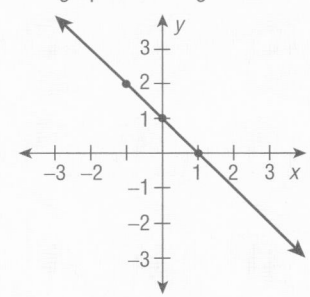

71. The algebraic expression $-n$ has the same meaning as the verbal expression *the opposite of n*.

72. The statement is false when $n \leq 0$.

73. The statement is false when $n < 0$.

74. The statement is true by the Distributive Property and the meaning of subtraction.

Answers

59.–62.

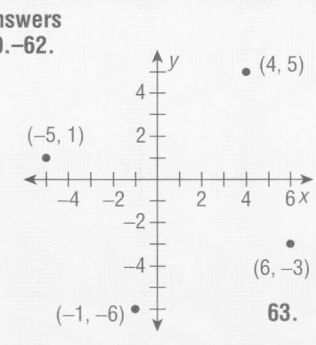

67.

x	-1	0	1
y	0	1	2
(x, y)	$(-1, 0)$	$(0, 1)$	$(1, 2)$

The graph is a straight line.

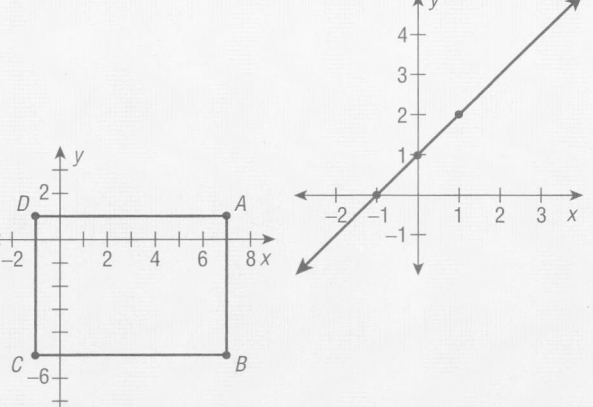

63.

Chapter Review   **141**

Real Life Connection

Gymnastics **In Exercises 75 and 76, use the following information.**

Gymnasts are judged by how well they perform their routine. A score of 10.00 is a perfect score. In women's gymnastics, seven judges score each performance. To determine a gymnast's score, the head judge eliminates the highest and lowest scores of the other six judges and averages the remaining four scores. (The head judge's score is usually not used.)

✪ **75.** Listed below are the judges' scores (excluding the head judge's) for the gold, silver, and bronze medalists in an international women's gymnastics competition. Which gymnast won the gold? Gymnast 3

Gymnast 1: 9.85, 9.30, 9.70, 9.65, 9.35, 9.50
Gymnast 2: 9.80, 9.60, 9.45, 9.30, 9.50, 9.25
Gymnast 3: 9.10, 9.45, 9.95, 9.70, 9.55, 9.65

✪ **76.** One gymnast finished with a final score of 9.2. What could her scores have been? (There are many correct answers.) Answers vary.

In gymnastics competitions, judges award a maximum of 3.4 points for the level of difficulty of the routine, 2.6 points for the combination of movements, and 4.0 points for originality and performance.

Word Puzzle **In Exercises 77–96, solve the equation. Then use the results to decode the message.**

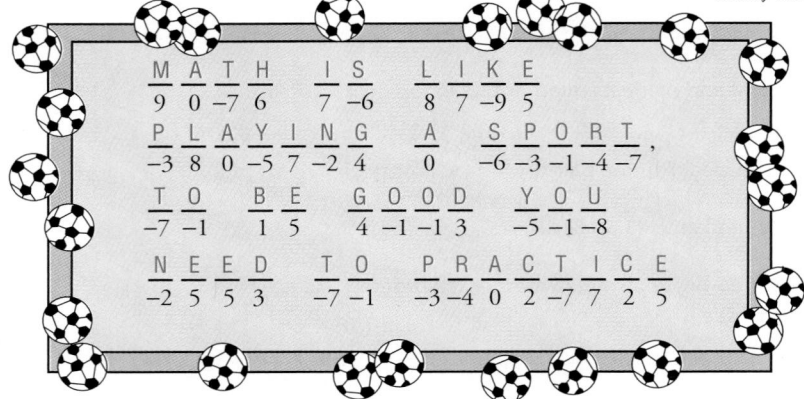

```
 M  A  T  H    I  S    L  I  K  E
 9  0 -7  6    7 -6    8  7 -9  5

 P  L  A  Y  I  N  G    A    S  P  O  R  T
-3  8  0 -5  7 -2  4    0   -6 -3 -1 -4 -7  ,

 T  O    B  E    G  O  O  D    Y  O  U
-7 -1    1  5    4 -1 -1  3   -5 -1 -8

 N  E  E  D    T  O    P  R  A  C  T  I  C  E
-2  5  5  3   -7 -1   -3 -4  0  2 -7  7  2  5
```

✪ **77.** $Y + 17 = 12$ −5   ✪ **78.** $4 = 0 + G$ 4   ✪ **79.** $N - 3 = -5$ −2

✪ **80.** $S - (-4) = -2$ −6   ✪ **81.** $-5I = -35$ 7   ✪ **82.** $8D = 24$ 3

✪ **83.** $\frac{U}{4} = -2$ −8   ✪ **84.** $\frac{H}{-1} = -6$ 6   ✪ **85.** $6 + K = -3$ −9

✪ **86.** $C - 7 = -5$ 2   ✪ **87.** $79B = 79$ 1   ✪ **88.** $-7 + M = 2$ 9

✪ **89.** $\frac{R}{-4} = 1$ −4   ✪ **90.** $16P = -48$ −3   ✪ **91.** $3 - O = 4$ −1

✪ **92.** $E + 11 = 16$ 5   ✪ **93.** $12T = -84$ −7   ✪ **94.** $\frac{A}{-249} = 0$ 0

✪ **95.** $4L = 32$ 8   ✪ **96.** What is the message? See above.

✪ More difficult exercises

Chapter TEST

Exercises 1 and 2, write the integer that represents the phrase. (3.1)

1. An altitude of 3000 feet   3000

2. A loss of $60   −60

Exercises 3 and 4, state the opposite and the absolute value of the integer. (3.1)

3. 120   −120, 120

4. −54   54, 54

5. Order the integers −4, 5, −3, 0, 2, and −1 from least to greatest.   (3.1)   −4, −3, −1, 0, 2, 5

6. Find the average of −5, 3, −4, −2, and −7.   (3.1)   −3

Exercises 7–12, simplify the expression. (3.2–3.6)

7. −4 + 8   4

8. −6 − (−3)   −3

9. (−2)(−5)   10

10. (−3)(−4)(−5)   −60

11. $\frac{-12}{-6}$ 2

12. $\frac{36}{-9}$ −4

Exercises 13–15, use the graph at the right. (3.8)

13. Write the coordinates of A, B, C, D, and E.   See below.

14. Which point lies in quadrant III?   E

15. The points A, B, and C form three vertices of a rectangle. Write the coordinates of the fourth vertex. Find the perimeter and area of the rectangle.   (−4, −2), 24 units, 35 units²

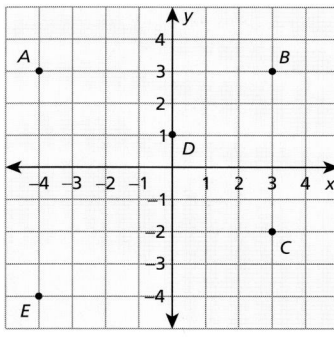

Exercises 16–18, use mental math to solve the equation. (3.7)

16. x + 2 = −4   −6

17. 2x = −6   −3

18. $\frac{x}{9}$ = −2   −18

13. A(−4, 3), B(3, 3), C(3, −2), D(0, 1), E(−4, −4)

Exercises 19 and 20, use the following information. (3.6)

The low temperatures for 6 days in a row are 7°, −3°, −6°, 3°, 0°, and −2°.

19. If the average low temperature for the week was −2°, what was the low temperature on the 7th day?   1°

20. If the average low temperature for the week was −1°, what was the low temperature on the 7th day?   8°

21. Your bowling-league average is the sum of your scores divided by the number of games bowled. On your first night you bowled games of 128, 99, and 109. On the second night you bowled 117, 101, and 130. What was your average after the two nights?   (3.6)   114

Cumulative Review

Resources

Color Transparency
  Picture for Ex. 71, 72, p. 15
Answer Masters, pp. 67–69

In Exercises 1–6, describe the pattern. Then list the next 3 numbers or letters. (1.1) For descriptions, see margin.

1. 20, 18, 16, 14, [?] [?] [?] 12, 10, 8

2. 1, 5, 9, 13, [?] [?] [?] 17, 21, 25

3. $\frac{1}{2}, \frac{3}{4}, \frac{5}{6}, \frac{7}{8},$ [?] [?] [?] $\frac{9}{10}, \frac{11}{12}, \frac{13}{14}$

4. $\frac{14}{13}, \frac{12}{11}, \frac{10}{9}, \frac{8}{7},$ [?] [?] [?] $\frac{6}{5}, \frac{4}{3}, \frac{2}{1}$

5. Z, W, T, Q, [?] [?] [?]   N, K, H

6. A, Z, C, X, [?] [?] [?]   E, V, G

In Exercises 7–15, evaluate the expression using a calculator. Round to two decimal places when necessary. (1.3, 1.4)

7. 4^8 65,536

8. $\left(\frac{3}{4}\right)^5$ 0.24

9. $\sqrt{48}$ 6.93

10. $\sqrt{352}$ 18.76

11. $(3.8)^7$ 11,441.56

12. $\sqrt{26.19}$ 5.12

13. $150 - 60 \div 3 \cdot 4$ 70

14. $35 \div (19 - 12) + 4^5$ 1029

15. $3^3 + (14 + 8) \cdot 12 - 11$ 280

In Exercises 16–24, evaluate the expression. (1.4, 3.1–3.6)

16. $|-3| - |5|$ -2

17. $-|-4| + |-3|$ -1

18. $-5 + 12 - 9 - 13$ -15

19. $21 - 32 - 1 + 4$ -8

20. $(10)(-11)$ -110

21. $\frac{-144}{-2}$ 72

22. $(-3)(-4)(6)$ 72

23. $2^2 + (3 - 4)^2 \cdot 9$ 13

24. $20 - (5 - 8)^3 \div 9$ 23

In Exercises 25–28, decide whether the figure is a polygon. If it is, name it. If it is not, explain. (1.7) 25. No, all sides not segments

25.

26.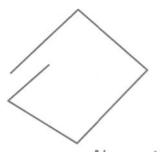

No, not closed

27.

Yes, hexagon

28.

Yes, quadrilateral

In Exercises 29–40, write the expression without parentheses and combine like terms when possible. Then evaluate it when $x = 3$, $y = 4$, and $z = 6$. (1.5, 2.1, 2.2, 3.1–3.5)

29. $3(x + y + 3)$ $3x + 3y + 9$, 30

30. $4(x + y + z + 3)$ $4x + 4y + 4z + 12$, 64

31. $2(z + 3y)$ $2z + 6y$, 36

32. $5(z - 2x)$ $5z - 10x$, 0

33. $7x + x + z + y$ $8x + z + y$, 34

34. $9y - 2y - z - 2$ $7y - z - 2$, 20

35. $4z + 6z - 9y - 25$ $10z - 9y - 25$, -1

36. $-16 + 5x - 3x + y$ $-16 + 2x + y$, -6

37. $6(5x - 3x + x)$ $18x$, 54

38. $3(2y + y) + 16$ $9y + 16$, 52

39. $z(y + 2) + |-y|$ $zy + 2z + |y|$, 40

40. $|-z| + 3(y - 1)$ $|z| + 3y - 3$, 15

In Exercises 41–44, plot the number on a number line. (3.1) See margin.

41. -3

42. 5

43. -4

44. 0

In Exercises 45–48, plot the ordered pairs on one coordinate plane. (3.8) See margin.

45. $A(2, -3)$

46. $B(-1, 0)$

47. $C(-4, -5)$

48. $D(2, 4)$

Answers

To get the next number:

1. Subtract 2 from the preceding number.
2. Add 4 to the preceding number.
3. Add 2 to both the numerator and the denominator of the preceding number.
4. Subtract 2 from both the numerator and the denominator of the preceding number.

To get the next letter:

5. Name the letter that is 3 positions earlier in the alphabet than the position in the alphabet of the preceding letter.
6. In every odd-numbered position: Name the letter of the alphabet in that position. In every even-numbered position: Subtract the position number from 28 and name the letter of the alphabet in that numbered position.

41.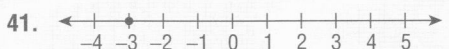

42.

43.

44.

45.–48.

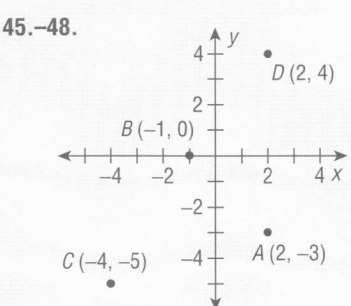

FORMAL ASSESSMENT ▶

A **Cumulative Test** of average difficulty for Chapters 1–3.

Available as copymasters, pages 46–53

144 Chapter 3

Cumulative Test

Cumulative Test **Chapters 1–3** Name _____
(Page 1 of 8 pages) Date _____

In Exercises 1–6, describe the pattern. Then list the next 3 numbers or letters. (1.1, 1.8)

1. 50, 45, 40, 35 Decreasing by 5 each time. 30, 25, 20 1. _____

2. $\frac{1}{2}, \frac{2}{3}, \frac{3}{4}, \frac{4}{5}$ Denominator of 1 fraction becomes numerator of the next, denominators are in sequential order. 5/6, 6/7, 7/8 2. _____

3. A, 1, B, 2 Letters of alphabet alternating with corresponding numerical placement of letters. C, 3, D 3. _____

4. Z, A, Y, B Outermost letters of alphabet, alternating beginning with end, working inward. X, C, W 4. _____

5. 1,000,000; 100,000; 10,000; 1,000 Decreasing by powers of 10. 100, 10, 1 5. _____

6. 100, 90, 81, 73 Decreasing by one less each time. 66, 60, 55 6. _____

In Exercises 7–12, evaluate the expression using a calculator. Round to two decimal places when necessary. (1.3)

7. 9^7 7. _4,782,969_

8. $\left(\frac{4}{5}\right)^6$ 8. _0.26_

9. $\sqrt{55}$ 9. _7.42_

10. $\sqrt{500}$ 10. _22.36_

11. $(2.7)^5$ 11. _143.49_

12. $\sqrt{43.27}$ 12. _6.58_

In Exercises 49–64, solve the equation or inequality.
(2.3–2.5, 2.9, 3.7)

49. $x + 7 = 16$ 9 **50.** $y + 5 = -6$ -11 **51.** $z - 8 = -16$ -8 **52.** $a - 8 = 13$ 21

53. $10b = 100$ 10 **54.** $-9x = 36$ -4 **55.** $\frac{y}{-12} = 8$ -96 **56.** $\frac{m}{4} = 16$ 64

57. $n + 6 < 7$ $n < 1$ **58.** $p + 4 > 12$ $p > 8$ **59.** $x - 2 \geq 5$ $x \geq 7$ **60.** $y - 11 \leq 9$ $y \leq 20$

61. $15c > 30$ $c > 2$ **62.** $26 > 13t$ $t < 2$ **63.** $\frac{q}{3} \leq 25$ $q \leq 75$ **64.** $40 \leq \frac{s}{9}$ $s \geq 360$

In Exercises 65–68, write an algebraic equation or inequality for the sentence. Then solve the equation or inequality. (2.7, 2.9, 3.7)

65. -12 is the sum of a number and 9. $-12 = n + 9, -21$

66. The difference of a number and 16 is less than or equal to 20. $n - 16 \leq 20, n \leq 36$

67. The product of 7 and a number is greater than 91. $7n > 91, n > 13$

68. Three is the quotient of a number and 4. $3 = \frac{n}{4}, 12$

In Exercises 69 and 70, write the coordinates of the vertices of each numbered figure. Then find the perimeter of each figure, and find the area of the entire shaded region. (1.4, 3.8) See margin.

69. 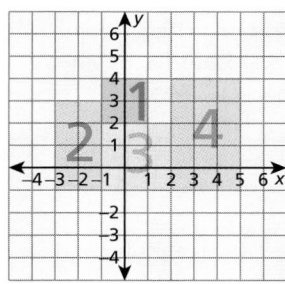 **70.**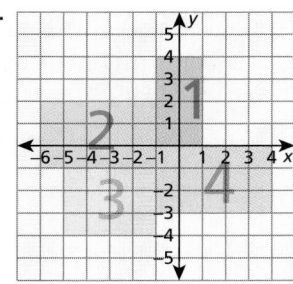

Roller Coaster   **In Exercises 71 and 72, use the following information. (1.5)**

You and a friend are riding on a racing roller coaster that is 1.4 miles long and has dual tracks, with two sets of cars running side by side. You are in one set of cars and your friend is in the other. You finish the ride in 1.3 minutes and your friend finishes in 1.4 minutes.

71. How fast did your set of cars travel in miles per hour?
About 64.6 mph   60 mph
72. How fast did your friend's set of cars travel in miles per hour?

73. *Amusement Park*   At an amusement park, you play x games that cost \$1 each and y games that cost \$2 each. Altogether, you spend \$12 on games. Construct a table that lists all possible values of x and y. **(3.8)**

x	0	2	4	6	8	10	12
y	6	5	4	3	2	1	0

Cumulative Review   **145**

Answers
69. Figure 1: $(-1, 4), (1, 4), (1, 2), (-1, 2)$; 8 units.
Figure 2: $(-3, 3), (-1, 3), (-1, -1), (-3, -1)$; 12 units.
Figure 3: $(-1, 2), (2, 2), (2, -1), (-1, -1)$; 12 units.
Figure 4: $(2, 4), (5, 4), (5, -1), (2, -1)$; 16 units.
36 units^2

70. Figure 1: $(-1, 4), (1, 4), (1, 0), (-1, 0)$; 12 units.
Figure 2: $(-6, 2), (-1, 2), (-1, -1), (-6, -1)$; 16 units.
Figure 3: $(-5, -1), (-1, -1), (-1, -4), (-5, -4)$; 14 units.
Figure 4: $(-1, 0), (4, 0), (4, -3), (-1, -3)$; 16 units.
50 units^2

CHAPTER 4 GOALS

Lesson	Pages	Goals	Meeting the NCTM Standards
Lesson Investigation 4.1	148	Solving Two-Step Equations	Algebra, Geometry, Measurement
4.1	149–152	1. Use two transformations to solve a two-step equation 2. Solve real-life problems using the work-backwards and make-a-table strategies	Problem Solving, Communication, Connections, Computation and Estimation, Algebra, Measurement
4.2	153–156	1. Use three or more transformations to solve an equation 2. Solve real-life problems using multi-step equations	Problem Solving, Communication, Connections, Patterns and Functions, Algebra, Geometry, Measurement
Using a Calculator	157	Checking Solutions	Technology, Algebra
4.3	158–161	1. Solve an equation by multiplying by a reciprocal 2. Use two-step equations to model real-life problems	Problem Solving, Communication, Connections, Number Relationships, Technology, Algebra, Statistics, Geometry, Measurement
Mixed Review	162	Review of arithmetic, algebra, and geometry	Algebra, Geometry
Milestones	162	Boolean Algebra	Connections
4.4	163–166	1. Use the Distributive Property to solve equations 2. Use the Distributive Property to model and solve real-life problems	Problem Solving, Communication, Algebra, Geometry, Measurement
Mid-Chapter Self-Test	167	Diagnose student weaknesses and remediate with correlated Reteaching Copymasters	Assessment
Lesson Investigation 4.5	168	Equations with Variables on Both Sides	Algebra, Geometry, Measurement
4.5	169–172	1. Solve equations with variables on both sides 2. Use equations to model problems in geometry	Problem Solving, Communication, Reasoning, Connections, Algebra, Geometry
4.6	173–177	1. Use tables and graphs to solve real-life problems 2. Use a general problem-solving plan	Problem Solving, Communication, Reasoning, Connections, Algebra, Statistics, Geometry, Measurement
Mixed Review	177	Review of arithmetic, algebra, and geometry	Algebra, Statistics
4.7	178–181	1. Solve equations involving rounding with decimals 2. Use a table to solve problems	Problem Solving, Communication, Reasoning, Connections, Computation and Estimation, Technology, Algebra, Statistics
4.8	182–185	1. Use formulas from geometry to solve equations 2. Use geometry formulas to solve real-life problems	Problem Solving, Communication, Reasoning, Connections, Algebra, Geometry, Measurement
Chapter Summary	186	A restatement of what has been learned, why it has been learned, and how it fits into the structure of mathematics	Communication, Connections
Chapter Review	187–190	Review of concepts and skills learned in the chapter.	Problem Solving, Connections
Chapter Test	191	Diagnose student weaknesses and remediate with correlated Reteaching Copymasters	Assessment

RESOURCES ORGANIZER

Lesson Pages	4.1 149–152	4.2 153–156	4.3 158–161	4.4 163–166	4.5 169–172	4.6 173–177	4.7 178–181	4.8 182–185
Lesson Plans	26	27	28	29	30	31	32	33
Problem of the Day	10	10	10	11	11	11	12	12
Warm-Up Exercises	10	10	10	11	11	11	12	12
Color Transparencies	—	16	16	—	—	17	18	18
Teaching Tools: Transparencies	—	T8	—	—	—	—	—	T2, T10
Copymasters	—	C10	—	—	—	—	—	C3, C13
Math Log	13	13	13	14	14	14, 15	15	15
Technology	—	—	17	—	18	19	—	—
Answer Masters	70, 71	72–74	75, 76	78	79	80, 81	83	84
Extra Practice Copymasters	26	27	28	29	30	31	32	33
Reteaching Copymasters	26	27	28	29	30	31	32	33
Enrichment Projects	—	—	18, 19	20, 21	—	—	—	—
Alternative Assessment: Projects	—	—	—	—	21	21, 22	22	—
Partner Quizzes	—	—	—	47	—	—	—	—
Group Assessment	—	—	—	—	—	—	—	65, 66
Formal Assessment: Short Quizzes	—	54	—	55	—	58	—	59
Tests	—	—	—	56, 57	—	—	—	60–68
Overhead Manipulatives Kit	Algebra Tiles	—	—	—	Algebra Tiles	—	—	—
Complete Solutions Manual	Includes step-by-step solutions for all exercises in the student text							
Computerized Test Bank	Creates customized tests that include graphics							
Interactive CD-ROM Project	Provides an interactive and interdisciplinary chapter project							

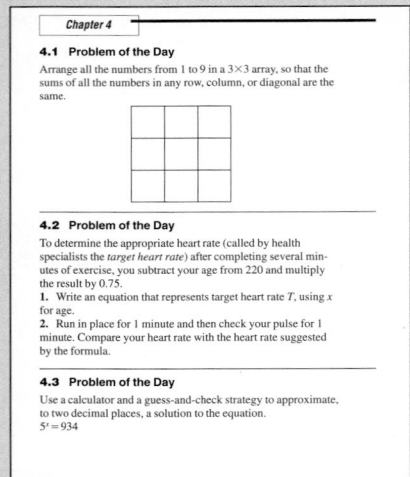

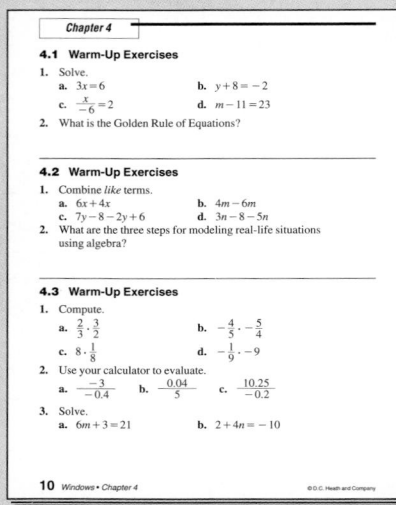

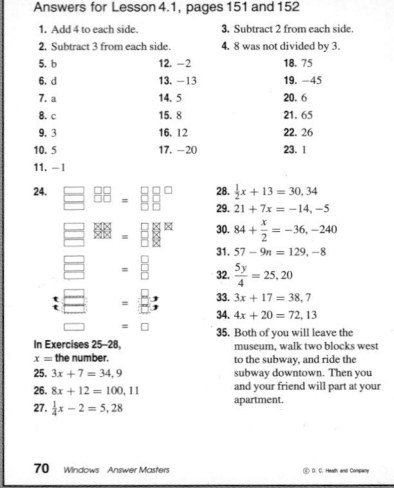

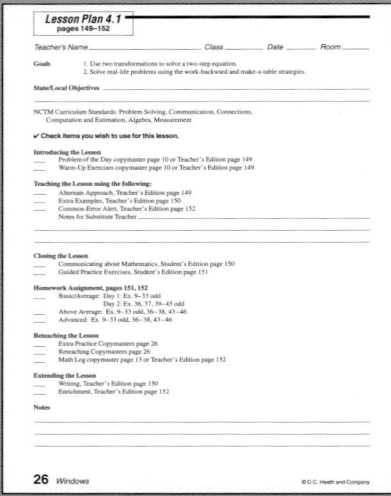

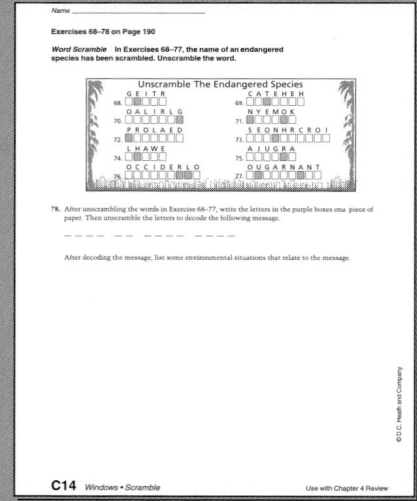

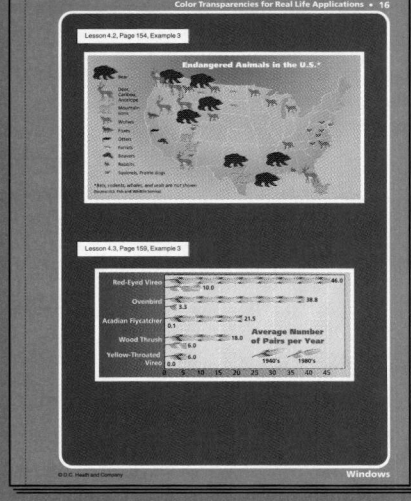

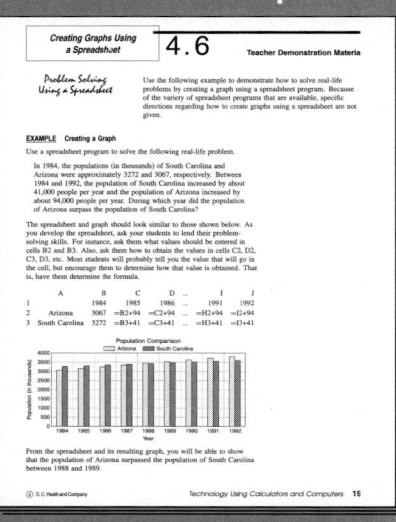

STARTERS

Problem of the Day

Warm-Up Exercises

FOR TEACHERS

Answer Masters

Lesson Plans

Teaching Tools

Teaching Tools includes:
Transparencies and Copymasters for classroom activities and study skills:

- Graph Paper
- Dot Paper (Geoboard)
- Algebra Tiles
- Number Counters
- Fraction Strips
- Models

REAL LIFE

Color Transparencies for Real-Life Applications

Technology: Using Calculators and Computers

Also Available:

- Complete Solutions Manual
- Overhead Manipulatives Kit
- Computerized Testing Program

- **Interactive CD-ROM Projects**
  Interactive projects for solving real-world problems using multimedia

- **Interactions: Real Math–Real Careers**
  A videodisc–based resource that connects math to real careers and on-the-job problem solving

- **PACKETS® Performance Assessment for Middle School Mathematics**
  A program that links assessment and instruction

ASSESSMENT

Alternative Assessment

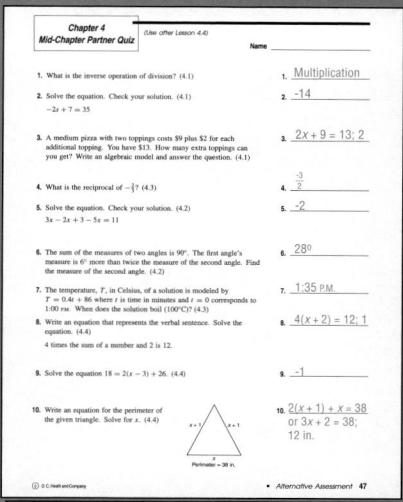

Alternative Assessment includes:
- Scoring Rubrics
- Portfolios
- Math Journals
- Projects
- Partner Quizzes
- Individual and Group Assessment

Formal Assessment

Formal Assessment includes:
- Short Quizzes (after every 2 lessons)
- Mid-Chapter Tests (2 forms)
- Chapter Tests (3 forms)
- Cumulative Tests (after every 3 Chapters)

MEETING INDIVIDUAL NEEDS

Extra Practice Copymasters

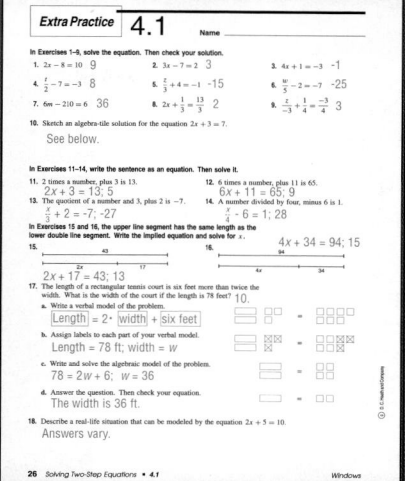

Reteaching Copymasters

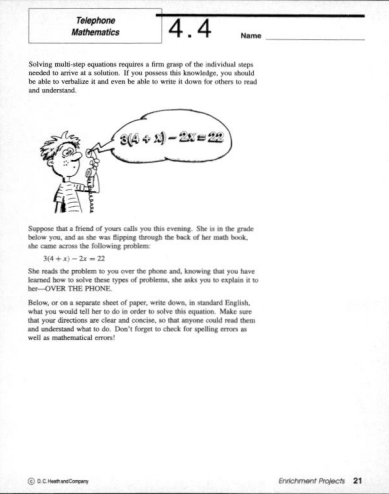

Enrichment Projects

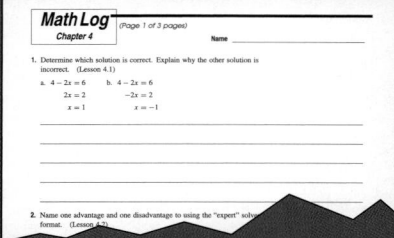

Math Log

Special Populations
Suggestions for providing equal access for:

Students Acquiring English Proficiency*
Encourage students to bring a native language dictionary to class. Students can create their own dictionaries by using pictures and diagrams to give further explanations of the vocabulary words (Lesson 4.3), properties (Lesson 4.4), and formulas (Lesson 4.8) taught in the chapter.

Students with Various Learning Styles*
Allow some students to continue to use algebra tiles to model equations when completing the exercises in Lessons 4.1 and 4.5.

When reading word problems and writing equations, students may benefit from using highlighters or colored pencils to identify the pertinent information relating to the labels and the equation as is done in the text.

Underachieving Students*
Allow students who have difficulty with multiplication and division to use calculators when solving equations.

The word problems in this chapter may require further explanation. Solving problems in pairs or in other cooperative group arrangements will benefit these students.

Gifted and Talented Students*
Challenge students to write a story consisting of a series of interrelated word problems that are based on topics of interest to them and to their classmates. Encourage the authors to write problems that require students to solve multi-step equations to find the answers. The authors can challenge groups of students to solve the problems, monitor the group work, and correct it.

* See page T19 for descriptions of these special populations.

Exploring the Language of Algebra

About the Chapter

Chapter 2 introduced students to basic techniques for solving simple single-step equations. This chapter develops those skills further, empowering students to deal with two-step and multistep equations. Students are encouraged to use inverse operations to isolate the variable in an equation, and further practice is given in applying the Distributive Property to simplify equations in which the variable occurs in more than one term. Students are next presented with a simple strategy for equations with the variable on both sides. Meanwhile, especially in Lessons 4.5 and 4.8, the strong connection between geometry and algebra is further emphasized by using one to model the other. The algebraic problem-solving plan introduced in Lesson 2.8 is once again the focus of Lesson 4.6, but not to the exclusion of other strategies such as the use of tables. Since real-life situations rarely involve whole numbers, Lesson 4.7 gives students practice using calculators to solve equations involving decimals.

The American bald eagle population has made a remarkable recovery over the past 30 years due in large part to the 1972 banning of the pesticide DDT and the 1973 passage of the Endangered Species Act. On July 4, 1994, the United States Fish and Wildlife Service announced that the bald eagle can now be upgraded to the threatened species list.

Equations can be used to model a wide variety of real-life situations. An example is the level of DDT residue found in eagle eggs. An approximate equation for the DDT residue levels R over time t is

$$R = 120 - 10(t - 1)$$

where 1967 is represented by $t = 0$.

In this chapter, you will learn how to use other multi-step equations to model real-world problems.

Materials

Teaching Tools
  Algebra tiles, pp. T4, C5

The goal of this investigation is to visually model the two-step process for solving equations outlined in Lesson 4.1. Be sure students have a clear understanding of the notion of discarding equal groups of tiles.

  To do this investigation, divide the class into small groups, tour the room, and listen to students' explanations of their work.

EXTENSION

Equations involving sums and positive numbers are modeled on this page. If you wish to model equations involving subtraction and negative numbers, you can use the Overhead Manipulative Kit that includes tiles and directions for handling negatives.

Materials Needed: algebra tiles

In this investigation, you will use algebra tiles to model and solve two-step equations.

Example   *Using Algebra Tiles*

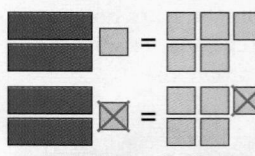

Original equation: $2x + 1 = 5$

To isolate the x-tiles, remove (subtract) a 1-tile from each side.

Transformed equation: $2x = 4$

To isolate one x-tile, divide each side into two groups and discard one group from each side.

Solution is $x = 2$. ■

Exercises

See margin.

In Exercises 1 and 2, an equation has been modeled and solved with algebra tiles. Write the equation and its solution. Explain your steps.

1.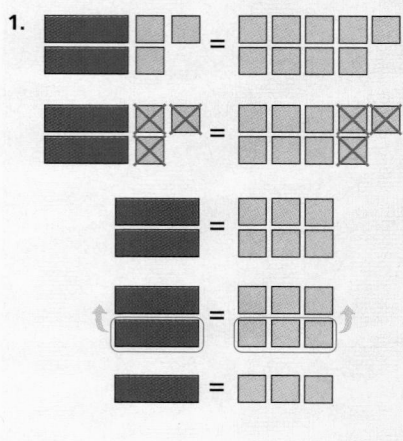

2.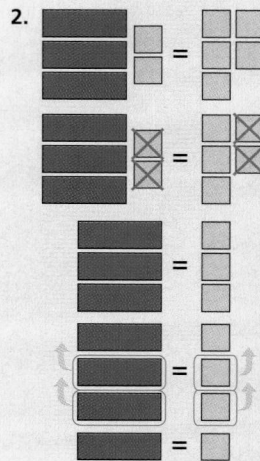

In Exercises 3–6, use algebra tiles to model and solve the equation. Check students' work.

3. $3x + 2 = 14$ 4

4. $15 = 2n + 1$ 7

5. $13 = 5 + 4y$ 2

6. $6m + 3 = 15$ 2

Answers

1. $2x + 3 = 9$
  Write original equation.
  $2x + 3 - 3 = 9 - 3$
  To isolate the *x*-term, subtract 3 from each side.
  $2x = 6$
  Simplify.
  $\frac{2x}{2} = \frac{6}{2}$
  To isolate *x*, divide each side by 2.
  $x = 3$
  Simplify.

2. $3x + 2 = 5$
  Write original equation.
  $3x + 2 - 2 = 5 - 2$
  To isolate the *x*-term, subtract 2 from each side.
  $3x = 3$

4.1 Solving Two-Step Equations

What you should learn:

 Goal 1
How to use two transformations to solve a two-step equation

 Goal 2
How to solve real-life problems using the work-backwards and make-a-table strategies

Why you should learn it:

You will need to use two or more transformations to solve most equations that model real-life situations, such as analyzing a tennis-club membership.

Goal 1 **Using Two Transformations**

Many equations require two or more transformations. Here are some guidelines that can help you decide how to start. Once you have found a solution, be sure to check it in the original equation.

1. Simplify both sides of the equation (if needed).

2. Use inverse operations (see Study Tip) to isolate the variable.

Example 1 · Solving an Equation

Solve $3x + 8 = 2$.

Solution Remember that your goal is to isolate the variable.

$$3x + 8 = 2 \qquad \textit{Rewrite original equation.}$$
$$3x + 8 - 8 = 2 - 8 \qquad \textit{To isolate the x-term, subtract 8 from each side.}$$
$$3x = -6 \qquad \textit{Simplify.}$$
$$\frac{3x}{3} = \frac{-6}{3} \qquad \textit{To isolate x, divide each side by 3.}$$
$$x = -2 \qquad \textit{Simplify.}$$

The solution is -2. Because $3(-2) + 8 = -6 + 8 = 2$, the solution checks in the original equation. ∎

Study Tip...
Remember that addition and subtraction are inverse operations and that multiplication and division are inverse operations.

Example 2 · Solving an Equation

Solve $\frac{x}{-4} - 8 = 1$.

Solution

$$\frac{x}{-4} - 8 = 1 \qquad \textit{Rewrite original equation.}$$
$$\frac{x}{-4} - 8 + 8 = 1 + 8 \qquad \textit{Add 8 to each side.}$$
$$\frac{x}{-4} = 9 \qquad \textit{Simplify.}$$
$$-4 \cdot \frac{x}{-4} = -4 \cdot 9 \qquad \textit{Multiply each side by } -4.$$
$$x = -36 \qquad \textit{Simplify.}$$

The solution is -36. Check this in the original equation.

4.1 · Solving Two-Step Equations **149**

▶ **PACING the Lesson**
Suggested Number of Days
Basic/Average 2 **Above Average** 1
Advanced 1

▶ **PLANNING the Lesson**
Lesson Plan 4.1, p. 26

ORGANIZER

Starters (reproduced below)
  Problem of the Day 4.1, p. 10
  Warm-Up Exercises 4.1, p. 10
Lesson Resources
  Math Log, p. 13
  Answer Masters 4.1, pp. 70, 71
  Extra Practice Copymaster 4.1, p. 26
  Reteaching Copymaster 4.1, p. 26
Special Populations
  Suggestions, Teacher's Edition, p. 146D

LESSON Notes

ALTERNATE APPROACH
Packaging and Unpackaging x
You may wish to explain that when we solve equations by isolating the variable, we undo the order of operations used to *put together* the variable expression. Thus, in an equation such as $3x + 8 = 2$ (see Example 1), the expression on the left was put together by multiplying x by 3 and adding 8. We undo these operations by first subtracting 8 and then dividing by 3. Encourage students to compare this reversible process to packaging and unpackaging a gift:

Package   Unpackage
Write an expression in x ↔ Isolate x

Example 1

Before starting the example, use a flowchart to further illustrate the packaging of the expression $3x + 8$:

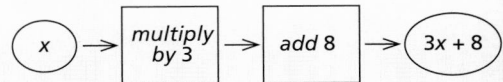

Example 2

Use a flowchart to build the algebraic expression on the left side of the equation. Then compare the steps of the solution with the sequence needed to put together that expression.

Most real-life situations are modeled by equations that require two or more steps to solve for the unknown.

Example 3

Note that the verbal model used here applies the problem-solving strategy of working backwards (from total dollars spent to playing time). Have students refer to their journals or to page 72 to review the use of unit canceling in checking solutions.

Communicating about MATHEMATICS

Discuss the two approaches for solving equations—tables versus algebraic models. Ask students which approach they prefer, and have them explain why.

Writing Prompt
Describe situations in which you have become "bogged down" while solving two-step equations.

Real Life
Monthly Dues

In 1993, there were about 220,000 tennis courts in the United States. Of these, about 14,000 were indoor courts. (Source: U.S. Tennis Association)

Goal 2 | **Modeling Real-Life Situations**

Example 3 | *Problem Solving: Work Backwards*

You are joining a community tennis club. The annual membership fee is $50, and a tennis court rents for $10 per hour. You plan to spend no more than $190 playing tennis during the year. How many hours can you play?

Solution   With some problems, you have to work backwards from the given facts to solve the problem.

Verbal Model

Total spent	=	Annual fee	+	Hourly rate	·	Hours of tennis

Labels
Total spent = 190   (dollars)
Annual fee = 50   (dollars)
Hourly rate = 10   (dollars per hour)
Number of hours played = n (hours)

Algebraic Model

$190 = 50 + 10 \cdot n$
$190 - 50 = 50 + 10n - 50$
$140 = 10n$
$\dfrac{140}{10} = \dfrac{10n}{10}$
$14 = n$

Answer and Check. You can play 14 hours. When you check this result, don't just check the numbers. You also need to check the units of measure.

$$(50 \text{ dollars}) + \frac{10 \text{ dollars}}{\text{hour}} \cdot (14 \text{ hours})$$
$$= 50 \text{ dollars} + 140 \text{ dollars} = 190 \text{ dollars}$$

Communicating about MATHEMATICS

▶ **SHARING IDEAS about the Lesson**

Make a Table Another way to answer the question in Example 3 is to use a table. Copy and complete the table. Then use the result to answer the question. 14 hours

Hours	1	2	3	4	5	6	7	8	9	10	11	12	13	14
Cost ($)	?	?	?	?	?	?	?	?	?	?	?	?	?	?

60   80   100   120   140   160   180
70   90   110   130   150   170   190

OPTION: Extra Examples

Here is an additional example similar to Example 1.

Solving an Equation
Solve $6x - 11 = 13$

Solution   Remember that your goal is to isolate the variable.

$6x - 11 = 13$	Rewrite original equation.
$6x - 11 + 11 = 13 + 11$	To isolate the x-term, add 11 to each side.
$6x = 24$	Simplify.
$\dfrac{6x}{6} = \dfrac{24}{6}$	To isolate x, divide each side by 6.
$x = 4$	Simplify.

The solution is 4. Because $6(4) - 11 = 13$, the solution checks in the original equation.

EXERCISES

Guided Practice

▶ CHECK for Understanding

In Exercises 1–3, describe the first step you would use to solve the equation.

1. $3x - 4 = 2$ Add 4 to each side.

2. $5x + 3 = 15$ Subtract 3 from each side.

3. $-2 = 2 - 4x$ Subtract 2 from each side.

4. *Error Analysis*   Describe the error.

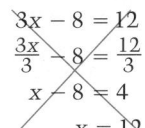

8 was not divided by 3.

In Exercises 5–8, match the equation with an equivalent equation.

a. $2x = -8$ **b.** $2x = 8$ **c.** $2x = -24$ **d.** $2x = 24$

5. $2x + 8 = 16$ b   **6.** $2x - 8 = 16$ d   **7.** $2x - 8 = -16$ a   **8.** $2x + 8 = -16$ c

Independent Practice

In Exercises 9–23, solve the equation. Then check your solution.

9. $3x + 15 = 24$ 3   **10.** $4x + 11 = 31$ 5   **11.** $6p + 8 = 2$ -1

12. $5q + 14 = 4$ -2 **13.** $-2r - 4 = 22$ -13 **14.** $-3s - 5 = -20$ 5

15. $\frac{t}{2} + 6 = 10$ 8   **16.** $\frac{z}{3} + 17 = 21$ 12   **17.** $\frac{x}{4} - 2 = -7$ -20

18. $\frac{n}{3} - 5 = 20$ 75   **19.** $\frac{x}{-5} + 1 = 10$ -45 **20.** $\frac{m}{-2} + 2 = -1$ 6

21. $7m - 105 = 350$ 65   **22.** $14t - 280 = 84$ 26   **23.** $3x + \frac{1}{2} = \frac{7}{2}$ 1

P **24.** *Modeling Equations*   Sketch an algebra-tile solution for the equation $3x + 4 = 7$. Use the samples on page 148.   See Additional Answers.

For equations, see Additional Answers.

In Exercises 25–32, write the sentence as an equation. Then solve it.

25. 3 times a number, plus 7, is 34.   9

26. 8 times a number, plus 12, is 100.   11

27. One fourth of a number, minus 2, is 5.   28

28. Half of a number, plus 13, is 30.   34

29. The sum of 21 and $7x$ is -14. -5

30. The sum of 84 and $\frac{x}{2}$ is -36. -240

31. The difference of 57 and $9n$ is 129. -8

32. The quotient of $5y$ and 4 is 25.   20

Diagramming Equations   In Exercises 33 and 34, the upper line segment has the same length as the lower double line segment. Write the implied equation and solve for x.

33.

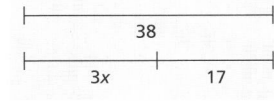

$3x + 17 = 38, 7$

34.

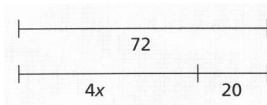

$4x + 20 = 72, 13$

P Portfolio Opportunity   *4.1* ▪ *Solving Two-Step Equations*   **151**

EXERCISE Notes

ASSIGNMENT GUIDE

Basic/Average:
  Day 1: Ex. 9–33 odd
  Day 2: Ex. 36, 37, 39–45 odd

Above Average: Ex. 9–33 odd, 36–38, 43–46

Advanced: Ex. 9–33 odd, 36–38, 43–46

Selected Answers: Ex. 1–7, 9–41 odd

Guided Practice

Use this section as a classroom "summary moment." Have students work in groups of three, and allow each student to describe for the other two what steps he/she would use to solve the problem.

▶ **Ex. 5–8**   Have students use a "think-share" approach. Each member of the group spends one to three minutes silently thinking about the solutions. Group members then share and compare their responses.

Independent Practice

▶ **Ex. 9–23**   Before assigning these exercises, select random problems and ask students to state the two steps they would use. Remind students that they are expected to use the format presented in Examples 1 and 2 on page 149; check that equal signs are aligned vertically

▶ **Ex. 33, 34**   These exercises are an intuitive introduction to the segment addition postulate in geometry.

▶ **Ex. 36** Students still need support in using the verbal model illustrated on page 150. This exercise prompts students to use the steps of our algebraic problem-solving plan. Use the exercise as a teacher-led in-class activity. Note that although the result of the computation is $4\frac{2}{3}$ minutes, phone charges are based on full minutes, that is, fractions of a minute are reckoned as a full minute. So the solution to the problem is 5 minutes.

▶ **Ex. 37** Unlike phone charges, automotive repair charges are based on actual time spent on labor. So the solution to this problem is $7\frac{1}{2}$ hours (not 8 hours).

Common-Error Alert!

In solving equations, some students become confused in deciding whether to multiply or divide in order to isolate variables. Encourage them to apply the packaging approach. Remind them also that checking the solution helps to identify errors of this kind.

Integrated Review

▶ **Ex. 39–42** The format used here is similar to the way units of measurement are used in most physical science computations.

Exploration and Extension

▶ **Ex. 43–46** These exercises provide excellent practice in applying the packaging approach described earlier in these notes.

Portfolio Opportunity: Math Log

Determine which solution is correct. Explain why the other solution is incorrect.

a. $4 - 2x = 6$
   $2x = 2$
   $x = 1$

b. $4 - 2x = 6$
   $-2x = 2$
   $x = -1$

Also available as a copymaster, p. 13, Ex. 1

152 *Chapter 4*

35., 36. See Additional Answers.

✪ **35.** *A Folk Art Museum*   You and a friend are going to visit an art museum. Your friend will meet you at your apartment. Then both of you will ride the subway uptown and walk 2 blocks east to the museum. Write the inverse of this plan.

✪ **36.** *Telephone Rates*   You are at a phone booth and need to make a long-distance call home. The call will cost 25 cents for the first minute and 15 cents for each additional minute or fraction of a minute. You have 95 cents in your pocket. How many minutes can you talk?

  a. Write a verbal model of the problem.

  b. Assign labels to each part of your verbal model.

  c. Write and solve an algebraic model of the problem.

  d. Answer the question. Then check your solution. 5 min

✪ **37.** *Automotive Repair*   You are the service manager at an automotive repair shop. You charge $22 per hour of labor plus the cost of any parts. One car needed $156 of new parts and the final bill for the car was $321. How long did it take to repair the car? $7\frac{1}{2}$ hours

✪ **38.** *Problem Solving*   Describe a real-life situation that can be modeled by the equation $5x - 7 = 120$. Answers vary.

Panamanian Molas *Folk museums of American art often contain molas that illustrate scenes of Kuna experiences of other cultures. This one, called* **Masked Dancers,** *shows African dancers and is from the Rio Sidra Island.*

Integrated Review
Making Connections within Mathematics

Measurement Sense   In Exercises 39–42, simplify the expression. Include the appropriate unit of measure in your result.

39. $\dfrac{22 \text{ miles}}{\text{hour}} \times (3 \text{ hours})$ 66 miles

40. $\dfrac{1.45 \text{ dollars}}{\text{pound}} \times (6 \text{ pounds})$ 8.7 dollars

41. $\dfrac{18 \text{ meters}}{\text{second}} \times (12 \text{ seconds})$ 216 meters

42. $\dfrac{12 \text{ dollars}}{\text{square yard}} \times (3 \text{ yards}) \times (5 \text{ yards})$ 180 dollars

Exploration and Extension

Writing Equations   In Exercises 43–46, write a two-step equation that has the given solution. (There are many correct answers.) Answers vary.

✪ **43.** $x = 1$ $3x - 1 = 2$ ✪ **44.** $x = 3$ $\frac{x}{3} - 2 = -1$ ✪ **45.** $x = -3$ $4x + 13 = 1$ ✪ **46.** $x = -2$ $\frac{x}{2} + 4 = 3$

✪ **47.** *You Be the Teacher*   A classmate asks you for help on Exercise 31.
🅿   Your classmate has written $9n - 57 = 129$ and determined that $n \approx 20.67$. Is your classmate correct? If not, explain how you could help your classmate solve the problem correctly. No; rewrite the equation correctly as $57 - 9n = 129$ to get $n = -8$.

✪ More difficult exercises
🅿 Portfolio Opportunity

▶ Enrichment

Segment $\overline{JK}$ is equal in length to segment $\overline{AM}$.

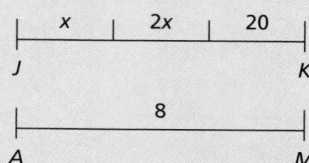

a. Write an equation that states that the length of $\overline{JK}$ is equal to the length of $\overline{AM}$.

b. Solve the equation.

c. Does your answer make sense? Explain.

4.2 Solving Multi-Step Equations

What you should learn:

Goal 1 How to use three or more transformations to solve an equation

Goal 2 How to solve real-life problems using multi-step equations

Why you should learn it:

Many real-life problems can be modeled with equations whose solutions require three or more transformations.

Goal 1 Solving Multi-Step Equations

Before applying inverse operations to solve an equation, you should check to see whether one or both sides of the equation can be simplified by *combining like terms*.

Example 1 Simplifying First

Solve the equation $2x + 3x - 4 = 11$.

Solution

$2x + 3x - 4 = 11$	*Rewrite original equation.*
$5x - 4 = 11$	*Combine like terms:*
	$2x + 3x = 5x.$
$5x - 4 + 4 = 11 + 4$	*Add 4 to each side.*
$5x = 15$	*Simplify.*
$\frac{5x}{5} = \frac{15}{5}$	*Divide each side by 5.*
$x = 3$	*Simplify.*

The solution is 3. Because $2(3) + 3(3) - 4 = 6 + 9 - 4 = 11$, the solution checks in the original equation. ∎

As you become more of an expert in solving equations, you may want to perform some of the solution steps mentally. If you do this, don't forget to check your solution.

> **Study Tip...**
> When some people use the "expert" solver format, they say they are skipping steps. That, however, isn't really what is happening. They aren't skipping steps—they are simply doing some of the steps mentally. For instance, in Example 2, which steps were performed mentally?

Example 2 "Expert" Equation Solver Format

Solve the equation $-13 = 3n + 3 + n$.

Solution

$-13 = 3n + 3 + n$	*Rewrite original equation.*
$-13 = 4n + 3$	*Combine like terms.*
$-16 = 4n$	*Subtract 3 from each side.*
$-4 = n$	*Divide each side by 4.*

The solution is -4. Because $3(-4) + 3 + (-4) = -12 + 3 + (-4) = -13$, the solution checks in the original equation. ∎

4.2 • *Solving Multi-Step Equations* **153**

PACING the Lesson

Suggested Number of Days
Basic/Average 0 **Above Average** 2
Advanced 1

PLANNING the Lesson

Lesson Plan 4.2, p. 27

ORGANIZER

Starters (reproduced below)
    Problem of the Day 4.2, p. 10
    Warm-Up Exercises 4.2, p. 10
Lesson Resources
    Color Transparencies
        Diagram for Example 3, p. 16
    Teaching Tools
        Coordinate plane, pp. T8, C10
    Math Log, p. 13
    Answer Masters 4.2, pp. 72–74
    Extra Practice Copymaster 4.2, p. 27
    Reteaching Copymaster 4.2, p. 27
Special Populations
    Suggestions, Teacher's Edition, p. 146D

LESSON Notes

Remind students how the Distributive Property is used to combine like terms in an algebraic expression. You may wish to demonstrate its application on three or more like terms. For example,
$4x + 8x - 5x = (4 + 8 - 5)x = 7x$

Example 1
You may wish to model the example using algebra tiles or sketch it, as on page 148.

Example 2
Explain to students that $-4 = n$ is equivalent to $n = -4$. This will prepare the way for solving equations with the variable on both sides. Have students answer the question posed in the Study Tip.

Ask students whether they know of any en-dangered mammals in your community or state. Do any of your students belong to in-school environmental groups?

Example 3

This is another realistic application of the algebraic problem-solving plan. Note how the example and the Communicating about Mathematics ask for progressive involvement by students in the details of the plan. Make sure that students list all the labels indicated in the verbal model.

Communicating about MATHEMATICS

EXTENSION
Once the algebraic model has been written and used to solve the problem in Example 3, challenge students to write other questions that could be answered using this model.

Writing Prompt
Ask students to write a poem that explains why checking solutions is important. Have some of the poems read in class.

Endangered Animals in the U.S.*

Bear
Deer, Caribou, Antelope
Mountain lions
Wolves
Foxes
Otters
Ferrets
Beavers
Rabbits
Squirrels, Prairie dogs

*Bats, rodents, whales, and seals are not shown
(Source: U.S. Fish and Wildlife Service)

Goal 2 **Modeling Multi-Step Problems**

Real Life
Poster Sales

Example 3 *Modeling a Real-Life Problem*

Your wildlife club has made the poster shown above. To print the poster, a printer charges $250, plus $2 per poster. You plan t sell each poster for $5. How many do you need to sell to make a profit of $300?

Solution Here is a partial solution. You are asked to complet the solution below.

Verbal Model

$$\text{Profit} = \text{Income} - \text{Expenses}$$

$$300 = 5 \cdot \boxed{\text{Number of posters}} - \left(250 + 2 \cdot \boxed{\text{Number of posters}}\right)$$

↓

Labels Number of posters = n

Communicating about MATHEMATICS

▶ **SHARING IDEAS about the Lesson**

Writing an Algebraic Model Write an equation that represents the verbal model in Example 3. Then solve the equation and answer the question given in Example 3.

$300 = 5n - (250 + 2n)$, $183.\overline{3}$, 184

154 Chapter **4** ▪ *Exploring the Language of Algebra*

OPTION: Extra Examples
Here are additional examples similar to some of those of the lesson.

1. Simplifying First
Solve $8m - 3m + 3 = 13$.
Solution

$8m - 3m + 3 = 13$	Rewrite original equation.
$5m + 3 = 13$	Combine like terms: $8m - 3m = 5m$.
$5m + 3 - 3 = 13 - 3$	Subtract 3 from each side.
$5m = 10$	Simplify.
$\frac{5m}{5} = \frac{10}{5}$	Divide each side by 5.
$m = 2$	Simplify.

The solution is 2. Check this in the original equation.

2. "Expert" Equation Solver Format
Solve $46 = 4x - 4 + 6x$.
Solution

$46 = 4x - 4 + 6x$	Rewrite original equation.
$46 = 10x - 4$	Combine like terms.
$50 = 10x$	Add 4 to each side.
$5 = x$	Divide each side by 10.

The solution is 5. Check this in the original equation.

EXERCISES

Guided Practice

CHECK for Understanding

Logical Reasoning   **In Exercises 1–3, explain each step of the solution.**   See margin.

1. $3x - x + 8 = -16$
$2x + 8 = -16$
$2x = -24$
$x = -12$

2. $4x + 7 - 5x = 9$
$-x + 7 = 9$
$-x = 2$
$(-1)x = 2$
$x = -2$

3. $-5 = -5x - 3x + 11$
$-5 = -8x + 11$
$-16 = -8x$
$2 = x$

Independent Practice

In Exercises 4–9, decide whether the given value is a solution of the equation. If not, find the solution.

4. $4x - x - 5 = -8; \ x = 1$ No, -1

5. $9y - 6 - 7y = -12; \ y = -9$ No, -3

6. $-13 = 3x + 2x - x + 7; \ x = -5$ Yes

7. $6y - y + 3y + 26 = -30; \ y = -2$ No, -7

8. $4t - 2t - 8 = 1; \ t = 3$ No, 4.5

9. $2 = 3a - 8a + 17; \ a = 3$ Yes

In Exercises 10–21, solve the equation. Check your solution.

10. $8x + 2x - 4 = 6$ 1

11. $6y - 3y + 2 = -16$ -6

12. $42 = 8a - 2a + 12$ 5

13. $6m - 2m - 6 = -60$ -13.5

14. $5x - 3x + 12 = 8$ -2

15. $n - 3n + 8 = -8$ 8

16. $2y - 7y - 4y = 81$ -9

17. $9p - 6p - 6p = 24$ -8

18. $\frac{3}{2}x - \frac{1}{2}x - 2 = 4$ 6

19. $\frac{5}{2}x - \frac{1}{2}x - 3 = 5$ 4

20. $4(x + 1) = 8$ 1

21. $-3(x + 1) = 0$ -1

In Exercises 22 and 23, write an equation that represents the sentence. Then solve.

22. The sum of $3x$ and $2x$ and $7x$ and 6 is 42. $3x + 2x + 7x + 6 = 42, 3$

23. 5 subtracted from the difference of $4y$ and y is -29. $4y - y - 5 = -29, -8$

Geometry   **In Exercises 24 and 25, use the given information to write an equation. Then solve the equation.**

24. The sum of the measures of two **complementary angles** is 90°.

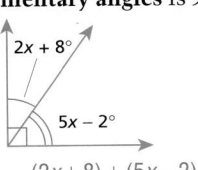

$(2x + 8) + (5x - 2) = 90, 12$

✪ **25.** The sum of the measures of the angles of a triangle is 180°.

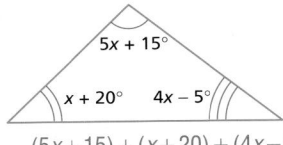

$(5x + 15) + (x + 20) + (4x - 5) = 180, 15$

✪ More difficult exercises

ASSIGNMENT GUIDE

*Basic/Average:
Day 1: Ex. 5–25 odd
Day 2: Ex. 26, 27, 31–35 odd

Above Average:
Day 1: Ex. 5–25 odd
Day 2: Ex. 26–28, 31–37 odd

Advanced: Ex. 5–9 odd, 15–25 odd, 26, 27, 33–37 odd

Selected Answers: Ex. 1–3, 5–33 odd
* You may wish to omit this lesson for these students.

Guided Practice

Ask students to examine Examples 1 and 2 on page 153, paying special attention to the comments (in blue) that explain each step of the solution.

Independent Practice

▶ **Ex. 10–21**   For these exercises, students may wish to try the "expert" method presented in Example 2 of the lesson. Before assigning the exercises, be aware that Ex. 16–21 introduce three variables, or fractional coefficients, or parentheses. You may wish to discuss these in class. In general, encourage students to write a brief explanation for each step. For example, in Ex. 14:

$5x - 3x + 12 = 8$
$2x + 12 = 8$ Simplify.
$2x = -4$ Subtract 12.
$x = -2$ Divide by 2.

Answers

1. Combine like terms, subtract 8 from each side, divide each side by 2.

2. Combine like terms, subtract 7 from each side, $(-1)x = -x$, divide each side by -1.

3. Combine like terms, subtract 11 from each side, divide each side by -8.

Extra Practice

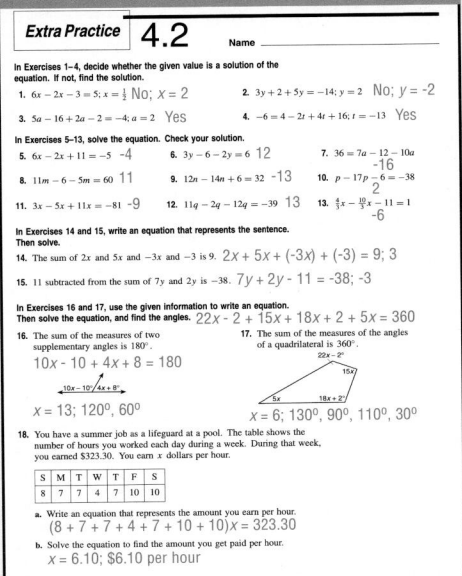

Reteaching

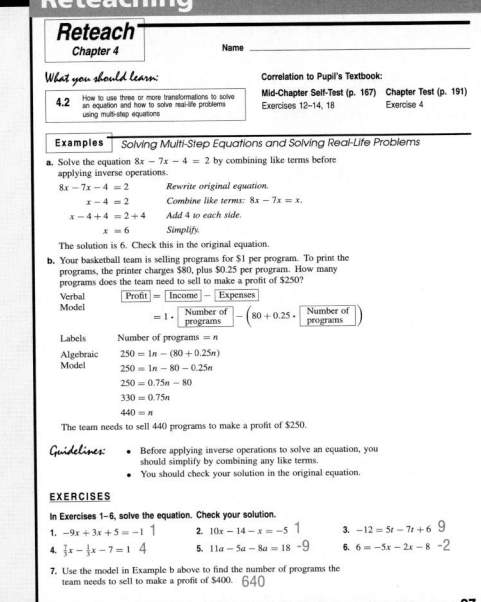

▶ **Ex. 27, 28** Work Ex. 27 in class, then assign Ex. 28.

Integrated Review

▶ **Ex. 29–34** Ask students which method they consider more efficient—to simplify, then evaluate or to evaluate, then simplify. These exercises provide good preparation for plotting ordered pairs.

Exploration and Extension

Common-Error Alert!

Evaluation of expressions such as those in Ex. 36 and 37 can be difficult because of the negative coefficients. Once again, encourage students to use parentheses when evaluating. For example, in Ex. 37:

$-2x+y=1 \rightarrow -2(-2)+y=1$ Substitute -2 for x.

$4+y=1$

$y=-3$ Subtract 4.

Portfolio Opportunity: Math Log

Name one advantage and one disadvantage to using the "expert" solver format.

Also available as a copymaster, p. 13, Ex. 2

Short Quiz

Covers Lessons 4.1 and 4.2

Available as a copymaster, p. 54

---

26. *Summer Job* You have a job mowing lawns Monday through Saturday. The table shows the number of lawns you mowed each day during a week. During that week, you earned $126. You earn x dollars per lawn.

M	T	W	Th	F	S
1	2	2	1	3	5

a. Write an equation that represents the amount you earn in a week. $(1 + 2 + 2 + 1 + 3 + 5)x = 126$

b. Solve the equation to find the amount you get paid per lawn. $9

27. *Printing Posters* In Example 3 on page 154, suppose the printer raises the price to $275 and $3 per poster. How many posters do you now need to sell to make a profit of $300? 288

28. *Starting a Business* You start a business selling bottled fruit juices. You invest $10,000 for equipment. Each bottle costs you $0.30 to make. You sell each bottle for $0.75. How many bottles must you sell to earn a profit of $2,000? 26,667

Tom Scott (top left) and Tom First (top right) a shown with 2 of their employees. They began fruit juice business called Nantucket Nectors. 1993, the business sold $1.3 million worth of juices. (Source: The Boston Sunday Globe)

Integrated Review

Describing Patterns **In Exercises 29–34, simplify the expression. Then complete the table for each expression and describe the pattern.** For completions of table and descriptions of pattern, see Additional Answers.

x	−2	−1	0	1	2
Value of Expression	?	?	?	?	?

29. $9x - 4x + 2x$ $7x$

30. $6x + 3x - x$ $8x$

31. $5x + 11x - 4x + 5 - 8$ $12x$

32. $8x - 7x + 2x - 6 + 12$ $3x + 6$

33. $2x - 5x - 8x$ $-11x$

34. $3x - 10x + 2x$ $-5x$

Exploration and Extension

Coordinate Geometry **In Exercises 35–37, for each equation complete the table showing several solutions of the equation. Write the solutions as ordered pairs. Then plot the ordered pairs in a coordinate plane. Describe the pattern. (For a sample, look at Lesson 3.8.)** For plots of ordered pairs and descriptions of patterns, see Additional Answers.

x	−2	−1	0	1	2
y	?	?	?	?	?

35. $x + y = 7$
$(-2, 9), (-1, 8), (0, 7), (1, 6), (2, 5)$

36. $2x - y = 5$
$(-2, -9), (-1, -7), (0, -5), (1, -3), (2, -1)$

37. $-2x + y = 1$
$(-2, -3), (-1, -1), (0, 1), (1, 3), (2, 5)$

✪ More difficult exercises

▶ ### Enrichment

Have students examine this pattern of numbers, fill in the blanks, and describe the pattern.

$1^2 + 2^2 + 2^2 = 9 = 3^2$

$2^2 + 3^2 + 6^2 = 49 = 7^2$

$3^2 + 4^2 + 12^2 = 169 = 13^2$

$4^2 + 5^2 + 20^2 = \_\_\_ = \_\_\_$ $441, 21^2$

$5^2 + 6^2 + 30^2 = \_\_\_ = \_\_\_$ $961, 31^2$

$6^2 + \_\_^2 + \_\_^2 = \_\_\_ = \_\_\_$ $7, 42, 1849, 43^2$

USING A CALCULATOR
Checking Solutions

When you check a solution that has been rounded, the solution will only make the original equation *approximately* true.

Example   *Checking a Rounded Solution*

Solve the equation $34x - 5 - 23x = 15$. Check your solution.

Solution

$34x - 5 - 23x = 15$	*Rewrite original equation.*
$11x - 5 = 15$	*Combine like terms.*
$11x - 5 + 5 = 15 + 5$	*Add 5 to each side.*
$11x = 20$	*Simplify.*
$\frac{11x}{11} = \frac{20}{11}$	*Divide each side by 11.*
$x \approx 1.82$	*Round to 2 decimal places.*

The solution is $\frac{20}{11}$ or approximately 1.82. You can check the solution in the original equation as follows.

$34x - 5 - 23x = 15$	*Original equation*
$34(1.82) - 5 - 23(1.82) \stackrel{?}{=} 15$	*Substitute 1.82 for x.*
$61.88 - 5 - 41.86 \stackrel{?}{=} 15$	*Use a calculator.*
$15.02 \approx 15$	*Approximate check* ✔

You could perform the check on a scientific calculator using the following keystrokes. (Some calculators will give you a wrong answer because they do not follow the order of operations.)

Calculator Keystrokes   **Display**

34 ☒ 1.82 ⊟ 5 ⊟ 23 ☒ 1.82 ⊜ 15.02

Exercises

In Exercises 1–8, solve the equation. Round your solution to 2 decimal places. Check your rounded solution in the original equation. Does it check exactly? If not, why?

1. $2x + 5x - 7 = 9$ 2.29, no

2. $3y - 7 + 4y = 10$ 2.43, no

3. $2n + 7n - 13 = -4$ 1, yes

4. $-5a + 17 + 2a = 8$ 3, yes

5. $12 = -2x + 5x - 9$ 7, yes

6. $-13 = 4y + 8y + 9$ -1.83, no

7. $-4n - 14 - 5n = 11$ -2.78, no

8. $5m + 8m - 14 = 23$ 2.85, no

Rounded answers do not check exactly.

TECHNOLOGY Notes

Show students who have calculators that do not follow the order of operations how to insert parentheses to check their solutions. In order to check the solution in the example, students should enter

34 ☒ 1.82 ⊟ 5 ⊟ $(23$ ☒ $1.82)$ ⊜ 15.02

Because basic calculators perform the operations in the order in which they are entered, parentheses are not needed around 34×1.82.

▶ **PACING** the Lesson

Suggested Number of Days
Basic/Average 2 **Above Average** 1
Advanced 1

▶ **PLANNING** the Lesson

Lesson Plan 4.3, p. 28

ORGANIZER

Starters (reproduced below)
  Problem of the Day 4.3, p. 10
  Warm-Up Exercises 4.3, p. 10
Lesson Resources
  Color Transparencies
    Graph for Example 3, p. 16
  Math Log, p. 13
  Technology, p. 17
  Answer Masters 4.3, pp. 75, 76
  Extra Practice Copymaster 4.3, p. 28
  Reteaching Copymaster 4.3, p. 28
  Enrichment Projects, pp. 18, 19
Special Populations
  Suggestions, Teacher's Edition, p. 146D

LESSON Notes

Having a variety of approaches to solving equations means that students can choose the one they prefer. Students must sample each approach to determine their preference.

Example 1

You may wish to refer to the teaching note on reciprocals on page 130. Students should record in their journals the definition of reciprocals: For all real numbers a and b (except 0), if $ab = 1$, then a and b are reciprocals.

Example 2

Point out to students that multiplying by a reciprocal is used to simplify equations.

4.3

Two-Step Equations and Problem Solving

What you should learn:

Goal 1 How to solve an equation by multiplying by a reciprocal

Goal 2 How to use two-step equations to model real-life problems

Why you should learn it:

You can use two-step equations as algebraic models for analyzing real-life graphical data, such as populations of songbirds.

> **Need to Know**
> When you multiply a number by its reciprocal, you obtain 1. Here are some examples.
>
> $5 \cdot \frac{1}{5} = 1$
>
> $\left(-\frac{1}{3}\right) \cdot (-3) = 1$
>
> $(-2) \cdot \left(-\frac{1}{2}\right) = 1$
>
> $\frac{1}{4} \cdot 4 = 1$

Goal 1   **Using Reciprocals**

Often, there is not just one way to solve a problem. For instance, Example 1 shows two ways to solve $3x - 4 = 11$.

Example 1	***Comparing Two Solutions***

a. $3x - 4 = 11$ *Original equation*
  $3x = 15$ *Add 4 to each side.*
  $\frac{3x}{3} = \frac{15}{3}$ *Divide each side by 3.*
  $x = 5$ *Simplify.*

b. $3x - 4 = 11$ *Original equation*
  $3x = 15$ *Add 4 to each side.*
  $\frac{1}{3} \cdot 3x = \frac{1}{3} \cdot 15$ *Multiply each side by $\frac{1}{3}$.*
  $x = 5$ *Simplify.*

The number $\frac{1}{3}$ is the **reciprocal** of 3. Notice that multiplying by the reciprocal of a number produces the same result as dividing by the number. ∎

The solution is 5. Because $3(5) - 4 = 15 - 4 = 11$, the solution checks in the original equation.

Example 2	***Multiplying by a Reciprocal***

a. $\frac{1}{3}x = 12$ *Original equation*
  $3 \cdot \frac{1}{3}x = 3 \cdot 12$ *Multiply each side by 3.*
  $x = 36$ *Simplify.*

b. $-\frac{1}{4}t + 2 = 6$ *Original equation*
  $-\frac{1}{4}t + 2 - 2 = 6 - 2$ *Subtract 2 from each side.*
  $-\frac{1}{4}t = 4$ *Simplify.*
  $-4 \cdot \left(-\frac{1}{4}t\right) = -4 \cdot 4$ *Multiply each side by -4.*
  $t = -16$ *Simplify.*

Check the solutions in the original equations. ∎

STARTER: Problem of the Day

Use a calculator and a guess-and-check strategy to approximate, to two decimal places, a solution to the equation.
$5^x = 934$ 4.25

Also available as a copymaster, p. 10

STARTER: Warm-Up Exercises

1. Compute.
  a. $\frac{2}{3} \cdot \frac{3}{2}$ **b.** $-\frac{4}{5} \cdot -\frac{5}{4}$
  c. $8 \cdot \frac{1}{8}$ **d.** $-\frac{1}{9} \cdot -9$
  a. 1, **b.** 1, **c.** 1, **d.** 1
2. Use your calculator to evaluate.
  a. $\frac{-3}{-0.4}$ **b.** $\frac{0.04}{5}$ **c.** $\frac{10.25}{-0.2}$
  a. 7.5, **b.** 0.008, **c.** -51.25
3. Solve.
  a. $6m + 3 = 21$ **b.** $2 + 4n = -10$
  a. $m = 3$, **b.** $n = -3$

Also available as a copymaster, p. 10

Each year from 1940 through the present, the number of breeding pairs of songbirds in Rock Creek Park in Washington, D.C., have been counted. Many factors have contributed to the birds' decline. (Source: National Audubon Society)

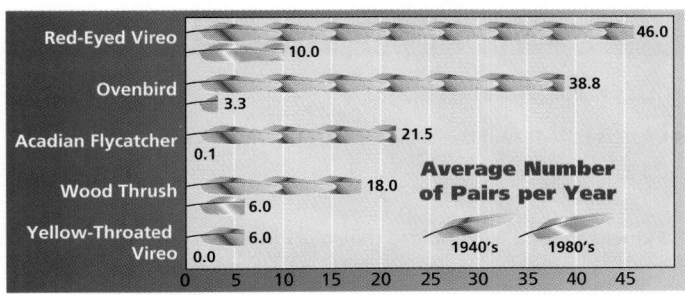

Red-Eyed Vireo 10.0 46.0
Ovenbird 3.3 38.8
Acadian Flycatcher 0.1 21.5
Wood Thrush 6.0 18.0
Yellow-Throated Vireo 0.0 6.0

Average Number of Pairs per Year

1940's 1980's

0 5 10 15 20 25 30 35 40 45

Real Life
Endangered Species

Example 3   *Modeling Real Life*

A biologist uses the data in the graph to model the number W of pairs of wood thrush in Rock Creek Park.

$$W = -0.3t + 18$$

In this model, $t = 0$ represents 1940. Use the model to predict the year in which no pairs of wood thrush ($W = 0$) will be seen in Rock Creek Park.

Need to Know

In Example 3, the year 1940 is represented by $t = 0$. This means that $t = 10$ represents 1950, $t = 20$ represents 1960, $t = 30$ represents 1970, and so on. The notation $0 \leftrightarrow 1940$ indicates that 1940 is represented by 0.

Solution Substitute 0 for W in the equation and solve for t.

$$W = -0.3t + 18 \qquad \textit{Model for number of pairs of wood thrush}$$
$$0 = -0.3t + 18 \qquad \textit{Substitute 0 for W.}$$
$$-18 = -0.3t \qquad \textit{Subtract 18 from each side.}$$
$$\frac{-18}{-0.3} = \frac{-0.3t}{-0.3} \qquad \textit{Divide each side by} -0.3.$$
$$60 = t \qquad \textit{Use a calculator.}$$

Because $t = 0$ represents 1940, it follows that $t = 60$ represents 2000. Thus, you can predict that no pairs of wood thrush will be seen in the year 2000. ∎

Communicating about MATHEMATICS

▶ **SHARING IDEAS about the Lesson**

Making a Prediction The number R of pairs of red-eyed vireo in Rock Creek Park can be modeled by $R = -0.9t + 46$, where $t = 0$ represents 1940. How many pairs would you expect to see in 1955? During which year would you expect to see no pairs? 32 or 33, 1991 or 1992

Let students suggest factors or reasons why the number of breeding pairs of songbirds have declined.

Example 3

The bar graph needs some explanation. There is no vertical scale. Each bar represents a decade (of years). The algebraic model used here relates only to one species of songbird — the wood thrush. For more help on the variable t, you may wish to refer to Ex. 7–10 in Guided Practice. Explain also that the data as given here are very limited, and consequently, the model is only approximate.

Communicating about MATHEMATICS

Once again you have an opportunity here to point out the versatility of an algebraic model, whereby predictions and projections can be made, limiting cases examined, and so on.

Writing Prompt
Write a letter to a friend explaining why, or why not, you would rather be a teacher than an accountant. You may wish to refer students to the Integrated Review.

Technology

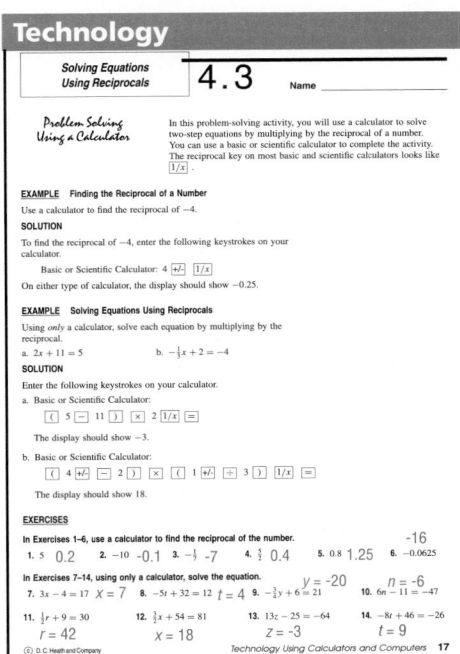

OPTION: Extra Examples

Here are additional examples similar to Example 1.

Comparing Two Solutions
Solve $-4x + 6 = -34$.

a. $\quad -4x + 6 = -34$ Original equation
$\quad\quad\quad -4x = -40$ Subtract 6 from each side.
$\quad\quad \frac{-4x}{-4} = \frac{-40}{-4}$ Divide each side by -4.
$\quad\quad\quad\quad x = 10$ Simplify.

b. $\quad -4x + 6 = -34$ Original equation
$\quad\quad\quad -4x = -40$ Subtract 6 from each side.
$-\frac{1}{4} \cdot -4x = -\frac{1}{4} \cdot -40$ Multiply each side by $-\frac{1}{4}$.
$\quad\quad\quad\quad x = 10$ Simplify.

EXERCISE Notes

ASSIGNMENT GUIDE

Basic/Average:
  Day 1: Ex. 11–29 odd, 30, 31
  Day 2: Ex. 32, 34–36
Above Average: Ex 11–37 odd, 35–46
Advanced: Ex. 11–37 odd, 38–46
Selected Answers: Ex. 1–10, 11–37 odd

Guided Practice

▶ **Ex. 4** Discuss with students why 0 does not have a reciprocal.

Independent Practice

▶ **Ex. 11–14** Use these exercises to generate a discussion about which method seems more efficient for isolating the variable (see Example 1).
▶ **Ex. 15–29** Be sure to remind students of the correct format for their solutions.
▶ **Ex. 30, 31** For setting up the sketches, you may wish to review some simple translation from verbal to symbolic.

EXERCISES

Guided Practice

▶ **CHECK for Understanding**

In Exercises 1–4, find the reciprocal of the number, if possible.

1. $\frac{1}{3}$ 3
2. $-\frac{1}{4}$ -4
3. -5 $-\frac{1}{5}$
4. 0 Not possible

In Exercises 5 and 6, complete the solution.

5.
$$7x = -28$$
$$\boxed{?} \cdot 7x = \boxed{?} \cdot (-28) \quad \tfrac{1}{7}, \tfrac{1}{7}$$
$$x = \boxed{?} \quad -4$$

6.
$$-\tfrac{1}{4}x = 12$$
$$\boxed{?} \cdot \left(-\tfrac{1}{4}x\right) = \boxed{?} \cdot 12 \quad -4, -4$$
$$x = \boxed{?} \quad -48$$

In Exercises 7–10, let $t = 0$ represent 1950. What year is represented by the given value of t?

7. $t = 17$ 1967
8. $t = 45$ 1995
9. $t = -10$ 1940
10. $t = -25$ 1925

Independent Practice

In Exercises 11–14, describe two different ways to solve the equation. See margin.

11. $3x = -15$
12. $-2x = 14$
13. $27 = 9n$
14. $-48 = -4y$

In Exercises 15–29, solve the equation.

15. $2y - 12 = 4$ 8
16. $5n - 21 = 24$ 9
17. $-\tfrac{1}{8}x + 14 = 6$ 64
18. $-\tfrac{1}{10}m - 11 = 1$ -120
19. $-12t - 7 = -15$ $\frac{2}{3}$
20. $21z - 16 = 12$ $1\frac{1}{3}$
21. $\tfrac{1}{5}x - 3 = -2$ 5
22. $-\tfrac{1}{3}y + 27 = 39$ -36
23. $5r + 15 = 10$ -1
24. $-11t + 16 = -6$ 2
25. $-\tfrac{1}{7}b + 2 = 1$ 7
26. $\tfrac{1}{7}p - 3 = 0$ 15
27. $\tfrac{2}{3}x - \tfrac{1}{3}x = 12$ 36
28. $3(x + 7) = 27$ 2
29. $-2(t + 2) = 6$ -5

In Exercises 30 and 31, use a sketch to find the answer.

✪ **30.** *Geometry*   A rectangle has a perimeter of 34 inches. Its length is 5 inches more than its width, x.

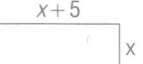

  a. Make a sketch of the rectangle and label its side lengths.
  b. Find the rectangle's dimensions. width: 6 in., length: 11

✪ **31.** *Geometry*   A triangle has a perimeter of 30 centimeters. Side a is 7 centimeters shorter than Side b, and Side c is 1 centimeter longer than Side b. Side b has a length of x centimeters.

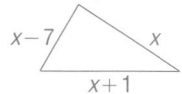

  a. Make a sketch of the triangle and label its side lengths.
  b. Find the lengths of the triangle's sides. 5 cm, 12 cm, 13 cm

---

Answers

11. Divide each side by 3, multiply each side by $\frac{1}{3}$.

12. Divide each side by -2, multiply each side by $-\frac{1}{2}$.

13. Divide each side by 9, multiply each side by $\frac{1}{9}$.

14. Divide each side by -4, multiply each side by $-\frac{1}{4}$.

Extra Practice

Extra Practice   4.3   Name _____

In Exercises 1 and 2, describe two different ways to solve the equation.
1. $4x = -24$ Divide both sides by 4 or multiply both sides by 1/4.
2. $-3x = -33$ Divide both sides by -3 or multiply both sides by -1/3.

In Exercises 3–14, solve the equation.
3. $3y - 12 = 18$ 10
4. $2x + 11 = -19$ -15
5. $-\tfrac{1}{4}z + 7 = -3$ 20
6. $\tfrac{1}{3}m - 4 = 2$ 18
7. $-4t + 6 = -10$ 4
8. $18y - 6 = -30$ $\frac{-4}{3}$
9. $-13t + 10 = -16$ 2
10. $\tfrac{1}{10}x - 1 = 0$ 10
11. $\tfrac{3}{7}x + \tfrac{1}{7}x - 6 = 1$ 7
12. $\tfrac{3}{5}x - \tfrac{1}{5}x = 2$ 10
13. $2(x + 5) = -8$ -9
14. $-3(x + 2) = 18$ -8

15. The sum of four times a number and 16 is 100. Find the number. Write an equation and solve it. $4n + 16 = 100; n = 21$

16. The difference of three times a number and 23 is 34. Find the number. Write an equation and solve it. $3n - 23 = 34; n = 19$

17. The sum of one-half a number and 27 is 40. Find the number. Write an equation and solve it. $\tfrac{1}{2}n + 27 = 40; n = 26$

18. 13 is the difference of one-fifth a number and 8. Find the number. Write an equation and solve it. $13 = \tfrac{1}{5}n - 8; n = 105$

19. A traffic sign has the shape of an equilateral triangle. The perimeter of the sign is 225 centimeters. Find the length of the sides of the sign. (An equilateral triangle is one whose sides have the same length.) 75 cm

YIELD

20. A rectangle has a perimeter of 78 inches. Its length is 6 inches more than twice its width.
  a. Make a sketch of the rectangle and label its sides.
  b. Find the rectangles dimensions. Width = 11 inches; length = 28 inches

21. In 1992, the salary of the governor of New York was about $25,000 more than three times the salary of the governor of Arkansas. The total of the two salaries was $165,000. Find the 1992 salaries of each state's governor. (Source: The Universal Almanac) Arkansas' governor salary = $35,000 New York's governor salary = $130,000

28   *Two-Step Equations and Problem Solving* ▪ *4.3*   Windows

---

Reteaching

Reteach **Chapter 4**   Name _____

What you should learn:
4.3 How to solve an equation by multiplying by a reciprocal and how to write two-step equations that model real-life problems

Correlation to Pupil's Textbook:
Mid-Chapter Self-Test (p. 167) Chapter Test (p. 191)
Exercises 1–5   Exercises 9, 10

Examples   *Using Reciprocals and Writing Real-Life Models*

a. Solve the equation by multiplying by a reciprocal.
$$-\tfrac{1}{3}x = 4 \quad \text{Original equation}$$
$$-3 \cdot \left(-\tfrac{1}{3}\right)x = -3 \cdot 4 \quad \text{Multiply each side by } -3.$$
$$x = -12 \quad \text{Simplify.}$$

b. The width of a rectangular garden is 4 feet less than its length. Write a model for the perimeter of the garden. Find the dimensions of the garden if you know that the perimeter is 52 feet.

Verbal Model	Perimeter of garden	=	Length	+	Width	+	Length	+	Width

Labels Length = x
  Width = $x - 4$

Algebraic Model
$$52 = x + (x - 4) + x + (x - 4)$$
$$52 = 4x - 8$$
$$60 = 4x$$
$$\tfrac{1}{4} \cdot 60 = \tfrac{1}{4} \cdot 4x$$
$$15 = x$$

The length of the garden is 15 feet and the width of the garden is $15 - 4 = 11$ feet.

Guidelines: • Multiplying by the reciprocal of a number produces the same result as dividing by the number.
• When you multiply a number by its reciprocal, you obtain 1.

EXERCISES

In Exercises 1–4, find the reciprocal of the number.
1. 13 $\frac{1}{13}$
2. $-\tfrac{1}{6}$ -6
3. -4 $\frac{-1}{4}$
4. $\tfrac{1}{2}$ 2

In Exercises 5–7, solve the equation.
5. $-\tfrac{1}{3}x + 4 = -5$ 27
6. $-18q - 12 = 24$ -2
7. $\tfrac{1}{4}w - 6 = 2$ 32

8. Use the model in Example b above to find the dimensions of a garden with a perimeter of 28 feet. 5 feet by 9 feet

29

32. *Population* In 1990, the population of Nebraska was about 71,700 less than 3 times the population of Alaska. The total population of the two states was about 2,128,400. Find the 1990 population of each state.
(Source: U.S. Bureau of the Census)

Verbal Model	Total Pop.	=	Pop. of Nebraska	+	Pop. of Alaska

Labels Total Population = 2,128,400
Population of Alaska = A
Population of Nebraska = $3A - 71,700$

a. Write the algebraic model. $2,128,400 = (3A - 71,700) + A$
b. Solve the algebraic model. 550,025
c. Answer the question. AK: 550,025; NE: 1,578,375

33. *Population* In 1990, the population of Utah was about 79,300 more than half the population of Connecticut. The total population of the two states was about 5,010,000. Find the 1990 population of each state.
(Source: U.S. Bureau of the Census) CT: ≈ 3,287,133; UT: ≈ 1,722,867

Although Alaska ranks 49th in population, it ranks first in area. Its area is about one-fifth that of the area of the lower 48 states.

Integrated Review
Making Connections within Mathematics

Analyzing Salary Data **In Exercises 34–37, use the data in the bar graph. The data represents the average starting salaries for public school teachers and accountants.** *(Source: Northwestern University Placement Center)*

34. Estimate the starting salary for a teacher in 1980.

35. Estimate the starting salary for an accountant in 1985.

36. From 1980 to 1990, which average starting salary increased by the larger amount?

37. From the data, what would you predict the average starting salary for a teacher to be in 1995? about $25,000

34. about $10,800 **35.** about $20,700 **36.** accountants

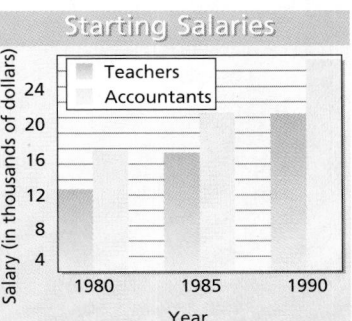

Exploration and Extension

In Exercises 38–45, use a calculator to find the reciprocal of the given number. Then verify that the product of the number and its reciprocal is 1.

Sample: To find the reciprocal of −0.5, enter 0.5 [+/−] [¹/ₓ].

38. 0.25 4
39. −0.125 −8
40. −25 −0.04
41. 32 0.03125
42. $\frac{1}{2}$ 2
43. $-\frac{5}{4}$ −0.8
44. −100 −0.01
45. 500 0.002

46. What happens if you try to use a calculator to find the reciprocal of 0? Explain. You get an error message, zero does not have a reciprocal

4.3 • Two-Step Equations and Problem Solving **161**

Milestones

Theme: Language and Communication

Students can use Venn diagrams to solve logic puzzles like the following.

Consider an all-school conference on the environment. Let E be the set of students attending the lecture on endangered species. Let R be the set of students attending the lecture on the rain forest, and let P be the set of students attending the lecture on pollution.

- $E = 21$ • $E + P = 40$
- $E \cap R \cap P = 3$
- $E \cap P = 8$ • $R \cap P = 4$
- $E \cap R = 7$ • $E \cup R = 34$

1. How many students only attended lecture P? 10

Venn Diagram

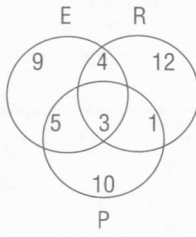

2. How many students attended the conference? 44

Library Skills

Have students use library resources to research the history of and determine the similarities and differences of symbolic computer languages such as FORTRAN (mid-1950's), and LISP (mid-1950's), COBOL (1960), BASIC (mid-1960's), FORTH (late-1960's), and Pascal (1980's).

Mixed REVIEW

4. Add 2 to each side, divide each side by 4.

In Exercises 1–3, evaluate the expression when $a = 4$ and $b = 5$. (3.4, 3.6)

1. $6b - 3$ 27   **2.** $8b \div (-a)$ -10 **3.** $a^2 - 2b - 3$ 3

4. Describe the steps used to solve the equation $4x - 2 = 12$. **(4.2)** See above.

5. Plot the points $(3, 2)$ and $(-2, 4)$ in a coordinate plane. **(3.8)** See margin.

In Exercises 6–8, write the expression without parentheses. (2.1)

6. $4(3 + 2y)$ $12 + 8y$ **7.** $4(2x - 3)$ $8x - 12$ **8.** $0.25(4m + 8)$ $m + 2$

In Exercises 9–14, solve the equation. (4.2, 4.3)

9. $2y - 14 = 0$ 7   **10.** $16a + 14 = 110$ 6   **11.** $2.06r + 1.14r = 8.32$ 2.6

12. $\frac{5}{2}x - \frac{1}{2}x = -1$ $-\frac{1}{2}$ **13.** $\frac{m}{5} + 1 = 7$ 30   **14.** $2c + 4c - c = 10$ 2

Milestones   BOOLEAN ALGEBRA

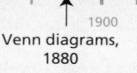

1700	1750	1800	1850	1900	1950	
Euler born, 1707		Rosetta stone, 1799	Braille, 1829	Morse code, 1838	Venn diagrams, 1880	BASIC, 1964 Fractals, 1975

A self-taught elementary school teacher in England named George Boole (1815–1864) revolutionized mathematics in 1847. In his algebra, statements and their logical relationships could be represented by symbols in a new kind of equation. The rules that he invented, now known as Boolean Algebra, are currently used in topology, fractal mathematics, circuitry, probability, computer science, and truth-function logic.

To avoid confusion with standard algebra, a new set of symbols was developed for Boolean Algebra, and John Venn (1834–1923) adapted Euler's logic circles as "Venn diagrams" to help people understand the relationships between the symbols.

George Boole

Venn Diagram

In symbols: $A \cap B = C$

Symbol	Meaning
$A, B, C,$ etc.	Individual sets that contain elements
$A \cup B$	The union of two sets A and B; contains all the elements in either A or B, or in both A and B
$A \cap B$	The intersection of sets A and B; contains only the elements that are in both A and B

- *What is the intersection of the set of multiples of 2 and the set of multiples of 3?* The set of multiples of 6   Answers v
- *Define two sets A and B. Determine $A \cup B$ and $A \cap B$ for your sets.*

Answer to Mixed Review

5.

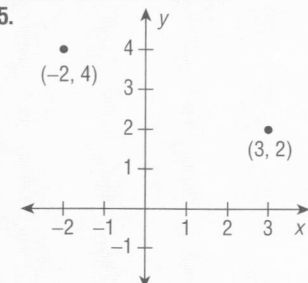

4.4

Solving Equations: The Distributive Property

PACING the Lesson
Suggested Number of Days
Basic/Average 2   Above Average 1
Advanced 1

PLANNING the Lesson
Lesson Plan 4.4, p. 29

What you should learn:

Goal 1 How to use the Distributive Property to solve equations

Goal 2 How to use the Distributive Property to model and solve real-life problems

Why you should learn it:

You can use the Distributive Property and the problem-solving plan to model and solve real-life problems, such as finding the sales necessary to obtain a bonus.

Goal 1 Using the Distributive Property

In Lesson 4.1, you studied the two guidelines for solving equations. The first guideline often involves the Distributive Property.

1. Simplify both sides of the equation (if needed).
2. Use inverse operations to isolate the variable.

Example 1 *Using the Distributive Property*

Solve $5y + 2(y - 3) = 92$.

Solution

$5y + 2(y - 3) = 92$	*Rewrite original equation.*
$5y + 2y - 6 = 92$	*Distributive Property*
$7y - 6 = 92$	*Combine like terms.*
$7y - 6 + 6 = 92 + 6$	*Add 6 to each side.*
$7y = 98$	*Simplify.*
$\frac{7y}{7} = \frac{98}{7}$	*Divide each side by 7.*
$y = 14$	*Simplify.*

The solution is 14. Check this in the original equation. ∎

Need to Know

Another way to solve the equation in Example 2 is to first multiply each side by the reciprocal of $\frac{1}{4}$.

$$24 = \frac{1}{4}(x - 8)$$

$$4 \cdot 24 = 4 \cdot \frac{1}{4}(x - 8)$$

$$96 = x - 8$$

$$96 + 8 = x - 8 + 8$$

$$104 = x$$

Which strategy do you think is easier?

Example 2 *Using the Distributive Property*

Solve $24 = \frac{1}{4}(x - 8)$.

Solution

$24 = \frac{1}{4}(x - 8)$	*Original equation*
$24 = \frac{1}{4}x - \frac{1}{4}(8)$	*Distributive Property*
$24 = \frac{1}{4}x - 2$	*Simplify.*
$24 + 2 = \frac{1}{4}x - 2 + 2$	*Add 2 to each side.*
$6 = \frac{1}{4}x$	*Simplify.*
$4 \cdot 26 = 4 \cdot \frac{1}{4}x$	*Multiply each side by 4.*
$104 = x$	*Simplify.*

The solution is 104. Check this in the original equation. ∎

4.4 • *Solving Equations: The Distributive Property* **163**

ORGANIZER

Starters (reproduced below)
  Problem of the Day 4.4, p. 11
  Warm-Up Exercises 4.4, p. 11
Lesson Resources
  Math Log, p. 14
  Answer Masters 4.4, p. 78
  Extra Practice Copymaster 4.4, p. 29
  Reteaching Copymaster 4.4, p. 29
  Enrichment Projects, pp. 20, 21
Special Populations
  Suggestions, Teacher's Edition, p. 146D

LESSON Notes

You may wish to set the stage for these examples by reviewing how the two applications of the Distributive Property (expanding and factoring) are used in simplifying equations.

Example 1

Use arrows to remind students of the expansion application of the Distributive Property:

$$a(b+c)$$

Example 2

Discuss the Need to Know box with students. Ask how the right side of the equation in Example 2 is different from the left side of the equation in Example 1.   The right side of the equation in Example 2 involves only one operation, multiplication.

STARTER: Problem of the Day

Replace each letter with a digit to make the subtraction correct. Different letters stand for different digits, but a letter must be replaced by the same digit whenever it occurs. There are 16 possible values for the number *KJE*! Examine *all* possibilities. How many can you find?

```
  A W K
- K J E
  K J E
```

Possible solutions for the number *KJE*: 206, 216, 231, 236, 271, 281, 286, 291, 407, 417, 427, 432, 452, 457, 467, 482.

Also available as a copymaster, p. 11

STARTER: Warm-Up Exercises

1. Apply the Distributive Property to find the product.
   a. $3(4y - 2)$ b. $\frac{1}{3}(9m + 6)$
      $12y - 6$ $3m + 2$
   c. $8(4 - 3x)$ d. $\frac{1}{6}(30 + 12n)$
      $32 - 24x$ $5 + 2n$

2. Find the reciprocal of each given number.
   a. -3 b. $\frac{4}{5}$ c. $\frac{-3}{2}$ d. $\frac{1}{13}$

   a. $\frac{1}{-3}$, b. $\frac{5}{4}$, c. $\frac{2}{-3}$, d. 13

Also available as a copymaster, p. 11

Algebra is used to model real life. Take a few moments to reflect with students about the variety of real-life situations that we have encountered in the text.

Real Life
Sales Bonus

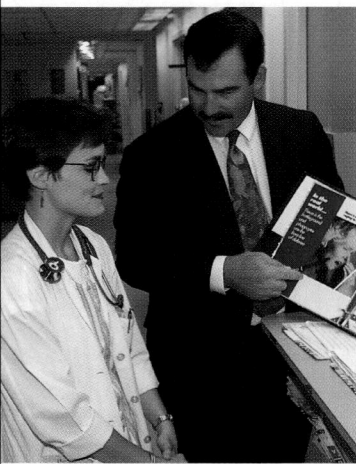

In 1993, over 9 million Americans worked in sales. Of these, more than half had salary plans that included commissions or bonuses based on sales. (Source: U.S. Bureau of Census)

Goal 2 **Real-Life Modeling**

Example 3 *Solving Real-Life Problems*

You are a sales representative for a company that sells medical equipment. Your annual salary is $30,000, plus a bonus. Your bonus is $\frac{1}{30}$ of the amount by which your sales exceed $500,000. Create a table showing the amounts you need to sell to earn a total salary of $30,000, $40,000, $50,000, and $60,000.

Solution

Verbal Model
$$\boxed{\text{Total salary}} = 30,000 + \frac{1}{30}\left(\boxed{\text{Total sales}} - 500,000\right)$$

Labels
Total salary = T (dollars)
Total sales = S (dollars)

Algebraic Model
$$\boxed{T} = 30,000 + \frac{1}{30}(\boxed{S} - 500,000), \qquad S > 500,000$$

To find the sales you need to earn a total salary of $40,000, substitute 40,000 for T, and solve for S.

$$40,000 = 30,000 + \frac{1}{30}(S - 500,000)$$

$$10,000 = \frac{1}{30}(S - 500,000)$$

$$30 \cdot 10,000 = 30 \cdot \frac{1}{30}(S - 500,000)$$

$$300,000 = S - 500,000$$

$$800,000 = S$$

To complete the table, you can solve for the values of S that will produce total salaries of $50,000 and $60,000 in a similar way.

Salary, T	$30,000	$40,000	$50,000	$60,000
Sales, S	Up to $500,000	$800,000	$1,100,000	$1,400,000

∎

Communicating *about* MATHEMATICS

Cooperative Learning

▷ **SHARING IDEAS about the Lesson**

Finding a Pattern Describe the pattern given in the table in Example 3 to your partner. Then use the pattern to predict the amount you would have to sell to earn a salary of $70,000. Finally, use the algebraic model to verify your answer.

164 Chapter **4** ▪ *Exploring the Language of Algebra*

EXERCISES

Guided Practice

▶ **CHECK for Understanding** 1.–3. Answers vary.

1. *Writing* In your own words, describe a set of guidelines for solving an equation.

2. Explain how your guidelines can be used to solve the equation $\frac{1}{7}(x - 5) = 9$.

3. For the equation in Exercise 2, is it easier to apply the Distributive Property first or multiply both sides by the reciprocal of $\frac{1}{7}$ first? Explain.

4. Distributive Property, combine like terms, add 12 to each side, simplify, divide each side by 10, simplify.

4. *Logical Reasoning* Justify each step of the solved equation. See below.

$$6x + 4(x - 3) = 8$$
$$6x + 4x - 12 = 8$$
$$10x - 12 = 8$$
$$10x - 12 + 12 = 8 + 12$$
$$10x = 20$$
$$\frac{10x}{10} = \frac{20}{10}$$
$$x = 2$$

Independent Practice

5. $2(x + 2) \neq 2x + 2, 0$ **6.** $(-2) \div (-2) \neq -1, 1$ **7.** $-2x - 4x \neq -2x, -\frac{2}{3}$

Error Analysis In Exercises 5–7, describe the error. Then solve the equation.

5.
$$2(x + 2) = 4$$
$$2x + 2 = 4$$
$$2x = 2$$
$$x = 1$$

6.
$$5x - 7x + 5 = 3$$
$$-2x + 5 = 3$$
$$-2x = -2$$
$$x = -1$$

7.
$$-2x - 4x + 6 = 10$$
$$-2x + 6 = 10$$
$$-2x = 4$$
$$x = -2$$

In Exercises 8–22, solve the equation. Check your solution.

8. $x + 4(x + 6) = -1$ -5
9. $1 = y + 3(y - 9)$ 7
10. $3x + 2(x + 8) = 21$ 1

11. $2z + 5(z - 2) = -31$ -3
12. $4(p - 2) + 7p = 14$ 2
13. $11 = 6(t - 4) - 13$ 8

14. $3(4 - s) - 5s = 52$ -5
15. $7(1 + r) - 5r = -5$ -6
16. $5(2n + 3) = 65$ 5

17. $\frac{3}{4}x - \frac{2}{4}x + 12 = -8$ -80
18. $14 = \frac{1}{4}(q - 9)$ 65
19. $-3(y + 4) = 18$ -10

20. $2 = -2(n - 3)$ 2
21. $8(4z - 7) = -56$ 0
22. $6(2n - 5) = 42$ 6

23. *It's Up to You* Solve the equation $\frac{1}{3}(x - 6) = 6$ in two ways. Which way do you prefer? Why? Answers vary.

 a. Use the Distributive Property first. $\frac{1}{3}x - 2 = 6, \frac{1}{3}x = 8, x = 24$

 b. Multiply by a reciprocal first. $x - 6 = 18, x = 24$

Geometry In Exercises 24–26, write an equation for the area of the rectangle. Then solve for x.

24.
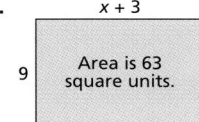
$x + 3$
9
Area is 63 square units.

$9(x + 3) = 63, 4$

25.
$x - 5$
12
Area is 48 square units.

$12(x - 5) = 48, 9$

26.
$2x - 1$
5
Area is 35 square units.

$5(2x - 1) = 35, 4$

P Portfolio Opportunity

4.4 ▪ *Solving Equations: The Distributive Property* **165**

EXERCISE Notes

ASSIGNMENT GUIDE
Basic/Average:
 Day 1: Ex. 5–25 odd
 Day 2: Ex. 29–35 odd, 37, 38
Above Average:
Ex. 5–29 odd, 31, 33, 37, 38
Advanced: Ex. 5–29 odd, 31, 33, 37, 38
Selected Answers: Ex. 1–4, 5–35 odd

Guided Practice
▶ **Ex. 1–3** Use these exercises as a small-group activity. The equation in Ex. 2 involves a format that students often find difficult.
▶ **Ex. 4** This exercise provides an excellent opportunity to review techniques.

Independent Practice
▶ **Ex. 5–7** Have students work in pairs for these exercises.
▶ **Ex. 24–26** Remind students how to set up the area model.

Extra Practice

Extra Practice 4.4 Name _____

In Exercises 1 and 2, describe the error. Then solve the equation.

1. $3x - 6x + 2 = 8$ The second line
$3x + 2 = 8$ should be
$3x = 6$ $-3x + 2 = 8;$
$x = 2$ $x = -2$

2. $4(x - 2) + 6 = 16$ The second line
$4x - 2 + 6 = 16$ should be
$4x + 4 = 16$ $4x - 8 + 6 = 16;$
$4x = 12$ $x = 9/2$ or 4.5.
$x = 3$

In Exercises 3–11, solve the equation. Check your solution.

3. $3x + 2(x - 1) = 8$ 2
4. $6 = 3y + 3(y - 6)$ 4
5. $6(2 - r) = -18$ 5
6. $8(p + 1) + 3p = -14$ -2
7. $3(t - 4) + 6 = 0$ 2
8. $6(x - 4) + 3x = 3$ 3
9. $\frac{5}{8}x - \frac{3}{8}x + 2 = -3$ -30
10. $16 = -\frac{1}{4}(q + 2)$ -34
11. $-5(y + 3) = 25$ -8

12. Solve the equation $2(x + 7) = -26$ in two ways.
 a. Use the Distributive Property first. -20
 b. Multiply by a reciprocal first. -20
 c. Which way do you prefer? Why? Answers vary.

13. Solve the equation $-\frac{1}{3}(x - 11) = 2$ in two ways.
 a. Use the Distributive Property first. -3
 b. Multiply by a reciprocal first. -3
 c. Which way do you prefer? Why? Answers vary.

14. Write an equation for the area of the rectangle. Then solve for x.
$x + 5$
6 Area is 42 square units
$6(x + 5) = 42; x = 2$

15. Write an equation, solve the equation for x, and find the measures of the angles.
$(3x - 2) + (2x - 1) + (7x + 3) = 180;$
$x = 15; 43°, 29°, 108°$

16. A grocer wants to mix x pounds of cashew nuts worth \$7.00 per pound with 9 pounds of peanuts worth \$3.00 per pound to obtain $9 + x$ pounds of mixture worth \$5.00 per pound. Use the verbal model and labels to write an equation and find the number of pounds of cashews required to obtain the specified mixture.

| Verbal model | Total cost of cashews | + | Total cost of peanuts | = | Total cost of mixed nuts |

Labels Cost per pound of cashews = \$7.00
 Number of pounds of cashews = x
 Cost per pound of peanuts = \$3.00
 Number of pounds of peanuts = 9
 Cost per pound of mixed nuts = \$5.00
 Number of pounds of mixed nuts = $9 + x$ pounds

$7(x) + 3(9) = 5(9 + x); x = 9;$ 9 pounds of cashews

Windows *4.4 ▪ Solving Equations: The Distributive Property* **29**

Reteaching

Reteach Chapter 4 Name _____

What you should learn:

4.4 How to use the Distributive Property to solve equations

Correlation to Pupil's Textbook:
Mid-Chapter Self-Test (p. 167) Chapter Test (p. 191)
Exercises 15, 19 Exercises 3, 6, 13

Examples *Using the Distributive Property*

a. Solve $6(x + 3) - 2x = 14$.

$6(x + 3) - 2x = 14$ Rewrite original equation.
$6x + 18 - 2x = 14$ Distributive Property
$4x + 18 = 14$ Combine like terms.
$4x + 18 - 18 = 14 - 18$ Subtract 18 from each side.
$4x = -4$ Simplify.
$\frac{4x}{4} = \frac{-4}{4}$ Divide each side by 4.
$x = -1$ Simplify.

The solution is -1. Check this in the original equation.

b. Use the Distributive Property and then solve $-43 = \frac{1}{5}(x - 15)$.

$-43 = \frac{1}{5}(x - 15)$ Original equation
$-43 = \frac{1}{5}x - \frac{1}{5}(15)$ Distributive Property
$-43 = \frac{1}{5}x - 3$ Simplify.
$-43 + 3 = \frac{1}{5}x - 3 + 3$ Add 3 to each side.
$-40 = \frac{1}{5}x$ Simplify.
$5(-40) = 5(\frac{1}{5}x)$ Multiply each side by 5.
$-200 = x$ Simplify.

Guidelines: • To solve an equation:
 1. Simplify both sides of the equation (if needed).
 2. Use inverse operations to isolate the variable.

EXERCISES

In Exercises 1–6, solve the equation. Check your solution.

1. $5x + 2(x + 3) = 20$ 2
2. $14 = 3(n - 4) - 2n$ 26
3. $-2(z + 3) = 10$ -8
4. $4(s - 3) + s = -17$ -1
5. $\frac{2}{3}y - \frac{1}{3}y + 7 = -2$ -27
6. $5(6 - a) - 8a = 4$ 2

Windows *Chapter 4 ▪ Exploring the Language of Algebra* **29**

► **Ex. 29** When assigning this exercise, refer students to Example 3 of this lesson.

Integrated Review

► **Ex. 35, 36** Ask students how they might check their estimates.

EXTENSION

Have students generate their own estimation problems using something they observe in the room, for example, the total height (in feet) of all students in the room, or the area (in feet²) of the door.

Exploration and Extension

Remind students of the techniques of changing from verbal statements to symbolic expressions.

PORTFOLIO

Challenge students to create their own number puzzle and have them include it in their portfolios, together with a solution.

Portfolio Opportunity: Math Log

Write a statement that describes the equation $2(x + 3) - 1 = 15$.

Also available as a copymaster, p. 14, Ex. 5

Short Quiz

Covers Lessons 4.3 and 4.4

Available as a copymaster, p. 55

In Exercises 27 and 28, write an equation and solve the equation for x.

✪ **27.** *Geometry*   The sum of the measures of the angles of a triangle is 180°.

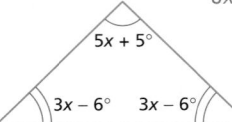

$5x + 5 + 2(3x - 6) = 180, 17$

- $5x + 5°$
- $3x - 6°$ $3x - 6°$

✪ **28.** *Volleyball Court*   The perimeter of a volleyball court is 180 feet.

$6x = 180, 30$

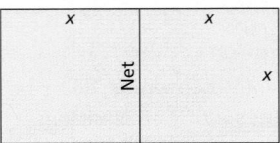

x		x
Net		x

✪ **29.** *Barbershop*   Imagine that you own a barbershop. You provide haircuts, stylings, and manicures for x dollars each, and perms for $(x + 40)$ dollars. This week your income came from providing 96 haircuts, 80 stylings, 14 manicures, and 24 perms. In a week, you pay $800 in expenses. **a.** See below

  a. Write an algebraic model that represents your income if this week's profit is $3,370.

  b. How much does a haircut cost? $15

✪ **30.** *Temperature*   To convert a Celsius temperature to a Fahrenheit temperature, you can use the equation $C = \frac{5}{9}(F - 32)$.

  a. What is 35°C on the Fahrenheit scale? 95°F

  b. What is 40°C on the Fahrenheit scale? 104°F

29a. $(96 + 80 + 14)x + 24(x + 40) = 3370 + 800$

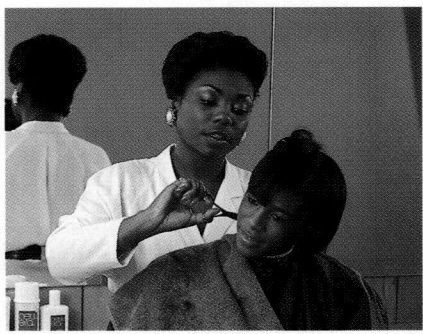

In 1987, approximately 390,700 Americans worked in barbershops and beauty shops.

Integrated Review

Making Connections within Mathematics

Mental Math   **In Exercises 31–34, each equation has two solutions. Use mental math to find both solutions.**

31. $x^2 = 4$ 2, -2   **32.** $x^2 = 9$ 3, -3   **33.** $|x| = 3$ 3, -3   **34.** $|x| = 5$ 5, -5

35. *Estimation*   Which of the following is the best estimate for the weight (in pounds) of this textbook? b

  a. $\frac{1}{2}$ **b.** 3   **c.** 6   **d.** 9

36. *Estimation*   Which of the following is the best estimate for the area (in square inches) of this textbook's front cover? c

  a. 20   **b.** 40   **c.** 80   **d.** 160

Exploration and Extension

Number Puzzles   **In Exercises 37 and 38, write an equation that represents the statements. Then solve the equation to find the number.**

✪ **37.** A number is added to 10. The result is multiplied by 2. The original number is added to the product to obtain 71. $2(n + 10) + n = 71, 17$

✪ **38.** A number is decreased by 6. The result is multiplied by $\frac{1}{3}$ to obtain 15. $\frac{1}{3}(n - 6) = 15, 51$

► **Enrichment**

Have students explore the following number pattern, then use a calculator to fill in the blanks. Ask students what pattern they notice in the results.

$1^2 = 1$
$11^2 = 121$
$111^2 = 12,321$
$1111^2 = \underline{\hspace{1cm}}$ 1,234,321
$11111^2 = \underline{\hspace{1cm}}$ 123,454,321
$111111^2 = \underline{\hspace{1cm}}$ 12,345,654,321

The results are a palindrome pattern with the middle digit increasing each time by 1.

Mid-Chapter Self-Test
Resources
Color Transparencies
  Diagram for Ex. 19, 20, p. 17

Take this test as you would take a test in class. The answers to the exercises are given in the back of the book.

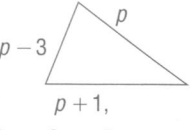
p
$p - 3$
$p + 1,$
3 cm, 6 cm, 7 cm

1. A triangle has a perimeter of 16 centimeters. Side a is 3 centimeters shorter than Side c. Side b is 1 centimeter longer than Side c. Side c is p centimeters in length. Sketch the triangle and find its dimensions. **(4.3)**

In Exercises 2–4, find the reciprocal. (4.3)

2. $\frac{3}{2}$ $\frac{2}{3}$

3. $-\frac{8}{21}$ $-\frac{21}{8}$

4. $\frac{16}{5}$ $\frac{5}{16}$

5. Choose any nonzero number. Multiply the number by its reciprocal. What is the result? 1

In Exercises 6–11, solve the equation. Then check your solution. (4.1)

6. $2y - 4 = 10$ 7

7. $4t + 16 = 0$ -4

8. $8 - 2b = 2$ 3

9. $\frac{1}{2}r + 6 = 8$ 4

10. $6m + 5 = -1$ -1

11. $20p - 8 = 32$ 2

In Exercises 12–15, solve the equation. Then check your solution. (4.2, 4.4)

12. $9s + 6s - 12s = 15$ 5

13. $7t - 10t - t = 24$ -6

14. $19 + 12p - 17p = -1$ 4

15. $3(n + 4) + 1 = 28$ 5

In Exercises 16–18, write an equation that represents the verbal sentence. Then solve the equation. (4.1, 4.2)

16. The sum of $2x$ and 3 is 21. $2x + 3 = 21, 9$

17. The difference of $16x$ and 30 is -2. $16x - 30 = -2, 1\frac{3}{4}$

18. 17 is the sum of $2x$, x, x, and -4.
$$17 = 2x + x + x + (-4), 5\frac{1}{4}$$

In Exercises 19 and 20, use the following information. (4.3)

You have just arrived in Little Rock, Arkansas. You see the road sign at the right. Two of the arrows are broken. Use the clues to find the distances to Washington, D.C. and New Orleans, Louisiana.

19. The distance from Little Rock to Dallas is equal to one-third the difference of the distance to Washington, D.C. and 57. What is the distance to Washington, D.C? 1005 miles

20. The distance from Little Rock to Phoenix is the sum of 74 and 3 times the distance to New Orleans. What is the distance to New Orleans? 417 miles

WELCOME TO LITTLE ROCK
Phoenix, 1325 Miles
Washington D.C.
New Orleans
Dallas, 316 Miles

Partner Quiz

Chapter 4
Mid-Chapter Partner Quiz (Use after Lesson 4.4)
Name _____

1. What is the inverse operation of division? (4.1) **1.** Multiplication

2. Solve the equation. Check your solution. (4.1) **2.** -14
$-2s + 7 = 35$

3. A medium pizza with two toppings costs $9 plus $2 for each additional topping. You have $13. How many extra toppings can you get? Write an algebraic model and answer the question. (4.1) **3.** $2x + 9 = 13; 2$

4. What is the reciprocal of $-\frac{2}{3}$? (4.3) **4.** $\frac{-3}{2}$

5. Solve the equation. Check your solution. (4.2) **5.** -2
$3x - 2x + 3 - 5x = 11$

6. The sum of the measures of two angles is 90°. The first angle's measure is 6° more than twice the measure of the second angle. Find the measure of the second angle. (4.2) **6.** 28°

7. The temperature, T, in Celsius, of a solution is modeled by $T = 0.4t + 86$ where t is time in minutes and $t = 0$ corresponds to 1:00 P.M. When does the solution boil (100°C)? (4.3) **7.** 1:35 P.M.

8. Write an equation that represents the verbal sentence. Solve the equation. (4.4) **8.** $4(x + 2) = 12; 1$
4 times the sum of a number and 2 is 12.

9. Solve the equation $18 = 2(x - 3) + 26$. (4.4) **9.** -1

10. Write an equation for the perimeter of the given triangle. Solve for x. (4.4) **10.** $2(x + 1) + x = 38$ or $3x + 2 = 38$; 12 in.
$x + 1$ $x + 1$
x
Perimeter = 38 in.

Mid-Chapter Test

Mid-Chapter **4** Test Form B Name _____
(Use after Lesson 4.4) Date _____

1. A rectangle has a perimeter of 48 feet. Its length, l, is 6 feet shorter than its width. Sketch the rectangle and find its dimensions. (4.3) **1.** $l = 9$ feet, $w = 15$ feet

2. Find the reciprocal of $-\frac{1}{8}$. (4.3) **2.** -8

3. Write any positive number. Then write its reciprocal. (4.3) **3.** _____
Answers will vary but must be positive and reciprocals of each other.

In Exercises 4–8, solve the equation. (4.1–4.4)

4. $5n - 9 = 71$ **4.** $n = 16$

5. $2x + 1 = 11$ **5.** $x = 5$

6. $\frac{1}{2}r + 3 = 9$ **6.** $r = 12$

7. $4(y + 2) = 24$ **7.** $y = 4$

8. $-8y - 11 = 13$ **8.** $y = -3$

In Exercises 9–11, write an equation that represents the verbal sentence or problem. Then solve the equation. (4.1)

9. -17 is the sum of 10 and $9h$. $-17 = 10 + 9h; h = -3$ **9.** _____

10. The difference of $3x$ and 8 is 25. $3x - 8 = 25; x = 11$ **10.** _____

11. A new oil tank holds 35 barrels of oil more than an old tank. Together they hold 365 barrels of oil. How much does each tank hold? (4.3) **11.** _____
$(35 + x) + x = 365$; old holds 165 barrels, new holds 200 barrels

◀ **Alternative Assessment**

A **Partner Quiz** assesses students' achievement and provides them with an opportunity to communicate about mathematics. Available as a copymaster, p. 47

◀ **Formal Assessment**

Two **Mid-Chapter Tests** of average difficulty. Available as copymasters, pp. 56, 57

Materials

Teaching Tools
  Algebra tiles, pp. T4, C5

The goal of this investigation is to use algebra tiles to help students visualize the solution of equations with variables on both sides. *x*-tiles can be removed from both sides, just as 1-tiles can be removed from both sides.

This investigation connects well with the strategy of collecting like variables on the same side, modeled in Examples 1 and 2 for Lesson 4.5 on page 169.

Remind students of the option of using sketches on graph paper rather than tiles for this investigation.

EXTENSION

Equations involving sums and positive numbers are modeled on this page. If you wish to model equations involving subtraction and negative numbers, you can use the Overhead Manipulative Kit that includes tiles and directions for handling negatives.

▶ **Ex. 2** Remind students of the "group and remove" technique used in the opening investigation on page 148.

Materials Needed: algebra tiles

In this investigation, you will use algebra tiles to model and solve equations that have variables on both sides.

Example **Using Algebra Tiles**

Solve the equation $2x + 2 = x + 4$.

Solution

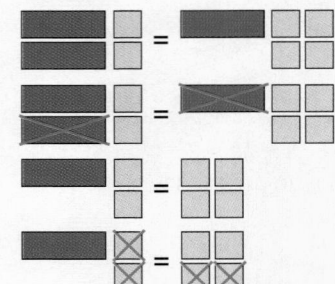

Original equation: $2x + 2 = x + 4$

Remove (subtract) an x-tile from each side so that you don't have x-tiles on each side.

Transformed equation: $x + 2 = 4$

To isolate x, remove (subtract) two 1-tiles from each side.

Solution is $x = 2$. ■

Exercises

In Exercises 1 and 2, an equation has been modeled and solved with algebra tiles. Write the equation and its solution.

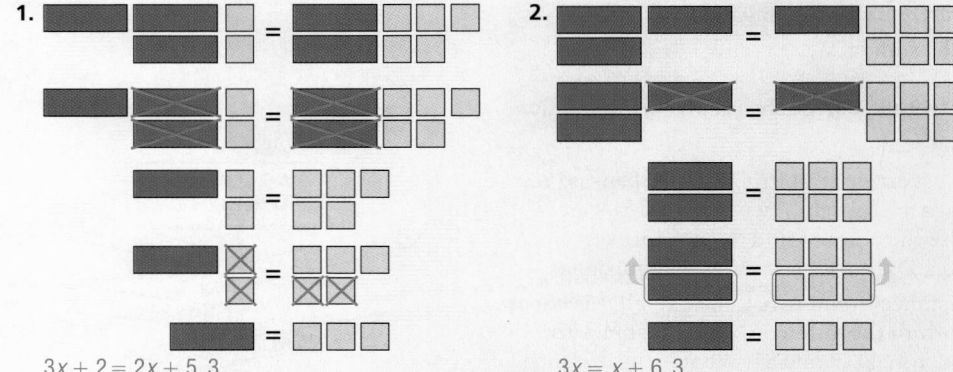

1. $3x + 2 = 2x + 5, 3$

2. $3x = x + 6, 3$

In Exercises 3–6, use algebra tiles to model and solve the equation. Check students' work.

3. $4x + 3 = 3x + 5$ 2   **4.** $y + 9 = 3y + 3$ 3

5. $3n + 5 = n + 11$ 3   **6.** $5m + 2 = 2m + 14$ 4

4.5 Solving Equations: Variables on Both Sides

▶ **PACING the Lesson**

Suggested Number of Days
Basic/Average 2 **Above Average** 1
Advanced 1

▶ **PLANNING the Lesson**

Lesson Plan 4.5, p. 30

What you should learn:

 Goal 1 How to solve equations with variables on both sides

 Goal 2 How use equations to model problems in geometry

Why you should learn it:

You can use algebra to solve problems in other branches of mathematics, such as finding the perimeter of a square or a triangle.

Goal 1 — Collecting Variables on One Side

Some equations, such as $2x + 3 = 3x + 5$, have variables on both sides. The strategy for solving such equations is to *collect like variables* on the same side. We suggest that you collect variables on the side with the term that has the greater variable coefficient.

Example 1 — Collecting Like Variables

Solve $2x + 3 = 3x + 5$.

Solution Remember that your goal is to isolate the variable.

$2x + 3 = 3x + 5$	*Rewrite original equation.*
$2x + 3 - 2x = 3x + 5 - 2x$	*Subtract 2x from each side.*
$3 = x + 5$	*Simplify.*
$3 - 5 = x + 5 - 5$	*Subtract 5 from each side.*
$-2 = x$	*Simplify.*

The solution is -2. Check this in the original equation. ∎

Example 2 — Collecting Like Variables

Solve $5x - 4 = 3(x - 8)$.

Solution

$5x - 4 = 3(x - 8)$	*Rewrite original equation.*
$5x - 4 = 3x - 24$	*Distributive Property*
$5x - 4 - 3x = 3x - 24 - 3x$	*Subtract 3x from each side.*
$2x - 4 = -24$	*Simplify.*
$2x - 4 + 4 = -24 + 4$	*Add 4 to each side.*
$2x = -20$	*Simplify.*
$\frac{2x}{2} = \frac{-20}{2}$	*Divide each side by 2.*
$x = -10$	*Simplify.*

The solution is -10. Check this in the original equation. ∎

Study Tip...

Some people prefer to always collect like variables on the left side. Notice what happens in Example 1 when you collect variables on the left side.

$$2x + 3 = 3x + 5$$
$$2x + 3 - 3x = 3x + 5 - 3x$$
$$-x + 3 = 5$$
$$-x + 3 - 3 = 5 - 3$$
$$-x = 2$$
$$\frac{-x}{-1} = \frac{2}{-1}$$
$$x = -2$$

Which strategy do you prefer?

4.5 • Solving Equations: Variables on Both Sides **169**

ORGANIZER

Starters (reproduced below)
  Problem of the Day 4.5, p. 11
  Warm-Up Exercises 4.5, p. 11
Lesson Resources
  Math Log, p. 14
  Technology, p. 18
  Answer Masters 4.5, p. 79
  Extra Practice Copymaster 4.5, p. 30
  Reteaching Copymaster 4.5, p. 30
Special Populations
  Suggestions, Teacher's Edition, p. 146D

LESSON Notes

Explain to students that collecting *like* variables on one side of an equation is a critical skill in solving equations. Students should describe this process in their journals. You may wish to link the first paragraph of the lesson to the investigation on page 168. Make sure that students understand the concept of "term that has the greater variable coefficient." Have students identify such terms from a number of samples.

Example 1

Note that all constant terms are *like* terms. The decision to subtract 2x from both sides of the equation was made because the coefficient 3 (of 3x) is greater than the coefficient 2 (of 2x). This guarantees that the coefficient of the isolated variable will be positive.

Study Tip Extension
Discuss the sequence of steps described here. Note that the coefficient of the isolated variable x is -1. We undo this product by dividing by -1. Because a negative divided by a negative is positive, the isolated variable, x, has a new coefficient of 1.

Example 2

In order to further emphasize the advantage of the technique presented on this page, challenge students to solve the equation by first subtracting 5x from both sides of the equation.

In Chapter 1, number patterns were often represented geometrically. The examples on this page emphasize that such modeling is reversible—properties and relationships of geometric figures can often be effectively described using algebraic relationships.

Example 3

Note that the Communicating about Mathematics offers an extension of this example.

Challenge students to make up other expressions for the sides of each figure and have them use the technique of the example to find the value of x for which the perimeters are equal.

Example 4

Make sure students understand why the equation $x + 3 = x + 3$ cannot be used in solving for x.

Communicating about MATHEMATICS

Have students work with a partner for this extension of Example 3.

Writing Prompt
Describe how an equation with the variable on both sides was used to solve a geometry problem in this lesson.

Connections
Geometry

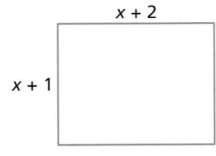

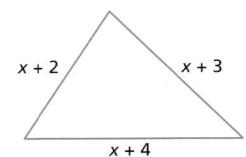

Connections
Geometry

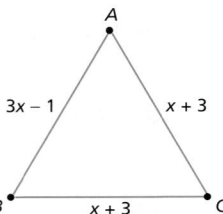

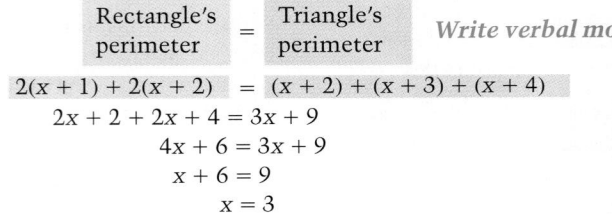

Example 3   *Comparing Perimeters*

Find the value of x so that the rectangle and the triangle have the same perimeter.

Solution

Rectangle's perimeter	=	Triangle's perimeter	*Write verbal model.*

$$2(x + 1) + 2(x + 2) = (x + 2) + (x + 3) + (x + 4)$$
$$2x + 2 + 2x + 4 = 3x + 9$$
$$4x + 6 = 3x + 9$$
$$x + 6 = 9$$
$$x = 3$$

When $x = 3$, each figure has a perimeter of 18.

Example 4   *Creating an Equilateral Triangle*

A triangle is **equilateral** if its sides all have the same length. Find a value of x so that $\triangle ABC$ is equilateral.

Solution

Length of side AB	=	Length of side AC or BC	*Write verbal model.*

$$3x - 1 = x + 3$$
$$2x - 1 = 3 \qquad \text{Subtract } x \text{ from each side.}$$
$$2x = 4 \qquad \text{Add 1 to each side.}$$
$$x = 2 \qquad \text{Divide each side by 2.}$$

When $x = 2$, each side will have a length of 5.

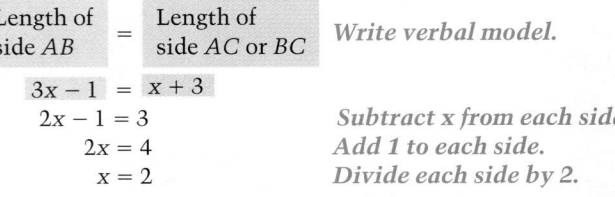

Communicating about MATHEMATICS

For table, see Additional Answers.
▶ **SHARING IDEAS about the Lesson**

Extending the Example In Example 3, which values of x make the rectangle's perimeter larger than the triangle's perimeter? Use a table to obtain your answer. $x > 3$

Technology

◤ **OPTION: Extra Examples**

Here is an additional example similar to Example 1.
Collecting Like Variables
Solve $-4x + 6 = x - 9$.
Solution
Remember that your goal is to isolate the variable.

$$-4x + 6 = x - 9 \qquad \text{Rewrite original equation.}$$
$$-4x + 6 + 4x = x - 9 + 4x \qquad \text{Add } 4x \text{ to each side.}$$
$$6 = 5x - 9 \qquad \text{Simplify.}$$
$$6 + 9 = 5x - 9 + 9 \qquad \text{Add 9 to each side.}$$
$$15 = 5x \qquad \text{Simplify.}$$
$$\frac{15}{5} = \frac{5x}{5} \qquad \text{Divide each side by 5.}$$
$$3 = x \qquad \text{Simplify.}$$

The solution is 3. Check this in the original equation.

EXERCISES

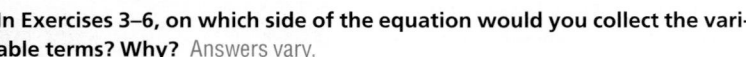

Guided Practice

▶ CHECK for Understanding

1. *Writing*   In your own words, describe a strategy for solving an equation that has variables on both sides.   Answers vary.

2. *Language Connections*   The preface *equi* means "equal" and the world *lateral* means "side." Explain how these words are related to the term *equilateral triangle*.   The sides of an equilateral triangle are equal in length.

In Exercises 3–6, on which side of the equation would you collect the variable terms? Why?   Answers vary.

3. $2x - 4 = x$ **4.** $4y + 10 = 6y$ **5.** $x + 15 = 4x + 6$ **6.** $3x - 5 = x + 3$

Independent Practice

In Exercises 7–10, match the equation with its solution.

a. $n = 9$ **b.** $n = 5$ **c.** $n = 4$ **d.** $n = 3$

7. $4n + 1 = 2n + 7$ d   **8.** $4n - 1 = 2n + 7$ c   **9.** $2(n - 1) = n + 7$ a   **10.** $2(n + 1) = n + 7$ b

In Exercises 11–22, solve the equation. Then check your solution.

11. $7x + 12 = 13x$ 2   **12.** $-2x + 6 = -x$ 6   **13.** $10x + 17 = 4x - 1$ -3

14. $-5x + 6 = x + 12$ -1 **15.** $6(x - 3) = 4(x + 3)$ 15   **16.** $2(x - 9) = 3(x - 6)$ 0

17. $-6 - 9t = 5(2 - t)$ -4 **18.** $4(7 + y) = 16 - 2y$ -2 **19.** $10(2n + 10) = 120n$ 1

20. $7y = 3(5y - 8)$ 3   **21.** $\frac{7}{2}t + 12 = 6 + \frac{5}{2}t$ -6 **22.** $-13 - \frac{1}{12}s = \frac{11}{12}s + 2$ -15

Diagramming Equations   In Exercises 23 and 24, write the equation implied by the model. Then solve it.   **23.** $x + x + 12 = 3x + 5, 7$ **24.** $2x + x + 41 = 5x + 15, 13$

23.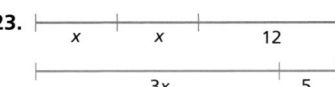

24.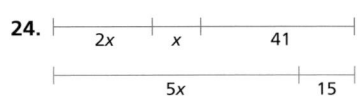

25. One less than three times a number is equal to the same number plus 19. What is the number?   10

✪ 26. Four times a number plus seventeen is equal to seven times the same number minus 7. What is the number?   8

27. *Geometry*   Find the value of x so that the rectangle and the triangle have the same perimeter. What is the perimeter?   5, 24

   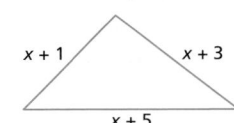

✪ More difficult exercises
P Portfolio Opportunity

4.5 • *Solving Equations: Variables on Both Sides*   **171**

ASSIGNMENT GUIDE

Basic/Average:
  Day 1: Ex. 7–27 odd
  Day 2: Ex. 29–33, 35–38

Above Average:
  Ex. 7–25 odd, 29–33, 35–38

Advanced: Ex. 7–25 odd, 29–33, 35–38

Selected Answers: Ex. 1–6, 7–33 odd

Guided Practice

▶ **Ex. 1, 3–6** This lesson suggests collecting variables on the side that has the term with the greater coefficient. This avoids ending up with a negative coefficient. However, allow students the option of collecting variables on the left side on condition that they can cope with a negative coefficient.

Independent Practice

▶ **Ex. 7–10** You may want to have students model these equations with tiles.
▶ **Ex. 11–22** It's important at this stage that students patiently work through each step of a solution. Encourage them to show explanations to the right of each step.
▶ **Ex. 23, 24, 27** These exercises (and Ex. 28, 29 on the following page) provide useful connections to geometry. Before assigning them, you may wish to review Example 3 of this lesson.

▶ **Ex. 30–32**

ALTERNATIVE ASSESSMENT
Since this group of exercises is quite challenging, assign them as a small-group in-class assessment activity. The "interpretation" referred to in Ex. 31 is simply a reminder that solving the equation and solving the problem are two distinct stages.

Exploration and Extension
Common-Error Alert!

Most students think there is always one solution to an equation. Use these exercises as a discussion of unusual cases. Remind students of the definition of a solution—the value (or values) of the variable which, when substituted into the equation, makes it a true statement. Students may need to be "walked through" the result of Ex. 37 in particular.

Portfolio Opportunity: Math Log

The strategy for solving equations with variables on both sides involves collecting variables on the side with the term that has the greater variable coefficient. Is this a rule which must be followed or just a suggestion? Explain your answer.

Also available as a copymaster, p. 14, Ex. 6

Alternative Assessment

A problem-solving project that develops equation-solving skills.

Available as a copymaster, p. 21

28. Geometry Find the value of x so that the triangle is equilateral. 7

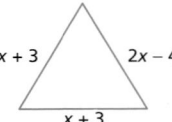

$x + 3$ $2x - 4$
$x + 3$

29. Geometry Find the value of x so that the figure is a square. $4\frac{3}{4}$

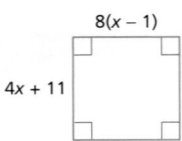

$8(x - 1)$
$4x + 11$

Rabbit versus Turtle **In Exercises 30–32, use the following information.**

A rabbit and a turtle are in a race. The rabbit is running 25 feet per second and the turtle is running 0.15 feet per second. The turtle was given a head start of 1000 feet. How long will it take the rabbit to catch up to the turtle? (Let t represent the time in seconds.)

✪ **30.** Which equation is a correct model for this problem? b
   a. $0.15t = 25t + 1000$
   b. $25t = 0.15t + 1000$
   c. $0.15t - 1000 = 25t$

✪ **31.** Solve the correct equation in Exercise 30 and interpret the result. ≈ 40.24 seconds

✪ **32.** If the race is 1010 feet long, who will win? Rabbit

The Lower Keys Rabbit is found in the Florida Keys. It is just one of 37 mammals in the United States that is on the endangered species list.

Integrated Review   *Making Connections within Mathematics*

Magic Squares **In Exercises 33 and 34, fill in the squares so that the sum of the integers in each row, column, and diagonal is the same.**

33.

1		
	2	
5		3

6, −1
0, 4
−2

34.

−5		
	−4	
−6		−3

−5, −2
−1, −7
−3

Exploration and Extension

Equation Sense **In Exercises 35–38, match the equation with the number of solutions. Explain your reasoning.** For explanations, see margin.

   a. No solution   **b.** Exactly one solution
   c. Exactly two solutions   **d.** Many solutions

✪ **35.** $10x + 35 = 5(7 + 2x)$ d   ✪ **36.** $3x + (1 - x) = 2x$ a
✪ **37.** $2|x| + 1 = 5$ c   ✪ **38.** $4x + 7 = 2 - x$ b

Answers
35. The equation is true for any value of x.
36. It simplifies to $1 = 0$.
37. Only 2 and -2 satisfy the equation.
38. Only -1 satisfies the equation.

▶ **Enrichment**

The following formula can be used as a "universal calendar" with which you can determine the day of the week for any date in history, where S is the sum and d is the day of the month. m is the month, with March $= 3$ and the following February $= 14$. y is the year, except for January and February dates when the number for the previous year is used. For expressions enclosed with square braces, [ ], use only the whole number part of the quotient and discard the remainder.

$S = d + 2m + [(3m + 3) \div 5] + y + [\frac{y}{4}]$
$- [\frac{y}{100}] + [\frac{y}{400}] + 2$

Example: What day of the week was December 24, 1976?
$d = 24, m = 12, y = 1976$
$S = 24 + 2(12) + [(3(12) + 3) \div 5] +$
$1976 + [\frac{1976}{4}] - [\frac{1976}{100}] + [\frac{1976}{400}] + 2$
$= 24 + 24 + 7 + 1976 + 494 - 19 + 4$
$+ 2 = 2512$
Now divide 2512 by 7 and write the remainder R.
$R = 0$ is Saturday, $R = 1$ is Sunday, and so on.
$\frac{2512}{7} = 358 \text{ R}6$

So, December 24, 1976 was a Friday. See whether the formula works for today's date.

Problem Solving Strategies

What you should learn:

Goal 1 How to use tables and graphs to solve real-life problems

Goal 2 How to use a general problem-solving plan

Why you should learn it:

To be an efficient problem solver, you should be able to solve real-life problems in more than one way.

Real Life
Nutrition

Goal 1 Using Tables and Graphs

When solving a real-life problem, remember that there are usually several ways to solve the problem. Often, it helps to solve the problem in more than one way and then compare results.

Example 1 *Using Tables and Graphs*

In 1970, Americans drank an average of 31 gallons of milk and 24 gallons of soda pop. For the next 20 years, milk consumption dropped by 0.26 gallons a year, and soda pop consumption increased by 0.89 gallons a year. During which year did Americans drink the same amount of each?

Solution The table shows the consumptions for 3-year intervals. During each 3-year interval milk consumption decreased by 3(0.26) or 0.78 gallons, and soda pop consumption increased by 3 (0.89) or 2.67 gallons.

Year	1970	1973	1976	1979	1982	1985	1988	1991
Milk	31.00	30.22	29.44	28.66	27.88	27.10	26.32	25.54
Soda	24.00	26.67	29.34	32.01	34.68	37.35	40.02	42.69

From the table, you can see that the consumption of milk and soda pop was about the same in 1976. A graph of the data in the table helps you visualize the two consumption rates.

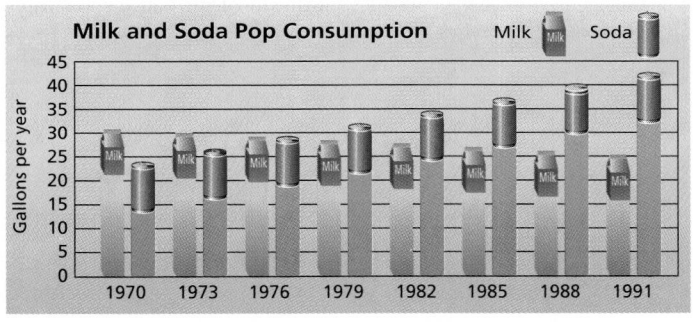

Milk and Soda Pop Consumption

■

▶ **PACING the Lesson**

Suggested Number of Days
Basic/Average 2 **Above Average** 1
Advanced 1

▶ **PLANNING the Lesson**

Lesson Plan 4.6, p. 31

ORGANIZER

Starters (reproduced below)
   Problem of the Day 4.6, p. 11
   Warm-Up Exercises 4.6, p. 11

Lesson Resources
   Color Transparencies
     Graph for Example 1, p. 17
   Math Log, pp. 14, 15
   Technology, p. 19
   Answer Masters 4.6, pp. 80, 81
   Extra Practice Copymaster 4.6, p. 31
   Reteaching Copymaster 4.6, p. 31

Special Populations
   Suggestions, Teacher's Edition, p. 146D

LESSON Notes

Real-life situations seldom indicate the type of mathematics needed to solve them. When we pose problems, we should avoid indicating the strategies that should be applied. Allow students flexibility in the way they attack problems. Encourage them to use strategies that reflect their understanding of the situation.

Example 1

Ask students: Would the results be the same if we looked at the consumption rates in 1-year intervals? In 2-year intervals? In 5-year intervals? Use this as a class discussion.

You may also wish to discuss the advantages and disadvantages of each method of displaying the results of this survey. See if there is a class consensus.

| **STARTER: Problem of the Day** |

Write any 3-digit number, for example, 692. Now form a 6-digit number by repeating the digits—692,692. Divide by 13. Divide by 11. Divide by 7. What do you notice? Explain this result.
The result is the original number because
$692 \times (13 \times 11 \times 7) = 692 \times 1001$
$= 692 (1000 + 1) = 692 \times 1000 + 692 \times 1$
$= 692,692.$

Also available as a copymaster, p. 11

| **STARTER: Warm-Up Exercises** |

1. What are the three steps of algebraic modeling? Write a verbal model, assign labels, write an algebraic model.

2. Using your math journal entry, indicate the last three steps of a general problem-solving plan. Solve the algebraic model, answer the original question, and check that your answer is reasonable.

3. Solve.
a. $51 - 3m = 26 + 2m$
b. $123 + 13x = 198 - 12x$
a. $m = 5,$ **b.** $x = 3$

Also available as a copymaster, p. 11

Be sure students have recorded the general problem-solving plan in their math journal. Although not shown in the flowchart at the top of the page, the final step in any problem-solving plan is to check the reasonableness of the answer.

Example 2

Take plenty of time to discuss the meaning of the initial verbal model. Return to the original statement of the problem. Milk consumption *decreased* from the 1970 average at a constant rate. How this decrease affected the milk consumption in a given *time* is expressed in the left side of the verbal model. During the *same* time, soda consumption *increased* from the 1970 average at a constant rate, and how this increase affected the soda consumption is expressed in the right side of the verbal model.

The time referred to is that particular time it takes to give equal values on each side of the equation. When students are comfortable with the verbal equation, proceed to discuss the labels. Note that the second label refers to milk rate of *decrease*. Be sure to explain the significance of *t* as the time elapsed since 1970. Finally, discuss how the algebraic equation is put together using the labels.

Communicating *about* MATHEMATICS

EXTENSION
You may wish to demonstrate the versatility of an algebraic model by generating further questions about this situation. For example, ask students how the model could be used to find the year in which soda pop consumption would approximately double milk consumption (at $t \approx 27$, or 1997). Encourage students to discuss the assumptions made in applying the model, the factors affecting realistic sampling (summer consumption versus winter consumption, and so on).

Writing Prompt
Write a bumper sticker slogan that would describe this chapter.

Problem Solving

Real Life
Nutrition

In Lesson 2.8, you studied a general problem-solving plan.

$$\boxed{\text{Write a verbal model.}} \rightarrow \boxed{\text{Assign labels.}} \rightarrow \boxed{\text{Write an algebraic model.}} \rightarrow \boxed{\text{Solve algebraic model.}} \rightarrow \boxed{\text{Answer the question.}} \rightarrow \boxed{\text{Check}}$$

Example 2 shows how to use this plan to solve the problem given in Example 1.

Example 2   *Using a Problem-Solving Plan*

Show how to use the general problem-solving plan to solve the "milk and soda pop problem" described in Example 1.

Solution

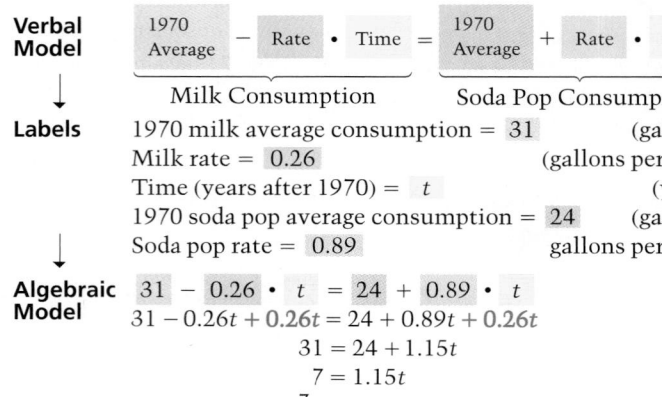

Verbal Model

$$\boxed{\text{1970 Average}} - \boxed{\text{Rate}} \cdot \boxed{\text{Time}} = \boxed{\text{1970 Average}} + \boxed{\text{Rate}} \cdot \boxed{\text{Time}}$$

$\underbrace{\qquad\qquad}_{\text{Milk Consumption}}$ $\underbrace{\qquad\qquad}_{\text{Soda Pop Consumption}}$

Labels
1970 milk average consumption = 31 (gallons)
Milk rate = 0.26 (gallons per year)
Time (years after 1970) = t (years)
1970 soda pop average consumption = 24 (gallons)
Soda pop rate = 0.89 gallons per year

Algebraic Model
$$31 - 0.26 \cdot t = 24 + 0.89 \cdot t$$
$$31 - 0.26t + 0.26t = 24 + 0.89t + 0.26t$$
$$31 = 24 + 1.15t$$
$$7 = 1.15t$$
$$\frac{7}{1.15} = t$$
$$6 \approx t$$

Because $t \approx 6$, it follows that Americans drank the same amount of milk and soda pop in 1976. ∎

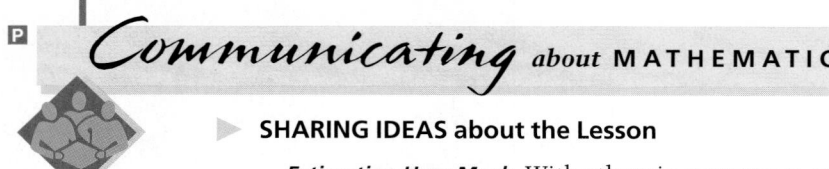

Communicating *about* MATHEMATICS

Cooperative Learning

▶ **SHARING IDEAS about the Lesson**

Estimating How Much With others in your group, estimate the number of gallons of milk and soda pop that you drink in a year. Answers vary.

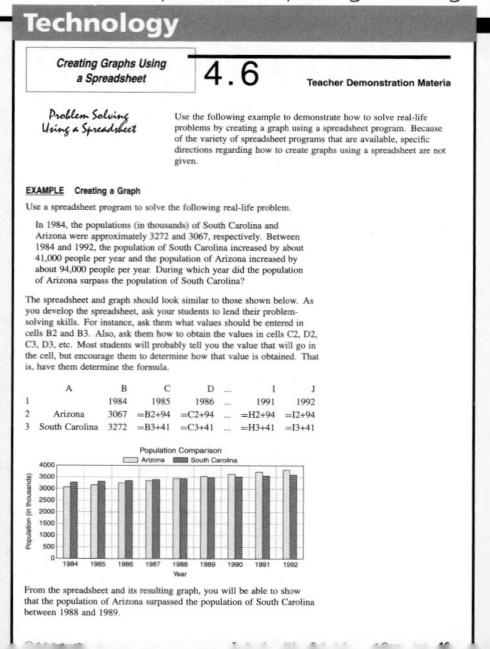

EXERCISES

Guided Practice

▶ **CHECK for Understanding**

1. *Writing*   In your own words, describe the general problem-solving plan. Answers vary.

Using a Problem-Solving Plan   **In Exercises 2–5, use the following.**

You are 60 inches tall and your cousin is 56 inches tall. Your cousin is growing at a rate of $\frac{4}{3}$ inch per year and you are growing at a rate of $\frac{1}{3}$ inch per year. When will you be the same height?

Your height now	+	Your rate of growth	·	Number of years	=	Cousin's height now	+	Cousin's rate of growth	·	Number of years
60 in.		$\frac{1}{3}$ in. per yr		n yr		56 in.		$\frac{4}{3}$ in. per yr		n yr

2. Assign labels to each part of the verbal model. Indicate the units of measure.

3. Write an algebraic model. $60 + \frac{1}{3}n = 56 + \frac{4}{3}n$

4. Solve the algebraic model. 4

5. When will you be the same height?
In 4 years

Independent Practice

6.–8. See Additional Answers.

Temperature   **In Exercises 6–12, use the following.**

At 3:00 P.M., the temperature is 86°F in Santa Fe, New Mexico, and is decreasing at a rate of 3 degrees per hour. At the same time, the temperature is 56°F in Minot, North Dakota, and is increasing at a rate of 2 degrees per hour. When will the temperatures be the same?

6. Show how to use a table and graph to solve the problem.

7. Write a verbal model.

8. Assign labels to each part of the model.

9. Write an algebraic model. $86 - 3h = 56 + 2h$

10. Solve the algebraic model. 6

11. How long will it take for the temperatures to be the same? 6 hours

12. At what time will the temperatures be the same? 9 P.M.

13. *It's Up to You*   You are considering joining one of two karate clubs in your area. At Club 1, there is no membership fee and lessons cost $6.00 per hour. At Club 2, there is an annual membership fee of $30, and lessons cost $4.50 per hour. Explain how you would decide which club to join.
Club 1 is cheaper for less than 20 hours, Club 2 is cheaper for more than 20 hours.

The temperature in the desert can drop as much as 80°F at night.

4.6 ▪ *Problem Solving Strategies*   **175**

EXERCISE Notes

ASSIGNMENT GUIDE

Basic/Average:
  Day 1: Ex. 6–13, 15, 17–19
  Day 2: Ex. 14, 16, 20–25
Above Average:
  Ex. 6–12, 14, 15, 20–25
Advanced: Ex. 6–12, 14, 15, 20–25
Selected Answers: Ex. 1–5, 7–23 odd

Guided Practice

▶ **Ex. 2–5**   Use these exercises as a small-group activity in order to summarize the lesson. Tour the room as groups share and compare.

Independent Practice

▶ **Ex. 6–12**   Assign these exercises as a group.

14. *Interactive CDs*   You want to join an interactive CD club to buy interactive books on compact discs. Your friend says that it is more economical to buy the CDs from a bookstore. You decide to consider your options. The CD club has a membership fee of $50 and each interactive book costs $25. The bookstore charges $35 for each interactive book.

a. See margin.
d. See Additional Answers.

a. Complete the table and interpret the results.

Number of CDs, x	1	2	3	4	5	6	7	8	9	10
Bookstore Cost ($)	?	?	?	?	?	?	?	?	?	?
CD Club Cost ($)	?	?	?	?	?	?	?	?	?	?

b. How many CDs do you have to buy for the costs of both options to be the same? 5

c. Is your friend correct? (S)he is if you buy more than 5, otherwise (s)he is not.

d. Show how the problem can be solved with a bar graph.

15. *Geometry*   The perimeters of the regular hexagon and the square shown below are equal. Find the side lengths and perimeter of each figure.

Hexagon: 8, 48
Square: 12, 48

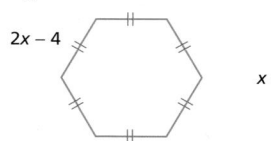
$2x - 4$

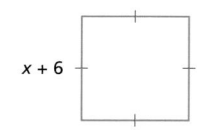
$x + 6$

16. *Breaking Even*   You own a small business that produces skateboards. You want to determine how many skateboards must be sold to break even. Your costs are $1500 plus $15 in materials for each skateboard. You sell each skateboard for $32. To break even, your total cost must be equal to your total income. Use the following model to find the number of skateboards you must sell to break even.

89

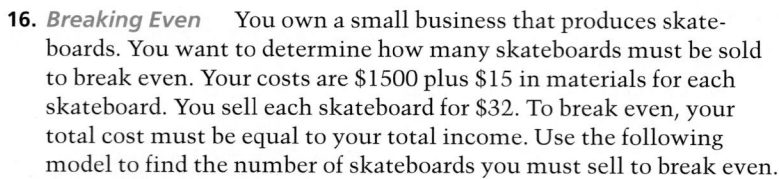

Total Cost	=	Total Income

$$\$1500 + 15 \cdot \text{Number sold} = 32 \cdot \text{Number sold}$$

Integrated Review   *Making Connections within Mathematics*

Equation Sense   In Exercises 17–22, solve the equation. Check your solution.

17. $6x + 12 = 84$ 12

18. $-3x - 25 = -4$ -7

19. $-4y + 10 + 7y = 37$ 9

20. $11y + 16 + 5y = -44$ $-3\frac{3}{4}$

21. $m + 2(m - 3) = 4m + 2$ -8

22. $9 - 2(n + 1) = 10 - 3n$ 3

Verbal Phrases   In Exercises 23 and 24, write an algebraic expression that represents the verbal phrase.

23. The change in temperature in h hours when it decreases at a rate of 7° per hour. $-7h$

24. The change in speed in s seconds when it increases at a rate of 6 feet per second. $6s$

Exploration and Extension

25. *Logic Puzzle*   Bev, Kim, Lee, Ron, and Sue each have a favorite sport. No two of them have the same favorite sport. Copy the table below. Then use the clues to determine their favorite sports. (Hint: In each box, put a O for true and an X for false.)

  a. Ron's favorite sport is not basketball.

  b. Bev does not like basketball or soccer.

  c. Sue's favorite sport is volleyball.

  d. Kim does not like golf.

  e. Lee's favorite sport is the sport that Kim does not like.

  f. Three of the sports are basketball, soccer, and tennis.

Sue: volleyball, Lee: golf, Bev: tennis, Ron: soccer, Kim: basketball

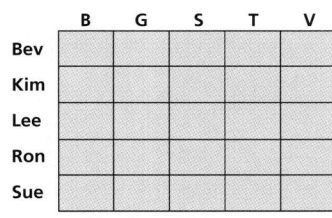

B=basketball, G=golf,
S=soccer, T=tennis,
V=volleyball

Mixed R E V I E W

In Exercises 1–8, solve the equation. (4.5)

1. $4a = 28$ 7

2. $6 - 9x = -48$ 6

3. $4.5r - 2 = 7$ 2

4. $12x + 3x = 30$ 2

5. $3a = 2 + 2a$ 2

6. $14s - 6 = 12s$ 3

7. $z + 2(4 - z) = 4$ 4

8. $\frac{4}{3}p = \frac{12}{3} + \frac{2}{3}p$ 6

In Exercises 9–12, write the verbal sentence as an algebraic equation and solve. (4.3)

9. Six times a number is 3. $6n = 3, \frac{1}{2}$

10. The sum of $3x$ and 2 is $8x$. $3x + 2 = 8x, \frac{2}{5}$

11. $5x$ is the difference of 1 and x. $5x = 1 - x, \frac{1}{6}$

12. 2 times the sum of x and 2 is $-x$. $2(x + 2) = -x, -1\frac{1}{3}$

In Exercises 13 and 14, find the average of the numbers. (3.6)

13. 14, 24, 20, 12, 17, 22, 7, 20 17

14. $-2.4, 1.1, 2.7, -1.4, -0.5$ -0.1

In Exercises 15–20, solve the inequality. (2.9)

15. $2x \geq 1$ $x \geq \frac{1}{2}$

16. $7y < 28$ $y < 4$

17. $48 < 16y$ $y > 3$

18. $3c < 21$ $c < 7$

19. $\frac{r}{4} \geq 6$ $r \geq 24$

20. $0.2p \leq 12$ $p \leq 60$

⊙ More difficult exercises

4.6 • *Problem Solving Strategies*   **177**

PACING the Lesson

Suggested Number of Days
Basic/Average 0 **Above Average** 1
Advanced 1

PLANNING the Lesson

Lesson Plan 4.7, p. 32

ORGANIZER

Starters (reproduced below)
Problem of the Day 4.7, p. 12
Warm-Up Exercises 4.7, p. 12
Lesson Resources
Color Transparencies
Picture for Ex. 35, p. 18
Math Log, p. 15
Answer Masters 4.7, p. 83
Extra Practice Copymaster 4.7, p. 32
Reteaching Copymaster 4.7, p. 32
Special Populations
Suggestions, Teacher's Edition, p. 146D

LESSON Notes

Having students work the Warm-Up Exercises
will help them review decimal numbers for
this lesson. Emphasize how the place value
system of whole numbers is extended to
decimal numbers. Use the following table to
have students identify the pattern moving
from left to right.

Thousands	Hundreds	Tens	Ones
1000	100	10	1

Tenths	Hundredths	Thousandths
0.1	0.01	0.001

Each place value is $\frac{1}{10}$ of the place value on its left.

Example 1

Ask students to give reasons for each step of
the solution. Discuss the checking of the
answer. Ask students how this check is different from others that we have done. In this
check, the left side does not turn out to be identical
to the right side; the two sides are equal only when
rounded to two decimal places.

4.7 Solving Equations Using Technology

What you should learn:

Goal 1 How to solve equations involving round-
ing with decimals

Goal 2 How to use a table to
solve problems

Why you should learn it:

Many real-life problems involve
decimal amounts, such as
money, distances, and averages.

Technology
Using a Calculator

Goal 1 Equations Involving Decimals

LESSON INVESTIGATION

■ **Investigating Round-Off Error**

Group Activity In the following solutions, the red numbers
are rounded to 2 decimal places. Which solution is more
accurate? What does that tell you about rounding before
the final step? See answer at left.

Rounding Early	Rounding at Final Step
$0.12(3.45x - 2.80) = 9.45$	$0.12(3.45x - 2.80) = 9.45$
$0.414x - 0.336 = 9.45$	$0.414x - 0.336 = 9.45$
$0.41x - 0.34 \approx 9.45$	$0.414x = 9.786$
$0.41x \approx 9.79$	$x = \frac{9.786}{0.414}$
$x \approx \frac{9.79}{0.41}$	$x \approx 23.64$
$x \approx 23.88$	

The second, you get a less accurate
solution. (23.88 yields 9.55032,
while 23.64 yields 9.45096.)

Example 1 *Solving an Equation*

Solve $3.56x + 4.78 = 2.69(1.20x - 4.18)$. Round the solution to
2 decimal places.

Solution

$$3.56x + 4.78 = 2.69(1.20x - 4.18)$$
$$3.56x + 4.78 = 3.228x - 11.2442$$
$$3.56x + 4.78 - 3.228x = 3.228x - 11.2442 - 3.228x$$
$$0.332x + 4.78 = -11.2442$$
$$0.332x + 4.78 - 4.78 = -11.2442 - 4.78$$
$$0.332x = -16.0242$$
$$\frac{0.332x}{0.332} = \frac{-16.0242}{0.332}$$
$$x \approx -48.26 \quad \text{\textit{Round to 2 decimal places.}}$$

The solution is ≈ -48.26. Check this in the original equation. ■

STARTER: Problem of the Day

The Magic of 1089
Write any 3-digit number with three
different digits.

Sample:	489
Reverse the digits.	984
Subtract the smaller from the larger.	495
Reverse the digits.	594
Add these last two numbers.	1089

Repeat the process with another number. Will the result always be 1089? Yes.

Also available as a copymaster, p. 12

STARTER: Warm-Up Exercises

1. Use your calculator to compute.
a. $0.42 + 0.032$ b. $3.1(0.03 - 0.823)$
c. $4.303 + 6.87 - 11.03 + 1.003$
d. $\frac{3.024 - 2.16}{0.8}$
a. 0.452, b. −2.4583, c. 1.146, d. 1.08

2. Round each answer in Exercise 1 to
the nearest hundredth.
a. 0.45, b. −2.46, c. 1.15, d. 1.08
(The Integrated Review exercises on
page 181 can also be used as a 3-minute
warm-up for this lesson.)

Also available as a copymaster, p. 12

Solving Problems with a Table

Real Life
Telephone Costs

Example 2   *Using a Table*

You are making a long-distance call to a friend. The call costs $3.56 for the first minute and $1.68 for each additional minute. You don't want to spend more than $20.00 on the call. How long can you talk?

Solution

Verbal Model

$$\text{Cost} = \boxed{\begin{array}{c}\text{Cost of first minute}\end{array}} + \boxed{\begin{array}{c}\text{Addl. minute rate}\end{array}} \cdot \boxed{\begin{array}{c}\text{Number of addl. minutes}\end{array}}$$

Labels

Cost = C	(dollars)
Cost of first minute = 3.56	(dollars)
Additional minute rate = 1.68	(dollars per minute)
Number of additional minutes = t	(minutes)

Algebraic Model

$$C = 3.56 + 1.68 \cdot t$$

You want to find the values of t such that C is less than or equal to $20.00. One way to do this is with a table. From the table, you can see that you can talk for up to 10 minutes (1 minute plus 9 additional minutes).

Almost all Americans live in homes with phones. Nearly half, however, choose to not have their phone number listed in the telephone book. (Source: Maritz Marketing Service, Inc.)

Additional minutes	1	2	3	4	5
Cost (dollars)	5.24	6.92	8.60	10.28	11.96

Additional minutes	6	7	8	9	10
Cost (dollars)	13.64	15.32	17.00	18.68	20.36

■

Communicating about MATHEMATICS

▶ **SHARING IDEAS about the Lesson**

Extending the Example You often make telephone calls to your cousin who lives in another state. Which long-distance company would you choose? Explain your reasoning.
See margin.
- **Company A** charges $1.48 for the first minute and $0.74 for each additional minute.
- **Company B** charges $2.74 for the first minute and $0.68 for each additional minute.

4.7 ▪ *Solving Equations Using Technology*   **179**

PROBLEM SOLVING
Remind students once again that in problem solving, usually several approaches are possible. Remind them that in previous chapters we have solved problems by inspecting tables and geometric patterns, by manipulating concrete materials, and by using our algebraic modeling plan. Example 2 combines algebraic modeling with the strategy of making a table.

Example 2
Have students show that the solution also can be obtained algebraically without using the table. Refer them to Lesson 2.9, in which we solved simple inequalities. Here, we use the inequality $3.56 + 1.68t < 20$, which has the solution $t < 9.8$. Since charges relate to whole minutes, this solution is equivalent to $t < 10$. So, talking for 9 minutes will cost less than $20.

Communicating
about MATHEMATICS

PROJECT
Suggest this as a project. Have students research telephone ads in your local newspaper and compare their cost plans, using the techniques presented in the lesson.

Writing Prompt
Examine the local newspaper and find an article or advertisement containing information similar to that presented in Ex. 35 on page 181. Identify a distance, rate, or time, and attach the newspaper article.

Answer to Communicating
When a call is 22 minutes, the two companies charge the same amount. Company A should be chosen when the calls are shorter than 22 minutes, and Company B should be chosen when the calls are longer than 22 minutes.

ASSIGNMENT GUIDE

*Basic/Average:
   Day 1: Ex. 5, 6, 7–21 odd
   Day 2: Ex. 23–26, 27–35 odd

Above Average:
   Ex. 5–21 odd, 25, 26, 27–35 odd

Advanced: Ex. 5–21 odd, 25, 26, 27–35 odd

Selected Answers: Ex. 1–4, 5–33 odd

*You may wish to omit this lesson for these students.

Guided Practice

▶ **Ex. 1, 3, 4** These exercises ask for student explanations and provide a good opportunity for assessing students' understanding of the difference between approximate and exact answers. To summarize the lesson, have students work in pairs using these exercises as a "think/share" activity.

Independent Practice

▶ **Ex. 7–20**

Common-Error Alert!

Remind students of the potential error of rounding off numbers too early in the process. Refer them to the investigation on page 178.

▶ **Ex. 21, 22** Be aware that students are used to seeing sales tax as a percent rather than a decimal. Remind them of the equivalence of 0.06 and 6%.

180 *Chapter 4*

EXERCISES

Guided Practice

▶ **CHECK for Understanding**

1. *Reasoning* Which of the following solutions of $9x = 1$ is more likely to have been obtained using a calculator or computer? Why?   a, because it is in decimal form
   a. $x \approx 0.111$ **b.** $x = \frac{1}{9}$

2. Solve $0.25(3.2x + 4.1) = 7.2$. Round the result to two decimal places.   7.72

3. Explain the difference between $x = 2.5$ and $x \approx 2.5$.   1st: exact, 2nd: approximate

4. *Measurement Sense* The total weight of 11 people is 1204 pounds. Which of the following is the better way to list their average weight? Why?   b, a person's weight varies at least a tenth of a pound each day.
   a. 109.45455 pounds   **b.** 109.5 pounds

Independent Practice

Error Analysis **In Exercises 5 and 6, describe the error. Write a correct solution.**   5., 6. Rounding was done too early (in 2nd step).

5. $1.1(2.5x - 3.5) = 11.2$
   $2.8x - 3.9 = 11.2$
   $2.8x = 15.1$
   $x \approx 5.39$ ~ 5.47

6. $0.26(2.39x - 4.91) = 10.64$
   $0.62x - 1.28 = 10.64$
   $0.62x = 11.92$
   $x = 19.23$ ~ 19.18

In Exercises 7–20, use a calculator to solve the equation. Round your result to two decimal places.

7. $3x + 12 = 17$ 1.67
8. $13y + 22 = 16$ −0.46
9. $29t - 17 = -86$ −2.38
10. $15 - 11x = 108$ −8.45
11. $6(4x - 12) = 8x + 9$ 5.06
12. $13x - 22 = 2(9x + 10)$ −8.4
13. $1.3y + 22.1 = 12.9$ −7.08
14. $-7.4m + 36.4 = 9.5$ 3.64
15. $0.15(9.85x + 3.70) = 4.65$ 2.77
16. $2.16(3.47x - 8.60) = 17.59$ 4.83
17. $0.19t - 1.57 = 0.46t$ −5.81
18. $2.4x + 13.7 = 8.1x - 22.5$ 6.35
19. $3.14x + 17.5 = 9.77x + 24.1$ −1.00
20. $19.5(13.3 - 4.4x) = 7.2(0.8x - 11.6)$ 3.74

21. *Sales Tax* You purchase an item. The sales tax rate is 0.06 and the total cost of the item is $6.35. Let p represent the price of the item (not including sales tax). Solve the following equation to find the price of the item. $5.99
   $$p + 0.06p = 6.35$$

22. *Sales Tax* You purchase an item. The sales tax rate is 0.05 and the total cost of the item is $2.62. Let p represent the price of the item (not including sales tax). Solve the following equation to find the price of the item. $2.50
   $$p + 0.05p = 2.62$$

180   *Chapter 4 ▪ Exploring the Language of Algebra*

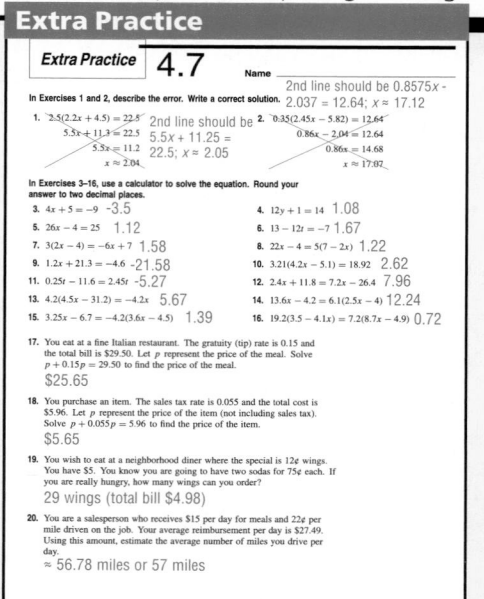

Extra Practice

Extra Practice 4.7 Name _____

2nd line should be 0.8575x −
In Exercises 1 and 2, describe the error. Write a correct solution. 2.037 = 12.64; x ≈ 17.12

1. $2.5(2.2x + 4.5) = 22.5$ 2nd line should be
   $5.5x + 11.3 = 22.5$ $5.5x + 11.25 =$
   $5.5x = 11.2$ $22.5; x \approx 2.05$
   $x \approx 2.04$

2. $0.35(2.45x - 5.82) = 12.64$
   $0.86x - 2.04 = 12.64$
   $0.86x = 14.68$
   $x \approx 17.02$

In Exercises 3–16, use a calculator to solve the equation. Round your answer to two decimal places.

3. $4x + 5 = -9$ −3.5
4. $12y + 1 = 14$ 1.08
5. $26x - 4 = 25$ 1.12
6. $13 - 12t = -7$ 1.67
7. $3(2x - 4) = -6x + 7$ 1.58
8. $22x - 4 = 5(7 - 2x)$ 1.22
9. $1.2x + 21.3 = -4.6$ −21.58
10. $3.21(4.2x - 5.1) = 18.92$ 2.62
11. $0.25t - 11.6 = 2.45t$ −5.27
12. $2.4x + 11.8 = 7.2x - 26.4$ 7.96
13. $4.2(4.5x - 31.2) = -4.2x$ 5.67
14. $13.6x - 4.2 = 6.1(2.5x - 4)$ 12.24
15. $3.25x - 6.7 = -4.2(3.6x - 4.5)$ 1.39
16. $19.2(3.5 - 4.1x) = 7.2(8.7x - 4.9)$ 0.72

17. You eat at a fine Italian restaurant. The gratuity (tip) rate is 0.15 and the total bill is $29.50. Let p represent the price of the meal. Solve $p + 0.15p = 29.50$ to find the price of the meal.
   $25.65

18. You purchase an item. The sales tax rate is 0.055 and the total cost is $5.96. Let p represent the price of the item (not including sales tax). Solve $p + 0.055p = 5.96$ to find the price of the item.
   $5.65

19. You wish to eat at a neighborhood diner where the special is 12¢ wings. You have $5. You know you are going to have two sodas for 75¢ each. If you are really hungry, how many wings can you order?
   29 wings (total bill $4.98)

20. You are a salesperson who receives $15 per day for meals and 22¢ per mile driven on the job. Your average reimbursement per day is $27.49. Using this amount, estimate the average number of miles you drive per day.
   ≈ 56.78 miles or 57 miles

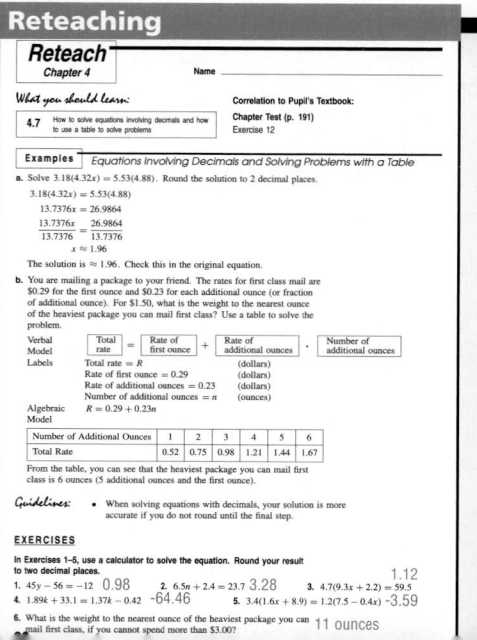

Reteaching

Reteach Chapter 4 Name _____

What you should learn:
   4.7 How to solve equations involving decimals and how to use a table to solve problems

Correlation to Pupil's Textbook:
   Chapter Test (p. 191)
   Exercise 12

Examples *Equations Involving Decimals and Solving Problems with a Table*

a. Solve $3.18(4.32x) = 5.53(4.88)$. Round the solution to 2 decimal places.
   $3.18(4.32x) = 5.53(4.88)$
   $13.7376x = 26.9864$
   $\frac{13.7376x}{13.7376} = \frac{26.9864}{13.7376}$
   $x \approx 1.96$

   The solution is ≈ 1.96. Check this in the original equation.

b. You are mailing a package to your friend. The rates for first class mail are $0.29 for the first ounce and $0.23 for each additional ounce (or fraction of additional ounce). For $1.50, what is the weight to the nearest ounce of the heaviest package you can mail first class? Use a table to solve the problem.

Verbal Model	Total rate	=	Rate of first ounce	+	Rate of additional ounces	·	Number of additional ounces

Labels   Total rate = R   (dollars)
   Rate of first ounce = 0.29   (dollars)
   Rate of additional ounces = 0.23   (dollars)
   Number of additional ounces = n   (ounces)

Algebraic Model $R = 0.29 + 0.23n$

Number of Additional Ounces	1	2	3	4	5	6
Total Rate	0.52	0.75	0.98	1.21	1.44	1.67

From the table, you can see that the heaviest package you can mail first class is 6 ounces (5 additional ounces and the first ounce).

Guidelines: • When solving equations with decimals, your solution is more accurate if you do not round until the final step.

EXERCISES

In Exercises 1–5, use a calculator to solve the equation. Round your result to two decimal places.
1.12
1. $45y - 56 = -12$ 0.98
2. $6.5n + 2.4 = 23.7$ 3.28
3. $4.7(9.3x + 2.2) = 59.5$
4. $1.89x + 33.1 = 1.37x - 0.42$ −64.46
5. $3.4(1.6x + 8.9) = 1.2(7.5 - 0.4x)$ −3.59

6. What is the weight to the nearest ounce of the heaviest package you can mail first class, if you cannot spend more than $3.00?   11 ounces

Mailing a Letter **In Exercises 23 and 24, use the following information.**

You are mailing a letter with pictures inside to your friend. Postage costs $.29 for the first ounce and $.23 for each additional ounce. How heavy can your letter be if you have $2.00 to spend?

23. Write a verbal model for the problem. See Additional Answers.

24. Create a table similar to the one in Example 2 to solve the problem. 8 oz

Using a Label **In Exercises 25 and 26, use the following information.**

You are renting a car. The rental costs are $35 plus 23 cents per mile. You don't want to spend more than $140 on the car rental. How many miles can you drive the rental car?

25. Write a verbal model for the problem. See Additional Answers.

26. Create a table similar to the one in Example 2 to solve the problem. 456

Integrated Review
Making Connections within Mathematics

Computation Sense **In Exercises 27–30, use a calculator to evaluate the expression. Round the result to two decimal places.**

27. $(4.21)(16.07)$ 67.65 **28.** $(0.965)(19.68)$ 18.99 **29.** $31.02 \div 5.76$ 5.39 **30.** $21.555 \div 4.148$
  5.20

Verbal Phrases **In Exercises 31–34, use a calculator to evaluate the expression. Round the result to two decimal places.**

31. The square root of 4.52 2.13   **32.** The square of 4.52 20.43

33. 0.9 raised to the fifth power 0.59   **34.** The reciprocal of 0.3 3.33

Exploration and Extension

35. *The Daytona 500* The Daytona 500 is one of the most famous stock car races in the world. The race is 500 miles long. In 1994, the winner of the Daytona 500 finished the race in 3 hours, 11 minutes, and 10 seconds. What was the average speed in miles per hour of the winner? (*Hint:* Convert 11 minutes and 10 seconds to hours and use the distance formula, $d = rt$.) ≈ 156.93 mph

36. To determine race position, all drivers must run two laps of the 2.5 mile track. The faster of the two laps is recorded. In 1994, #1 pole position was won by Loy Allen at 190.158 miles per hour. What was his lap time in seconds? ≈ 47.33 seconds

The 1994 Daytona 500 winner, Sterling Marlin, won $253,575. It was his first victory in 279 races.

⊕ More difficult exercises

▶ **Ex. 25, 26**
EXTENSION
The model established in these exercises is linear, as in Example 2 of this lesson. Have students plot their table values to observe the linear trend.

Exploration and Extension

Have students work this exercise in their groups.

Portfolio Opportunity: Math Log

If the solution to an equation represents one of the following quantities, would you round off your answer to the integer, to one decimal place, or to two decimal places? Explain your answer.
a. price   **b.** population

Also available as a copymaster, p. 15, Ex. 9

Alternative Assessment

A cooperative learning project that develops appreciation for the effect of round-off error.

Available as a copymaster, p. 22

▶ **Enrichment**

TECHNOLOGY
If an overhead graphing calculator or computer is available, you can demonstrate solutions to Ex. 7–20 using the table or spreadsheet feature. Show how changing the decimal setting from "float" to 0, 1, 2, 3, 4, 5, or 6 decimal places changes the round-off error.

ORGANIZER

Starters (reproduced below)
    Problem of the Day 4.8, p. 12
    Warm-Up Exercises 4.8, p. 12
Lesson Resources
    Color Transparencies
        Map for Example 2, p. 18
    Teaching Tools
        Parallelogram, pp. T10, C13
        Dot paper, pp. T2, C3
    Math Log, p. 15
    Answer Masters 4.8, p. 84
    Extra Practice Copymaster 4.8, p. 33
    Reteaching Copymaster 4.8, p. 33
Special Populations
    Suggestions, Teacher's Edition, p. 146D

LESSON Notes

Ask students to sketch and label a square, a rectangle, and a parallelogram. Then have them state the formulas for the perimeter and area of each. Discuss how these formulas are alike. Then have students do the Lesson Investigation.

Example 1

Some students may prefer to switch the dimensions and let x represent the length. In this case, the expression for the width becomes $\frac{1}{2}(x+3)$ but, of course, the final solution is the same.

What you should learn:

Goal 1   How to use formulas from geometry to solve equations

Goal 2   How to use geometry formulas to solve real-life problems

Why you should learn it:

You can use formulas from geometry to model real-life problems, such as approximating the area of a city.

$$\text{Area} = \tfrac{1}{2}\,\text{base} \times \text{height}$$

Goal 1   **Using Formulas from Geometry**

The following investigation shows how you can use the formula for the area of a rectangle (Area = length × width) to find a formula for the area of a triangle.

LESSON INVESTIGATION

■ Investigating the Area of a Triangle

Group Activity Use dot paper to draw several triangles. (Two samples are shown below.) For each triangle, draw a rectangle whose area is twice the area of the triangle. Use the result to write a formula for the area of a triangle.

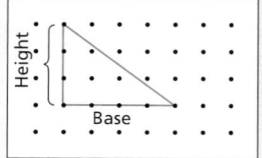
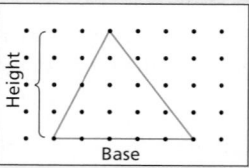

Example 1   *Finding the Dimensions of a Rectangle*

The length of a rectangle is 3 less than twice its width. The perimeter is 24 units. Find the dimensions of the rectangle.

Solution   Let x represent the width of the rectangle. Then the length of the rectangle is $2x - 3$.

Perimeter	= 2 ·	Width	+ 2 ·	Length

$$24 = 2 \cdot x + 2 \cdot (2x - 3)$$
$$24 = 2x + 4x - 6$$
$$30 = 6x$$
$$5 = x$$

The width is 5 units and the length is $2(5) - 3$ or 7 units. ■

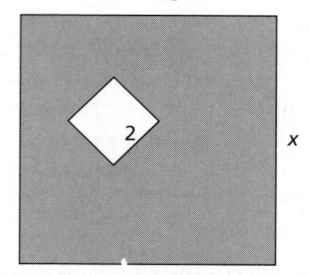
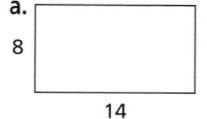

Goal 2 — Modeling Real Life with Formulas

Connections
Geometry

Example 2 — *Estimating an Area*

Use the map to approximate the area of Detroit, Michigan.

Solution One way to answer this question is to sketch a triangle whose area appears to be about the same as Detroit's area.

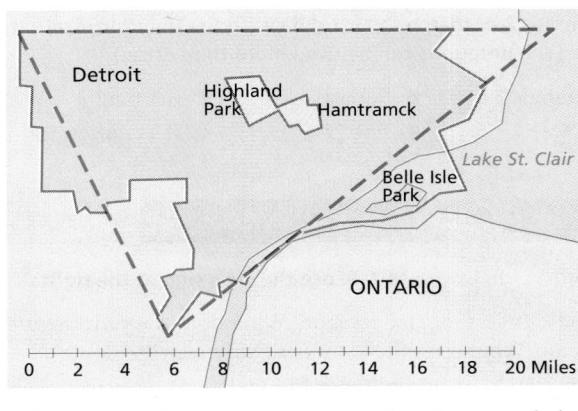

From the scale on the map, you can see that the triangle has a base of about 22 miles and a height of about 13 miles.

$$\text{Area of Detroit} \approx \text{Area of triangle}$$

$$\text{Area} = \tfrac{1}{2}(\text{base})(\text{height})$$
$$= \tfrac{1}{2}(22)(13)$$
$$= 143 \text{ square miles}$$

You can estimate Detroit's area to be about 143 square miles. ■

Detroit is the largest city in Michigan. It was founded in 1701 and is one of the world's greatest manufacturing centers.

Communicating about MATHEMATICS

▶ **SHARING IDEAS about the Lesson**

Comparing Perimeter and Area The triangle described in Example 2 gives a good approximation for the area of Detroit. (In fact, it is correct to the nearest square mile.) Do you think the triangle could be used to approximate the perimeter of Detroit? Explain your reasoning.

Explanations may be given to support "yes" or "no."

4.8 • *Formulas and Variables in Geometry* **183**

Students should be aware that in real-life measurement situations it is frequently easier to use an approximation such as the one used in Example 2.

Example 2

Demonstrate how the scale and a straight-edge can be used to measure the base and height of the triangle. Discuss, in terms of small areas excluded or included, why the given area of the triangle is a reasonable approximation of the area of Detroit.

Communicating about MATHEMATICS

This geometric discussion could be enlivened with graph paper or unit square diagrams such as the following.

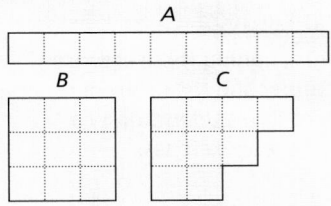

Writing Prompt
Describe what you liked best about this chapter and what you liked least.

OPTION: Extra Examples

Here is an additional example similar to Example 1.

Finding the Dimensions of a Rectangle
The width of a rectangle is 3 more than half its length. The perimeter is 30 units. Find the dimensions of the rectangle.

Solution
Let x represent the length of the rectangle. The width of the rectangle is $\frac{1}{2}x + 3$.

$$\text{Perimeter} = 2 \cdot \text{Length} + 2 \cdot \text{Width}$$
$$30 = 2x + 2(\tfrac{1}{2}x + 3)$$
$$30 = 2x + x + 6$$
$$30 = 3x + 6$$
$$24 = 3x$$
$$8 = x$$

The length is 8 units and the width is $\frac{1}{2}(8) + 3$ or 7 units.

ASSIGNMENT GUIDE

*Basic/Average:
  Day 1: Ex. 7–23 odd
  Day 2: Ex. 8–24 even, 25
Above Average:
  Ex. 7–9, 11–25 odd
Advanced: Ex. 7–9, 11–25 odd
Selected Answers: Ex. 1–6, 7–23 odd

*You may wish to omit this lesson for these students.

Guided Practice

▶ **Ex. 2–6** Use these exercises to discuss the word *polygon* in class with the students.

Independent Practice

▶ **Ex. 7–9** Before assigning these exercises, review the term *regular* and the prefix *octa*.
▶ **Ex. 10–15** Make sure students draw a diagram for each of these exercises.
▶ **Ex. 16–18**

Common-Error Alert!

Many students may simply find the value of *x*, without computing the measures of the angles.

Answers
2. The area of a square is the square of a side.
3. The perimeter of a rectangle is the sum of twice the length and twice the width.
4. The area of a triangle is one-half the product of the base and height.
5. The perimeter of a square is four times a side.
6. The area of a rectangle is the product of the base and height.
7. Regular: All sides are congruent and all angles are congruent. Octagon: A polygon with 8 sides.

EXERCISES

Guided Practice

▶ **CHECK for Understanding**

1. *Draw a Diagram* State a formula used in geometry. Sketch a figure that corresponds to the formula. Label the variables on the figure. Answers vary.

In Exercises 2–6, match the formula with the polygon. State the formula in words. (The polygons can be used more than once.) For words, see margin.

a. Triangle   **b.** Square   **c.** Rectangle

2. $A = s^2$ 3. $P = 2l + 2w$ 4. $A = \frac{1}{2}bh$ 5. $P = 4s$ 6. $A = bh$
   b   c (also b)   a   b   c (also b)

Independent Practice

Stop Sign   In Exercises 7–9, use the stop sign at the right.

7. The sign is a regular octagon. What does the term *regular* mean? What does the term *octagon* mean? See margin.
8. The sign has a perimeter of 126 inches. How long is each side? $15\frac{3}{4}$ in.
9. If each side were 16 inches long, what would the perimeter be? 128 in.

In Exercises 10–15, solve for *x* and find the dimensions of the polygon.

10. *Rectangle* 4
    Perimeter: 36 units
    Width: x 4 units
    Length: $4x - 2$ 14 units

11. *Rectangle* 3
    Perimeter: 58 units
    Width: $6x - 4$ 14 units
    Length: $3x + 6$ 15 units

12. *Square* 9
    Perimeter: 16 units
    Side: $x - 5$ 4 units

13. *Regular Pentagon* 5
    Perimeter: 90 units
    Side: $5x - 7$ 18 units

14. *Triangle* 7
    Area: 155 square units
    Height: 10 units
    Base: $3x + 10$ 31 units

15. *Rectangle* 8
    Area: 225 square units
    Width: 9 units
    Length: $2x + 9$ 25 units

Geometry   In Exercises 16–18, find the measure of each angle.

16. The sum of the measures of ∠1 and ∠2 is 90°.

    55°
    35°
    $7x - 1°$
    1
    2 $4x + 3°$

17. The sum of the measures of ∠1 and ∠2 is 180°.

    $112\frac{3}{11}°$ $67\frac{8}{11}°$
    $7x - 1°$ $4x + 3°$
    1 2

18. The sum of the measures of ∠1, ∠2, and ∠3 is 180°.

    1 74°
    $4x - 2°$
    2 $2x - 2°$ $3x + 13°$ 3
    36°

Extra Practice

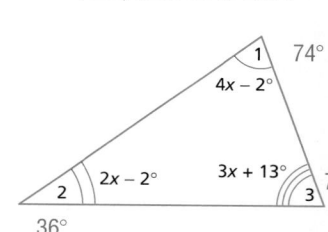

Extra Practice **4.8**   Name _____

In Exercises 1–3, solve for *x* and find the dimensions of the polygon.

1. Square
   Perimeter: 24 units
   Side: $x - 2$
   8; each side is 6 units.

2. Rectangle   4;
   Perimeter: 64 units width = 22;
   Width: $5x + 2$ length = 10
   Length: $3x - 2$

3. Regular Pentagon
   Perimeter: 65 units
   Side: $4x + 1$
   $x = 3$; each side is 13 units.

In Exercises 4 and 5, find the measures of each angle.

4. The sum of the measures of ∠1 and ∠2 is 180°.

   $3x - 5°$ $4x + 10°$
   $x = 25$; m∠1 = 70°,
   m∠2 = 110°

5. The sum of the measures of ∠1, ∠2, and ∠3 is 180°.

   $5x + 1°$ $4x - 6°$
   $3x + 3°$
   $x = 14$; m∠1 = 45°;
   m∠2 = 50°; m∠3 = 85°

6. Find the area of the swimming pool if the total swimming area, including the sidewalk, is 2400 square feet and the sidewalk is 3 feet wide.

   1836 square feet

7. Find the area of the triangle if the area of the rectangle is 120 square inches.

   52 square inches

8. Find the area of a rectangular tennis court if the perimeter is 480 feet. The length of the court is six feet more than twice the width.

   Perimeter = 480 feet
   12,636 square feet

9. Use the map below to approximate the area of Tennessee. Explain your method.

   TENNESSEE
   0 50 100
   Miles
   53,125 square miles;
   area of rectangle + area of triangle

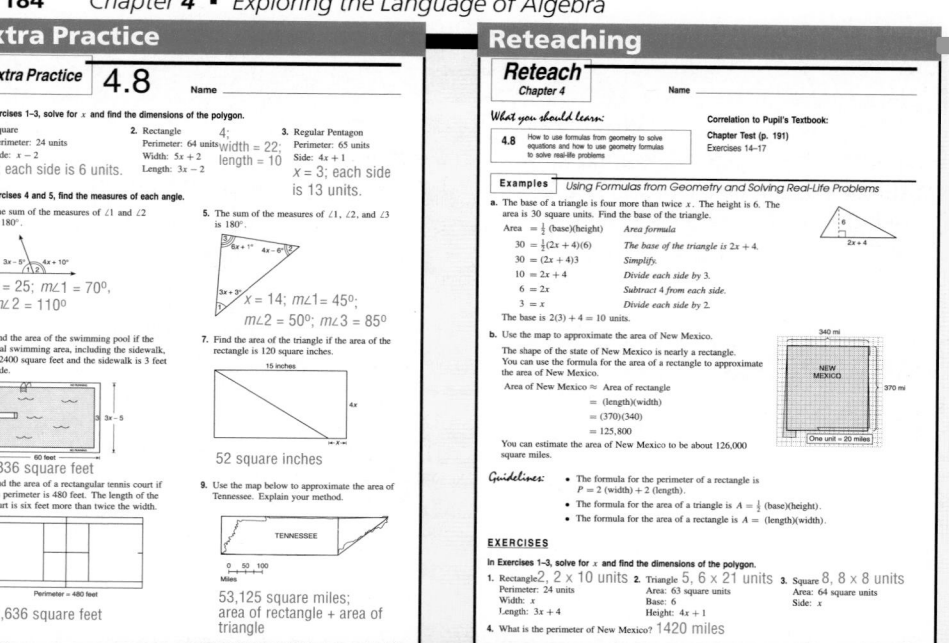

Reteaching

Reteach Chapter 4   Name _____

What you should learn:

| 4.8 | How to use formulas from geometry to solve equations and how to use geometry formulas to solve real-life problems |

Correlation to Pupil's Textbook:
Chapter Test (p. 191)
Exercises 14–17

Examples Using Formulas from Geometry and Solving Real-Life Problems

a. The base of a triangle is four more than twice *x*. The height is 6. The area is 30 square units. Find the base of the triangle.

Area $= \frac{1}{2}$(base)(height)   *Area formula*
$30 = \frac{1}{2}(2x + 4)(6)$ *The base of the triangle is 2x + 4.*
$30 = (2x + 4)3$ *Simplify.*
$10 = 2x + 4$ *Divide each side by 3.*
$6 = 2x$ *Subtract 4 from each side.*
$3 = x$ *Divide each side by 2.*
The base is 2(3) + 4 = 10 units.

b. Use the map to approximate the area of New Mexico.

The shape of the state of New Mexico is nearly a rectangle. You can use the formula for the area of a rectangle to approximate the area of New Mexico.

Area of New Mexico ≈ Area of rectangle
= (length)(width)
= (370)(340)
= 125,800

You can estimate the area of New Mexico to be about 126,000 square miles.

NEW MEXICO
340 mi
370 mi
One unit = 20 miles

Guidelines: • The formula for the perimeter of a rectangle is $P = 2$ (width) + 2 (length).
• The formula for the area of a triangle is $A = \frac{1}{2}$ (base)(height).
• The formula for the area of a rectangle is $A =$ (length)(width).

EXERCISES

In Exercises 1–3, solve for *x* and find the dimensions of the polygon.

1. Rectangle 2, 2 × 10 units
   Perimeter: 24 units
   Width: x
   Length: $3x + 4$

2. Triangle 5, 6 × 21 units
   Area: 63 square units
   Base: 6
   Height: $4x + 1$

3. Square 8, 8 × 8 units
   Area: 64 square units
   Side: x

4. What is the perimeter of New Mexico? 1420 miles

19. *Television Screen*   The region shown below has a total area of 285 square inches. Find the area of the television screen.

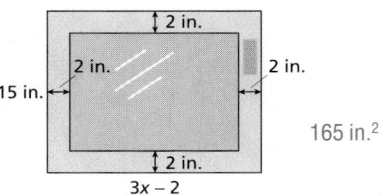

2 in.

2 in.   2 in.

15 in.

2 in.

3x − 2

165 in.²

20. *Bricklaying*   The fronts of the 7 bricks have a total area of 112 square inches. Find the dimensions of the front of each brick.

2 in. × 8 in.

(2x + 6) in.

2 in.

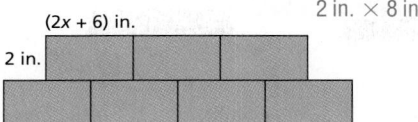

21. *Baseball Diamond*   The perimeter of a baseball diamond is 360 feet. Find the distance between 1st base and 2nd base.

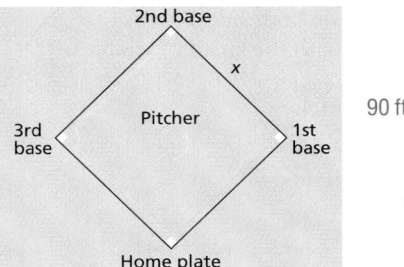

2nd base

x

3rd base

Pitcher

1st base

Home plate

90 ft

22. *Nevada*   Use the map below to approximate the area of Nevada. Explain your method.   See margin.

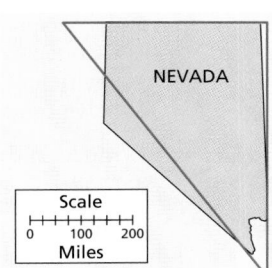

NEVADA

Scale

0   100   200

Miles

▶ **Ex. 22**   Remind students again of the technique of small areas included or excluded.

Integrated Review

Have students draw diagrams for these exercises.

Exploration and Extension

Use this exercise as a 5-minute in-class verification of the area formula for a parallelogram.

Portfolio Opportunity: Math Log

One-inch by one-inch squares are cut at the corners of an *s* by *s* square ($s > 2$). Find an algebraic expression that gives the perimeter of the resulting shape. How is this perimeter related to the perimeter of the *s* by *s* square?

Also available as a copymaster, p. 15, Ex. 10

Short Quiz

Covers Lessons 4.7 and 4.8

Available as a copymaster, p. 59

Alternative Assessment

Chapter 4 Group Assessment
An exploration for 3 or 4 students that leads to discovery of the area formula of an isosceles trapezoid.

Chapter 4 Individual Assessment
A similar follow-up activity for individual students. Adds incentive for the group activity and measures individual competence in the activity.

Available as copymasters, pp. 65, 66

Integrated Review

Making Connections within Mathematics

Perimeter   In Exercises 23 and 24, find the perimeter of the square.

23. The perimeter of a square that has the same area as a 2 × 8 rectangle.   16

24. The perimeter of a square that has the same area as a 4 × 16 rectangle.   32

Exploration and Extension

25. *Investigating the Area of a Parallelogram*
A parallelogram is a quadrilateral with its opposite sides parallel, as shown. Cut a parallelogram out of paper. Cut the parallelogram as shown and rearrange the pieces to form a rectangle. Use the result to write a formula for the area of a parallelogram.   Area = base × height

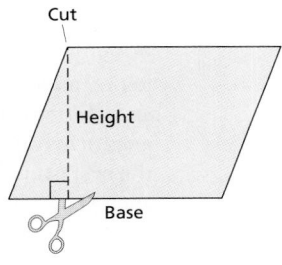

Cut

Height

Base

✪ More difficult exercises

4.8 • *Formulas and Variables in Geometry*   **185**

▶ **Enrichment**

There are triangular, square, and pentagonal numbers.

Based on these patterns, find the 5th triangular, square, and pentagonal numbers.

15, 25, 35

Triangular	Square	Pentagonal
1	1	1
3	4	5
6	9	12
10	16	22

Answer
22. 1 unit = 25 mi

Area of triangle is $\frac{1}{2}$ (16 units × 20.4 units)

$= \frac{1}{2}$ (400 mi × 510 mi) = 102,000 mi²

Chapter SUMMARY

The underlying purpose of building students' algebraic skills is to empower them to model and solve real-life problems by writing and solving algebraic equations. In this chapter, students progressed from the simplest equations of Chapter 2 to more complex, multi-step equations. Students learned to use the Distributive Property to collect terms containing the variable. They learned to isolate the variable by applying inverse operations, using appropriate reciprocals to undo multiplication and division. They learned a strategy to be used when an equation has the variable on both sides. They were given practice at using a calculator for equations involving decimals, and so on. This empowerment to cope with increasingly complex linear equations is in turn reflected in the increasing authenticity of the models that students can now build and apply. For example, the models used in Lesson 4.6 are considerably more complex and more applicable to real-life situations than those available in Chapter 2.

4 Chapter Summary

What did you learn?

Skills

1. Solve two-step equations.
   - **General Guidelines**
     a. Simplify both sides of an equation (if needed).
     b. Use inverse operations to isolate the variable.
2. Solve multi-step equations.
   - Use an "expert" equation-solver format.
3. Use reciprocals to solve equations.
4. Use the Distributive Property to solve equations.
5. Solve equations with variables on both sides.
   - Collect variables on the side with the greater variable coefficient.
6. Solve equations involving decimals.

Problem-Solving Strategies

7. Model and solve real-life problems.   (4.1
8. Model and solve geometry problems.   (4.5

Exploring Data

9. Use tables and graphs to solve problems.   (4.6

Why did you learn it?

One of the most common ways to model a real-life situation is with an equation. Knowing how to solve equations helps you answer questions about these real-life situations. For instance, in this chapter you learned how to use equations to analyze a tennis club membership, plan the sa a wildlife poster, predict the number of songbirds in a region, compute your sales bonus, and approximate the area of a city.

How does it fit into the bigger picture of mathema

Throughout this course, you will be given many opportunities to practice problem solving. One of the things you learned in this chapter is that the are many ways to solve problems. For instance, you learned that dividing both sides of an equation by a number produces the same result as multiplying both sides of the equation by the reciprocal of the number. You also st ied examples of real-life problems that can be solved algebraically (by sol an equation), numerically (by using a table), and graphically (by using a graph). In future chapters and in future mathematics courses, remember the best overall problem-solving strategy is to consider a variety of approaches. In fact, solving problems in more than one way and compari the results is an excellent way to become an expert problem solver.

In Exercises 1–4, state the inverse of each. (4.1) See margin.

1. Subtracting 3 from a number

2. Adding 17 to a number

3. Multiplying a number by -4.2

4. Dividing a number by 6.5

In Exercises 5–10, solve the equation. Check your solution. (4.1)

5. $4x + 11 = 35$ 6

6. $9y + 19 = -8$ -3

7. $5t - 72 = 28$ 20

8. $-7t - 25 = 38$ -9

9. $15 - \frac{1}{2}n = 7$ 16

10. $36 - \frac{1}{3}m = 52$ -48

In Exercises 11–14, write an example of the given type of equation. Then solve the equation. (4.2–4.6) Answers vary.

11. One-step equation

12. Two-step equation

13. Three-step equation

14. Equation with variables on both sides

In Exercises 15–20, solve the equation. Check your solution. (4.2)

15. $7x - 5x + 9 = 21$ 6

16. $5s + 11s - 6 = 74$ 5

17. $3r - 7r + 22 = -14$ 9

18. $21p - 73 - 46p = 27$ -4

19. $\frac{2}{5}m + 9 - \frac{1}{5}m = 15$ 30

20. $-31 = \frac{2}{3}n - 26 + \frac{1}{3}n$ -5

Diagramming Equations   **In Exercises 21 and 22, write the equation implied and solve. (4.1, 4.2)**

21.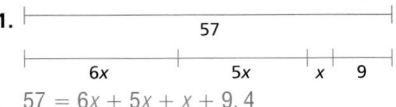

$57 = 6x + 5x + x + 9, 4$

22.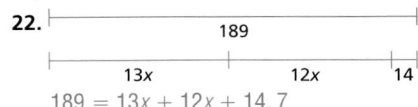

$189 = 13x + 12x + 14, 7$

23. *Writing*   In your own words describe the reciprocal of a number. **(4.3)**   See margin.

24. *Number Sense*   There are only two numbers that are their own reciprocals. What are they? **(4.3)**   1 and -1

In Exercises 25–28, find the reciprocal of the number. (4.3)

25. 7 $\frac{1}{7}$

26. -24 $-\frac{1}{24}$

27. $-\frac{1}{2}$ -2

28. $\frac{15}{8}$ $\frac{8}{15}$

In Exercises 29–34, solve the equation. (4.3, 4.4)

29. $\frac{1}{4}(z + 8) = 10$ 32

30. $\frac{1}{3}(t - 9) = 4$ 21

31. $11(x - 6) - 17 = 38$ 11

32. $15(2m + 5) = -60$ $-4\frac{1}{2}$

33. $\frac{1}{2}n + \frac{1}{2}(n - 2) = -10$ -9

34. $17 = 3n + \frac{1}{5}(15n - 5)$ 3

In Exercises 35–40, solve the equation. Then check your solution. (4.5)

35. $15x - 56 = 7x$ 7

36. $-18y + 175 = 7y$ 7

37. $3(3 - t) = 5(2t + 7)$ -2

38. $23(2n + 3) = 89n + 26$ 1

39. $\frac{3}{4}m + 8 = 22 - \frac{1}{4}m$ 14

40. $\frac{2}{3}t - 18 = \frac{1}{3}t - 20$ -6

Chapter REVIEW

Have students begin this Review in class and complete it as a homework assignment.

ASSIGNMENT GUIDE

*Basic/Average:
 Ex. 15–39 odd, 41–43, 45–47 odd, 49, 50
 Ex. 53–55 odd, 57–66

Above Average:
 Ex. 15–39 odd, 41–43, 45–47 odd, 49, 50
 Ex. 53–55 odd, 57–66

Advanced:
 Ex. 15–39 odd, 41–43, 45–47 odd, 49, 50
 Ex. 53–55 odd, 57–66

 *For these students, you will need to limit assignments to cover only those lessons you chose to teach from this chapter.

Resources
Color Transparencies, p. 19
Answer Masters, pp. 85, 86

Answers
 1. Adding 3 to a number
 2. Subtracting 17 from a number
 3. Dividing a number by -4.2
 4. Multiplying a number by 6.5
 23. The reciprocal of a number is equal to 1 divided by that number.

Analyzing Advertising Expenses **In Exercises 41–44, use the following information. (4.3)**

The graph at the right shows the amount A (in billions of dollars) spent on advertising in the United States. This amount can be modeled by the equation

$$A = 22.33 + 7.12t$$

where $t = 0$ represents 1975. *(Source: McCann-Erickson, Inc.)*

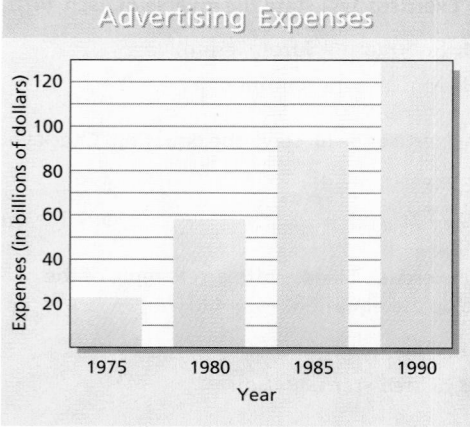

Advertising Expenses

41. What year is represented by $t = 12$?   1987
42. What value of t represents 1983?   8
43. Use the model to find the amount of money spent on advertising in 1990. $129.13 billion
44. Use the model to predict the amount of money spent on advertising in the year 2000. $200.33 billion
✪ 45. Explain how to solve the equation $12n - 39 = 6n + 3$. **(4.5)**   See margin.
✪ 46. Explain how to solve the equation $3(n + 6) = 4n + 6 - 2n$. **(4.3–4.5)**   See margin.
47. *Geometry*   Find x so that the triangle is equilateral **(4.5)**   9

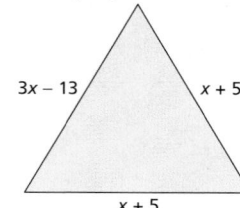

48. *Geometry*   Find n so that the square and the triangle have the same perimeter. **(4.5)**   2

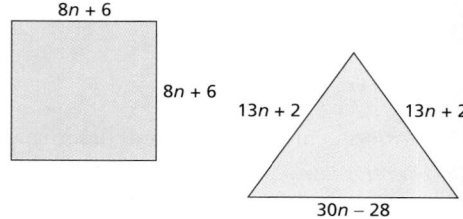

Canoeing   **In Exercises 49 and 50, use the following information. (4.6)**   50. For table, see margin.

You and your friends go canoeing. The first canoe departs at 11:00 A.M. and travels at a rate of 4 miles per hour. Your canoe leaves an hour later and travels at a rate of 6 miles per hour.   4 mph for 1 hour is 4 miles.

49. Explain why the first canoe is 4 miles ahead of your canoe when you begin.
50. Use a table to find the time that your canoe will catch up to the first canoe.   At 2 P.M.

The highest speed obtained in a canoe is 13.29 miles per hour. The Norwegian four-man team achieved that speed in the 1988 Olympic Games.

Answers
45. Subtract $6n$ from each side, add 39 to each side, divide each side by 6.
46. Combine like terms on the right side, distribute the 3 on the left side, subtract $2n$ from each side, subtract 18 from each side.
50.

Time	12	1	2
First canoe's distance (miles)	4	8	12
Your canoe's distance (miles)	0	6	12

51. *Estimation*   Round each number to two decimal places. **(4.7)**

   a. 8.39154   8.39   **b.** -13.657 -13.66 **c.** 25.9981   26.00

52. *Error Analysis*   Describe the error. Write a correct solution. **(4.7)**

$$0.14(3.72x - 5.84) = 20.91$$
$$0.52x - 0.82 = 20.91$$
$$0.52x = 21.73$$
$$x \approx 41.79$$

  Rounding was
  done too early
  (in 2nd step).
  ≈ 41.72

In Exercises 53–56, use a calculator to solve the equation. Round your result to 2 decimal places. (4.7)

53. $4.7x - 9.5 = 13.2$ 4.83   **54.** $-3.69y + 14.24 = 57.83$ -11.81

55. $2.12(4.86t - 3.79) = 19.21$ 2.64   **56.** $7.05(13.29n - 6.95) = -194.56$ -1.55

Using a Table   **In Exercises 57 and 58, use the following information.**

You want to purchase a new video game. You
have saved $52.89. The sales tax rate is 0.055.
The price of the game plus the sales tax cannot
be more than the money you have saved. What
is the maximum price the game can cost? **(4.6, 4.7)**
57.–58. See margin.

57. Write a verbal model for the problem.

58. Create a table to answer the question. $50.13

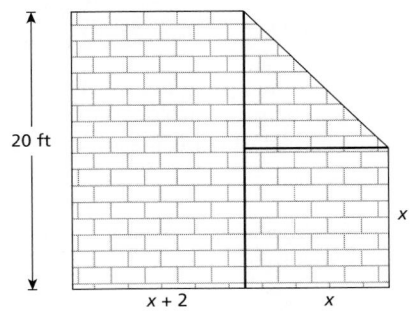

Geometry   **In Exercises 59 and 60, find the area of the triangle. (4.8)**

59.

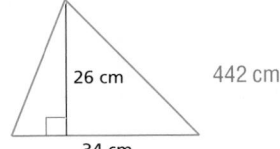

442 cm²

60.

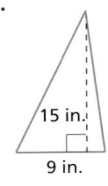

67.5 in.²

Patio Area   **In Exercises 61–65, use the patio diagram shown at the right. (4.8)**

61. The area of the nonsquare rectangle is 240 square
    feet. Find the width of this rectangle.   12 ft

62. Find the area of the square.   100 ft²

63. Find the base and height of the triangle.   10 ft, 10 ft

64. Find the area of the triangle.   50 ft²

65. Find the total area of the patio.   390 ft²

✪ More difficult exercises

Answers

57.

Price of game	+	Tax rate	×	Price of game	=	Money saved

58.

Price ($)	Price ÷ tax($)
10	10.55
50	52.75
50.10	52.86
50.12	52.88
50.13	52.89
50.14	52.90

Real Life
Connection

66. *California Condors*   Solve the following equation to find the number of miles a California condor can fly without flapping its wings.   10

$$3.56x + 4.92x - 10.79x = 17.81x + 50.2 - 251.4$$

67. *The Duck and the Falcon*   You are studying the flying speeds of two endangered species of birds: the Laysan duck and the Peregrine falcon. You observed a Laysan duck fly a distance of 2000 feet in the same time that a Peregrine falcon flew a distance of 5000 feet. From previous observations, you know that a Laysan duck can fly at a rate of about 80 feet per second. Use the following model to find how fast the Peregrine falcon was flying.
200 feet per second

Verbal Model $\dfrac{2000\ \text{feet}}{\text{Duck's speed}} = \dfrac{5000\ \text{feet}}{\text{Falcon's speed}}$

Labels   Duck's speed = 80   (feet per second)
Falcon's speed = *s*   (feet per second)

The California condor is the largest flying land bird found in North America. In 1991, it was reported that about 32 survive, all in captivity.

✪ *Word Scramble*   **In Exercises 68–77, the name of an endangered species has been scrambled. Unscramble the word.**   See margin.

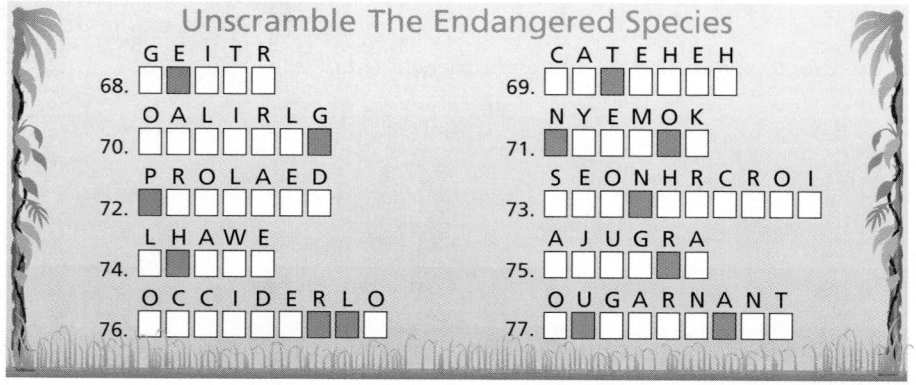

Unscramble The Endangered Species

68. G E I T R
69. C A T E H E H
70. O A L I R L G
71. N Y E M O K
72. P R O L A E D
73. S E O N H R C R O I
74. L H A W E
75. A J U G R A
76. O C C I D E R L O
77. O U G A R N A N T

✪ **78.** After unscrambling the words in Exercises 68–77, write the letters in the purple boxes on a piece of paper. Then unscramble the letters to decode the following message.

M A T H   I N   R E A L   L I F E

79. *Problem Solving*   After decoding the message, list some environmental situations that relate to the message.   Answers vary.

Answers
68. TIGER
69. CHEETAH
70. GORILLA
71. MONKEY
72. LEOPARD
73. RHINOCEROS
74. WHALE
75. JAGUAR
76. CROCODILE
77. ORANGUTAN

In Exercises 1–8, solve the equation. (4.1– 4.5)

1. $4y - 2 = 18$ 5

2. $3 - 3a = 21$ -6

3. $12(r - 2) = 36$ 5

4. $8x + 4 - 3x = 19$ 3

5. $7s - 12 = s$ 2

6. $\frac{1}{2}(x + 8) = 4$ 0

7. $0.7x = 1.3x - 1.2$ 2

8. $p + 2(p - 1) = 2p$ 2

In Exercises 9 and 10, write the reciprocal of the number. (4.3)

9. $-\frac{1}{2}$ -2

10. 10 $\frac{1}{10}$

In Exercises 11–13, use a calculator to solve the equation. Round your answer to 2 decimal places. (4.7)

11. $4x + 2 = 17$ 3.75

12. $1.1(2.2x + 3.3) = 4.4$ 0.32

13. $5(3 + x) - 2x = 17$ 0.67

14. The sum of the two angles is 180°. Find the measure of each angle. (4.8)

121°, 59°

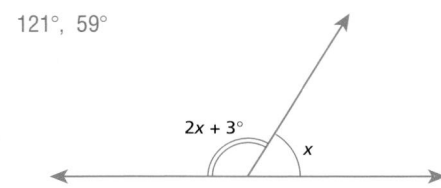

$2x + 3°$ x

In Exercises 15–17, use the diagram of the swimming pool. The pool is surrounded by a fence whose length is 172 feet. (4.8)

16. $18\ ft \times 50\ ft$

15. Write an equation for the length of the fence and solve for x. $2(2x) + 2(5x + 2) = 172, 12$

16. What are the dimensions of the swimming pool?

17. What is the area of the swimming pool? $900\ ft^2$

6 ft

3 ft   3 ft

$5x + 2$

In Exercises 18–20, use the following information. (4.6)

When you started your homework assignment, your friend already had 6 exercises done. You can do about 3 exercises per minute, whereas your friend can only do 2 exercises per minute.

18. How many minutes will it take you to catch up to your friend?   6

19. When you catch up, how many exercises will you have done?   18

20. Copy and complete the table.

6 ft

$2x$

			6	9	12	15	18	21	24
Minutes	0	1	2	3	4	5	6	7	8
Number of Exercises You Have Solved	0	3	?	?	?	?	?	?	?
Number of Exercises Your Friend Has Solved	6	8	?	?	?	?	?	?	?
			10	12	14	16	18	20	22

Chapter Test

Chapter **4** Test   Form C
(Page 1 of 3 pages)

Name _____
Date _____

In Exercises 1 and 2, state the inverse. (4.1)

1. Dividing a number by 3 and subtracting 7 from its quotient.   1. _____
   Adding 7 to a number and multiplying the sum by 3.

2. Adding 5 to a number and multiplying its sum by 6.   2. _____
   Dividing a number by 6 and subtracting 5 from the quotient.

In Exercises 3–5, write the sentence as an equation. Then solve it. (4.1, 4.3, 4.5)

3. 4 times a number increased by 13 is 69.   3. _____
   $4n + 13 = 69; n = 14$

4. The sum of 32 and 7 times a number is −3.   4. _____
   $32 + 7n = -3; n = -5$

5. One third a number decreased by 12 is 5.   5. _____
   $\frac{1}{3}n - 12 = 5; n = 51$

6. Write an equation in its verbal form (as in Exercises 3–5). Then   6. _____
   write its algebraic model and solve.
   Answers will vary.

In Exercises 7 and 8, use the figure below.
Assume that the sum of angles in any
quadrilateral is 360°. (4.8)

$4x - 9°$ $4x + 2°$
D C
A B
$2x$ $2x - 5°$

7. What is the value of x?   7. _____
   $x = 31$

8. What is the measure of each angle in the figure?   8. _____
   $A = 62°, B = 57°, C = 126°, D = 115°$

In Exercises 9 and 10, state the reciprocal. (4.3)

9. $-\frac{1}{5}$ -5   9. _____

10. 32 $\frac{1}{32}$ 10. _____

◀ **Formal Assessment**

Three **Chapter Tests**. Form A is of average difficulty, Form B is of average difficulty in multiple choice format, and Form C is more challenging.
Available as copymasters, pp. 60–68

CHAPTER 5 GOALS

CHAPTER 5 ■ OVERVIEW

RESOURCES ORGANIZER

Lesson Pages	5.1 195–198	5.2 199–202	5.3 203–206	5.4 209–212	5.5 214–217	5.6 218–222	5.7 224–227	5.8 229–232
Lesson Plans	34	35	36	37	38	39	40	41
Problem of the Day	13	13	13	14	14	14	15	15
Warm-Up Exercises	13	13	13	14	14	14	15	15
Color Transparencies	20, 21	—	21	—	—	23	—	—
Teaching Tools: Transparencies Copymasters	T1 C2	T1 C2	T1 C2	T1 C2, C15	T1 C2	T1 C2	T1 C2	T1 C2
Math Log	16	16	16	17	17	17	18	18
Technology	22	23–26	27	—	—	—	28, 29	—
Answer Masters	88	89, 90	91	93	94	95	97, 98	99
Extra Practice Copymasters	34	35	36	37	38	39	40	41
Reteaching Copymasters	34	35	36	37	38	39	40	41
Enrichment Projects	22–25	—	—	26–28	—	—	—	—
Alternative Assessment: Projects Partner Quizzes Group Assessment	23 — —	23 — —	— — —	— 48 —	— — 67, 68	— — —	24 — —	24 — —
Formal Assessment Short Quizzes Tests	— —	69 —	— —	70 71, 72	— —	73 —	— —	74 75–83
Overhead Manipulatives Kit	—	—	—	—	—	—	—	—
Complete Solutions Manual	Includes step-by-step solutions for all exercises in the student text							
Computerized Test Bank	Creates customized tests that include graphics							
Interactive CD-ROM Project	Provides an interactive and interdisciplinary chapter project							

CHAPTER 5 · RESOURCES

STARTERS

Problem of the Day

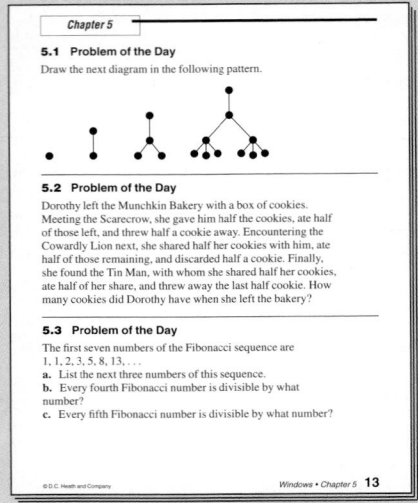

Warm-Up Exercises

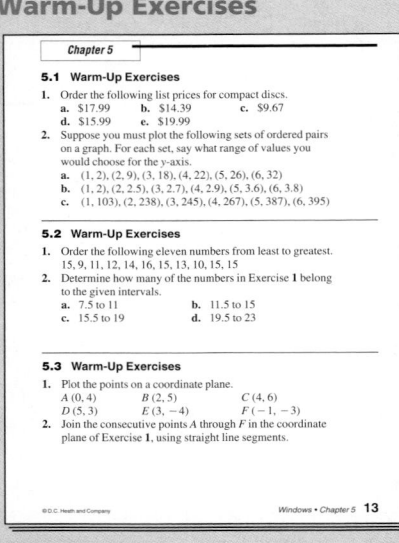

FOR TEACHERS

Answer Masters

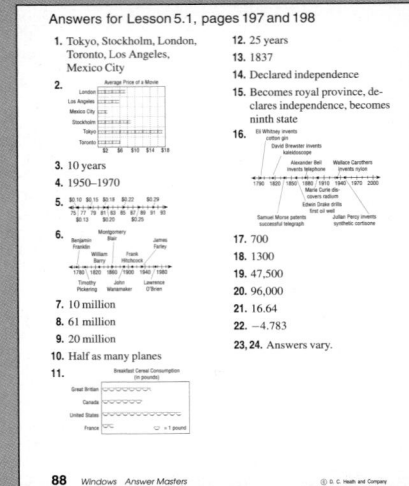

Lesson Plans

Teaching Tools

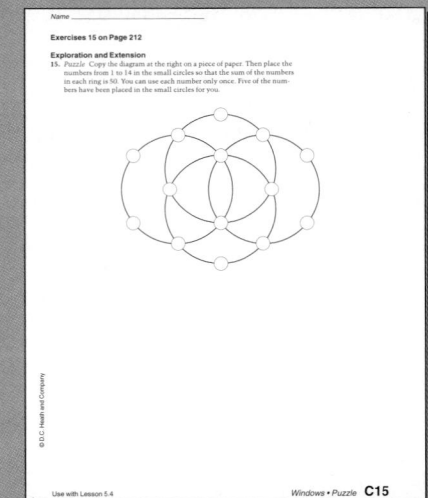

Teaching Tools includes:
Transparencies and Copymasters for classroom activities and study skills:

- Graph Paper
- Dot Paper (Geoboards)
- Algebra Tiles
- Number Counters
- Fraction Strips
- Models

REAL LIFE

Color Transparencies for Real-Life Applications

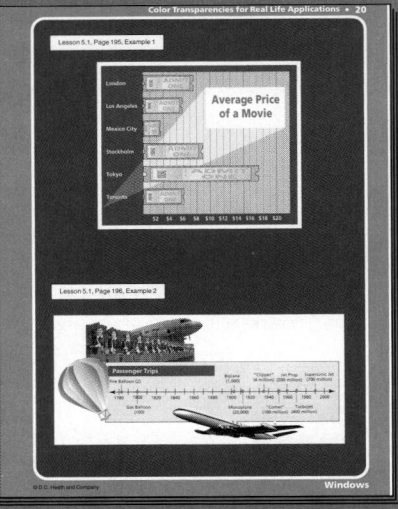

Technology: Using Calculators and Computers

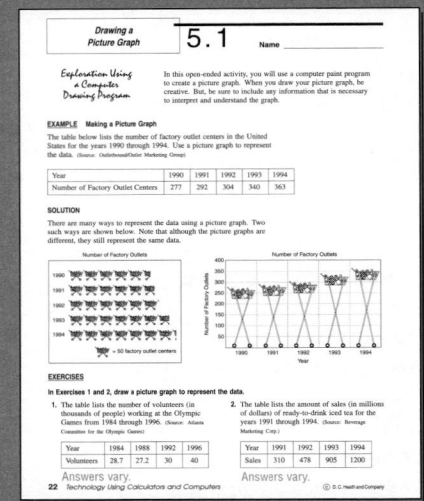

Also Available:

- Complete Solutions Manual
- Overhead Manipulatives Kit
- Computerized Testing Program

- **Interactive CD-ROM Projects**
  Interactive projects for solving real-world problems using multimedia

- **Interactions: Real Math–Real Careers**
  A videodisc–based resource that connects math to real careers and on-the-job problem solving

- **PACKETS® Performance Assessment for Middle School Mathematics**
  A program that links assessment and instruction

ASSESSMENT

Alternative Assessment

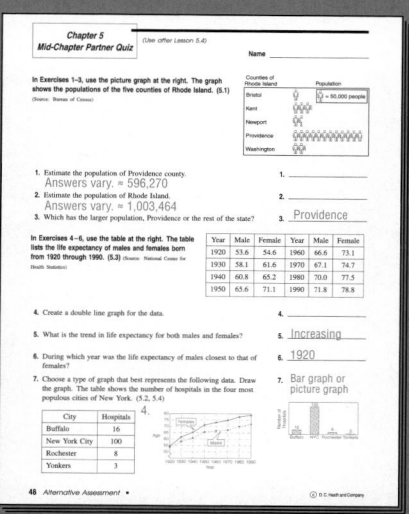

Alternative Assessment includes:
- Scoring Rubrics
- Portfolios
- Math Journals
- Projects
- Partner Quizzes
- Individual and Group Assessment

Formal Assessment

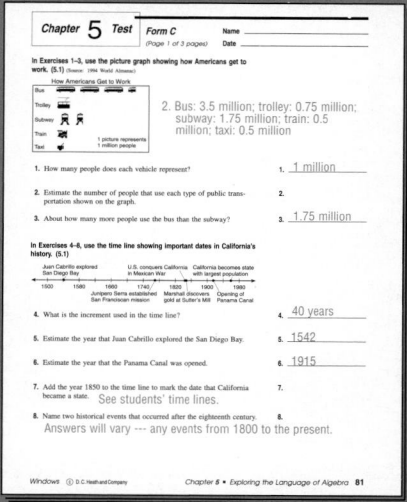

Formal Assessment includes:
- Short Quizzes (after every 2 lessons)
- Mid-Chapter Tests (2 forms)
- Chapter Tests (3 forms)
- Cumulative Tests (after every 3 Chapters)

MEETING INDIVIDUAL NEEDS

Extra Practice Copymasters

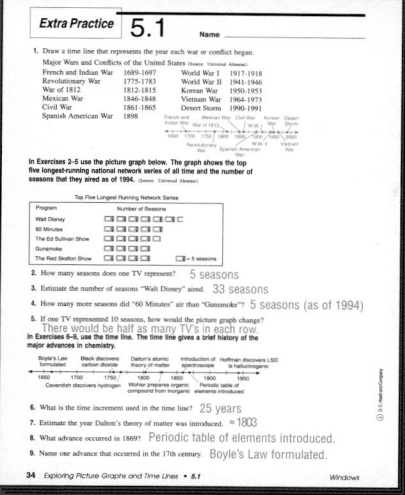

Reteaching Copymasters

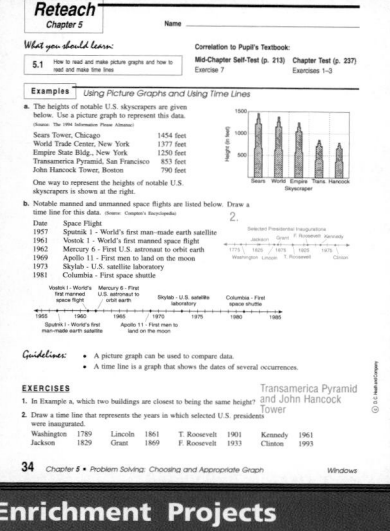

Enrichment Projects

Math Log

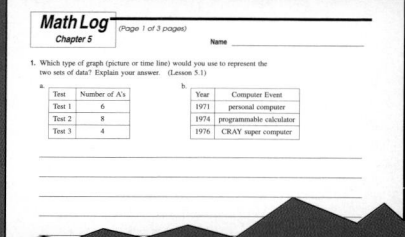

Special Populations
Suggestions for providing equal access for:

Students Acquiring English Proficiency*
To help students develop and practice new vocabulary, have them read graphs and describe the data in complete sentences (either orally or in writing).

In Lesson Investigation 5.1, encourage students to choose a survey topic that is of interest to them such as favorite foods, favorite television shows, number of people in a family, or countries of origin. In addition to displaying the results of their surveys graphically, have students summarize their findings in writing.

Students with Various Learning Styles*
Students with spatial and/or visual problems may have difficulty constructing and reading graphs. Allow these students extra time to complete the exercises. Encourage them to use graph paper and rulers. Some students may require assistance in creating scales and organizing data.

Underachieving Students*
In Lesson Investigation 5.1, assign students specific responsibilities to carry out within the group. Some students are good graphic artists and should be encouraged to draw or design letter displays.

In Lesson 5.8, keep students interested by providing them with spinners, number cubes, coins, and so on, to perform the activities in the exercises.

Gifted and Talented Students*
Have students extend Lesson Investigation 5.4 by researching a fact of interest for each country in a continent of their choice. Students may choose to research topics such as population, number of animal species, or average temperature. Have students trace a map of the continent, create a color code, and color the map accordingly.

* See page T19 for descriptions of these special populations.

Exploring Data and Graphs

About the Chapter

In this chapter, students are introduced to strategies for the organization, representation, and analysis of data.

The chapter begins with picture graphs and time lines, two types of graphs popularized by many daily newspapers. In Lesson 5.2, students are shown how to organize data in the most appropriate version of a bar graph, to represent a frequency distribution, and to use a histogram. Students are constantly reminded of the *purpose* of these strategies, namely, the analysis or interpretation of the organized data. Lesson 5.3 demonstrates the usefulness of line graphs for showing trends over intervals of time and for detecting a change in patterns. Having learned the basic options for representing data, students are guided in Lesson 5.4 to an appropriate choice of graphs, and in Lesson 5.5 to an in-depth look at what constitutes a misleading graph. The last three lessons of the chapter deal with statistics and probability. Lessons 5.6 and 5.7 introduce students to the construction and interpretation of line plots and scatter plots, and to the concept of *x, y* correlation. The investigation for Lesson 5.8 shows students three approaches to probability, and the lesson itself introduces a formula for the theoretical probability of an event. Be sure to have students read the second and third paragraphs of the student text on page 233 for a further view of data analysis.

Because over 160,000,000 metric tons of garbage are generated annually in the United States, space to put it is filling up at an alarming rate. Almost half the states will fill up all their existing landfills within 10 years. To solve this problem, we need to use less packaging and recycle more of it.

CODE

1

PETE

Poly-Ethylene
Terephthalate (PET)

In 1990, over 8 million pounds of packaging was produced in the United States. Because it is very versatile, plastic is one of the most popular materials used in packaging today. Plastic containers often have symbols like the one shown here to identify what type of material is in them.

In this chapter you will learn to interpret data and graphs in a variety of different forms. This will help you to determine the truth of advertising claims made about a product's environmental impact.

Using the Page

Plastic recycling benefits the environment by reducing the volume of solid waste. In addition, it benefits the economy because recycled plastic costs about two-thirds as much as new plastic. Recycled plastic can be used to make polyester carpet, automobile parts, tennis ball felt, and "plastic lumber." The plastic used in soda bottles is recycled more than any other plastic.

Have students work in groups to research another material that is recycled. Have them present the information to the class using graphs and other visual displays to illustrate what they have learned.

Multimedia Resources

Interactive CD-ROM Projects
A project for this chapter combines print, animation, sound and video presentations to capture students' interest in Car Sales. This interactive approach shows students how the math concepts and problem-solving strategies they are learning will be used in the future in dealing with important personal, national, and world issues.
The theme of Car Sales correlates to Exercise 5 on page 220.

Interactions: Real Math—Real Life
The theme of this chapter, Recycling, correlates with an episode of **Interactions** which is a videodisc-based multimedia resource that connects middle school math topics with real-life careers. In each of the twelve episodes, students go on-site with a variety of professionals to witness real-life applications of the math they are studying. Students see math concepts and problem-solving strategies in a context that helps them connect what they are studying to the world outside the classroom. **Interactions** was developed by the Foundation for Advancements in Science and Education (FASE) and is published by D.C. Heath and Company.
The theme of Recycling is continued throughout the chapter on pages 205, 207, 219, and 236.

Performance Assessment Resource

The PACKETS® Program: Performance Assessment for Middle School Mathematics was developed by Educational Testing Service and is published by D.C. Heath. **PACKETS** helps you assess your students' performances as they learn. You can use a wide variety of **PACKETS** Activity Units with this chapter because, in every activity, students will use ideas from all topic areas of mathematics. However, you can use the chart on page T16 to help you choose the **PACKETS** Activity Unit(s) that may fit best with this chapter.

Materials

Teaching Tools
  Graph paper, pp. T1, C2

In this investigation, allow students to work in groups of four. Each group could give a five-minute oral presentation of their project for an assessment. Students could be graded based on eye contact, neatness and accuracy of graphs, description of audience surveyed, and ability to listen to others' presentations.

  Make sure students understand the significance of fractions of icons on the modified bar graph. Have students explain why the total number of people in all categories is greater than 200.

EXTENSION

Each group could create its own survey questions such as: What is your favorite food? What sport do you enjoy watching the most? What are your personal goals? (See page 199.)

Materials Needed: colored pencils, graph paper

In this investigation you will conduct a survey and organize the results graphically.

| Example | *Conducting a Survey* |

In the exercises below, you are asked to conduct a survey to find things that people are afraid of. Such a survey was conducted with 200 people by the magazine *Psychology Today*. The results of that survey are shown below.

Scary Thing	Number of People
Snakes	81
Public Speaking	51
High Places	37
Mice	32
Flying on a Plane	32
Spiders and Insects	22

These results can be shown graphically in several ways. You could use a standard bar graph, or you could modify the bar graph with symbols, as shown below.

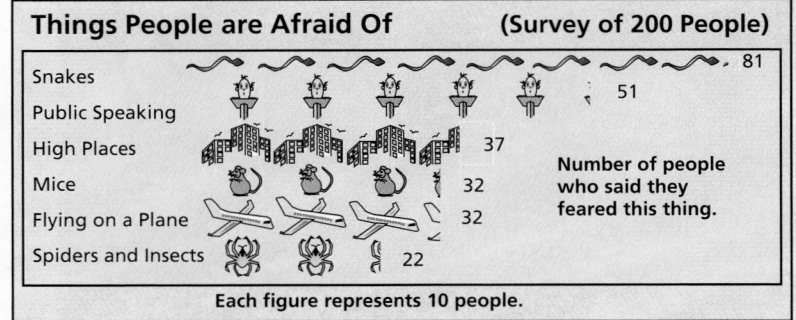

Things People are Afraid Of (Survey of 200 People)

Snakes — 81
Public Speaking — 51
High Places — 37
Mice — 32
Flying on a Plane — 32
Spiders and Insects — 22

Number of people who said they feared this thing.

Each figure represents 10 people.

Exercises

1. *Group Project*   With others in your group, decide how to conduct a survey to find things that people are afraid of. After conducting the survey, organize your results. Then represent your results graphically.   Check students' work.

2. How do the results of your survey compare with the survey reported in *Psychology Today*?   Check students' work.

5.1

Exploring Picture Graphs and Time Lines

PACING the Lesson

Suggested Number of Days
Basic/Average 2 **Above Average** 1
Advanced 1

PLANNING the Lesson

Lesson Plan 5.1, p. 34

What you should learn:

 Goal 1 How to read and make picture graphs

 Goal 2 How to read and make time lines

Why you should learn it:

Being able to draw and interpret picture graphs and time lines helps you understand the graphs and time lines you see in newspapers and magazines.

Real Life
Economics

Goal 1 ## Using Picture Graphs

One of your goals in this course is to learn to use mathematics to communicate with others. In this chapter, you will learn many ways that graphs are used to communicate. For instance, Example 1 shows how a **picture graph** can be used to compare the prices of a movie in different cities.

Example 1 *Making a Picture Graph*

The average price of a movie in 1993 in each of several cities is shown below. Use a picture graph to represent this data. (*Source: Runzheimer International*)

City	Price	City	Price
London, England	$7.50	Los Angeles, U.S.A.	$5.84
Mexico City, Mexico	$2.57	Stockholm, Sweden	$8.91
Tokyo, Japan	$17.31	Toronto, Canada	$6.07

Solution One way to represent the price of a movie ticket in the 6 cities is shown below.

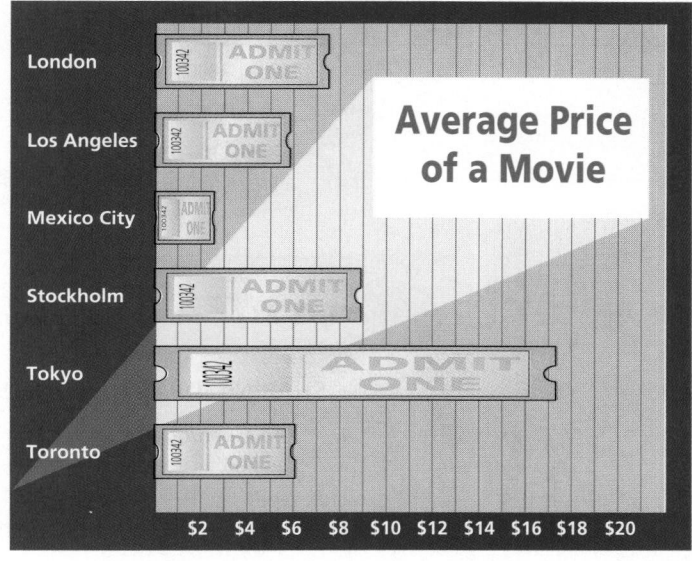

Average Price of a Movie

5.1 ▪ *Exploring Picture Graphs and Time Lines* **195**

ORGANIZER

Starters (reproduced below)
  Problem of the Day 5.1, p. 13
  Warm-Up Exercises 5.1, p. 13
Lesson Resources
  Color Transparencies
    Diagram for Examples 1, 2 and Ex. 12–15, pp. 20, 21
  Teaching Tools
    Graph paper, pp. T1, C2
  Math Log, p. 16
  Technology, p. 22
  Answer Masters 5.1, p. 88
  Extra Practice Copymaster 5.1, p. 34
  Reteaching Copymaster 5.1, p. 34
  Enrichment Projects, pp. 22–25
Special Populations
  Suggestions, Teacher's Edition, p. 192D

LESSON Notes

Discuss ways that have already been developed to describe real-life situations. Algebraic models, verbal models, tables, and graphs have already been used in this text.

Example 1

You may wish to present this graph as a horizontal bar graph, in which the bars have been drawn as movie tickets. Direct students' attention to the essentials of the graph, namely, the position of the right edge of each movie ticket relative to the "price" axis. Discuss whether the picture graph would have a greater impact if ticket prices were displayed in order, or if the vertical axis were used as the price axis, and so on.

Lesson 5.1 **195**

Emphasize that a time line is really a number line that is often enhanced with additional information and pictures.

Example 2

Ask students to identify which period of time witnessed the most advances in passenger flights. In the Enrichment feature on page 198 of these notes, students are given an opportunity to draw a similar type of time line based on the birth dates of noted African-American scientists.

EXTENSION

Challenge students to draw a time line of important events in their lives.

Communicating about MATHEMATICS

As a research project, have students make a time line of modern science inventions since 1900.

Writing Prompt

Complete the following sentence:
The one set of data I would like to have more information about is . . .

See if you can find any information on this data set somewhere in the textbook. For example, if you want to know more about the places where dogs sleep, look on page 214.

Goal 2   Using Time Lines

A **time line** is a graph that shows the dates of several occurrences. For instance, Example 2 shows a time line that gives information about the history of aviation.

Real Life
Aviation History

In the 1930's, United Airlines became the first American airline to employ stewardesses. All applicants had to be registered nurses.

Example 2   *Drawing a Time Line*

The numbers of air passenger trips in America for several years is shown below. The most advanced passenger aircraft at the time is also listed. Draw a time line for this data. (**Source:** *America by the Numbers*)

Date	Passenger Trips	Aircraft
1783	2	Fire Balloon
1800	100	Gas Balloon
1906	1,000	Biplane
1913	20,000	Monoplane
1935	4,000,000	"Clipper"
1952	100,000,000	"Comet"
1960	200,000,000	Jet Prop
1970	400,000,000	Turbojet
1990	700,000,000	Supersonic Jet

Solution   One way to draw the time line is shown below. Notice that the dates are placed on a number line.

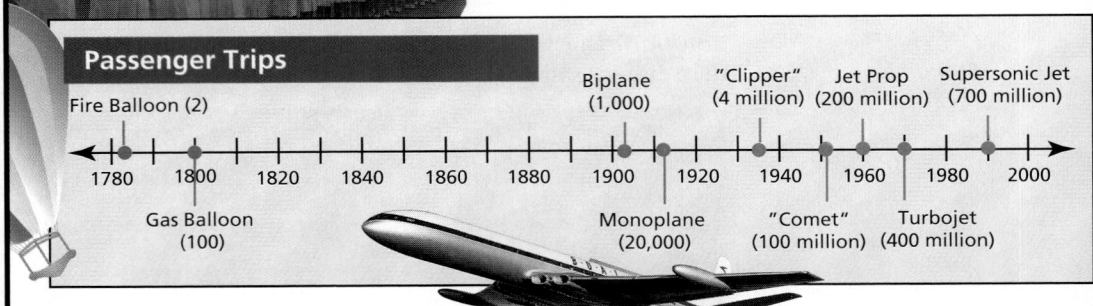

Passenger Trips

Fire Balloon (2), Gas Balloon (100), Biplane (1,000), Monoplane (20,000), "Clipper" (4 million), "Comet" (100 million), Jet Prop (200 million), Turbojet (400 million), Supersonic Jet (700 million)

1780 1800 1820 1840 1860 1880 1900 1920 1940 1960 1980 2000

Communicating about MATHEMATICS

▶ **SHARING IDEAS about the Lesson**

Connections
Language Arts

The Meaning of Words   The prefix "bi" means *two* and the prefix "mono" means *one*. What do you think the words "biplane" and "monoplane" mean? Answers vary.

Technology

| Drawing a Picture Graph | 5.1 | Name _____ |

Exploration Using a Computer Drawing Program

In this open-ended activity, you will use a computer paint program to create a picture graph. When you draw your picture graph, be creative. But, be sure to include any information that is necessary to interpret and understand the graph.

EXAMPLE   Making a Picture Graph

The table below lists the number of factory outlet centers in the United States for the years 1990 through 1994. Use a picture graph to represent the data. (Source: Outletbound/Outlet Marketing Group)

Year	1990	1991	1992	1993	1994
Number of Factory Outlet Centers	277	292	304	340	363

SOLUTION

There are many ways to represent the data using a picture graph. Two such ways are shown below. Note that although the picture graphs are different, they still represent the same data.

EXERCISES

In Exercises 1 and 2, draw a picture graph to represent the data.

1. The table lists the number of volunteers (in thousands of people) working at the Olympic Games from 1984 through 1996. (Source: Atlanta Committee for the Olympic Games)

Year	1984	1988	1992	1996
Volunteers	28.7	27.2	30	40

Answers vary.

2. The table lists the amount of sales (in millions of dollars) of ready-to-drink iced tea for the years 1991 through 1994. (Source: Beverage Marketing Corp.)

Year	1991	1992	1993	1994
Sales	310	478	905	1200

Answers vary.

22   *Technology Using Calculators and Computers*

EXERCISES

Guided Practice

▶ **CHECK for Understanding**

In Exercises 1 and 2, refer to Example 1.

1. Use the picture graph to rank the cities from highest to lowest according to average ticket price.

2. Redraw the picture graph using the symbol [ADMIT ONE] to represent $2.00. See margin.

In Exercises 3 and 4, refer to Example 2.

1. Tokyo, Stockholm, London, Toronto, Los Angeles, Mexico City

3. How many years does each unit on the time line represent? 10

4. According to the time line, in which 20-year period were the most changes made in passenger aircraft? 1950–1970

Independent Practice

In Exercises 5–6, draw a time line that represents each set of data. See Additional Answers.

5. *Price of a U.S. Postage Stamp* Between 1975 and 1991, the cost of a first-class postage stamp increased several times.

Sep. 14, 1975 10¢	May 29, 1978 15¢	Nov. 1, 1981 20¢	Apr. 3, 1988 25¢
Dec. 31, 1975 13¢	Mar. 22, 1981 18¢	Feb. 17, 1985 22¢	Feb. 3, 1991 29¢

6. *Postmaster Generals* The years in which selected postmaster generals took office are listed below.

Benjamin Franklin, 1775; Timothy Pickering, 1795; William Barry, 1829; Montgomery Blair, 1861; John Wanamaker, 1889; Frank Hitchcock, 1909; James Farley, 1933; Lawrence O'Brien, 1965

Air Travel **In Exercises 7–10, use the picture graph at the right. The graph shows the number of passengers that traveled on the five most heavily traveled airlines in 1991.** (*Source: Air Transportation Association of America*) 8. 61 million 9. 20 million

Top Five Airlines
Number of passengers in 1991:

Northwest	✈✈✈✈·
USAir	✈✈✈✈✈✈
United	✈✈✈✈✈✈·
Delta	✈✈✈✈✈✈✈—
American	✈✈✈✈✈✈✈✈

✈ = 10 million passengers

7. How many passengers does one airplane represent? 10 million

8. Estimate the number of passengers that traveled on *United*.

9. How many more people traveled on *American* than on *USAir*?

10. If one airplane represented 20 million passengers, how would the picture graph change? Half as many planes

11. *International Breakfasts* The table at the right lists the 1993 annual consumption of breakfast cereal per person in the United States, Great Britain, Canada, and France. Use the data to create a picture graph. (*Source: Gale Book of Averages*)
See Additional Answers.

Country	Consumption (in pounds)
Great Britain	7.34
Canada	6.02
United States	11.9
France	1.78

5.1 • *Exploring Picture Graphs and Time Lines* **197**

Answer
2.

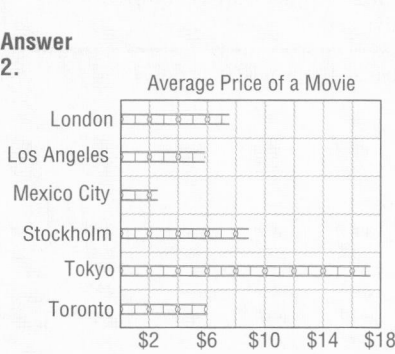

Average Price of a Movie

London, Los Angeles, Mexico City, Stockholm, Tokyo, Toronto

$2 $6 $10 $14 $18

▶ **Ex. 12–15** Assign these exercises as a group. Be sure students understand which years belong to the 18th century.

EXTENSION
Ask students: For how many years was New Hampshire a royal province? In what year was the date of the New Hampshire primary moved to remain the first primary in the nation?

▶ **Ex. 16** Again encourage your student artists to be creative here, and remind them to use equal time increments. Suggest that they use movable "event" labels to help in planning a satisfactory layout.

EXTENSION
This is a great opportunity for interdisciplinary research. Have students plan a time line of events for their own state. Research could be done as a social studies project, while the time line can be completed in math period.

Integrated Review ────────

▶ **Ex. 17–20** Ask students in what context such expressions would be used. For example, in computing interest on an investment or loan

Exploration and Extension

▶ **Ex. 23** Use this exercise as a history connection project. Ask the social studies teacher to supply possible resources for this out-of-class project.

Portfolio Opportunity: Math Log

Which type of graph (picture or time line) would you use to represent the two sets of data? Explain your answer.

a.

Test	Number of A's
Test 1	6
Test 2	8
Test 3	4

b.

Year	Computer Event
1971	personal computer
1974	programmable calculator
1976	CRAY super computer

Also available as a copymaster, page 16, Ex. 1

Alternative Assessment

A research project that develops data organizing skills.

Available as a copymaster, page 23

History of New Hampshire   In Exercises 12–15, use the time line.
The time line gives a brief history of New Hampshire. (*Source: PCUSA*)

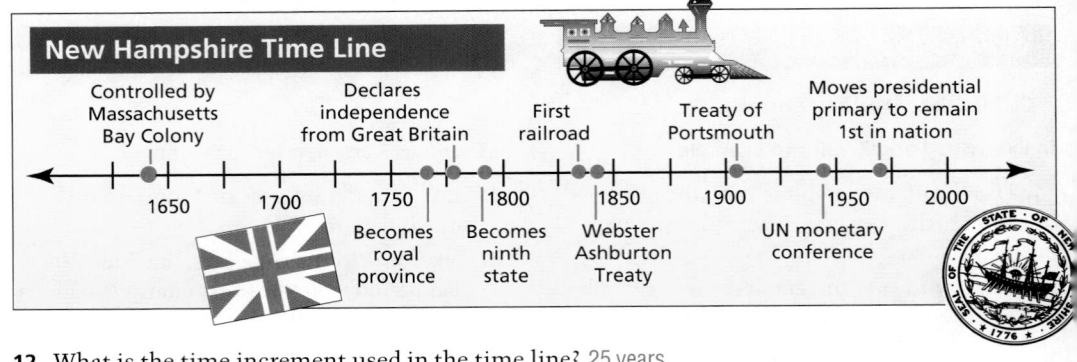

New Hampshire Time Line

12. What is the time increment used in the time line? 25 years
13. Estimate the year that the first railroad appeared in New Hampshire. 1837
14. What event in New Hampshire's history occurred in 1776? Declared independence
15. Name 2 events that occurred in the 18th century. Becomes royal province, declares independence, becomes ninth state
16. *History* The data at the right lists several events and the years in which they occurred. Make a time line for this data.

See Additional Answers.

Year	Event
1793	Eli Whitney invents cotton gin.
1816	David Brewster invents kaleidoscope.
1837	Samuel Morse patents successful telegraph.
1859	Edwin Drake drills first oil well.
1876	Alexander Bell invents telephone.
1898	Marie Curie discovers radium.
1934	Wallace Carothers invents nylon.
1948	Julian Percy invents synthetic cortisone.

Integrated Review   ***Making Connections within Mathematics***
─────────

Mental Math   **In Exercises 17–20, evaluate the expression.**   96,000

17. $200 \times 3\frac{1}{2}$ 700   **18.** $300 \times 4\frac{1}{3}$ 1300   **19.** $(10,000)\left(4\frac{3}{4}\right)$ 47,500   **20.** $(15,000)\left(6\frac{2}{5}\right)$

Average   **In Exercises 21 and 22, find the average of the numbers.**

21. 18.4, 16.8, 17.5, 19.0, 14.7, 17.9, 16.1, 15.2, 14.9, 15.9   16.64
22. $-5.61, -3.25, -4.50, -6.13, -4.75, -4.34, -5.07, -6.00, -4.21, -3.97$ -4.783

Exploration and Extension
─────────

P *Creating a Time Line*   **In Exercises 23 and 24, research the given topic.**
Create a time line that shows the important events that occurred.   Check students' work.

✪ **23.** The history of your state, province, or region
✪ **24.** The history of mathematics from A.D. 1000 to A.D. 2000

✪ More difficult exercises
P Portfolio Opportunity

198   *Chapter 5* ▪ *Exploring Data and Graphs*

▶ **Enrichment**

GROUP PROJECT
Based on Example 2, have students prepare a time line of noted African-American scientists, showing the names, birth dates, and discoveries listed below. Have student artists add appropriate sketches in the style of Example 2.
■ George E. Carruthers (1940), physicist, developed the Apollo 16 lunar surface ultraviolet camera/spectrograph.
■ Dr. Charles R. Drew (1904), pioneer in the development of blood plasma; director of the American Red Cross blood donor project in World War II.
■ Jan Matzeliger (1852), invented the lasting machine, which revolutionized the shoe industry.

■ Dr. Alexa Canady (1950), first African-American woman neurosurgeon in the United States.
■ Dr. Daniel Hale Williams (1858), performed the first open-heart operation, founded Provident (Chicago's first hospital for African-Americans).
■ Katherine Johnson (1918), mathematician and physicist, developed new navigation procedures for NASA for tracking manned and unmanned space flights.
■ Norbert Rillieux (1806), invented a vacuum pan evaporator that revolutionized the sugar-refining industry.

5.2 Exploring Bar Graphs and Histograms

PACING the Lesson

Suggested Number of Days
Basic/Average 2   **Above Average** 1
Advanced 1

PLANNING the Lesson

Lesson Plan 5.2, p. 35

What you should learn:

 Goal 1 How to use bar graphs to represent data

 Goal 2 How to use histograms to represent data

Why you should learn it:

Being able to draw and interpret bar graphs and histograms helps you communicate about real-life situations, such as comparing goals and achievements.

Real Life
American Dream

...e you ever dreamed of owning your ...business? That dream came true for ...e Sanchez, who started a successful direct marketing business.

Goal 1   Using Bar Graphs

There are three basic types of **bar graphs:** simple bar graphs, double (or triple) bar graphs, and stacked bar graphs. When you use a bar graph to represent real-life data, you first need to decide which type of bar graph will best represent the data.

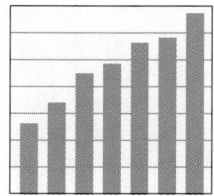
Simple Bar Graph

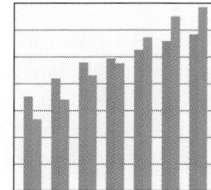
Double Bar Graph

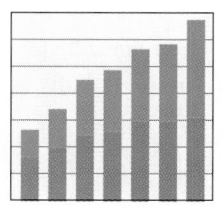
Stacked Bar Graph

Example 1   *Drawing a Bar Graph*

A survey asked 250 adults about their personal goals, and whether they had achieved their goals. Represent these results with a bar graph. (*Source: Roper Organization*)

Goal	Have/Had Goal	Achieved Goal
Own a home	157	109
Happy marriage	140	100
Own a car	131	150
Have children	131	113
Become rich	113	7
Interesting job	111	60

Solution   This data is best represented by a double bar graph.

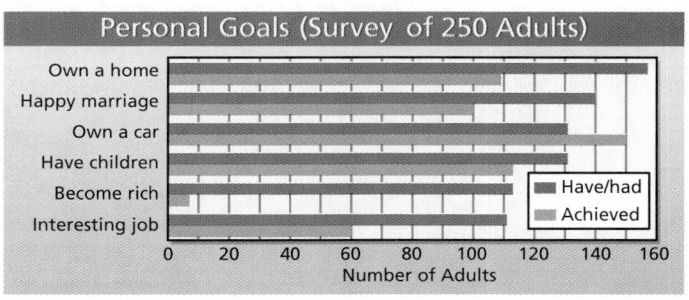

5.2 ▪ *Exploring Bar Graphs and Histograms*   **199**

ORGANIZER

Starters (reproduced below)
  Problem of the Day 5.2, p. 13
  Warm-Up Exercises 5.2, p. 13
Lesson Resources
  Teaching Tools
    Graph paper, pp. T1, C2
  Math Log, p. 16
  Technology, pp. 23–26
  Answer Masters 5.2, pp. 89, 90
  Extra Practice Copymaster 5.2, p. 35
  Reteaching Copymaster 5.2, p. 35
Special Populations
  Suggestions, Teacher's Edition, p. 192D

LESSON Notes

Bring in examples of bar graphs from magazines and newspapers. Ask students to identify each graph as one of the three basic types: simple bar graph, double (or triple) bar graph, and stacked bar graph.

Example 1

Explain that a double bar graph is convenient when a comparison is made within each category. For each goal (category), this graph compares the number of people who had that goal with the number who achieved it. Have students compare the layout of this graph with that on page 195. Observe that a double bar graph must include a color key. Encourage students to suggest explanations for the "Own a car" results.

STARTER: Problem of the Day

Dorothy left the Munchkin Bakery with a box of cookies. Meeting the Scarecrow, she gave him half the cookies, ate half of those left, and threw half a cookie away. Encountering the Cowardly Lion next, she shared half her cookies with him, ate half of those remaining, and discarded half a cookie. Finally, she found the Tin Man, with whom she shared half her cookies, ate half of her share, and threw away the last half cookie. How many cookies did Dorothy have when she left the bakery?
42

Also available as a copymaster, p. 13

STARTER: Warm-Up Exercises

1. Order the following eleven numbers from least to greatest.
15, 9, 11, 12, 14, 16, 15, 13, 10, 15, 15
9, 10, 11, 12, 13, 14, 15, 15, 15, 15, 16
2. Determine how many of the numbers in **1.** belong to the given intervals.
a. 7.5 to 11   **b.** 11.5 to 15
c. 15.5 to 19   **d.** 19.5 to 23
a. 3, **b.** 7, **c.** 1, **d.** none

Also available as a copymaster, p. 13

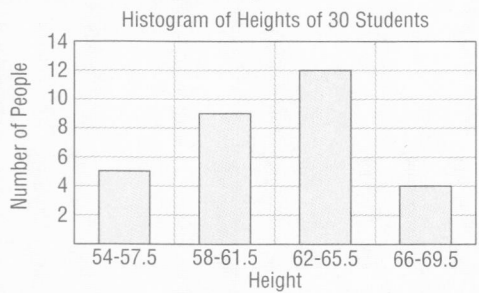

Real Life
Student Heights

Frequency Distribution

Internal	Tally	Total
54–55.5	II	2
56–57.5	III	3
58–59.5	IIIII	5
60–61.5	IIII	4
62–63.5	IIIIII	7
64–65.5	IIIII	5
66–67.5	III	3
68–69.5	I	1

Goal 2 Using Histograms

A **histogram** is a bar graph in which the bars represent intervals of numbers.

Example 2 *Drawing a Histogram*

You have taken a survey of the heights (in inches) of 30 students. Show how this data can be organized by a histogram.

$$58\tfrac{1}{2},\ 65,\ 60,\ 61\tfrac{1}{2},\ 58\tfrac{1}{2}, 63,\ 64\tfrac{1}{2}, 66\tfrac{1}{2}, 62,\ 67,$$

$$59,\ 62\tfrac{1}{2}, 55\tfrac{1}{2}, 68,\ 56\tfrac{1}{2}, 59,\ 60,\ 62,\ 63\tfrac{1}{2}, 54,$$

$$56,\ 57,\ 64,\ 65,\ 67,\ 58, 60\tfrac{1}{2}, 62,\ 64\tfrac{1}{2}, 62$$

Solution You should begin by deciding which intervals will help you see the patterns of the heights. Then, use the intervals to construct a **frequency distribution** that shows the number of events or items in each interval. Notice that the frequency distribution shows how many heights are in each interval. Using the numbers in the frequency distribution, you can draw a histogram to represent the data.

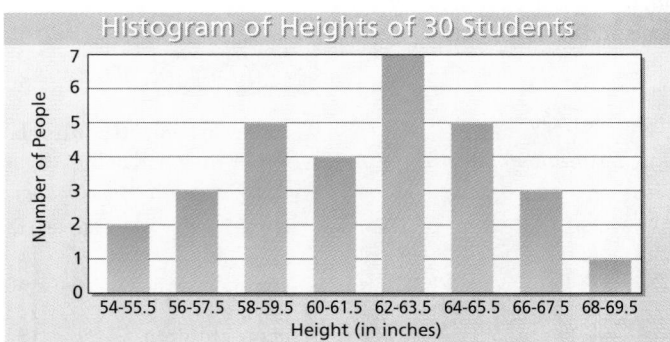

Communicating about MATHEMATICS

▶ **SHARING IDEAS about the Lesson**

It's Up to You Use the intervals 54–57.5, 58–61.5, 62–65.5, and 66–69.5 to organize the data in Example 2. Then compare the resulting histogram to the one above. Which histogram do you think gives a fairer representation of the data? Explain. See margin.

Technology

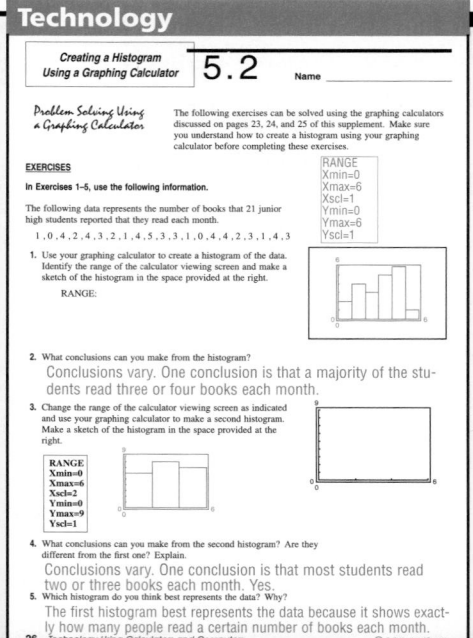

Creating a Histogram Using a Graphing Calculator **5.2** Name _____

Problem Solving Using a Graphing Calculator The following exercises can be solved using the graphing calculators discussed on pages 23, 24, and 25 of this supplement. Make sure you understand how to create a histogram using your graphing calculator before completing these exercises.

EXERCISES

In Exercises 1–5, use the following information.

The following data represents the number of books that 21 junior high students reported that they read each month.

1, 0, 4, 2, 4, 3, 2, 1, 4, 5, 3, 3, 1, 0, 4, 4, 2, 3, 1, 4, 3

1. Use your graphing calculator to create a histogram of the data. Identify the range of the calculator viewing screen and make a sketch of the histogram in the space provided at the right.
   RANGE:

RANGE
Xmin=0
Xmax=6
Xscl=1
Ymin=0
Ymax=6
Yscl=1

2. What conclusions can you make from the histogram?
   Conclusions vary. One conclusion is that a majority of the students read three or four books each month.

3. Change the range of the calculator viewing screen as indicated and use your graphing calculator to make a second histogram. Make a sketch of the histogram in the space provided at the right.

RANGE
Xmin=0
Xmax=6
Xscl=2
Ymin=0
Ymax=9
Yscl=1

4. What conclusions can you make from the second histogram? Are they different from the first one? Explain.
   Conclusions vary. One conclusion is that most students read two or three books each month. Yes.

5. Which histogram do you think best represents the data? Why?
   The first histogram best represents the data because it shows exactly how many people read a certain number of books each month.

EXERCISES

Guided Practice

▶ **CHECK for Understanding**

1. How do you make a frequency distribution from given data?   See page 200.
2. How is a frequency distribution used?   To make a histogram

In Exercises 3 and 4, refer to Example 1.

3. What was achieved by the most people? By the fewest?   Own a car, become rich

4. What goal did most adults have? How many did not achieve that goal?
   Own a home, 48

In Exercises 5 and 6, refer to Example 2.

5. What interval contains the greatest number of students? What interval contains the least?

6. What two intervals contain the same number of students?   56–57.5 and 66–67.5, or 58–59.5 and 64–65.5

5. 62–63.5, 68–69.5

Independent Practice

In Exercises 7 and 8, which type of bar graph do you think would best represent the data? Explain.

7. *An Apple a Day*   In a survey, people were asked which type of apple   Simple, 1 question for 1 period of time
they preferred: 39 preferred Red Delicious, 24 preferred Golden Delicious, 20 preferred Granny Smith, and 10 preferred McIntosh.
(*Source: USA Today*)

8. *Food Preferences*   The data below shows the average number of meals that were pizza, turkey, or pasta (consumed at home) out of 100, for different years. (*Source: NPD Group's National Eating Trends Service*)   Triple, 3 kinds of food for more than 1 period of time

1983	Pizza: 3	Turkey: 2	Pasta: 4
1986	Pizza: 4	Turkey: 1	Pasta: 4
1989	Pizza: 4	Turkey: 2	Pasta: 4
1992	Pizza: 5	Turkey: 2	Pasta: 5

9. *Interpreting Data*   For the survey in Exercise 7, eight people preferred other types of apples and 17 people said they didn't like any kind of apples. Should these results be included in a bar graph? If so, how?   Yes, include 2 more bars

10. *Computers*   A survey asked 100 parents of children ages 6 to 17 the skills that they believe their children develop from using computers. Represent the results with a bar graph. Then explain why you chose the type of bar graph you did. (*Source: Fuji Photo Film USA, Inc.*)   Simple, 1 question for 1 period of time. For graph, see margin.

Skill	Number of Parents
Word processing/typing	32
Reading	26
Mathematics	26
Hand-eye coordination	22
Writing	18
Thinking/reasoning	18
Analytical problem solving	9
Speed	2

☻ More difficult exercises

5.2 ▪ *Exploring Bar Graphs and Histograms*   **201**

EXERCISE Notes

ASSIGNMENT GUIDE

Basic/Average:
Day 1: Ex. 7–9, 11–16
Day 2: Ex. 10, 17–19

Above Average:
Ex. 7–10, 16–19

Advanced: Ex. 7–10, 16–19

Selected Answers: Ex. 1–6, 7–17 odd

Guided Practice

Assign these exercises as a classroom summary. Encourage small groups of three or four students to use the think-share method of finding and discussing answers.

Independent Practice

▶ **Ex. 7, 8**   In choosing the appropriate bar graph, students may need to refer to the displays above Example 1 on page 199.

Extra Practice

Extra Practice 5.2   Name _____

In Exercises 1 and 2, which type of bar graph do you think would best represent the data. Explain.

Number of correct answers	Number of men who scored that number	Number of women who scored that number
55-60	5	6
50-54	12	11
45-49	14	16
40-44	12	7
35-39	8	4
30-34	1	3
25-29	0	1
20-24	0	0
15-19	0	0
10-14	0	0
5-9	0	0
0-4	0	0

1. In a survey, 100 people were asked to state their blood type: 38 said A+, 3 said A-, 10 said B+, 1 said B-, 1 said AB-, 2 said AB+, 35 said O+, 3 said O-, and 7 did not know.
Simple bar graph, one bar for each type of blood

2. One hundred people, fifty men and fifty women, were given a timed quiz. There were 60 arithmetic problems to answer in 60 seconds. The table at the right shows the number of correct answers and the number of men and women who scored that number.
Double bar graph or stacked bar graph

In Exercises 3–6, use the histogram which represents the total number of U.S. immigrants by decade.

3. Which decade shows the largest number of immigrants?   1901-10

4. Between which two decades did the number of immigrants decrease the most?
1921-1930 and 1931-1940

5. Do you see a trend in the bar graph?   Number was highest from 1901-1910. The number decreased, then up again from 1931-1940. Since then, number increases each decade.

6. Make an estimate of the number of immigrants from 1991-2000 based on the data in the bar graph.
If trend continues, there should be more than 8000 immigrants from 1991-2000.

7. The following are the times in seconds for 20 eighth grade students running a 40 yard dash. Show how this data can be organized by a histogram.   See students' graphs. Time intervals may vary.

5.8	6.3	7.4	4.9	5.5
6.2	5.1	5.8	5.6	4.7
6.5	6.8	6.2	5.9	5.4
5.8	7.3	6.7	6.9	5.1

Windows   **5.2 ▪** *Exploring Bar Graphs and Histograms*   **35**

Reteaching

Reteach Chapter 5   Name _____

What you should learn:

5.2   How to use bar graphs to represent data and how to use histograms to represent data

Correlation to Pupil's Textbook:
Chapter Test (p. 237)
Exercises 10-13

Examples   *Using Bar Graphs and Using Histograms*

a. The average annual income for year-round full-time workers ages 25 and above is given below for various years. Represent the data with a double bar graph. (Source: Statistical Abstract of the U.S., 1990)

Year	Men	Women	Year	Men	Women
1970	9,521	5,616	1982	22,857	14,477
1974	12,786	7,370	1986	27,335	17,675
1978	16,882	10,121			

b. You have taken a survey of the weights (in pounds) of each member of your drama club. Organize this data by a histogram.

112, 135, 140, 109, 105, 122, 129, 147, 117, 105, 143, 110, 148, 102

Construct a frequency distribution that shows the number of weights in an interval. Use the numbers in the frequency distribution to draw a histogram.

Frequency Distribution

Interval	Tally	Total
100 - 109	IIII	4
110 - 119	II	3
120 - 129	II	2
130 - 139	I	1
140 - 149	IIII	4

Guidelines:
• The 3 types of bar graphs are simple bar graphs, double (or triple) bar graphs, and stacked bar graphs.
• A histogram is a bar graph in which the bars represent intervals of numbers.

EXERCISES

1. The revenues for the top 5 all-time motion picture money makers are given below. Represent the data with a bar graph.
E.T. The Extra-Terrestrial, $228,618,939; Star Wars, $193,777,000; Return of the Jedi, $169,193,000; Batman, $150,500,000; The Empire Strikes Back, $141,672,000 (Source: Variety, Inc.)

2. For Example b, construct a frequency distribution using these intervals: 101–110, 111–120, 121–130, 131–140, and 141–150.
Totals will change to 5, 2, 2, 2, and 3.

Windows   Chapter 5 ▪ *Problem Solving: Choosing and Appropriate Graph*   **35**

Answer

10.

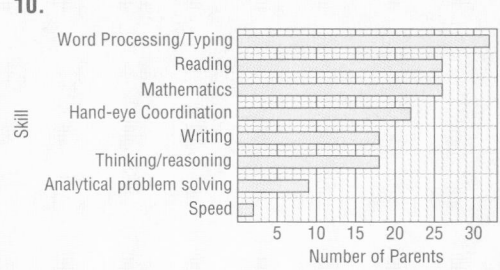

Lesson 5.2   **201**

► **Ex. 11–15** Assign these as a group. Be sure to help students get a feeling for what's going on in this graph. It can be read in several ways, depending on whether you want to focus on a particular age group or on a particular year. You may wish to explain that Census Bureau information is gathered every ten years. These data are from the 1990 Census.

► **Ex. 15** Have students brainstorm and list as many conclusions as possible.

Integrated Review

► **Ex. 17, 18** These exercises take time. Use them as an in-class small-group activity. If geoboards are not available, use 5 x 5 arrays of dot paper.

Exploration and Extension

You may wish to have students work with partners. This is their first attempt at a stacked bar graph, so you will probably have to explain that in this kind of graph you can show a total by stacking the component subtotals on one bar. In this case, for each year the subtotals for public and private schools can be stacked on one bar. Students may need a prompt regarding appropriate scale units.

Portfolio Opportunity: Math Log

In your own words, describe the difference between a simple bar graph and a histogram.

Also available as a copymaster, page 16, Ex. 2

Short Quiz

Covers Lessons 5.1 and 5.2

Available as a copymaster, page 69

Alternative Assessment

1. A journal entry activity that develops writing skills.
2. An interview project that develops students' ability to collect and organize data.

Available as a copymaster, page 23

Youth Population **In Exercises 11–15, use the histogram that represents the projected population (in millions) of young people ages 3–17 for the years 1993, 1995, and 2005.** *(Source: Census Bureau Projections)*

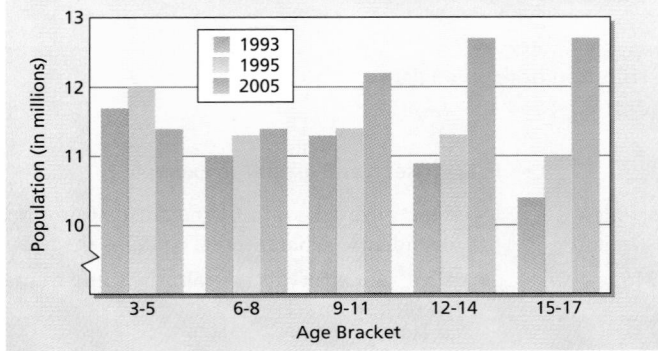

11. Which age brackets have about the same population in 2005? 3–5 and 6–8; 12–14 and 15–17
12. Which age bracket shows a decrease in population from 1993 to 2005? 3–5
13. Which age bracket shows the largest increase through the years? 15–17
14. How much did the 9–11 age group increase from 1995 to 2005? About 0.8 million
15. What conclusions can you make from the bar graph? See Additional Answers.

✪ 16. *Environment* You have taken a survey of the ages of 40 volunteers cleaning a local park. Show how this data can be organized by a histogram. See Additional Answers.

13	17	8	9	12	13	13	16	14	10
15	9	15	10	11	16	13	11	10	17
13	10	12	9	6	14	16	11	9	9
15	14	11	12	10	7	9	13	11	10

Integrated Review   *Making Connections within Mathematics*

Geoboard Shapes **In Exercises 17 and 18, use the geoboard.**

P 17. Count the number of "non-tilted" squares that can be formed on the geoboard. Organize the squares according to their perimeters and illustrate the results with a histogram.

P 18. Count the number of "non-tilted" rectangles that can be formed on the geoboard. Organize the rectangles according to their areas and illustrate the results with a histogram.
17., 18. See Additional Answers.

Exploration and Extension

✪ 19. *School Enrollment* The table shows the fall enrollment (in millions of students) in grades K–8 for public and private schools. Represent the results with a stacked bar graph. *(Source: Bureau of Census)*
See Additional Answers.

Type of School	1980	1985	1990	1995
Public	27.7	27.0	29.7	31.7
Private	4.0	4.2	4.1	4.3

✪ More difficult exercises
P Portfolio Opportunity

202   *Chapter 5 ▪ Exploring Data and Graphs*

Enrichment

Ask students to choose a bar graph from a newspaper or magazine and write a report. Students should provide the graph, list the source, explain any patterns from the graph, and discuss the types of units used.

5.3

Exploring Line Graphs

 What you should learn:

Goal 1 How to use line graphs to represent data

Goal 2 How to use line graphs to explore patterns in geometry

 Why you should learn it:

Line graphs can help you communicate about real-life situations, such as the numbers of female and minority members of congress.

Real Life
U.S. Congress

Student reporters for National Geographic World, Mark Fleming and Charis Willis, talk with Carrie Meek, who became a U.S. Congresswoman from Florida in 1993.

Goal 1 Using Line Graphs

Line graphs are often used to show trends over intervals of time. A *simple* line graph shows changes in one quantity. A *double* line graph shows changes in two quantities.

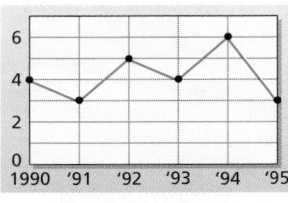
Simple Line Graph

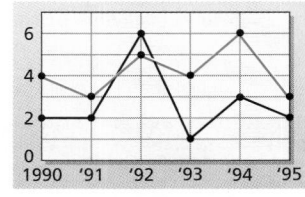
Double Line Graph

Example 1 *Interpreting a Line Graph*

The *triple* line graph below shows the numbers of female, African American, and Hispanic members of the United States House of Representatives from 1981 to 1993. (Representatives are elected for 2-year terms.) During which years did every group increase in members?

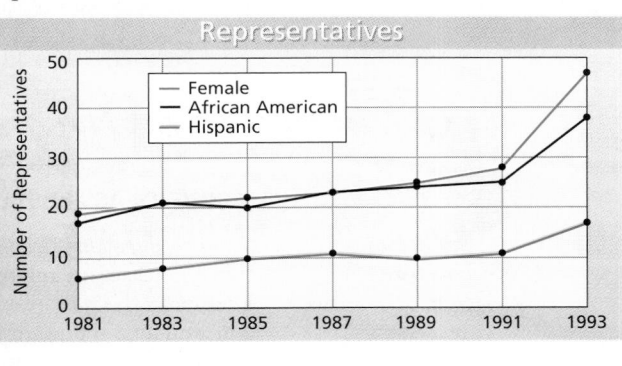

Solution The number of females increased every 2 years. The number of African Americans increased every 2 years except from 1983 to 1985. The number of Hispanics increased every 2 years except from 1987 to 1989. So every group increased in members in 1981–1983, 1985–1987, and 1989–1993. ∎

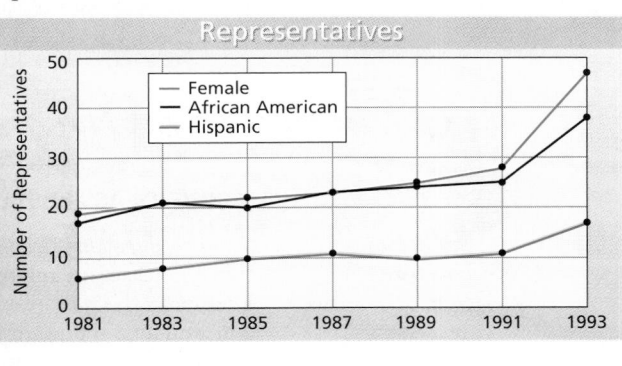

5.3 • *Exploring Line Graphs* **203**

PACING the Lesson

Suggested Number of Days
Basic/Average 2   **Above Average** 1
Advanced 1

PLANNING the Lesson

Lesson Plan 5.3, p. 36

ORGANIZER

Starters (reproduced below)
  Problem of the Day 5.3, p. 13
  Warm-Up Exercises 5.3, p. 13
Lesson Resources
  Color Transparencies
    Picture for Example 2, p. 21
  Teaching Tools
    Graph paper, pp. T1, C2
  Math Log, p. 16
  Technology, p. 27
  Answer Masters 5.3, pp. 91, 92
  Extra Practice Copymaster 5.3, p. 36
  Reteaching Copymaster 5.3, p. 36
Special Populations
  Suggestions, Teacher's Edition, p. 192D

LESSON Notes

Have students include this type of graph in their math journals. Ask students how this type of graph is similar to a time line. It can provide information over time.

You may wish to remind students that data from surveys of any kind are valid only for specific years.

Example 1

Have students determine the current number of representatives in the Congress from their own state, and on what basis the number changes. The number of representatives of a state is based upon the population of that state.

STARTER: Problem of the Day

The first seven numbers of the Fibonacci sequence are 1, 1, 2, 3, 5, 8, 13, . . .
a. List the next three numbers of this sequence. 21, 34, 55
b. Every fourth Fibonacci number is divisible by what number? 3
c. Every fifth Fibonacci number is divisible by what number? 5

Also available as a copymaster, p. 13

STARTER: Warm-Up Exercises

1. Plot the points on a coordinate plane.
$A(0,4)$ $B(2,5)$ $C(4,6)$
$D(5,3)$ $E(3,-4)$ $F(-1,-3)$
Check students' work.
2. Join the consecutive points A through F in the coordinate plane of **Ex. 1**, using straight line segments.

Also available as a copymaster, p. 13

Help students recognize that a variety of methods exists by which we can communicate relationships in real-life situations using mathematics.

Example 2

Be careful to clearly describe the characteristics of a pentagon, hexagon, and heptagon.

Communicating about MATHEMATICS

Ask students what geometric pattern is described by the line graph in Example 2.
Straight line

Writing Prompt
Explain how you used the characteristics of the graph to decide on labels for the vertical axis in the graph for Ex. 18 of the Independent Practice.

The star in this Amish quilt is made up of triangular pieces of cloth.

Angle Measures of Polygons

Sum of Angle Measures (in degrees) vs *Number of Sides*

Exploring Patterns in Geometry

Example 2 *Finding a Geometric Pattern*

The sum of the measures of the angles of a triangle is 180°. Use this result to find the sum of the measures of the angles of a quadrilateral, pentagon, hexagon, and heptagon. Use a line graph to represent your results.

Triangle   Pentagon   Quadrilateral   Hexagon   Heptagon

Solution In the figure above, notice that a quadrilateral can be divided into two triangles. Because the sum of the measures of the angles of each triangle is 180°, it follows that the sum of the measures of the angles of the quadrilateral is

$$2(180°) \text{ or } 360°.$$

You can find the sum of the measures of the angles of the other polygons in a similar way.

$2(180°) = 360°$	*Sum of angle measures of quadrilateral*
$3(180°) = 540°$	*Sum of angle measures of pentagon*
$4(180°) = 720°$	*Sum of angle measures of hexagon*
$5(180°) = 900°$	*Sum of angle measures of heptagon*

These results are summarized in the line graph at the left. ∎

Communicating about MATHEMATICS

Cooperative Learning

▶ **SHARING IDEAS about the Lesson**

Interpreting a Line Graph Graphs can help you see how two quantities are related to each other. For instance, in Example 2, let n represent the number of sides of the polygon, and let S represent the sum of the angle measures of the polygon. Use the line graph shown above to describe to your partner how n and S are related. Use the graph to predict the value of S when $n = 8$. Explain how you could verify your prediction.

$S = (n-2)180°, 1080°$; draw an 8-sided figure, measure each angle, and add the measures of the angles.

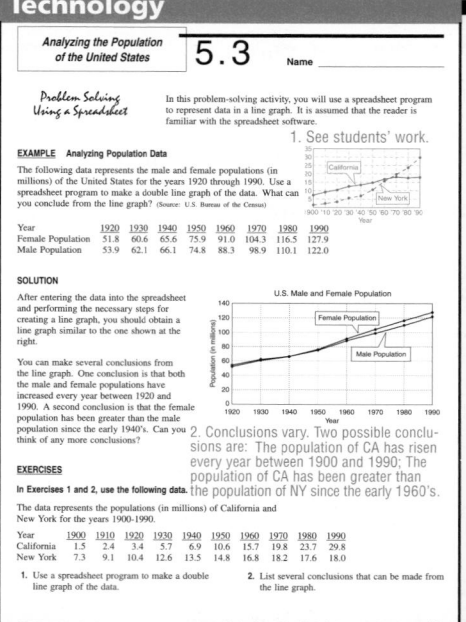

Technology

Analyzing the Population of the United States   **5.3**   Name _____

Problem Solving Using a Spreadsheet

In this problem-solving activity, you will use a spreadsheet program to represent data in a line graph. It is assumed that the reader is familiar with the spreadsheet software.

1. See students' work.

EXAMPLE Analyzing Population Data

The following data represents the male and female populations (in millions) of the United States for the years 1920 through 1990. Use a spreadsheet program to make a double line graph of the data. What can you conclude from the line graph? (Source: U.S. Bureau of the Census)

Year	1920	1930	1940	1950	1960	1970	1980	1990
Female Population	51.8	60.6	65.6	75.9	91.0	104.3	116.5	127.9
Male Population	53.9	62.1	66.1	74.8	88.3	98.9	110.1	122.0

SOLUTION

After entering the data into the spreadsheet and performing the necessary steps for creating a line graph, you should obtain a line graph similar to the one shown at the right.

You can make several conclusions from the line graph. One conclusion is that both the male and female populations have increased every year between 1920 and 1990. A second conclusion is that the female population has been greater than the male population since the early 1940's. Can you think of any more conclusions?

U.S. Male and Female Population

2. Conclusions vary. Two possible conclusions are: The population of CA has risen every year between 1900 and 1990; The population of CA has been greater than the population of NY since the early 1960's.

EXERCISES

In Exercises 1 and 2, use the following data. The data represents the populations (in millions) of California and New York for the years 1900-1990.

Year	1900	1910	1920	1930	1940	1950	1960	1970	1980	1990
California	1.5	2.4	3.4	5.7	6.9	10.6	15.7	19.8	23.7	29.8
New York	7.3	9.1	10.4	12.6	13.5	14.8	16.8	18.2	17.6	18.0

1. Use a spreadsheet program to make a double line graph of the data.

2. List several conclusions that can be made from the line graph.

EXERCISES

Guided Practice

▶ **CHECK for Understanding**

Interpreting a Line Graph   **In Exercises 1–4, use the line graph in Example 1.** Estimates vary.

1. Estimate the number of female representatives in 1993. 47

2. Estimate the number of Hispanic representatives in 1993. 17

3. Estimate the increase in female representatives from 1991 to 1993. 19

4. Estimate the increase in African American representatives from 1991 to 1993. 13

Independent Practice

Handling Garbage   **In Exercises 5–12, use the line graph.**
(Source: Franklin Associates) See margin.

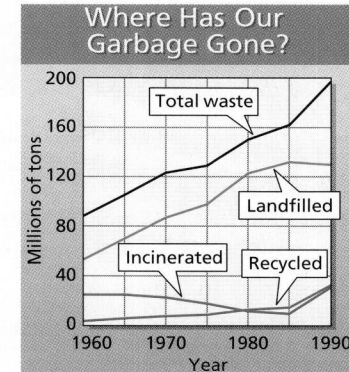

Where Has Our Garbage Gone?

5. Name the units of the horizontal and vertical axes.

6. What are the four quantities shown in the line graph?

7. Estimate the total waste in 1980 and 1990.

8. Estimate the amount of incinerated garbage in 1970.

9. Which quantities increased every year?

10. During which time period did the amount of incinerated garbage decrease?

11. *Reasoning*   What is the relationship between the four quantities in the line graph?

12. *Think about It*   Why do you think landfill garbage is decreasing?

A Geometric Pattern   **In Exercises 13 and 14, use the triangles shown below.**

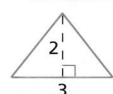 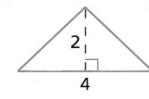 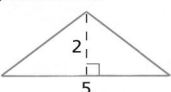

13. Create a table that lists the base, height, and area of each triangle. See margin.

14. Make a line graph showing the relationship between the base and the area. See Additional Answers.

15. *Airline Profits*   The total profit or loss (in billions of dollars) for airlines in the United States is given in the table. Construct a line graph for this data. *(Source: Air Transport Association)* See Additional Answers.

Year	1983	1984	1985	1986	1987	1988	1989	1990	1991	1992
Profit or Loss	−0.2	0.8	0.8	−0.2	0.7	1.7	0.1	−3.9	−1.9	−4.0

P Portfolio Opportunity

5.3 ▪ Exploring Line Graphs   **205**

Extra Practice

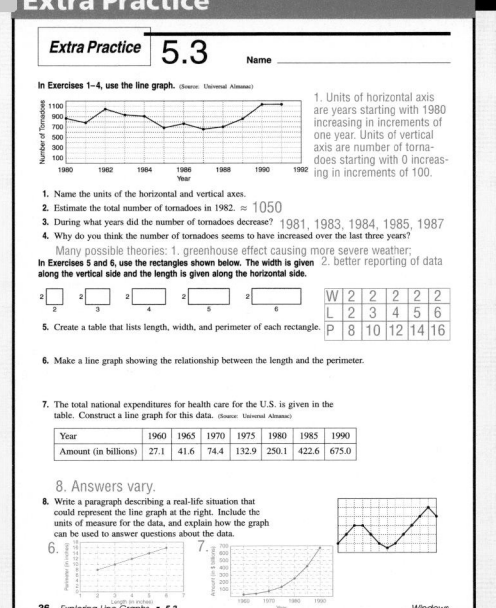

Reteaching

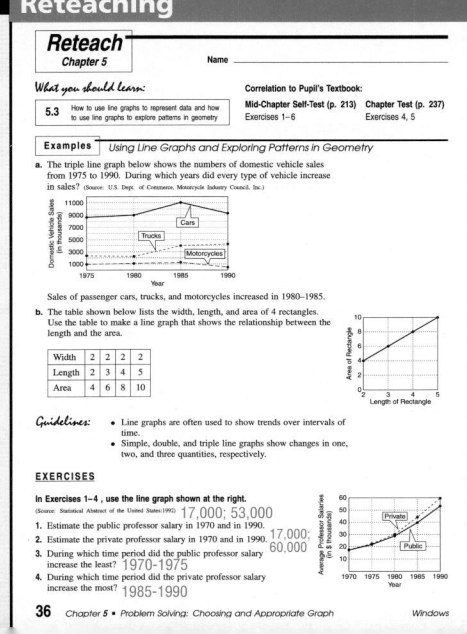

► **Ex. 18**

CRITICAL THINKING

This is great opportunity for students to reason about the characteristics of a graph. Point out to them that the time axis does not specify AM or PM, which gives students even more room for conjecture. It might help to have a student verbalize the "behavior" of the graph with observations about the peaks and valleys, and so on.

Integrated Review

► **Ex. 24**

EXTENSION

Ask students for their best estimate of the area of the page in square centimeters.

Exploration and Extension

EXTENSION

Have students discuss why the price of gasoline was so high in 1980. Ask them what happened in the 1970's.

Portfolio Opportunity: Math Log

A double line graph is used to show the total revenue and cost associated with a company over a 10-year period. Describe the company's profits when the revenue graph lies above the cost graph, when the cost graph lies above the revenue graph, and when the line graphs intersect.

Also available as a copymaster, page 16, Ex. 3

College Costs   In Exercises 16 and 17, use the table, which lists the average annual cost (in dollars) of tuition and fees of four-year public and private colleges for several years. *(Source: The College Board)*

Year	Public	Private
1981	909	4113
1983	1148	5093
1985	1318	6121
1987	1537	7116
1989	1781	8446
1991	2137	10,017

✪ **16.** Make a line graph of the data. See margin.

✪ **17.** Are the costs for a public college increasing at a faster or slower rate than the costs for a private college? Explain your reasoning. Slightly slower, explanations vary

✪ **18.** *Writing*   Write a paragraph describing
Ⓟ a real-life situation that could be represented by the line graph at the right. Include the units of measure for the data, and explain how the graph can be used to answer questions about the data. Answers vary.

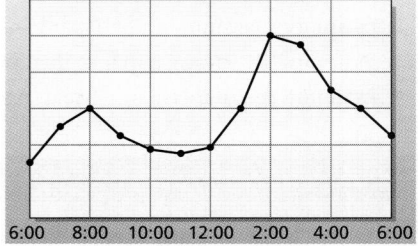

Integrated Review   *Making Connections within Mathematics*

Mental Math   In Exercises 19–22, evaluate the expression.

19. $\frac{1}{2}(8)(4)$ 16   **20.** $\frac{1}{2}(16)(7)$ 56   **21.** $\sqrt{5^2+12^2}$ 13   **22.** $\sqrt{6^2+8^2}$ 10

23. *Estimation*   Which is the best estimate for the distance (in miles) between Madison, Wisconsin, and Atlanta, Georgia? c

    a. 7   **b.** 70   **c.** 700   **d.** 7000

24. *Estimation*   Which is the best estimate for the area (in square inches) of this page? d

    a. 20   **b.** 40   **c.** 60   **d.** 80

Exploration and Extension

Reading Graphs   In Exercises 25–30, use the line graph to find the missing coordinate of the ordered pair. *(Source: U.S. Department of Energy)*

✪ **25.** (1950, [?]) 27
✪ **26.** ([?], 119.1) 1980
✪ **27.** ([?], 56.7) 1975
✪ **28.** ([?], 114.9) 1990
✪ **29.** (1955, [?]) 30
✪ **30.** ([?], 31.2) 1965

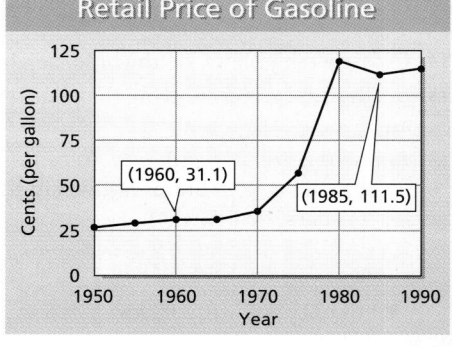

✪ More difficult exercises
Ⓟ Portfolio Opportunity

Enrichment

Extend the Problem of the Day by having students square each Fibonacci number in the sequence of the first ten terms. Then have students add each set of adjacent terms to form a new term. Have them describe the new sequence.

Original sequence: 1, 1, 2, 3, 5, 8, 13, 21, 34, 55
Squares: 1, 1, 4, 9, 25, 64, 169, 441, 1156, 3025
New sequence   2, 5, 13, 34, 89, 233, . . .
Sum of adjacent squares forms a sequence of alternate Fibonacci numbers.

Answer
16.

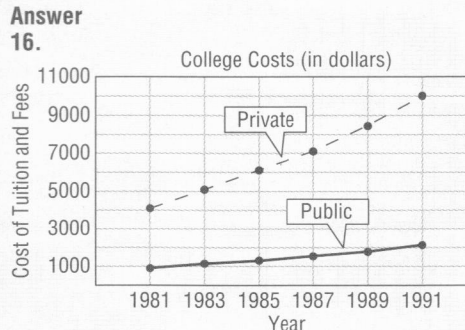

In Exercises 1–5, use the graph at the right. (5.2)
(Source: American Veterinary Association)

1. What type of graph is used? Triple bar
2. Which types of pet owners increased? Cat, bird
3. Estimate the number of cat owners in 1983.
4. Estimate the number of dog owners in 1991.
5. Draw a line graph to represent the data. Use the horizontal axis for the year and the vertical axis for the number of owners. Which graph gives a better representation? Explain. Answers vary. For graph, see margin.

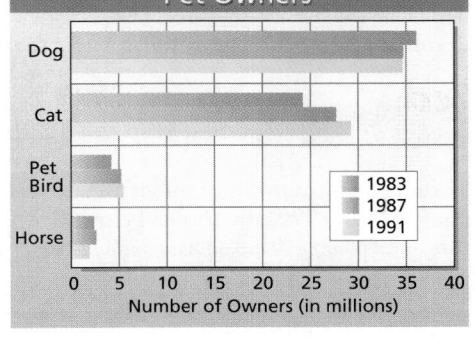

Pet Owners

1983
1987
1991

Number of Owners (in millions)

In Exercises 6–9, solve the equation. (4.3–4.5)

6. $3x + 4 = x$ -2
7. $2(2x + 1) = 8$ $1\frac{1}{2}$
8. $\frac{1}{3}(6x - 3) = 9x$ $-\frac{1}{7}$
9. $4t + 6t = 8t - 13$ $-6\frac{1}{2}$

Career Interview

Recycling Engineer

Stephen Morgan designs, starts up and troubleshoots systems to recycle paper at paper mills. He travels all over the United States, and to foreign countries and helps to insure that the paper brought from the recycling bins is quickly and easily made into new paper products.

Q: *What led you into this career?*
A: When I learned about it in college, I felt it was an interesting, new and exciting field.
Q: *What is your favorite part of your job?*
A: I like to travel, and the different people I meet together with the variety of the work keeps it exciting and fun.
Q: *Do you use high school mathematics in your work?*
A: Yes, I use algebra a great deal in my work, solving equations for unknown values. For example, I use it when I calculate mass balances as treated pulp is being moved from one place to another inside the mills. In addition, I also need to understand geometry when planning an installation.
Q: *What would you like to tell students about math?*
A: Math is very important, it makes life easier to understand. Knowing math makes you aware of your surroundings.

Answer to Mixed Review
5.

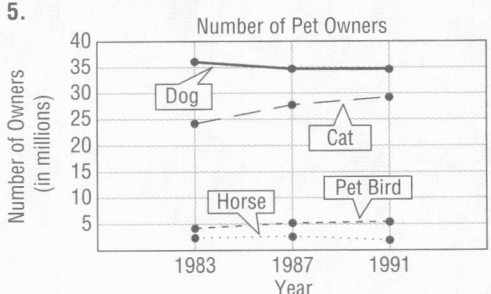

Materials
Color Transparencies
  U.S. map, p. 22
Teaching Tools
  U.S. map, p. C34

This investigation provides a useful connection to geography. Have students use the library reference section and a book such as the State Book of Lists to obtain a new data set for creating a color map model.

EXTENSION
Have students draw a histogram based on the frequency of states in each interval listed for the data. This provides a format for connecting data presentation to Lesson 5.2. Ask students which data-organizing technique seems more useful for interpreting the data.

Materials Needed: colored pencils, paper

In this investigation you will use a map to organize data.

Example   *Using a Map to Organize Data*

The numbers (in millions) of visitors to state parks and recreation areas for 1991 are shown below. Use a map to organize this data. (*Source: National Association of State Park Directors*)

AK	6.8	HI	19.1	ME	2.4	NJ	11.0	SD	5.9
AL	6.1	IA	12.1	MI	25.3	NM	4.3	TN	27.0
AR	6.9	ID	2.5	MN	8.0	NV	2.6	TX	24.0
AZ	2.2	IL	34.6	MO	15.0	NY	60.7	UT	4.9
CA	70.4	IN	10.5	MS	3.9	OH	67.2	VA	3.9
CO	8.7	KS	4.1	MT	1.7	OK	16.0	VT	1.0
CT	6.7	KY	27.3	NC	9.5	OR	39.5	WA	46.8
DE	3.2	LA	1.1	ND	1.0	PA	36.3	WI	12.3
FL	13.1	MA	12.0	NE	9.2	RI	5.1	WV	8.3
GA	16.3	MD	7.8	NH	2.8	SC	8.0	WY	2.0

0-5.9	6-11.9
12-17.9	18-23.9
24-29.9	30-35.9
36-41.9	42-47.9
48-53.9	54-59.9
60-65.9	66-71.9

Solution Begin with a state map. Then choose different colors to represent different intervals. Color each state accordingly.

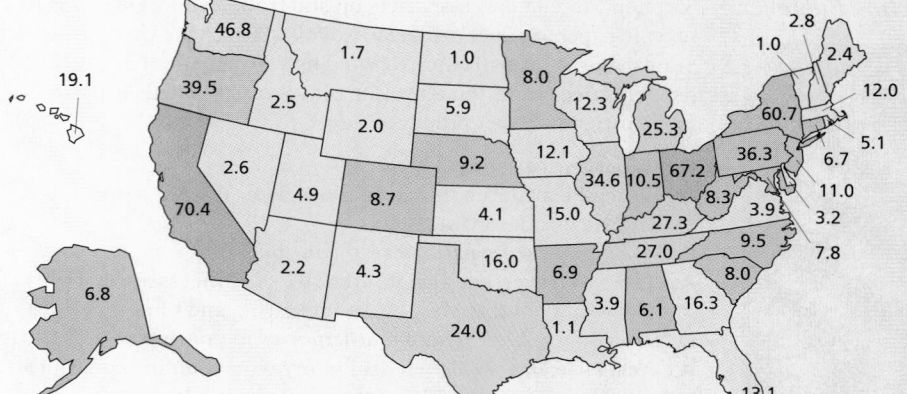

Exercises

1. Which 8 states had the most visitors?
   CA, OH, NY, WA, OR, PA, IL, KY

2. Which 8 states had the least visitors?
   ND, VT, LA, MT, WY, AZ, ME, ID

3. Yellowstone Park, in Wyoming and Montana, is the most popular park in the United States. How does this information fit with that given above?

Yellowstone is a national park, so it is not included in the data.

5.4

Problem Solving: Choosing an Appropriate Graph

PACING the Lesson

Suggested Number of Days
Basic/Average 0   **Above Average** 1
Advanced 1

PLANNING the Lesson

Lesson Plan 5.4, p. 37

What you should learn:

Goal 1 How to choose an appropriate graph to represent data

Goal 2 How to use graphs to make presentations

Why you should learn it:

Graphs can help you communicate about real-life situations, such as showing the numbers of miles walked by individuals in different occupations.

Real Life
Occupations

Study Tip...

When deciding which type of graph to use, here are some guidelines.

1. *Use a bar graph when the data falls into distinct categories and you want to compare totals.*
2. *Use a line graph when you want to show the relationship between consecutive amounts or data over time.*
3. *Use a picture graph for informal presentations in which you want a high visual appeal.*

Goal 1   Choosing Appropriate Graphs

So far in the chapter, you have studied picture graphs, time lines, bar graphs, and line graphs. When you are using a graph to organize and present data, you must first decide which type of graph to use.

Example 1   *Organizing Data with a Graph*

The following data lists the daily average numbers of miles walked by people while working at their jobs. Organize the data graphically. *(Source: American Podiatry Association)*

Occupation	Miles Walked per Day
Actor	3.2 miles
Mail Carrier	4.4 miles
Medical Doctor	3.5 miles
Nurse	3.9 miles
Police Officer	6.8 miles
Retail Salesperson	3.4 miles
Secretary	3.3 miles
Television Reporter	4.2 miles

Solution   You can use either a picture graph or a bar graph. The bar graph below is horizontal. This makes it easier to label each bar. Also notice that the occupations are listed in order of the number of miles walked.

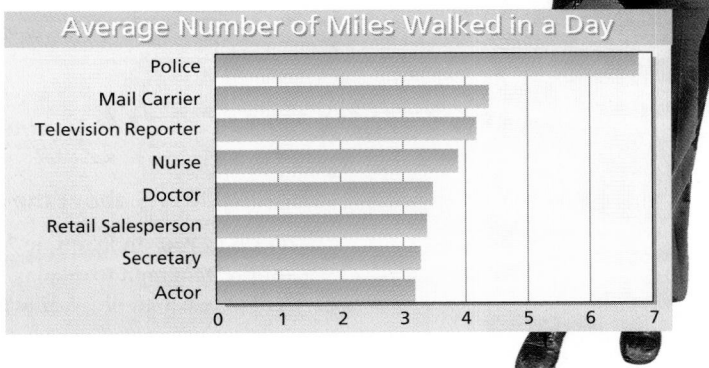

Average Number of Miles Walked in a Day

(Horizontal bar graph, from top to bottom: Police, Mail Carrier, Television Reporter, Nurse, Doctor, Retail Salesperson, Secretary, Actor; horizontal axis 0 to 7)

ORGANIZER

Starters (reproduced below)
   Problem of the Day 5.4, p. 14
   Warm-Up Exercises 5.4, p. 14
Lesson Resources
   Teaching Tools
      Graph paper, pp. T1, C2
      Puzzle, p. C15
   Math Log, p. 17
   Answer Masters 5.4, p. 93
   Extra Practice Copymaster 5.4, p. 37
   Reteaching Copymaster 5.4, p. 37
   Enrichment Projects, pp. 26–28
Special Populations
   Suggestions, Teacher's Edition, p. 192D

LESSON Notes

MATH JOURNAL
The type of graph you use in any real-life situation depends on the data you want to represent. Encourage students to use the Study Tip to record guidelines for the use of each type of graph in their journals.

Example 1
Point out that by *ordering* data, as in this graph, information can often be processed more effectively.

EXTENSION
Have students discuss what categories of people might be particularly interested in this information and why.   For example, footwear companies

---

Example 2

Explain to students that this is basically a pictograph similar to that on page 197, but it also has some of the elements of a stacked graph. Note that labeling has been minimized by the use of gender icons and color.

EXTENSION

Have students conduct a similar survey in class and graph the results.

Communicating about MATHEMATICS

EXTENSION

You may wish to suggest a class survey to determine students' television viewing preferences over weekends. Have small groups of students create appropriate graphs to display the results.

Writing Prompt

What I liked best about math this week is . . .

Real Life
Fashion Color Preferences

Example 2 *Making a Presentation*

In 1993, the *Pantone Color Institute* took a survey asking adults which color of clothing they preferred for dressy occasions. The results are listed below. You work for a clothing designer and want to use this data in a presentation. How would you organize the data graphically? (*Source: Pantone Color Institute of Carlstadt, New Jersey*)

Color	Number of Women	Number of Men
Black	727	702
Blue	551	473
Gray	223	649
Red	222	78
Brown	102	198

Solution One possibility is to use a picture graph, like that shown below.

Color Preference for Dressy Occasions
Each symbol represents 100 people who preferred the indicated color.

	Men	Women
Black		
Blue		
Gray		
Red		
Brown		

What do young people wear for dressy occasions? The data in this graph represents the color preferences of adults. If you were to survey your classmates, do you think your results would be similar?

Communicating about MATHEMATICS

▶ **SHARING IDEAS about the Lesson**

It's Up to You In Example 2, would it make sense to use a simple bar graph to display the data? A stacked bar graph? A double bar graph? A line graph? Explain your reasoning.

See margin.

Answer to Communicating

Answers vary. Because two kinds of people (men and women) choose among the same five colors, only a double or stacked bar graph or a double line graph would make sense.

Answer

5.

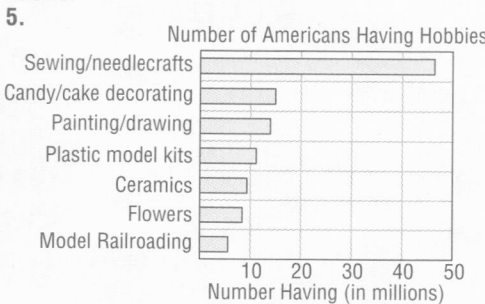

Number of Americans Having Hobbies

Sewing/needlecrafts
Candy/cake decorating
Painting/drawing
Plastic model kits
Ceramics
Flowers
Model Railroading

10 20 30 40 50
Number Having (in millions)

EXERCISES

Guided Practice

▶ CHECK for Understanding

In Exercises 1 and 2, refer to Example 1.

1. On the average, how many more miles a _2.4_ day do police officers walk than mail carriers?

2. On the average, which occupation walks half as many miles in a day as police officers?
Retail Salesperson

In Exercises 3 and 4, refer to Example 2.

3. How many more men than women prefer to wear gray? _426_

P 4. Describe how this picture graph would be effective in giving a presentation.
Answers vary.

Independent Practice

In Exercises 5–8, choose a type of graph that best represents the data. Explain why you chose that type, and then draw the graph. Answers vary. For graphs, see margin, pages 210 and 211.

5. *Hobbies* The number (in millions) of people who have a hobby *(Source: Hobby Industries of America)*

Craft or Hobby	Number
Sewing/needlecrafts	46.4
Candy making/ cake decorating	14.9
Painting/drawing	13.9
Plastic model kits	11.1
Ceramics	9.3
Flowers	8.4
Model railroading	5.6

6. *Videocassette Recorders* The average number (out of 100) of people who own videocassette recorders *(Source: The Roper Organization)*

Year	Number
1980	3
1983	10
1985	19
1987	50
1988	64
1990	65
1992	68

7. *Owning Cats* The average number (out of 100) of cat owners who state the reason for owning a cat *(Source: Gallup Poll)*

Reason for Owning a Cat	Number
Someone to play with	93
Companionship	84
Help children learn responsibility	78
Someone to communicate with	62
Security	51

8. *Dog Tricks* The number (in millions) of dogs who can perform tricks *(Source: Pet Food Institute)*

Trick	Number
Sit	5.3
Shake paw	3.8
Roll over	2.9
Speak	2.7
Stand on hind legs	1.9
Sing	0.8
Fetch newspaper	0.4

5.4 • Problem Solving: Choosing an Appropriate Graph **211**

EXERCISE Notes

ASSIGNMENT GUIDE

***Basic/Average:**
Day 1: Ex. 5–15 odd
Day 2: Ex. 6–14 even

Above Average:
Ex. 5–9 odd, 10, 13–15

Advanced: Ex. 5–9 odd, 10, 13–15

Selected Answers: Ex. 1–4, 5–13 odd

*You may wish to omit this lesson for these students.

Guided Practice

Assign these exercises as an in-class small-group activity.

Independent Practice

▶ **Ex. 5–8** Encourage students to refer to the Study Tip on page 209 for help with these exercises. The Warm-Up Exercises were designed to prepare students for drawing the appropriate graphs. Remind students also of the need for appropriate labeling.

Answers

6.
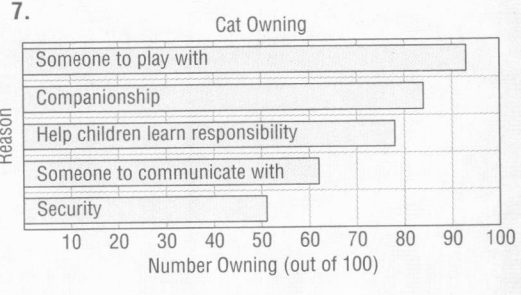

7.
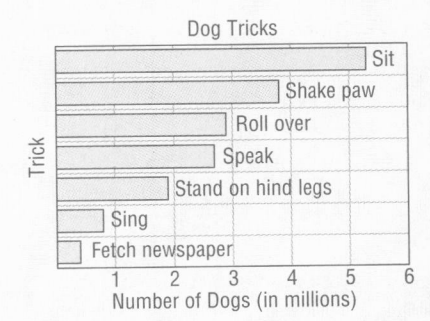

8.

Lesson 5.4 **211**

► **Ex. 9** This is a good opportunity for class discussion.

► **Ex. 10** Have students work with partners, and again refer them to the Study Tip on page 209.

Exploration and Extension

This could be used as a small-group competition in class. Advise students to write numbers on slips of sticky paper that can be moved around. Have students start with the circle at the top. If no progress is being made, you may wish to tell them where the 5 is.

Portfolio Opportunity: Math Log

Give an example of a set of data in which a bar graph would be the appropriate type of graph. Explain your answer.

Also available as a copymaster, page 17, Ex. 4

Short Quiz

Covers Lessons 5.3 and 5.4

Available as a copymaster, page 70

---

9. *Little League* The graph shows the number of kids playing Little League baseball around the world from 1940 through 1993.

a. Estimate the number of kids who played in 1980, 1985, and 1990. 0.8 million, 1.3 million, 1.8 million

b. Estimate the increase in players from 1940 to 1993. 2.4 million

c. During which decade did the number of players remain about the same? 1940–1950

d. During which decade did the greatest increase occur? 1980–1990

e. Why is a line graph a good choice for presenting this information? It shows clearly how it has changed over the years.

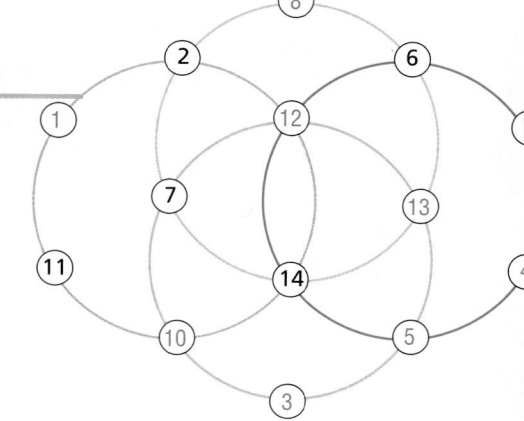

Kids Playing Little League Baseball around the World

10. *Organizing Data* You work for a telephone company and are asked to find the number of telephones that Americans have in their homes. You research the question and obtain the data shown at the right. (The number of people is shown in millions.) You are to present the data in a company meeting. How would you organize the data graphically? Answers vary.

Number of Phones in Home	Number of People
1	61.8
2	80.2
3	50.4
4	22.9
5 or more	13.7

Integrated Review   *Making Connections within Mathematics*

Modeling Numbers **In Exercises 11–14, draw the number line that is described.** See margin.

11. Low number: 0, High number: 15, 5 intervals

12. Low number: 0, High number: 16, 4 intervals

13. Low number: 0, High number: 64, 8 intervals

14. Low number: 0, High number: 150, 6 intervals

Exploration and Extension

15. *Puzzle* Copy the diagram at the right on a piece of paper. Then place the numbers from 1 to 14 in the small circles so that the sum of the numbers in each ring is 50. You can use each number only once. Six of the numbers have been placed in the small circles for you.

Enrichment

Have students locate a graph in a local newspaper or magazine. Ask them to write the data from the graph into a table similar to those in Exercises 5–8. Ask students whether they feel that the graph used was appropriate, and have them explain their answer.

Answers

11.
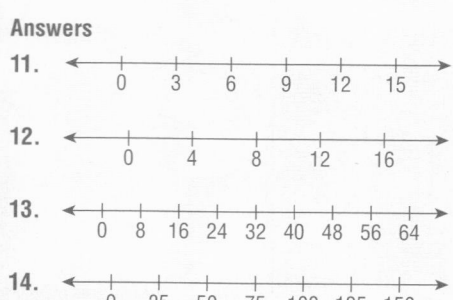

12.

0 4 8 12 16

13.

0 8 16 24 32 40 48 56 64

14.

0 25 50 75 100 125 150

Take this test as you would take a test in class. The answers to the exercises are given in the back of the book. **4.** Travel, Hotels, and Resorts; Gas

In Exercises 1–6, use the graph, which shows the expenses for network advertising. *(Source: Television Bureau of Advertising)* **(5.3)**

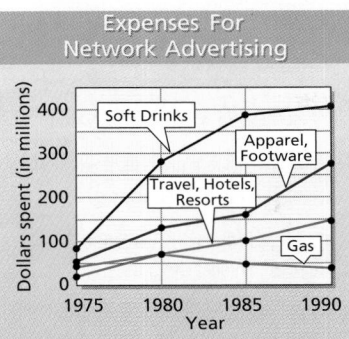

Expenses For Network Advertising

1. What type of graph is this? Line

2. Which group had the steadiest increase? Travel, Hotels, and Resorts

3. Name the only group whose expenses decreased. Gas

4. Which two groups spent about the same amount in 1980?

5. Which group had the sharpest increase from 1985 to 1990? Apparel and Footwear

6. Which group spent about $49 million in 1985? Gas

7. *Literature* The table lists the year of birth of several famous authors. Create a time line using the given information. **(5.1)** See margin.

Author	Year of Birth
Emily Dickinson	1830
Mark Twain	1835
Jack London	1876
John Steinbeck	1902
Alice Walker	1944

8. The table below shows the price of a share of stock for each company in March of 1994. Draw a graph that best represents the data. Explain why you chose that type of graph. **(5.4)** See margin.

Company	Stock Price
Sears, Roebuck	$48
Wal-Mart Stores	$28
JC Penney	$55
K Mart Corp.	$19
The Gap, Inc.	$45

9. Draw a graph that best represents the net profit (in millions of dollars) of Blockbuster Entertainment for the years given. Explain why you chose that type of graph. **(5.4)** See margin.

1993: $243.6 1992: $142.0 1991: $93.7
1990: $68.7 1989: $44.2 1988: $15.5

In Exercises 10–13, use the data in the graph, which shows the number of people who doodle. *(Source: Faber-Castell)* **(5.2)**

10. What type of graph is this? Bar

11. What seems to be the most common reason for doodling? Talking on the telephone

12. Estimate the number of people who doodle while they are thinking or solving problems. 75 million

13. What is the reason that about 82 million people doodle? Boredom

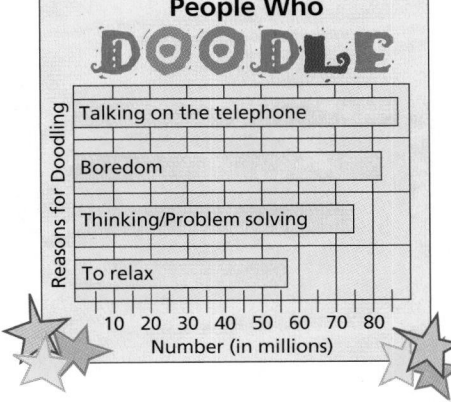

People Who DOODLE

Answers

7.

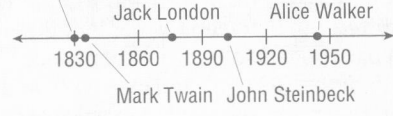

Emily Dickinson, Jack London, Alice Walker
1830 1860 1890 1920 1950
Mark Twain, John Steinbeck

8. Answers vary.

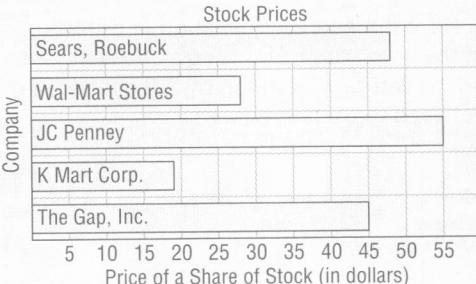

Stock Prices

9. Answers vary.

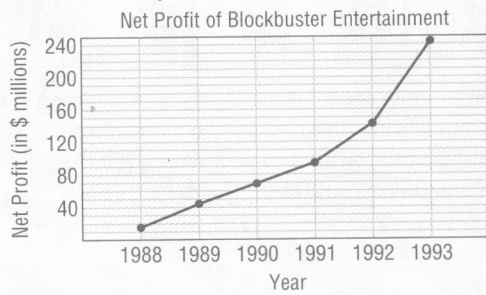

Net Profit of Blockbuster Entertainment

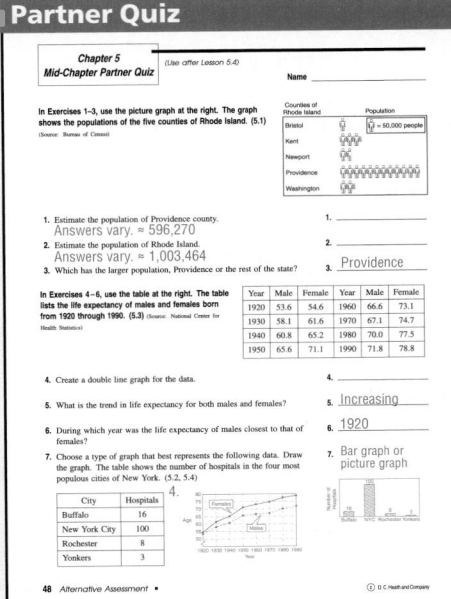

Partner Quiz

Chapter 5 Mid-Chapter Partner Quiz (Use after Lesson 5.4)

Mid-Chapter Test

Mid-Chapter 5 Test Form B (Use after Lesson 5.4)

PACING the Lesson

Suggested Number of Days
Basic/Average 0   Above Average 2
Advanced 2

PLANNING the Lesson

Lesson Plan 5.5, p. 38

ORGANIZER

Starters (reproduced below)
Problem of the Day 5.5, p. 14
Warm-Up Exercises 5.5, p. 14
Lesson Resources
Teaching Tools
Graph paper, pp. T1, C2
Math Log, p. 17
Answer Masters 5.5, p. 94
Extra Practice Copymaster 5.5, p. 38
Reteaching Copymaster 5.5, p. 38
Special Populations
Suggestions, Teacher's Edition, p. 192D

LESSON Notes

Explain to students that the effect of using a broken vertical scale is to permit larger intervals on the axis. This in turn may exaggerate the difference between the bar lengths—the 1994 bar appears to be more than twice the length of the 1991 bar. You may wish, at this point, to refer to the Guided Practice exercises.

Have students consider another distortion of the graph caused by using a *different* scale on the vertical axis. In this case, the difference between the bars is reduced.

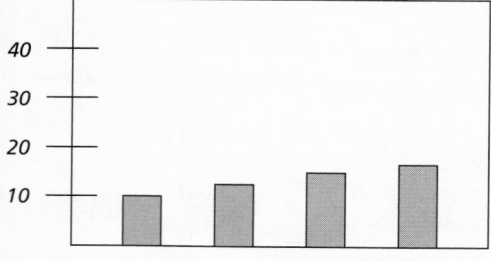

Then show students examples of misleading graphs from newspapers and magazines. Discuss the techniques that were used that seemed to misrepresent the data.

Common Error Alert!

Although this lesson demonstrates the sometimes misleading effect of using a broken scale, make sure that students understand that there is a perfectly legitimate use of broken scales in data representation where, for example, there is no risk of visual deception. Basically, a broken scale makes it possible to exclude from the graph a whole range of values that are unimportant to the representation of the given data.

5.5 Problem Solving: Misleading Graphs

What you should learn:

Goal 1 How to recognize misleading bar graphs

Goal 2 How to recognize misleading line graphs

Why you should learn it:

Knowing when a graph is misleading helps you interpret real-life information that is presented graphically.

Real Life
Pet Behavior

Goal 1   Misleading Bar Graphs

LESSON INVESTIGATION

■ Investigating Bar Graphs

Group Activity Both bar graphs represent the same data. Which graph is misleading? Why?

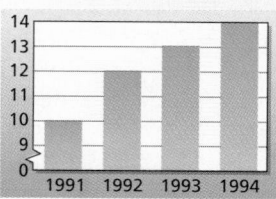
Broken Vertical Scale

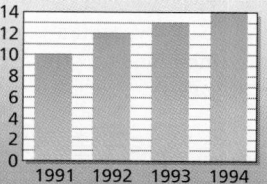
Unbroken Vertical Scale

Example 1   *Interpreting a Bar Graph*

From the graph, about how many more dogs sleep in or on their owners' beds as outside or in a garage? *(Source: Gallup)*

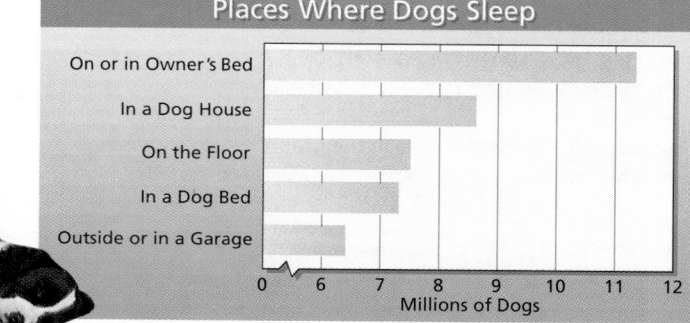

Solution   The size of the bars makes it appear that about 4 times as many dogs sleep in or on their owners' beds as sleep outside or in a garage. From the scale, however, you can see that it is really only about twice as many.   ■

214   Chapter 5 ▪ Exploring Data and Graphs

Goal 2 Misleading Line Graphs

Example 2 *Interpreting Line Graphs*

Each of the line graphs shows the numbers of paperback books and hardback books sold in the United States from 1985 through 1991. Which graph is misleading? *(Source: Book Industry Study Group)*

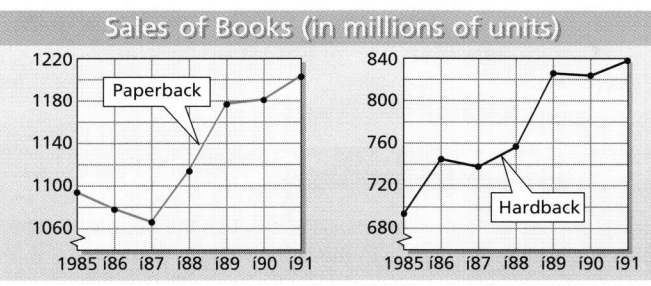

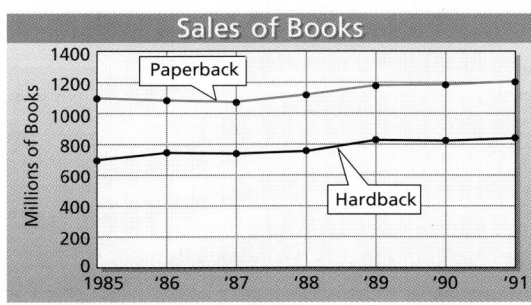

Solution The first graph is misleading; the second is not. The visual impression of the first graph makes it appear that paperbacks and hardbacks sold equally well. Moreover, the broken vertical scales accentuate the changes from one year to the next. ∎

P **Communicating** *about* MATHEMATICS

▶ **SHARING IDEAS about the Lesson**

Research Look through newspapers or magazines to find examples of graphs that are misleading. Bring the graphs to class. Do you think the graphs were intended to be misleading? Explain your reasoning. Check students' work.

ASSIGNMENT GUIDE

*Basic/Average:
Day 1: Ex. 3–6, 11, 12, 14, 15
Day 2: Ex. 7–10, 13, 16–18

Above Average:
Day 1: Ex. 3–6, 11, 12, 14, 15
Day 2: Ex. 7–10, 13, 16–18

Advanced:
Day 1: Ex. 3–6, 11, 12, 14, 15
Day 2: Ex. 7–10, 13, 16–18

Selected Answers: Ex. 1, 2, 3–17 odd

*You may wish to omit this lesson for these students.

Guided Practice

Use these exercises as part of the investigation discussion at the start of the lesson.

Independent Practice

▶ **Ex. 3–6** Have students observe the difference between a numerical doubling in size versus a visual doubling. For example, the flute bar is four times the size of the trumpet bar, but the numerical value for the flute is less than twice the numerical value for trumpets.

▶ **Ex. 6** The key to this exercise (and Ex. 10) is to create a graph in which the visual relationship matches the numerical relationship.

▶ **Ex. 7–10** Make sure students observe that the small divisions on the time axis represent months, and that the graph begins in February, 1991.

Guided Practice

▶ **CHECK for Understanding**

Business   In Exercises 1 and 2, use the graphs in the Lesson Investigation on page 214.

1. Suppose that the graphs represent your company's profits. Which graph makes your profits appear to have increased more rapidly? *The one with the broken vertical scale*

2. Suppose that the graphs represent your company's expenses. Which graph makes your expenses appear to have increased more slowly? *The one with the unbroken vertical scale*

Independent Practice

Playing an Instrument   In Exercises 3–6, use the bar graph. The graph shows the number of people in the United States (in millions) that play each instrument. (*Source: The* Unofficial *U.S. Census*) 3.–5. See margin.

3. Judging only from the length of the bars, compare the number of flutists to the number of drummers.

4. Use the scale to determine the answer to Exercise 3.

5. Is this graph misleading? Explain.

6. Use the information in the graph to create another bar graph that is *not* misleading. See Additional Answers.

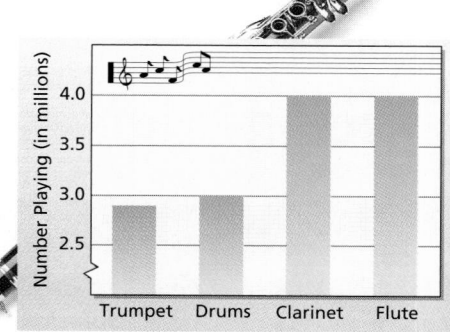

P *Weekly Earnings*   In Exercises 7–10, use the line graph. This line graph is similar to the one that appeared in *The Wall Street Journal.* The graph shows the weekly earnings for factory workers from February, 1991 through January, 1994. 7.–9. See margin.

7. Without looking at the vertical scale, compare the weekly pay in February, 1991 to the weekly pay in December, 1993.

8. Use the scale to determine the answer to Exercise 7.

9. Write a paragraph explaining why this graph is misleading.

10. Use the information in the line graph to create another line graph that is *not* misleading. See Additional Answers.

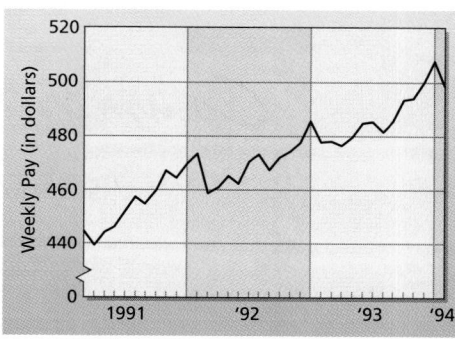

Answers

3. There appears to be 2 times as many flutists as drummers.

4. There are about $1\frac{1}{3}$ times as many flutists as drummers.

5. Yes, the broken vertical scale makes it appear that there are 2 times as many flutists instead of about $1\frac{1}{3}$ times as many flutists.

7. The pay in December 1993 appears to be 4 times as much as the pay in February 1991.

8. The pay in December 1993 is about 1.1 times as much as the pay in February 1991.

9. The broken vertical scale makes it appear that the pay in December 1993 is 4 times as much pay instead of about 1.1 times as much pay.

Extra Practice

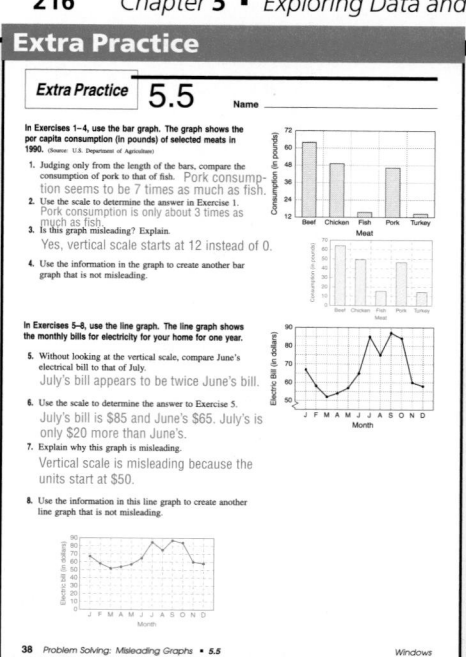

Reteaching

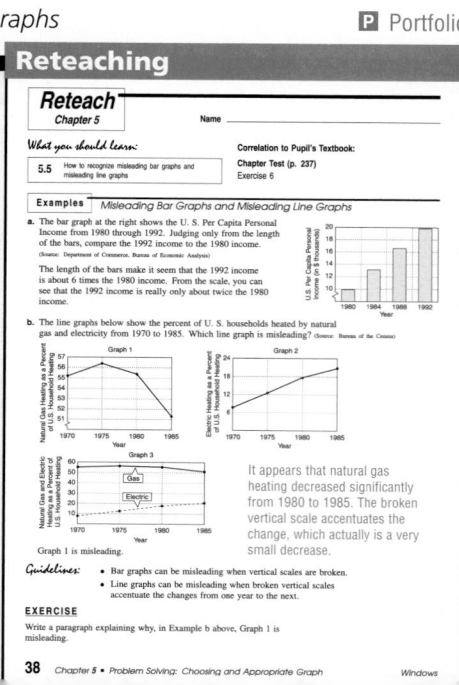

Comparing Graphs   In Exercises 11 and 12, use the two graphs below.

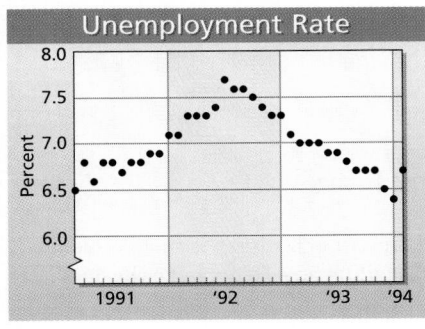

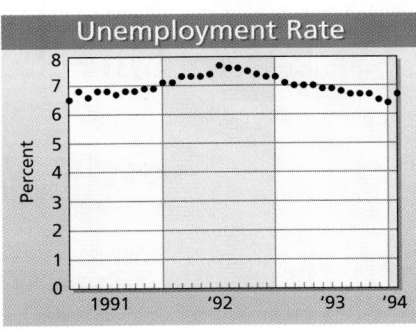

11. A candidate who has been in office is seeking reelection. Which graph might the candidate use? Why? Answers vary.

12. A candidate who has not been in office is seeking election. Which graph might the candidate use? Why? Answers vary.

13. *Research Project*   Use a table or graph of information to create a misleading graph. Explain how the graph is misleading.
   Check students' work.

Integrated Review   *Making Connections within Mathematics*

Logical Thinking   In Exercises 14–17, decide whether the information in the graph allows you to conclude that the statement is true. Explain your reasoning. *(Source: Bureau of the Census)*

14. More new homes in 1990 have fireplaces than new homes in 1970. True, 64% > 35%

15. In 1970, more than half of all new homes had only one bathroom. True, 100% − 48% = 52%

16. The percent of new homes built with airconditioning in 1990 is triple that of 1970. False, 78% ≠ 3 (34%)

17. In 1970, more than 50% of all new homes were built without a garage. False, 100% − 58% < 50%

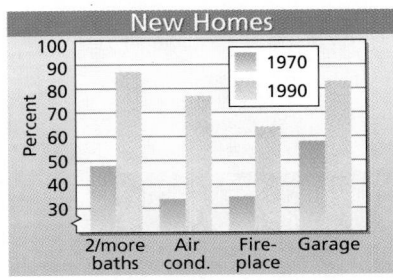

Exploration and Extension

18. *Average Home Prices*   The picture graph shows the average sales price of a new one-family house in 1970 and in 1990. Explain why the graph is misleading.
   The house sizes are different, but each house represents the same amount.

Average Home Price

KEY
One house represents $27,000

1970   1990

✪ More difficult exercises
P Portfolio Opportunity

▶ **Ex. 13**   Assign this as a small-group presentation project

Explain to students that these exercises do not, per se, involve a misleading graph but rather what can be deduced from the graph.

Exploration and Extension

Note that this graph might easily be interpreted in a contradictory sense—that in 1990 you could buy nearly six houses for the price you paid for one in 1970!

Portfolio Opportunity: Math Log

In your own words, explain how a broken vertical scale can lead to a misleading bar graph.

Also available as a copymaster, page 17, Ex. 5

Alternative Assessment

Chapter 5 Group Assessment
A data analysis and graphing activity that develops students' awareness of misleading graphs.

Chapter 5 Individual Assessment
A similar follow-up activity for individual students. Adds incentive for the group activity and measures individual competence in the activity.

Available as copymasters, pages 67, 68

▶ **Enrichment**

Have students choose a graph from a newspaper or magazine. Have them redraw the graph so that the data shows different results (either more accurate or misleading). Then have them create a new slogan for the graph.

PACING the Lesson

Suggested Number of Days
Basic/Average 2 **Above Average** 1
Advanced 1

PLANNING the Lesson

Lesson Plan 5.6, p. 39

ORGANIZER

Starters (reproduced below)
 Problem of the Day 5.6, p. 14
 Warm-Up Exercises 5.6, p. 14
Lesson Resources
 Color Transparencies
  Picture for Example 1, p. 23
 Teaching Tools
  Graph paper, pp. T1, C2
 Math Log, p. 17
 Answer Masters 5.6, pp. 95, 96
 Extra Practice Copymaster 5.6, p. 39
 Reteaching Copymaster 5.6, p. 39
Special Populations
 Suggestions, Teacher's Edition, p. 192D

LESSON Notes

Have students record the definition of *statistics* in their math journals—the science of gathering, classifying, and analyzing data.

Lesson Investigation
Encourage students to be creative. One obvious way of organizing the data is to count the number of deer at a given age. Another is to cluster the data into age groups (perhaps based upon the development stages of deer). Students should then indicate the type of graph that they would use to display the data.

Addressing Misconceptions

Make sure students understand that drawing a line plot is not the same as plotting a line.

Example 1

A line plot is a frequency distribution. The similarity to a bar graph is easily observable.

5.6 Statistics: Line Plots

What you should learn:

Goal 1 How to use line plots to organize data

Goal 2 How to use organized data to help make decisions

Why you should learn it:

Data is more meaningful and useful when it is organized.

Real Life
Wildlife

Goal 1 Using Line Plots

When data from an experiment or a survey is first collected, it is usually not organized. Deciding how to organize the data is a critical part of a branch of mathematics called *statistics*.

LESSON INVESTIGATION

■ Investigating Data Organization

Group Activity The "raw data" (unorganized data) below lists the ages of a herd of deer at Presque Isle State Park. With other members of your group, discuss different ways that the data could be organized. As a group, choose one method and use it to organize the data.

3, 1, 1, 5, 11, 12, 5, 7, 7, 3, 2, 4, 1, 10, 11, 4, 4, 4,
1, 5, 6, 6, 7, 4, 1, 3, 2, 1, 9, 2, 12, 4, 4, 1, 8, 9,
1, 3, 3, 2, 5, 1, 3, 1, 2, 2, 1, 1, 2, 2, 1, 1, 3, 3,
1, 6, 2, 6, 1, 1, 8, 3, 2, 2, 2, 2, 5, 5, 1, 3, 8, 2

Example 1 *Using a Line Plot*

One way to organize the data shown above is with a line plot. To begin, draw a number line that includes all integers from 1 through 12. For each number in the list, place an × above the coordinate on the number line, as shown below.

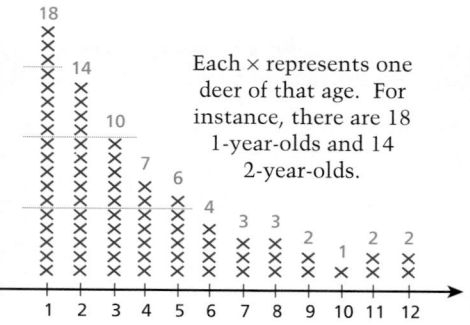

Each × represents one deer of that age. For instance, there are 18 1-year-olds and 14 2-year-olds.

Real Life
Recycling

Example 2   *Interpreting a Survey*

You are trying to determine the "environmental awareness" of a group of people. You ask each person in the group to complete a survey. One of the questions asks about the importance of recycling aluminum cans. The results are shown below. What would you conclude from the survey?

1. Very important. I always recycle aluminum cans.
2. Quite important. I usually recycle aluminum cans.
3. Somewhat important. I sometimes recycle aluminum cans.
4. Not very important. I recycle aluminum cans if it is convenient.
5. Not at all important. I never recycle aluminum cans.

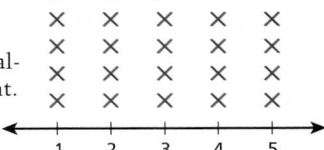

Solution   From the survey, it appears that many of the people in the group are not as aware of the importance of recycling as they should be. Four of the people said that they never recycle aluminum cans and another seven said that they only recycle if it is convenient (they might happen to be near a recycling container). ■

ch year in the United States, millions tons of waste are buried in landfills.

P *Communicating* about **MATHEMATICS**

Connections
Art and Design

▶ **SHARING IDEAS about the Lesson**

Poster Design   You are designing a poster to increase the environmental awareness of a group of people. Which of the following do you think would be useful on the poster? How would you present the information? *(Source: Environmental Protection Agency)* Answers vary.

• In 1993, over 200 million tons of nonindustrial waste was created in the United States.
• In 1993, the national average was 4.2 pounds of nonindustrial waste per person per day.
• In 1993, 3.6 billion pounds of aluminum cans were recycled in the United States.

Surveys are common tools for gathering opinions. For example, in shopping malls, customers are asked to answer questions about services and products. Ask students if any of them have ever participated in any type of survey.

Example 2

You may wish to point out that in a line plot, each "X" can be used to represent some value other than 1 (10, 100, and so on).
Ask students: For the results given in this example, could a case be made that most people are aware of the importance of recycling?   Answers will vary. For example, 63% of respondents have some awareness.

Communicating
about **MATHEMATICS**

Challenge students to create and conduct an environment-related survey for their class. Then allow them to report on the results as a class project.

Writing Prompt
Describe the images that come to mind when you think about statistics.

ASSIGNMENT GUIDE

Basic/Average:
 Day 1: Ex. 4–6, 9, 10, 12–14
 Day 2: Ex. 7, 11, 15–18
Above Average:
 Ex.5, 6, 8, 9, 11, 15–18
Advanced: Ex. 5, 6, 8, 9, 11, 15–18
Selected Answers: Ex. 1–3, 5–17 odd

Guided Practice

▶ **Ex. 3** You may wish to point out once more that some real-life facts often become quite obvious when data is organized.

Guided Practice

P CHECK for Understanding

1. *Writing* In your own words, describe the meaning of statistics. Answers vary.

In Exercises 2 and 3, refer to Example 1 on page 218.

2. How many 5-year-old deer are there? 6

3. What do you notice about the population of the deer as they increase in age? Decreases

Independent Practice

Organizing Data **In Exercises 4 and 5, decide whether the data could have been organized with a line plot. Explain your reasoning.** Explanations vary.

4. The following data shows the heights (in inches) of 35 eighth graders. Yes

Height (in inches)	Number of 8th graders
60	3
62	5
64	8
65	9
66	5
68	3
72	2

5. A survey was taken of the number of cars on the road of different ages. No (*Source: Motor Vehicle Manufacturers Association*)

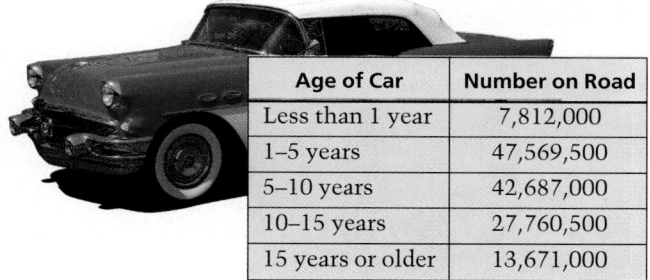

Age of Car	Number on Road
Less than 1 year	7,812,000
1–5 years	47,569,500
5–10 years	42,687,000
10–15 years	27,760,500
15 years or older	13,671,000

6. *Homework* Sixty students in a class were asked to keep track of the number of hours each spent doing homework during a specific week. The results are shown below. Organize the data in a line plot. See margin.

3, 8, 1, 12, 6, 8, 3, 7, 11, 10, 8, 10, 15, 2, 1,
6, 14, 4, 15, 9, 10, 13, 14, 4, 11, 7, 6, 7, 10, 9,
5, 11, 10, 8, 15, 4, 12, 9, 5, 8, 11, 15, 10, 6, 5,
13, 5, 12, 10, 12, 5, 10, 11, 5, 10, 8, 12, 8, 12, 15

7. *Siblings* Thirty students in a class were asked the number of brothers and/or sisters each has. The results are shown below. Organize the data in a line plot. See margin.

4, 8, 2, 1, 3, 0, 2, 7, 0, 5, 4, 3, 1, 5, 3,
2, 2, 5, 3, 6, 3, 2, 4, 2, 6, 2, 3, 5, 3, 4

P Portfolio Opportunity

Answers
6.

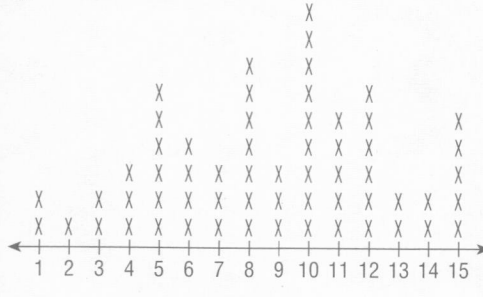

7.

Extra Practice

Extra Practice 5.6 Name _____

In Exercises 1 and 2, decide whether the data could have been organized with a line plot. Explain your reasoning.

1. The following data shows the number of games played in the Stanley Cup Finals from 1917-1993. (Source: Universal Almanac)

Games played	Years occured
2	5
3	2
4	22
5	24
6	14
7	9

Yes. Explanations vary.

2. The following data shows the number of seeds of a particular plant that germinated within a specified number of weeks.

Week	Number of seeds
1	6
2	9
3	13
4	16
5	7
6	2

Yes. Explanations vary.

3. The following data shows the resulting sum when a pair of six-sided dice is tossed 100 times. Organize the data in a line plot.

```
8   4   3   5   6   7   5   7   7
8   6   7   8   4   8   8   4   9   10
7   9   5   7   5   9   10  6   2   7
2   8   7   9   7   9   4   9   7   6
5   10  6   4   10  9   7   10  6   9
6   9   7   2   10  9   7   5   11
8   3   5   9   10  3   5   10  9   3
7   6   10  4   6   7   8   6   12  5
9   4   8   8   11  8   12  11  12  11
7   10  11  6   5   12  4   6   4   8
```

4. A baseball fan examined the records of a favorite baseball player's performance during his last 50 games. The number of games in which the player had 0, 1, 2, 3 and 4 hits are recorded in the line plot.

a. Determine the average number of hits per game.
 1 hit per game

b. Determine the player's batting average if he had 200 at bats during the 50 game series. (batting average = number of hits ÷ number of at bats)
 0.250 batting average

Reteaching

Reteach Chapter 5 Name _____

What you should learn:

5.6 How to use line plots to organize data and how to use organized data to help make decisions

Correlation to Pupil's Textbook:
Chapter Test (p. 237)
Exercises 8, 9

Examples *Using Line Plots and Using Data in Decision Making*

a. Thirty students in a ninth-grade social studies class were asked to record the number of hours they spent watching television during a specific week. The results are shown below. Organize the data in a line plot.

14, 16, 23, 20, 22, 19, 19, 17, 20, 21, 15, 12, 17, 16, 23,
15, 19, 22, 21, 18, 14, 23, 16, 16, 23, 17, 18, 22, 17, 15

Draw a number line that includes all integers from 12 through 23. For each number in the list, place an X above the coordinate on the line.

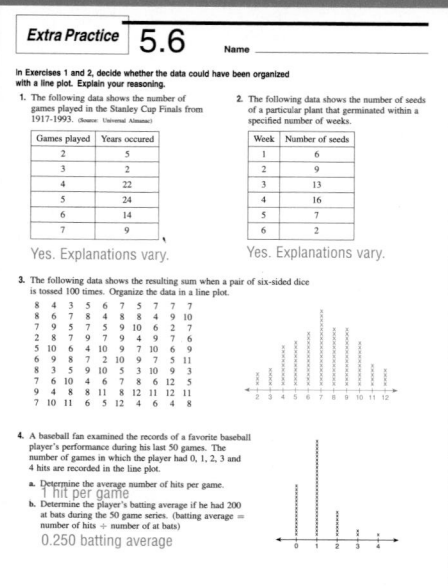

b. You are trying to determine how seriously a group of people view their responsibility to vote. You ask each person in the group to complete a survey question about how often they vote. The results are shown at the right. What would you conclude from the survey question?

1. I always vote.
2. I usually vote.
3. I usually don't vote.
4. I never vote.

From the survey question, it appears that more than half of the people in the group take their responsibility to vote seriously. Ten of the sixteen people said that they usually or always vote.

Guidelines: • Deciding how to organize data is a critical part of a branch of mathematics called statistics.
• One way to organize data is with a line plot.

EXERCISE It appears that 16 of the 20 students passed the biology exam.

Twenty students completed a biology test. The scores are shown below. Organize the data in a line plot. What can you conclude from the results?
85, 85, 75, 75, 75, 65, 95, 95, 75, 75, 75, 95, 65, 85, 75, 55, 55, 95, 75, 85

8. Phone Numbers You take a survey of the digits in the phone numbers of ten students in your class. You organize the data in a line plot, as shown at the right. Let × represent that digit occurring in a phone number.

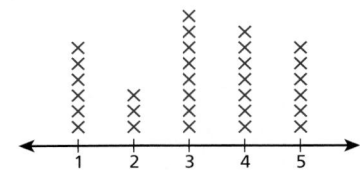

   a. Which digit occurs the most in the phone numbers? Which occurs the least? 4, 6

   b. All the phone numbers have the same exchange (first three digits). List all possible combinations of the exchange.

9. Jogging You conduct a survey among 30 joggers to find the average number of miles each jogs in a day. You organize the numbers in a line plot, as shown at the right. Let × represent a person who jogs that number of miles.

8.b. 347, 374, 437, 473, 734, 743

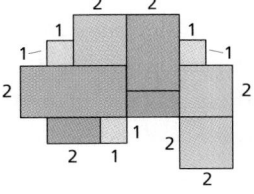

   a. How many people jog 5 miles a day? What is the total number of miles jogged by all who jog 5 miles a day? 6, 30

   b. Find the average of the number of miles that all 30 people jogged. $3\frac{2}{15}$

10. NFL Wins The table at the right shows the number of wins of the teams in the 1993 NFL regular season. Organize the number of wins with a line plot. *(Source: National Football League)* See margin.

Team Name	Wins	Team Name	Wins
Buffalo Bills	12	Washington Redskins	4
New York Jets	8	Dallas Cowboys	12
Miami Dolphins	9	Philadelphia Eagles	8
New England Patriots	5	New York Giants	11
Indianapolis Colts	4	Phoenix Cardinals	7
Houston Oilers	12	Detroit Lions	10
Pittsburgh Steelers	9	Chicago Bears	7
Cleveland Browns	7	Minnesota Vikings	9
Cincinnati Bengals	3	Green Bay Packers	9
Denver Broncos	9	Tampa Bay Buccaneers	5
Kansas City Chiefs	11	New Orleans Saints	8
Los Angeles Raiders	10	Atlanta Falcons	6
Seattle Seahawks	6	San Francisco 49ers	10
San Diego Chargers	8	Los Angeles Rams	5

11. Geometry The region at the right contains many different sizes of squares and rectangles.

   a. Find the area of each figure in the region.

   b. Organize the data in a line plot.

   c. What is the total area of the region? 33

   a., b. See margin.

✪ More difficult exercises

▶ **Ex. 4, 5** Students should observe that some sample sizes are not conveniently shown on a line plot. The only way the numbers in Ex. 5 could be shown in a line plot would be to have each "X" represent the nearest 10,000,000!

▶ **Ex. 9b** Students may need some prompts on how to approach this problem.

▶ **Ex. 10** Make sure students understand that this exercise asks for a frequency distribution of numbers of wins.

▶ **Ex. 11** Explain to students that part **b** involves a frequency distribution of each area value.

Answers
10.

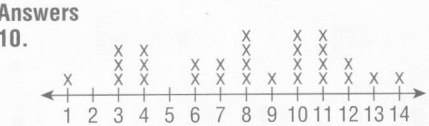

11. a. Each of 3 tan figures:1, each of 2 purple figures:2, each of 3 green figures:4, 1 brown figure:6, 1 blue figure:8

   b.

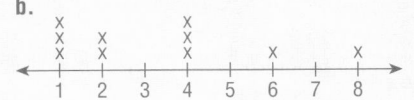

Integrated Review

▶ **Ex. 12–17** Use these exercises to review Chapter 4 concepts. Remind students of the expected format for solutions.

Exploration and Extension

▶ **Ex. 18** Use this exercise as a small-group project and presentation. Each group can use others in the class for the 20 people to be surveyed.

Portfolio Opportunity: Math Log

Explain why organizing raw data is important in presenting information.

Also available as a copymaster, page 17, Ex. 6

Short Quiz

Covers Lessons 5.5 and 5.6

Available as a copymaster, page 73

Integrated Review *Making Connections within Mathematics*

Mental Math   In Exercises 12–17, solve the equation. Then check your solution.

12. $7x + 3x + 12 = 32$ 2

13. $16 = 3y - 8y - 9$ −5

14. $-13 = \frac{p}{8} - 11$ −16

15. $\frac{p}{12} + 14 = 17$ 36

16. $5n - 20 = 3n$ 10

17. $-9z = 18 - 3z$ −3

Exploration and Extension

✪ **18.** *Data Analysis*   Conduct a survey of 20 people on a topic of your
Ⓟ   choice. Organize the data in a line plot. Write five questions that will require a classmate to interpret your line plot. Check students' work.

Mixed REVIEW

In Exercises 1–3, use the graphs, which compare auto sales in January, 1993 and January, 1994. *(Source: Auto Data)* **(5.5)** See margin.

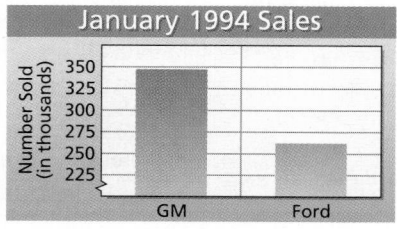

1. Both graphs are misleading, but which is more misleading? Why?

2. From the graph, it appears that Ford sold fewer cars in 1994 than in 1993. Why is this?

3. How could you represent this data with a single graph that was not misleading?

In Exercises 4–9, solve the equation. **(4.1–4.7)**

4. $5(n - 2) = 0$ 2

5. $6r - 2 = 2r$ $\frac{1}{2}$

6. $2r + 6r = 4r - 28$ −7

7. $2(p + 1) = -2(p + 1)$ −1 **8.** $\frac{4}{5}s + 3.2 = -\frac{1}{5}s$ −3.2

9. $\frac{1}{7}(x + 1) = 6$ 41

In Exercises 10–13, use the figure at the right. **(4.8)**

10. What are the inside dimensions of the picture frame?

11. What is the inside perimeter of the picture frame? 134 in.

12. What is the area of the picture? 1066 in.²

13. What is the area of the picture frame? 284 in.²

10. 41 in. × 26 in.

✪ More difficult exercises
Ⓟ Portfolio Opportunity

▶ ## Enrichment

Suppose the survey of classmates for Ex. 18 was used to determine extra-curricular activity involvement at your school. Have students draw a Venn diagram based on the results from three activities such as sports, drama, and music. Students who take part in more than one activity should be listed accordingly.

Sample:
Extracurricular Activities
5 students sports only
3 students drama only
4 students music only

3 students drama and sports
3 students drama and music
2 students sports and music
1 student sports, music, and drama

Answers to Mixed Review
 1. The 2nd graph, because the vertical scale on it has a bigger break.
 2. Because the vertical scale on the 2nd graph has a bigger break.
 3. With a line graph having an unbroken vertical scale.

There are many ways that technology can help you organize data. For instance, this bar graph was produced with a graphing calculator. The bar graph represents the data given in Example 1 on page 218.

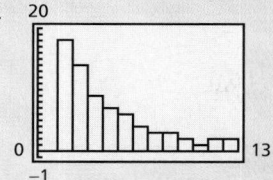

Age of Deer	1	2	3	4	5	6	7	8	9	10	11	12
Number of Deer	18	14	10	7	6	4	3	3	2	1	2	2

The following keystrokes show how to create the bar graph on several graphing calculators.*

TI-82

Window   Xmin = 0   Ymin = −1
            Xmax = 13   Ymax = 20
            Xscl = 1   Yscl = 1

STAT ENTER (Edit)
L1(1) = 1 L2(1) = 18   L1(7) = 7 L2(7) = 3
L1(2) = 2 L2(2) = 14   L1(8) = 8 L2(8) = 3
L1(3) = 3 L2(3) = 10   L1(9) = 9 L2(9) = 2
L1(4) = 4 L2(4) = 7   L1(10) = 10 L2(10) = 1
L1(5) = 5 L2(5) = 6   L1(11) = 11 L2(11) = 2
L1(6) = 6 L2(6) = 4   L1(12) = 12 L2(12) = 2
2nd STAT ENTER (Plot1)
     PLOT

Choose the following:
   On, Type: 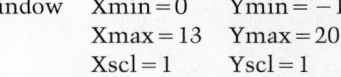, Xlist: L1, Freq: L2
GRAPH

Casio *fx-7700GE, fx-9700GE*

Range   Xmin = 0   Ymin = −1
           Xmax = 13   Ymax = 20
           Xscl = 1   Yscl = 1

MENU 3 (SD)
SHIFT SET UP
Choose: GRAPH TYPE :RECT
         DRAW TYPE :PLOT
         STAT DATA   :STO
         STAT GRAPH :DRAW
         M-DISP/COPY:M-DISP
EXIT SHIFT Defm 12 EXE
1 F3 18 F1   5 F3 6 F1   9 F3 2 F1
2 F3 14 F1   6 F3 4 F1   10 F3 1 F1
3 F3 10 F1   7 F3 3 F1   11 F3 2 F1
4 F3 7 F1   8 F3 3 F1   12 F3 2 F1
GRAPH EXE

Exercises

In Exercises 1 and 2, use a graphing calculator or a computer program to draw a bar graph of the data in the table.

1.

Age of Deer	1	2	3	4	5	6	7	8	9	10	11	12
Number of Deer	15	12	8	9	5	3	2	0	1	1	0	1

Check students' work.

2.

Age of Deer	1	2	3	4	5	6	7	8	9	10	11	12
Number of Deer	24	22	18	15	12	8	9	5	4	6	2	1

Check students' work.

* Keystrokes for other calculators are listed in *Technology—Keystrokes for Other Graphing Calculators* found at the end of this text.

To draw a bar graph on a graphing calculator, data is entered in pairs. The second number in each pair indicates the frequency in which the first number occurs in the set of data. For example, for the value of 1, you enter L1(1) = 1 L2(2) = 18 on the TI-82, or 1 F3 18 F1 on the Casio *fx-7700GE* and *fx-9700GE* to indicate that there are 18 one-year old deer.

Students will need to change the value of Ymax to 25 in order to make a graph in Exercise 2.

Additional activities that use graphing calculators to draw bar graphs are available on pages 23–26 of the Technology supplement.

PACING the Lesson

Suggested Number of Days
Basic/Average 2   Above Average 2
Advanced 2

PLANNING the Lesson

Lesson Plan 5.7, p. 40

ORGANIZER

Starters (reproduced below)
  Problem of the Day 5.7, p. 15
  Warm-Up Exercises 5.7, p. 15
Lesson Resources
  Teaching Tools
    Graph paper, pp. T1, C2
  Math Log, p. 18
  Technology, pp. 28, 29
  Answer Masters 5.7, pp. 97, 98
  Extra Practice Copymaster 5.7, p. 40
  Reteaching Copymaster 5.7, p. 40
Special Populations
  Suggestions, Teacher's Edition, p. 192D

LESSON Notes

Vocabulary ALERT!

Have students record the definitions of *scatter plot* and *correlations* in their journals. Emphasize that we have seen plots of data that formed special geometric patterns such as straight lines. Not all plots, however, result in such perfect patterns. Correlations can provide an index of how closely a given data plot resembles a straight line.

Point out to students that although the opening paragraph uses *x* and *y* values, in actual data sets these values would be physical quantities, as in Example 1.

Example 1

Have students check that there are about as many points above as below the dashed line (see the Need to Know box). A close inspection of the plotted points reveals that about 8 points are above the dashed line, 8 points are below the line, and 5 lie on the dashed line. Notice that some points lie on each other. You may wish to describe the dashed line as a *line of best fit*.

5.7

Statistics: Scatter Plots

What you should learn:

Goal 1 How to use scatter plots to organize data

Goal 2 How to use scatter plots to help make decisions

Why you should learn it:

Scatter plots can help you understand how two real-life quantities are related.

Connections
Biology

Need to Know

The dashed line approximates the pattern of the data points. There should be as many points above the line as below the line.

Goal 1 Using Scatter Plots

A **scatter plot** is the graph of a collection of ordered pairs of numbers (x, y). If the y-coordinates tend to increase as the x-coordinates increase, then x and y have a **positive correlation.** If the y-coordinates tend to decrease as the x-coordinates increase, then x and y have a **negative correlation.** If no pattern exists between the coordinates, then x and y have **no correlation.**

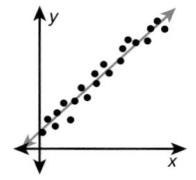
Positive Correlation

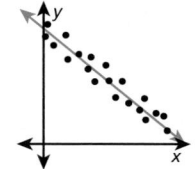
Negative Correlation

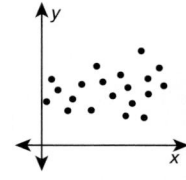
No Correlation

Example 1   *Drawing a Scatter Plot*

The ordered pairs below show the wrist measurements and elbow-to-fingertip measurements for 21 students. Draw a scatter plot of this data. What can you conclude?

(12, 32), (16, 42), (15, 40), (15, 39), (15, 37), (16, 41), (17, 43),
(14, 38), (15, 39), (16, 42), (17, 44), (14, 34), (15, 41), (13, 34),
(13, 35), (14, 37), (16, 40), (17, 43), (13, 31), (15, 39), (14, 38)

Solution   From the scatter plot, you can see that the two measurements have a positive correlation. So, people with larger wrists tend to have longer arms and vice versa.

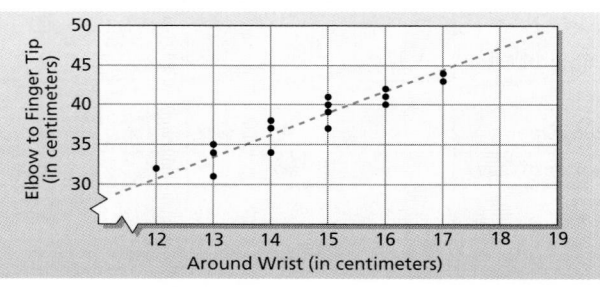

224   Chapter 5 · Exploring Data and Graphs

Real Life
Farming

In 1990, South Dakota produced about 223,000,000 bushels of grain corn, mostly in the area around Sioux Falls.

Cooperative Learning

P Portfolio Opportunity

Goal 2 **Decision Making with Scatter Plots**

Example 2 *Interpreting a Scatter Plot*

The scatter plot below shows several temperatures per week (in degrees Celsius) taken from January through May in Sioux Falls, South Dakota. Each temperature represents the low temperature for that day. You live near Sioux Falls and are planning a garden. You should plant your corn when you are fairly certain that the low temperature will remain *above* freezing. From last year's temperatures, when do you think it would be safe to plant corn in your garden? *(Source: PC USA)*

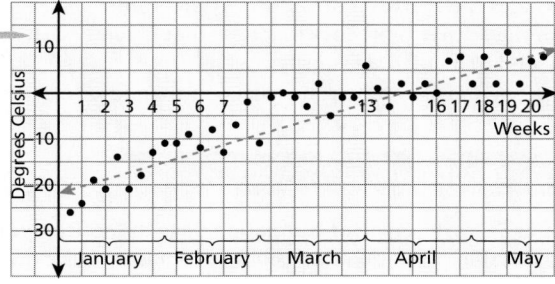

Solution Because freezing is 0° on the Celsius scale, it seems that it would be good to wait until the middle of April to plant corn in your garden. ∎

P *Communicating about* **MATHEMATICS**

▶ **SHARING IDEAS about the Lesson**

Determining Correlations Discuss with your partner the correlation of each of the following pairs. Do you think they have a positive correlation, a negative correlation, or no correlation? In each case, explain how you could collect and organize data that would test your hypothesis. Explanations vary.

A. A person's height and shoe size Positive

B. A baseball player's batting average and shoe size No

C. The number of games a baseball team won during a season and the team's ranking during the season Negative

D. A person's salary and the number of years that he or she went to school Positive

---

Knowing how one measurement is related to another can often provide information that is useful in making real-life decisions.

Example 2
Ask students: How are temperatures correlated to months (January through May) in Sioux Falls? There is a positive correlation.
Note that the first three lessons of Chapter 14 will provide an opportunity to further explore how to represent and analyze data using stem-and-leaf and box-and-whisker plots.

Communicating *about* **MATHEMATICS**

This is a good opportunity for some critical thinking in groups.

EXTENSION
Have the groups collect, organize, and analyze data for the circumference of a person's neck and his/her wrist.

Writing Prompt
Explain in your own words what a scatter plot is.

Technology

After entering the proper keystrokes on your calculator, your viewing screen should look similar to the one shown at the right.

From the scatter plot, you can see that the two quantities, T and P, have a negative correlation. This is good because you can conclude that the more time you spend training, the better you should place.

EXERCISES

In Exercises 1 and 2, use a graphing calculator to represent the data in a scatter plot. Make a sketch of the scatter plot in the space provided.

1. (4, 19), (3, 16), (7, 29), (10, 36), (9, 40), (3, 18), (8, 35), (6, 28), (2, 10), (5, 25)

2. (18, 80), (17, 89), (15, 93), (13, 90), (20, 74), (21, 74), (23, 70), (19, 81), (12, 100), (24, 63)

In Exercises 3–5, use the following information.
The following data represents the amount of money (in millions of dollars) that was spent on jogging and running shoes for the years 1986 through 1992. (Note: 6↔1986) (Source: National Sporting Goods Association)
(6, 476), (7, 475), (8, 460), (9, 515), (10, 519), (11, 555), (12, 572)

3. Use a graphing calculator to represent the data in a scatter plot. Make a sketch of the scatter plot in the space provided.

4. Does the data have a positive correlation, a negative correlation, or no correlation?
Positive correlation

5. What can you conclude from the scatter plot?
Each year, more money was spent on jogging and running shoes than the previous year.

Technology Using Calculators and Computers **29**

EXERCISE Notes

ASSIGNMENT GUIDE

Basic/Average:
Day 1: Ex. 5–14, 22–25
Day 2: Ex. 16–21, 26, 27

Above Average:
Day 1: Ex. 5–14, 22–25
Day 2: Ex. 16–21, 26, 27

Advanced:
Day 1: Ex. 5–14, 22–25
Day 2: Ex. 16–21, 26, 27

Selected Answers: Ex. 1–4, 5–25 odd

Guided Practice

You may need to explain the concepts of "hits" and "runs batted in" to students unfamiliar with baseball.

Independent Practice

▶ **Ex. 12–15** Assign these exercises as a group. For Ex. 12 you may need to help students establish an appropriate scale for the "pressure" axis.

EXERCISES

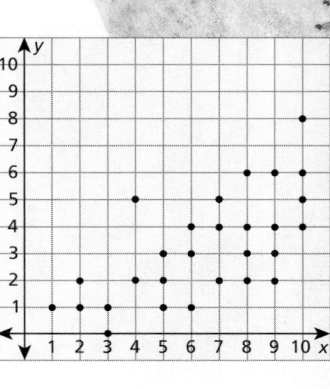

Guided Practice

▶ **CHECK for Understanding**

Interpreting a Scatter Plot **In Exercises 1–4, use the scatter plot at the right. The scatter plot compares the number of hits x of 30 softball players during the first half of the season with the number of runs y batted in.**

1. Do x and y have a positive correlation, a negative correlation, or no correlation? Positive

2. Why does the scatter plot show only 28 points? Some duplication

3. From the scatter plot, does it appear that players with more hits tend to have more runs batted in? Yes

4. Can a player have more runs batted in than hits? Explain.
Yes, 1 hit can bring in up to 4 runs.

Independent Practice

P **In Exercises 5–7, what type of correlation does the scatter plot have? Describe a real-life situation that could be represented by the scatter plot.** Descriptions vary.

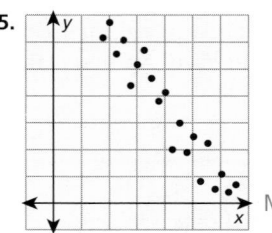

5. Negative   **6.** Positive   **7.** No

Think about It **In Exercises 8–11, decide whether a scatter plot relating the** Explanations vary.
two quantities would tend to have a positive, negative, or no correlation. Explain.

Positive

8. The age and value of a car Negative

9. A student's study time and test scores

10. The height and age of a pine tree Positive

11. A student's height and test scores No

Making a Scatter Plot **In Exercises 12–15, use the data in the table. The table compares the altitude A (in thousands of feet) with the air pressure P (in pounds per square feet).**

Altitude	0	5	10	15	20	25	30	35	40	45	50
Pressure	14.7	12.3	10.2	8.4	6.8	5.4	4.5	3.5	2.8	2.1	1.8

Estimates vary.
12. See margin.

Have a negative

12. Construct a scatter plot of the data.   **13.** How are A and P related? correlation

14. Estimate the air pressure at 42,500 feet.   **15.** Estimate the altitude at which the air pressure is 5.0 pounds per square foot. 28,000 ft
2.45 lb/ft²

Answers
12.

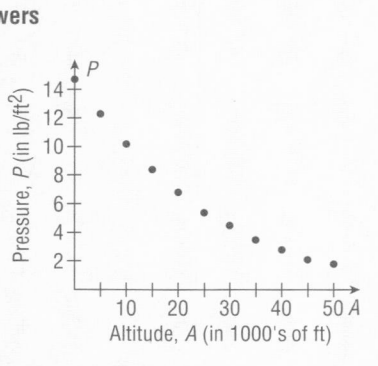

Altitude, A (in 1000's of ft)

Extra Practice

Extra Practice **5.7** Name _____

In Exercises 1–3, what type of correlation does the scatter plot have? Describe a real-life situation that could be represented by the scatter plot.

Positive correlation. Answers vary.

1.   2. Negative correlation. Answers vary.   3.

No correlation. Answers vary.

In Exercises 4–6, decide whether a scatter plot relating the two quantities would tend to have a positive, negative, or no correlation. Explain.

4. The number of study hours and test scores
Positive. As the number of hours increases, scores should increase.
5. The number of pets you own and your age
No correlation. Number of pets you own and your age have no pattern.
6. The number of hours you watch TV and your test scores
Negative. As the number of hours increases, scores should decrease.

In Exercises 7–10, use the data in the table. The table compares h, the   7.
altitude in thousands of feet, and v, the speed of sound in feet per second.

h	0	5	10	15	20	25	30	35
v	1116	1097	1077	1057	1036	1015	995	973

7. Sketch a scatter plot of the data.   8. How are v and h related?
Negative correlation

9. Estimate the speed of sound at 12,500 feet.   10. Estimate the altitude at which the speed of
About 1065 ft/sec   sound is 1000 feet/second.
About 27,000 feet

In Exercises 11–13, use the scatter plot at the right. The scatter plot shows the pre-primary school enrollment (in millions) for years 1985 through 1991 where t = 5 corresponds to 1985.

11. What was the enrollment in 1987?
About 10.9 million
12. How is the enrollment and the year related? Explain.
Positive. As years go by, enrollment increases.
13. Estimate the enrollment in the year 1995.
Answers will vary slightly. In 1995, the enrollment should be about 11.7 million.

40   *Statistics: Scatter Plots • 5.7*   Windows

Reteaching

Reteach *Chapter 5*   Name _____

What you should learn: Correlation to Pupil's Textbook:

5.7	How to use scatter plots to organize data and how to use scatter plots to help make decisions

Chapter Test (p. 237)
Exercises 10, 11

Examples *Using Scatter Plots and Decision Making with Scatter Plots*

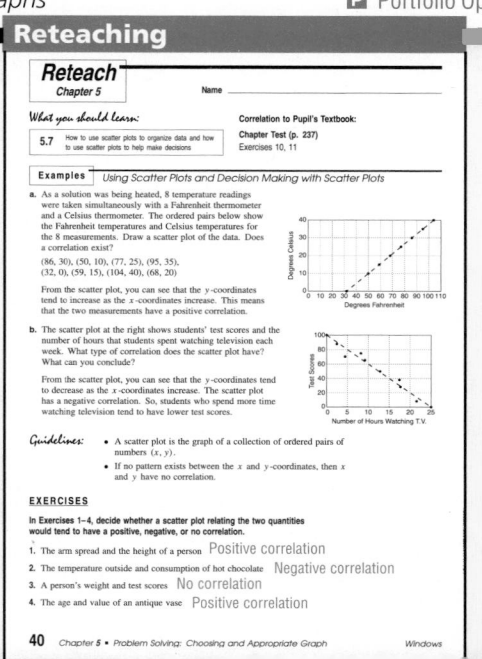

a. As a solution was being heated, 8 temperature readings were taken simultaneously with a Fahrenheit thermometer and a Celsius thermometer. The ordered pairs below show the Fahrenheit temperatures and Celsius temperatures for the 8 measurements. Draw a scatter plot of the data. Does a correlation exist?

(86, 30), (50, 10), (77, 25), (95, 35), (32, 0), (59, 15), (104, 40), (68, 20)

From the scatter plot, you can see that the y-coordinates tend to increase as the x-coordinates increase. This means that the two measurements have a positive correlation.

b. The scatter plot at the right shows students' test scores and the number of hours that students spent watching television each week. What type of correlation does the scatter plot have? What can you conclude?

From the scatter plot, you can see that the y-coordinates tend to decrease as the x-coordinates increase. The scatter plot has a negative correlation. So, students who spend more time watching television tend to have lower test scores.

Guidelines: • A scatter plot is the graph of a collection of ordered pairs of numbers (x, y).
• If no pattern exists between the x- and y-coordinates, then x and y have no correlation.

EXERCISES

In Exercises 1–4, decide whether a scatter plot relating the two quantities would tend to have a positive, negative, or no correlation.

1. The arm spread and the height of a person Positive correlation
2. The temperature outside and consumption of hot chocolate Negative correlation
3. A person's weight and test scores No correlation
4. The age and value of an antique vase Positive correlation

40   *Chapter 5 • Problem Solving: Choosing and Appropriate Graph*   Windows

Interpreting a Scatter Plot   **In Exercises 16–19, use the scatter plot at the right. The scatter plot shows the number of subscribers to basic cable TV from 1983 through 1992.** *(Source: A. C. Nielsen)*

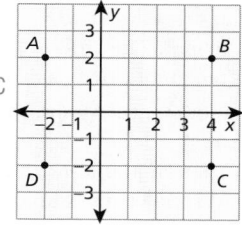

16. How many subscribers were there in 1989?

17. How are the years and subscribers related? Explain.

18. Copy the scatter plot on graph paper and draw a line that appears to best fit the points.

19. Use the results of Exercise 18 to estimate the number of subscribers in the year 2000.

16. 48 million   **17., 18.** See margin.   **19.** Estimates vary. 79 million

Geometry   **In Exercises 20 and 21, use the rectangle at the right.**

20. Complete the table.   5, 4, 3, 2, 1

Length, ℓ	1	2	3	4	5
Width, w	?	?	?	?	?
Perimeter	12	12	12	12	12

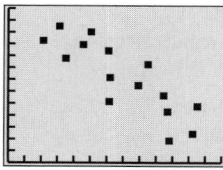

21. Construct a scatter plot using the lengths ℓ and widths w and discuss how they relate to each other.
Negative correlation; For graph, see Additional Answers.

Integrated Review

Making Connections within Mathematics

Coordinate Geometry   **In Exercises 22–25, use the coordinate plane at the right.**

22. Which pairs of points have the same x-coordinate? A and D, B and C

23. Which pairs of points have the same y-coordinate? A and B,

24. State the quadrant in which each point lies. C and D

25. Find the perimeter and area of rectangle $ABCD$. 20, 24
24. A: II, B: I, C: IV, D: III

Exploration and Extension

In Exercises 26 and 27, draw a scatter plot and describe the result. A sample is shown at the right. See Additional Answers.

Technology   To draw a scatter plot using a graphing calculator, enter the data as shown on page 223. Then, follow your calculator's procedure for drawing a scatter plot.

26. (1, 12), (2, 11), (3, 9), (3, 10), (4, 8), (5, 8), (6, 7), (7, 5), (8, 6), (9, 5), (10, 6)

27. (1, 3), (2, 3), (2, 4), (3, 6), (4, 5), (5, 5), (6, 7), (7, 7), (8, 9), (9, 11), (10, 10)

⭐ More difficult exercises

▶ **Ex. 16–19**   These exercises introduce the concept of *line of best fit* and offer a preview to concepts developed further in Chapter 13. Review the significance of the label under the horizontal axis.
▶ **Ex. 20, 21**   Use these as an in-class small-group activity.

Exploration and Extension

If graphing calculators are not available for class use, try to demonstrate these exercises using an overhead model of a graphing calculator.

Portfolio Opportunity: Math Log

Describe a real-life situation that is represented by a scatter plot that initially has a positive correlation and then changes to a negative correlation.

Also available as a copymaster, page 18, Ex. 7

Alternative Assessment

An investigation of the "learning curve" that develops students' ability to draw a scatter plot and find correlations.

Available as a copymaster, page 24

Enrichment

As a further extension of the Communicating about Mathematics, have your students measure the circumferences of their wrists and necks. Have them also list the number of books they read per week. Ask them to draw a scatter plot of wrist size to neck size and a second scatter plot of wrist size to number of books read weekly. Have them describe any relationships that seem to exist.

Answers
17. Have a positive correlation, cable TV subscribers tend to increase as the years increase

18.

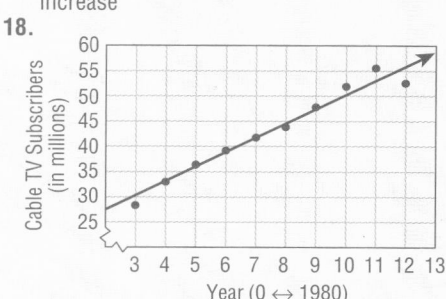

Explain to the students that the probability of an outcome is the likelihood or chance of that outcome occurring.

For those who are unfamiliar with the rules of high school basketball, explain that although Laurie is awarded two free throws for being fouled, the "1 and 1" rule allows her the second free throw only if she makes the first one.

EXTENSION
Ask students to repeat the investigation using the assumption that Laurie is a $\frac{5}{10}$ shooter, a $\frac{7}{10}$ shooter, or an $\frac{8}{10}$ shooter.

LESSON INVESTIGATION 5.8
Probability

Materials Needed: cardboard, paper clip, pencil

In this investigation you will investigate the probability of an event.

Description of the Problem Stevenson High School is playing Liberty High School for the state championship. The score is 65 to 66 in favor of Liberty. With one second left, a Liberty player fouls Laurie, a player from Stevenson. Laurie makes 6 out of every 10 free throws. Which of the following is more likely to happen?

a. **Stevenson Wins** Laurie makes two shots.

b. **Stevenson Loses** Laurie misses her first shot. (In this case, she doesn't shoot again.)

c. **Overtime Play** Laurie makes her first shot but misses her second shot. (In this case, the winner is determined in overtime play.)

There are three approaches to this problem. Try each approach in class. Compare the results of the three approaches.

1. **The Intuitive Approach** What outcome do you *think* is more likely? Each person in the class should write his or her guess on a slip of paper. The slips of paper should be collected and tallied. Answers vary.

2. **The Experimental Approach** Copy the circle at the right on a piece of cardboard. Hold a pencil point at the center of the circle, and spin a paper clip that encircles the pencil point. Record the outcomes for several "shots." Which outcome occurred more often? Answers vary.

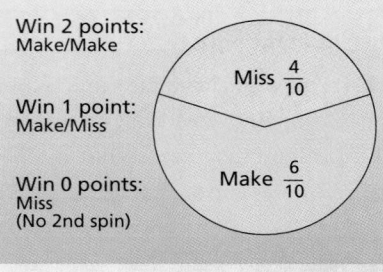

Win 2 points: Make/Make

Win 1 point: Make/Miss

Win 0 points: Miss (No 2nd spin)

Miss $\frac{4}{10}$

Make $\frac{6}{10}$

3. **The Theoretical Approach** The area model at the right can be used to determine the following probabilities.

The probability of Stevenson winning in regulation time is ⟨?⟩. 0.36

The probability of Stevenson losing in regulation time is ⟨?⟩. 0.4

The probability of overtime play is ⟨?⟩. 0.24

Which outcome has the greatest probability? Stevenson loses

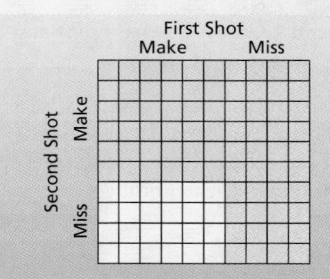

First Shot
Make   Miss

Second Shot
Make
Miss

5.8

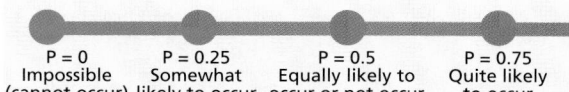

Exploring Probability

▶ PACING the Lesson

Suggested Number of Days
Basic/Average 2   **Above Average** 1
Advanced 1

▶ PLANNING the Lesson

Lesson Plan 5.8, p. 41

What you should learn:

 Goal 1 How to compute the probability of an event

 Goal 2 How to use concepts of probability to solve real-life problems

Why you should learn it:

Many events in real life are not certain. Probability can help you determine the likelihood that such events will actually occur.

Goal 1 **Finding the Probability of an Event**

The **probability of an event** is a measure of the likelihood that the event will occur. Probability is measured on a scale from 0 to 1.

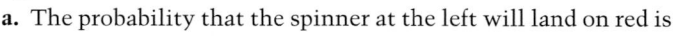

P = 0	P = 0.25	P = 0.5	P = 0.75	P = 1
Impossible	Somewhat	Equally likely to	Quite likely	Certain
(cannot occur)	likely to occur	occur or not occur	to occur	to occur

To find the probability that an event will be "favorable," divide the number of ways that it can occur favorably by the total number of ways that the event can occur.

> **Probability of an Event**
>
> Let S be a set that has equally likely outcomes. IF E is a subset of S, then the probability that E will occur is
>
> $$\text{Probability of } E = \frac{\text{Number of outcomes in } E}{\text{Number of outcomes in } S}.$$

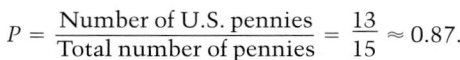 **Example 1** *Finding Probabilities*

a. The probability that the spinner at the left will land on red is

$$P = \frac{\text{Number of red regions}}{\text{Total number of regions}} = \frac{3}{12} = 0.25.$$

This means that if you spin the spinner 100 times, it should land on a red region about 25 times.

b. You have 15 pennies in your pocket. Two are Canadian and the rest are U.S. pennies. If you randomly choose one penny, the probability that it will be a U.S. penny is

$$P = \frac{\text{Number of U.S. pennies}}{\text{Total number of pennies}} = \frac{13}{15} \approx 0.87.$$

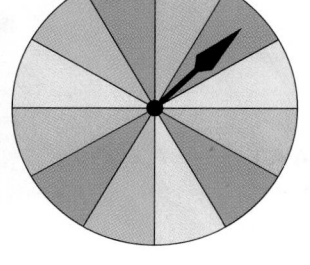

*The spinner can land on 12 different regions. This set of 12 possible outcomes is called the **sample space**.*

5.8 · *Exploring Probability* **229**

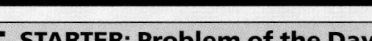

ORGANIZER

Starters (reproduced below)
　Problem of the Day 5.8, p. 15
　Warm-Up Exercises 5.8, p. 15
Lesson Resources
　Math Log, p. 18
　Answer Masters 5.8, p. 99
　Extra Practice Copymaster 5.8, p. 41
　Reteaching Copymaster 5.8, p. 41
Special Populations
　Suggestions, Teacher's Edition, p. 192D

LESSON Notes

Briefly discuss the terminology—probability as a mathematical word for "chance" and the concept of *equally likely outcomes*. The coin toss of Warm–Up Exercise 2 is an example of an equally likely event. Students should record the Probability of an Event formula in their math journals. Be sure students understand the terms *set* and *subset*. Encourage students to copy the probability scale at the start of the lesson for future reference.

Example 1

You may wish to use this example as an investigation.
　Discuss reasons why theoretical probabilities might not actually occur. Stress that the equally likely assumption means that none of the conditions that could have a skewing effect exist.

Locate polls from newspapers and magazines to share with your class. Discuss the samples used to conduct the polls and whether the samples are appropriate.

Example 2

You may wish to discuss the meaning of random selection. Describe some ways that the sample might have been taken that is not representative of adults. Ask students what sort of factors (social, physical, climatic) might skew the selection in this survey.

Communicating
about MATHEMATICS

Conduct a coin-tossing experiment. Have each student toss 10 times, combine the results, and then discuss reasons why the outcome may not match the expected results.

Writing Prompt
Describe the process you used in answering Ex. 21.

Goal 2 **Using Probability in Real Life**

To find characteristics of large groups, such as the population of the United States, pollsters sample a small group within the large group. If the small group is selected randomly, then its characteristics can be used to model those of the large group.

Real Life
Water Conservation

A typical shower uses 5 gallons of water per minute. If people limited their showers to 5 minutes, millions of gallons of water could be saved each day.

Example 2 *Conducting a Poll*

You are taking a poll to find how long adults take showers. You ask 600 adults and obtain the following data.

Length of Shower	Number Taking	
1 minute or less	1	≈ 0.002
Between 1 and 5 minutes	111	0.185
Between 5 and 10 minutes	360	
Between 10 and 15 minutes	109	≈ 0.182
Between 15 and 20 minutes	16	≈ 0.027
20 minutes or more	3	0.005

If you ask another adult how long he or she takes a shower, what is the probability that he or she will answer "between 5 and 10 minutes"? *(Source: John O. Butler Company)*

Solution Of the 600 people sampled, 360 answered "between 5 and 10 minutes." Assuming that the sample is representative of the entire population, you can reason that the probability is

$$P = \frac{\text{Number of people answering "5 to 10 minutes"}}{\text{Number of people in survey}}$$

$$= \frac{360}{600} = 0.6.$$

The probability that a person will answer "between 5 and 10 minutes" is 0.6. ∎

P *Communicating about* MATHEMATICS

▶ **SHARING IDEAS about the Lesson**
See above.
Extending the Example Use the data in Example 2 to compute the probabilities that an adult chosen at random will take showers that last for the other indicated times.

OPTION: Extra Examples
Here are additional examples similar to Example 1 of the lesson.

1. Finding Probabilities
a. The probability that the spinner below will land on a shaded region is
$$P = \frac{\text{Number of shaded regions}}{\text{Total number of regions}} = \frac{4}{10} = 0.4.$$
This means that if you spin the spinner 100 times, it should land on a shaded region about 40 times.

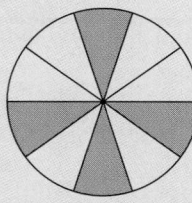

b. You have 24 marbles in a bag. Nine are yellow and the rest are blue. If you randomly choose one marble, the probability that it will be blue is
$$P = \frac{\text{Number of blue marbles}}{\text{Total number of marbles}} = \frac{15}{24} = 0.625.$$

EXERCISES

Guided Practice

▶ CHECK for Understanding

1. How do you find the probability of an event? See page 229.

2. Describe what a "probability of 0.5" means. See page 229.

3. If the probability of rain is 0.8, is it likely to rain? Explain. Yes, 8 out of 10 times it will rain.

4. *School Day* Think about events that may occur during a school day. Answers vary.
   a. Name three events whose probability of occurring is 1.
   b. Name three events whose probability of occurring is 0.
   c. Name three events whose probability of occurring is about 0.8.

Independent Practice

Spinning a Spinner **In Exercises 5–8, find the probability of the spinner landing on the color.**

5. Green $\frac{1}{4}$ 6. Red $\frac{5}{12}$ 7. Purple $\frac{1}{12}$ 8. Blue $\frac{1}{6}$

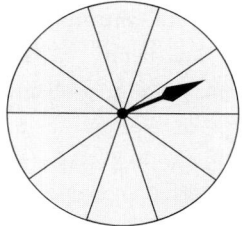

Choosing Letters **In Exercises 9–12, consider the following.**

Write each letter in the word **ALABAMA** on a separate scrap of paper and put them in a bag. Without looking, choose one.

9. What is the probability of choosing an A? $\frac{4}{7}$

10. What is the probability of choosing an M? $\frac{1}{7}$

11. Choose a scrap of paper from the bag, record the letter, and replace the scrap. Do this 50 times. Which letter did you choose most often?
    Check students' work.

12. Divide the number of times you choose "A" by 50. This number is the experimental probability. Compare this to the probability obtained in Exercise 9.
    Check students' work.

Tossing a Coin **In Exercises 13–16, consider the probability of tossing a coin.**

13. What is the probability of tossing a head in one coin toss? $\frac{1}{2}$

14. Toss a coin 30 times and record your results.

15. Divide the number of times you tossed a head by 30. This is the experimental probability of tossing a head.

16. Compare the experimental probability with the probability obtained in Exercise 13.
    14.–16. Check students' work.

17. *Coloring a Spinner* Copy the spinner shown at the right. Then use the following statements to color the spinner.
    • Probability of red is 0.1   • Probability of blue is 0.4
    • Probability of yellow is 0.3   • Probability of green is 0.2
    Check students' work.

18. *Reasoning* Is there only one way to color the spinner in Exercise 17? If not, show how the spinner could be colored a different way. No, check students' work.

⭐ More difficult exercises

5.8 • *Exploring Probability*   **231**

EXERCISE Notes

ASSIGNMENT GUIDE
Basic/Average:
 Day 1: Ex. 5–12, 17, 23–31 odd
 Day 2: Ex. 18–21, 33–35
Above Average:
 Ex. 9–12, 17–21, 23–31 odd, 33–35
Advanced: Ex. 9–12, 17–21, 23–31 odd, 33–35
Selected Answers: Ex. 1–4, 5–31 odd

Guided Practice
You may need to discuss decimal and fraction formats for expressing the probability of an event. Percent and probability will be discussed further in Chapter 8.
▶ **Ex. 4** This is an opportunity for some good discussion.

Independent Practice
▶ **Ex. 9–12** Assign these as a group. Have small groups work Ex. 11 in class, then assign Ex. 9, 10, and 12 for homework. Be sure students understand the difference between theoretical and experimental probability.
▶ **Ex. 13–16** Assign these exercises as a group.
▶ **Ex. 17** Assign this exercise, together with a sample spinner, as a problem that is to be handed in separately.

Lesson 5.8   **231**

Integrated Review

▶ **Ex. 30–32** Remind students that the sum of all the probabilities in each of these exercises must be 1.

Exploration and Extension

▶ **Ex. 35** This is a good opportunity for critical thinking and involves both inductive and deductive reasoning.

Portfolio Opportunity: Math Log

1. Is it possible for there to be a 1.3 probability that an event will occur? Explain your answer.
2. In a coin tossing game, seven tosses results in seven heads. What is the probability that the next toss will also be a head? Explain your answer.

Also available as a copymaster, page 18, Ex. 8, 9

Short Quiz

Covers Lessons 5.7 and 5.8

Available as a copymaster, page 74

Alternative Assessment

A coin-tossing activity that develops students' understanding of probability.

Available as a copymaster, page 24

Taking a Poll In Exercises 19–21, you are taking a poll to find the blood types of 200 people. You obtain the results shown in the table at the right. *(Source: American Association of Blood Banks)*

Blood Type	Number
O^+	74
A^+	71
B^+	17
O^-	14
A^-	12
AB^+	6
B^-	4
AB^-	2

19. From the results of your survey, what is the probability that a randomly chosen person has the following blood type?
    a. O^+ **b.** B^- **c.** A^+ or A^- 0.37, 0.02, 0.415

20. What is the probability that a person has a positive blood type? 0.84

✪ 21. Using only the result from Exercise 20, what is the probability that a person has a negative blood type? Explain your reasoning. 0.16, $1 - 0.84 = 0.16$

Integrated Review   *Making Connections within Mathematics*

Decimal Sense In Exercises 22–29, use a calculator to write the fraction as a decimal. Round your result to 2 decimal places.

22. $\frac{12}{15}$ 0.8   **23.** $\frac{8}{15}$ 0.53   **24.** $\frac{3}{7}$ 0.43   **25.** $\frac{4}{7}$ 0.57

26. $\frac{13}{24}$ 0.54   **27.** $\frac{7}{24}$ 0.29   **28.** $\frac{11}{20}$ 0.55   **29.** $\frac{9}{20}$ 0.45

More Spinners In Exercises 30–32, all but one probability is given. Find the missing probability.

30.
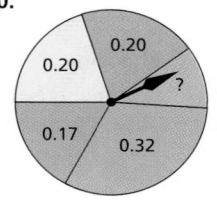
0.11

31.
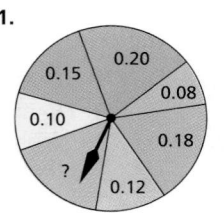
0.17

32.
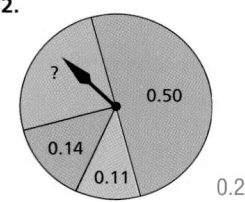
0.25

Exploration and Extension

Making a Conjecture In Exercises 33–35, use the following information.

A coin bank has 26 pennies, 15 nickels, 21 dimes, and 18 quarters. When you pick the bank up, a single coin falls out.

✪ **33.** Find the probability that the coin is a   0.325, 0.1875, 0.2625, 0.225
    a. penny.   **b.** nickel.   **c.** dime.   **d.** quarter.

✪ **34.** Find the probability that the coin is *not* a   0.675, 0.8125, 0.7375, 0.775
    a. penny.   **b.** nickel.   **c.** dime.   **d.** quarter.

✪ **35.** Write a conjecture about the relationship between the probability that an event *will* occur and the probability that the event will *not* occur. The sum of the probability that an event will occur and the probability that an event will not occur is 1.

✪ More difficult exercises
P Portfolio Opportunity

▶ ### Enrichment

Stadium scoreboards use an array of lights in the pattern shown below. Suppose a number (0–9) is chosen at random. Have students compute the probability that the segment marked x will be lit. $\frac{9}{10}$

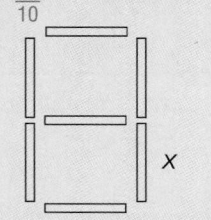

5

Chapter Summary

What did you learn?

Skills

1. Represent data using a
   - picture graph. **(5.1)**
   - time line. **(5.1)**
   - bar graph. **(5.2)**
   - line graph. **(5.3)**
   - scatter plot. **(5.7)**
2. Use a frequency distribution to organize data. **(5.2)**
3. Choose appropriate graphs to represent data. **(5.4)**
4. Recognize misleading bar graphs and line graphs. **(5.5)**
5. Use a line plot to organize data. **(5.6)**
6. Find the probability of an event. **(5.8)**

Problem-Solving Strategies

7. Model and solve real-life problems. **(5.1–5.8)**
8. Model and solve geometry problems. **(5.1–5.8)**

Exploring Data

9. Use tables and graphs to solve problems. **(5.1–5.8)**
10. Use probability concepts to solve problems.

Why did you learn it?

Almost every part of your life involves data. At school, on television, in magazines, and in newspapers, you are presented with data. Data is easier to understand when it is organized and presented visually with a graph. For instance, in this chapter you saw how a graph can be used to compare movie prices, trace the history of aircraft, compare people's goals and achievements, find patterns in geometry, analyze color preferences for clothing, compare the sales of hardback books and paperback books. From these examples, you can see that graphs are helpful in analyzing data in many walks of life.

How does it fit into the bigger picture of mathematics?

Organizing data is part of a branch of mathematics called *statistics.* In this chapter, you were introduced to some basic strategies for organizing, presenting, and interpreting data. One thing you learned is that there is seldom a "best" way to present data graphically. There are, however, some "bad" ways to present data graphically. For instance, you learned that breaks in the vertical scale can create false impressions with bar graphs and line graphs.

Throughout your study of mathematics, remember that a graph can help you recognize patterns. In fact, "drawing a graph" is an important problem-solving strategy in almost every branch of mathematics.

SUMMARY and REVIEW

COOPERATIVE LEARNING

Encourage students to study together. Emphasize the importance of teaching a classmate how to perform a skill or how to recall a procedure. When students work together, everyone wins. The students receiving help get additional instruction, and the students giving help gain a deeper understanding of the skills and concepts involved.

Chapter SUMMARY

The topic of exploring data was introduced informally as early as Lesson 1.6 with simple tables and bar graphs. This chapter developed systematic strategies for organizing and representing data through the use of several types of display—picture graphs, time lines, bar graphs, histograms, line graphs. Based on the kind of data to be organized, students were given guidelines for the correct choice of graph. Students were reminded that displaying data is merely a stepping stone towards the goal of interpreting results and detecting patterns. The choice of correct axes and scales was emphasized indirectly by having students study misleading graphs. The final three lessons then prepared the ground for some statistics and probability by means of line plots, scatter plots, and the formula for the theoretical probability of an event.

Have students begin this Review in class and complete it as a homework assignment.

ASSIGNMENT GUIDE

*Basic/Average: All exercises except Ex. 7–9
Above Average: All exercises
Advanced: All exercises
*For these students, you will need to limit assignments to cover only those lessons you chose to teach from this chapter

Resources

Color Transparencies
    Graph for Ex. 1–3, p. 23
Answer Masters, pp. 100, 101

Answers

2. Estimates vary. Bicycling: 9.2 million, Camping: 5.2 million, Volleyball: 5.0 million, Bowling: 4.7 million, Fishing: 4.1 million

6.

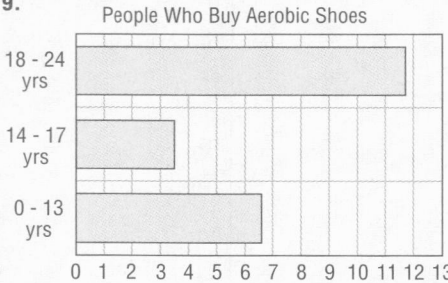

Annual Yogurt Consumption per Person

7. The number of buyers under 14 appears to be 3 times the number of buyers 14 to 17.

9.

People Who Buy Aerobic Shoes

Sports Activities   In Exercises 1–3, use the picture graph at the right. The graph shows the number of young people ages 12–17 that participate in selected sports activities. *(Source: National Sporting Goods Association)* **(5.1)**

                                                1 million

1. How many people does each picture represent?

2. Estimate the number of young people who participate in each activity.   See margin.

3. About how many more young people camp than bowl?   About 0.5 million

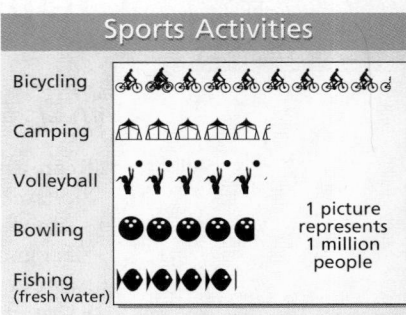

Sports Activities

Bicycling
Camping
Volleyball
Bowling
Fishing (fresh water)

1 picture represents 1 million people

Yogurt Consumption   In Exercises 4–6, use the graph at the right. The graph shows the average number of pounds of yogurt eaten in the United States in a year. *(Source: The National Yogurt Association)* **(5.1, 5.2)**

                                          0.5

4. How many pounds does each yogurt cup symbol represent?

5. From 1971 to 1991, how much did yogurt consumption increase?   About 3.3 lb per person

6. Represent the results in a bar graph.   See margin.

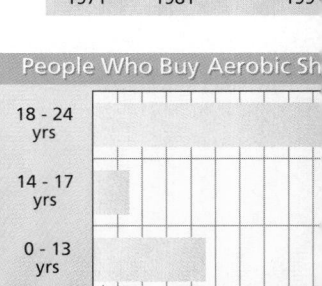

Annual Yogurt Consumption Per Person

One yogurt cup = 0.5 pounds

1971   1981   1991

Aerobic Shoes   In Exercises 7–9, use the bar graph at the right. The graph shows the average number of aerobic shoe buyers (out of 100 buyers) who are different ages. *(Source: National Sporting Goods Association)* **(5.2, 5.5)**

                                     See margin.

7. Without looking at the scale, compare the number of buyers who are under 14 to those who are in the 14 to 17 age group.

8. Why is this graph misleading?   Because the horizontal scale is broken

9. Redraw the bar graph so that it is not misleading.   See margin.

People Who Buy Aerobic Shoes

18 - 24 yrs
14 - 17 yrs
0 - 13 yrs

   3 4 5 6 7 8 9 10 11

The History of Computers   In Exercises 10–13, use the time line. *(Source: The 1993 Universal Almanac)* **(5.1)**

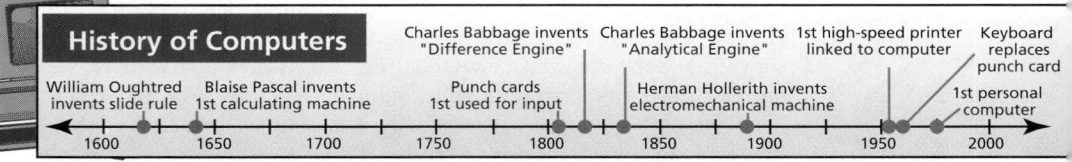

History of Computers

Charles Babbage invents "Difference Engine"   Charles Babbage invents "Analytical Engine"   1st high-speed printer linked to computer   Keyboard replaces punch card

William Oughtred invents slide rule   Blaise Pascal invents 1st calculating machine   Punch cards 1st used for input   Herman Hollerith invents electromechanical machine   1st personal computer

1600   1650   1700   1750   1800   1850   1900   1950   2000

10. What is the time increment used in the time line?   25 years

11. Estimate the year that the first calculating machine was invented.   About 1640

12. Estimate the year the Difference Engine was invented.   About 1822

13. Name two computer developments of the 20th century.   Any two of the last three shown on the time line

In Exercises 14 and 15, organize the data and represent your results graphically. Explain why you used the type of graph you chose. (5.1–5.6)

14. *Mall Shoppers*   A pollster in a mall is surveying opinions of shoppers who are from 13 to 20 years old. At the end of the day, the pollster had surveyed 50 people in this age group. The ages of the 50 people are listed below. Explanations vary. For graph, see margin.

20, 18, 16, 19, 14, 17, 15, 20, 16, 13, 17, 15, 18,
16, 20, 15, 17, 17, 14, 15, 19, 18, 16, 18, 20, 20,
19, 15, 16, 17, 19, 16, 14, 16, 19, 16, 15, 17, 18,
16, 14, 19, 15, 18, 13, 16, 17, 15, 17, 18

15. *Test Grades*   The following data shows the grades received by students on a math test. Explanations vary. For graph, see margin.

84, 90, 63, 79, 83, 63, 84, 79, 60, 73, 76, 87,
99, 95, 75, 82, 85, 71, 95, 87, 76, 84, 100, 95,
90, 100, 87, 98, 93, 82, 94, 95, 81, 100, 96, 87

16. *Geometric Pattern*   Each of the five triangles is an isosceles right triangle, which means that each has a right angle and two sides of the same length. Draw a scatter plot that relates the length of a shorter side with the length of the longer side. Describe the relationship between the two side lengths. **(5.7)**

For scatter plot, see margin. Positive correlation. (The longer side is $\sqrt{2}$ times a shorter side.)

 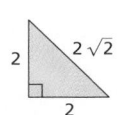 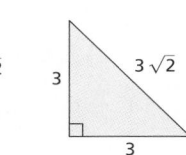 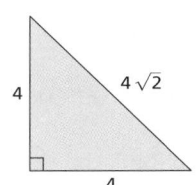 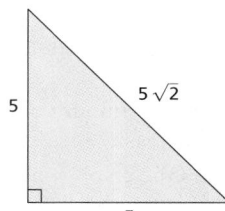

See margin.

17. *U.S. Population*   The ordered pairs below show the year and the United States population (in millions) for that year. Draw a scatter plot of this data. Describe the pattern. *(Source: U.S. Bureau of Census)* **(5.7)**

(1980, 227), (1981, 228), (1982, 231), (1983, 233),
(1984, 235), (1985, 237), (1986, 239), (1987, 241),
(1988, 243), (1989, 246), (1990, 248), (1991, 251)

18. *Probability*   A bag contains 9 red marbles, 7 blue marbles, and 8 white marbles. Without looking at the color, you choose one marble from the bag. What is the probability that the marble is

a. red? $\frac{3}{8}$ **b.** blue? $\frac{7}{24}$ **c.** white? $\frac{1}{3}$

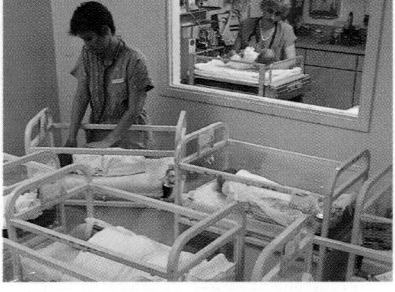

Since 1980, the population of the United States has been increasing due to the rise in the birth rate, increases in immigration, and the increased life expectancy of its citizens.

⊕ More difficult exercises

Answers
14.

15.

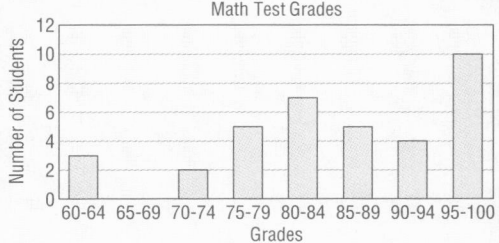

16.

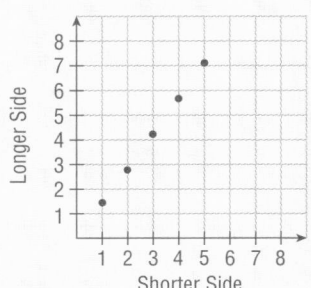

17.

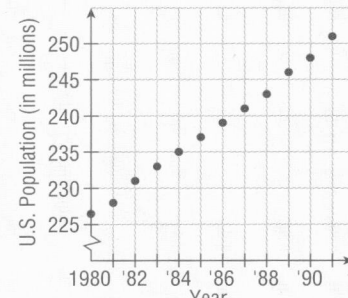

The population is slowly and steadily increasing.

Real L.

Connect

Analyzing a Company In Exercises 19–22, use the table, which lists the gross income and profit (in millions of dollars) for *WMX Technologies, Inc.* for 1984 through 1993. In 1993, this company was the world's largest solid waste collection and disposal company. *(Source: WMX Technologies, Inc.)*

Year	1984	1985	1986	1987	1988	1989	1990	1991	1992	1993
Gross Income	1,315	1,625	2,018	2,758	3,566	4,459	6,034	7,551	8,661	9,110
Profit	143	172	222	327	464	562	709	787	830	775

19. Create a double line graph for this data. See margin.

20. From the graph, which appears to be increasing more rapidly: gross income or profit? Explain. Answers vary.

21. In which year was the difference between gross income and profit the greatest? 1993

✪ **22.** When a company's gross income increases, does it necessarily follow that its profit increases? Explain. No, expenses may also increase

What's in the Trash? In Exercises 23–26, use the picture graph. *(Source: U.S. Environmental Protection Agency)* **26.** Paper/Paperboard

✪ **23.** How much trash does each trash can symbol represent? 5 lb

✪ **24.** Estimate the amount of food in 100 pounds of trash. About 7 lb

✪ **25.** Estimate the amount of paper products in 100 pounds of trash. About 38 lb

✪ **26.** Based on the graph, where do you think the greatest effort should be placed on recycling?

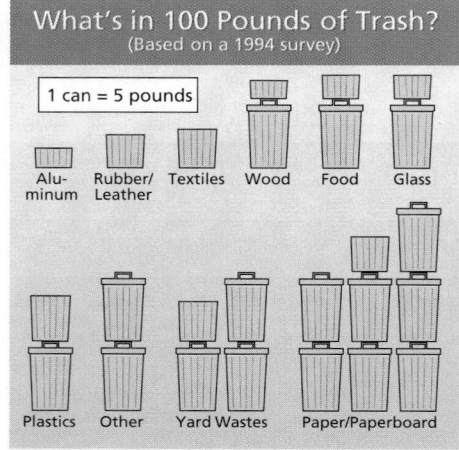

Recycling of aluminum cans, plastic and glass containers, and newspapers can reduce the 100 pounds of trash by about 15 pounds.

✪ More difficult exercises

Answer 19.

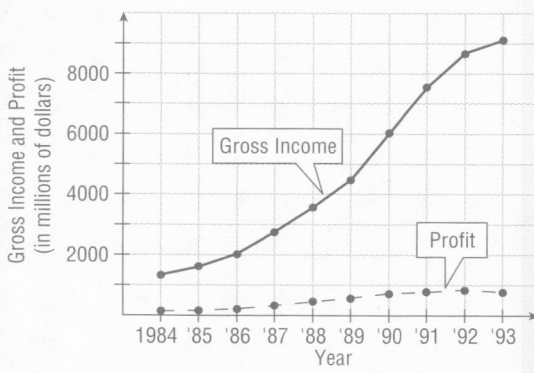

In Exercises 1–3, use the graph at the right. *(Source: Leading National Advertisers, Inc.)* (5.1)

1. Name the type of graph. Picture

2. Which company spent the most money on advertising in 1990? Proctor and Gamble

3. Estimate the difference in the amount of money General Motors spent on advertising in 1990 and 1991. About $325 million

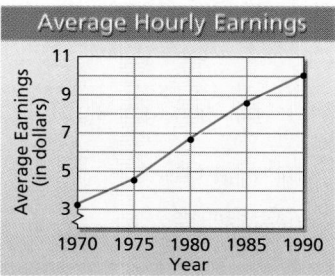

In Exercises 4–6, use the graph at the right. *(Source: U.S. Bureau of Labor Statistics)* (5.3, 5.5)

4. Name the type of graph. Line

5. *Without looking* at the scale, compare the 1970 average hourly wage to the 1990 average hourly wage. See margin.

6. Explain why this graph is misleading. The vertical scale is broken.

7. *Sports Records* The table lists the number of pitchers who were twenty-game winners in Major League Baseball by decade. Choose a graph that best represents the data. Then draw the graph. (5.4) See margin.

Decade	1940's	1950's	1960's	1970's	1980's	1990's
Number of 20-game winners	55	60	73	96	37	45

Business Records **In Exercises 8 and 9, use the following information.** (5.6)

The management of a company is recording the arrival times of its employees. They are keeping track of the number of minutes each employee is late for a specific day. The results are shown below.

0, 5, 7, 2, 1, 0, 0, 1, 0, 0, 2, 0, 7, 10,
0, 8, 4, 5, 0, 12, 0, 0, 3, 1, 2, 5, 6, 10

8. Organize the data in a line plot. See margin.

9. How many people arrived at work on time? 10

Scatter Plots **In Exercises 10 and 11, use the data at the right.** (5.7)

10. Create a scatter plot of the data (x, y) shown at the right. See margin.

11. Do x and y have a positive correlation, negative correlation, or no correlation? (5.7) Positive

(0, 1)	(4, 6)	(3, 3)
(2, 3)	(7, 9)	(5, 7)
(6, 6)	(1, 2)	(8, 11)

12. *Probability* A box contains 12 Ping-Pong balls numbered from 1 through 12. One ball is chosen at random. What is the probability that the number on the ball is less than 4? (5.8) $\frac{1}{4}$

Chapter Test **237**

Answers

5. The 1990 average hourly wage appears to be over 6 times as much as the 1970 average hourly wage.

7.

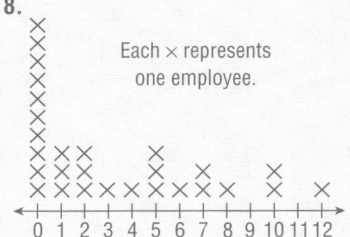

8.

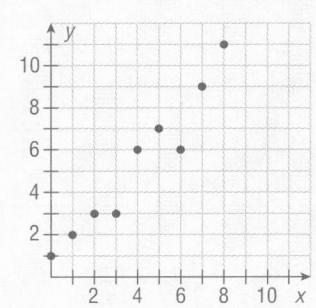

Each × represents one employee.

10.

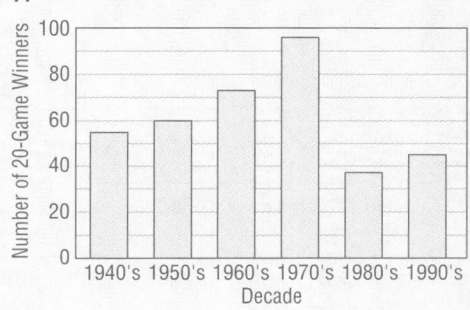

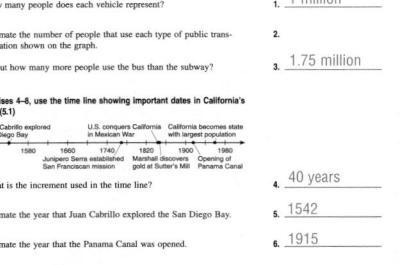
◄ Formal Assessment

Three **Chapter Tests.** Form A is of average difficulty, Form B is of average difficulty in multiple choice format, and Form C is more challenging.

Available as copymasters, pages 75–83

CHAPTER 6 GOALS

CHAPTER 6 ■ OVERVIEW

RESOURCES ORGANIZER

Lesson Pages	6.1 240–243	6.2 245–248	6.3 250–253	6.4 255–258	6.5 259–262	6.6 265–268	6.7 269–273	6.8 274–277	6.9 279–282
Lesson Plans	42	43	44	45	46	47	48	49	50
Problem of the Day	16	16	16	17	17	17	18	18	18
Warm-Up Exercises	16	16	16	17	17	17	18	18	18
Color Transparencies	—	24	25	—	25	—	26	26	—
Teaching Tools: Transparencies	T1	—	—	T2	T11	—	—	—	—
Copymasters	C2	C16	—	C2	C17	—	—	—	—
Math Log	19	19	20	20	20	21	21	21	21
Technology	—	—	32	33, 34	—	—	—	—	35
Answer Masters	103–105	106, 107	108, 109	111–113	114	115, 116	117, 118	120, 121	122, 123
Extra Practice Copymasters	42	43	44	45	46	47	48	49	50
Reteaching Copymasters	42	43	44	45	46	47	48	49	50
Enrichment Projects	—	29, 30	—	—	31, 32	—	—	—	33, 34
Alternative Assessment: Projects	25	—	—	—	25, 26	—	—	—	26
Partner Quizzes	—	—	—	—	49	—	—	—	—
Group Assessment	—	—	—	—	—	—	69, 70	—	—
Formal Assessment: Short Quizzes	—	84	—	85	—	88	—	89	—
Tests	—	—	—	—	86, 87	—	—	—	90–98
Overhead Manipulatives Kit	—	—	—	—	—	—	—	—	—
Complete Solutions Manual	Includes step-by-step solutions for all exercises in the student text								
Computerized Test Bank	Creates customized tests that include graphics								
Interactive CD-ROM Project	Provides an interactive and interdisciplinary chapter project								

STARTERS

Problem of the Day

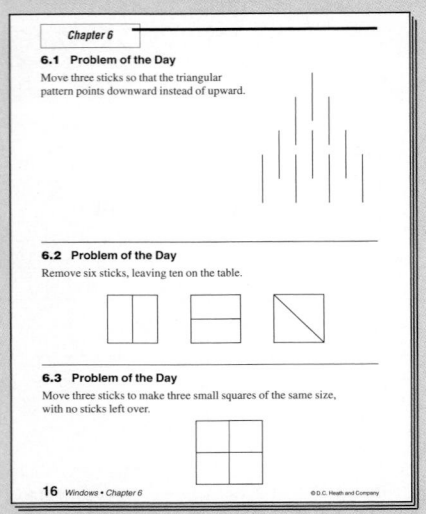

Chapter 6

6.1 Problem of the Day
Move three sticks so that the triangular pattern points downward instead of upward.

6.2 Problem of the Day
Remove six sticks, leaving ten on the table.

6.3 Problem of the Day
Move three sticks to make three small squares of the same size, with no sticks left over.

16 Windows • Chapter 6

© D.C. Heath and Company

Warm-Up Exercises

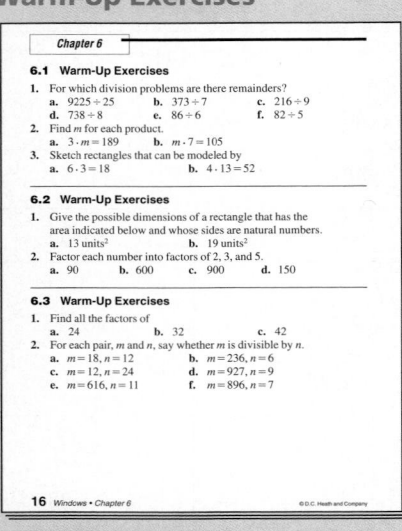

Chapter 6

6.1 Warm-Up Exercises
1. For which division problems are there remainders?
   a. $9225 \div 25$ b. $373 \div 7$ c. $216 \div 9$
   d. $738 \div 8$ e. $86 \div 6$ f. $82 \div 5$
2. Find m for each product.
   a. $3 \cdot m = 189$ b. $m \cdot 7 = 105$
3. Sketch rectangles that can be modeled by
   a. $6 \cdot 3 = 18$ b. $4 \cdot 13 = 52$

6.2 Warm-Up Exercises
1. Give the possible dimensions of a rectangle that has the area indicated below and whose sides are natural numbers.
   a. 13 units² b. 19 units²
2. Factor each number into factors of 2, 3, and 5.
   a. 90 b. 600 c. 900 d. 150

6.3 Warm-Up Exercises
1. Find all the factors of
   a. 24 b. 32 c. 42
2. For each pair, m and n, say whether m is divisible by n.
   a. $m = 18, n = 12$ b. $m = 236, n = 6$
   c. $m = 12, n = 24$ d. $m = 927, n = 9$
   e. $m = 616, n = 11$ f. $m = 896, n = 7$

16 Windows • Chapter 6

© D.C. Heath and Company

FOR TEACHERS

Answer Masters

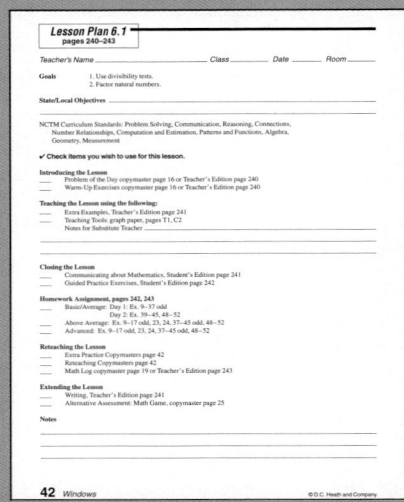

Answers for Lesson 6.1, pages 242 and 243

1. If one natural number divides evenly into another natural number, then the second number is said to be divisible by the first.
2. Divisible only by 3 and 5
3. 1, 2, 3, 4, 6, 9, 12, 18, 36
4. The side lengths are the factors.
5. False. 6 is divisible by 3, but is not divisible by 9.
6. True. $10 = 2 \times 5$
7. True. $6 \times 12 = 72$
8. False. The factors of 9 are 1, 3, and 9.
9. Divisible by all
10. Divisible by all
11. Divisible by 2, 3, 4, 6, 8
12. Divisible by 2, 3, 4, 6, 9
13. Divisible by 2
14. Divisible by 5
15. Divisible by none
16. Divisible by none
17. 2, 5, 8
18. 7
19. 0 or 9
20. 0 or 9
21. 4
22. 60, 120, 180
23. 360 $2 \times 2 \times 2$ is divisible by 2, 4, and 8. 2×3 is divisible by 2, 3, and 6. 3×3 is divisible by 3 and 9. 5 is divisible by 5. So $2 \times 2 \times 2 \times 3 \times 3 \times 5$ is divisible by 2, 3, 4, 5, 6, 8, and 9. $2 \times 2 \times 2 \times 3 \times 3 \times 5 = 360$
24. a, b, and c. Let $a = 3x$ and $b = 3y$, and let x and y be integers. Then
   a. $a + b = 3x + 3y = 3(x + y)$
   b. $a - b = 3x - 3y = 3(x - y)$
   c. $ab = 3x(3y)$
   d. $\frac{a}{b} = \frac{3x}{3y} = \frac{x}{y}$
   In a, b, and c, the expressions are always divisible by 3. In d, $\frac{x}{y}$ may be a fraction or an integer that is not divisible by 3.

© D.C. Heath and Company

Windows Answer Masters 103

Lesson Plans

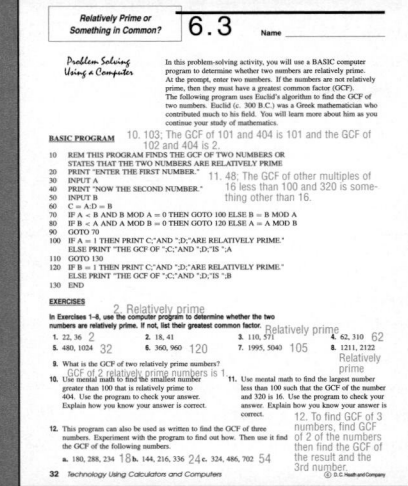

Lesson Plan 6.1
pages 240–243

Teacher's Name _____ Class ____ Date ____ Room ____

Goals
1. Use divisibility tests.
2. Factor natural numbers.

State/Local Objectives

NCTM Curriculum Standards: Problem Solving, Communication, Reasoning, Connections, Number Relationships, Computation and Estimation, Patterns and Functions, Algebra, Geometry, Measurement

✔ Check items you wish to use for this lesson.

Introducing the Lesson
___ Problem of the Day copymaster page 16 or Teacher's Edition page 240
___ Warm-Up Exercises copymaster page 16 or Teacher's Edition page 240

Teaching the Lesson using the following:
___ Extra Examples, Teacher's Edition page 241
___ Teaching Tools: graph paper, pages T1, C2
___ Notes for Substitute Teacher

Closing the Lesson
___ Communicating about Mathematics, Student's Edition page 241
___ Guided Practice Exercises, Student's Edition page 241

Homework Assignment, pages 242, 243
___ Basic/Average: Day 1: Ex. 9–37 odd
  Day 2: Ex. 39–45, 48–52
___ Above Average: Ex. 9–17 odd, 23, 24, 37–43 odd, 48–52
___ Advanced: Ex. 9–17 odd, 23, 24, 37–45 odd, 48–52

Reteaching the Lesson
___ Extra Practice Copymasters page 42
___ Reteaching Copymasters page 42
___ Math Log copymaster page 19 or Teacher's Edition page 243

Extending the Lesson
___ Writing, Teacher's Edition page 241
___ Alternative Assessment: Math Game, copymaster page 25

Notes

42 Windows

© D.C. Heath and Company

Teaching Tools

Name _____

Exercise 49 and 50 on Page 248

Exploration and Extension

Crossnumber Puzzle In Exercises 49 and 50, copy and complete the puzzle using single digits. Each digit must be a factor of the number at the beginning of its row and column. You can use each digit only once.

	18	8	35
42			
60			
72			

	36	30	56
35			
24			
18			

C16 Windows • Puzzle

Use with Lesson 6.2

© D.C. Heath and Company

Teaching Tools includes:
Transparencies and Copymasters for classroom activities and study skills:
- Graph Paper
- Dot Paper (Geoboards)
- Algebra Tiles
- Number Counters
- Fraction Strips
- Models

REAL LIFE

Color Transparencies for Real-Life Applications

Color transparencies for Real Life Applications • 26

Lesson 6.7, Page 269, Example 1

Lesson 6.8, Page 277, Exercise 39

© D.C. Heath and Company

Windows

Technology: Using Calculators and Computers

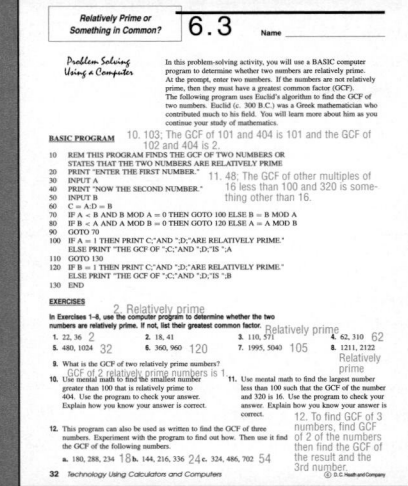

Relatively Prime or Something in Common? 6.3

Name _____

Problem Solving Using a Computer

In this problem-solving activity, you will use a BASIC computer program to determine whether two numbers are relatively prime. At the prompt, enter two numbers. If the numbers are not relatively prime, then they must have a greatest common factor (GCF). The following program uses Euclid's algorithm to find the GCF of two numbers. Euclid (c. 300 B.C.) was a Greek mathematician who contributed much to this field. You will learn more about him as you continue your study of mathematics.

BASIC PROGRAM
```
10  REM THIS PROGRAM FINDS THE GCF OF TWO NUMBERS OR
    STATES THAT THE TWO NUMBERS ARE RELATIVELY PRIME
20  PRINT "ENTER THE FIRST NUMBER."
30  INPUT A
40  PRINT "NOW THE SECOND NUMBER."
50  INPUT B
60  IF A < B THEN C = A : A = B : B = C
70  IF A > B AND B MOD A = 0 THEN GOTO 100 ELSE B = B MOD A
80  IF B < A AND A MOD B = 0 THEN GOTO 120 ELSE A = A MOD B
90  GOTO 70
100 IF A = 1 THEN PRINT C;"AND ";D;"ARE RELATIVELY PRIME."
    ELSE PRINT "THE GCF OF ";C;"IS ";A
110 GOTO 130
120 IF B = 1 THEN PRINT C;"AND ";D;"ARE RELATIVELY PRIME."
    ELSE PRINT "THE GCF OF ";C;"IS ";B
130 END
```

EXERCISES

2. Relatively prime

In Exercises 1–8, use the computer program to determine whether the two numbers are relatively prime. If not, list their greatest common factor.
1. 22, 36 2. 18, 41 3. 110, 571 4. 62, 310 62
5. 480, 1024 32 6. 360, 960 120 7. 1995, 5040 105 8. 1211, 2122 Relatively prime

9. What is the GCF of two relatively prime numbers? GCF of 2 relatively prime numbers is 1
10. Use mental math to find the smallest number greater than 100 that is relatively prime to 404. Use the program to check your answer. Explain how you know your answer is correct.
11. Use mental math to find the largest number less than 100 such that the GCF of the number and 320 is 16. Use the program to check your answer. Explain how you know your answer is correct.
12. This program can also be used as written to find the GCF of three numbers. Experiment with the program to find out how. Then use it to find the GCF of the following numbers.
   a. 180, 288, 234 18 b. 144, 216, 336 24 c. 342, 486, 702 54

12. To find GCF of 3 numbers, find GCF of 2 of the numbers then find the GCF of the result and the 3rd number.

10. 103; The GCF of 101 and 404 is 101 and the GCF of 102 and 404 is 2.
11. 48; The GCF of other multiples of 16 less than 100 and 320 is something other than 16.

32 Technology Using Calculators and Computers

© D.C. Heath and Company

Also Available:

- Complete Solutions Manual
- Overhead Manipulatives Kit
- Computerized Testing Program

- **Interactive CD-ROM Projects**
  Interactive projects for solving real-world problems using multimedia

- **Interactions: Real Math–Real Careers**
  A videodisc–based resource that connects math to real careers and on-the-job problem solving

- **PACKETS® Performance Assessment for Middle School Mathematics**
  A program that links assessment and instruction

Alternative Assessment

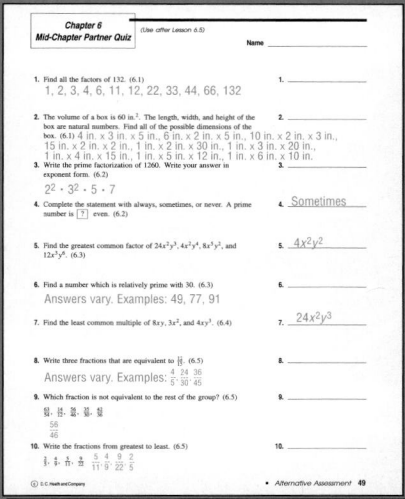

Alternative Assessment includes:
- Scoring Rubrics
- Portfolios
- Math Journals
- Projects
- Partner Quizzes
- Individual and Group Assessment

Formal Assessment

Formal Assessment includes:
- Short Quizzes (after every 2 lessons)
- Mid-Chapter Tests (2 forms)
- Chapter Tests (3 forms)
- Cumulative Tests (after every 3 Chapters)

MEETING INDIVIDUAL NEEDS

Extra Practice Copymasters

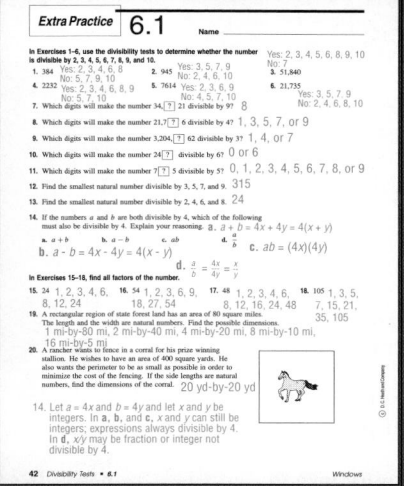

Reteaching Copymasters

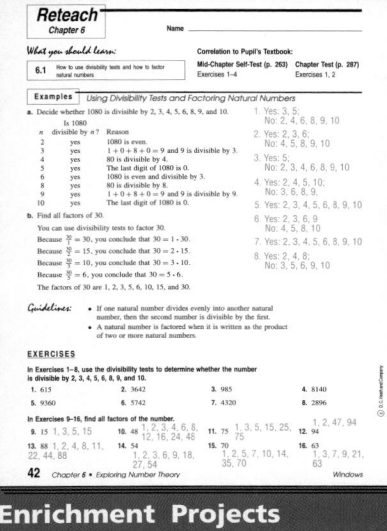

Enrichment Projects

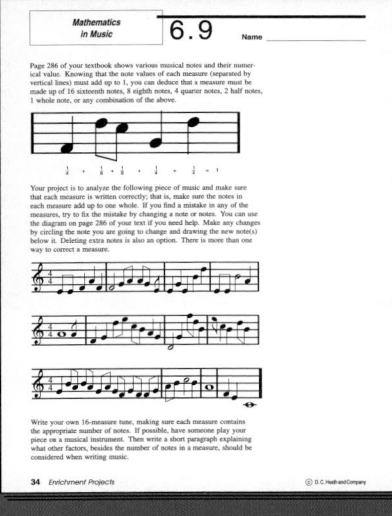

Math Log

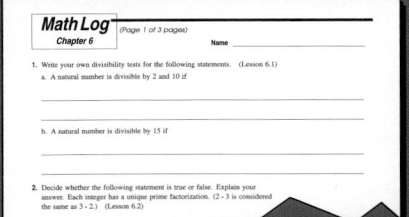

Special Populations

Suggestions for providing equal access for:

Students Acquiring English Proficiency*

Make sure students know the terms of the parts of multiplication and division equations. A poster displaying this information can be helpful. Other terms that may need clarification include: *prime, composite, greatest common factor, least common multiple, power, exponent, and perfect number.*

Practice vocabulary with students by dictating fractions. Students should write the fractions down and read them back to you, identifying the numerators and denominators.

Students with Various Learning Styles*

Allow some students to continue to use tiles to model factors as done in Lesson Investigation 6.2, until they are ready to think more abstractly. Visual learners will benefit from the use of pattern blocks, fraction strips, and measuring cups when dealing with fractions.

For the investigation in Lesson 6.2, suggest the students use graph paper and rulers to organize their list of primes.

Underachieving Students*

A discussion about "What is a fraction?" and "Why do we need fractions?" before beginning Lesson 6.5 will help students develop a frame of reference for proceeding with the lesson.

In Lesson 6.8, encourage students interested in space, computers, and science to find real-life examples of numbers in scientific notation.

Gifted and Talented Students*

Have students create a table that shows the decimal equivalents of all the proper fractions with denominators 2 through 9. Have students describe patterns they notice. Allow students to use calculators. Have them put an asterisk next to any decimal equivalents that they find by using mental math. Ask students if they discovered any patterns that helped them to find some of the decimals mentally.

* See page T19 for descriptions of these special populations.

PACING CHART

Lesson	Basic/ Average Course	Above Average Course	Advanced Course
6.1	0 days	0 days	1 day
6.2	0 days	0 days	1 day
6.3	0 days	0 days	1 day
6.4	0 days	0 days	1 day
6.5	2 days	1 day	1 day
6.6	2 days	1 day	1 day
6.7	2 days	1 day	1 day
6.8	2 days	1 day	1 day
6.9	0 days	0 days	1 day

About the Chapter

After the strong emphasis on mathematical modeling and data analysis that was the thrust of previous chapters, students may find this chapter somewhat abstract. However, the ability to use mathematics to model real-life situations requires a sound grasp of basic number theory. After a general introduction to divisibility in Lesson 6.1, students learn to identify prime numbers and composite numbers and the technique of prime factorization in Lesson 6.2. In the next two lessons, students learn further techniques, finding the Greatest Common Factor and the Least Common Multiple of a set of numbers or of algebraic expressions. Lessons 6.5 and 6.6 deal with the manipulation of fractions and with rational numbers in general. Simple powers and exponents were first introduced in Chapter 1. Lesson 6.7 extends these concepts to include zero and negative exponents, and students learn how to multiply and divide powers. Lesson 6.8 deals with scientific notation and, in Example 2, offers students an opportunity to use scientific notation in the context of the algebraic problem-solving plan. Finally, Lesson 6.9 revisits the exploration of number patterns.

CHAPTER 6

Exploring Number Theory

LESSONS

Computers have changed the way music is produced and recorded. They ease and speed the process of both composition and communication with other artists. Using synthesizers, composers can now write, edit, and listen to their pieces all in one sitting, and without needing musicians.

Real Life
Making Music

Treble Clef

Staff

$\dfrac{4}{4}$

Time Signature

The symbolic language of music is designed to tell the person reading it many things, including meter, tempo, melody, pitch, and key. The clef at the beginning of each staff tells the reader the name and pitch of each note, and the time signature indicates the music's meter.

Numbers can be used to describe musical notes, meter, and tempo. They can also be used to express a great many patterns in nature. These uses of numbers will be explored in this chapter.

Using the Page

Allow students time to talk about their musical interests. Take a survey of the class to determine how many students play musical instruments and what type of instruments they play. On page 277, you are told that the piano and the guitar are the most popular instruments played by Americans. Is this true for your class?

Encourage students who study music to give examples of how they use fractions when reading music. Discuss what information is given in the time signature.

In the Chapter Review, students will learn about musical notes and how many beats they represent.

Multimedia Resources

Interactive CD-Rom Projects A project for this chapter combines print, animation, sound and video presentations to capture students' interest in Playing the Stock Market. This interactive approach shows students how the math concepts and problem-solving strategies they are learning will be used in the future in dealing with important personal, national, and world issues. The theme of Playing the Stock Market correlates to Lesson 6.6.

Interactions: Real Math–Real Life The theme of this chapter, Making Music, correlates with an episode of **Interactions** which is a videodisc-based multimedia resource that connects middle school math topics with real-life careers. In each of the twelve episodes, students go on-site with a variety of professionals to witness real-life applications of the math they are studying. Students see math concepts and problem-solving strategies in a context that helps them connect what they are studying to the world outside the classroom. **Interactions** was developed by the Foundation for Advancements in Science and Education (FASE) and is published by D.C. Heath and Company.

The theme of Making Music is continued throughout the chapter on pages 251, 254, 277, and 286.

Performance Assessment Resource

The PACKETS® Program: Performance Assessment for Middle School Mathematics was developed by Educational Testing Service and is published by D.C. Heath. **PACKETS** helps you assess your students' performances as they learn. You can use a wide variety of **PACKETS** Activity Units with this chapter because, in every activity, students will use ideas from all topic areas of mathematics. However, you can use the chart on page T16 to help you choose the **PACKETS** Activity Unit(s) that may fit best with this chapter.

PLANNING the Lesson

Lesson Plan 6.1, p. 42

ORGANIZER

Starters (reproduced below)
 Problem of the Day 6.1, p. 16
 Warm-Up Exercises 6.1, p. 16
Lesson Resources
 Teaching Tools
  Graph paper, pp. T1, C2
 Math Log, p. 19
 Answer Masters 6.1, pp. 103–105
 Extra Practice Copymaster 6.1, p. 42
 Reteaching Copymaster 6.1, p. 42
Special Populations
 Suggestions, Teacher's Edition, p. 238D

LESSON Notes

Review natural numbers with students. Be sure they recognize that "divides evenly" means "divides with no remainder."

Example 1

MATH JOURNAL
Along with the Divisibility Tests, students may want to include this example in their journals. Observe that no divisibility rule for 7 is given. Students will benefit from translation exercises.

Division Statement	Corresponding Multiplication Statement	
$39 \div 3 = 13$	$3 \cdot 13 = 39$	
$44 \div 4 = 11$	$4 \cdot 11 = 44$	
$378 \div 6 = 63$	$? \cdot 63 = 378$	6
$518 \div 14 = 37$	$? \cdot 37 = 518$	14
$? \div 7 = 26$	$7 \cdot 26 = 182$	182
$? \div 13 = 41$	$13 \cdot 41 = 533$	533

6.1 Divisibility Tests

What you should learn:

Goal 1 How to use divisibility tests

Goal 2 How to factor natural numbers

Why you should learn it:

You can use divisibility tests to determine some possible dimensions of a rectangular region with a given area.

Goal 1 ## Using Divisibility Tests

If one natural number divides evenly into another natural number, then the second number is **divisible** by the first. For instance, 198 is divisible by 9 because $198 \div 9 = 22$, but 198 is not divisible by 4 because 4 does not divide evenly into 198.

Divisibility Tests

A natural number is divisible by
2 if the number is even.
3 if the sum of its digits is divisible by 3.
4 if the number formed by its last 2 digits is divisible by 4.
5 if its last digit is 0 or 5.
6 if the number is even and divisible by 3.
8 if the number formed by its last 3 digits is divisible by 8.
9 if the sum of its digits is divisible by 9.
10 if its last digit is 0.

Example 1 *Using a Divisibility Test*

Decide whether 534 is divisible by 2, 3, 4, 5, 6, 8, 9, and 10.

Solution

Study Tip
To decide whether a 3-digit number is divisible by 8, divide the number by 2, and test whether the result is divisible by 4. For instance, 534 is not divisible by 8 because $534 \div 2 = 267$, and 267 is not divisible by 4.

n	Is 534 divisible by n?	Reason
2	Yes	534 is even.
3	Yes	$5 + 3 + 4 = 12$, and 12 is divisible by 3.
4	No	34 is not divisible by 4.
5	No	The last digit of 534 is not 0 or 5.
6	Yes	534 is even and divisible by 3.
8	No	$534 \div 8 = 66.75$.
9	No	$5 + 3 + 4 = 12$, and 12 is not divisible by 9.
10	No	The last digit of 534 is not 0.

You can also use a calculator to decide whether one number is divisible by another. For instance, 3007 is divisible by 31 because $3007 \div 31 = 97$.

240 Chapter 6 • Exploring Number Theory

STARTER: Problem of the Day

Move three sticks so that the triangular pattern points downward instead of upward.

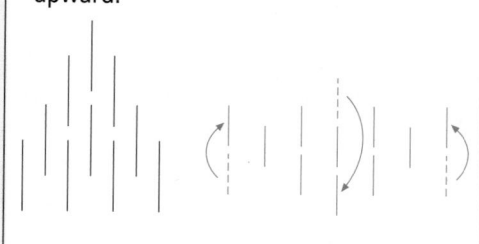

Also available as a copymaster, page 16

STARTER: Warm-Up Exercises

1. For which division problems are there remainders?
a. $9225 \div 25$ **b.** $373 \div 7$ **c.** $216 \div 9$
d. $738 \div 8$ **e.** $86 \div 6$ **f.** $82 \div 5$
b, d, e, f
2. Find m for each product.
a. $3 \cdot m = 189$ **b.** $m \cdot 7 = 105$
a. $m = 63$, **b.** $m = 15$
3. Sketch rectangles that can be modeled by
a. $6 \cdot 3 = 18$ **b.** $4 \cdot 13 = 52$.
Check students' work.

Also available as a copymaster, page 16

Goal 2 Factoring Natural Numbers

A natural number is **factored** when it is written as the product of two or more natural numbers. For instance, 28 can be factored as 4 • 7. The numbers 4 and 7 are **factors** of 28. Divisibility tests can be used to factor a number. For instance, because $39 \div 3 = 13$, you can conclude that $39 = 3 \cdot 13$.

Quotient

$$39 \div 3 = 13$$

Dividend   Divisor

Product

$$3 \cdot 13 = 39$$

Factor   Factor

Connections
Geometry

Factor

Factor

Area is the product.

The area of a rectangle is the product of its length and width.

Example 2   *Finding Factors of a Number*

A rectangle has an area of 24 square units. The lengths of the sides are natural numbers. Name the possible dimensions. Find the factors of 24.

Solution   You are hunting for pairs of numbers whose product is 24. That is, you are hunting for ways to factor 24 into the product of two numbers. From the rectangles below, you can see that the possible side lengths are 1 by 24, 2 by 12, 3 by 8, and 4 by 6. The factors of 24 are 1, 2, 3, 4, 6, 8, 12, and 24.

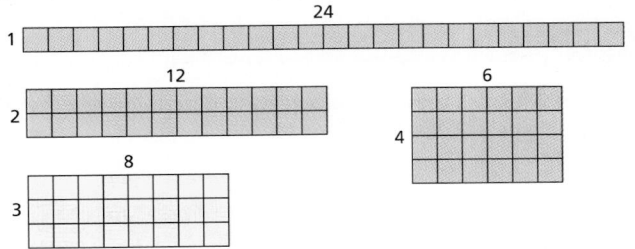

Real Life
Banking

Cooperative Learning

Communicating *about* MATHEMATICS

▶ **SHARING IDEAS about the Lesson**

Cashing a Check You work as a bank teller. A person brings you a check for $80. The person asks for bills that are all the same denomination. Explain to your partner how you can use divisibility tests to decide how many ways this can be done. Then explain how you can use factors to decide how many bills of each denomination you would give the person. See margin.

OPTION: Extra Example

Here is an additional example similar to Example 1 of the lesson.

Using a Divisibility Test
Decide whether 1305 is divisible by 2, 3, 4, 5, 6, 7, 8, 9, and 10.

Solution

n	Is 1305 divisible by n?	Reason
2	No	1305 is not even.
3	Yes	$1+3+0+5=9$, and 9 is divisible by 3.
4	No	1305 is not even.
5	Yes	The last digit of 1305 is 5.

n	Is 1305 divisible by n?	Reason
6	No	1305 is not even.
8	No	1305 is not even.
9	Yes	$1+3+0+5=9$, and 9 is divisible by 9.
10	No	The last digit of 1305 is not 0.

Example 2

Be sure that students understand that all possible rectangles of area 24 are shown (given that the sides are natural numbers). For example, the 2 x 12 rectangle is equivalent to a 12 x 2 rectangle, and so on.

Communicating *about* MATHEMATICS

Challenge students to determine the number of ways that bills of exactly two denominations can be used to cash the $80 check.

Writing Prompt
Use any of the problems from Ex. 42–45. Any of these will give insight into the students' comprehension of the concept of divisibility.

Answer to Communicating
Use divisibility tests for 2, 5, 10, and 20 (use divisibility tests for 4 and 5) to determine whether two-dollar, five-dollar, ten-dollar, and twenty-dollar bills, respectively, can be given in exchange for the check. Then divide by 2, 5, 10, and 20 to determine the number of two-dollar, five-dollar, ten-dollar, and twenty-dollar bills, respectively, that can be given in exchange for the check.

ASSIGNMENT GUIDE

*Basic/Average:
Day 1: Ex. 9–37 odd
Day 2: Ex. 39–45, 48–52

*Above Average:
Ex. 9–17 odd, 23, 24, 37–45 odd, 48–52

Advanced: Ex. 9–17 odd, 23, 24, 37–45 odd, 48–52

Selected Answers: Ex. 1–8, 9–49 odd
*You may wish to omit this lesson for these students.

Guided Practice

▶ **Ex. 1**
MATH JOURNAL
This would be a good question to include in students' math journals.
▶ **Ex. 4** This exercise is based on Example 2.
▶ **Ex. 5–8** As students explain their reasoning, be aware of whether they use the correct vocabulary.

Independent Practice

▶ **Ex. 9–16** These exercises assess students' understanding of the lesson.
▶ **Ex. 18–21**
EXTENSION
Ask students whether the solution would be unique if we were trying to make the numbers divisible by 3.
▶ **Ex. 22–24**
GROUP ACTIVITY
These exercises could be assigned as a group activity, after which each group shares explanations with the entire class.
▶ **Ex. 25–32** Have students compare the results of Ex. 25 and 26, 29 and 30, 26 and 31. Ask students whether doubling a number results in doubling the number of factors.

Answers
5. 6 is divisible by 3, but is not divisible by 9.
6. $10 = 2 \times 5$
7. $6 \times 12 = 72$
8. The factors of 9 are 1, 3, and 9.

Guided Practice

▶ **CHECK for Understanding**

1. Explain what it means to say that one natural number is divisible by another natural number.   See page 240.
2. Decide whether 4485 is divisible by 2, 3, 4, 5, 6, 8, 9, and 10.   Divisible only by 3 and 5
3. Name all the natural numbers that are factors of 36.
4. *Geometry* Each of the rectangles at the right has an area of 30 square units. Explain how to use these rectangles to find the factors of 30.

True or False? **In Exercises 5–8, decide whether the statement is true or false. Explain.**

5. A number divisible by 3 is also divisible by 9.   False
6. A number divisible by 10 is also divisible by 2.   True
7. The numbers 6 and 12 are factors of 72.   True
8. The number 18 is a factor of 9.   False
   5.–8. For explanations, see margin.

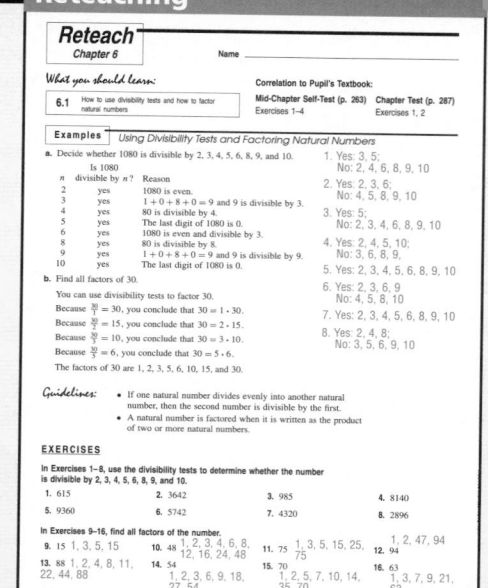

3. 1, 2, 3, 4, 6, 9, 12, 18, 36
4. The side lengths are the factors.

Independent Practice

In Exercises 9–16, use the divisibility tests to determine whether the number is divisible by 2, 3, 4, 5, 6, 8, 9, or 10.   Divisible by

9. 2160   all
10. 25,920   all
11. 192   2, 3, 4, 6, 8
12. 9756   2, 3, 4, 6, 9
13. 1234   2
14. 3725   5
15. 6859   none
16. 2401   none
17. *Reasoning* Which digits will make the number 34,?21 divisible by 3?   2, 5, and 8

In Exercises 18–21, find the digit that makes the number divisible by 9.

18. 39,9?8   7
19. 5,43?,216,789   0 or 9
20. 12,?51   0 or 9
21. 2,546,?24   4
☆ 22. List all natural numbers less than 200 that are divisible by 3, 4, *and* 5.   60, 120, 180
Ⓟ 23. *It's Up to You* Find the smallest natural number divisible by 2, 3, 4, 5, 6, 8, *and* 9. Explain how you found your answer.   360; for explanation, see Additional Answers.
☆ 24. *Logical Reasoning* If the numbers a and b are each divisible by 3, which of the following must also be divisible by 3? Explain your reasoning.   a, b, and c
   a. $a + b$ **b.** $a - b$ **c.** ab **d.** $\frac{a}{b}$ for explanation, see Additional Answers.

In Exercises 25–32, find all factors of the number.

25. 18   1, 2, 3, 6, 9, 18
26. 36   1, 2, 3, 4, 6, 9, 12, 18, 36
27. 42   1, 2, 3, 6, 7, 14, 21, 42
28. 45   1, 3, 5, 9, 15, 45   1, 2, 3, 4, 6, 8, 12,
29. 50   1, 2, 5, 10, 25, 50
30. 100   1, 2, 4, 5, 10, 20, 25, 50, 100
31. 72   1, 2, 3, 4, 6, 8, 9, 12, 18, 24, 36, 72
32. 96   16, 24, 32, 48, 96

☆ More difficult exercises
Ⓟ Portfolio Opportunity

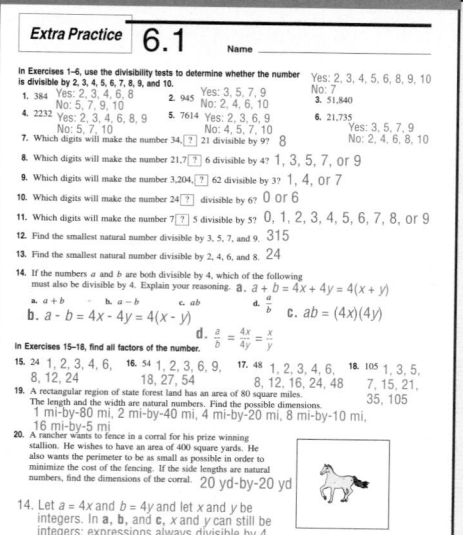

Extra Practice 6.1   Name _____

In Exercises 1–6, use the divisibility tests to determine whether the number is divisible by 2, 3, 4, 5, 6, 7, 8, 9, and 10.   Yes: 2, 3, 4, 5, 6, 8, 9, 10
1. 384   Yes: 2, 3, 4, 6, 8   No: 5, 7, 9, 10
   2. 945   Yes: 3, 5, 7, 9   No: 2, 4, 6, 10
   3. 51,840
4. 2232   Yes: 2, 3, 4, 6, 8, 9   No: 5, 7, 10
   5. 7614   Yes: 2, 3, 6, 9   No: 4, 5, 7, 10
   6. 21,735   Yes: 3, 5, 7, 9   No: 2, 4, 6, 8, 10
7. Which digits will make the number 34,?21 divisible by 9?   8
8. Which digits will make the number 21,7?6 divisible by 4?   1, 3, 5, 7, or 9
9. Which digits will make the number 3,204,?62 divisible by 3?   1, 4, or 7
10. Which digits will make the number 24?7 divisible by 6?   0 or 6
11. Which digits will make the number 7?5 divisible by 5?   0, 1, 2, 3, 4, 5, 6, 7, 8, or 9
12. Find the smallest natural number divisible by 3, 5, 7, and 9.   315
13. Find the smallest natural number divisible by 2, 4, 6, and 8.   24
14. If the numbers a and b are both divisible by 4, which of the following must also be divisible by 4. Explain your reasoning. **a.** $a + b = 4x + 4y = 4(x + y)$
b. $a - b = 4x - 4y = 4(x - y)$ **c.** $ab = (4x)(4y)$
d. $\frac{a}{b} = \frac{4x}{4y} = \frac{x}{y}$

In Exercises 15–18, find all factors of the number.
15. 24   1, 2, 3, 4, 6, 8, 12, 24
16. 54   1, 2, 3, 6, 9, 18, 27, 54
17. 48   1, 2, 3, 4, 6, 8, 12, 16, 24, 48
18. 105   1, 3, 5, 7, 15, 21, 35, 105
19. A rectangular region of state forest land has an area of 80 square miles. The length and the width are natural numbers. Find the possible dimensions.
   1 mi-by-80 mi, 2 mi-by-40 mi, 4 mi-by-20 mi, 8 mi-by-10 mi, 16 mi-by-5 mi
20. A rancher wants to fence in a corral for his prize winning stallion. He wishes to have an area of 400 square yards. He also wants the perimeter to be as small as possible in order to minimize the cost of the fencing. If the side lengths are natural numbers, find the dimensions of the corral.   20 yd-by-20 yd

42   *Divisibility Tests • 6.1*   Windows

Reteach Chapter 6   Name _____

What you should learn: **Correlation to Pupil's Textbook:**
6.1 How to use divisibility tests and how to factor natural numbers   Mid-Chapter Self-Test (p. 263)   Chapter Test (p. 287)
Exercises 1–4   Exercises 1, 2

Examples *Using Divisibility Tests and Factoring Natural Numbers*

a. Decide whether 1080 is divisible by 2, 3, 4, 5, 6, 8, 9, and 10.
Is 1080

n	divisible by n?	Reason
2	yes	1080 is even.
3	yes	$1 + 0 + 8 + 0 = 9$ and 9 is divisible by 3.
4	yes	80 is divisible by 4.
5	yes	The last digit of 1080 is 0.
6	yes	1080 is even and divisible by 3.
8	yes	80 is divisible by 8.
9	yes	$1 + 0 + 8 + 0 = 9$ and 9 is divisible by 9.
10	yes	The last digit of 1080 is 0.

1. Yes: 3, 5;   No: 2, 4, 6, 8, 9, 10
2. Yes: 2, 3, 6;   No: 4, 5, 8, 9, 10
3. Yes: 5;   No: 2, 3, 4, 6, 8, 9, 10
4. Yes: 2, 4, 5, 10;   No: 3, 6, 8, 9,
5. Yes: 2, 3, 4, 5, 6, 8, 9, 10
6. Yes: 2, 3, 5;   No: 4, 5, 8, 10
7. Yes: 2, 3, 4, 5, 6, 8, 9, 10
8. Yes: 2, 4, 8;   No: 3, 5, 6, 9, 10

b. Find all factors of 30.
You can use divisibility tests to factor 30.
Because $\frac{30}{1} = 30$, you conclude that $30 = 1 \cdot 30$.
Because $\frac{30}{2} = 15$, you conclude that $30 = 2 \cdot 15$.
Because $\frac{30}{3} = 10$, you conclude that $30 = 3 \cdot 10$.
Because $\frac{30}{5} = 6$, you conclude that $30 = 5 \cdot 6$.
The factors of 30 are 1, 2, 3, 5, 6, 10, 15, and 30.

Guidelines: • If one natural number divides evenly into another natural number, then the second number is divisible by the first.
• A natural number is factored when it is written as the product of two or more natural numbers.

EXERCISES

In Exercises 1–4, use the divisibility tests to determine whether the number is divisible by 2, 3, 4, 5, 6, 8, 9, and 10.
1. 615   2. 3642   3. 985   4. 8140
5. 9360   6. 5742   7. 4320   8. 2896

In Exercises 9–16, find all factors of the number.
9. 15   1, 3, 5, 15
10. 48   1, 2, 3, 4, 6, 8, 12, 16, 24, 48
11. 75   1, 3, 5, 15, 25, 75
12. 94   1, 2, 47, 94
13. 88   1, 2, 4, 8, 11, 22, 44, 88
14. 54   1, 2, 3, 6, 9, 18, 27, 54
15. 70   1, 2, 5, 7, 10, 14, 35, 70
16. 63   1, 3, 7, 9, 21, 63

42   *Chapter 6 • Exploring Number Theory*   Windows

33.–36. See Additional Answers.

In Exercises 33–36, write each number as the product of three factors. (Don't use 1 as a factor.)

33. 24   **34.** 36

35. 210   **36.** 144

37. *Geometry*   The box at the right has a volume of 60 cubic units. The volume is the product of the box's length, width, and height. Use the box to write 60 as the product of three factors. $3 \times 4 \times 5$

38. *Geometry*   A rectangle has an area of 64 square units. The lengths of the sides are natural numbers. Find the possible dimensions.
$1 \times 64, 2 \times 32, 4 \times 16,$ or 8×8

Conservation Project   **In Exercises 39–41, imagine you are part of a team that is planting 350 tree seedlings.**

39. Your team is instructed to plant the seedlings in straight rows with the same number of trees in each row. One team member wants to plant 15 rows. Is that possible? Explain why or why not.   **39., 40.** See Additional Answers.

40. Your team is instructed to plant the trees in a rectangular region. You can use any rectangle, so long as its area is 1600 square feet. If the side lengths (in feet) are natural numbers, what are the possible dimensions of the region?

41. Your team wants to construct a temporary fence around the seedlings. Of the dimensions found in Exercise 40, which have the smallest perimeter?   40 ft × 40 ft

A young tree needs moist soil to become well rooted. Fall and spring are good times to plant trees.

42. Why can a number be divisible by 3 and not be divisible by 9?

43. Why is a number that is divisible by 8 also divisible by 4?   **42.–45.** See margin.

✪ 44. *Number Theory*   State a rule for divisibility by 50.

✪ 45. *Number Theory*   State a rule for divisibility by 20.

Integrated Review   *Making Connections within Mathematics*

Probability   **In Exercises 46–49, one of the digits 2, 3, 5, 7, or 8 is randomly selected and used to form the indicated 3-digit number. Find the probability that the number is divisible by 4.**

46. 6?4 $\frac{2}{5}$ **47.** 87? $\frac{1}{5}$ **48.** ?32   1   **49.** ?94   0

Exploration and Extension

✪ 50. *A Division Pattern*   Complete each statement. Then describe the pattern. See margin.

$56 \div 4 = \boxed{?}$, $156 \div 4 = \boxed{?}$, $256 \div 4 = \boxed{?}$, $356 \div 4 = \boxed{?}$

✪ 51. Using your pattern, predict $756 \div 4$. Check your answer.   189

✪ 52. *Writing*   Write a paragraph explaining why the divisibility test for 4
P   works.   See margin.

▶ **Ex. 37**   For students unfamiliar with the term *volume*, the model should help in answering the question.

▶ **Ex. 39–41**   Assign these as a group.

Integrated Review ────

These exercises offer a good review of probability.

Exploration and Extension

Assign these as a group.

Portfolio Opportunity: Math Log

Write your own divisibility tests for the following statements.
a. A natural number is divisible by 2 and 10 if . . .
b. A natural number is divisible by 15 if . . .

Also available as a copymaster, page 19, Ex. 1

Alternative Assessment

A Math Game that evaluates students' ability to recognize factors of natural numbers

Available as a copymaster, page 25

Answers

42. Because 3 is not divisible by 9.

43. Because 8 is divisible by 4.

44. A natural number is divisible by 50 if (a) its last digit is 0 and (b) its next-to-last digit is 0 or 5.

45. A natural number is divisible by 20 if (a) its last digit is 0 and (b) its next-to-last digit is even (or (b) the number formed by its last two digits is divisible by 4).

50. 14, 39, 64, 89: each number, after the first, is 25 more than the preceding number.

52. In a natural number, the digits in the places beyond the tens place represent multiples of 100 (such as 300, 9000, or 70,000), which are all multiples of 4 ($300 = 3 \times 4 \times 25$, $9000 = 9 \times 4 \times 250$, $70,000 = 7 \times 4 \times 2500$). So, if the number represented by the last two digits is divisible by 4, then the natural number is divisible by 4.

The investigation can be completed with little assistance from the teacher. Manipulating the square tiles helps students develop a better understanding of the concept of area. If square tiles are not available, have students draw the possible rectangles on graph paper ($\frac{1}{4}$ inch or cm) *or* have them cut the rectangles out of graph paper (at least $\frac{1}{2}$ inch).

Materials Needed: square tiles or graph paper

In this activity, you will investigate factors of natural numbers.

Example   *Finding Factors of a Number*

Find all possible factors of 16.

Solution   As shown below, 16 tiles can be used to form 3 sizes of rectangles: a 1-by-16 rectangle, a 2-by-8 rectangle, and a 4-by-4 rectangle. This implies that 16 has five factors: 1, 2, 4, 8, and 16.

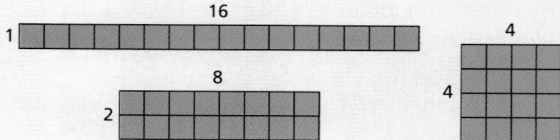

Exercises

Copy and complete the table.

Number, n	Number of Rectangles	Dimensions of Rectangles	Factors of n
1	1 ?	1 by 1 ?	1 ?
2	1 ?	1 by 2 ?	1, 2 ?
3	1 ?	1 by 3 ?	1, 3 ?
4	2 ?	1 by 4, ? 2 by 2	1, 2, ? 4
5	1 ?	1 by 5 ?	1, 5 ?
6	2 ?	1 by 6, ? 2 by 3	1, 2, ? 3, 6
7	1 ?	1 by 7 ?	1, 7 ?
8	2 ?	1 by 8, ? 2 by 4	1, 2, ? 4, 8
9	2 ?	1 by 9, ? 3 by 3	1, 3, ? 9
10	2 ?	1 by 10, ? 2 by 5	1, 2, ? 5, 10
11	1 ?	1 by 11 ?	1, 11 ?
12	3 ?	1 by 12, ? 2 by 6, 3 by 4	1, 2, 3, ? 4, 6, 12
13	1 ?	1 by 13 ?	1, 13 ?
14	2 ?	1 by 14, ? 2 by 7	1, 2, ? 7, 14
15	2 ?	1 by 15, ? 3 by 5	1, 3, ? 5, 15
16	3	1 by 16, 2 by 8, 4 by 4	1, 2, 4, 8, 16

6.2

Factors and Primes

What you should learn:

Goal 1 How to classify natural numbers as prime or composite

Goal 2 How to actor algebraic expressions and use factorizations to solve real-life problems.

Why you should learn it:

You can use the factors of a number to determine ways the number can be written as a product.

Except for 2 and 3, all the primes are in the first and fifth rows.

7, 13, 19, 31, 37, 43, 61, 67, 73, 79

2

3

11, 17, 23, 29, 41, 47, 53, 59, 71, 83, 89

Goal 1 Classifying Primes and Composites

Natural numbers can be classified according to the number of factors they have.

> **Prime and Composite Numbers**
>
> **1.** A natural number is **prime** if it has exactly two factors, itself and 1. For instance, 2, 3, 5, and 7 are prime.
>
> **2.** A natural number is **composite** if it has three or more factors. For instance, 4, 6, and 8 are composite.
>
> **3.** The natural number 1 is neither prime nor composite.

LESSON INVESTIGATION

■ Investigating Prime Patterns

Group Activity Write the natural numbers from 1 through 96 as shown below. Circle all primes. Describe any pattern you observe.

1	7	13	19	25	31	37	43	49	55	61	67	73	79	85	91
2	8	14	20	26	32	38	44	50	56	62	68	74	80	86	92
3	9	15	21	27	33	39	45	51	57	63	69	75	81	87	93
4	10	16	22	28	34	40	46	52	58	64	70	76	82	88	94
5	11	17	23	29	35	41	47	53	59	65	71	77	83	89	95
6	12	18	24	30	36	42	48	54	60	66	72	78	84	90	96

Example 1 *Prime Factorization*

The **prime factorization** of 24 is $2 \cdot 2 \cdot 2 \cdot 3$. Write the prime factorization of 30.

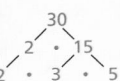

First factor 30 as 3 times 10. Then factor 10 as 2 times 5.

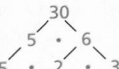

First factor 30 as 2 times 15. Then factor 15 as 3 times 5.

First factor 30 as 5 times 6. Then factor 6 as 2 times 3.

Solution Begin by factoring 30 as the product of two numbers other than 1 and itself. Continue factoring until all factors are prime. The **tree diagrams** at the left show three ways this can be done. In each case, you obtain the factors 2, 3, and 5. This implies that the prime factorization of 30 is

$$30 = 2 \cdot 3 \cdot 5. \qquad \text{Prime factorization of 30.} \qquad ■$$

6.2 • Factors and Primes **245**

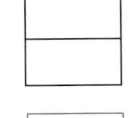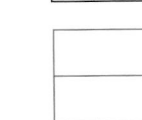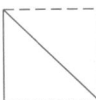

> **STARTER: Problem of the Day**
>
> Remove six sticks, leaving ten on the table.
>
> Also available as a copymaster, page 16

> **STARTER: Warm-Up Exercises**
>
> **1.** Give the possible dimensions of a rectangle that has the area indicated below and whose sides are natural numbers.
> **a.** 13 units²   **b.** 19 units²
> **a.** 1×13, **b.** 1×19
>
> **2.** Factor each number into factors of 2, 3, and 5.
> **a.** 90   **b.** 600   **c.** 900   **d.** 150
> **a.** $2 \cdot 3 \cdot 3 \cdot 5$, **b.** $2 \cdot 2 \cdot 2 \cdot 3 \cdot 5 \cdot 5$,
> **c.** $2 \cdot 2 \cdot 3 \cdot 3 \cdot 5 \cdot 5$, **d.** $2 \cdot 3 \cdot 5 \cdot 5$
>
> Also available as a copymaster, page 16

PACING the Lesson

Suggested Number of Days
Basic/Average 0   **Above Average** 0
Advanced 1

PLANNING the Lesson

Lesson Plan 6.2, p. 43

ORGANIZER

Starters (reproduced below)
   Problem of the Day 6.2, p. 16
   Warm-Up Exercises 6.2, p. 16
Lesson Resources
   Color Transparencies
     Pictures for Example 3 and Ex. 43–46, p. 24
   Teaching Tools
     Puzzle, p. C16
   Math Log, p. 19
   Answer Masters 6.2, pp. 106, 107
   Extra Practice Copymaster 6.2, p. 43
   Reteaching Copymaster 6.2, p. 43
   Enrichment Projects, pp. 29, 30
Special Populations
   Suggestions, Teacher's Edition, p. 238D

LESSON Notes

> **Vocabulary Alert!**
>
> The definitions of *prime* and *composite* numbers are very important in algebra. Students should include them in their math journals.

Lesson Investigation
As a research project, have students investigate the "Sieve of Eratosthenes." (See Guided Practice Exercises 1–4.) Eratosthenes was a Greek mathematician who lived from approximately 276 to 194 B.C.

Example 1

In constructing a factorization tree, rather than continuing to write the same prime factor at each level, students can use a shortcut by labeling each prime (with a circle) as it appears. For example:

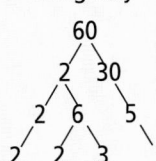   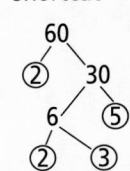

Long way   Shortcut

Note also that it is customary to write the prime factorization of a natural number with

Lesson 6.2 **245**

Emphasize that the definition of powers of variables indicates how to write them in expanded form. For example, a^5 is defined as $a \cdot a \cdot a \cdot a \cdot a$. Also explain to the students that any negative real number can be rewritten as a product involving -1. For example, $-5 = (-1) \cdot 5$.

Example 2

Students should be able to write algebraic expressions in either exponent form or expanded form.

Example 3

Have students repeat this activity using 500 yen.

Group Size	Amount given to each person (yen)
1	500
2	250
4	125
5	100
10	50
20	25
25	20
50	10
100	5

Communicating
about MATHEMATICS

Make sure that students consider and write down plenty of examples.

Writing Prompt
Describe the images that come to mind when you think about FACTOR.

Answer to Communicating
Every natural number can be written as products of pairs of numbers. When no two numbers in a pair are identical, there must be an even number of factors; when two numbers in a pair are identical, there must be an odd number of factors. Conversely, if a natural number has an odd number of factors, then there must be two numbers in a pair written as a product that are identical; so the natural number must be a square.

The factoring technique shown in Example 1 can be extended to negative integers and expressions involving variables. For instance, $-6ab^2$ can be written as $-6ab^2 = (-1) \cdot 2 \cdot 3 \cdot a \cdot b \cdot b$.

Example 2 *Factoring Algebraic Expressions*

Expression	Expanded Form	Exponent Form
a. -24	$(-1) \cdot 2 \cdot 2 \cdot 2 \cdot 3$	$(-1) \cdot 2^3 \cdot 3$
b. $63a^3$	$3 \cdot 3 \cdot 7 \cdot a \cdot a \cdot a$	$3^2 \cdot 7 \cdot a^3$
c. $18x^2y$	$2 \cdot 3 \cdot 3 \cdot x \cdot x \cdot y$	$2 \cdot 3^2 \cdot x^2 \cdot y$

Real Life
Finance

Japanese Money *The Japanese yen is issued in denominations of 5, 10, 50, 100, and 500. Using only these denominations, how could you evenly divide 500 yen with each person in a group?*

Example 3 *Problem Solving: Consider All Causes*

$5 is to be divided evenly among the people in a group. How many people can be in the group?

Solution $5 is equal to 500 pennies. You must find all the factors of 500 since each factor is a possible group size.

Group Size	Amount Given to Each Person	Check
1	$5.00	$1 \cdot \$5.00 = \$5.00$
2	$2.50	$2 \cdot \$2.50 = \$5.00$
4	$1.25	$4 \cdot \$1.25 = \$5.00$
5	$1.00	$5 \cdot \$1.00 = \$5.00$
10	$0.50	$10 \cdot \$0.50 = \$5.00$
20	$0.25	$20 \cdot \$0.25 = \$5.00$
25	$0.20	$25 \cdot \$0.20 = \$5.00$
50	$0.10	$50 \cdot \$0.10 = \$5.00$
100	$0.05	$100 \cdot \$0.05 = \$5.00$
125	$0.04	$125 \cdot \$0.04 = \$5.00$
250	$0.02	$250 \cdot \$0.02 = \$5.00$
500	$0.01	$500 \cdot \$0.01 = \$5.00$

Communicating about MATHEMATICS

▶ **SHARING IDEAS about the Lesson**

Square Numbers Explain why every square number must have an *odd* number of factors. If a natural number has an odd number of factors, must it be square? Explain. See margin.

◀ **OPTION: Extra Example**

Here is an additional example similar to Example 1 of the lesson.
Prime Factorization
The prime factorization of 40 is $2^3 \cdot 5$. Write the prime factorization of 63.
Solution
Begin by factoring 63 as the product of two numbers other than 1 and itself. Continue factoring until all factors are prime. The tree diagrams show two ways this can be done. In each case, you obtain the factors 3, 3, and 7. This implies that the prime factorization of 63 is $63 = 3^2 \cdot 7$.

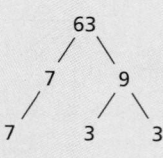
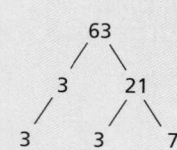

EXERCISES

Guided Practice

▶ **CHECK for Understanding**

Number Sense   **In Exercises 1–4, use the number sieve.**

1. Multiples of 2 other than 2, multiples of 3 other than 3, multiples of 5 other than 5

2, 3, ~~4~~, 5, ~~6~~, 7, ~~8~~, 9, ~~10~~, 11, ~~12~~, 13, ~~14~~, 15, ~~16~~, 17, ~~18~~, 19, ~~20~~, 21, ~~22~~, 23, ~~24~~, 25, ~~26~~, 27, ~~28~~, 29, ~~30~~

2, 3, 4, 5, ~~6~~, 7, 8, ~~9~~, 10, 11, ~~12~~, 13, 14, ~~15~~, 16, 17, ~~18~~, 19, 20, ~~21~~, 22, 23, ~~24~~, 25, 26, ~~27~~, 28, 29, ~~30~~

2, 3, 4, 5, 6, 7, 8, 9, ~~10~~, 11, 12, 13, 14, ~~15~~, 16, 17, 18, 19, ~~20~~, 21, 22, 23, 24, ~~25~~, 26, 27, 28, 29, ~~30~~

1. What type of number is crossed out in the 1st row? The 2nd row? The 3rd row?

2. What type of number has not been crossed out in any row?   Prime

3. Extend each row to 40. Which of the numbers 31–40 would not be crossed out?   31, 37

4. What natural number is neither prime nor composite?   1

Independent Practice

In Exercises 5–8, is the number prime or composite? Explain.

5. 17 Prime, exactly two factors

6. 9 Composite, $9 = 3^2$

7. 35 Composite, $35 = 5 \cdot 7$

8. 27 Composite, $27 = 3^3$

In Exercises 9–12, write the factorization represented by the tree diagram.

9.
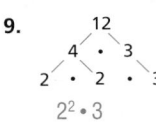
$2^2 \cdot 3$

10.
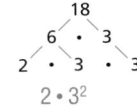
$2 \cdot 3^2$

11.
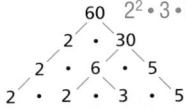 $2^2 \cdot 3 \cdot 5$

12.
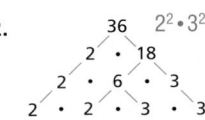 $2^2 \cdot 3^2$

In Exercises 13–20, write the prime factorization of the number. Write your answer in exponent form.

13. 36 $2^2 \cdot 3^2$
14. 63 $3^2 \cdot 7$
15. 84 $2^2 \cdot 3 \cdot 7$
16. 100 $2^2 \cdot 5^2$

17. 32 2^5
18. 64 2^6
19. 72 $2^3 \cdot 3^2$
20. 90 $2 \cdot 3^2 \cdot 5$

In Exercises 21–28, write the expression in expanded form and exponent form.   See margin.

21. -27
22. -28
23. $9x^3$
24. $125y^4$

25. $8a^3b^2$
26. $12p^4q$
27. $-45mn^3$
28. $-50s^2t^5$

In Exercises 29–32, evaluate the expression.

29. $2^3 \cdot 3 \cdot 5$ 120
30. $3^2 \cdot 2 \cdot 13$ 234
31. $-1 \cdot 3^2 \cdot 5 \cdot 13$ -585
32. $-1 \cdot 2^3 \cdot 3 \cdot 7$ -168

In Exercises 33–36, list all possible factors of the number.

33. 8 1, 2, 4, 8
34. 16 1, 2, 4, 8, 16
35. 32 1, 2, 4, 8, 16, 32
36. 64 1, 2, 4, 8, 16, 32, 64

6.2 • Factors and Primes   **247**

Extra Practice

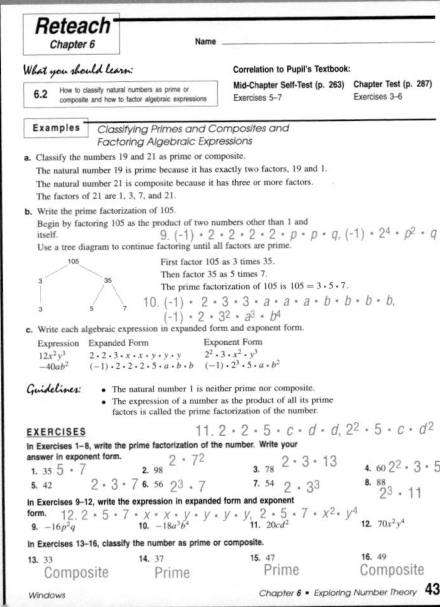

Reteaching

ASSIGNMENT GUIDE

*Basic/Average:
Day 1: Ex. 5–31 odd, 37
Day 2: Ex. 39–49 odd

*Above Average:
Ex. 9–31 odd, 37–40, 47–49

Advanced: Ex. 9–31 odd, 37–40, 47–49

Selected Answers: Ex. 1–4, 5–47 odd
*You may wish to omit this lesson for these students.

Guided Practice

Make sure all students know what a sieve is.

Independent Practice

▶ **Ex. 13–20** Check to see that all factors are prime.
▶ **Ex. 21–28** The simplified version of each expression has been given. Students are asked to write both the expanded from *and* the exponent form. Be sure to do an example of this in class.
▶ **Ex. 31, 32** Note that negative numbers are also factors.

Answers
21. $(-1) \cdot 3 \cdot 3 \cdot 3$, $(-1) \cdot 3^3$
22. $(-1) \cdot 2 \cdot 2 \cdot 7$, $(-1) \cdot 2^2 \cdot 7$
23. $3 \cdot 3 \cdot x \cdot x \cdot x$, $3^2 \cdot x^3$
24. $5 \cdot 5 \cdot 5 \cdot y \cdot y \cdot y \cdot y$, $5^3 \cdot y^4$
25. $2 \cdot 2 \cdot 2 \cdot a \cdot a \cdot a \cdot b \cdot b$, $2^3 \cdot a^3 \cdot b^2$
26. $2 \cdot 2 \cdot 3 \cdot p \cdot p \cdot p \cdot p \cdot q$, $2^2 \cdot 3 \cdot p^4 \cdot q$
27. $(-1) \cdot 3 \cdot 3 \cdot 5 \cdot m \cdot n \cdot n \cdot n$, $(-1) \cdot 3^2 \cdot 5 \cdot m \cdot n^3$
28. $(-1) \cdot 2 \cdot 5 \cdot 5 \cdot s \cdot s \cdot t \cdot t \cdot t \cdot t \cdot t$, $(-1) \cdot 2 \cdot 5^2 \cdot s^2 \cdot t^5$

Lesson 6.2   **247**

37.–41. See Additional Answers.

Portfolio Opportunity: Math Log

1. Decide whether the following statement is true or false. Explain your answer.
   Each integer has a unique prime factorization (2 • 3 is considered the same as 3 • 2.)
2. Decide whether the following statements are true or false. Explain your answer.
   a. If *a* and *b* are prime, *a* • *b* is prime.
   b. If *a* and *b* are prime, *a* + *b* is prime.

Short Quiz
Covers Lessons 6.1 and 6.2

---

37. *Number Sense* Consider the results of Exercises 33–36. If you double a number, does the list of all possible factors of the number double? Explain your reasoning. No

38. *Geometry* If the lengths of the sides of a triangle are consecutive integers, could the perimeter be a prime number? Explain. No

39. *Goldbach's Conjecture* A famous unproven conjecture by Christian Goldbach (1690–1764) states that every even natural number except 2 is the sum of two prime numbers. Write the even numbers from 20 to 40 as the sum of two primes.

40. *Twin Primes* Another famous unproven conjecture deals with primes whose difference is 2, such as 3 and 5, 5 and 7, and 11 and 13. Write the next five twin prime pairs.

41. *Dividing Money* $4.50 is divided evenly among the people in a group. How many people can be in the group?

42. *Dividing into Groups* A class is divided into more than two groups. If each group is the same size, could the number of students in the class be prime? Explain. See margin.

U.S. Flag History In Exercises 43–46, design a rectangular pattern for the stars in the United States flag. Make one star for each state and make the rectangle's sides as close to the same lengths as possible.

43. Flag of 1795: 15 states
44. Flag of 1818: 20 states
45. Flag of 1861: 34 states
46. Flag of 1994: 50 states

43.–46. See Additional Answers.

The flag from 1912 to 1959 served as the national flag longer than any other. The 13 stripes represent the 13 original states.

Integrated Review   *Making Connections within Mathematics*

Probability   In Exercises 47 and 48, consider the following. The natural numbers from 1 through 30 are written on slips of paper and placed in a box. One number is randomly selected from the box.

47. What is the probability that the number is prime? $\frac{1}{3}$

48. What is the probability that the number is composite? $\frac{19}{30}$

Exploration and Extension

Crossnumber Puzzles   In Exercises 49 and 50, copy and complete the puzzle using single digits. Each digit must be a factor of the number at the beginning of its row and column. You can use each digit only once.

49.

✕	18	8	35
42	3/6	2	7
60	6/3	4	5
72	9	8	1

50.

✕	36	30	56
35	1	5	7
24	4	3/6	8
18	9	6/3	2

✪ More difficult exercises
Ⓟ Portfolio Opportunity

248   *Chapter 6 ▪ Exploring Number Theory*

Answers
42. Assuming each group consists of more than one student, no (otherwise, yes). The number of students in the class would be equal to the product of two numbers (the number of groups and the number of students in each group), neither of which is 1.

Enrichment

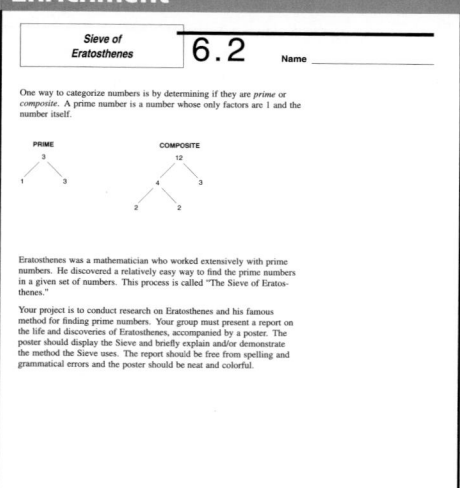

Sieve of Eratosthenes   **6.2**   Name _____

One way to categorize numbers is by determining if they are *prime* or *composite*. A prime number is a number whose only factors are 1 and the number itself.

PRIME
3

COMPOSITE
12

Eratosthenes was a mathematician who worked extensively with prime numbers. He discovered a relatively easy way to find the prime numbers in a given set of numbers. This process is called "The Sieve of Eratosthenes."

Your project is to conduct research on Eratosthenes and his famous method for finding prime numbers. Your group must present a report on the life and discoveries of Eratosthenes, accompanied by a poster. The poster should display the Sieve and briefly explain and/or demonstrate the method the Sieve uses. The report should be free from spelling and grammatical errors and the poster should be neat and colorful.

Materials Needed: graph paper, pencil

In this activity, you will investigate common factors of numbers.

Example · *Finding Common Factors*

You are tiling a 12-by-16 floor with square tiles. The tiles cannot overlap, and you can't cut any of the tiles. Can the room be tiled using only 1-by-1 tiles? 2-by-2 tiles? 3-by-3 tiles? 4-by-4 tiles? 5-by-5 tiles? 6-by-6 tiles?

Solution The solutions are shown below. Notice that the 1-by-1, 2-by-2, and 4-by-4 tiles are the only ones that work. The reason is that 1, 2, and 4 are common factors of 12 and 16. The greatest common factor of 12 and 16 is 4.

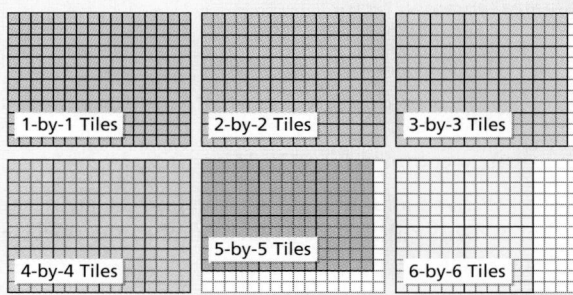

■

Exercises · For sketches, see margin.

In Exercises 1–4, decide which size tiles can be used to tile the room. Sketch your results. Which numbers are common factors of the width and length of the room? What is the greatest common factor?

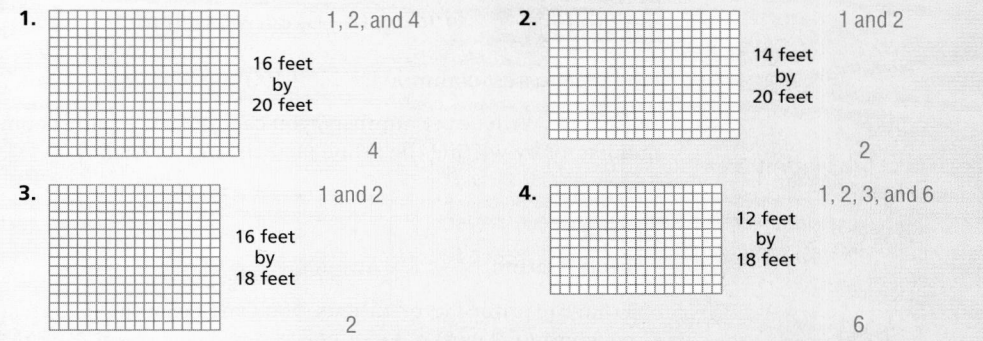

1. 16 feet by 20 feet — 1, 2, and 4 — 4

2. 14 feet by 20 feet — 1 and 2 — 2

3. 16 feet by 18 feet — 1 and 2 — 2

4. 12 feet by 18 feet — 1, 2, 3, and 6 — 6

This investigation is a fun activity for students. Students should cut out and manipulate the tiles in an attempt to simulate the tiling process. This simulation could also be done with the overhead projector. The goal is to introduce the idea of a common factor.

Resources
Teaching Tools
  Graph paper pp. T1, C2

Answers
1.

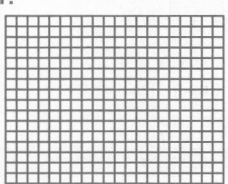 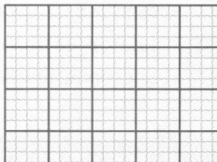

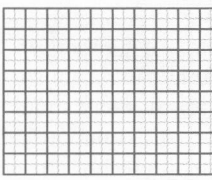

1, 2, and 4, are the common factors. 4 is the greatest common factor.

2.

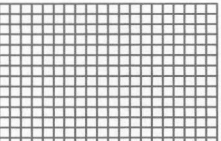 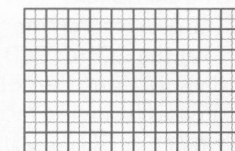

1 and 2 are the common factors. 2 is the greatest common factor.

3.

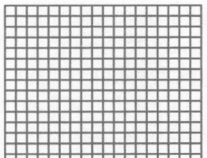 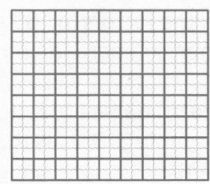

1 and 2 are the common factors. 2 is the greatest common factor.

4.

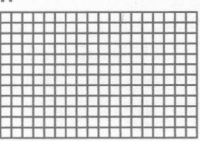 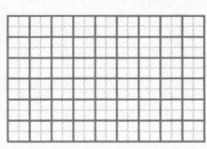

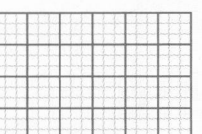 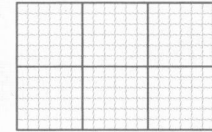

1, 2, 3, and 6 are the common factors. 6 is the greatest common factor.

PACING the Lesson

Suggested Number of Days
Basic/Average 0   **Above Average** 0
Advanced 1

PLANNING the Lesson

Lesson Plan 6.3, p. 44

ORGANIZER

Starters (reproduced below)
 Problem of the Day 6.3, p. 16
 Warm-Up Exercises 6.3, p. 16
Lesson Resources
 Color Transparencies
  Picture for Example 3, p. 25
 Math Log, p. 20
 Technology, p. 32
 Answer Masters 6.3, pp. 108, 109
 Extra Practice Copymaster 6.3, p. 44
 Reteaching Copymaster 6.3, p. 44
Special Populations
 Suggestions, Teacher's Edition, p. 238D

LESSON Notes

Begin by discussing strategies for finding
common factors of two natural numbers, *m*
and *n*. Ask students how they can recognize
the greatest common factor. Students should
then include the definitions of "common
factor" and "greatest common factor" in
their math journals.

Example 1

The greatest common factor is often referred
to as the GCF (or GCD, for greatest common
divisor). Using the abbreviated form, the
greatest common factor of 16 and 20 can be
written as GCF(16,20).

Example 2

Encourage students to find the GCF by listing
all the factors of 180 and 378, as in Example 1.
Then compare the time it takes to find the
GCF that way versus the time it takes to find
the prime factorization and find the GCF as in
Example 2. Discuss the differences with students.
 The margin note on the pupil page extends
the concept of GCF to algebraic expressions.
You may wish to discuss this. Have students
note that the prime factorization of $18x^2y$ is
$2 \cdot 3 \cdot 3 \cdot x \cdot x \cdot y$. The prime factorization of
$12xy$ is $2 \cdot 2 \cdot 3 \cdot x \cdot y$. So, the common prime
factors are $2 \cdot 3 \cdot x \cdot y$. Hence, the GCF of
$18x^2y$ and $12xy$ is $6xy$.

6.3
Greatest Common Factor

What you should learn:

Goal 1 How to find the
greatest common
factor of two num-
bers or expressions

Goal 2 How to use the greatest common factor of
numbers to solve real-
life problems

Why you should learn it:

You can use the greatest common factor of two numbers to
solve real-life problems, such as
comparing frequencies of notes
on a musical scale.

Greatest Common Factor of Algebraic Expressions

The concept of a greatest
common factor also applies
to algebraic expressions. For
instance, the greatest common factor of $18x^2y$ and
$12xy$ is $6xy$.

Goal 1 ## Finding Common Factors

In Lessons 6.1 and 6.2, you studied factors of numbers. In this
lesson, you will study common factors of two numbers.

> **Common Factors and Greatest Common Factor**
> Let *m* and *n* be natural numbers.
> 1. A number that is a factor of both *m* and *n* is a **common factor**
>   of *m* and *n*.
> 2. Of all common factors of *m* and *n*, the largest is called the
>   **greatest common factor.**

Example 1   *Finding the Greatest Common Factor*

Find the greatest common factor of 16 and 20.

Solution   With small numbers, you can find the greatest common factor by listing all factors of each number and selecting
the largest common factor.

Number	16	20
Factors	1, 2, 4, 8, 16	1, 2, 4, 5, 10, 20

From the lists, you can see that 1, 2, and 4 are common factors
of 16 and 20. Of these, 4 is the greatest common factor. ∎

Example 2   *Finding the Greatest Common Factor*

Find the greatest common factor of 180 and 378.

Solution   With larger numbers, you can find the greatest common factor by writing the prime factorization of each.

Number	180	378
Prime Factorization	$2 \cdot 2 \cdot 3 \cdot 3 \cdot 5$	$2 \cdot 3 \cdot 3 \cdot 3 \cdot 7$

From the prime factorizations, you can reason that the greatest common factor is $2 \cdot 3 \cdot 3$ or 18. ∎

STARTER: Problem of the Day	STARTER: Warm-Up Exercises
Move three sticks to make three small squares of the same size, with no sticks left over. 	**1.** Find all the factors of **a.** 24 **b.** 32 **c.** 42 **a.** 1, 2, 3, 4, 6, 8, 12, 24; **b.** 1, 2, 4, 8, 16, 32; **c.** 1, 2, 3, 6, 7, 14, 21, 42 **2.** For each pair, *m* and *n*, say whether *m* is divisible by *n*. **a.** $m = 18, n = 12$ **b.** $m = 236, n = 6$ **c.** $m = 12, n = 24$ **d.** $m = 927, n = 9$ **e.** $m = 616, n = 11$ **f.** $m = 896, n = 7$ **a.** no, **b.** no, **c.** no, **d.** yes, **e.** yes, **f.** yes
Also available as a copymaster, page 16	Also available as a copymaster, page 16

Modern symphony orchestras have from 90 to 120 players. The violins, the highest pitched string instruments, usually carry the melody in orchestral music.

Goal 2 **Using Greatest Common Factors**

Example 3 **Using Greatest Common Factors**

Notes on a musical scale are characterized by their frequencies. The higher the frequency, the higher the note. On a piano, the A above middle C has a frequency of 440. What is the greatest common factor of the three A's shown on the following piano keyboard? What is the greatest common factor of the three G's?

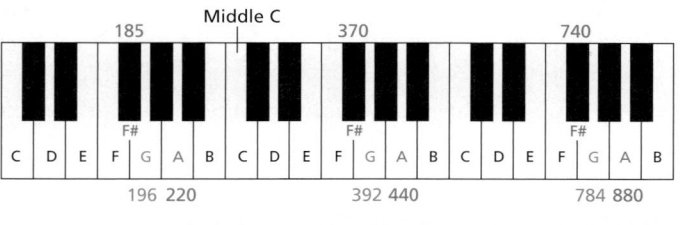

Solution The three A's have frequencies of 220, 440, and 880. Because 440 and 880 are each divisible by 220, it follows that 220 is the greatest common factor of the three numbers.

The three G's have frequencies of 196, 392, and 784. Because 392 and 784 are each divisible by 196, it follows that 196 is the greatest common factor of the three numbers. ∎

In music, the notes A-220 and A-440 are an *octave* apart. The notes F#-185 and F#-370 are also an octave apart. (F# is read as F-sharp.) From Example 3, you can see that if two notes are an octave apart, then the higher note has twice the frequency of the lower note.

Communicating about MATHEMATICS

▶ **SHARING IDEAS about the Lesson**

Relatively Prime Numbers Two natural numbers are **relatively prime** if their greatest common factor is 1. For instance, the numbers 8 and 21 are relatively prime. Find the greatest common factor of the following pairs. State whether the two numbers are relatively prime.

A. 1, yes
B. 45, no
C. 2, no

A. 135 and 224   **B.** 135 and 225   **C.** 134 and 224

Must two prime numbers be relatively prime? Explain.

See margin, page 252.

6.3 • *Greatest Common Factor* **251**

The greatest common factor is used in many real-life situations, including determination of the frequency at which traffic lights should change.

Example 3

Have students use the library to find the frequencies of some other musical notes.

Communicating about MATHEMATICS

EXTENSION
Another way to find the GCF of two numbers is the *Euclidean Algorithm*, as in the following examples.

Find GCF(8,12).
$12 \div 8 = 1, R = 4; 8 \div 4 = 2, R = 0$
GCF(8,12) = **4**

Find GCF(42,24).
$42 \div 24 = 1, R = 18; 24 \div 18 = 1, R = 6; 18 \div 6 = 3, R = 0$
GCF(42,24) = **6**

Find GCF(70,143):
$143 \div 70 = 2, R = 3; 70 \div 3 = 23, R = 1; 3 \div 1 = 3, R = 0$
GCF(70,143) = **1** (So, 70 and 143 are relatively prime.)

Describe the process shown above and then use it to find the GCF of these pairs:
135 and 225, 134 and 224, 135 and 224,
45, 2; 135 and 224 are relatively prime.

Writing Prompt
Write a multiple choice question about greatest common factors and explain how each of the wrong answers could be considered logical.

Technology

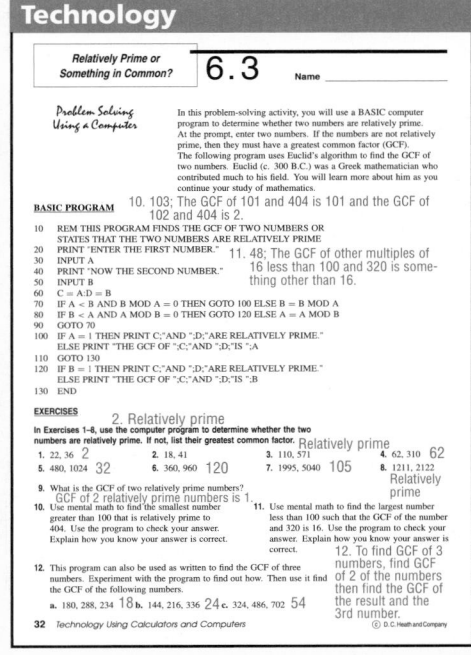

◆ **OPTION: Extra Examples**
Here are additional examples similar to some of those of the lesson.
Finding the Greatest Common Factor
1. Find the greatest common factor of 28 and 42.
Solution
With small numbers, you can find the greatest common factor by listing all factors of each number and selecting the largest common factor.

Number	Factors
28	1, 2, 4, 7, ⑭, 28
42	1, 2, 3, 6, 7, ⑭, 21, 42

From the lists, you can see that 1, 2, 7, and 14 are common factors of 28 and 42. Of these, 14 is the greatest common factor.

2. Find the greatest common factor of 297 and 540.
Solution
With larger numbers, you can find the greatest common factor by writing the prime factorization of each.

Number	Prime Factorization
297	③·③·③·11
540	2·2·③·③·③·5

From the prime factorizations, you can reason that the greatest common factor is 3·3·3 or 27.

Lesson 6.3 **251**

ASSIGNMENT GUIDE

*Basic/Average:
Day 1: Ex. 7–31 odd, 35, 37
Day 2: Ex. 33, 34, 36, 39, 41–47 odd

*Above Average:
Ex. 11–33 odd, 34, 36, 39–47 odd

Advanced: Ex. 11–33 odd, 34, 36, 39–47 odd

Selected Answers: Ex. 1–6, 7–45 odd
*You may wish to omit this lesson for these
students.

Guided Practice

▶ **Ex. 1–4** The numbers in these exercises
are small enough so that it is efficient to list
all factors.
▶ **Ex. 6** The numbers here are large
enough so that prime factorization is more
efficient.

Independent Practice

▶ **Ex. 9** Have students compare the result
of this exercise with GCF(9,21).
▶ **Ex. 13** Students should recognize that
$128 \times 2 = 256$, so GCF(128,256) = 128.
▶ **Ex. 15–18**

Common-Error Alert!

In these exercises, students may recognize the common variable in each
expression but may not use the correct
exponent.

▶ **Ex. 31, 32** These exercises preview the
next lesson on multiples.

EXERCISES

Guided Practice

▶ **CHECK for Understanding**

**In Exercises 1–4, find the common factors of the two numbers. What is the
greatest common factor?**

1. Factors of 12: 1, 2, 3, 4, 6, 12   1, 2, 3, 6;
   Factors of 18: 1, 2, 3, 6, 9, 18   6

2. Factors of 24: 1, 2, 3, 4, 6, 8, 12, 24   1, 2, 4, 8
   Factors of 16: 1, 2, 4, 8, 16   8

3. Factors of 20: 1, 2, 4, 5, 10, 20   1, 5; 5
   Factors of 35: 1, 5, 7, 35

4. Factors of 39: 1, 3, 13, 39   1; 1
   Factors of 25: 1, 5, 25

5. Two natural numbers are relatively prime if their greatest common factor is ? .   1

6. Decide whether 160 and 189 are relatively prime.   Yes

Independent Practice

In Exercises 7–14, find the greatest common factor of the numbers.

7. 20, 32   4
8. 36, 54   18
9. 90, 210   30
10. 126, 216   18
11. 1008, 1080   72
12. 546, 1995   21
13. 128, 256   128
14. 255, 256   1

In Exercises 15–18, find the greatest common factor of the expressions.

15. $2y^2z, 8yz^2$ $2yz$
16. $3x^2y^2, 15x^2y$ $3x^2y$
17. $9r^2z, 21rz$ $3rz$
18. $42s^3t^4, 70s^4t^3$
   $14s^3t^3$

**In Exercises 19–22, find two pairs of numbers that have the given greatest
common factor. (There are many correct answers.)**   Answers vary.

19. 4   16 and 20, 16 and 28
20. 6   18 and 24, 18 and 30
21. 21   21 and 42, 21 and 63
22. 18   36 and 54, 54 and 72

In Exercises 23–26, decide whether the numbers are relatively prime.

23. 384, 945   No
24. 80, 189   Yes
25. 120, 336   No
26. 220, 315   No

Geometry   **In Exercises 27–30, find the area and perimeter of the rectangle. Are the two measures relatively prime? Explain.**   See margin.

27.
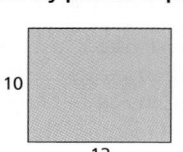

3

5

28.
10

12

29.
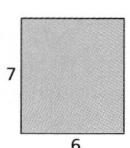

7

6

30.
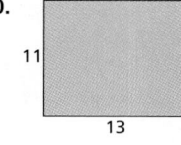

11

13

31. *Sequences*   Find the greatest common factor of the terms in the following sequence: 6, 12, 18, 24, 30, ...   6

32. *Sequences*   Find the greatest common factor of the terms in the following sequence:
8, 12, 16, 20, 24, ...   4

Extra Practice

In Exercises 1–6, find the greatest common factor of the numbers.

1. 12, 30   6
2. 48, 54   6
3. 60, 130   10
4. 108, 198   18
5. 720, 1200   240
6. 660, 1155   165

In Exercises 7–10, find the greatest common factor of the expressions.

7. $2x^2y, 10xy^2$ $2xy$
8. $4x^2y^3, 18xy^2$ $2xy^2$
9. $5r^2p^3, 20r^3p$ $5r^2p$
10. $36x^2y^3, 63x^2y^4$ $9x^2y^3$

**In Exercises 11–13, find two pairs of numbers that have the given greatest
common factor. (There are many correct answers.)**

11. 5   10 and 15, 20 and 25, . . .
12. 3   3 and 6, 9 and 12, . . .
13. 12   12 and 24, 36 and 48, . . .

In Exercises 14–16, decide whether the numbers are relatively prime.

14. 256 and 315   Yes
15. 321 and 405   No, GCF = 3
16. 190 and 343   Yes

**In Exercises 17–19, find the area and perimeter of the rectangle. Are the
two measures relatively prime? Explain.**

17. $A = 28, P = 22$ 4   7   Not relatively prime, GCF = 2
18. $A = 108, P = 42$ 9   12   Not relatively prime, GCF = 6
19. $A = 77, P = 36$ 7   11   Relatively prime

20. Find the greatest common factor of the terms in the following sequence:
2, 6, 10, 14, 18, . . .   GCF = 2

21. Find the greatest common factor of the terms in the following sequence:
3, 9, 15, 21, 27, . . .   GCF = 3

22. A group of children walk to the corner store and buy cans of soda pop for
a total of \$3.36 and candy bars for a total of \$2.45. Each child has one
can of pop and one candy bar. How many children were in the group?
What is the cost of one can of soda and one candy bar?
7 children; A can of soda costs \$0.48 and one
candy bar costs \$0.35.

Reteaching

What you should learn:

6.3 How to find the greatest common factor of two
numbers and how to use the greatest common
factor to solve real-life problems

Correlation to Pupil's Textbook:
Mid-Chapter Self-Test (p. 263)   Chapter Test (p. 287)
Exercises 8–10   Exercises 7, 8

Examples   *Finding Common Factors and Using Greatest Common Factors*

a. Find the greatest common factor of 32 and 56.

A number that is a factor of both natural numbers 32 and 56 is called a
common factor of 32 and 56. Of all common factors of 32 and 56, the
largest is called the greatest common factor.

List all the factors of 32 and 56 and select the largest.
The factors of 32 are 1, 2, 4, 8, 16, and 32.
The factors of 56 are 1, 2, 4, 7, 8, 14, 28, and 56.
The common factors are 1, 2, 4, and 8. Of these, 8 is the greatest common
factor.

b. Your field hockey team raised \$360 for new uniforms and \$420 for new
equipment. Each team member raised an equal share of the \$360 and
\$420. How much did each team member raise?
Use prime factorization to find the greatest common factor of 360 and 420.

Number	Prime Factorization
360	$2 \cdot 2 \cdot 2 \cdot 3 \cdot 3 \cdot 5$
420	$2 \cdot 2 \cdot 3 \cdot 5 \cdot 7$

From the prime factorization, you conclude that the greatest common
factor is $2 \cdot 2 \cdot 3 \cdot 5$ or 60. Each member raised \$60.

Guidelines: • With small numbers, you can find the greatest common factor
by listing all factors and selecting the largest.
• With larger numbers, you can find the greatest common factor
by writing the prime factorization of each.

EXERCISES

**In Exercises 1–8, find the greatest common factor of the numbers or
expressions.**

1. $18x, 30x^2$ $6x$
2. 336, 378   42
3. 101, 202   101
4. $75ab^2, 175a^3b$ $25ab$
5. 686, 980   98
6. 235, 245   5
7. 90, 135   45
8. $40p^2, 84p^3$ $4p^2$

Answer to Communicating (page 251)
Yes, unless they are the same number. Each prime
number has only itself and 1 as factors, so only 1 is
the greatest common factor of two different prime
numbers.

Answers
27. 15. 16; yes, greatest common factor is 1.
28. 120, 44; no, greatest common factor is not 1.
29. 42. 26; no, greatest common factor is not 1.
30. 143. 48; yes, greatest common factor is 1.

33. *Physical Fitness Equipment*   You and some of your classmates have raised money to purchase a stair climber for $285 and a weight set for $418 for a community gym. Each person raised an equal share of the $285 and $418. How many people are in your fundraising group?   19

34. *Geometry*   Three strings have lengths of 39 centimeters, 52 centimeters, and 65 centimeters. You want to cut the strings so that the resulting pieces are all the same length. How can you make the pieces as long as possible? Cut them into 13-cm pieces.

39 cm
52 cm
65 cm

35. *True or False?*   The greatest common factor of $2^2 \cdot 3 \cdot 5 \cdot 19$ and $2 \cdot 3^2 \cdot 7 \cdot 19$ is 19.   False

36. *True or False?*   If n and m are different primes, then they are relatively prime.   True

Number Theory   **In Exercises 37–40, choose two different prime numbers p and q. Decide whether the statement about the greatest common factor (GCF) is true. Could your answer change by choosing different prime numbers? Explain.**   No, a prime number has only itself and 1 as factors.

37. The GCF of p and pq is p.   True

38. The GCF of q and q^2 is q.   True

39. The GCF of p^2q and pq^2 is pq.   True

40. The GCF of p^2 and q^2 is 1.   True

Integrated Review

Making Connections within Mathematics

Factor Form   **In Exercises 41–44, write the prime factorization of the number.**

41. 124 $2^2 \cdot 31$

42. 196 $2^2 \cdot 7^2$

43. 900 $2^2 \cdot 3^2 \cdot 5^2$

44. 3300 $2^2 \cdot 3 \cdot 5^2 \cdot 11$

Exponent Form   **In Exercises 45 and 46, write the expression in exponent form. Then simplify the expression.**

45. $2 \cdot 2 \cdot 3 \cdot 3 \cdot 3 \cdot 5 \cdot 7 \cdot 7$ $2^2 \cdot 3^3 \cdot 5 \cdot 7^2$; 26,460

46. $2 \cdot 3 \cdot 3 \cdot 5 \cdot 5 \cdot 5 \cdot 11 \cdot 11$ $2 \cdot 3^2 \cdot 5^3 \cdot 11^2$; 272,250

Exploration and Extension

Tiling   **In Exercises 47 and 48, you are tiling two rooms with a single size of square tile. The tiles cannot overlap or be cut. Find the largest size tile that you can use to tile both rooms. Illustrate your solution with a sketch.**   For sketches, see Additional Answers.

47. Room 1: 8 feet by 10 feet
Room 2: 14 feet by 16 feet
2-ft by 2-ft tiles

48. Room 1: 8 feet by 16 feet
Room 2: 12 feet by 20 feet
4-ft by 4-ft tiles

✪ More difficult exercises

6.3 ▪ *Greatest Common Factor*   **253**

▶ **Ex. 34**   Give students a hint that a different number of cuts will be made in each piece of string.
▶ **Ex. 37–40**   Assign these as a group. Have students discuss the statements in their groups and then share results with the entire class.

Integrated Review

▶ **Ex. 43, 44**   Students should recognize that using a factor tree that begins with one small number and one large number is not efficient. Advise them to begin with two factors near the middle range. For example, $3300 = 33 \times 100$ versus $3300 = 2 \times 1650$.

Exploration and Extension

Point out to students that they must find the GCF of *four* numbers.

Portfolio Opportunity: Math Log

Find two pairs of algebraic expressions that have $24xy^2$ as their greatest common factor.

Also available as a copymaster, page 20, Ex. 4

Enrichment

Suppose that a hall in your school includes a row of 100 lockers, all initially open. 100 students walk past the row of lockers, changing the status of the lockers as described below.
The 1st student closes each open locker.
The 2nd student opens lockers 2, 4, 6, 8, and so on.
The 3rd student changes the status of every third locker starting with locker 3.
The 4th student changes the status of every fourth locker starting with locker 4.
And so on...
How many lockers will be closed after all the students have passed by?   10 lockers will be closed.

Milestones

Theme: Number Theory of Music

1. The study of "agreeable sounds" led the Pythagoreans to a definition of "amicable" or "nice" numbers. Two natural numbers are amicable if the sum of the factors of each number (except for the number itself) is equal to the other number. If 220 is one number of an amicable number pair, what is the other number in the pair?

> 284; The factors of 220 are 1, 2, 4, 5, 10, 11, 20, 22, 44, 55, and 110. Their sum is 284. Check: The factors of 284 are 1, 2, 4, 71, and 142 which sum to 220.

2. To the Pythagoreans, odd numbers greater than one were "good" because the sum of the first n odd numbers is the square number n^2. For example, the sum of the first 3 odd numbers, $1 + 3 + 5$, is $9 = 3^2$. Try summing the even numbers. Can you discover a pattern?

> The sum of the first n even numbers is $n(n + 1)$. For example, the sum of the first 3 even numbers, $2 + 4 + 6$, is $23 = 3(4)$. The Pythagoreans called these numbers "oblong" numbers.

Library Skills

Have students use library resources to research the history of other types of musical instruments, like the wind instruments or percussion instruments, to determine if there is a mathematical connection.

Mixed REVIEW

Yes: 2, 3, 4, 6, 9; no: 5, 8, 10

1. Use the divisibility tests to decide whether 612 is divisible by 2, 3, 4, 5, 6, 8, 9, and 10. **(6.1)**

2. Use a calculator to decide whether 612 is divisible by 11, 12, 13, 14, 15, 16, 17, 18, 19, and 20. **(6.1)** Yes: 12, 17, 18; no: 11, 13, 14, 15, 16, 19, 20

In Exercises 3–6, you randomly select one letter from the word DIVISIBILITY. What is the probability that the letter is as described? (5.8)

3. S $\frac{1}{12}$

4. I $\frac{5}{12}$

5. D or Y $\frac{1}{6}$

6. Not an I $\frac{7}{12}$

In Exercises 7–10, write the prime factorization of the number. (6.2)

7. 87 $3 \cdot 29$

8. 98 $2 \cdot 7^2$

9. 76 $2^2 \cdot 19$

10. 88 $2^3 \cdot 11$

In Exercises 11–14, solve the equation. Show your work. (4.2, 4.4, 4.5)

11. $\frac{1}{2}(x + 2) = 4$ 6

12. $\frac{1}{4}(r - 1) = 0$ 1

13. $7(y + 2) = 5y$ -7

14. $3.2 + 1.2s = -0.4s$

Milestones   MUSIC OF THE GREEKS

600 B.C.		200 B.C.	200 A.D.	600 A.D.	1000 A.D.	1400 A.D.	
Harp	Pythagoras, Greece		Plainsong	Bowed Instruments, China	Sitar, India	Violin, Cello,	Banjo,
? B.C.	540 B.C.		400–800	900	1200	Italy, 1500's	17?

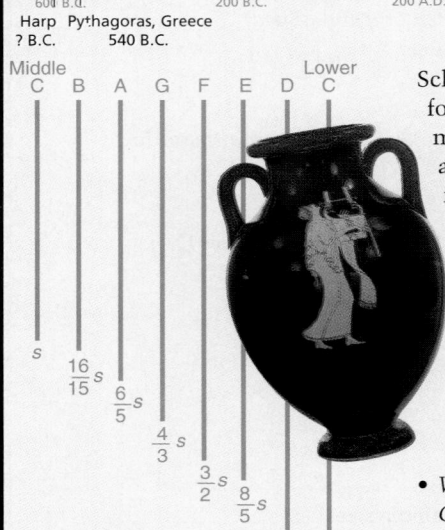

Middle C B A G F E D C Lower

s, $\frac{16}{15}s$, $\frac{6}{5}s$, $\frac{4}{3}s$, $\frac{3}{2}s$, $\frac{8}{5}s$, $\frac{16}{9}s$, $2s$

This Greek vase of a boy playing a Kithara is from about 490 B.C.

Scholars in ancient Greece (600 B.C.–500 B.C.) believed that four subjects ruled their universe—music, geometry, arithmetic, and astronomy. Pythagoras, a Greek mathematician and philosopher, and his followers looked for a numerical interpretation for all natural phenomena.

Pythagoreans found that musical sounds made by equally tight lyre strings were related to their lengths. So, starting with any note, you can go down the scale merely by changing the length of the string as shown in the chart. Strings whose lengths were in ratios made up of small integers, like 1 to 2, had a more "agreeable" sound than strings whose ratios were made up of larger integers, like 23 to 13.

- *Which notes do you think are "more agreeable" to Middle C?* A, G, F, E, Lower C

- *Which notes would be "less agreeable"?* B, D

Try playing the notes together to check your answers.

6.4

Least Common Multiple

► **PACING the Lesson**

Suggested Number of Days
Basic/Average 0   **Above Average** 0
Advanced 1

► **PLANNING the Lesson**

Lesson Plan 6.4, p. 45

What you should learn:

al 1 How to find the least common multiple of two numbers

al 2 How to use a least common multiple to solve problems in geometry

Why you should learn it:

u can use the least common ultiple of two numbers to ve real-life problems, such as alyzing the movements of ars.

Least Common Multiple of Algebraic Expressions

The concept of a least common multiple also applies to algebraic expressions. For instance, the least common multiple of 6*x* and 4*xy* is 12*xy*.

Goal **1** **Finding a Least Common Multiple**

Least Common Multiple

Let *m* and *n* be natural numbers.

1. A number that is a multiple of both *m* and *n* is a **common multiple** of *m* and *n* .

2. Of all common multiples of *m* and *n*, the smallest is called the **least common multiple.**

Example 1 *Finding the Least Common Multiple*

Find the least common multiple of 6 and 9.

Solution With small numbers, you can find the least common multiple by listing multiples of each number. The smallest duplicate in the two lists is the least common multiple.

Number	Multiples
6	6, 12, 18, 24, 30, . . .
9	9, 18, 27, 36, . . .

From the lists, you can see that 18 is the least common multiple. ∎

Example 2 *Finding the Least Common Multiple*

Find the least common multiple of 180 and 378.

Solution With larger numbers, you can find the least common multiple by writing the prime factorization of each.

Number	Prime Factorization
180	$2 \cdot 2 \cdot 3 \cdot 3 \cdot 5$
378	$2 \cdot 3 \cdot 3 \cdot 3 \cdot 7$

From the prime factorizations, you can reason that the least common multiple must contain the factors $2 \cdot 2$, $3 \cdot 3 \cdot 3$, 5, and 7. So the least common multiple is $2 \cdot 2 \cdot 3 \cdot 3 \cdot 3 \cdot 5 \cdot 7 = 3780$. Check to see that 3780 is divisible by 180 and by 378. ∎

6.4 • Least Common Multiple **255**

ORGANIZER

Starters (reproduced below)
    Problem of the Day 6.4, p. 17
    Warm-Up Exercises 6.4, p. 17
Lesson Resources
    Teaching Tools
        Graph paper, pp. T1, C2
    Math Log, p. 20
    Technology, pp. 33, 34
    Answer Masters 6.4, pp. 111–113
    Extra Practice Copymaster 6.4, p. 45
    Reteaching Copymaster 6.4, p. 45
Special Populations
    Suggestions, Teacher's Edition, p. 238D

LESSON Notes

MATH JOURNAL
Discuss strategies for finding common multiples of two natural numbers, *m* and *n*. Students should record the definition of Least Common Multiple in their journals.

Example 1
The Least Common Multiple is often referred to as the LCM (or LCD, for Least Common Denominator). The Least Common Multiple of 6 and 9 can be rewritten as LCM(6, 9).

Example 2
Have students compare the two methods for finding the LCM—the method of listing multiples used in Example 1 and the prime factorization approach used in Example 2.

Common-Error Alert!
Emphasize that in Example 2 the LCM must have all the factors of 180 and 378. Including only the two factors of 3 found in 180 would not produce the LCM(180,378), because we need *three* factors of 3 to produce 378.

The margin note on the pupil page extends the concept of LCM to algebraic expressions. You may wish to discuss this. Have students note that the prime factorization of 6*x* is $2 \cdot 3 \cdot x$ and that of 4*xy* is $2 \cdot 2 \cdot x \cdot y$. The LCM must have all the factors of 6*x* and 4*xy*. Thus, the LCM is the product of the two 2's from **4xy**, the 3 from **6x**, the *x* from either expression, and the *y* from **4xy**.

Thus, LCM(6*x*, 4*xy*) = $2 \cdot 2 \cdot 3 \cdot x \cdot y$ = 12*xy*

STARTER: Problem of the Day	**STARTER: Warm-Up Exercises**
The nearer gable end of the house is facing left. Move the position of one stick so that the nearer gable end is facing right. 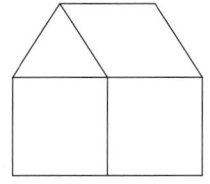 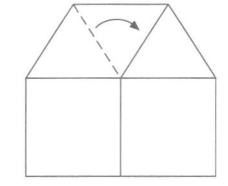	**1.** Multiply each number by 1, 2, 3, 4, 5, and 6. **a.** 8 **b.** 7 **c.** 4 **a.** 8, 16, 24, 32, 40, 48; **b.** 7, 14, 21, 28, 35, 42; **c.** 4, 8, 12, 16, 20, 24 **2.** Find values for *m* and *n* so that the given equation is true. **a.** 8*m* = 10*n* **b.** 12*m* = 14*n* **c.** 34*m* = 28*n* **a.** *m* = 5, *n* = 4; **b.** *m* = 7, *n* = 6; **c.** *m* = 14, *n* = 17
Also available as a copymaster, page 17	Also available as a copymaster, page 17

Students might enjoy constructing and manipulating cutouts to answer these questions.

Communicating about MATHEMATICS

EXTENSION

Have students extend this exercise on the LCM of triples to include algebraic expressions, as follows.

Find the LCM of

a. $8xy^2z$, $6x^2yz^3$, and $4y^3z$

b. $18x^2y$, $10xz^3$, and $11xy^2z^2$

a. $24x^2y^3z^3$, **b.** $990x^2y^2z^3$

Writing Prompt

For a student who missed today's class write an explanation of how to find the Least Common Multiple of a pair of numbers.

Answers to Communicating

A. $6 = 2 \cdot 3, 8 = 2^3, 5 = 5$; least common multiple is $2^3 \cdot 3 \cdot 5 = 120$.

B. $3 = 3, 4 = 2^2, 6 = 2 \cdot 3$; least common multiple is $2^2 \cdot 3 = 12$.

C. $10 = 2 \cdot 5, 6 = 2 \cdot 3, 15 = 3 \cdot 5$; least common multiple is $2 \cdot 3 \cdot 5 = 30$.

Technology

EXERCISES

In Exercises 1–8, use the computer program to find the least common multiple of the numbers.

1. 4, 6 12   2. 5, 15 15   3. 8, 14 56   4. 10, 16 80
5. 24, 36 72   6. 19, 40 760   7. 23, 37 851   8. 74, 76 2812

9. Two race cars are racing on a circular track. One car completes a lap in 54 seconds and the other car completes a lap in 57 seconds. At the start of the race, the cars are even. In how many seconds will the cars be even again? 1026 seconds

10. Two teams of students are designing a small bridge. After finding the width of the stream, one team decides to build the walkway using boards that are 14 inches wide and the other team using boards that are 10 inches wide. Upon completion, the bridges will span the same distance. What is the least possible width of the stream? 70 inches

11. This program can also be used as written to find the LCM of three numbers. Experiment with the program to find out how. Then use it to find the LCM of the following numbers.
  a. 8, 10, 12 120   b. 6, 9, 24 72   c. 14, 16, 20 560

  To find the LCM of 3 numbers, find the LCM of 2 of the numbers then find the LCM of the result and the third number.

12. Do you notice that when you use the program to find the LCM of larger numbers, it seems to take longer to find the answer? Why do you think this is so? Write a paragraph detailing your explanation. (HINT: To answer this question, you need to determine how the program works.)

  The program finds the LCM of 2 numbers by examining the multiples of each. It compares multiples of the 2nd number to the 1st number and if no match is found, it compares multiples of the 2nd number to twice the 1st number. It repeats this process until the LCM is found. It may take a long time to find the LCM of the 2 numbers if many multiples are examined.

34 *Technology Using Calculators and Computers* © D.C. Heath and Company

---

Connections
Geometry

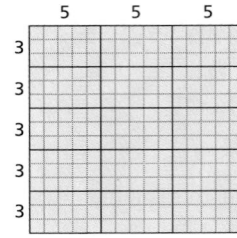

When the lengths of the sides are relatively prime, the number of tiles is equal to the least common multiple.

Example 3 *Using a Least Common Multiple*

You have a box of tiles, each of which is 3 inches by 5 inches. Without overlapping or cutting the tiles, what is the least number of tiles you must use to form a square region?

Solution As shown at the left, the least number of tiles is 15. This follows from the fact that 15 is the least common multiple of 3 and 5.

LESSON INVESTIGATION

P ■ **Investigating Least Common Multiples**

Group Activity Assume that you are given a box of tiles of each size shown below. For each size, find the least number of tiles you can use to form a square. How do the results relate to the least common multiple of the lengths of the sides of each tile?

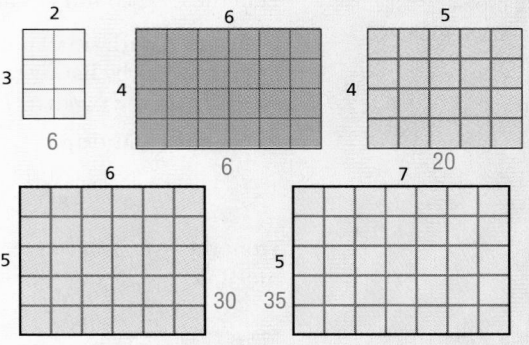

Communicating about MATHEMATICS

▶ **SHARING IDEAS about the Lesson**

Least Common Multiple The least common multiple of 4, 5, and 6 is 60. Find the least common multiple of each of the following triples. Explain your reasoning. For explanations, see margin.
  120   12   30
A. 6, 8, 5   **B.** 3, 4, 6   **C.** 10, 6, 15

OPTION: Extra Examples

Here are additional examples similar to some of those of the lesson.

1. Finding the Least Common Multiple

Find the least common multiple of 12 and 14.

Solution With small numbers, you can find the least common multiple by listing multiples of each number. The smallest duplicate in the two lists is the least common multiple.

Number	Multiples
12	12, 24, 36, 48, 60, 72, ⑧④, 96, ...
14	14, 28, 42, 56, 70, ⑧④, 112, ...

From the lists, you can see that 84 is the least common multiple.

2. Finding the Least Common Multiple

Find the least common multiple of 168 and 462.

Solution With larger numbers, you can find the least common multiple by writing the prime factorization of each.

Number	Prime Factorization
168	②·②·②·③·⑦
462	2·3·7·⑪

From the prime factorizations, you can reason that the least common multiple must contain the factors 2, 2, 2, 3, 7, and 11. So the least common multiple is $2 \cdot 2 \cdot 2 \cdot 3 \cdot 7 \cdot 11 = 1848$. Check to see that 1848 is divisible by 168 and 462.

EXERCISES

Guided Practice

▶ **CHECK for Understanding**

1. 4, 12, 24   **2.** 12, 24, 36

In Exercises 1 and 2, find the three missing multiples of the number.

1. Multiples of 4: [?], 8, [?], 16, 20, [?]   **2.** Multiples of 6: 6, [?], 18, [?], 30, [?]

3. What is the least common multiple (LCM) of 4 and 6? 12

4. *It's Up to You*   In your own words, describe two ways to find the least common multiple of two numbers. Which way would you use to find the least common multiple of 10 and 16? Which way would you use to find the least common multiple of 112 and 204?
See page 255, as in Example 1, as in Example 2

In Exercises 5–7, match the number with its prime factorization. Then find the least common multiple of the three numbers.   1800

a. $2^2 \cdot 3 \cdot 5^2$ **b.** $2 \cdot 3^2 \cdot 5$ **c.** $2^3 \cdot 5^2$

5. 200 c   **6.** 90 b   **7.** 300 a

8. What is the least common multiple of $2a^2b^3$ and $4ab^4$? $4a^2b^4$

Independent Practice

In Exercises 9–20, list the first several multiples of each number. Use the lists to find the least common multiple.   For lists, see Additional Answers.

9. 3, 7 21   **10.** 7, 8 56   **11.** 6, 8 24   **12.** 3, 9 9

13. 8, 10 40   **14.** 10, 15 30   **15.** 10, 26 130   **16.** 4, 22 44

17. 3, 4, 18 36   **18.** 3, 6, 9 18   **19.** 5, 10, 20 20   **20.** 6, 9, 18 18

In Exercises 21–32, write the prime factorization of each expression. Use the results to find the least common multiple.   For prime factorizations, see Additional Answers.

21. 90, 108 540   **22.** 7, 8 56   **23.** 125, 500 500   **24.** 160, 432 4320

25. 135, 375 3375   **26.** 225, 324 8100   **27.** 144, 162 1296   **28.** $16x, 32x^4$ $32x^4$

29. $7s^2t, 49st^2$ $49s^2t^2$ **30.** $2x^3y, 3xy^5$ $6x^3y^5$ **31.** $3m^4n^4, 7m^6n^2$ $21m^6n^4$ **32.** $4a^6b^3, 8a^7b^5$ $8a^7b^5$

33. *Reasoning*   If two numbers are relatively prime, then what is their least common multiple? Give two examples.   Their product, check students' work

34. *Reasoning*   If one number is a multiple of another, then what is their least common multiple? Give two examples.
The number that is the multiple, check students' work

In Exercises 35–38, use the results of Exercises 33 and 34 to find the least common multiple.

35. 3, 8 24   **36.** 8, 9 72   **37.** 3, 6 6   **38.** 8, 24 24

✪ More difficult exercises

6.4 • *Least Common Multiple*   **257**

Extra Practice

Extra Practice **6.4** 1–12. See page 129 for complete answer.
Name _____

In Exercises 1–6, list the first several multiple of each number. Use the list to find the least common multiple.
1. 5, 7 35   **2.** 3, 8 24   **3.** 9, 12 36
4. 12, 14 84   **5.** 3, 5, 6 30   **6.** 5, 6, 12 60

In Exercises 7–12, write the prime factorization of each expression. Use the result to find the least common multiple.
7. 36, 54 108   **8.** 15, 35 105   **9.** 145, 275 7975
10. 81, 216 648   **11.** $13xy^2, 26x^2y^3$ $26x^2y^3$ **12.** $3x^2, 5y^2$ $15x^2y^2$

In Exercises 13–16, find a pair of numbers that satisfy the conditions.
13. Two prime numbers whose LCM is 39.
3 and 13
14. Two composite numbers whose LCM is 36.
Possible answer: 4 and 9
15. Two square numbers whose LCM is 100.
4 and 25
16. Two even numbers whose LCM is 72.
Possible answer: 8 and 18

17. You have collected empty pop bottles to return for a 8¢ per bottle refund. You want to use the money to buy packs of trading cards for $1.50 per pack. After buying the packs you had no money left over. What is the fewest number of pop bottles you could have returned? How many packs of cards did you buy?
75 bottles, 4 packs

18. Angel's car gets 32 miles per gallon and Mo's car gets 22 miles per gallon. When traveling from Morgan Run to Clinton, they each use a whole number of gallons of gasoline. What is the closest that Morgan Run and Clinton could be? How many gallons did Angel's car use? How many gallons did Mo's car use?
352 miles; Angel's car used 11 gallons. Mo's car used 16 gallons.

19. Mr. Wilson has a problem. He can't sleep when the dogs in his neighborhood start howling at the full moon. Luckily, it takes the sound of two dogs barking at the same time to awake him. Last night, Sparky started barking at 1:00 A.M. and barked every 12 minutes. Trigger also started at 1:00 A.M. and barked every 14 minutes. After Mr. Wilson fell back to sleep, he woke up again when Sparky and Trigger barked simultaneously. What time was it?
84 minutes later at 2:24 A.M.

Windows   6.4 • Least Common Multiples **45**

Reteaching

Reteach *Chapter 6*
Name _____

What you should learn:
| 6.4 | How to find the least common multiple of two numbers and how to use a least common multiple to solve problems in geometry |

Correlation to Pupil's Textbook:
Mid-Chapter Self-Test (p. 263) Chapter Test (p. 287)
Exercises 11–13, 17–20   Exercises 9–11

Examples   *Finding a Least Common Multiple and Using Least Common Multiples*

a. Find the least common multiple of 14 and 21. $1 \cdot 2 \cdot 5, 5 \cdot 5, 100$
List all the multiples of 14 and 21 and select the smallest.
The multiples of 14 are 14, 28, 42, 56, … $2 \cdot 7 \cdot x, 2 \cdot 5 \cdot x \cdot x \cdot x, 70x^3$
The multiples of 21 are 21, 42, 63, 84, …
The smallest duplicate in the two lists, 42, is the least common multiple.

b. Use prime factorization to find the least common multiple of 280 and 300. $3 \cdot 5 \cdot 29, 5 \cdot 31, 4495$

Number	Prime Factorization
280	$2 \cdot 2 \cdot 2 \cdot 5 \cdot 7$
300	$2 \cdot 2 \cdot 3 \cdot 5 \cdot 5$

$4 \cdot 2 \cdot 3 \cdot 2, 2 \cdot 11, 198$

The least common multiple is $2 \cdot 2 \cdot 2 \cdot 3 \cdot 5 \cdot 5 \cdot 7 = 4200$. You should check that 4200 is divisible by 280 and by 300. $5, 2 \cdot 2 \cdot a \cdot a \cdot b, 5 \cdot a \cdot b \cdot b, 20a^2b^2$

c. You are tiling a floor with 14-inch and 10-inch square tiles. Each row contains the same size tile. What is the shortest length you can make the rows if the rows must have the same length? $6, 13 \cdot p \cdot p, 2 \cdot 13 \cdot p \cdot p, 26p^3$
The least common multiple of 14 and 10 is 70. Each row is 70 inches long. $7, 2 \cdot 2 \cdot 3 \cdot 5, 2 \cdot 2 \cdot 5 \cdot 5, 600$

Guidelines: • With small numbers, you can find the least common multiple by listing multiples of each number and selecting the smallest.
• With larger numbers, you can find the least common multiple by writing the prime factorization of each.

EXERCISES $8, 2 \cdot 2 \cdot 7 \cdot 7, 2 \cdot 2 \cdot 5 \cdot 11, 10,780$
In Exercises 1–8, write the prime factorization of each expression. Use the result to find the least common multiple.
1. 20, 25   **2.** $7x, 10x^3$ **3.** 145, 155   **4.** 18, 22
5. $4a^2b, 5ab^2$ **6.** $13p^2, 26p^3$ **7.** 120, 200   **8.** 196, 220

Windows   Chapter 6 • Exploring Number Theory **45**

► **Ex. 39–42** Assign these exercises as a group. They review various concepts and vocabulary.

► **Ex. 43** This exercise refers back to Example 3 and the Lesson Investigation on page 256.

► **Ex. 44, 45**
GROUP ACTIVITY
Have students work in cooperative groups to solve these problems. As an extension, have students relate information about bicycle gears and traffic lights in their city.

Integrated Review

Have students give explanations for their solutions. Ask them to develop other patterns such as the LCM of consecutive odd numbers taken in pairs.

Exploration and Extension

These exercises offer students an opportunity to solve problems by *listing all possibilities*.

Portfolio Opportunity: Math Log

Explain why the lowest common multiple of any two numbers is divisible by the greatest common factor of the numbers.

Also available as a copymaster, page 20, Ex. 5

Short Quiz

Covers Lessons 6.3 and 6.4

Available as a copymaster, page 85

Number Sense **In Exercises 39–42, find all pairs of numbers that satisfy the conditions.** See margin.

39. Two prime numbers whose LCM is 35
40. Two composite numbers whose LCM is 16
41. Two square numbers whose LCM is 36
42. Two even numbers whose LCM is 12

✪ 43. *Tiling* You have a box of tiles, each of which is 4 inches by 14 inches. Without overlapping or cutting the tiles, what is the least number of tiles you must use to form a square region? Draw a diagram and explain your answer. 14, See margin.

✪ 44. *Stoplights* Consider three stoplights on a street. The first stoplight is red 3 minutes out of every 6 minutes. The second stoplight is red 4 minutes out of every 8 minutes. The third stoplight is red 5 minutes out of every 10 minutes. At 2:00 P.M., each stoplight turns red. When is the next time all three stoplights turn red? 4 P.M.

✪ 45. *Gears* The gears at the right are rotating. Gear *A* has 14 teeth and Gear *B* has 12 teeth. How many complete revolutions must each gear make for the gears to align again as shown? A: 6, B: 7

Some clocks operate with gears. These clocks are called analog clocks. As the gears revolve, the hands of the clock move.

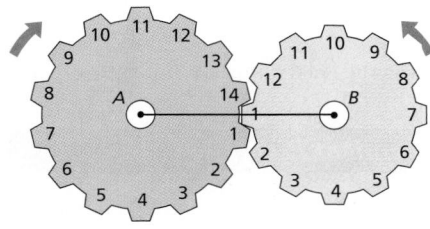

Integrated Review

Number Patterns **In Exercises 46 and 47, find the least common multiple of each pair. Then describe the pattern formed by the common multiples.**

46. 1 and 2, 2 and 3, 3 and 4, 4 and 5, 5 and 6, 6 and 7
47. 2 and 4, 4 and 6, 6 and 8, 8 and 10, 10 and 12, 12 and 14
   46. 2, 6, 12, 20, 30, 42 **47.** 4, 12, 24, 40, 60, 84

Exploration and Extension

Making Connections within Mathematics

For descriptions, see Additional Answers.

Age Riddles **In Exercises 48 and 49, find the age of each person.**

✪ 48. I have lived less than a half century. My age is a multiple of 8. Next year my age will be a multiple of 11. 32

✪ 49. I have lived more than 2 decades but less than 4 decades. Last year my age was a multiple of 3. This year my age is a multiple of 4. What is my age? 28

According to the 1990 census, the median age in the United States is 32.9 years, up 2.9 years from 1980.

Answers
39. 5 and 7
40. 4 and 16, 8 and 16, 16 and 16
41. 1 and 36, 4 and 9, 4 and 36, 9 and 36, 36 and 36
42. 2 and 12, 4 and 6, 4 and 12, 6 and 12, 12 and 12
43.

14 in.	14 in.

4 in.
4 in.
4 in.
4 in. ⎫ 7(4) = 28
4 in.
4 in.
4 in.
   2(14) = 28

The LCM of 4 and 14 is 28, so each side of the square region is 28 in. Then two 14's and seven 4's are needed for the sides of the square region; 2 × 7 = 14.

6.5 Simplifying and Comparing Fractions

What you should learn:

Goal 1 How to simplify a fraction

Goal 2 How to compare two fractions

Why you should learn it:

Rewriting a fraction in a different form helps you decide whether one fraction is larger than another.

As fractions, $\frac{3}{4}$ and $\frac{6}{8}$ are equivalent. In music, however, three-quarter time is not equivalent to six-eights time. The first has 3 beats to a measure and the second has 6. African drum songs are often in six-eights time to build excitement or to wake people up.

Goal 1 Simplifying a Fraction

Two fractions are **equivalent** if they have the same decimal form. For instance, the fractions $\frac{1}{2}$ and $\frac{2}{4}$ are equivalent because each is equal to 0.5. The following hexagons show that the fractions $\frac{2}{3}$, $\frac{4}{6}$, and $\frac{8}{12}$ are also equivalent. The first of these, $\frac{2}{3}$, is in **simplest form**. Writing a fraction in reduced form is called **simplifying** the fraction.

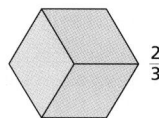 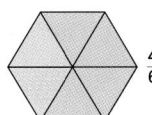 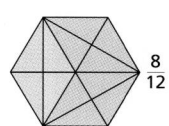

Example 1 Simplifying a Fraction

Simplify the fraction $\frac{12}{20}$.

Solution To simplify the fraction, factor its numerator and denominator. Then divide the numerator and denominator by any common factors.

$$\frac{12}{20} = \frac{\cancel{2} \cdot \cancel{2} \cdot 3}{\cancel{2} \cdot \cancel{2} \cdot 5} = \frac{3}{5}$$

Another way to simplify a fraction is to divide the numerator and denominator by their greatest common factor.

$$\frac{12}{20} = \frac{12 \div 4}{20 \div 4} = \frac{3}{5}$$

Example 2 Simplifying a Fraction with Variables

Simplify the fraction $\frac{4x^2}{6x}$.

Solution

$$\frac{4x^2}{6x} = \frac{\cancel{2} \cdot 2 \cdot \cancel{x} \cdot x}{\cancel{2} \cdot 3 \cdot \cancel{x}} = \frac{2x}{3}$$

▶ **PACING the Lesson**

Suggested Number of Days
Basic/Average 2 **Above Average** 1
Advanced 1

▶ **PLANNING the Lesson**

Lesson Plan 6.5, p. 46

ORGANIZER

Starters (reproduced below)
  Problem of the Day 6.5, p. 17
  Warm-Up Exercises 6.5, p. 17
Lesson Resources
  Color Transparencies
    Graph for Ex. 40–42, p. 25
  Teaching Tools
    Fraction strips, pp. T11, C17
  Math Log, p. 20
  Answer Masters 6.5, p. 114
  Extra Practice Copymaster 6.5, p. 46
  Reteaching Copymaster 6.5, p. 46
  Enrichment Projects, pp. 31, 32
Special Populations
  Suggestions, Teacher's Edition, p. 238D

LESSON Notes

Use fraction strips or attribute blocks to model the fraction concept of equivalence. Manipulatives allow us to exploit the area interpretation of fractions to show equivalence.

Example 1

Have students discuss the two techniques for simplifying fractions. Poll students to see which they prefer.

Example 2

Common-Error Alert!

Notice that the expanded form of the factorization is used to simplify the expression. This is a good practice because it avoids errors associated with using the exponent form of the expression.

Fraction strips are especially useful when comparing fractions. If you do not have a commercially available set, you could consider making your own set.

Study Tip
Another way to compare two fractions is to write them as decimals. From
$$\frac{7}{12} = 0.5833\cdots$$
and
$$\frac{9}{16} = 0.5625,$$
you can see that $\frac{7}{12}$ is larger than $\frac{9}{16}$.

Real Life
Food Service

Example 3 *Comparing Fractions*

Which fraction is larger, $\frac{7}{12}$ or $\frac{9}{16}$?

Solution   Begin by rewriting the fractions with a common denominator. The common denominator should be the least common multiple of the two original denominators. The least common multiple of 12 and 16 is 48. The fraction $\frac{7}{12}$ can be rewritten as

$$\frac{7}{12} \times \frac{4}{4} = \frac{28}{48} \quad \textit{Multiply by } \frac{4}{4} \textit{ to get a denominator of 48.}$$

The fraction $\frac{9}{16}$ can be written as

$$\frac{9}{16} \times \frac{3}{3} = \frac{27}{48} \quad \textit{Multiply by } \frac{3}{3} \textit{ to get a denominator of 48.}$$

By comparing the rewritten forms, you can see that $\frac{7}{12}$ is larger than $\frac{9}{16}$. ∎

Example 4 *Comparing Fractions*

You ate 4 pieces of a small pizza that was cut into 6 equal pieces. Your friend ate 5 pieces of a small pizza that was cut into 8 equal pieces. Who ate more pizza?

Solution   You ate $\frac{4}{6}$ of a pizza and your friend ate $\frac{5}{8}$ of a pizza. Because

$$\frac{4}{6} \times \frac{4}{4} = \frac{16}{24} \text{ and } \frac{5}{8} \times \frac{3}{3} = \frac{15}{24}$$

it follows that you ate more pizza. ∎

Communicating *about* **MATHEMATICS**

▶ **SHARING IDEAS about the Lesson**

Comparing Fractions In Example 3, the fraction $\frac{7}{12}$ was multiplied by $\frac{4}{4}$. Explain why this procedure produced an equivalent fraction. Multiplying a fraction by 1 does not change the value of the fraction.

EXERCISES

Guided Practice

▶ **CHECK for Understanding**

Modeling Fractions   In Exercises 1–4, write a fraction that represents the portion of the region that is blue. Then simplify the fraction.

1. 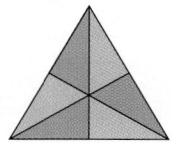 $\frac{3}{6}, \frac{1}{2}$

2.  $\frac{5}{8}, \frac{5}{8}$

3. 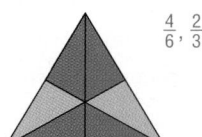 $\frac{4}{6}, \frac{2}{3}$

4. 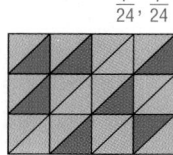 $\frac{7}{24}, \frac{7}{24}$

Fraction Strips   In Exercises 5 and 6, write the fraction that is represented by each fraction strip. Then rewrite the fractions with a common denominator and decide which is larger.

5.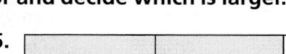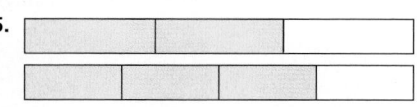

$\frac{2}{3}, \frac{8}{12}$
$\frac{3}{4}, \frac{9}{12}$
$\frac{3}{4}$

6.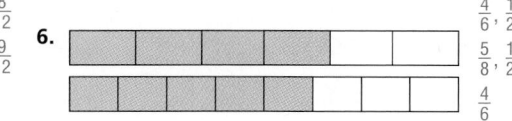

$\frac{4}{6}, \frac{16}{24}$
$\frac{5}{8}, \frac{15}{24}$
$\frac{4}{6}$

Independent Practice

In Exercises 7–14, what is the greatest common factor of the numerator and denominator? Use your answer to simplify the fraction.

7. $\frac{14}{20}$ $2, \frac{7}{10}$

8. $\frac{16}{36}$ $4, \frac{4}{9}$

9. $\frac{9}{42}$ $3, \frac{3}{14}$

10. $\frac{63}{105}$ $21, \frac{3}{5}$

11. $\frac{10}{75}$ $5, \frac{2}{15}$

12. $\frac{8}{28}$ $4, \frac{2}{7}$

13. $\frac{36}{54}$ $18, \frac{2}{3}$

14. $\frac{117}{143}$ $13, \frac{9}{11}$

In Exercises 15–22, simplify the variable expression.

15. $\frac{2ab}{8b^2}$ $\frac{a}{4b}$

16. $\frac{3x^2y}{9y}$ $\frac{x^2}{3}$

17. $\frac{25z^2}{150z^3}$ $\frac{1}{6z}$

18. $\frac{22s^3t}{55s^3t^2}$ $\frac{2}{5t}$

19. $\frac{6yz}{8y}$ $\frac{3z}{4}$

20. $\frac{15x}{21x^2}$ $\frac{5}{7x}$

21. $\frac{28p^2q^2}{42p^3q^3}$ $\frac{2}{3pq}$

22. $\frac{34m^2}{68mn}$ $\frac{m}{2n}$

23. *Reasoning*   Explain how you can determine whether a fraction is in simplest form.
See margin.

24. Which of the following is not equivalent to $\frac{7}{8}$: $\frac{14}{16}, \frac{17}{18}, \frac{21}{24}$? $\frac{17}{18}$

In Exercises 25–28, write 3 fractions that are equivalent to the given fraction.   Answers vary.

25. $\frac{1}{2}$ $\frac{2}{4}, \frac{3}{6}, \frac{4}{8}$

26. $\frac{2}{5}$ $\frac{4}{10}, \frac{6}{15}, \frac{8}{20}$

27. $\frac{10}{22}$ $\frac{5}{11}, \frac{15}{33}, \frac{20}{44}$

28. $\frac{8}{18}$ $\frac{4}{9}, \frac{12}{27}, \frac{16}{36}$

Comparing Fractions   In Exercises 29–36, complete the statement with $<$, $>$, or $=$.

29. $\frac{1}{7}$ ⟨?⟩ $\frac{1}{6}$ $<$

30. $\frac{18}{38}$ ⟨?⟩ $\frac{27}{57}$ $=$

31. $\frac{1}{12}$ ⟨?⟩ $\frac{1}{13}$ $>$

32. $\frac{8}{14}$ ⟨?⟩ $\frac{6}{13}$ $>$

33. $\frac{7}{8}$ ⟨?⟩ $\frac{8}{9}$ $<$

34. $\frac{0}{2}$ ⟨?⟩ $\frac{0}{100}$ $=$

35. $\frac{15}{39}$ ⟨?⟩ $\frac{5}{13}$ $=$

36. $\frac{26}{50}$ ⟨?⟩ $\frac{27}{51}$ $<$

✪ More difficult exercises

6.5 ▪ *Simplifying and Comparing Fractions*   **261**

Extra Practice

Extra Practice **6.5** Name _____

In Exercises 1–6, what is the greatest common factor of the numerator and denominator? Use your answer to simplify the fraction.

1. $\frac{14}{18}$ $4, \frac{3}{7}$
2. $\frac{8}{36}$ $4, \frac{2}{9}$
3. $\frac{9}{36}$ $9, \frac{1}{5}$
4. $\frac{99}{77}$ $11, \frac{7}{7}$
5. $\frac{3}{54}$ $2, \frac{2}{19}$
6. $\frac{88}{168}$ $12, \frac{7}{9}$

In Exercises 7–12, simplify the variable expression.

7. $\frac{2xy}{6xy^2}$ $\frac{1}{3y}$
8. $\frac{3ab}{12a^2}$ $\frac{b}{4a}$
9. $\frac{49z^2}{147z^5}$ $\frac{1}{3z^3}$
10. $\frac{16yz^2}{18z}$ $\frac{8yz}{9}$
11. $\frac{24x^2y}{40xy^5}$ $\frac{3x^2}{5y^4}$
12. $\frac{38z^2}{95xy^3}$ $\frac{2x}{5y^2}$

In Exercises 13–16, determine which of the fractions are not equivalent to the given fraction.

13. $\frac{9}{16}$ $\frac{9}{16}$
14. $\frac{7}{49}$ $\frac{7}{49}$
15. $\frac{9}{64}$, $\frac{15}{64}$
16. $\frac{25}{64}$

In Exercises 17–19, write 3 fractions that are equivalent to the given fraction.

17. $\frac{4}{5}$ $\frac{8}{10}, \frac{12}{15}, \frac{16}{20}$
18. $\frac{7}{8}$ $\frac{14}{16}, \frac{21}{24}, \frac{28}{32}$
19. $\frac{1}{3}$ $\frac{2}{6}, \frac{3}{9}$

In Exercises 20–25, complete the statement with $<$, $>$, or $=$.

20. $\frac{1}{4}$ ▢ $\frac{1}{7}$ $>$
21. ▢ ▢ $=$
22. ▢ ▢ $<$
23. $\frac{5}{6}$ ▢ $\frac{8}{12}$
24. ▢ ▢ $>$
25. ▢ ▢ $=$

In Exercises 26 and 27, use the table which shows the number of miles ridden per day during a 7 day bike trip from the town of Osceola to the town of Fairview.

Day	1	2	3	4	5	6	7
Number of miles	20	30	30	40	30	40	30

26. Express the number of miles ridden on day 1 as a fraction of the total miles. $\frac{1}{11}$

27. Express the number of miles ridden on day 6 as a fraction of the total miles. $\frac{2}{11}$

28. Miss Curtis and Mr. Morgan gave the same test to their eighth grade math classes. In Miss Curtis' class, 21 out of 35 students received a grade of B or higher. In Mr. Morgan's class, 24 out of 36 students received a grade of B or higher. Which class did better? Explain.
Mr. Morgan's class did better because $\frac{24}{36} > \frac{21}{35}$.

46 *Simplifying and Comparing Fractions ▪ 6.5*   Windows

Reteaching

Reteach Chapter 6 Name _____

What you should learn:

6.5 How to simplify a fraction and how to compare two fractions

Correlation to Pupil's Textbook:
Mid-Chapter Self-Test (p. 263)   Chapter Test (p. 287)
Exercises 14–16   Exercises 12, 13

Examples *Simplifying a Fraction and Comparing Fractions*

a. Simplify the fraction $\frac{18x^3}{24x}$.
To simplify a fraction, factor the numerator and denominator. Then divide the numerator and denominator by any common factors.

$\frac{18x^3}{24x} = \frac{2 \cdot 3 \cdot 3 \cdot x \cdot x \cdot x}{2 \cdot 2 \cdot 2 \cdot 3 \cdot x} = \frac{3x^2}{4}$

b. Which fraction is larger, $\frac{11}{20}$ or $\frac{8}{15}$?
To compare two fractions, rewrite the fractions with a common denominator. The common denominator should be the least common multiple of the original denominators. The least common multiple of 20 and 15 is 60.

$\frac{11}{20} \cdot \frac{3}{3} = \frac{33}{60}$ *Multiply $\frac{11}{20}$ by $\frac{3}{3}$ to get a denominator of 60.*

$\frac{8}{15} \cdot \frac{4}{4} = \frac{32}{60}$ *Multiply $\frac{8}{15}$ by $\frac{4}{4}$ to get a denominator of 60.*

Because $\frac{33}{60}$ is larger than $\frac{32}{60}$, you can see that $\frac{11}{20}$ is larger than $\frac{8}{15}$.

Another way to compare two fractions is to write them as decimals.
$\frac{11}{20} = 0.55$ and $\frac{8}{15} = 0.7333\ldots$
You can see that $\frac{8}{15}$ is larger than $\frac{11}{20}$.

Guidelines:
▪ Two fractions are equivalent if they have the same decimal form.
▪ Writing a fraction in reduced form is called simplifying the fraction.

EXERCISES

In Exercises 1–4, find the greatest common factor of the numerator and denominator. Use your answer to simplify the fraction.

1. $\frac{12}{18}$ $6, \frac{2}{3}$
2. $\frac{24}{28}$ $8, \frac{4}{7}$
3. $\frac{45}{75}$ $15, \frac{3}{4}$
4. $\frac{48}{56}$ $14, \frac{3}{7}$

In Exercises 5–8, complete the statement with $<$, $>$, or $=$.

5. $\frac{1}{9}$ ▢ $\frac{1}{8}$ $<$
6. $\frac{7}{15}$ ▢ $\frac{7}{16}$ $>$
7. $\frac{7}{9}$ ▢ $\frac{7}{8}$ $<$
8. $\frac{6}{8}$ ▢ $\frac{9}{12}$ $=$

46 Chapter 6 ▪ *Exploring Number Theory*   Windows

EXERCISE Notes

ASSIGNMENT GUIDE
Basic/Average:
Day 1: Ex. 7–35 odd
Day 2: Ex. 37–39, 43–49 odd
Above Average:
Ex. 11–31 odd, 38–41, 45–49 odd
Advanced: Ex. 11–31 odd, 38–41, 45–49 odd
Selected Answers: Ex. 1–5, 7–47 odd

Guided Practice

▶ **Ex. 1–4** After the students have simplified the fractions, they could sketch figures that model the simplified fraction that are similar to the given figures.

Independent Practice

▶ **Ex. 7–14** Remind students of the methods studied to find the GCF of two numbers.
▶ **Ex. 15–22** For many students, the strategy of writing the variable expressions in expanded form (as in Example 2) is helpful.
▶ **Ex. 23**
MATH JOURNAL
This exercise should be answered in students' journals.
▶ **Ex. 25–28**
EXTENSION
Ask students if the fraction $\frac{2x}{5x}$ would be acceptable in Ex. 26.
▶ **Ex. 29–36**

Common-Error Alert!

Some students may observe (or may have seen) the following: $\frac{a}{b} > \frac{c}{d}$ if $ad > bc$. While this relationship is true, along with a similar one for *less than*, it is not recommended to propose this as a method for comparing fractions. It is too easy for students to forget the order in which the relationship is written.

Answer
23. A fraction is in simplest form if the only common factor of the numerator and denominator is 1.

Lesson 6.5 **261**

37. *Ordering Fractions* Order $\frac{2}{3}, \frac{6}{18}, \frac{8}{10}, \frac{1}{1}, \frac{3}{6}, \frac{5}{12}$ from least to greatest. $\frac{6}{18}, \frac{5}{12}, \frac{3}{6}, \frac{2}{3}, \frac{8}{10}, \frac{1}{1}$

Photography **In Exercises 38 and 39, use the following information.** For explanations, see margin.

Shutter speed is the length of time the shutter is open. Many cameras allow a photographer to adjust the shutter speed. A slow shutter speed allows more light to expose film than does a fast shutter speed.

✪ **38.** The shutter speed on your camera is $\frac{1}{250}$ of a second. You want to decrease the shutter speed. Which of the following would be appropriate: $\frac{1}{500}$ of a second or $\frac{1}{125}$ of a second? Explain. $\frac{1}{125}$

✪ **39.** Your friend's camera is letting in too much light. You tell him that he needs to increase the shutter speed. The shutter speed setting is at $\frac{1}{250}$ of a second. Which of the following would be appropriate: $\frac{1}{500}$ of a second or $\frac{1}{125}$ of a second? Explain. $\frac{1}{500}$

This photograph appears blurry because the moving vehicles were photographed using a slow shutter speed.

Simplifying Fractions **In Exercises 40–42, use the bar graph, which shows the average number (in millions) of M & Ms sold in a day.** *(Source: Mars Company)* **40.** $\frac{30}{80}, \frac{3}{8}$ **41.** $\frac{20}{80}, \frac{1}{4}$

40. Express the number of brown M & Ms as a fraction of all brown, red, yellow, and orange M & Ms. Simplify.

41. Express the number of red M & Ms as a fraction of all brown, red, yellow, and orange M & Ms. Simplify.

42. How is the fraction $\frac{1}{3}$ related to the bar graph?
Sales of Orange $= \frac{1}{3}$ Sales of Brown

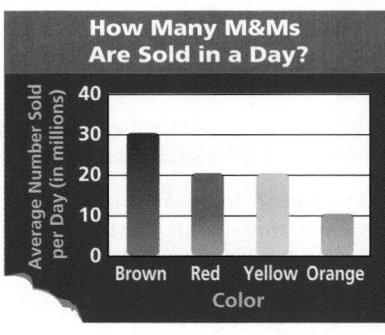

How Many M&Ms Are Sold in a Day?

Integrated Review

Making Connections within Mathematics

GCF and LCM **In Exercises 43–46, find the GCF and LCM of the numbers.**

43. 10, 12   2, 60
44. 15, 18   3, 90
45. 75, 100   25, 300
46. 36, 84   12, 252

47. *Estimation* Which best estimates the height of the Washington Monument?   c
  a. 5.55 feet **b.** 55.5 feet
  c. 555 feet   **d.** 5550 feet

48. *Estimation* Which best estimates the length of the Mississippi River?   b
  a. 234 miles   **b.** 2340 miles
  c. 23,400 miles **d.** 234,000 miles

Exploration and Extension

1, $.50 more per hour

✪ **49.** *Comparing Pay Scales* Which pay scale would you prefer? Explain.
  Pay scale 1: $4 for each $\frac{1}{2}$ hour worked. **Pay scale 2:** $5 for each $\frac{2}{3}$ hour worked.

✪ **50.** Find the hourly rates for the pay scales in Exercise 49.   1: $8 per hour, 2: $7.50 per hour

262 Chapter **6** · *Exploring Number Theory*   ✪ More difficult exercises

---

Left margin

▶ **Ex. 38, 39** Assign these as a group.
▶ **Ex. 40–42** Offer students a hint: In order to begin this set of exercises, students need to find the sum of all sales (80 million).

Integrated Review

▶ **Ex. 47, 48** Many students may need the help of some convenient "benchmark" for estimating heights and distances, for example, the height of the classroom in feet, the distance from New York to Los Angeles in miles.

Exploration and Extension

WRITING
Have students work with partners to write other comparison problems similar to these that can be exchanged with other groups.

Portfolio Opportunity: Math Log

Explain the following statement: When rewriting fractions with a common denominator, the common denominator can be any common multiple of the two original denominators, however, using the least common multiple is the most convenient choice.

Also available as a copymaster, page 20, Ex. 6

Alternative Assessment

A Math Game that develops students' ability to compare fractions.

Available as copymasters, pages 25, 26

Answers
38. To decrease the shutter speed means to leave it open for a longer period of time, so the fraction would have to be larger than $\frac{1}{250}$;
$\frac{1}{125} = \frac{2}{250} > \frac{1}{250}$.
39. To increase the shutter speed means to leave it open for a shorter period of time, so the fraction would have to be smaller than $\frac{1}{250}$;
$\frac{1}{500} < \frac{2}{500} = \frac{1}{250}$.

262 *Chapter 6*

Enrichment

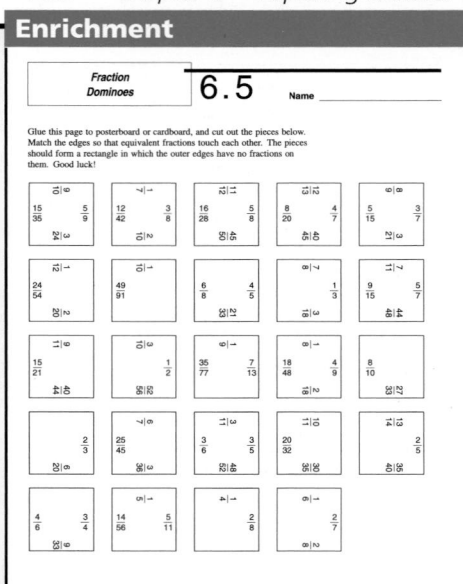

Fraction Dominoes **6.5** Name _____

Glue this page to posterboard or cardboard, and cut out the pieces below. Match the edges so that equivalent fractions touch each other. The pieces should form a rectangle in which the outer edges have no fractions on them. Good luck!

32 Enrichment Projects

Take this test as you would take a test in class. The answers to the exercises are given in the back of the book.

In Exercises 1 and 2, use the divisibility tests to decide whether the number is divisible by 2, 3, 4, 5, 6, 8, 9, and 10. (6.1)

1. 510   Yes: 2, 3, 5, 6, 10; no: 4, 8, 9

2. 1360   Yes: 2, 4, 5, 8, 10; no: 3, 6, 9

3. Use a calculator to decide whether 816 is divisible by 11, 12, 13, 14, 15, 16, 17, 18, 19, or 20. **(6.1)**   Yes: 12. 16. 17; no: 11, 13, 14, 15, 18, 19, 20

4. List all the factors of the number 56.   1, 2, 4, 7, 8, 14, 28, 56

In Exercises 5–7, write the prime factorization of the number. (6.2)

5. 80 $2^4 \cdot 5$

6. 44 $2^2 \cdot 11$

7. 105 $3 \cdot 5 \cdot 7$

In Exercises 8–10, find the greatest common factor. (6.3)

8. 12, 60   12

9. 36, 15   3

10. 135, 45, 25   5

In Exercises 11–13, find the least common multiple. (6.4)

11. 13, 5   65

12. 14, 21   42

13. $6x, 9x^2$ $18x^2$

In Exercises 14–16, simplify the expression. (6.5)

14. $\frac{5}{25}$ $\frac{1}{5}$

15. $\frac{45}{306}$ $\frac{5}{34}$

16. $\frac{8y^2}{24y}$ $\frac{y}{3}$

In Exercises 17 and 18, find the least number of tiles that can be used to form a square given a box of tiles of the size shown. How is the length of the square's sides related to the lengths of the sides of the tile? (6.4)

17.
2

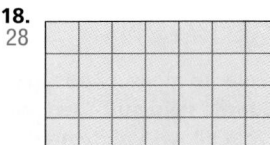

The length of the square's side is the LCM of the lengths of the tile's sides.

18.
28

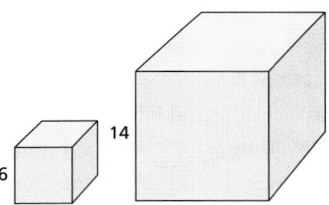

In Exercises 19 and 20, imagine that you are stacking 2 different-sized boxes as shown at the right. One box size is 6 inches high and the other is 14 inches high. (6.4)

19. To obtain two stacks of the same height, what is the least number of boxes of each size that must be used?   6-in.: 7, 14-in.: 3

20. In Exercise 19, is the height of each stack the least common multiple of 6 and 14 or the greatest common factor of 6 and 14?   Least common multiple

14

6

Partner Quiz

Chapter 6
Mid-Chapter Partner Quiz
(Use after Lesson 6.5)
Name _____

1. Find all the factors of 132. (6.1)   1. _____
   1, 2, 3, 4, 6, 11, 12, 22, 33, 44, 66, 132

2. The volume of a box is 60 in.². The length, width, and height of the   2. _____
   box are natural numbers. Find all of the possible dimensions of the
   box. (6.1) 4 in. x 3 in. x 5 in., 6 in. x 2 in. x 5 in., 10 in. x 2 in. x 3 in.,
   15 in. x 2 in. x 2 in., 1 in. x 2 in. x 30 in., 1 in. x 3 in. x 20 in.,
   1 in. x 4 in. x 15 in., 1 in. x 5 in. x 12 in., 1 in. x 6 in. x 10 in.
3. Write the prime factorization of 1260. Write your answer in   3. _____
   exponent form. (6.2)
   $2^2 \cdot 3^2 \cdot 5 \cdot 7$
4. Complete the statement with always, sometimes, or never. A prime   4. Sometimes
   number is [?] even. (6.2)

5. Find the greatest common factor of $24x^2y^3, 4x^2y^4, 8x^5y^2$, and   5. $4x^2y^2$
   $12x^3y^6$. (6.3)

6. Find a number which is relatively prime with 30. (6.3)   6. _____
   Answers vary. Examples: 49, 77, 91

7. Find the least common multiple of $8xy, 3x^2$, and $4xy^3$. (6.4)   7. $24x^2y^3$

8. Write three fractions that are equivalent to $\frac{2}{3}$. (6.5)   8. _____
   Answers vary. Examples: $\frac{4}{5}, \frac{24}{30}, \frac{36}{45}$

9. Which fraction is not equivalent to the rest of the group? (6.5)   9. _____
   $\frac{8}{9}, \frac{16}{18}, \frac{56}{63}, \frac{64}{90}, \frac{80}{90}$
   $\frac{56}{46}$
10. Write the fractions from greatest to least. (6.5)   10. _____
    $\frac{2}{9}, \frac{4}{11}, \frac{5}{22}, \frac{9}{5}$ $\frac{9}{5}, \frac{4}{11}, \frac{9}{22}, \frac{2}{5}$

© D.C. Heath and Company   • Alternative Assessment **49**

Mid-Chapter Test

Mid-Chapter **6** Test   Form B   Name _____
(Use after Lesson 6.5)   Date _____

For Exercises 1 and 2, use the divisibility tests to decide whether the
number is divisible by 2, 3, 4, 5, 6, 8, 9, and 10. (6.1)

1. 234   Yes: 2, 3, 6, 9; No: 4, 5, 8, 10   1. _____

2. 5780   Yes: 2, 4, 5, 10; No: 3, 6, 8, 9   2. _____

3. List all of the factors of 300. (6.2)   3. _____
   1, 2, 3, 4, 5, 6, 10, 12, 15, 20, 25, 30, 50, 60, 75, 100, 150, 300
In Exercises 4 and 5, write the prime factorization. (6.2)

4. 72   4. $2^3 \cdot 3^2$

5. 126   5. $3^2 \cdot 7 \cdot 2$

6. Write a pair of numbers whose greatest common factor is 24. (6.3)   6. _____
   Answers will vary. Possible answer: 24 and 48
7. Find the least common multiple of 15 and 20. (6.4)   7. 60

8. Write a pair of numbers whose least common multiple is 12. (6.4)   8. _____
   Answers will vary. Possible answer: 3 and 4
In Exercises 9–11, simplify the expression. (6.5)

9. $\frac{9}{63}$ 9. $\frac{1}{7}$

10. $\frac{96}{176}$ 10. $\frac{6}{11}$

11. $\frac{15a^4}{35a^3b}$ 11. $\frac{3a}{7b}$

In Exercises 12 and 13, imagine that you are laying a tile design using
alternating rows of 8-inch and 10-inch tiles. (6.4)

12. After how many inches will the tile design be the same length in   12. 40 inches
    each row?

13. How many 8-inch tiles will be in the row at that point? How many   13. 5 8-in. tiles;
    10-inch tiles?   4 10-in. tiles

Windows © D.C. Heath and Company   Chapter 6 • Exploring Number Theory **87**

The investigation presents the division model for fractions versus the part-to-whole model. Initially, this model may be difficult for students to understand. It is suggested that instead of having the students read the example, supply students with 3-inch strips of paper, set students the task of producing a $\frac{3}{4}$-inch strip, and see what methods they come up with. The last two exercises use the area of a circle as a model, but the concept involved is equivalent to strips and lengths.

LESSON INVESTIGATION 6.6
Folding Fraction Strips

Materials Needed: paper, scissors

In this activity, you will investigate properties of fractions by folding strips of paper to specified lengths.

Example — *Folding Fractions*

Each person in your group is given a strip of paper that is 3 inches long. Without using a ruler, each person is asked to fold the strip and mark a portion that is $\frac{3}{4}$ inch long. The following three methods were used. Is each method correct? Explain your reasoning. **Yes**

a. 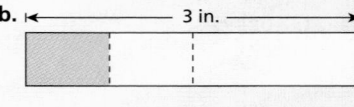 |← 3 in. →|
Fold the strip in half. Then fold it in half again. Each of four parts has a length of $\frac{3}{4}$ inch.

$\frac{1}{4}$ of 3 $= \frac{3}{4}$

b. |← 3 in. →|
Fold the strip in half. Unfold it and fold one of the halves in half. Each of two smaller parts has a length of $\frac{3}{4}$ inch.

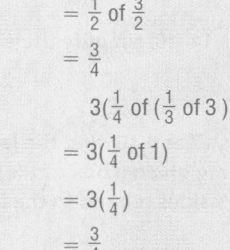

$\frac{1}{2}$ of ($\frac{1}{2}$ of 3)
$= \frac{1}{2}$ of $\frac{3}{2}$
$= \frac{3}{4}$

c. |← 3 in. →|
Fold the strip into 3 equal parts. Unfold it and fold one of the parts into 4 equal parts. Shade 3 of the smaller parts. ■

$3(\frac{1}{4}$ of ($\frac{1}{3}$ of 3))
$= 3(\frac{1}{4}$ of 1)
$= 3(\frac{1}{4})$
$= \frac{3}{4}$

Exercises   Check students' work.

In Exercises 1–4, use a ruler to measure a strip of paper that has the indicated length. Cut the strip out. Then, without using the ruler, fold the strip in a way that allows you to mark a portion of the strip that has the indicated length.   See margin.

1. Length of paper strip: 4 inches
   Length of portion: $\frac{3}{4}$ inch

2. Length of paper strip: 4 inches
   Length of portion: $\frac{4}{3}$ inch

3. Length of paper strip: 5 inches
   Length of portion: $\frac{5}{6}$ inch

4. Length of paper strip: 3 inches
   Length of portion: $\frac{4}{3}$ inch

5. Draw a circle and label its area as 5 square units. Then shade a portion of the circle whose area is $\frac{5}{4}$ square units.   Shade $\frac{1}{4}$ of the circle.

6. Draw a circle and shade one-thrd of the circle. Label the area of the shaded region as $\frac{4}{3}$ square units. What is the area of the unshaded region? $\frac{8}{3}$ square units

Answers
1. Fold the strip in half, then fold it in half again. Fold 1 of the 4 parts in half, then fold it in half again. Shade 3 adjacent smaller parts.
2. Fold the strip into 3 equal parts. Shade any 1 of the 3 parts.
3. Fold the strip into 3 equal parts. Fold 1 of the 3 parts into 2 equal parts. Shade either 1 of the 2 smaller parts.
4. Fold the strip into 3 equal parts. Fold each of 2 adjacent parts into 3 equal parts. Shade 4 adjacent smaller parts.

6.6 Rational Numbers and Decimals

PACING the Lesson

Suggested Number of Days
Basic/Average 2   **Above Average** 1
Advanced 1

PLANNING the Lesson

Lesson Plan 6.6, p. 47

Goal 1   **Identifying Rational Numbers**

Throughout history, when people have studied numbers, they found that some numbers have special properties. For instance, you studied special properties of prime numbers in Lesson 6.2. In this lesson, you will study properties of **rational numbers.**

Rational Number

A number is **rational** if it can be written as the quotient of two integers. Numbers that cannot be written as the quotient of two integers are called **irrational.**

Rational Numbers	Irrational Numbers
$\frac{1}{2}, \frac{-3}{5}, \frac{9}{4}, \frac{5}{1}$	$\sqrt{2}, \sqrt{3}, \sqrt{5}$

Example 1   *Recognizing Rational Numbers*

Show that the following numbers are rational.
a. 4   **b.** 0.5   **c.** -3

Solution   To show that a number is rational, you must show that it can be written as the quotient of two integers.

a. 4 is rational because it can be written as $4 = \frac{4}{1}$.

b. 0.5 is rational because it can be written as $0.5 = \frac{1}{2}$.

c. -3 is rational because it can be written as $-3 = \frac{-3}{1}$. ∎

Example 2   *Showing a Mixed Number Is Rational*

Show that the mixed number $1\frac{1}{4}$ is rational.

Solution $1\frac{1}{4}$ can be written as

$$1\frac{1}{4} = 1 + \frac{1}{4} = \frac{4}{4} + \frac{1}{4} = \frac{5}{4}.$$

Since $1\frac{1}{4}$ can be written as the quotient of the integers 5 and 4, it is rational. ∎

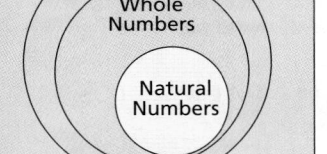

The Set of Rational Numbers

This Venn diagram shows that each natural number, whole number, and integer is a rational number.

6.6 • Rational Numbers and Decimals   **265**

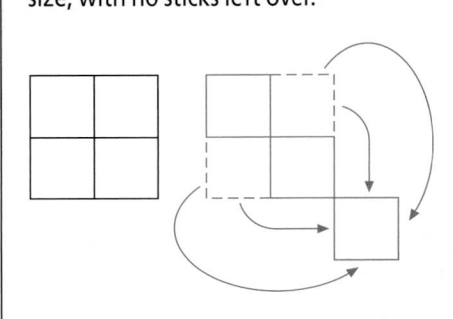

In describing rational and irrational numbers, you can avoid some confusion about the difference between *nonrepeating* and *having no pattern*. A repeating pattern duplicates a finite cluster of digits over and over. The following irrational numbers have a pattern (in the sense that we can anticipate what comes next) but are neither repeating nor terminating.

0.313113111311113111113...

0.232902329123292232932 3...

Example 3

Note that decimals that terminate have names that indicate the denominator of the equivalent fraction (tenths, hundredths, and so on).

You may wish to have students show the subtraction step in part **b** of the Example, as follows:

2nd equation: $100x = 9.090909$
1st equation: $\underline{-x = 0.090909}$
$99x = 9.000000$

Note that decimal parts in the first and second lines of the subtraction match.

Communicating
about **MATHEMATICS**

Can the following decimal numbers be rewritten as fractions? Explain.

a. 3.125454454445...

b. 0.304005000600007...
No, both are irrational.

Writing Prompt

I could really use some help with . . .
or
What I understand best about _____ is . . .
(Fill in the blank with an appropriate concept or topic.)

$0.45 = \dfrac{45}{100}$

Each small square has an area of 0.01 or $\frac{1}{100}$.

Need to Know

In part **b**, each side was multiplied by 100 because 0.090909 . . . has *two* repeating digits. For one repeating digit, multiply by 10. For three repeating digits, multiply by 1000.

Goal **2**   **Writing Decimals as Fractions**

Decimals can be *terminating, repeating,* or *nonrepeating.* In decimal form, every rational number is either terminating or repeating, and every irrational number is nonrepeating.

Number	Decimal Form	Comment
$\frac{3}{8}$	0.375	Rational, terminating
$\frac{16}{11}$	$1.454545 \ldots = 1.\overline{45}$	Rational, repeating
$\sqrt{2}$	$1.414213562 \ldots$	Irrational, nonrepeating

Example 3   *Writing Decimals as Fractions*

Write the following decimals as fractions.

a. 0.45   **b.** $0.090909 \ldots = 0.\overline{09}$

Solution

a. This terminating decimal represents 45 hundredths, as shown in the figure at the left. You can write it as a fraction as follows.

$$0.45 = \frac{45}{100} \qquad \textit{Write as 45 hundredths.}$$
$$= \frac{5 \cdot 9}{5 \cdot 20} \qquad \textit{Factor.}$$
$$= \frac{9}{20} \qquad \textit{Simplify.}$$

b. To write a repeating decimal as a fraction, use the following strategy.

$$x = 0.090909 \ldots \qquad \textit{Let x represent the number.}$$
$$100x = 9.090909 \ldots \qquad \textit{Multiply each side by 100.}$$
$$99x = 9 \qquad \textit{Subtract 1st equation from 2nd.}$$
$$x = \frac{9}{99} \qquad \textit{Divide each side by 99.}$$
$$x = \frac{1}{11} \qquad \textit{Simplify.}$$

Communicating about **MATHEMATICS**

For explanations, see
▶ **SHARING IDEAS about the Lesson** Additional Answers.

Writing Fractions Write each decimal number as a fraction. Explain your reasoning.

A. $0.6666 \ldots = 0.\overline{6}$ $\frac{2}{3}$ **B.** $1.6666 \ldots = 1.\overline{6}$ $\frac{5}{3}$

C. 2.25 $\frac{9}{4}$ **D.** $0.2222 \ldots = 0.\overline{2}$ $\frac{2}{9}$

OPTION: Extra Examples

1. Recognizing Rational Numbers
Show that the following numbers are rational.
a. 7   **b.** 0.6   **c.** −0.8

Solution
To show that a number is rational, you must show that it can be written as the quotient of two integers.

a. 7 is rational because it can be written as $7 = \frac{7}{1}$.

b. 0.6 is rational because it can be written as $0.6 = \frac{3}{5}$.

c. −0.8 is rational because it can be written as $-0.8 = \frac{-4}{5}$.

2. Showing a Mixed Number Is Rational
Show that the mixed number
$2 + \frac{4}{5}$ is rational.

Solution
$2\frac{4}{5}$ can be written as
$$2 + \frac{4}{5} = \frac{10}{5} + \frac{4}{5} = \frac{14}{5}.$$

Since $2\frac{4}{5}$ can be written as the quotient of the integers 14 and 5, it is rational.

EXERCISES

Guided Practice

▶ **CHECK for Understanding**

In Exercises 1–5, state whether the number is rational or irrational. Write the rational number as the quotient of two integers.

1., 3.–5. Rational
2. Irrational

1. -3 $\frac{-3}{1}$ **2.** $\sqrt{6}$ **3.** $2\frac{3}{5}$ $\frac{13}{5}$ **4.** 7 $\frac{7}{1}$ **5.** 0.4 $\frac{2}{5}$

Modeling Decimals   In Exercises 6–9, write the decimal that is represented by the blue portion of the grid. Then write the number as a fraction and simplify. (Each small square has an area of 0.01.)

6. 0.36, $\frac{36}{100}$, $\frac{9}{25}$ **7.** 0.75, $\frac{75}{100}$, $\frac{3}{4}$
8. 0.64, $\frac{64}{100}$, $\frac{16}{25}$ **9.** 0.05, $\frac{5}{100}$, $\frac{1}{20}$

6. 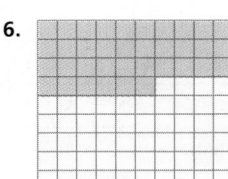   **7.** 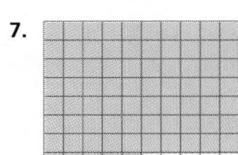   **8.** 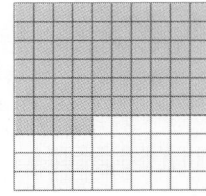   **9.**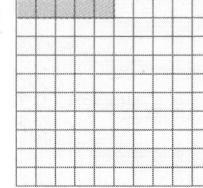

10. *Writing*   Explain how to write a mixed number as a quotient of two integers.

Write the whole number as a fraction with the same denominator as the fraction, then add.

Independent Practice

In Exercises 11–18, write the number as a fraction in simplest form.

11. 5 $\frac{5}{1}$ **12.** 0.75 $\frac{3}{4}$ **13.** 0.25 $\frac{1}{4}$ **14.** -9 $-\frac{9}{1}$
15. $1\frac{1}{6}$ $\frac{7}{6}$ **16.** $2\frac{2}{9}$ $\frac{20}{9}$ **17.** $-1\frac{5}{8}$ $-\frac{13}{8}$ **18.** $-2\frac{4}{5}$ $-\frac{14}{5}$

In Exercises 19–26, decide whether the number is rational or irrational. Then write the decimal form of the number and state whether the decimal is terminating, repeating, or nonrepeating.

19., 20., 22.–26. Rational
21. Irrational

19. $\frac{3}{5}$ 0.6, terminating   **20.** $\frac{9}{11}$ $0.\overline{81}$, repeating   **21.** $\sqrt{8}$ 2.8284 . . ., nonrepeating   **22.** $\sqrt{9}$ 3, terminating
23. $\frac{8}{15}$ $0.5\overline{3}$, repeating   **24.** $\frac{7}{10}$ 0.7, terminating   **25.** $\frac{7}{2}$ 3.5, terminating   **26.** $\frac{13}{12}$ $1.08\overline{3}$, repeating

In Exercises 27–34, write the decimal as a fraction. Simplify the result.

27. 0.8 $\frac{8}{10}, \frac{4}{5}$ **28.** 0.35 $\frac{35}{100}, \frac{7}{20}$ **29.** 0.84 $\frac{84}{100}, \frac{21}{25}$ **30.** 0.64 $\frac{64}{100}, \frac{16}{25}$
31. $0.\overline{45}$ $\frac{45}{99}, \frac{5}{11}$ **32.** $0.\overline{86}$ $\frac{86}{99}, \frac{86}{99}$ **33.** $2.\overline{3}$ $\frac{21}{9}, \frac{7}{3}$ **34.** $1.\overline{135}$ $\frac{1134}{999}, \frac{42}{37}$

In Exercises 35–40, match the rational number with its decimal form.

a. 0.4   **b.** 3.08   **c.** 2.12   **d.** 0.27   **e.** 0.083   **f.** 0.296

35. $\frac{10}{120}$ e   **36.** $\frac{6}{15}$ a   **37.** $2\frac{3}{25}$ c   **38.** $\frac{5}{18}$ d   **39.** $\frac{8}{27}$ f   **40.** $3\frac{6}{75}$ b

P Portfolio Opportunity   **6.6** ▪ *Rational Numbers and Decimals*   **267**

EXERCISE Notes

ASSIGNMENT GUIDE

Basic/Average:
Day 1: Ex. 11–39 odd
Day 2: Ex. 41–45 odd. 46–54

Above Average:
Ex. 11–53 odd

Advanced: Ex. 11–53 odd

Selected Answers: Ex. 1–10, 11–49 odd

Guided Practice

These exercises could be completed by groups and the results shared with the entire class.

Independent Practice

▶ **Ex. 19–26**
EXTENSION
Have students investigate the patterns for various "families" of fractions when they are written as decimals. For instance, the ninths and elevenths have patterns that are recognizable by most students.

▶ **Ex. 31–34**   Students need practice with converting repeating decimals to fractions.
EXTENSION
In an exercise such as Ex. 32, the students are directed to multiply by 100. However, ask students to determine what happens if they multiply by 1000 instead.

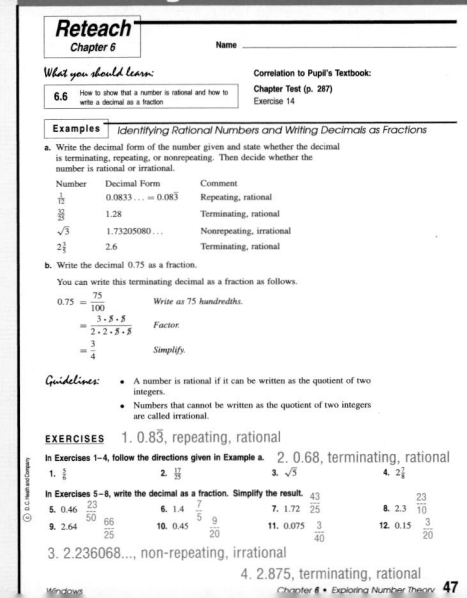

Fraction Patterns **In Exercises 41 and 42, write each rational number in decimal form. Then describe the pattern.** See margin.

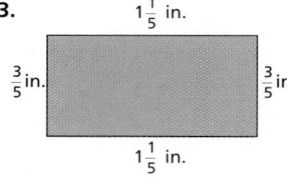

41. $\frac{1}{11}, \frac{2}{11}, \frac{3}{11}, \frac{4}{11}, \frac{5}{11}, \frac{6}{11}$

42. $\frac{1}{2}, \frac{3}{4}, \frac{5}{6}, \frac{7}{8}, \frac{9}{10}, \frac{11}{12}$

Geometry **In Exercises 43–45, find the perimeter of the figure. Write the result in three ways: in fraction form, as a mixed number, and as a decimal.**

45. $\frac{20}{3}$ in., $6\frac{2}{3}$ in., $6.\overline{6}$ in.

⊘ 43. $1\frac{1}{5}$ in. / $\frac{3}{5}$ in. / $\frac{3}{5}$ in. / $1\frac{1}{5}$ in.

$\frac{18}{5}$ in., $3\frac{3}{5}$ in., 3.6 in.

⊘ 44. $\frac{3}{11}$ in. / $\frac{5}{11}$ in. / $\frac{6}{11}$ in.

$\frac{14}{11}$ in., $1\frac{3}{11}$ in., $1.\overline{27}$ in.

⊘ 45. $\frac{2}{3}$ in. / $1\frac{1}{3}$ in. / $1\frac{1}{3}$ in. / $1\frac{2}{3}$ in. / $1\frac{2}{3}$ in.

46. *Favorite Foods* A survey was taken to determine the favorite foods of students between the ages of 6 and 12. The top five choices are shown at the right. The fraction indicates the portion of those surveyed who chose that food as one of their favorites. Write each fraction in decimal form. Then order the top five foods from most favorite to least favorite. Pizza, chicken nuggets, hot dogs, cheeseburgers, macaroni and cheese

Favorite Food	Number	
Cheeseburgers	$\frac{21}{50}$	0.4
Chicken nuggets	$\frac{13}{25}$	0.5
Hot dogs	$\frac{9}{20}$	0.4
Macaroni and cheese	$\frac{41}{100}$	0.4
Pizza	$\frac{41}{50}$	0.8

Integrated Review

Making Connections within Mathematics

P *Logical Reasoning* **In Exercises 47–50, use the Venn diagram on page 265 to help you decide whether the statement is true or false. Explain.** See margin.

47. All integers are rational numbers. True

48. All whole numbers are natural numbers. Fals

49. All rational numbers are whole numbers. False

50. All natural numbers are integers. True

Exploration and Extension

Percents **In Exercises 51–54, write the percent as a fraction, then write the fraction in decimal form. What do you notice?**

Percent means "per hundred." A percent is a fraction whose denominator is 100. The symbol for percent is %. For instance, 25 percent can be written as 25% or $\frac{25}{100}$.

⊘ 51. 24% $\frac{24}{100}$, 0.24

⊘ 52. 83% $\frac{83}{100}$, 0.83

⊘ 53. 56% $\frac{56}{100}$, 0.56

⊘ 54. 12% $\frac{12}{100}$, 0.12

The digits after the decimal point are the same as those in the numerator of the fraction.

⊘ More difficult exercises

P Portfolio Opportunity

6.7

Powers and Exponents

What you should learn:

Goal 1 How to evaluate powers that have negative and zero exponents

Goal 2 How to multiply and divide powers

Why you should learn it:

Knowing how to evaluate numbers with negative and zero exponents helps you interpret results given by calculators and computers.

Sand is composed of tiny pieces of rocks that vary in width from 20^{-2} inch to 12^{-1} inch. Can you write these widths as fractions?

Goal 1 Using Negative and Zero Exponents

You already know how to evaluate powers that have positive integer exponents. For instance, $2^3 = 2 \cdot 2 \cdot 2 = 8$ and $(-3)^2 = (-3) \cdot (-3) = 9$. In this lesson, you will learn how to evaluate powers that have negative integer or zero exponents.

LESSON INVESTIGATION

■ Investigating Negative and Zero Exponents

Group Activity Use a calculator to write each power in decimal form.

$$10^3 \quad 10^2 \quad 10^1 \quad 10^0 \quad 10^{-1} \quad 10^{-2} \quad 10^{-3}$$
$$2^3 \quad \ \ 2^2 \quad \ \ 2^1 \quad \ \ 2^0 \quad \ \ 2^{-1} \quad \ \ 2^{-2} \quad \ \ 2^{-3}$$

What patterns can you discover? What does it mean to have a zero or negative exponent?

Sample Keystrokes for 10^{-2}: $\quad 10 \ \boxed{y^x} \ 2 \ \boxed{+/-} \ \boxed{=}$

In this investigation, you may have discovered the following definitions.

> #### Negative and Zero Exponents
>
> Let n be a positive integer and let a be a nonzero number.
> $$a^{-n} = \frac{1}{a^n} \qquad \text{and} \qquad a^0 = 1$$

Example 1 — Evaluating Powers

a. $2^{-2} = \frac{1}{2^2} = \frac{1}{4}$

b. $-3^{-2} = -\frac{1}{3^2} = -\frac{1}{9}$

c. $(-4)^{-2} = \frac{1}{(-4)^2} = \frac{1}{16}$

d. $4^0 = 1$

e. $x^{-1} = \frac{1}{x^1} = \frac{1}{x}$

f. $2b^{-2} = 2(b^{-2}) = 2(\frac{1}{b^2}) = \frac{2}{b^2}$ ■

▶ **PACING the Lesson**

Suggested Number of Days
Basic/Average 2   Above Average 1
Advanced 1

▶ **PLANNING the Lesson**

Lesson Plan 6.7, p. 48

ORGANIZER

Starters (reproduced below)
  Problem of the Day 6.7, p. 18
  Warm-Up Exercises 6.7, p. 18
Lesson Resources
  Color Transparencies
    Picture for Example 1, p. 26
  Math Log, p. 21
  Answer Masters 6.7, pp. 117, 118
  Extra Practice Copymaster 6.7, p. 48
  Reteaching Copymaster 6.7, p. 48
Special Populations
  Suggestions, Teacher's Edition, p. 238D

LESSON Notes

ALTERNATE APPROACH
Using Tables   Patterns are effective in extending the rules for evaluating powers with zero and negative exponents. In the Lesson Investigation, the use of a calculator is suggested for examining the pattern. However, students can easily observe the pattern in a table.

Powers	Decimals
2^3	8
2^2	4 (= 8 ÷ 2)
2^1	2 (= 4 ÷ 2)
2^0	? (= 2 ÷ 2)
2^{-1}	?
2^{-2}	?
2^{-3}	?

Students should record the rules for negative and zero exponents in their journals.

Example 1

Common-Error Alert!

Direct students' attention to parts **b** and **c** of Example 1. In part **b**, the exponent, -2, does not include the negative sign of -3. Part **c** shows that parentheses must be used if the exponent is to include the negative sign. Similarly, in part **f**, the exponent -2 does not include the coefficient, 2. Ask students how to rewrite part **f** so that the exponent, -2, includes the coefficient, 2. $(2b)^{-2}$

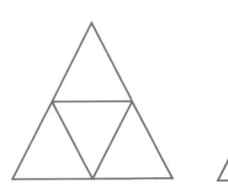

The rules for multiplying and dividing powers should be included in students' journals. As students apply these rules, occasionally check that students easily recognize which number is the base and which is the exponent.

Example 2

In part **d**, notice that using the exponent rule results in a negative exponent. It is customary to rewrite the result as $\frac{1}{5^2}$, using a positive exponent.

Example 3

Note that another approach to this problem is to recognize that the largest cube has dimensions $9 \times 9 \times 9$.

Communicating about MATHEMATICS

EXTENSION
Have students explain to partners why $-2m^{-3}$ is $-\frac{2}{m^3}$.

Writing Prompt
I am still unclear about . . .

Multiplying and Dividing Powers

To multiply two powers with the same base, add their exponents. To divide two powers with the same base, subtract the exponent of the denominator from the exponent of the numerator.

> **Multiplying and Dividing Powers**
> 1. $a^m \cdot a^n = a^{m+n}$ 2. $\frac{a^m}{a^n} = a^{m-n}$

Example 2 *Multiplying and Dividing Powers*

Using Exponent Rules   **Using Factors**

a. $4^2 \cdot 4^3 = 4^{2+3} = 4^5$ $4^2 \cdot 4^3 = \overbrace{4 \cdot 4}^{4^2} \cdot \overbrace{4 \cdot 4 \cdot 4}^{4^3} = 4^5$

b. $\frac{3^3}{3^2} = 3^{3-2} = 3^1 = 3$ $\frac{3^3}{3^2} = \frac{3 \cdot 3 \cdot 3}{3 \cdot 3} = 3$

c. $2^4 \cdot 2^{-2} = 2^{4+(-2)} = 2^2$ $2^4 \cdot \frac{1}{2^2} = \frac{2 \cdot 2 \cdot 2 \cdot 2}{2 \cdot 2} = 2^2$

d. $\frac{5}{5^3} = 5^{1-3} = 5^{-2}$ $\frac{5}{5^3} = \frac{5}{5 \cdot 5 \cdot 5} = \frac{1}{5^2}$

Connections
Geometry

Example 3 *Rubik's Cubes*

You have a stack of Rubik's Cubes, as shown at the left. How many small cubes are in the stack?

Solution Each Rubik's Cube is composed of 3^3 small cubes, and there are 3^3 Rubik's Cubes in the stack. This means that the stack has $3^3 \cdot 3^3 = 3^{3+3} = 3^6 = 729$ small cubes.

You can check this result by reasoning that each Rubik's Cube is composed of 27 small cubes, which means that the stack has $27 \cdot 27 = 729$ small cubes.

P Communicating about MATHEMATICS

▶ **SHARING IDEAS about the Lesson**

Cooperative Learning

You Be the Teacher How would you explain to a partner that $3^4 \cdot 3^5$ is equal to 3^9? See margin.

OPTION: Extra Examples

Here are additional examples similar to Example 2.
Multiplying and Dividing Powers.

Using Exponent Rules   Using Factors

a. $3^5 \cdot 3 = 3^{5+1} = 3^6$ $3^5 \cdot 3 = 3 \cdot 3 \cdot 3 \cdot 3 \cdot 3 \cdot 3 = 3^6$

b. $\frac{4^6}{4} = 4^{6-1} = 4^5$ $\frac{4^6}{4} = \frac{4 \cdot 4 \cdot 4 \cdot 4 \cdot 4 \cdot 4}{4} = 4^5$

c. $5^3 \cdot 5^{-7} = 5^{3+(-7)} = 5^{-4}$ $5^3 \cdot \frac{1}{5^7} = \frac{5 \cdot 5 \cdot 5}{5 \cdot 5 \cdot 5 \cdot 5 \cdot 5 \cdot 5 \cdot 5} = \frac{1}{5^4}$

d. $\frac{2^3}{2^8} = 2^{3-8} = 2^{-5}$ $\frac{2^3}{2^8} = \frac{2 \cdot 2 \cdot 2}{2 \cdot 2 \cdot 2 \cdot 2 \cdot 2 \cdot 2 \cdot 2 \cdot 2} = \frac{1}{2^5}$

Answer to Communicating
$3^4 \cdot 3^5 = \underbrace{3 \cdot 3 \cdot 3 \cdot 3}_{3^4} \cdot \underbrace{3 \cdot 3 \cdot 3 \cdot 3 \cdot 3}_{3^5} = 3^9$

EXERCISES

Guided Practice

▶ **CHECK for Understanding**

1. *Writing* In your own words, state the definitions for negative integer and zero exponents. See page 269.

In Exercises 2–5, rewrite the expression without using negative or zero exponents.

2. 4^{-1} $\frac{1}{4}$

3. 5^{-2} $\frac{1}{5^2}$ or $\frac{1}{25}$

4. 100^0 1

5. x^{-3} $\frac{1}{x^3}$

6. *Writing* In your own words, state how to multiply and divide two powers that have the same base. See page 270.

In Exercises 7–10, simplify the expression, if possible.

7. $p^5 \cdot p^2$ p^7

8. $r^2 \cdot s^3$ $r^2 s^3$

9. $\frac{m^6}{n^4}$ $\frac{m^6}{n^4}$

10. $\frac{x^4}{x^2}$ x^2

Independent Practice

In Exercises 11–18, simplify the expression.

11. 3^{-2} $\frac{1}{9}$

12. -10^{-3} $-\frac{1}{1000}$

13. 16^0 1

14. $(-9)^2$ 81

15. t^{-4} $\frac{1}{t^4}$

16. $2x^{-3}$ $\frac{2}{x^3}$

17. $3s^{-2}$ $\frac{3}{s^2}$

18. r^0 1

In Exercises 19–26, simplify the expression.

19. $(-6)^{-3} \cdot (-6)^5$ 36

20. $8^0 \cdot 8^4$ 4096

21. $x^{25} \cdot x^{-10}$ x^{15}

22. $y^{-6} \cdot y^4$ $\frac{1}{y^2}$

23. $\frac{7^5}{7^4}$ 7

24. $\frac{-9^2}{-9^4}$ $\frac{1}{81}$

25. $\frac{a^{12}}{a^0}$ a^{12}

26. $\frac{b^7}{b^{10}}$ $\frac{1}{b^3}$

In Exercises 27–30, use a calculator to evaluate the expression. If necessary, round the result to 3 decimal places.

27. 2.5^{-4} 0.026

28. 5.5^{-2} 0.033

29. $5.5^3 \cdot 5.5^2$ 5032.844

30. $\frac{0.5^3}{0.5^6}$ 8

✪ *Mental Math* In Exercises 31–34, solve the equation for n.

31. $\frac{2^5}{2^2} = 2^n$ 3

32. $\left(\frac{1}{2}\right)^n = 1$ 0

33. $3^{-3} \cdot 3^n = 3^3$ 6

34. $4^{-5} = \frac{1}{4^n}$ 5

35. *Guess, Check, and Revise* Find the largest value of n such that $2^n < 100,000$. 16

36. *Guess, Check, and Revise* Find the largest value of n such that $3^{-n} > 0.00001$. 10

In Exercises 37 and 38, write an expression for the verbal phrase.

✪ **37.** The product of seven raised to the tenth power and seven raised to the negative fourth power $7^{10} \cdot 7^{-4}$

✪ **38.** The quotient of two raised to the negative fifth power and two raised to the third power $\frac{2^{-5}}{2^3}$

✪ More difficult exercises

ASSIGNMENT GUIDE

Basic/Average:
Day 1: Ex. 11–45 odd
Day 2: Ex. 47–50, 51–59 odd

Above Average:
Ex. 15–21 odd, 27–59 odd

Advanced: Ex. 15–21 odd, 27–59 odd

Selected Answers: Ex. 1–10, 11–57 odd

Guided Practice

▶ **Ex. 1–6**
MATH JOURNAL
Have students work these exercises in their journals.
▶ **Ex. 5** Remind students that the rules for zero and negative exponents are not defined for a zero base. Throughout these exercises, wherever variables are used, we must assume that none of the variables has a zero value.
▶ **Ex. 8, 9**

Common-Error Alert!

Students may ignore the fact that the bases in each of these exercises are not the same. You may wish to substitute numbers for variables to help explain the issue.

Independent Practice

▶ **Ex. 14** An answer of −81 here signals, of course, that students have ignored the parentheses.
▶ **Ex. 16, 17**

Common-Error Alert!

In these exercises, students may make the mistake of writing the coefficient together with the variable in the denominator. Remind them that this would be correct only if parentheses had been used.

Extra Practice

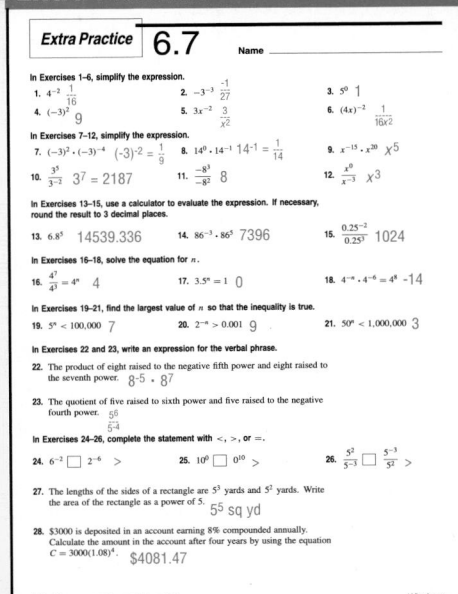

Extra Practice 6.7 Name _____

In Exercises 1–6, simplify the expression.
1. 4^{-2} $\frac{1}{16}$
2. -3^{-3} $\frac{-1}{27}$
3. 5^0 1
4. $(-3)^2$ 9
5. $3x^{-2}$ $\frac{3}{x^2}$
6. $(4x)^{-2}$ $\frac{1}{16x^2}$

In Exercises 7–12, simplify the expression.
7. $(-3)^2 \cdot (-3)^{-4}$ $(-3)^{-2} = \frac{1}{9}$
8. $14^0 \cdot 14^{-1}$ $14^{-1} = \frac{1}{14}$
9. $x^{-15} \cdot x^{20}$ x^5
10. $\frac{3^5}{3^{-2}}$ $3^7 = 2187$
11. $\frac{-8^3}{-8^2}$ 8
12. $\frac{x^0}{x^{-3}}$ x^3

In Exercises 13–15, use a calculator to evaluate the expression. If necessary, round the result to 3 decimal places.
13. 6.8^5 14539.336
14. $86^{-3} \cdot 86^5$ 7396
15. $\frac{0.25^{-2}}{0.25^3}$ 1024

In Exercises 16–18, solve the equation for n.
16. $\frac{4^7}{4^3} = 4^n$ 4
17. $3.5^n = 1$ 0
18. $4^{-n} \cdot 4^{-6} = 4^8$ -14

In Exercises 19–21, find the largest value of n so that the inequality is true.
19. $5^n < 100,000$ 7
20. $2^{-n} > 0.001$ 9
21. $50^n < 1,000,000$ 3

In Exercises 22 and 23, write an expression for the verbal phrase.
22. The product of eight raised to the negative fifth power and eight raised to the seventh power. $8^{-5} \cdot 8^7$
23. The quotient of five raised to sixth power and five raised to the negative fourth power. $\frac{5^6}{5^{-4}}$

In Exercises 24–26, complete the statement with <, >, or =.
24. 6^{-2} ☐ 2^{-6} $>$
25. 10^0 ☐ 0^{10} $>$
26. $\frac{5^2}{5^{-3}}$ ☐ $\frac{5^{-3}}{5^2}$ $>$

27. The lengths of the sides of a rectangle are 5^3 yards and 5^2 yards. Write the area of the rectangle as a power of 5. 5^5 sq yd
28. $3000 is deposited in an account earning 8% compounded annually. Calculate the amount in the account after four years by using the equation $C = 3000(1.08)^4$. $4081.47

48 *Powers and Exponents* ▪ *6.7* Windows

Reteaching

Reteach Chapter 6 Name _____

What you should learn:
6.7 How to evaluate powers that have negative and zero exponents and how to multiply and divide powers

Correlation to Pupil's Textbook:
Chapter Test (p. 287)
Exercise 15

Examples *Using Negative and Zero Exponents and Multiplying and Dividing Powers*

a. Rewrite each expression without using negative or zero exponents.
$2^{-3} = \frac{1}{2^3} = \frac{1}{8}$ $17^0 = 1$
$(-5)^{-2} = \frac{1}{(-5)^2} = \frac{1}{25}$ $-5^{-2} = -\frac{1}{5^2} = -\frac{1}{25}$

b. Simplify each expression, using factors.
$5^6 \cdot 5^{-2} = 5^6 \cdot \frac{1}{5^2} = \frac{\cancel{5} \cdot \cancel{5} \cdot 5 \cdot 5 \cdot 5 \cdot 5}{\cancel{5} \cdot \cancel{5}} = 5^4$
$\frac{6}{6^4} = \frac{\cancel{6}}{\cancel{6} \cdot 6 \cdot 6 \cdot 6} = \frac{1}{6^3}$

c. Simplify each expression, using exponent rules.
$3^5 \cdot 3^{-2} = 3^{5+(-2)} = 3^3$ *To multiply two powers with the same base, add their exponents.*
$\frac{q^3}{q^8} = q^{3-8} = q^{-5} = \frac{1}{q^5}$ *To divide two powers with the same base, subtract the exponent of the denominator from the exponent of the numerator.*

Guidelines:
• Let n be a positive integer and let a be a nonzero number. The definition of negative and zero exponents is as follows.
$a^{-n} = \frac{1}{a^n}$ and $a^0 = 1$
• The definition of multiplying and dividing powers is as follows.
$a^m \cdot a^n = a^{m+n}$ and $\frac{a^m}{a^n} = a^{m-n}$

EXERCISES
In Exercises 1–8, simplify the expression.
1. 12^{-1} $\frac{1}{12}$
2. 18^0 1
3. -7^{-2} $\frac{-1}{49}$
4. $x^4 \cdot x^3$ x^7
5. $\frac{8^6}{8^3}$ 8^4 or 4096
6. $\frac{t^4}{t^7}$ $\frac{1}{t^3}$
7. $2^0 \cdot 2^5$ 2^5 or 32
8. $d^{12} \cdot d^{-7}$ d^5

48 *Chapter 6 ▪ Exploring Number Theory* Windows

Comparing Powers   **In Exercises 39–42, complete the statement with** $<$, $>$, **or** $=$.

39. 3^{10} [?] $3 \cdot 3^9$ $=$

40. 2^{-5} [?] 5^{-2} $<$

41. $\frac{4^3}{4^2}$ [?] $\frac{4^2}{4^3}$ $>$

42. $\frac{4^{14}}{4^3}$ [?] 4^{10} $>$

Sequences   **In Exercises 43 and 44, rewrite the sequence as powers of 10. Describe the pattern and write the next three terms.** See margin.

43. 1, 10, 100, 1000, [?], [?], [?]

44. 1, 0.1, 0.01, 0.001, 0.0001, [?], [?], [?]

45. *Geometry*   The lengths of the sides of a rectangle are 2^3 meters and 2^4 meters. Write the area of the rectangle as a power of 2. 2^7

46. *Geometry*   Suppose a Rubik's Cube contained 4^3 cubes. How many small cubes would be in the stack of Rubik's Cubes shown at the right? 4^6 or 4096

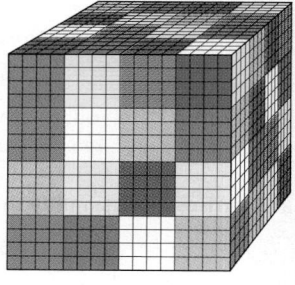

47. *U.S. Population*   In 1990, the United States had a population of about 250 million. Which of the following expressions represents this number? *(Source: U.S. Bureau of Census)*

   a. $2.5(10^6)$ b. $2.5(10^7)$ c. $2.5(10^8)$ c

48. *Beef Consumption*   In 1990, the United States had a population of about 250 million. In that year, Americans ate about 16 billion pounds of beef. Find the average amount eaten by each American by simplifying the following expression. *(Source: U.S. Department of Agriculture)*

   $\frac{1.6 (10^{10}) \text{ pounds}}{2.5 (10^8) \text{ people}}$ 64 pounds

49. *Biology*   Most cells of living organisms are about 10 micrometers wide. One micrometer is 10^{-6} meters, which means that a typical cell is about $10 \cdot 10^{-6}$ meters wide. Write this measurement as a power of 10. 10^{-5}

50. *Lasers*   A laser is a device that amplifies light. A laser beam can be focused on a point that is just 0.05^2 millimeters wide. Write this measure as a fraction. $\frac{1}{400}$

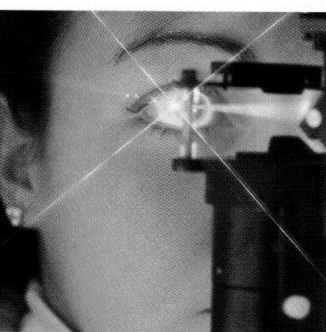

*Laser is an acronym for **L**ight **A**mplification by **S**timulated **E**mission of **R**adiation.*

╔══╗
║ *Integrated Review*   **Making Connections within Mathematics** ║
╚══╝

Error Analysis   **In Exercises 51–54, explain why the answer is incorrect. Then correct it.** For explanations, see margin.

P **51.** $3^{-2} = 3 \cdot -2$
   $= -6$
   $\frac{1}{9}$

52. $4^2 + 4^3 = 4^{2+3}$
   $= 4^5$
   80

53. $7^2 \cdot 7^3 = 7^{2 \cdot 3}$
   $= 7^6$
   7^5

54. $\frac{6^4}{6^8} = 6^{8-4}$
   $= 6^4$
   6^{-4}

Reasoning   **In Exercises 55–58, decide whether the answer is positive or negative. Explain.** For explanations, see margin.

55. $(-1)^{16}$ Positive

56. $(-2)^{37}$ Negative

57. $(-3)^{42}$ Positive

58. $(-4)^{51}$ Negative

Exploration and Extension

59. *Think About It*   Each cube below is made of smaller cubes. Each small yellow cube contains a $20 bill. Each small red cube contains a $10 bill. Each small blue cube contains a $5 bill. If you were allowed to keep the money contained in one of the large cubes, which cube would you choose? Explain your reasoning.

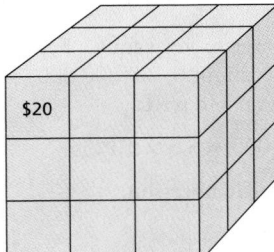 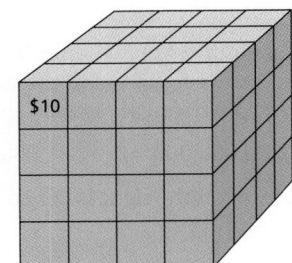 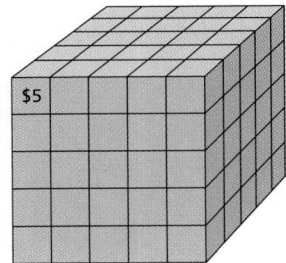

The red cube; for explanation, see margin.

Mixed REVIEW

In Exercises 1–6, write the number in decimal form. Is the decimal terminating, repeating, or nonrepeating? (6.6)

1. $\frac{1}{27}$ $0.0\overline{37}$, repeating

2. $\frac{3}{8}$ 0.375, terminating

3. $\frac{3}{9}$ $0.\overline{3}$, repeating

4. $\frac{19}{18}$ $1.0\overline{5}$, repeating

5. $\frac{14}{9}$ $1.\overline{5}$, repeating

6. $\frac{61}{111}$ $0.\overline{549}$, repeating

In Exercises 7–15, solve the equation. Give the answer in decimal form. If necessary, round the result to 3 decimal places. (4.4, 6.6, 6.7)

7. $18x = 25$ 1.389

8. $25y + 18 = 0$ -0.72

9. $2(10a + 15) = 10$ -1

10. $4x - \frac{1}{2} = \frac{5}{2}$ 0.75

11. $0.5 - 50a = 200a$ 0.002

12. $\frac{1}{10}(p + 2) = 1$ 8

13. $32p - 10 = 10^{-2}$ 0.313

14. $3(33x) = 313$ 3.162

15. $3^2(111x) + 3142 = 0$ -3.145

Coordinate Geometry   For Exercises 16–18, plot the points in the same coordinate plane. State in what quadrant the point is located. (3.8).   For plots, see margin.

16. $A(-2, 4)$ II

17. $B(0, 2)$ None

18. $C(3, -1)$ IV

19. The points in Exercises 16–18 all lie on a line. Find another point that lies on the same line. (3.8) Answers vary. (1, 1)

20. Find the average of $0.1, -0.4, 0.2, -0.3, 0.1$. -0.06

✪ More difficult exercises

6.7 ▪ *Powers and Exponents*   **273**

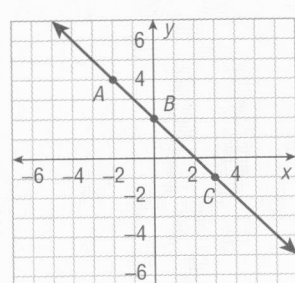

PACING the Lesson

Suggested Number of Days
Basic/Average 2 **Above Average** 1
Advanced 1

PLANNING the Lesson

Lesson Plan 6.8, p. 49

ORGANIZER

Starters (reproduced below)

Problem of the Day 6.8, p. 18
Warm-Up Exercises 6.8, p. 18

Lesson Resources

Color Transparencies
Picture for Ex. 39, p. 26
Math Log, p. 21
Answer Masters 6.8, pp. 120, 121
Extra Practice Copymaster 6.8, p. 49
Reteaching Copymaster 6.8, p. 49

Special Populations

Suggestions, Teacher's Edition, p. 238D

LESSON Notes

Have students record the definition of scientific notation in their math journals. Motivate its use by showing students newspaper and magazine articles in which scientific notation can be found.

Example 1

You may wish to show how scientific notation is displayed on a scientific or graphing calculator. See the Lesson Investigation on page 278.

6.8

Scientific Notation

What you should learn:

Goal 1 How to use scientific notation to represent numbers

Goal 2 How to use scientific notation to solve real-life problems

Why you should learn it:

Scientific notation is a convenient way to represent numbers whose absolute values are very small or very large.

Need to Know

When writing powers of 10, remember that positive exponents correspond to large numbers and negative exponents correspond to small numbers.

1,000,000	10^6
100,000	10^5
10,000	10^4
1,000	10^3
100	10^2
10	10^1
1	10^0
0.1	10^{-1}
0.01	10^{-2}
0.001	10^{-3}

Goal 1 ## Using Scientific Notation

Many numbers in real life are very large or very small. For instance, the population of the world is about 5,500,000,000. Instead of writing this many zeros, you can write

$$5,500,000,000 = 5.5 \times 1,000,000,000 = 5.5 \times 10^9.$$

The form on the right is called **scientific notation.**

Scientific Notation

A number is written in **scientific notation** if it has the form

$$c \times 10^n$$

where c is greater than or equal to 1 and less than 10.

Example 1 *Writing Numbers in Scientific Notation*

	Decimal Form	Product Form	Scientific Notation
a.	3,400	3.4×1000	3.4×10^3
b.	56,000,000	$5.6 \times 10,000,000$	5.6×10^7
c.	0.00923	9.23×0.001	9.23×10^{-3}
d.	0.0000004	4×0.0000001	4×10^{-7}

In Example 1, notice that the exponent of 10 indicates the number of places the decimal point is moved. For instance, in part **a** the decimal point is moved 3 places and in part **d** the decimal point is moved 7 places.

Decimal Form	Scientific Notation
3,400.00	3.4×10^3

Move decimal point 3 places to the left.

0.0000004	4×10^{-7}

Move decimal point 7 places to the right.

STARTER: Problem of the Day

A formula for converting Celsius to Fahrenheit is

$$F = \frac{9}{5}C + 32.$$

When are the two temperature scales numerically equal?
$-40°F = -40°C$

Also available as a copymaster, page 18

STARTER: Warm-Up Exercises

1. Multiply.
a. $5.3 \cdot 10^3$ **b.** $2.7 \cdot 10^{-2}$ **c.** $10^3 \cdot 10^4$
a. 5300, **b.** 0.027, **c.** 10,000,000 or 10^7

2. For each of the following decimal numbers, relocate the decimal point so that the new number lies between 1 and 10.

a. 34.63   **b.** 0.00257   **c.** 0.000056
a. 3.463, **b.** 2.57, **c.** 5.6

Also available as a copymaster, page 18

Goal 2 Using Scientific Notation in Real Life

To multiply two numbers that are written in scientific notation, you can use the rule for multiplying powers with like bases. Here is an example.

$(3.2 \times 10^5) \times (4 \times 10^6)$
$= 3.2 \times 4 \times 10^5 \times 10^6$ *Reorder.*
$= (3.2 \times 4) \times (10^5 \times 10^6)$ *Regroup.*
$= 12.8 \times 10^{11}$ *Multiply.*
$= 1.28 \times 10^{12}$ *Scientific notation.*

This can also be written as 1,280,000,000,000 or 1.28 trillion.

Real Life
Warehousing

In 1990, Americans used an average of about 600 pounds of paper and cardboard per person.

Example 2 *Multiplying with Scientific Notation*

You work in a warehouse that stores paper. You are storing paper that has a thickness of 4.4×10^{-3} inch. The paper comes in packages of 500 sheets. Each carton of paper has a stack of 5 packages. How tall is a stack of 10 cartons?

Solution

Verbal Model	Height of stack	$=$	Number of sheets	$\times$	Thickness of sheet

↓

Labels   Number of sheets $= 10(5)(500) =$ 25,000   (sheets)
          Thickness of sheet $= 4.4 \times 10^{-3}$ (inches per sheet)

↓

Algebraic   Height $=$ 25,000 $\times$ (4.4×10^{-3})

Model $= (2.5 \times 10^4) \times (4.4 \times 10^{-3})$
               $= (2.5 \times 4.4) \times (10^4 \times 10^{-3})$
               $= 11 \times 10^1$
               $= 110$

The stack is 110 inches high. ■

Communicating about MATHEMATICS

▶ **SHARING IDEAS about the Lesson**

Scientific Notation State whether the number is in scientific notation. If it isn't, rewrite the number in scientific notation.

A. 12.4×10^{-3} **B.** 3.8×10^{-2} **C.** 0.5×10^4

A. No, 1.24×10^{-2} **B.** Yes **C.** No, 5×10^3

6.8 • Scientific Notation   **275**

Draw students' attention to the word *reorder*, used as a comment on the first line of the multiplication process shown here. Ask students to name the multiplication properties used in this reordering.   Associative and Commutative Properties   Students may benefit from seeing the next-to-last statement expanded as follows.

$12.8 \times 10^{11} = (1.28 \times 10^1) \times 10^{11}$
               $= 1.28 \times (10^1 \times 10^{11})$
               $= 1.28 \times 10^{12}$

Example 2

Explain to students that the algebraic model used in the example does not include the thickness of the wrapping used to package the paper.

   Ask students what tools could be used to measure such small thicknesses as that of a sheet of paper.
micrometers and vernier calipers

Communicating about MATHEMATICS

PROJECT
Have students identify five real-life situations in which scientific notation is used.

Writing Prompt
To multiply 42,000,000 by 1,800,000,000 without a calculator, I would . . .

ASSIGNMENT GUIDE

Basic/Average:
Day 1: Ex. 7—33 odd
Day 2: Ex. 35–37, 39, 40–44

Above Average:
Ex. 7–41 odd, 42–44

Advanced: Ex. 7–41 odd, 42–44

Selected Answers: Ex. 1–6, 7–41 odd

Guided Practice

▶ **Ex. 1** Have students explain why all three expressions are equivalent.
▶ **Ex. 2, 3** Have students check their answers for these exercises with a calculator.
▶ **Ex. 6** Remind students to focus on the exponent rather than on a comparison of 2.6 and 1.5.

Independent Practice

▶ **Ex. 23–28** If students have difficulty with these problems, you may wish to suggest that they write an intermediate step, for example (Ex. 24):

$0.392 \times 10^6 = 0.392 \times 10 \times 10 \times 10 \times 10 \times 10 \times 10$
$= 3.92 \times 10^5$

They should only need to do this a few times in order to gain understanding and confidence in the process.
▶ **Ex. 29–32** Remind students of the implied multiplication in the use of parentheses.

Guided Practice

▶ **CHECK for Understanding**

1. Which of the following is written in scientific notation? b
   a. 12.3×10^3 **b.** 1.23×10^4 **c.** 0.123×10^5

In Exercises 2 and 3, find the power of 10.

2. $350{,}000 = 3.5 \times 10^{\boxed{?}}$ 5

3. $0.00943 = 9.43 \times 10^{\boxed{?}}$ -3

In Exercises 4 and 5, write the number in decimal form.

4. 6.25×10^5 625,000

5. 8.7×10^{-6} 0.0000087

6. *World Populations* One of the following is the approximate 1990 population of China. The other is the approximate 1990 population of Canada. Which is which? Explain your reasoning.
   a. 2.6×10^7 **b.** 1.5×10^9 a: Canada, b: China; China has more people and $9 > 7$.

Independent Practice

In Exercises 7–14, write the number in scientific notation.

7. 5000 5×10^3
8. 643,000 6.43×10^5
9. 0.00041 4.1×10^{-4}
10. 0.18 1.8×10^{-1}
11. 32,610,000 3.261×10^7
12. 5,730,000,000 5.73×10^9
13. 0.000000012 1.2×10^{-8}
14. 0.000008 8×10^{-6}

In Exercises 15–22, write the number in decimal form. See margin.

15. 5.7×10^{-3}
16. 3.41×10^{-6}
17. 2.50×10^4
18. 2.4×10^9
19. 6.2×10^{10}
20. 8.59×10^5
21. 3.63×10^{-7}
22. 5.99×10^{-1}

In Exercises 23–28, decide whether the number is in scientific notation. If it is not, rewrite the number in scientific notation.

23. 5.3×10^{-5} Yes
24. 0.392×10^6 No, 3.92×10^5
25. 25.6×10^8 No, 2.56×10^9
26. 3.7×10^9 Yes
27. 791×10^{-4} No, 7.91×10^{-2}
28. 68.8×10^3 No, 6.88×10^4

In Exercises 29–32, evaluate the product. Write the result in scientific notation and in decimal form.

29. $(6.2 \times 10^2)(8 \times 10^3)$ 4.96×10^6; 4,960,000
30. $(4.5 \times 10^{-3})(3.4 \times 10^5)$ 1.53×10^3, 1530
31. $(0.3 \times 10^{-4})(0.6 \times 10^{-1})$ 1.8×10^{-6}, 0.0000018
32. $(9.7 \times 10^4)(2.4 \times 10^2)$ 2.328×10^7; 23,280,000

Number Sense **In Exercises 33 and 34, decide which is larger. Explain.**

33. 1×10^9 or 9×10^8 1×10^9, $9 > 8$
34. 5×10^{-5} or 1×10^{-4} 1×10^{-4}, $-4 > -5$

Answers

15. 0.0057
16. 0.00000341
17. 25,000
18. 2,400,000,000
19. 62,000,000,000
20. 859,000
21. 0.000000363
22. 0.599

Extra Practice

Extra Practice 6.8 Name _____

In Exercises 1–6, write the number in scientific notation.
1. 3500 3.6×10^3
2. 62,000 6.2×10^4
3. 0.000375 3.75×10^{-4}
4. 0.0205 2.05×10^{-2}
5. 62,153,000 6.2153×10^7
6. 0.0000105 1.05×10^{-5}

In Exercises 7–12, write the number in decimal form.
7. 3.2×10^5 320,000
8. 6.35×10^{-4} 0.000635
9. 4.3×10^{-3} 0.0043
10. 9.75×10^4 97,500
11. 8.27×10^{-6} 0.00000827
12. 3.25×10^5 325,000

In Exercises 13–18, decide whether the number is in scientific notation. If it is not, rewrite the number in scientific notation.
13. 2.5×10^6 Yes
14. 0.35×10^6 No, 3.5×10^5
15. 26.5×10^{-3} No, 2.65×10^{-2}
16. 3.2×10^{-6} Yes
17. 764×10^{-3} No, 7.64×10^{-1}
18. 5.25×10^{-1} Yes

In Exercises 19–22, evaluate the product. Write the result in scientific notation and in decimal form.
19. $(3.2 \times 10^5)(4 \times 10^2)$ 1.28×10^8; 128,000,000
20. $(3.0 \times 10^5)(6.5 \times 10^{-2})$ 1.95×10^6; 1,950,000
21. $(5.2 \times 10^{-4})(7.2 \times 10^{-6})$ 3.744×10^{-9}; 0.000000003744
22. $(9.5 \times 10^3)(2.3 \times 10^{-1})$ 2.185×10^3; 2185

In Exercises 23 and 24, decide which is larger. Explain.
23. 1×10^6 or 6×10^5 $1 \times 10^6 > 6 \times 10^5$ because 1,000,000 > 600,000.
24. 1×10^{-4} or 4×10^{-3} $1 \times 10^{-4} < 4 \times 10^{-3}$ because 0.0001 < 0.004.

25. The star Beta Andromeda is approximately 76 light years from Earth. Estimate the distance to this star if a light year is approximately 5.88×10^{12} miles. Write your estimate in scientific notation.
   Approximately 4.4688×10^{14} miles

26. The hydraulic cylinder in a large press contains 2 gallons of oil. When the cylinder is under full pressure the actual volume of oil will decrease by $2(150)(2.0 \times 10^{-5})$ gallons. Write this decrease in decimal and scientific notation. What is the actual volume when the cylinder is under full pressure?
   0.006, 6.0×10^{-3} gal; 1.994 gal

Windows   *6.8 • Scientific Notation* 49

Reteaching

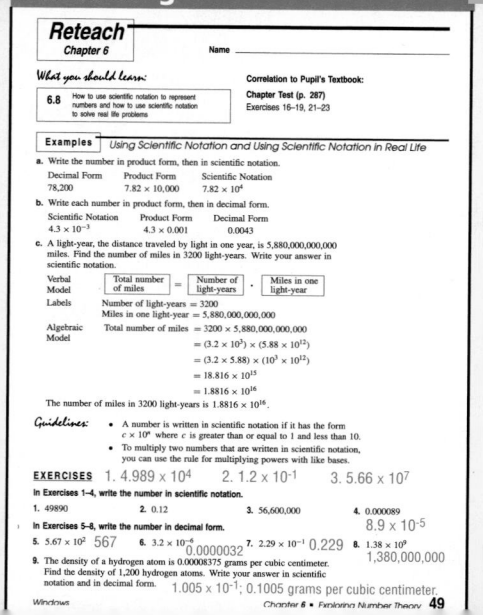

Reteach Chapter 6 Name _____

What you should learn:

6.8 How to use scientific notation to represent numbers and how to use scientific notation to solve real life problems

Correlation to Pupil's Textbook:
Chapter Test (p. 267)
Exercises 16–19, 21–23

Examples *Using Scientific Notation and Using Scientific Notation in Real Life*

a. Write the number in product form, then in scientific notation.

Decimal Form	Product Form	Scientific Notation
78,200	$7.82 \times 10{,}000$	7.82×10^4

b. Write each number in product form, then in decimal form.

Scientific Notation	Product Form	Decimal Form
4.3×10^{-3}	4.3×0.001	0.0043

c. A light-year, the distance traveled by light in one year, is 5,880,000,000,000 miles. Find the number of miles in 3200 light-years. Write your answer in scientific notation.

Verbal Model	Total number of miles	=	Number of light-years	•	Miles in one light-year

Labels   Number of light-years = 3200
   Miles in one light-year = 5,880,000,000,000

Algebraic Model   Total number of miles $= 3200 \times 5{,}880{,}000{,}000{,}000$
   $= (3.2 \times 10^3) \times (5.88 \times 10^{12})$
   $= (3.2 \times 10^3) \times (5.88 \times 10^{12})$
   $= (3.2 \times 5.88) \times (10^3 \times 10^{12})$
   $= 18.816 \times 10^{15}$
   $= 1.8816 \times 10^{16}$

The number of miles in 3200 light-years is 1.8816×10^{16}.

Guidelines: • A number is written in scientific notation if it has the form $c \times 10^n$ where c is greater than or equal to 1 and less than 10.
   • To multiply two numbers that are written in scientific notation, you can use the rule for multiplying powers with like bases.

EXERCISES 1. 4.989×10^4 2. 1.2×10^{-1} 3. 5.66×10^7

In Exercises 1–4, write the number in scientific notation.
1. 49890
2. 0.12
3. 56,600,000
4. 0.000089 8.9×10^{-5}

In Exercises 5–8, write the number in decimal form.
5. 5.67×10^2 567
6. 3.2×10^{-6} 0.0000032
7. 2.29×10^{-1} 0.229
8. 1.38×10^9 1,380,000,000

9. The density of a hydrogen atom is 0.00008375 grams per cubic centimeter. Find the density of 1,200 hydrogen atoms. Write your answer in scientific notation and in decimal form. 1.005×10^{-1}; 0.1005 grams per cubic centimeter.

Windows   Chapter 6 • Exploring Number Theory 49

In Exercises 35 and 36, write the number in scientific notation.

35. A thunderstorm cloud holds about 6,000,000,000,000 raindrops. 6×10^{12}

36. The adult human body contains about 100,000,000,000,000 cells. 1×10^{14}

37. *Musical Instruments*   You are writing a report and have collected the information in the table, which shows the number of people who play the six most popular instruments. Rewrite the table so that the numbers are in decimal form. Which table do you think would be better to include in your report? Explain your reasoning. *(Source: American Music Conference)*   Answers vary.

Instrument	Piano	Guitar	Organ	Flute	Clarinet	Drums
	20,600,000		6,300,000		4,000,000	
Number	2.06×10^7	1.89×10^7	6.3×10^6	4×10^6	4×10^6	3×10^6
		18,900,000		4,000,000		3,000,000

38. *Density*   The density of an element is related to its weight. Light elements such as oxygen have a smaller density (in grams per cubic centimeter) than heavy elements such as iron. Write each of the following densities in scientific notation. Then order the elements from lightest to heaviest.
Hydrogen, Helium, Nitrogen, Oxygen, Chlorine

Element	Density	Order
Chlorine	0.00295	2.95×10^{-3}, 5 (heaviest)
Helium	0.0001664	1.664×10^{-4}, 2
Hydrogen	0.00008375	8.375×10^{-5}, 1 (lightest)
Nitrogen	0.001165	1.165×10^{-3}, 3
Oxygen	0.001332	1.332×10^{-3}, 4

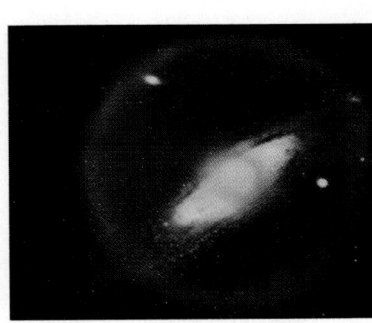

The Milky Way galaxy contains the sun, Earth, and the rest of the solar system. Its diameter is about 100,000 light-years. Can you find its diameter in miles?

39. *Milky Way*   Some stars in the Milky Way are 8×10^4 light-years from Earth. A light-year is 5.88×10^{12} miles. Write 8×10^4 light-years in miles. 4.704×10^{17}

Integrated Review   *Making Connections within Mathematics*

Geometry   **In Exercises 40 and 41, find the area of the figure.**

40.

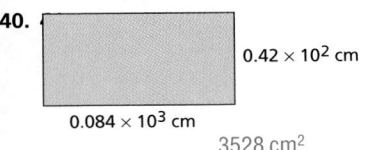

0.42×10^2 cm

0.084×10^3 cm

3528 cm²

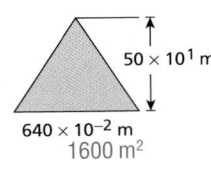

50×10^1 m

640×10^{-2} m
1600 m²

Exploration and Extension

Division   **In Exercises 42–44, divide. Explain your process.**

42. $\dfrac{3.6 \times 10^8}{1.2 \times 10^8}$ 3

43. $\dfrac{3.6 \times 10^8}{1.2 \times 10^7}$ 30

44. $\dfrac{3.6 \times 10^8}{1.2 \times 10^6}$ 300

Divide 3.6 by 1.2, divide 10^8 by the other power of 10, and multiply the two quotients.

✪ More difficult exercises

6.8 ▪ *Scientific Notation*   **277**

Make sure students follow the steps of each example on their calculators.

Students who have a graphing calculator may find a 10x key which can be used in Example 1.

Since the ability to interpret how a calculator displays very large numbers and very small positive numbers has a wide application in real-life situations, have students pay particular attention to Example 2.

Some scientific calculators can be used to write a number in scientific notation. For example, to write 354,000 in scientific notation, enter the following keystrokes:

354000 EE = .

The display should show 3.54 05, which represents 3.54×10^5.

With a scientific calculator, you may enter and display numbers whose absolute values are very small or very large using scientific notation.

Example 1   *Entering Numbers in Scientific Notation*

Number	Keystrokes	Display
8.75×10^{-15}	8.75 [EE] 15 [+/-]	8.75 -15
3.629×10^{12}	3.629 [EE] 12	3.629 12

With a scientific calculator, you enter the decimal portion of the number and the exponent. The base of 10 is not entered or displayed. Some scientific calculators have an [EXP] key instead of an [EE] key. ∎

Example 2   *Reading the Calculator Display*

Perform the indicated operation.

a. $232,000 \times 1,500,000$ **b.** $0.003 \div 1,500,000$

Solution

a. The calculator displays 3.48   11. Because it is understood that the base of the exponent is 10, the display is read as 3.48×10^{11} or "three and forty-eight hundredths times ten to the eleventh power."

b. The calculator displays 2 -09. The display is read as 2×10^{-9} or "two times ten to the negative ninth power." ∎

Exercises   1. 2.268×10^7 3. 1.107×10^{-11} 5. 5.697×10^{10}

In Exercises 1–8, write the result of the operation.

1. $(3.6 \times 10^4)(6.3 \times 10^2)$ **2.** $(9.83 \times 10^{10})(5.2 \times 10^8)$ 5.1116×10^{19}

3. $(1.35 \times 10^{-3})(8.2 \times 10^{-9})$ **4.** $(4.7 \times 10^{-7})(2.65 \times 10^{-5})$ 1.2455×10^{-11}

5. $(422,000)(135,000)$ **6.** $(9,364,000)(2150)$ 2.01326×10^{10}

7. $(0.014) \div (560,000)$ 2.5×10^{-8} **8.** $(9.12 \times 10^{-3}) \div (2.4 \times 10)$ 3.8×10^{-4}

P **9.** Use the power key as shown to evaluate the expressions in Exercises 2 and 8.

Exercise 2: 9.83 [×] 10 [yˣ] 10 [×] 5.2 [×] 10 [yˣ] 85.1116 × 10¹⁹

Exercise 8: 9.12 [×] 10 [yˣ] 3 [+/-] [÷] 2.4 [×] 10 3.8 × 10⁻²

What do you notice? Why is it a good idea to use the [EE] key, rather than the power key, when computing with scientific notation? The answer to Exercise 8 is different. The power key followed order of operations and evaluated $((9.12 \times 10^{-3}) \div 2.4) \times 10$.

6.9

Exploring Patterns

What you should learn:

Goal 1 How to recognize number patterns

Goal 2 How to recognize patterns in a coordinate plane

Why you should learn it:

Being able to recognize patterns helps you find the patterns in real-life processes.

Goal 1 Recognizing Number Patterns

In earlier lessons, you studied several number patterns.

Name	Numbers	Pattern
Square (1.3)	1, 4, 9, 16, 25, ...	n^2
Cubic (1.8)	1, 8, 27, 64, 125, ...	n^3
Triangular (1.8)	1, 3, 6, 10, 15, ...	$\frac{1}{2}n(n+1)$
Prime (6.2)	2, 3, 5, 7, 11, ...	None is known.
Fibonacci (1.8)	1, 1, 2, 3, 5, ...	Each (after 1, 1) is the sum of two previous numbers.

For thousands of years, people have studied number patterns. Some patterns are simple, but some are very difficult. No one has been able to write a formula for the nth prime number.

Example 1 *Perfect Numbers*

A natural number is called **perfect** if it is equal to the sum of its factors except itself. It is **deficient** if the sum of its factors, except itself, is less than the number, and it is **abundant** if the sum of its factors, except itself, is greater than the number. Classify the natural numbers from 2 through 12.

Solution

Number	Factors	Sum of Factors	Type
2	1	1	Deficient
3	1	1	Deficient
4	1, 2	$1 + 2 = 3$	Deficient
5	1	1	Deficient
6	1, 2, 3	$1 + 2 + 3 = 6$	Perfect
7	1	1	Deficient
8	1, 2, 4	$1 + 2 + 4 = 7$	Deficient
9	1, 3	$1 + 3 = 4$	Deficient
10	1, 2, 5	$1 + 2 + 5 = 8$	Deficient
11	1	1	Deficient
12	1, 2, 3, 4, 6	$1 + 2 + 3 + 4 + 6 = 16$	Abundant

Notice that the only perfect number in the table is 6. ∎

African Wall Painting
Women from Ghana use earth colors and bold geometric patterns for wall decorations.

▶ **PACING** the Lesson

Suggested Number of Days
Basic/Average 0   **Above Average** 0
Advanced 1

▶ **PLANNING** the Lesson

Lesson Plan 6.9, p. 50

ORGANIZER

Starters (reproduced below)
  Problem of the Day 6.9, p. 18
  Warm-Up Exercises 6.9, p. 18

Lesson Resources
  Math Log, p. 21
  Technology, p. 35
  Answer Masters 6.9, pp. 122, 123
  Extra Practice Copymaster 6.9, p. 50
  Reteaching Copymaster 6.9, p. 50
  Enrichment Projects, pp. 33, 34

Special Populations
  Suggestions, Teacher's Edition, p. 238D

LESSON Notes

Number patterns have been a source of amazement and amusement for hundreds of years. Secret societies whose members held the knowledge of special number patterns and relationships have existed throughout recorded history. Students may want to research one such famous society, known as the Pythagoreans.

Example 1

Have students discuss why most numbers seem to be deficient by this definition. Encourage their conjectures.

STARTER: Problem of the Day

Use six sticks to make four triangles, all of the same size.

Tetrahedron

Also available as a copymaster, page 18

STARTER: Warm-Up Exercises

1. Find all the factors.
a. 28   **b.** 56   **c.** 169
a. 1, 2, 4, 7, 14, 28; **b.** 1, 2, 4, 7, 8, 14, 28, 56; **c.** 1, 13, 169

2. Plot the points on a coordinate plane.
a. $(-3, -8)$ **b.** $(-2, 10)$
c. $(8, 12)$ **d.** $(6, -9)$
Check students' work.

Also available as a copymaster, page 18

Visual representations of patterns often have a more dramatic and satisfying effect than that provided by tables or equations. This is why it is important to investigate geometric patterns connected with algebraic relationships.

Example 2

Ask students how the four fractions in each part of the example are related to one another.   They are equivalent.

Communicating about MATHEMATICS

You may wish to extend the reasoning used in this section to *all* points on a line. The rational numbers formed by writing the *y*-coordinate of each point on a line as numerator and the corresponding *x*-coordinate as denominator are all equivalent, and this constant *ratio* is called the slope of the line.

Writing Prompt

Use a calculator to compute $x = \dfrac{1+\sqrt{5}}{2}$ and $y = \dfrac{2}{1+\sqrt{5}}$. How are *x* and *y* related?

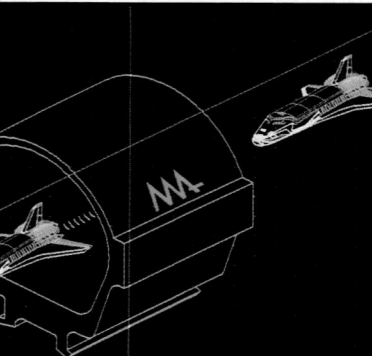

This art was produced on a computer. Computer programs that produce graphics such as this use coordinate systems to identify points on the computer screen.

Goal 2 **Patterns in a Coordinate Plane**

Geometry can help you find patterns among numbers. For instance, on page 39, geometry was used to find a pattern for triangular numbers.

Example 2   *Graphical Model for Rational Numbers*

For each of the following rational numbers, $\dfrac{a}{b}$, plot the ordered pair (b, a). Then describe the pattern.

a. $\dfrac{1}{2}, \dfrac{2}{4}, \dfrac{3}{6}, \dfrac{4}{8}$ b. $\dfrac{3}{-2}, \dfrac{-3}{2}, \dfrac{6}{-4}, \dfrac{-6}{4}$

Solution

a. For $\dfrac{1}{2}$, plot the point $(2, 1)$.

For $\dfrac{2}{4}$, plot the point $(4, 2)$.

For $\dfrac{3}{6}$, plot the point $(6, 3)$.

For $\dfrac{4}{8}$, plot the point $(8, 4)$.

From the coordinate plane at the right, you can see that all four points lie on a line.

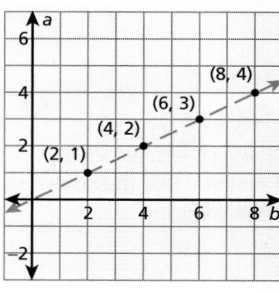

b. For $\dfrac{3}{-2}$, plot the point $(-2, 3)$.

For $\dfrac{-3}{2}$, plot the point $(2, -3)$.

For $\dfrac{6}{-4}$, plot the point $(-4, 6)$.

For $\dfrac{-6}{4}$, plot the point $(4, -6)$.

From the coordinate plane at the right, you can see that all four points lie on a line.

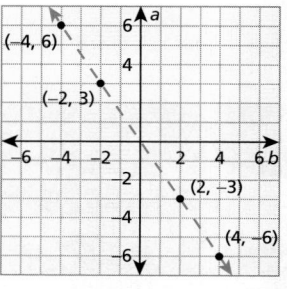

Communicating about MATHEMATICS

▶ **SHARING IDEAS about the Lesson**

Making a Conjecture In Part **a** of Example 2, each of the four points lies on a line. Each of the four rational numbers is equivalent. Use these observations to write a conjecture. Test your conjecture by choosing other equivalent rational numbers and plotting the points that correspond to them.

For equivalent rational numbers, $\dfrac{a}{b}$, the points (b, a) are collinear. Check students' work.

280   *Chapter 6* • *Exploring Number Theory*

Technology

| Patterns of Figurate Numbers | **6.9** | Name _____ |

Exploration Using a Spreadsheet

Figurate numbers are numbers that are associated with polygons. In Exercises 15–18 on page 281 of the textbook, you learned how to write figurate numbers geometrically. In this activity, you will use a spreadsheet program to generate the first ten triangular, square, pentagonal, and hexagonal numbers and discover patterns that exist between them. It is assumed that the user is familiar with the spreadsheet software.

Set up the spreadsheet as shown below. Copy the formulas in Column B to the corresponding cells in Columns C through K.

```
   A                    B  C  ...  J   K
1  n                    1  2  ...  9   10
2  Triangular Numbers  =B1*(B1+1)/2  3  ...  45  55
3  Square Numbers      =B1^2  4  ...  81  100
4  Pentagonal Numbers  =B1*(3*B1-1)/2  5  ...  117 145
5  Hexagonal Numbers   =B1*(4*B1-2)/2  6  ...  153 190
```

EXERCISES
See students' work. See table in back of supplement.
1. Complete the spreadsheet.

2. Describe the pattern that gives each type of figurate number.   Answers vary. One possible pattern is given for each type of number. Triangular: Product of *n* and *n* + 1 divided by 2. Square: Square of *n*. Pentagonal: Product of *n* and the quantity, 3 times *n* minus 1, divided by 2. Hexagonal: Product of *n* and the quantity, 4 times *n* minus 2, divided by 2.

3. Notice in Column D the sequence of numbers: 3, 6, 9, 12, and 15. Describe the pattern. Then describe the pattern that exists in each Column E, F, G, H, I, J, and K.
D: 3 more than previous; E: 6 more than previous; F: 10 more than previous; G: 15 more than previous; H: 21 more than previous; I: 28 more than previous; J: 36 more than previous; K: 45 more than previous.

4. Find the sum of the first two triangular numbers. What type of number results? Now find the sum of any two consecutive triangular numbers. What appears to be true about the sum of any two consecutive triangular numbers?
The sum of the first two triangular numbers is 4 which is a square number. The sum of any two consecutive triangular numbers is a square number.

5. There are other patterns that exist between sets of figurate numbers. Can you find any more?
Answers vary.

© D.C. Heath and Company   *Technology Using Calculators and Computers* **35**

EXERCISES

Guided Practice

▶ **CHECK for Understanding**

1. List all the factors of 28. Then use the factors to show that 28 is a perfect number. 1, 2, 4, 7, 14, 28; $1 + 2 + 4 + 7 + 14 = 28$

2. Complete the table.

n	1	2	3	4	5	6
$2n^2 + 1$	?	?	?	?	?	?

3, 9, 19, 33, 51, 73

In Exercises 3 and 4, use the coordinate plane at the right.

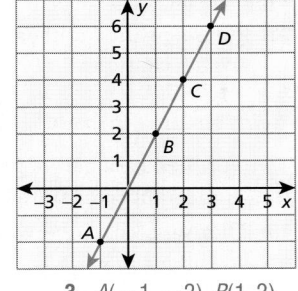

3. Identify the coordinate of points A, B, C, and D.

4. *A Coordinate Pattern* Describe the pattern of the coordinates. If the x-coordinate is 11, what is the y-coordinate?
Each y-coordinate is twice the x-coordinate, 22.

3. $A(-1, -2)$, $B(1, 2)$
$C(2, 4)$, $D(3, 6)$

Independent Practice

In Exercises 5–8, use the formula to construct a table similar to that shown in Exercise 2. See Additional Answers.

5. $n^2 + 1$ 6. $n^2 + n$ 7. 2^{n-1} 8. 2^{1-n}

Sequences **In Exercises 9–12, describe the pattern. Then list the next three terms in the sequence.** See margin.

9. 0, 3, 8, 15, ? ? ?

10. $1, \frac{1}{3}, \frac{1}{9}, \frac{1}{27},$? ? ?

11. 1, 2, 2, 4, 8, ? ? ?

12. 2, 4, 12, 48, 240, ? ? ?

13. *Fibonacci Sequence* The sequence 1, 1, 2, 4, 7, 13, 24, ... is similar to the Fibonacci sequence. Describe the pattern. Then list the next three terms. See margin.

14. *It's Up to You* Make up your own "Fibonacci-like" sequence. Answers vary.

Figurate Numbers **In Exercises 15–18, each figure represents a figurate number. Predict the next two numbers in the sequence. Then draw figures to check your predictions.** For figures, see Additional Answers.

15.
1   3   6   10   15, 21

16.
1   4   9   16   25, 36

17.
1   5   12   22   35, 51

18.
1   6   15   28   45, 66

✪ More difficult exercises
P Portfolio Opportunity

6.9 ▪ *Exploring Patterns*   **281**

EXERCISE Notes

ASSIGNMENT GUIDE

*Basic/Average:
Day 1: Ex. 5–17 odd, 19–22
Day 2: Ex. 23–26, 29–33

*Above Average:
Ex. 5–17 odd, 23–26, 29–33

Advanced: Ex. 5–17 odd, 23–26, 29–33

Selected Answers: Ex. 1–4, 5–29 odd
*You may wish to omit this lesson for these students.

Guided Practice

▶ **Ex. 1, 4** Extend the exercises by asking students to generate other patterns.

Independent Practice

▶ **Ex. 5–8**

Common-Error Alert!

Be aware that, having seen exponents that were sums (Lessons 6.7 and 6.8), students may confuse the expression $n^2 + 1$ with n^{2+1}.

▶ **Ex. 9–12** The patterns may be described by students in a variety of ways. Be careful to listen for equivalent descriptions and expressions.

▶ **Ex. 13, 14** A great deal has been written about the Fibonacci sequence. It is a good research project for students.

Answers

To get the next number:

9. Square the position number of the number and subtract 1, 24, 35, 48.

10. Divide the preceding number by 3, $\frac{1}{81}$, $\frac{1}{243}$, $\frac{1}{729}$

11. Multiply together the two preceding numbers, 32, 256, 8192

12. Multiply the preceding number by 2, by 3, by 4, etc. 1440; 10,080; 80,640

13. To get the next number after the first three, add the preceding three numbers, 44, 81, 149

Lesson 6.9   **281**

Extra Practice

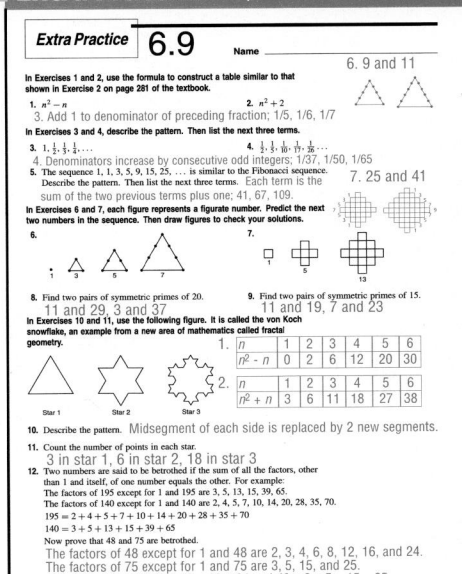

Extra Practice 6.9   Name

In Exercises 1 and 2, use the formula to construct a table similar to that shown in Exercise 2 on page 281 of the textbook.

1. $n^2 - n$ 2. $n^2 + 2$
3. Add 1 to denominator of preceding fraction; 1/5, 1/6, 1/7

In Exercises 3 and 4, describe the pattern. Then list the next three terms.

3. $1, \frac{1}{4}, \frac{1}{9}, \frac{1}{16}, \ldots$ 4. $\frac{1}{3}, \frac{1}{5}, \frac{1}{10}, \frac{1}{17}, \frac{1}{26}, \ldots$

4. Denominators increase by consecutive odd integers; 1/37, 1/50, 1/65

5. The sequence 1, 1, 3, 5, 9, 15, 25, ... is similar to the Fibonacci sequence. Describe the pattern. Then list the next three terms. Each term is the sum of the two previous terms plus one; 41, 67, 109.

In Exercises 6 and 7, each figure represents a figurate number. Predict the next two numbers in the sequence. Then draw figures to check your solutions.

6.
1   3   5

7. 25 and 41

8. Find two pairs of symmetric primes of 20. 11 and 29, 3 and 37

9. Find two pairs of symmetric primes of 15. 11 and 19, 7 and 23

In Exercises 10 and 11, use the following figure. It is called the von Koch snowflake, an example from a new area of mathematics called fractal geometry.

1.

n	1	2	3	4	5	6
$n^2 - n$	0	2	6	12	20	30

Star 1   Star 2   Star 3

2.

n	1	2	3	4	5	6
$n^2 + n$	3	6	11	18	27	38

10. Describe the pattern. Midsegment of each side is replaced by 2 new segments.

11. Count the number of points in each star. 3 in star 1, 6 in star 2, 18 in star 3

12. Two numbers are said to be betrothed if the sum of all the factors, other than 1 and itself, of one number equals the other. For example:
The factors of 195 except for 1 and 195 are 3, 5, 13, 15, 39, 65.
$195 = 2 + 4 + 5 + 7 + 10 + 14 + 20 + 28 + 35 + 70$
The factors of 140 except for 1 and 140 are 2, 4, 5, 7, 10, 14, 20, 28, 35, 70.
$140 = 3 + 5 + 13 + 15 + 39 + 65$
Now prove that 48 and 75 are betrothed.
The factors of 48 except for 1 and 48 are 2, 3, 4, 6, 8, 12, 16, and 24.
The factors of 75 except for 1 and 75 are 3, 5, 15, and 25.
$75 = 2 + 3 + 4 + 6 + 8 + 12 + 16 + 24$ and $48 = 3 + 5 + 15 + 25$

Reteaching

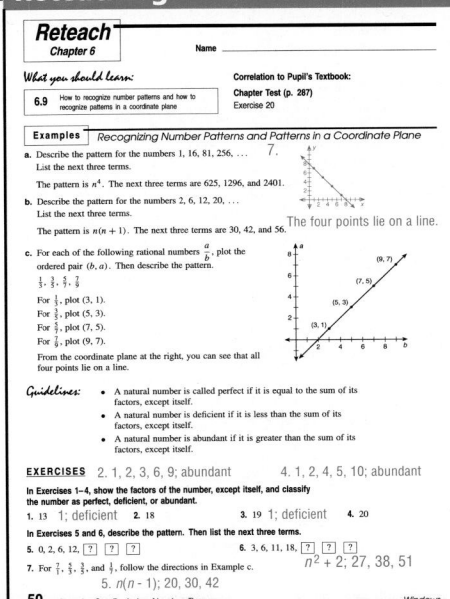

Reteach Chapter 6   Name

What you should learn:

6.9	How to recognize number patterns and how to recognize patterns in a coordinate plane

Correlation to Pupil's Textbook:
Chapter Test (p. 287)
Exercise 20

Examples *Recognizing Number Patterns and Patterns in a Coordinate Plane*

a. Describe the pattern for the numbers 1, 16, 81, 256, ...
List the next three terms.
The pattern is n^4. The next three terms are 625, 1296, and 2401.

b. Describe the pattern for the numbers 2, 6, 12, 20, ...
List the next three terms.
The pattern is $n(n + 1)$. The next three terms are 30, 42, and 56.

c. For each of the following rational numbers $\frac{a}{b}$, plot the ordered pair (b, a). Then describe the pattern.
$\frac{1}{3}, \frac{3}{5}, \frac{5}{7}, \frac{7}{9}$
For $\frac{1}{3}$, plot $(3, 1)$.
For $\frac{3}{5}$, plot $(5, 3)$.
For $\frac{5}{7}$, plot $(7, 5)$.
For $\frac{7}{9}$, plot $(9, 7)$.
From the coordinate plane at the right, you can see that all four points lie on a line.

The four points lie on a line.

Guidelines:
• A natural number is called perfect if it is equal to the sum of its factors, except itself.
• A natural number is deficient if it is less than the sum of its factors, except itself.
• A natural number is abundant if it is greater than the sum of its factors, except itself.

EXERCISES   2. 1, 2, 3, 6, 9; abundant   4. 1, 2, 4, 5, 10; abundant

In Exercises 1–4, show the factors of the number, except itself, and classify the number as perfect, deficient, or abundant.

1. 13   1; deficient   2. 18   3. 19   1; deficient   4. 20

In Exercises 5 and 6, describe the pattern. Then list the next three terms.

5. 0, 2, 6, 12, ? ? ?   6. 3, 6, 11, 18, ? ? ?
$n^2 + 2$; 27, 38, 51
7. For $\frac{7}{2}, \frac{5}{3}, \frac{3}{4},$ and $\frac{1}{5},$ follow the directions in Example c.
5. $n(n-1)$; 20, 30, 42

50   Chapter 6 ▪ Exploring Number Theory

Exploration and Extension

For the formula given in the textbook, here are several values of p that yield perfect numbers:

$p = 2 \rightarrow 6$
$p = 3 \rightarrow 28$
$p = 5 \rightarrow 496$
$p = 7 \rightarrow 8{,}128$
$p = 13 \rightarrow 33{,}550{,}336$

The twentieth perfect number was found in 1961. It contains 2,663 digits. There are 23 known perfect numbers. The largest of these is $2^{11{,}212}(2^{11{,}213} - 1)$, which has 6751 digits. (Historical Topics for the Classroom, NCTM, 1989)

Portfolio Opportunity: Math Log

A pair of numbers is called amicable if one number is equal to the sum of the factors of the other number (excluding the number itself), and vice versa. Verify that 220 and 284 are amicable.

Also available as a copymaster, page 21, Ex. 10

Alternative Assessment

A cooperative learning project that evaluates students' ability to recognize patterns and to work with powers.

Available as a copymaster, page 26

✪ **Symmetric Primes**   **In Exercises 19–22, use the following information.**

Let n be a natural number. Two primes are *symmetric primes of n* if their average is n. For instance, 7 and 13 are symmetric primes of 10 because the average of 7 and 13 is 10.

19. Find the other pair of symmetric primes of 10.   3 and 17

20. Explain why 2 and 18 are not symmetric primes of 10.   18 is not prime

21. List the six pairs of symmetric primes of 50.   47 and 53, 41 and 59, 29 and 71, 17 and 83, 11 and 89, 3 an

22. If n is a prime number, can it have a pair of symmetric primes? If so, give an example.   Yes, 3 and 7 are symmetric primes of 5.

✪ **Twin Primes**   **In Exercises 23–26, use the following information.**

Twin primes are a pair of prime numbers whose difference is 2. For instance, the prime numbers 3 and 5 are twin primes.

23. There are 8 pairs of twin primes that are less than 100. List all 8 pairs.   **23.–25.** See margin.

24. Find the average of each pair in Exercise 23. For instance, the average of 5 and 7 is 6. Except for 3 and 5, do you think that the average of each pair of twin primes is divisible by 6? Explain your reasoning.

25. Consider the following pairs of twin primes: 11 and 13, 41 and 43, and 71 and 73. Describe the pattern and determine the next pair. Is it a pair of twin primes?

26. Is the number 211 and another number a twin prime? Explain how you obtained your answer.   No, 209 is divisible by 11 and 213 is divisible by 3.

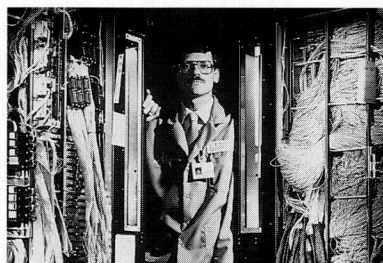

David Slowinski has designed software for Cray supercomputers to find prime numbers of the form $2^p - 1$, where p is prime. In 1994, his software produced the largest known prime number $2^{859{,}433} - 1$, a number that is 258,716 digits long.

Integrated Review   *Making Connections within Mathematics*

Factors   **In Exercises 27–33, list all the factors of the number.**

27. 20   1, 2, 4, 5, 10, 20   **28.** 42   1, 2, 3, 6, 7, 14, 21, 42   **29.** 72   1, 2, 3, 4, 6, 8, 9, 12, 18, 24, 36, 72   **30.** 90   1, 2, 3, 5, 6, 9, 10, 15, 18, 30, 45, 90

Exploration and Extension

✪ **Perfect Numbers**   **In Exercises 31–33, use the following information.**

The ancient Greeks were the first to discover perfect numbers. Every even perfect number is of the form $2^{p-1}(2^p - 1)$ where p and $2^p - 1$ are prime.

31. Complete the columns in the table for 2^{p-1} and $2^p - 1$ when $p = 5$. Is $2^p - 1$ a prime number?   16, 31; yes

32. Complete the last column to find the third perfect number.

33. List all the factors of the third perfect number and show the sum of the factors equals the number.   496   1, 2, 4, 8, 16, 31, 62, 124, 248, 496;

$1 + 2 + 4 + 8 + 16 + 31 + 62 + 124 + 248 = 496$

p	2^{p-1}	$2^p - 1$	$2^{p-1}(2^p - 1)$
2	2	3	6
3	4	7	28
5	?	?	?

Enrichment

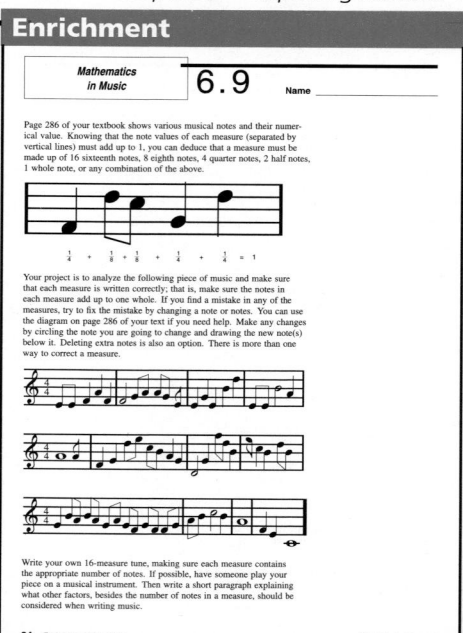

| Mathematics in Music | 6.9 | Name _____ |

Page 286 of your textbook shows various musical notes and their numerical value. Knowing that the note values of each measure (separated by vertical lines) must add up to 1, you can deduce that a measure must be made up of 16 sixteenth notes, 8 eighth notes, 4 quarter notes, 2 half notes, 1 whole note, or any combination of the above.

Your project is to analyze the following piece of music and make sure that each measure is written correctly; that is, make sure the notes in each measure add up to one whole. If you find a mistake in any of the measures, try to fix the mistake by changing a note or notes. You can use the diagram on page 286 of your text if you need help. Make any changes by circling the note you are going to change and drawing the new note(s) below it. Deleting extra notes is also an option. There is more than one way to correct a measure.

Write your own 16-measure tune, making sure each measure contains the appropriate number of notes. If possible, have someone play your piece on a musical instrument. Then write a short paragraph explaining what other factors, besides the number of notes in a measure, should be considered when writing music.

34   *Enrichment Projects*   ©︎ D.C. Heath and Company

Answers
23. 3 and 5, 5 and 7, 11 and 13, 17 and 19, 29 and 31, 41 and 43, 59 and 61, 71 and 73
24. The average of each pair in Exercise 23, respectively, is 4, 6, 12, 18, 30, 42, 60, and 72. Yes. If two numbers are twin primes, then they are symmetric primes of a number, n, that equals the average of the two numbers. Except for 3 and 5, the number n is apparently always divisible by 6.
25. To get the next twin primes, add 30 to each prime in the preceding twin primes. 101 and 103, yes

282   *Chapter 6*

6

Chapter Summary

What did you learn?

Why did you learn it?

Knowing properties of natural numbers helps you understand many different types of real-life situations. For instance, suppose you are an employer who is determining the annual salary of an employee. If you pay your employees each month, you would want the annual salary to be divisible by 12, but if you pay them each week, you would want the annual salary to be divisible by 52. Knowing how to use negative exponents, zero exponents, and scientific notation helps you solve problems that involve very large or very small numbers. For instance, if you become an astronomer, you will need to measure distances to other planets and other solar systems.

How does it fit into the bigger picture of mathematics?

Number theory is one of the oldest branches of mathematics. In this chapter, you learned the names of several types of numbers, such as prime numbers, composite numbers, and rational numbers. You also learned that each type of number has special properties. For instance, rational numbers are the only type of numbers whose decimal forms are either terminating or repeating.

SUMMARY and REVIEW

COOPERATIVE LEARNING

Encourage students to study together. Emphasize the importance of teaching a classmate how to perform a skill or how to recall a procedure. When students work together, everyone wins. The students receiving help get additional instruction, and the students giving help gain a deeper understanding of the skills and concepts involved.

Chapter SUMMARY

In this chapter, students were first introduced to the concept of divisibility, prime and composite numbers, and to the techniques of prime factorization. Students then learned how to find the Greatest Common Factor and the Least Common Multiple of sets of numbers and algebraic expressions. They were then introduced to techniques for simplifying and comparing fractions, to the concept of rational numbers, and to methods for expressing terminating or repeating decimals as rational numbers. Next, the concept of powers and exponents was broadened to include zero and negative exponents, and students learned the rules for multiplying and dividing powers. Scientific notation was introduced and used in the context of algebraic modeling.

Have students begin this Review in class and complete it as a homework assignment.

ASSIGNMENT GUIDE

*Basic/Average:
Ex. 21–55 odd, 61–67 odd, 69–79 odd, 88–92

*Above Average:
Ex. 21–55 odd, 61–67 odd, 69–79 odd, 88–92

Advanced:
Ex. 5–15 odd, 21–55 odd, 61–67 odd, 69–85 odd, 86, 88–92

*For these students, you will need to limit assignments to cover only those lessons you chose to teach from this chapter.

Resources

Transparencies
  Picture for Ex. 88, p. 27
  Graph for Ex. 77–80, p. 27
Answer Masters, pp. 124–126

In Exercises 1–8, use the Divisibility Tests to determine whether the number is divisible by 2, 3, 4, 5, 6, 8, 9, or 10. (6.1) Number is divisible by

1. 2560 2, 4, 5, 8, 10   **2.** 16,480 2, 4, 5, 8, 10   **3.** 342 2, 3, 6, 9   **4.** 4212 2, 3, 4, 6, 9

5. 245 5   **6.** 3845 5   **7.** 4968 2, 3, 4, 6, 8, 9   **8.** 2721 3

In Exercises 9–16, decide whether the number is prime or composite. If it is composite, list all its factors. (6.1, 6.2) For factors, see margin.

9. 15 Composite   **10.** 9 Composite   **11.** 13 Prime   **12.** 38 Composite

13. 46 Composite   **14.** 50 Composite   **15.** 64 Composite   **16.** 29 Prime

In Exercises 17–28, write the prime factorization of the expression. (6.2)

17. 80 $2^4 \cdot 5$ **18.** 96 $2^5 \cdot 3$ **19.** 120 $2^3 \cdot 3 \cdot 5$ **20.** 136 $2^3 \cdot 17$

21. -135 $(-1) \cdot 3^3 \cdot 5$ **22.** -252 $(-1) \cdot 2^2 \cdot 3^2 \cdot 7$ **23.** $40x^4$ $2^3 \cdot 5 \cdot x^4$ **24.** $108y^2$ $2^2 \cdot 3^3 \cdot y^2$

25. $12a^6b^2$ $2^2 \cdot 3 \cdot a^6 \cdot b^2$ **26.** $21p^3q$ $3 \cdot 7 \cdot p^3 \cdot q$ **27.** $-81st^5$ $(-1) \cdot 3^4 \cdot s \cdot t^5$ **28.** $-48m^4n^7$ $(-1) \cdot 2^4 \cdot 3 \cdot m^4 \cdot$

In Exercises 29–36, find the greatest common factor and the least common multiple. (6.3, 6.4)

29. 5, 15 5, 15   **30.** 8, 18 2, 72   **31.** 216, 240 24, 2160   **32.** 405, 450 45, 4050

33. $2x^4y^3, 4xy^8$ $2xy^3, 4x^4y^8$ **34.** $9ab^5, 18a^2b^3$ $9ab^3, 18a^2b^5$ **35.** $6y^5z^4, 14y^4z^5$ $2y^4z^4, 42y^5z^5$ **36.** $9mn^4, 12mn$ $3mn, 36mn^4$

In Exercises 37–44, simplify the expression. (6.5)

37. $\frac{4}{28}$ $\frac{1}{7}$ **38.** $\frac{5}{50}$ $\frac{1}{10}$ **39.** $\frac{8}{46}$ $\frac{4}{23}$ **40.** $\frac{12}{32}$ $\frac{3}{8}$

41. $\frac{2a^2b}{18a}$ $\frac{ab}{9}$ **42.** $\frac{7rs}{63r^2}$ $\frac{s}{9r}$ **43.** $\frac{36z}{54z^8}$ $\frac{2}{3z^7}$ **44.** $\frac{44x^4y}{99x^4y^3}$ $\frac{4}{9y^2}$

In Exercises 45–48, complete the statement with <, >, or =. (6.5)

45. $\frac{1}{3}$ ⬚ $\frac{1}{4}$ $>$ **46.** $\frac{2}{5}$ ⬚ $\frac{8}{20}$ $=$ **47.** $\frac{6}{14}$ ⬚ $\frac{21}{49}$ $=$ **48.** $\frac{26}{34}$ ⬚ $\frac{13}{17}$ $=$

In Exercises 49–56, decide whether the number is rational or irrational. Then write the number in decimal form and state whether the decimal is terminating, repeating, or nonrepeating. (6.6)

49., 51.–54., 56. Rational
50., 55. Irrational

49. $\frac{3}{18}$ $0.1\bar{6}$, repeat.   **50.** $\sqrt{11}$ $3.3166\ldots$, nonrepeat.   **51.** $-\frac{5}{8}$ $-.625$, term.   **52.** $\frac{15}{20}$ 0.75, term.

53. $\frac{18}{15}$ 1.2, term.   **54.** $-\frac{8}{9}$ $0.\bar{8}$, repeat.   **55.** $\sqrt{43}$ $6.5574\ldots$, nonrepeat.   **56.** $\frac{29}{27}$ $1.\overline{074}$, repeat.

In Exercises 57–68, simplify the expression. (6.7)

57. 4^{-1} $\frac{1}{4}$ **58.** $(-5)^{-3}$ $-\frac{1}{125}$ **59.** $(-7)^{-2}$ $\frac{1}{49}$ **60.** 12^0 1

61. x^{-4} $\frac{1}{x^4}$ **62.** $(-y)^{-2}$ $\frac{1}{y^2}$ **63.** $3^{-4} \cdot 3$ $\frac{1}{27}$ **64.** $\frac{8^5}{8^3}$ 64

65. $-10a^5 \cdot 10a$ $-100a^6$ **66.** $2y^7 \cdot 4x^9y^2$ $8x^9y^9$ **67.** $\frac{6m^4n^5}{3m^6n}$ $\frac{2n^4}{m^2}$ **68.** $\frac{9r^2st}{15r^2s^6}$ $\frac{3t}{5s^5}$

284 *Chapter **6** ▪ Exploring Number Theory*

Answers
 9. 1, 3, 5, 15
10. 1, 3, 9
12. 1, 2, 19, 38
13. 1, 2, 23, 46
14. 1, 2, 5, 10, 25, 50
15. 1, 2, 4, 8, 16, 32, 64

In Exercises 69–72, write the number in decimal form. (6.8)

69. 3.9×10^7
39,000,000

70. 6.8×10^{-6}
0.0000068

71. 9.46×10^{-4}
0.000946

72. 7.52×10^5
752,000

In Exercises 73–76, write the number in scientific notation. (6.8)

73. 1,200,000,000
1.2×10^9

74. 456,000
4.56×10^5

75. 0.00045
4.5×10^{-4}

76. 0.0000592
5.92×10^{-5}

In Exercises 77–80, find the product. Write the result in scientific notation. (6.8)

77. $(1.5 \times 10^3)(2.5 \times 10^4)$ 3.75×10^7

78. $(2.4 \times 10^{-1})(5.0 \times 10^8)$ 1.2×10^8

79. $(1.0 \times 10^{-8})(1.0 \times 10^8)$ 1.0×10^0

80. $(3.6 \times 10^{-4})(2.0 \times 10^{-2})$ 7.2×10^{-6}

Sequences　**In Exercises 81–84, describe the pattern. Then write the next three terms in the sequence. (6.9)**　For descriptions, see margin.

81. $\frac{1}{2}, \frac{1}{3}, \frac{1}{4}, \frac{1}{5}, \boxed{?}\ \boxed{?}\ \boxed{?}$　$\frac{1}{6}, \frac{1}{7}, \frac{1}{8}$

82. $-\frac{1}{2}, -\frac{2}{3}, -\frac{3}{4}, -\frac{4}{5}, \boxed{?}\ \boxed{?}\ \boxed{?}$　$-\frac{5}{6}, -\frac{6}{7}, -\frac{7}{8}$

83. $-\frac{7}{1}, -\frac{6}{2}, -\frac{5}{3}, -\frac{4}{4}, \boxed{?}\ \boxed{?}\ \boxed{?}$　$-\frac{3}{5}, -\frac{2}{6}, -\frac{1}{7}$

84. $\frac{1}{2}, \frac{1}{4}, \frac{1}{6}, \frac{1}{8}, \boxed{?}\ \boxed{?}\ \boxed{?}$　$\frac{1}{10}, \frac{1}{12}, \frac{1}{14}$

85. *Number Sense*　Is it possible to find a number that is divisible by 2 and not divisible by 4? If so, give an example. **(6.1)**　Yes, 2

⭐ **86.** *Number Sense*　Is it possible to find a number that is divisible by 4 and not divisible by 2? If so, give an example. **(6.1)**　No

87. *Bring on the Sun*　A survey was conducted to determine how important "a lot of sun" is to people when selecting a vacation spot. The table shows the fractions of the people who answered "very," "not very," and "not at all." Write each fraction as a decimal. What do you notice about the sum of the fractions? (*Source: USA Today*) **(6.5, 6.6)**　Sum is 1.

How Important?	Fraction	
Very	$\frac{69}{100}$	0.69
Not very	$\frac{16}{100}$	0.16
Not at all	$\frac{15}{100}$	0.15

88. *World Waters*　The table below shows the names of some oceans and seas of the world and their areas in square miles. Write each area in scientific notation. **(6.8)**

Ocean or Sea	Area (in square miles)	
Pacific	64,186,000	6.4186×10^7
Atlantic	33,420,000	3.342×10^7
Indian	28,350,000	2.835×10^7
Arctic	5,105,000	5.105×10^6
Caribbean	971,400	9.714×10^5

Earth contains about 140 million square miles of water, which is about $\frac{7}{10}$ of its total surface.

⭐ More difficult exercises

Answers
To get the next number:
81. Add 1 to the preceding denominator.
82. Add 1 to the absolute values of both the numerator and the denominator of the preceding number and keep the negative sign.
83. Subtract 1 from the absolute value of the numerator of the preceding number, add 1 to the absolute value of the denominator of the preceding number, and keep the negative sign.
84. Add 2 to the preceding denominator.

Chapter 6 Review　**285**

Real Lif
Connectic

Musical Notes   In Exercises 89–92, use the diagram of musical notes.

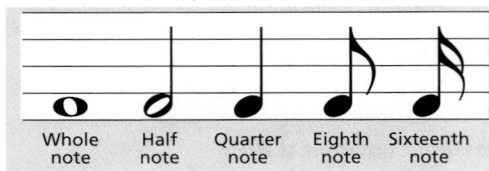

| Whole note | Half note | Quarter note | Eighth note | Sixteenth note |

Note	Number of Beats
Half	2
Dotted half	3
Quarter	1
Dotted quarter	$1\frac{1}{2}$
Eighth	$\frac{1}{2}$
Dotted eighth	$\frac{3}{4}$
Sixteenth	$\frac{1}{4}$
Dotted sixteenth	$\frac{3}{8}$

89. Write the names of the notes as fractions. $\frac{1}{1}, \frac{1}{2}, \frac{1}{4}, \frac{1}{8}, \frac{1}{16}$

90. Describe the pattern of the fractions in Exercise 89.

91. If a whole note is held for four beats and a half note is held for two beats, how long would you hold a quarter note, an eighth note, and a sixteenth note?

⭐ 92. Describe the pattern of the beats of the notes in Exercise 91.   **91.** 1 beat, $\frac{1}{2}$ beat, $\frac{1}{4}$ beat,

90., 92. See margin.

Use this table with Exercises 93 and 94.

Dotted Notes   In Exercises 93 and 94, use the following diagram and the table at the upper right.

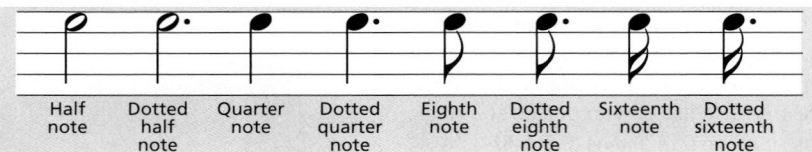

| Half note | Dotted half note | Quarter note | Dotted quarter note | Eighth note | Dotted eighth note | Sixteenth note | Dotted sixteenth note |

93. Dotting a note changes the number of beats that the note is held. The number of beats to hold a note and its related dotted note are given in the table above. How does the dot change the length of time a note is held?   It adds $\frac{1}{2}$ the length of time.

⭐ 94. Describe the pattern for the number of beats of the dotted-half note, dotted-quarter note, dotted-eighth note, and dotted-sixteenth note.

Each number of beats after the first is $\frac{1}{2}$ the preceding number of beats.

Reading Music   In Exercises 95 and 96, use the musical phrase below.

95. 2, 1, 1 occurs four times.   **96.** See margin.

⭐ 95. Describe a pattern for the number of beats for the notes in this phrase.

⭐ 96. Describe a pattern for the position of the notes on the musical staff.

⭐ 97. If you can play an instrument or read music, create your own musical compositions. Describe any patterns used in creating your piece.
Answers vary.

⭐ More difficult exercises

Answers
90. Each fraction after the first is $\frac{1}{2}$ the preceding one.
92. Each number of beats after the first is $\frac{1}{2}$ the preceding number of beats.
96. The first three positions of the notes are followed by the same three positions in reverse order, then that 6-position sequence is repeated one position higher.

1. Use the divisibility tests to decide whether 1224 is divisible by 2, 3, 4, 5, 6, 8, 9, or 10. **(6.1)** Yes: 2, 3, 4, 6, 8, 9; No: 5, 10

2. Decide whether 1224 is divisible by 11, 12, 13, 14, 15, 16, 17, 18, 19, or 20. **(6.1)** Yes: 12, 17, 18; No: 11, 13, 14, 15, 16, 19, 20

In Exercises 3 and 4, write the prime factorization of the number. (6.2)

3. 120 $2^3 \cdot 3 \cdot 5$

4. 125 5^3

In Exercises 5 and 6, write the prime factorization of the expression. (6.2)

5. $99ab$ $3^2 \cdot 11 \cdot a \cdot b$

6. $121x^2$ $11^2 \cdot x^2$

In Exercises 7 and 8, find the greatest common factor. (6.3)

7. 48, 36 12

8. 56, 98 14

In Exercises 9–11, find the least common multiple. (6.4)

9. 10, 35 70

10. 5, 18 90

11. 7, 10, 14 70

12. Simplify the fraction $\frac{20}{800}$. **(6.5)** $\frac{1}{40}$

13. Decide which fraction is larger: $\frac{3}{11}$ or $\frac{5}{22}$. **(6.5)** $\frac{3}{11}$

14. Write 0.65 as a fraction and simplify. **(6.5, 6.6)** $\frac{65}{100}, \frac{13}{20}$

15. Simplify the expression $x^9 \cdot x^{-4}$. **(6.7)** x^5

In Exercises 16–19, match the scientific notation with its decimal form. (6.8)

a. 0.00016

b. 0.016

c. 160

d. 16,000

16. 1.6×10^4 d

17. 1.6×10^{-4} a

18. 1.6×10^{-2} b

19. 1.6×10^2 c

20. The first 3 square numbers are represented below. Draw the next 2 square numbers. **(6.9)** See margin.

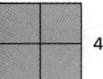 4 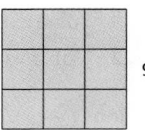 9  16

In Exercises 21–23, use the following information. (6.8)

Scientists have measured the speed of light to be about 300,000 kilometers per second. It takes light about 500 seconds to travel from the sun to Earth. 3×10^5 kilometers per second

21. Write the speed of light in scientific notation.

22. Write the time (in seconds) that it takes light to travel from the sun to Earth in scientific notation. 5×10^2 seconds

23. Approximate the distance between the sun and Earth by simplifying the following expression. 1.5×10^8 kilometers

$$\text{Distance} = \left(300{,}000\ \frac{\text{kilometers}}{\text{second}}\right)(500 \text{ seconds}).$$

It takes light about 8 minutes and 20 seconds to travel from the sun to Earth. Direct sunlight can be harmful to the eyes.

Chapter Test

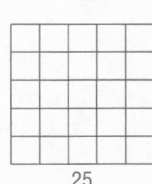

Chapter 6 Test | **Form C**
(Page 1 of 3 pages)

Name _____
Date _____

In Exercises 1–3, use the number 23,87⌊?⌋. (6.1)

1. Which digit would make the number divisible by 9? 1. _7_

2. Which digit would make the number divisible by 8? 2. _2_

3. If you used the last digit you found in Exercise 2, by which other digits would the completed number be divisible? 3. _2 and 4_

4. State a rule for divisibility by 15. (6.1) 4. Possible answer: The number ends in 0 or 5 and the sum of its digits is divisible by 3.

5. A box has a volume of 30 cubic units (Volume = length × width × height). List the factors of 30. Use the list to identify three possible dimensions for the length, width, and height of the box.(6.2) 5. 1, 2, 3, 5, 6, 10, 15, 30 Possible dimensions: 2 × 5 × 3; 1 × 10 × 3; 5 × 6 × 1, etc.

In Exercises 6 and 7, draw a tree diagram to show the prime factorization. Then write the prime factorization in exponent form. (6.2)

6. 60 6. $2^2 \cdot 3 \cdot 5$

7. 192 7. $2^6 \cdot 3$

In Exercises 8 and 9, write the expanded form and the exponent form of the expression. (6.2)

8. $32ab^4c^5$ $2 \cdot 2 \cdot 2 \cdot 2 \cdot 2 \cdot a \cdot b \cdot b \cdot b \cdot b \cdot c \cdot c \cdot c \cdot c \cdot c$; 8. $2^5 \cdot a \cdot b^4 \cdot c^5$

9. $-54t^2uv^3$ 9. _____ $-1 \cdot 2 \cdot 3 \cdot 3 \cdot 3 \cdot t \cdot t \cdot u \cdot v \cdot v \cdot v$, $-1 \cdot 2 \cdot 3^3 \cdot t^2 \cdot u \cdot v^3$

96 *Chapter 6 • Exploring Number Theory* © D.C. Heath and Company *Windows*

Answer 20.

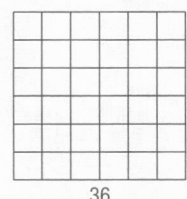 25 36

◄ Formal Assessment

Three **Chapter Tests.** Form A is of average difficulty, Form B is of average difficulty in multiple choice format, and Form C is more challenging.

Available as copymasters, pages 90–98

For descriptions and drawings, see margin.

Geometric Patterns In Exercises 1 and 2, describe the pattern and draw the next figure. Then write an expression for the perimeter of the regular polygon and evaluate the expression when $x = 2$. (1.7, 2.2)

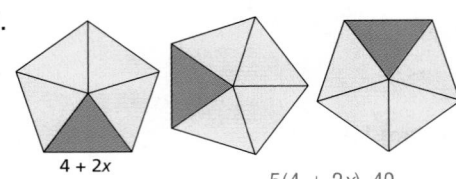

1. $4 + 2x$ $5(4 + 2x), 40$

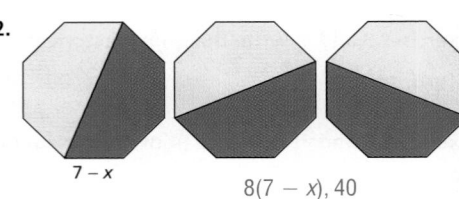

2. $7 - x$ $8(7 - x), 40$

In Exercises 3–10, use a calculator to evaluate the expression. Round to two decimal places if necessary. (1.3, 1.4)

3. 5^7 78,125

4. $\left(\frac{4}{9}\right)^4$ 0.04

5. $\sqrt{84}$ 9.17

6. $(5^4 - 20) \div 11 + 9$ 64

7. $\sqrt{512}$ 22.63

8. $(6.3)^6$ 62,523.50

9. $\sqrt{17.82}$ 4.22

10. $2^5 + (24 - 6) \cdot 3$ 86

In Exercises 11–16, evaluate the expression. (1.4, 3.1–3.6)

11. $-|-8| + 17 - 13 - 5$ -9

12. $|-6| - 9 - 4 + 21$ 14

13. $(-5)(3)(-6)(-2)$ -180

14. $\frac{-625}{-5}$ 125

15. $4^3 + (2 - 7)^2 \div 5$ 69

16. $32 - (4 - 7)^3 \cdot 3$ 113

In Exercises 17–22, match the term or property with its definition. (1.5, 2.1, 2.4, 2.5)

a. A collection of numbers, variables, operations, and grouping symbols

b. A letter used to represent one or more numbers

c. $ab + ac = a(b + c)$

d. $a(bc) = (ab)c$

e. $a + b = b + a$

f. Replacing a variable by a number

17. Variable   b

18. Distributive Property   c

19. Substitution   f

20. Associative Property   d

21. Algebraic expression   a

22. Commutative Property   e

In Exercises 23–28, write the expression without parentheses and combine like terms when possible. Then evaluate it when $x = -2$, $y = 4$, and $z = 5$. (3.1–3.5)

23. $5(x + y + z)$ $5x + 5y + 5z, 35$

24. $-4(x - y + 2z)$ $-4x + 4y - 8z, -16$

25. $3y - 6x + 3z - 5y$ $-2y - 6x + 3z, 19$

26. $-2(4x + 3x + y)$ $-14x - 2y, 20$

27. $-7 + x(z + y)$ $-7 + xz + xy, -25$

28. $2(3z - z) - |-y|$ $4z - |y|, 16$

In Exercises 29–36, write an algebraic equation or inequality for the sentence. Then solve. (2.3–2.5, 2.7, 2.9, 3.7)   See margin.

29. -18 is the difference of x and 9.

30. The sum of n and 16 is 3.

31. The product of y and -8 is -104.

32. 12 is the quotient of y and 4.

33. 5 is greater than or equal to the quotient of a and 13.

34. The difference of b and 8 is greater than or equal to -15.

35. -5 is less than the sum of z and 9.

36. 147 is greater than the product of m and 7.

Answers

1. To get the next polygon, rotate it 90° clockwise.

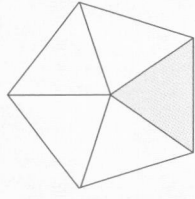

2. To get the next polygon, rotate it 45° clockwise.

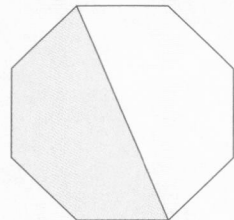

29. $-18 = x - 9, -9$
30. $n + 16 = 3, -13$
31. $-8y = -104, 13$
32. $12 = \frac{y}{4}, 48$

33. $5 \geq \frac{a}{13}, a \leq 65$
34. $b - 8 \geq -15, b \geq -7$
35. $-5 < z + 9, z > -14$
36. $147 > 7m, m < 21$

Cumulative Test

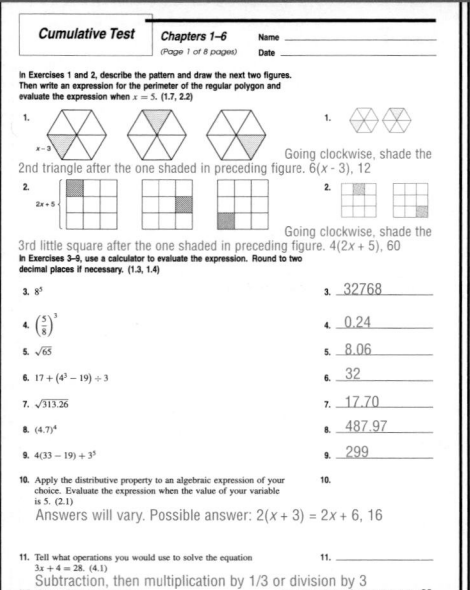

Coordinate Geometry **In Exercises 37–40, plot the points in a coordinate plane. Connect the points to form a rectangle. Then find the perimeter and area of the rectangle. (3.8)** See margin.

37. $(-2, 2), (-2, 4), (-4, 2), (-4, 4)$ **38.** $(1, 1), (6, 1), (1, -2), (6, -2)$

39. $(0, -1), (0, -4), (-3, -1), (-3, -4)$ **40.** $(-2, 3), (-6, 3), (-2, 0), (-6, 0)$

41. *Problem-Solving Plan* Order the steps (from 1 through 6) of the problem-solving plan. **(2.8)**

- Solve. 4
- Check your answer. 6
- Answer the question. 5
- Write a verbal model. 1
- Assign labels. 2
- Write an algebraic model. 3

UPC Code **In Exercises 42–45, use the following information to decide whether the UPC code checks. Explain your reasoning.** For explanations, see margin.

Most retail products contain a bar code called the Universal Product Code (UPC), as shown at the right. When a computer scanner reads a bar code, the computer checks the code using the following steps.

- Add the digits in the odd-numbered positions together. Multiply by 3.
- Add the digits in the even-numbered positions together.
- Add the results of steps 1 and 2.
- Subtract the result of step 3 from the next highest multiple of 10.

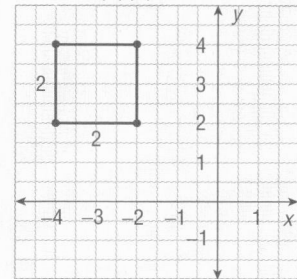

0 28400 01869 2

Check digit

$3(0 + 8 + 0 + 0 + 8 + 9) +$
$(2 + 4 + 0 + 1 + 6) = 88$

The next highest multiple of 10 is 90. Therefore, $90 - 88 = 2$, which is the check digit.

42. 0 43699 20450 2 Yes **43.** 0 35902 11234 9 No

44. 0 25401 42232 1 No **45.** 0 38322 56613 3 Yes

46. *Operation Sense* Identify the inverse of each operation. **(4.1)**

a. Addition **b.** Subtraction **c.** Multiplication **d.** Division
   Subtraction Addition Division Multiplication

Mental Math **In Exercises 47 and 48, what operation would you use to solve the equation? (4.1)**

47. $x - 4 = 18$ Addition **48.** $3x = 27$ Division by 3 or multiplication by $\frac{1}{3}$

In Exercises 49–52, find the reciprocal of the number. (4.3)

49. 5 $\frac{1}{5}$ **50.** -1 -1 **51.** $-\frac{1}{4}$ -4 **52.** $\frac{2}{9}$ $\frac{9}{2}$

In Exercises 53–58, solve the equation. Then check your solution. (4.1, 4.2)

53. $6x - 17 = 7$ 4 **54.** $4y + 13 = -19$ -8 **55.** $-\frac{n}{7} + 9 = 5$ 28

56. $8m + 3m - 2 = 9$ 1 **57.** $\frac{3}{4}z - \frac{1}{4}z + 6 = 12$ 12 **58.** $15t + 14 - 7t = 30$ 2

Cumulative Review **289**

Answers

37. Perimeter = 4(2) = 8 units
Area = (2)(2) = 4 units²

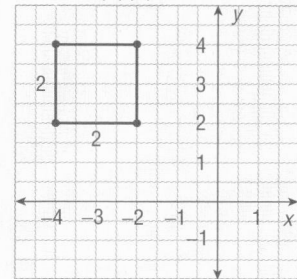

38. Perimeter = 2(5) + 2(3) = 16 units
Area = (3)(5) = 15 units²

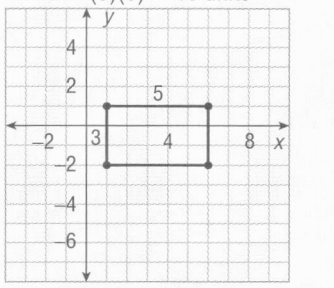

39. Perimeter = 4(3) = 12 units
Area = (3)(3) = 9 units²

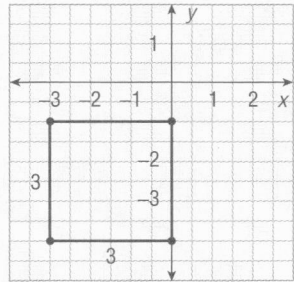

40. Perimeter = 2(4) + 2(3) = 14 units
Area = (4)(3) = 12 units²

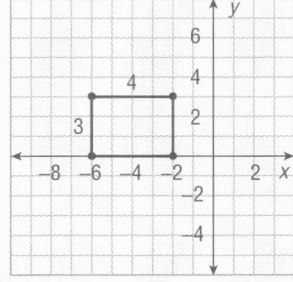

42. $3(0 + 3 + 9 + 2 + 4 + 0) + (4 + 6 + 9 + 0 + 5) = 78, 80 - 78 = 2$

43. $3(0 + 5 + 0 + 1 + 2 + 4) + (3 + 9 + 2 + 1 + 3) = 54, 60 - 54 = 6 \neq 9$

44. $3(0 + 5 + 0 + 4 + 2 + 2) + (2 + 4 + 1 + 2 + 3) = 51, 60 - 51 = 9 \neq 1$

45. $3(0 + 8 + 2 + 5 + 6 + 3) + (3 + 3 + 2 + 6 + 1) = 87, 90 - 87 = 3$

Geometry In Exercises 59 and 60, write an equation that equates the sum of the measures of the angles of the triangle to 180°. Then solve for *x* and find the measures of each angle. **(4.4)**

59.

54°
2x − 10°
90° 3x − 6° x + 4° 36°
$(2x − 10°) + (3x − 6°) + (x + 4°) = 180°, 32°$

60.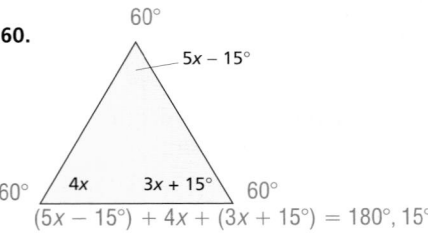

60°
5x − 15°
60° 4x 3x + 15° 60°
$(5x − 15°) + 4x + (3x + 15°) = 180°, 15°$

Distributive Property In Exercises 61–64, simplify the expression. **(4.4)**

61. $3x + 2(x + 1)$ $5x + 2$

62. $4(y − 1) − 2y$ $2y − 4$

63. $−3n + 2(4n − 5)$ $5n − 10$

64. $−5(6s − 3) + 7s$ $−23s + 15$

In Exercises 65–72, solve the equation. Then check your solution. **(4.4, 4.5)**

65. $10y − 27 = y$ 3

66. $13x − 80 = 60 − 7x$ 7

67. $18x + 53 = 4x − 31$ $−6$

68. $5t + 3t + 15 = 39$ 3

69. $3(4t + 3) = 2t$ $−\frac{9}{10}$

70. $b + 6 = 2(b − 2)$ 10

71. $2(4n + \frac{1}{2}) = 10n$ $\frac{1}{2}$

72. $3(y − 2) + 2 = −y$ 1

In Exercises 73 and 74, solve the equation. Round the result to 2 decimal places. **(4.7)**

73. $15x − 21 = −42x + 89$ 1.93

74. $14.1(2.37y + 5.6) = 0.71y − 29.3$ $−3.31$

75. Geometry Find the area of a triangle with height 4 inches and base 3 inches. **(4.8)** 6 in.^2

76. Geometry Find the area of a square that has a perimeter of 36 centimeters. **(4.8)** 81 c

Population In Exercises 77–80, use the graph at the right, which shows the populations (in millions) of males and females in the United States for 1920 through 1990. In the graph, t = 0 represents 1920. *(Source: U.S. Bureau of Census)* **(5.3, 5.5)**

78. 91 million   Yes
77. Does each graph increase during each decade?

78. Estimate the female population in 1960.

79. During which decade did the female population first exceed the male population?
1940's
80. Is this graph misleading? Explain.
Yes, the vertical scale is broken.

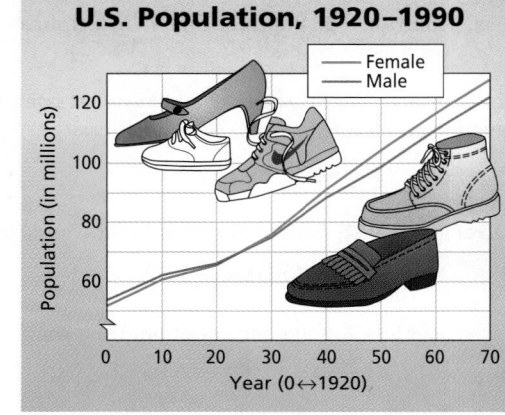

U.S. Population, 1920–1990

Female
Male

Population (in millions)

120
100
80
60

0 10 20 30 40 50 60 70
Year (0↔1920)

Gas Mileage In Exercises 81–84, use the scatter plot at the right, which compares the speed and gas mileage of a typical automobile. (5.7)

81. Do the speed and gas mileage have a positive correlation, a negative correlation, or no correlation? Explain your reasoning.

82. Write a sentence that describes the relationship between speed and gas mileage.

83. Estimate the gas mileage for a speed of 60 miles per hour.   27 mpg

84. Estimate the speed that corresponds to the maximum gas mileage.   45 mph

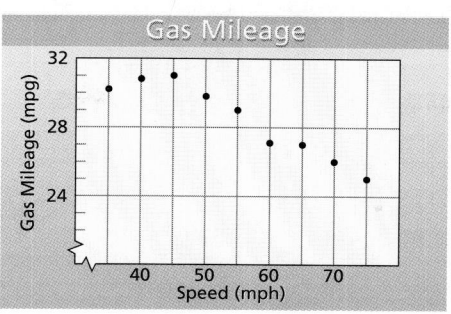

81., 82., 85. See margin.

85. **Radio Stations** The table lists the number of types of radio stations in the United States in 1991. Represent this data graphically. *(Source: Radio Information Center)* (5.4)

Type of Music	Number of Stations
Country	2314
Adult Contemporary	1898
Golden Oldies	729
Contemporary Hits	705
Easy Listening	268
Soft Contemporary	182
Classic Rock	127

Probability In Exercises 86–88, find the probability that the spinner will land on the given color. (5.8)

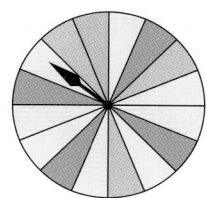

86. Blue $\frac{1}{16}$ 87. Red   0   88. Orange $\frac{3}{16}$

89. What is the probability that the spinner will not land on green? $\frac{3}{4}$

In Exercises 90–95, find the greatest common factor and least common multiple. (6.2–6.4)

90. 7, 49   7, 49

91. 4, 18   2, 36

92. 270, 450   90, 1350

93. 864, 972   108, 7776

94. $6x^2y, 8xy^3$ $2xy, 24x^2y^3$

95. $9a^2b, 12ab^4$ $3ab, 36a^2b^4$

In Exercises 96–99, simplify the fraction. Then write in decimal form. Round your answer to 3 decimal places, if necessary. (6.5, 6.6)

96. $\frac{6}{48}$ $\frac{1}{8}$, 0.125

97. $\frac{25}{45}$ $\frac{5}{9}$, 0.556

98. $\frac{10}{15}$ $\frac{2}{3}$, 0.667

99. $\frac{52}{54}$ $\frac{26}{27}$, 0.963

In Exercises 100–107, simplify the expression. (6.7)

100. 5^0 1

101. 3^{-2} $\frac{1}{9}$

102. a^{-4} $\frac{1}{a^4}$

103. $\frac{x}{x^3}$ $\frac{1}{x^2}$

104. $\frac{8a}{10a^2}$ $\frac{4}{5a}$

105. $4^2 \cdot 4^{-2}$ 1

106. $\frac{3^4}{3^5}$ $\frac{1}{3}$

107. $\frac{10^0}{10^4}$ $\frac{1}{10,000}$

108. Write 1.45×10^4 in decimal form.
   14,500

109. Write 0.000052 in scientific notation.
   5.2×10^{-5}

Answers
81. There appears to be a positive correlation between 35 mph and 45 mph because the gas mileage increases as the speed increases. There appears to be a negative correlation between 45 mph and 75 mph because the gas mileage decreases as the speed increases.
82. As the speed increases to 45 mph the gas mileage increases; and as the speed increases beyond 45 mph, the gas mileage decreases.
85.

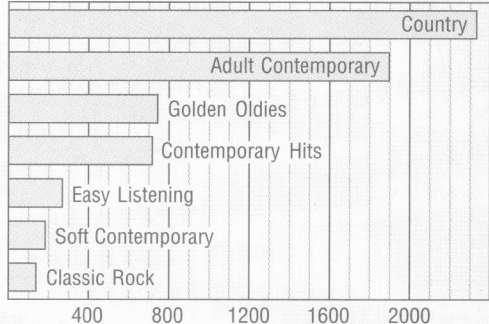

CHAPTER 7 GOALS

Lesson	Pages	Goals	Meeting the NCTM Standards
7.1	294–297	1. Add like fractions 2. Subtract like fractions	Problem Solving, Communication, Connections, Computation and Estimation, Technology
Lesson Investigation 7.2	298	A Model for Adding and Subtracting Fractions	Computation and Estimation
7.2	299–302	1. Add and subtract unlike fractions 2. Use addition and subtraction of fractions to solve real-life problems	Problem Solving, Communication, Connections, Computation and Estimation, Technology, Patterns and Functions, Algebra, Statistics, Geometry, Measurement
7.3	303–306	1. Add and subtract fractions by writing the fractions as decimals 2. Use addition and subtraction of decimals to solve real-life problems	Problem Solving, Communication, Connections, Number Relationships, Computation and Estimation, Technology, Algebra, Statistics, Geometry, Measurement
Mixed Review	307	Review of arithmetic, algebra, and geometry	Number Relationships, Computation and Estimation
Career Interview	307	Plumber	Connections
7.4	308–311	1. Multiply rational numbers 2. Use multiplication of rational numbers to solve real-life problems	Problem Solving, Communication, Connections, Number Relationships, Computation and Estimation, Technology, Algebra, Geometry, Measurement
7.5	312–315	1. Divide rational numbers 2. Use division of rational numbers to solve real-life problems	Problem Solving, Communication, Number Relationships, Computation and Estimation, Patterns and Functions, Algebra, Geometry, Measurement
Mid-Chapter Self-Test	316	Diagnose student weaknesses and remediate with correlated Reteaching Copymasters	Assessment
Lesson Investigation 7.6	317	Modeling Portions of Regions	Number Relationships, Geometry, Measurement
7.6	318–321	1. Write portions as percents 2. Use percents to solve real-life problems	Communication, Connections, Number Relationships, Computation and Estimation, Geometry
7.7	322–326	1. Write percents as decimals and write decimals as percents 2. Write fractions as percents and write percents as fractions	Communication, Connections, Number Relationships, Computation and Estimation, Statistics, Geometry
Mixed Review	326	Review of arithmetic, algebra, and geometry	Connections, Algebra, Probability
7.8	327–330	1. Find a percent of a number 2. Use percents to solve real-life problems	Problem Solving, Communication, Connections, Number Relationships, Computation and Estimation, Technology, Patterns and Functions, Geometry, Measurement
Using a Spreadsheet or a Graphing Calculator	331	Interest in a Savings Account	Connections, Computation and Estimation, Technology, Algebra
7.9	332–335	1. Use percents to solve real-life problems 2. Use percents to help organize data	Problem Solving, Communication, Reasoning, Connections, Computation and Estimation, Statistics
Chapter Summary	336	A restatement of what has been learned, why it has been learned, and how it fits into the structure of mathematics	Communication, Connections
Chapter Review	337–340	Review of concepts and skills learned in the chapter	Problem Solving, Connections
Chapter Test	341	Diagnose student weaknesses and remediate with correlated Reteaching Copymasters	Assessment

RESOURCES ORGANIZER

Lesson Pages	7.1 294–297	7.2 299–302	7.3 303–306	7.4 308–311	7.5 312–315	7.6 318–321	7.7 322–326	7.8 327–330	7.9 332–335
Lesson Plans	51	52	53	54	55	56	57	58	59
Problem of the Day	19	19	19	20	20	20	21	21	21
Warm-Up Exercises	19	19	19	20	20	20	21	21	21
Color Transparencies	—	28	29	—	—	29	30	—	—
Teaching Tools: Transparencies	—	T1	—	—	T1	T1	—	T1	—
Copymasters	—	C2	—	—	C2	C2	—	C2	—
Math Log	22	22	22	22	23	23	23, 24	24	24
Technology	—	37	38	—	39	—	—	—	40, 41
Answer Masters	132, 133	134, 135	136, 137	139	140, 141	142	143—145	147, 148	149
Extra Practice Copymasters	51	52	53	54	55	56	57	58	59
Reteaching Copymasters	51	52	53	54	55	56	57	58	59
Enrichment Projects	—	35, 36	—	—	—	—	—	37, 38	—
Alternative Assessment: Projects	—	27	—	—	—	27	—	27, 28	28
Partner Quizzes	—	—	—	—	50	—	—	—	—
Group Assessment	—	—	—	71, 72	—	—	—	—	—
Formal Assessment Short Quizzes	—	107	—	108	—	111	—	112	—
Tests	—	—	—	—	109, 110	—	—	—	113–121
Overhead Manipulatives Kit	—	—	—	—	—	—	—	—	—
Complete Solutions Manual	Includes step-by-step solutions for all exercises in the student text								
Computerized Test Bank	Creates customized tests that include graphics								
Interactive CD-ROM Project	Provides an interactive and interdisciplinary chapter project								

STARTERS

Problem of the Day

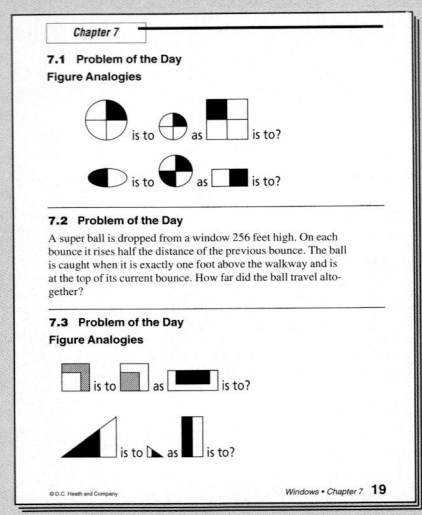

Chapter 7

7.1 Problem of the Day
Figure Analogies

is to ⬕ as ⬛ is to?

is to ◗ as ☐ is to?

7.2 Problem of the Day

A super ball is dropped from a window 256 feet high. On each bounce it rises half the distance of the previous bounce. The ball is caught when it is exactly one foot above the walkway and is at the top of its current bounce. How far did the ball travel altogether?

7.3 Problem of the Day
Figure Analogies

is to ⬜ as ⬛ is to?

is to ◺ as ▮ is to?

© D.C. Heath and Company   Windows • Chapter 7 **19**

Warm-Up Exercises

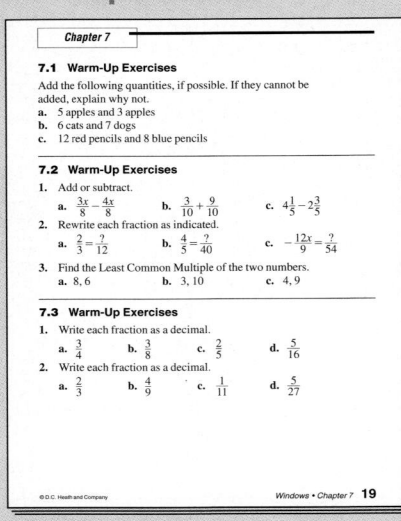

Chapter 7

7.1 Warm-Up Exercises

Add the following quantities, if possible. If they cannot be added, explain why not.
a. 5 apples and 3 apples
b. 6 cats and 7 dogs
c. 12 red pencils and 8 blue pencils

7.2 Warm-Up Exercises

1. Add or subtract.
   a. $\frac{3x}{8} - \frac{4x}{8}$ b. $\frac{3}{10} + \frac{9}{10}$ c. $4\frac{1}{5} - 2\frac{3}{5}$
2. Rewrite each fraction as indicated.
   a. $\frac{2}{3} = \frac{?}{12}$ b. $\frac{4}{5} = \frac{?}{40}$ c. $-\frac{12x}{9} = \frac{?}{54}$
3. Find the Least Common Multiple of the two numbers.
   a. 8, 6 b. 3, 10 c. 4, 9

7.3 Warm-Up Exercises

1. Write each fraction as a decimal.
   a. $\frac{3}{4}$ b. $\frac{3}{8}$ c. $\frac{2}{5}$ d. $\frac{5}{16}$
2. Write each fraction as a decimal.
   a. $\frac{2}{3}$ b. $\frac{4}{9}$ c. $\frac{1}{11}$ d. $\frac{5}{27}$

© D.C. Heath and Company   Windows • Chapter 7 **19**

FOR TEACHERS

Answer Masters

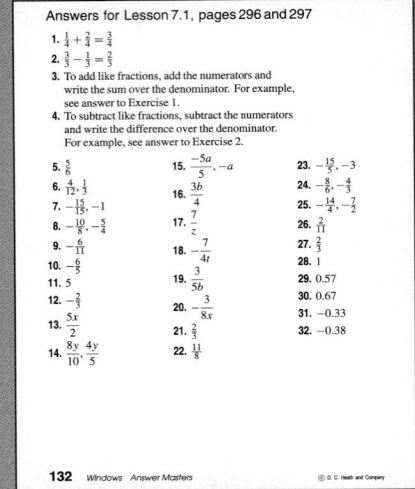

Answers for Lesson 7.1, pages 296 and 297

1. $\frac{1}{4} + \frac{2}{4} = \frac{3}{4}$
2. $\frac{3}{3} - \frac{1}{3} = \frac{2}{3}$
3. To add like fractions, add the numerators and write the sum over the denominator. For example, see answer to Exercise 1.
4. To subtract like fractions, subtract the numerators and write the difference over the denominator. For example, see answer to Exercise 2.

5. $\frac{5}{6}$
6. $\frac{4}{12}, \frac{1}{3}$
7. $-1\frac{3}{5}, -1$
8. $-\frac{10}{8}, -\frac{5}{4}$
9. $-\frac{6}{11}$
10. $-\frac{5}{9}$
11. 5
12. $-\frac{2}{3}$
13. $\frac{5x}{2}$
14. $\frac{8y}{10}, \frac{4y}{5}$
15. $\frac{-5a}{5}, -a$
16. $\frac{3b}{4}$
17. $\frac{7}{z}$
18. $-\frac{7}{4t}$
19. $\frac{3}{5b}$
20. $-\frac{3}{8x}$
21. $\frac{2}{5}$
22. $\frac{11}{8}$
23. $-\frac{15}{5}, -3$
24. $-\frac{8}{6}, -\frac{4}{3}$
25. $-\frac{14}{4}, -\frac{7}{2}$
26. $\frac{2}{11}$
27. $\frac{2}{3}$
28. 1
29. 0.57
30. 0.67
31. −0.33
32. −0.38

132 Windows Answer Masters   © D.C. Heath and Company

Lesson Plans

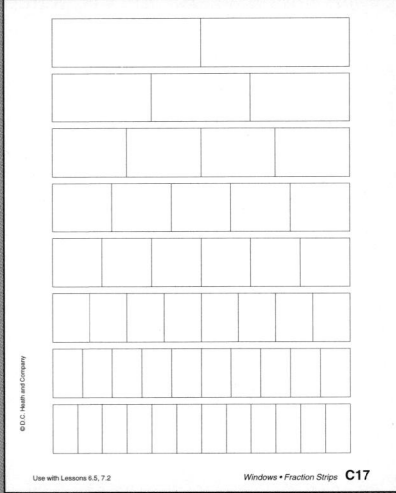

Lesson Plan 7.1
pages 294–297

Teacher's Name _____ Class _____ Date _____ Room _____

Goals 1. Add like fractions.
2. Subtract like fractions.

State/Local Objectives

NCTM Curriculum Standards: Problem Solving, Communication, Connections, Computation and Estimation, Technology, Patterns and Functions, Algebra, Geometry, Measurement

✔ Check items you wish to use for this lesson.

Introducing the Lesson
___ Problem of the Day copymasters page 19 or Teacher's Edition page 294
___ Warm-Up Exercises copymasters page 19 or Teacher's Edition page 294

Teaching the Lesson using the following:
___ Extra Examples, Teacher's Edition page 295
___ Common-Error Alert, Teacher's Edition page 296
___ Notes for Substitute Teacher

Closing the Lesson
___ Communicating about Mathematics, Student's Edition page 295
___ Guided Practice Exercises, Student's Edition page 296

Homework Assignment, pages 296, 297
___ Basic/Average: Day 1: Ex. 5–33
___ Day 2: Ex. 35, 37, 40–42, 44–46
___ Above Average: Ex. 5–37 odd, 38, 40–42, 44–46
___ Advanced: Ex. 5–37, 38, 44–46

Reteaching the Lesson
___ Extra Practice Copymasters page 51
___ Reteaching Copymasters page 51
___ Math Log copymasters page 22 or Teacher's Edition page 297

Extending the Lesson
___ Writing, Teacher's Edition page 295

Notes

© D.C. Heath and Company   Windows **51**

Teaching Tools

[table/grid of fraction strips]

Use with Lessons 6.5, 7.2   Windows • Fraction Strips **C17**

Teaching Tools includes:
Transparencies and Copymasters for classroom activities and study skills:
■ Graph Paper
■ Dot Paper (Geoboards)
■ Algebra Tiles
■ Number Counters
■ Fraction Strips
■ Models

REAL LIFE
Color Transparencies for Real-Life Applications

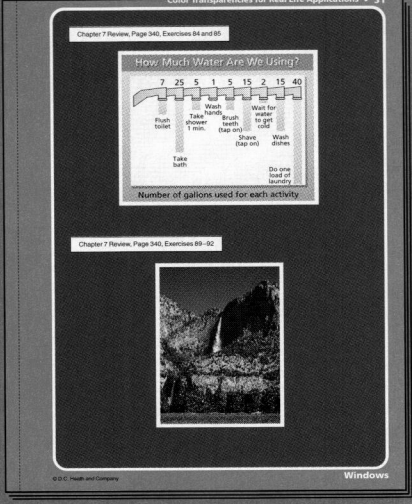

Chapter 7 Review, page 340, Exercises 84 and 85

How Much Water Are We Using?

Number of gallons used for each activity

Chapter 7 Review, Page 340, Exercises 89–92

© D.C. Heath and Company   Windows

Technology: Using Calculators and Computers

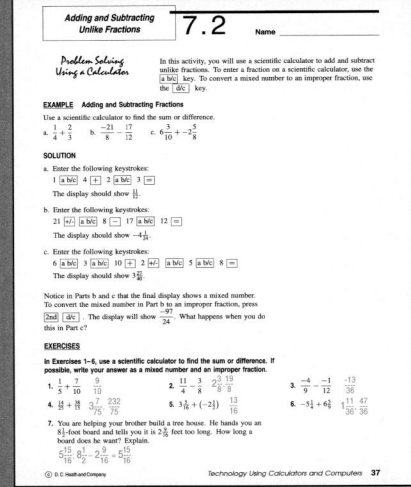

Adding and Subtracting Unlike Fractions   **7.2** Name _____

Problem Solving Using a Calculator

In this activity, you will use a scientific calculator to add and subtract unlike fractions. To enter a fraction on a scientific calculator, use the [a b/c] key. To convert a mixed number to an improper fraction, press the [d/c] key.

EXAMPLE Adding and Subtracting Fractions
Use a scientific calculator to find the sum or difference.
a. $\frac{1}{4} + \frac{2}{3}$ b. $-\frac{21}{8} - \frac{17}{12}$ c. $\frac{3}{10} + -2\frac{5}{8}$

SOLUTION
a. Enter the following keystrokes:
   1 [a b/c] 4 [+] 2 [a b/c] 3 [=]
   The display should show $\frac{11}{12}$.
b. Enter the following keystrokes:
   21 [+/–] [a b/c] 8 [−] 17 [a b/c] 12 [=]
   The display should show $-4\frac{1}{24}$.
c. Enter the following keystrokes:
   6 [a b/c] 3 [a b/c] 10 [+] 2 [+/–] [a b/c] 5 [a b/c] 8 [=]
   The display should show $3\frac{23}{40}$.

Notice in Parts b and c that the final display shows a mixed number. To convert the mixed number in Part b to an improper fraction, press [2nd] [d/c]. The display will show $-\frac{97}{24}$. What happens when you do this in Part c?

EXERCISES
In Exercises 1–6, use a scientific calculator to find the sum or difference. If possible, write your answer as a mixed number and an improper fraction.
1. $\frac{5}{8} + \frac{7}{10}$ $1\frac{13}{40}$ 2. $\frac{11}{4} - \frac{3}{8}$ $2\frac{3}{8}$ 3. $\frac{-4}{9} + \frac{-1}{12}$ $\frac{-13}{36}$
4. $\frac{14}{15} + \frac{9}{25}$ $1\frac{7}{75}, \frac{232}{75}$ 5. $3\frac{1}{8} + (-2\frac{1}{2})$ $\frac{13}{16}$ 6. $-5\frac{1}{4} + 6\frac{1}{9}$ $\frac{11}{36}, \frac{47}{36}$
7. You are helping your brother build a tree house. He hands you an $8\frac{1}{2}$-foot board and tells you it is $2\frac{9}{16}$ feet too long. How long a board does he want? Explain. $5\frac{15}{16}$; $8\frac{1}{2} - 2\frac{9}{16} = 5\frac{15}{16}$

© D.C. Heath and Company   Technology Using Calculators and Computers **37**

Also Available:

■ Complete Solutions Manual
■ Overhead Manipulatives Kit
■ Computerized Testing Program

■ **Interactive CD-ROM Projects**
Interactive projects for solving real-world problems using multimedia

■ **Interactions: Real Math–Real Careers**
A videodisc–based resource that connects math to real careers and on-the-job problem solving

■ **PACKETS® Performance Assessment for Middle School Mathematics**
A program that links assessment and instruction in real-life settings

ASSESSMENT

Alternative Assessment

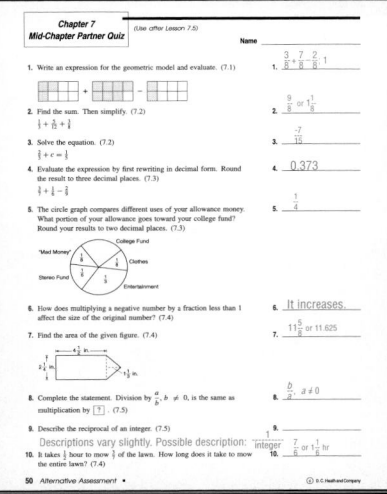

Alternative Assessment includes:
- Scoring Rubrics
- Portfolios
- Math Journals
- Projects
- Partner Quizzes
- Individual and Group Assessment

Formal Assessment

Formal Assessment includes:
- Short Quizzes (after every 2 lessons)
- Mid-Chapter Tests (2 forms)
- Chapter Tests (3 forms)
- Cumulative Tests (after every 3 Chapters)

MEETING INDIVIDUAL NEEDS

Extra Practice Copymasters

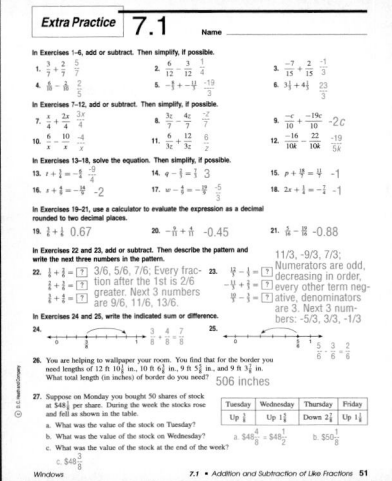

Reteaching Copymasters

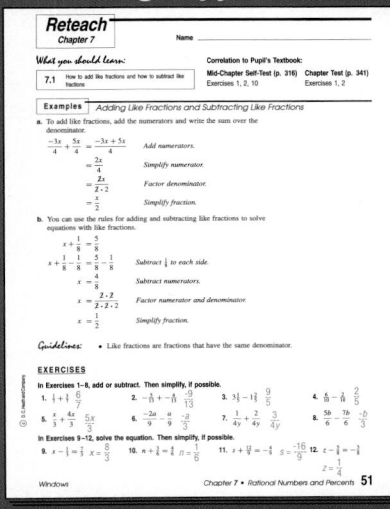

Enrichment Projects

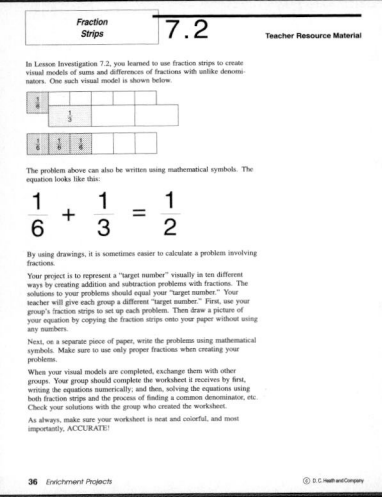

Math Log

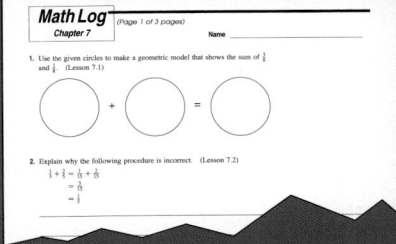

Special Populations
Suggestions for providing equal access for:

Students Acquiring English Proficiency*
Computing fractions and finding percents will be more easily understood when applied to real-life situations. Finding distances on road maps provide a practical application of computing fractions. Give students practice computing percents using advertisements from a variety of newspapers.

The language of percents in Lesson 7.8 can be confusing if it is not clear to students that *of* means multiply and *is* means equals.

Students with Various Learning Styles*
Encourage students who benefit from a **tactile** approach to continue to make use of fraction strips, area models, and pictorial representations as shown in Lessons 7.1–7.5.

Provide visual learners with 10 by 10 grid paper to represent fractions, decimals, and percents.

Underachieving Students*
Outside the classroom, students will primarily use fractions with small denominators such as 2, 3, 4, and 6. Encourage simple mental calculations using these denominators.

Many students will be familiar with the application of percents for tips. Teach students to estimate 10%, 15%, and 20% tips by rounding an amount, finding 10% of that amount, then adding half of that 10% figure to itself to get 15%, or doubling it to get 20%.

Gifted and Talented Students*
After Lesson 7.4 is taught, extend the Exploration and Extension in Lesson 7.3 by having students compute the shaded area if each circle has an area of $\frac{1}{2}$ square units, $\frac{1}{3}$ square units, and so on.

* See page T19 for descriptions of these special populations.

PACING CHART

Lesson	Basic/ Average Course	Above Average Course	Advanced Course
7.1	0 days	1 day	1 day
7.2	0 days	1 day	1 day
7.3	2 days	1 day	1 day
7.4	2 days	1 day	1 day
7.5	2 days	1 day	1 day
7.6	2 days	1 day	1 day
7.7	2 days	1 day	1 day
7.8	0 days	1 day	1 day
7.9	0 days	1 day	1 day

About the Chapter

This chapter deals with some of the most frequently used math skills in everyday life, those that are used to compare the measure of part of a quantity to the measure of the whole quantity—the number of hours spent *working* compared to the whole twenty four hours, or the amount of electricity produced from *gas* compared to the total amount of electricity produced, or the number of people describing themselves in a survey as *very attractive* compared to the total number of people surveyed. These quantitative comparisons can be expressed as fractions, as decimals, or as percents.

Lessons 7.1 and 7.2 present the skills of adding and subtracting *fractions*. The technique of changing fractions to *decimals*, first presented in Chapter 6 (Lesson 6), is applied in Lesson 7.3 as an alternative method, much better suited to calculators, of adding and subtracting fractions. Lessons 7.4 and 7.5 introduce techniques for multiplying and dividing rational numbers, including algebraic expressions. *Percents* are introduced in Lesson 7.6 and, in 7.7, fractions, decimals, and percents are shown in relation to one another. The two final lessons make it clear that real-life problem solving often involves all three methods of representing quantitative comparisons.

Rational Numbers and Percents

According to scientists, the world's water supply neither grows nor diminishes, it recycles itself by changing form and location. Three quarters of the earth's surface is covered by about 1350 million cubic kilometers of water in the form of oceans, rivers, lakes, snowcaps, and ice fields.

Real Life
Water Resources

Earth's Fresh-Water Resources

- Atmosphere 0.0004%
- Lakes & Rivers 0.4%
- Arctic Icecap 7.7%
- Antarctic Icecap 69.3%
- Surface Ground Water 11.3%
- Deep Ground Water 11.3%

About 97% of the earth's water resources are in the form of salt water as oceans and seas. Over 2% of the remaining fresh-water resources are frozen in the Arctic and Antarctic ice-caps or buried deep beneath the earth's surface. Less than 0.5% of the total water resources is available to maintain all life on earth.

Much of the real-life data you will encounter is given in the form of rational numbers as decimals or percents. In this chapter, you will explore how to use rational numbers in describing real-life situations.

Using the Page

Give students models to help them visualize 0.5%. Use a pie model or a 10×10 piece of grid paper.

Have students list how their family uses water. Compare the students' list with the table below which shows the average daily water use for a family of four. Have students suggest ways they could conserve water.

Use	Gallons	Use	Gallons
Lawn	100 gal.	Dishes	15 gal.
Toilet	95 gal.	Drinking	8 gal.
Bathing	100 gal.	Laundry	35 gal.

Multimedia Resources

Interactive CD-ROM Projects
A project for this chapter combines print, animation, sound and video presentations to capture students' interest in Electoral Votes and Popular Votes. This interactive approach shows students how the math concepts and problem-solving strategies they are learning will be used in the future in dealing with important personal, national, and world issues. The theme of Electoral Votes and Popular Votes correlates to Example 3 on page 328.

Interactions: Real Math—Real Life
The theme of this chapter, Water Resources, correlates with an episode of **Interactions** which is a videodisc-based multimedia resource that connects middle school math topics with real-life careers. In each of the twelve episodes, students go on-site with a variety of professionals to witness real-life applications of the math they are studying. Students see math concepts and problem-solving strategies in a context that helps them connect what they are studying to the world outside the classroom. **Interactions** was developed by the Foundation for Advancements in Science and Education (FASE) and is published by D.C. Heath and Company.

The theme of Water Resources is continued throughout the chapter on pages 307, 319, 321, 330, and 340.

Performance Assessment Resource

The PACKETS® Program: Performance Assessment for Middle School Mathematics was developed by Educational Testing Service and is published by D.C. Heath. **PACKETS** helps you assess your students' performances as they learn. You can use a wide variety of **PACKETS** Activity Units with this chapter because, in every activity, students will use ideas from all topic areas of mathematics. However, you can use the chart on page T16 to help you choose the **PACKETS** Activity Unit(s) that may fit best with this chapter.

Addition and Subtraction of Like Fractions

PACING the Lesson

Suggested Number of Days
Basic/Average 0   **Above Average** 1
Advanced 1

PLANNING the Lesson

Lesson Plan 7.1, p. 51

ORGANIZER

Starters (reproduced below)
  Problem of the Day 7.1, p. 19
  Warm-Up Exercises 7.1, p. 19
Lesson Resources
  Math Log, p. 22
  Answer Masters 7.1, pp. 132, 133
  Extra Practice Copymaster 7.1, p. 51
  Reteaching Copymaster 7.1, p. 51
Special Populations
  Suggestions, Teacher's Edition, p. 292D

LESSON Notes

Emphasize that the concrete interpretation of *like denominators* is: having whole objects of the same size divided into parts of equal size. Fraction strips and attribute blocks are useful for modeling *like* denominators.
  Remind students that we can add only *like* things. Objects added together must be viewed as alike (using some attribute common to both) before we can combine them into a single term.
  Suggest that students record in their journals the Variable Example of the rule for Adding Like Fractions.

Example 1

Emphasize that once the sum is found, it is customary to simplify the result. In parts **a, c,** and **d,** note that the results are expressed as improper fractions rather than mixed numbers.

What you should learn:

 Goal 1 How to add like fractions

Goal 2 How to subtract like fractions

Why you should learn it:

You can use addition and subtraction of like fractions to solve real-life problems, such as comparing the times of two runners.

Goal 1 **Adding Like Fractions**

Like fractions are fractions that have the same denominator.

Like Fractions	Unlike Fractions
$\frac{1}{5}$ and $\frac{3}{5}$	$\frac{1}{2}$ and $\frac{1}{3}$
$\frac{a}{c}$ and $\frac{b}{c}$	$\frac{a}{c}$ and $\frac{a}{d}$

Adding Like Fractions

To add like fractions, add the numerators and write the sum over the denominator.

Numerical Example
$$\frac{1}{5} + \frac{3}{5} = \frac{1+3}{5} = \frac{4}{5}$$

Variable Example
$$\frac{a}{c} + \frac{b}{c} = \frac{a+b}{c}$$

Model for $\frac{1}{5}$

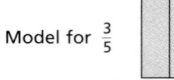
Model for $\frac{3}{5}$

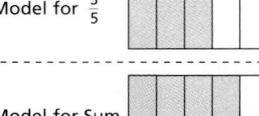
Model for Sum

$\frac{4}{5}$

This geometric model shows that the sum of $\frac{1}{5}$ and $\frac{3}{5}$ is $\frac{4}{5}$.

Example 1 *Adding Like Fractions*

a. $\frac{5}{8} + \frac{7}{8} = \frac{5+7}{8}$ *Add numerators.*

$= \frac{12}{8}$ *Simplify numerator.*

$= \frac{4 \cdot 3}{4 \cdot 2}$ *Factor numerator and denominator.*

$= \frac{3}{2}$ *Simplify fraction.*

b. $\frac{-3}{10} + \frac{-5}{10} = \frac{-3+(-5)}{10}$ *Add numerators.*

$= \frac{-8}{10}$ *Simplify numerator.*

$= \frac{-4 \cdot 2}{5 \cdot 2}$ *Factor numerator and denominator.*

$= -\frac{4}{5}$ *Simplify fraction.*

c. $1\frac{2}{6} + 1\frac{3}{6} = \frac{8}{6} + \frac{9}{6}$ *Rewrite as improper fractions.*

$= \frac{8+9}{6}$ *Add numerators.*

$= \frac{17}{6}$ *Simplify numerator.*

d. $\frac{6x}{5} + \frac{3x}{5} = \frac{6x+3x}{5}$ *Add numerators.*

$= \frac{9x}{5}$ *Simplify numerator.*

STARTER: Problem of the Day
Figure Analogies

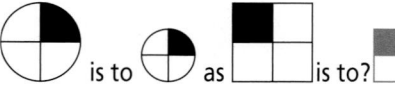

STARTER: Warm-Up Exercises
Add the following quantities, if possible. If they cannot be added, explain why not.

a. 5 apples and 3 apples

b. 6 cats and 7 dogs

c. 12 red pencils and 8 blue pencils

a. 8 apples; **b.** Can't add and get a sum of cats or a sum of dogs because they are not alike. However, if we view these as animals, we can add to get 13 animals; **c.** 20 pencils (without color indication)

Also available as a copymaster, page 19

Also available as a copymaster, page 19

Goal 2 Subtracting Like Fractions

Subtracting Like Fractions

To subtract like fractions, subtract the numerators and write the difference over the denominator.

Numerical Example	Variable Example
$\dfrac{3}{5} - \dfrac{1}{5} = \dfrac{3-1}{5} = \dfrac{2}{5}$	$\dfrac{a}{c} - \dfrac{b}{c} = \dfrac{a-b}{c}$

Example 2 *Subtracting Like Fractions*

You are helping two of your friends train for a track meet. You time your friends on a 100-meter sprint. One friend's time is $71\frac{3}{4}$ seconds and the other's time is $73\frac{1}{4}$ seconds. How much longer did your second friend take to complete the sprint?

Solution Subtract the first friend's time from the second friend's time.

Difference in times	=	Second friend's time	−	First friend's time

$\text{Difference} = 73\frac{1}{4} - 71\frac{3}{4}$ *Substitute for times.*

$= \dfrac{293}{4} - \dfrac{287}{4}$ *Write mixed numbers as fractions.*

$= \dfrac{293-287}{4}$ *Subtract numerators.*

$= \dfrac{6}{4}$ *Simplify.*

$= \dfrac{3}{2}$ *Simplify.*

Your second friend took $1\frac{1}{2}$ seconds longer to complete the sprint. ∎

Real Life Track

By the age of 14, Angela T. Williams, from Ontario, California, had won 15 national sprinting championships and set 6 national sprinting records.

Communicating about MATHEMATICS

▶ **SHARING IDEAS about the Lesson**

Solving Equations Use the rules for adding and subtracting fractions to solve the equations.

A. $x - \frac{6}{7} = \frac{2}{7}$ $\frac{8}{7}$ **B.** $y - \frac{4}{3} = \frac{5}{3}$ 3

C. $m + \frac{5}{4} = \frac{7}{4}$ $\frac{1}{2}$ **D.** $n + \frac{1}{8} = \frac{5}{8}$ $\frac{1}{2}$

ASSIGNMENT GUIDE

*Basic/Average:
Day 1: Ex. 5–33
Day 2: Ex. 35, 37, 38, 40–42, 44–46

Above Average:
Ex. 5–37 odd, 38, 40–42, 44–46

Advanced: Ex. 5–37, 38, 44–46

Selected Answers: Ex. 1–4, 5–43 odd

*You may wish to omit this lesson for these students.

Guided Practice

MATH JOURNAL
Use these four problems as a five-minute in-class writing activity in which students reflect on the key concepts of the lesson.

Independent Practice

▶ **Ex. 9, 12**

Common-Error Alert!

Students are apt to ignore the order of terms and give positive answers.

▶ **Ex. 17–20** Be sure to check for correct denominators in this set of exercises.

▶ **Ex. 21–26** Encourage students to solve these problems using mental math.

▶ **Ex. 29–32** Students should use calculators only to perform the division. You may wish to point out the rounding feature of many scientific calculators if students have never used this feature.

Guided Practice

▶ **CHECK for Understanding**

In Exercises 1 and 2, write the indicated sum or difference.

1. 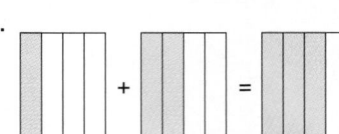 $\frac{1}{4} + \frac{2}{4} = \frac{3}{4}$

2. 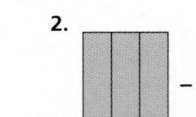 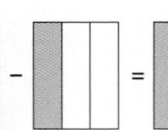 $\frac{3}{3} - \frac{1}{3} = \frac{2}{3}$

P 3. *Writing* In your own words, describe how to add like fractions. Give an example. See page 294. See answer to Exercise 1.

P 4. *Writing* In your own words, describe how to subtract like fractions. Give an example. See page 295. See answer to Exercise 2.

Independent Practice

In Exercises 5–12, add or subtract. Then simplify, if possible.

5. $\frac{2}{6} + \frac{3}{6}$ $\frac{5}{6}$

6. $\frac{8}{12} - \frac{4}{12}$ $\frac{4}{12}, \frac{1}{3}$

7. $\frac{-8}{15} - \frac{7}{15}$ $\frac{-15}{15}, -1$

8. $\frac{-3}{8} + \frac{-7}{8}$ $\frac{-10}{8}, -$

9. $\frac{4}{11} - \frac{10}{11}$ $\frac{-6}{11}$

10. $\frac{-8}{5} + \frac{2}{5}$ $\frac{-6}{5}$

11. $3\frac{1}{2} + 1\frac{1}{2}$ 5

12. $3\frac{2}{3} - 4\frac{1}{3}$ $-\frac{2}{3}$

In Exercises 13–20, add or subtract. Then simplify, if possible.

13. $\frac{x}{2} + \frac{4x}{2}$ $\frac{5x}{2}$

14. $\frac{12y}{10} - \frac{4y}{10}$ $\frac{8y}{10}, \frac{4y}{5}$

15. $\frac{-a}{5} - \frac{4a}{5}$ $\frac{-5a}{5}, -a$

16. $\frac{-3b}{4} + \frac{6b}{4}$ $\frac{3b}{4}$

17. $\frac{1}{z} + \frac{6}{z}$ $\frac{7}{z}$

18. $\frac{2}{4t} - \frac{9}{4t}$ $-\frac{7}{4t}$

19. $\frac{4}{5b} - \frac{1}{5b}$ $\frac{3}{5b}$

20. $\frac{1}{8x} + \frac{3}{8x} - \frac{7}{8x}$ $-\frac{3}{8x}$

In Exercises 21–28, solve the equation. Then simplify, if possible.

21. $x + \frac{2}{3} = \frac{4}{3}$ $\frac{2}{3}$

22. $y - \frac{6}{8} = \frac{5}{8}$ $\frac{11}{8}$

23. $m + \frac{19}{5} = \frac{4}{5}$ $-\frac{15}{5}, -3$

24. $n - \frac{1}{6} = \frac{-9}{6}$ $-\frac{8}{6}, -$

25. $s + \frac{5}{4} = \frac{-9}{4}$ $-\frac{14}{4}, -\frac{7}{2}$

26. $t - \frac{8}{11} = \frac{-6}{11}$ $\frac{2}{11}$

27. $3x + \frac{1}{2} = \frac{5}{2}$ $\frac{2}{3}$

28. $2z - \frac{8}{7} = \frac{6}{7}$ 1

In Exercises 29–32, use a calculator to evaluate the expression as a decimal rounded to two decimal places.

29. $\frac{1}{7} + \frac{3}{7}$ 0.57

30. $\frac{7}{6} - \frac{3}{6}$ 0.67

31. $\frac{5}{9} - \frac{8}{9}$ -0.33

32. $\frac{5}{16} - \frac{11}{16}$ -0.38

Patterns **In Exercises 33 and 34, add or subtract. Then describe the pattern and write the next three numbers in the pattern.** For descriptions, see margin.

33. $\frac{1}{8} + \frac{2}{8} = $? $\frac{3}{8}$

$\frac{3}{8} + \frac{4}{8} = $? $\frac{7}{8}$

$\frac{5}{8} + \frac{6}{8} = $? $\frac{11}{8}$

$\frac{7}{8} + \frac{8}{8} = $? $\frac{15}{8}$

$\frac{19}{8}, \frac{23}{8}, \frac{27}{8}$

34. $\frac{10}{2} - \frac{1}{2} = $? $\frac{9}{2}$

$\frac{-9}{2} - \frac{2}{2} = $? $-\frac{11}{2}$

$\frac{8}{2} - \frac{3}{2} = $? $\frac{5}{2}$

$\frac{-7}{2} - \frac{4}{2} = $? $-\frac{11}{2}$

$\frac{1}{2}, -\frac{11}{2}, -\frac{3}{2}$

P Portfolio Opportunity

Answers

33. Every fraction after the first is $\frac{4}{8}$ greater than the preceding fraction.

34. Every fraction, in every odd-numbered position after the first, is $\frac{4}{2}$ less than the preceding fraction in an odd-numbered position. Every fraction in an even-numbered position is $-\frac{11}{2}$.

Extra Practice

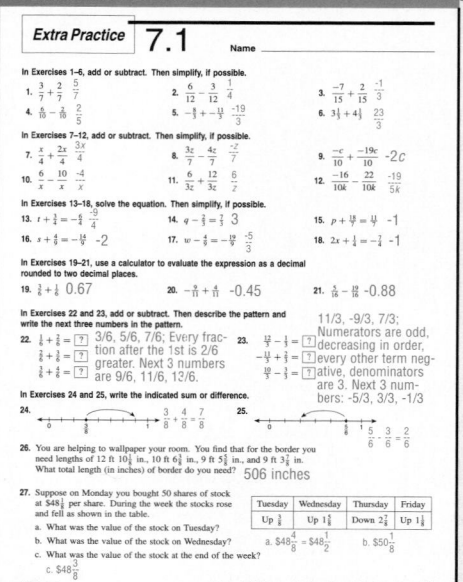

Reteaching

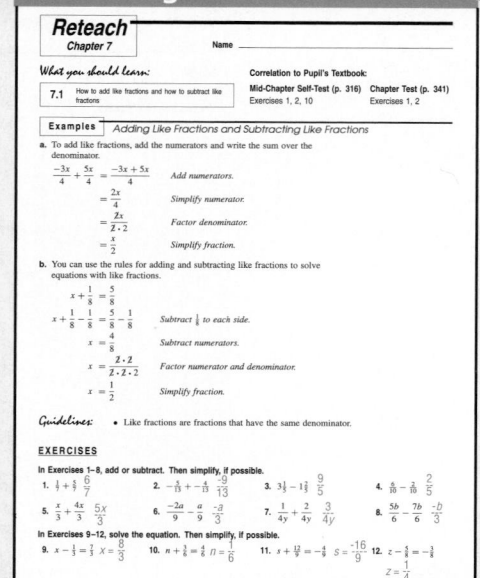

Correct or Incorrect? In Exercises 35 and 36, decide whether the addition is correct or incorrect. If it is incorrect, write a correct version.

35. $\frac{3}{5} + \frac{1}{5} = \frac{3+1}{5+5}$ Incorrect

$= \frac{4}{10}$ $\frac{3}{5} + \frac{1}{5} = \frac{3+1}{5}$

$= \frac{2}{5}$ $= \frac{4}{5}$

✪ 36. $1\frac{1}{3} + 2\frac{1}{3} = 1 + \frac{1}{3} + 2 + \frac{1}{3}$ Correct

$= 3 + \frac{2}{3}$

$= 3\frac{2}{3}$

Modeling Fractions In Exercises 37 and 38, write the indicated sum or difference.

37.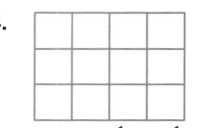
     $\frac{1}{4} + \frac{2}{4} = \frac{3}{4}$

38.
     $\frac{6}{8} - \frac{5}{8} = \frac{1}{8}$

39. *Baking*   The recipe below will make a single batch of banana bread. Rewrite the recipe for a double batch. See below.

Recipe for ___Banana Bread___
From ___Grandma___
Ingredients

1 3/4 cups all- purpose flour
2/3 cup of sugar
2 teaspoons baking powder
1/2 teaspoon baking soda
1/4 teaspoon salt
1 cup mashed ripe banana
1/3 cup shortening, margerine, or butter
2 tablespoons milk
2 eggs
1/4 cup chopped nuts

Mammals In Exercises 40–42, use the table, which shows the nose-to-tail lengths of some mammals.

40. How much longer is the Siberian tiger than the African lion? $1\frac{1}{4}$ ft

41. How much shorter is the polar bear than the Siberian tiger? $2\frac{7}{12}$ ft

42. How much shorter is the polar bear than the African lion? $1\frac{1}{3}$ ft

Mammal	Length in feet
Siberian tiger	$10\frac{4}{12}$
African lion	$9\frac{1}{12}$
Polar bear	$7\frac{9}{12}$

Integrated Review

Making Connections within Mathematics

Geometry In Exercises 43 and 44, find the perimeter of the figure.

43. $4\frac{2}{3}$ in.

Each tile is $\frac{1}{3}$ in. $\times \frac{2}{3}$ in.

44. $3\frac{1}{2}$ in.

Each tile is $\frac{1}{4}$ in. $\times \frac{1}{4}$ in.

Exploration and Extension

Fraction Riddles In Exercises 45 and 46, find the fraction that is described by the clues given.

45. The fraction is between 0 and 1. It is more than $\frac{1}{4}$. If you add $\frac{2}{8}$ to it, the fraction will be equivalent to $\frac{10}{16}$. $\frac{3}{8}$

✪ 46. The fraction is between -1 and 0. It is less than $-\frac{3}{8}$. If you subtract $\frac{2}{4}$ from it, the fraction will be equal to $-1\frac{1}{4}$. $-\frac{3}{4}$

39. New numbers, in order, are $3\frac{1}{2}$, $1\frac{1}{3}$, 4, 1, $\frac{1}{2}$, 2, $\frac{2}{3}$, 4, 4, $\frac{1}{2}$

✪ More difficult exercises

▶ **Ex. 35, 36** Have students draw a visual model of each of these problems.
▶ **Ex. 37, 38** These exercises provide important practice in reading a scale.

Integrated Review

Encourage students to give mixed number answers here.

Exploration and Extension

Each problem can be solved in several ways. Ask for volunteers to present their solution method to the class.

Portfolio Opportunity: Math Log

Use the given circles to make a geometric model that shows the sum of $\frac{3}{8}$ and $\frac{1}{8}$.

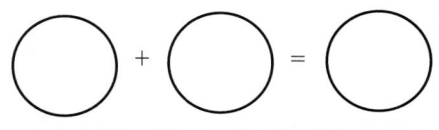

Also available as a copymaster, page 22, Ex. 1

This investigation could be done with commercial models of fractions if they are available. Otherwise, have students cut strips from the master provided in the supplement Teaching Tools, pages T11, C17. The goal is to have students understand that, with unlike denominators, it is necessary to find a common denominator for the sum or difference.

Materials Needed: fraction strips

In this activity, you will use fraction strips to investigate the sum and difference of fractions with unlike denominators.

| **Example** | ***Adding and Subtracting Unlike Fractions*** |

Use fraction strips to model the following.

a. $\frac{2}{3} + \frac{1}{6}$ **b.** $\frac{2}{3} - \frac{1}{4}$

Solution Begin by choosing fraction strips to represent $\frac{2}{3}$, $\frac{1}{6}$, and $\frac{1}{4}$.

a. To add the fractions, place the shaded parts together and find another fraction strip that has this length. From this, you can conclude that the sum is $\frac{5}{6}$.

| $\frac{1}{3}$ | $\frac{1}{3}$ | $\frac{1}{6}$ | | | | |

| $\frac{1}{6}$ | $\frac{1}{6}$ | $\frac{1}{6}$ | $\frac{1}{6}$ | $\frac{1}{6}$ | |

b. To subtract the fractions, overlap the shaded parts and find another fraction strip that has the same length as the difference. From this, you can conclude that the difference is $\frac{5}{12}$.

| $\frac{1}{3}$ | $\frac{1}{4}$ | | | |

| $\frac{1}{12}$ | $\frac{1}{12}$ | $\frac{1}{12}$ | $\frac{1}{12}$ | $\frac{1}{12}$ | | | | | | | |

∎

Exercises

In Exercises 1, and 2, write the sum or difference modeled by the fraction strips.

1.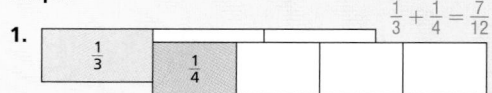

2.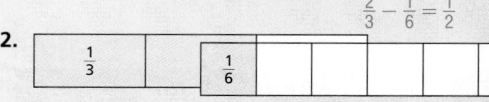

In Exercises 3–10, use fraction strips to find the sum or difference.

3. $\frac{2}{5} + \frac{1}{10}$ $\frac{1}{2}$ **4.** $\frac{2}{3} + \frac{1}{4}$ $\frac{11}{12}$ **5.** $\frac{1}{4} + \frac{1}{6}$ $\frac{5}{12}$ **6.** $\frac{1}{6} + \frac{3}{4}$ $\frac{11}{12}$

7. $\frac{2}{5} - \frac{1}{10}$ $\frac{3}{10}$ **8.** $\frac{2}{3} - \frac{1}{4}$ $\frac{5}{12}$ **9.** $\frac{5}{6} - \frac{1}{4}$ $\frac{7}{12}$ **10.** $\frac{3}{4} - \frac{1}{6}$ $\frac{7}{12}$

7.2

Addition and Subtraction of Unlike Fractions

▶ **PACING the Lesson**

Suggested Number of Days
Basic/Average 0   **Above Average** 1
Advanced 1

▶ **PLANNING the Lesson**

Lesson Plan 7.2, p. 52

What you should learn:

 Goal 1 How to add and subtract unlike fractions

 Goal 2 How to use addition and subtraction of fractions to solve real-life problems

What you should learn:

You can use addition and subtraction of unlike fractions to solve real-life problems, such as comparing the ways electric power is produced.

Goal 1 Add and Subtract Unlike Fractions

The **least common denominator** of two fractions is the least common multiple of their denominators. For instance, the least common denominator of $\frac{1}{2}$ and $\frac{1}{3}$ is 6. In this lesson, you will learn how to use least common denominators to add and subtract unlike fractions.

Addition and Subtraction of Unlike Fractions

To add or subtract unlike fractions, rewrite the fractions so that they have a common denominator. Then add or subtract the resulting like fractions.

Numerical Example

$$\frac{1}{2} + \frac{1}{3} = \frac{3}{6} + \frac{2}{6} = \frac{5}{6}$$

Variable Example

$$\frac{3}{x} - \frac{1}{2x} = \frac{6}{2x} - \frac{1}{2x} = \frac{5}{2x}$$

Example 1 Add and Subtract Unlike Fractions

a. $\frac{5}{6} + \frac{3}{8} = \frac{5}{6} \cdot \frac{4}{4} + \frac{3}{8} \cdot \frac{3}{3}$ *Least common denominator is 24.*

$= \frac{20}{24} + \frac{9}{24}$ *Rewrite as like fractions.*

$= \frac{29}{24}$ *Add like fractions.*

b. $\frac{7}{12} - \frac{3}{4} = \frac{7}{12} - \frac{3}{4} \cdot \frac{3}{3}$ *Least common denominator is 12.*

$= \frac{7}{12} - \frac{9}{12}$ *Rewrite as like fractions.*

$= \frac{-2}{12}$ *Subtract like fractions.*

$= -\frac{1}{6}$ *Simplify fraction.*

c. $\frac{2}{a} + \frac{3}{2} = \frac{2}{a} \cdot \frac{2}{2} + \frac{3}{2} \cdot \frac{a}{a}$ *Least common denominator is 2a.*

$= \frac{4}{2a} + \frac{3a}{2a}$ *Rewrite as like fractions.*

$= \frac{4 + 3a}{2a}$ *Add like fractions.*

d. $\frac{x}{4} - \frac{x}{5} = \frac{x}{4} \cdot \frac{5}{5} - \frac{x}{5} \cdot \frac{4}{4}$ *Least common denominator is 20.*

$= \frac{5x}{20} - \frac{4x}{20}$ *Rewrite as like fractions.*

$= \frac{x}{20}$ *Subtract like fractions.* ∎

Need to Know

The rule for adding and subtracting unlike fractions can be thought of as having two steps.

1. Rewrite fractions as like fractions.

2. Add or subtract the like fractions.

7.2 • Addition and Subtraction of Unlike Fractions   **299**

ORGANIZER

Starters (reproduced below)
   Problem of the Day 7.2, p. 19
   Warm-Up Exercises 7.2, p. 19
Lesson Resources
   Color Transparencies,
      Picture for Example 2, p. 28
      Graph for Ex. 33–35, p. 28
   Teaching Tools
      Graph paper, pp. T1, C2
   Math Log, p. 22
   Technology, p. 37
   Answer Masters 7.2, pp. 134, 135
   Extra Practice Copymaster 7.2, p. 52
   Reteaching Copymaster 7.2, p. 52
   Enrichment Projects, pp. 35, 36
Special Populations
   Suggestions, Teacher's Edition, p. 292D

LESSON Notes

Review the strategy for adding and subtracting unlike fractions. Emphasize that there is only one new step: find the Least Common Denominator. Insist that students record the rule for the Addition and Subtraction of Unlike Fractions in their journals.

Example 1

Changing the given denominator into the Least Common Denominator is called "raising to higher terms." Raising to higher terms is the method we use to obtain equivalent fractions with equal-size parts.

Most applications of adding and subtracting fractions involve unlike fractions. Because of this, working with unlike fractions is an important skill.

Example 2   *Adding Unlike Fractions*

The circle graph below compares the different ways that electricity is produced in the United States. Show that the sum of the five fractions is 1. *(Source: Electrical Power Annual)*

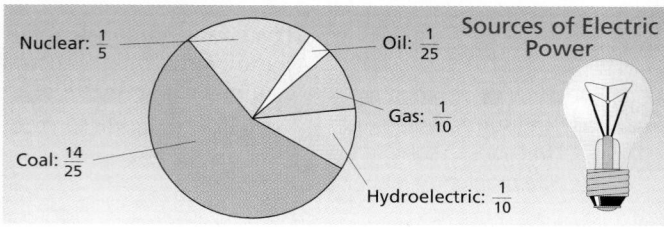

Nuclear: $\frac{1}{5}$ Oil: $\frac{1}{25}$ **Sources of Electric Power**   Gas: $\frac{1}{10}$ Coal: $\frac{14}{25}$ Hydroelectric: $\frac{1}{10}$

Solution   The least common denominator of the five fractions is 50.

$$\frac{14}{25} + \frac{1}{5} + \frac{1}{25} + \frac{1}{10} + \frac{1}{10}$$

$$= \frac{14}{25} \cdot \frac{2}{2} + \frac{1}{5} \cdot \frac{10}{10} + \frac{1}{25} \cdot \frac{2}{2} + \frac{1}{10} \cdot \frac{5}{5} + \frac{1}{10} \cdot \frac{5}{5}$$

$$= \frac{28}{50} + \frac{10}{50} + \frac{2}{50} + \frac{5}{50} + \frac{5}{50}$$

$$= \frac{28 + 10 + 2 + 5 + 5}{50}$$

$$= \frac{50}{50}$$

$$= 1$$

Thus, the sum of the five fractions is 1.

The Grand Coulee Dam in Washington is the largest dam in the United States. It contains 12 million cubic yards of concrete.

Communicating about MATHEMATICS

▶ **SHARING IDEAS about the Lesson**

Geoboard Fractions   Assume that the area of the region inside the pegs of each geoboard is 1. Write the fraction that represents the area of each shaded region. Then find the total area of the two shaded regions. $1\frac{1}{4}$ units²

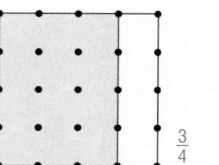
$\frac{3}{4}$

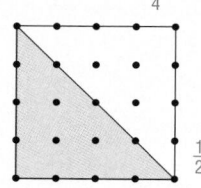
$\frac{1}{2}$

EXERCISES

Guided Practice

▶ CHECK for Understanding

In Exercises 1 and 2, the area of each region is 1. Write the fraction that represents the area of each blue region. Then add the fractions.

1.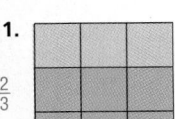

$\frac{2}{3}$

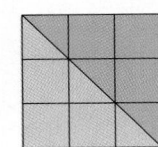 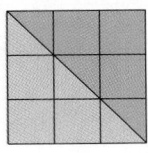 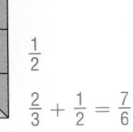

$\frac{1}{2}$

$\frac{2}{3} + \frac{1}{2} = \frac{7}{6}$

2.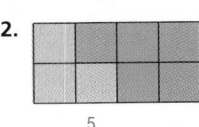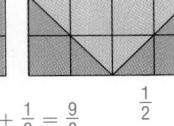

$\frac{5}{8}$ $\frac{5}{8} + \frac{1}{2} = \frac{9}{8}$ $\frac{1}{2}$

In Exercises 3–6, find the sum or difference. Then simplify, if possible. Explain your steps and identify the least common denominator of the fractions. For explanations, see margin.

3. $\frac{2}{5} + \frac{1}{3}$
$\frac{11}{15}$; 15

4. $\frac{4}{5} - \frac{3}{10}$
$\frac{5}{10}, \frac{1}{2}$; 10

5. $\frac{a}{2} - \frac{a}{3}$
$\frac{a}{6}$; 6

6. $\frac{4}{t} + \frac{1}{2t}$
$\frac{9}{2t}$; 2t

Independent Practice

In Exercises 7–14, find the sum or difference. Then simplify, if possible.

7. $\frac{1}{6} + \frac{7}{12}$ $\frac{9}{12}, \frac{3}{4}$

8. $\frac{2}{3} - \frac{3}{8}$ $\frac{7}{24}$

9. $\frac{-1}{2} + \frac{-7}{12}$ $-\frac{13}{12}$

10. $\frac{7}{9} - \frac{4}{5}$ $-\frac{1}{45}$

11. $\frac{-11}{15} + \frac{2}{5}$ $-\frac{5}{15}, -\frac{1}{3}$

12. $\frac{-3}{7} - \frac{1}{3}$ $-\frac{16}{21}$

13. $\frac{-3}{10} + \frac{7}{8}$ $\frac{23}{40}$

14. $\frac{1}{2} + \frac{5}{6} - \frac{7}{9}$ $\frac{10}{18}, \frac{5}{9}$

In Exercises 15–22, find the sum or difference. Then simplify, if possible.

15. $\frac{x}{3} + \frac{x}{6}$ $\frac{3x}{6}, \frac{x}{2}$

16. $\frac{a}{8} - \frac{a}{12}$ $\frac{a}{24}$

17. $\frac{2}{x} + \frac{9}{10}$ $\frac{20 + 9x}{10x}$

18. $\frac{4}{a} - \frac{11}{b}$ $\frac{4b - 11a}{ab}$

19. $\frac{-2}{3t} - \frac{4}{9t}$ $-\frac{10}{9t}$

20. $\frac{-7}{rs} + \frac{4}{s}$ $\frac{-7 + 4r}{rs}$

21. $\frac{2}{mn} - \frac{1}{3mn}$ $\frac{5}{3mn}$

22. $1\frac{2}{3} + 1\frac{3}{4}$ $3\frac{5}{12}$

In Exercises 23–26, use a calculator to find the sum or difference as a decimal rounded to two decimal places.

23. $\frac{13}{18} + \frac{9}{10}$ 1.62

24. $\frac{5}{28} + \frac{4}{7}$ 0.75

25. $\frac{8}{9} - \frac{23}{135}$ 0.72

26. $\frac{16}{27} - \frac{63}{108}$ 0.01

Geometry In Exercises 27 and 28, find the perimeter of the figure.

27.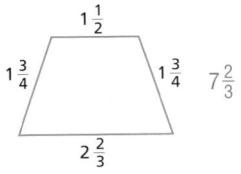

$1\frac{1}{2}$

$1\frac{3}{4}$ $1\frac{3}{4}$ $7\frac{2}{3}$

$2\frac{2}{3}$

28.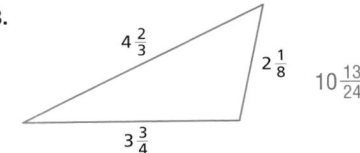

$4\frac{2}{3}$ $2\frac{1}{8}$ $10\frac{13}{24}$

$3\frac{3}{4}$

7.2 ▪ *Addition and Subtraction of Unlike Fractions*   **301**

EXERCISE Notes

ASSIGNMENT GUIDE
*Basic/Average:
Day 1: Ex. 7–27 odd, 29–32
Day 2: Ex. 33–36, 37–45 odd

Above Average:
Ex. 7–35 odd, 36, 37–45 odd

Advanced: Ex. 7–35 odd, 36, 37–45 odd

Selected Answers: Ex. 1–6, 7–41 odd
*You may wish to omit this lesson for these students.

Guided Practice
▶ **Ex. 1, 2** These exercises are modeled after the Communicating about Mathematics feature.
▶ **Ex. 6** Make sure that students work through this problem.

Independent Practice
▶ **Ex. 7–22** These problems are modeled in the lesson on page 299.
▶ **Ex. 23–26** Students should use a calculator to perform both the operation and the division. Encourage them to estimate the answer first.

Answers

3. $\frac{2}{5} + \frac{1}{3} = \frac{2}{5} \cdot \frac{3}{3} + \frac{1}{3} \cdot \frac{5}{5}$
$= \frac{6}{15} + \frac{5}{15}$
$= \frac{11}{15}$

4. $\frac{4}{5} - \frac{3}{10} = \frac{4}{5} \cdot \frac{2}{2} - \frac{3}{10}$
$= \frac{8}{10} - \frac{3}{10}$
$= \frac{5}{10}$
$= \frac{1}{2}$

5. $\frac{a}{2} - \frac{a}{3} = \frac{a}{2} \cdot \frac{3}{3} - \frac{a}{3} \cdot \frac{2}{2}$
$= \frac{3a}{6} - \frac{2a}{6}$
$= \frac{a}{6}$

6. $\frac{4}{t} + \frac{1}{2t} = \frac{4}{t} \cdot \frac{2}{2} + \frac{1}{2t}$
$= \frac{8}{2t} + \frac{1}{2t}$

Lesson 7.2 **301**

Integrated Review

These problems review the skill of estimating the size of each fraction by approximating the fraction to one of three values: 0, $\frac{1}{2}$, or 1.

Exploration and Extension

It takes practice to be able to select the appropriately sized square or rectangle on the graph paper so that the two fractions can be represented with new subdivisions based on the LCD. Since $\text{LCD}(4,9)=36$, a 6×6 square works well. For Ex. 44, $\text{LCD}(6,5)=30$, so a rectangle with dimensions 5×6 would work well.

Sequence In Exercises 29–32, consider the following sequence.

$$\frac{1}{2}, \ -\frac{2}{3}, \ \frac{3}{4}, \ -\frac{4}{5}, \ \ldots \qquad \frac{5}{6}, \ -\frac{6}{7}$$

✪ **29.** Describe the pattern. See margin.

✪ **30.** Write the next 2 terms of the sequence.

✪ **31.** Find the sum of the first 3 terms. $\frac{7}{12}$

✪ **32.** Find the sum of the first 5 terms. $\frac{37}{60}$

Science In Exercises 33–35, use the circle graph at the right, which shows what most influences students in grades 3–12 in their interest in science. The fractions represent portions of the student population. (*Source: USA Today*) **35.** See margin.

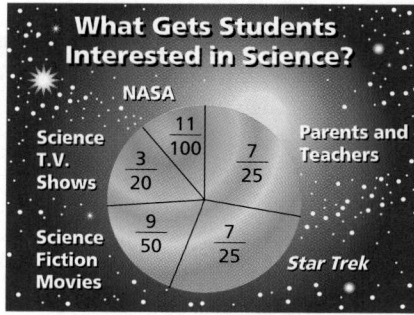

33. What portion of students are influenced most by Star Trek and science fiction movies? $\frac{23}{50}$

34. Find the difference in the portions influenced by science television shows and by NASA. $\frac{1}{25}$

35. Show that the sum of the five fractions is 1.

36. *Comics* You are making a comic book that is $4\frac{1}{2}$ inches by $6\frac{1}{3}$ inches. Each page of the comic book has a bottom and a top margin of $\frac{2}{3}$ inch and a left and right margin of $\frac{1}{4}$ inch, as shown at the right.

a. What is the perimeter of the page? $21\frac{2}{3}$ in.

b. What are the dimensions of the printed portion of the page? 4 in. by 5 in.

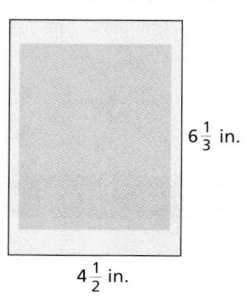

$6\frac{1}{3}$ in.

$4\frac{1}{2}$ in.

Integrated Review — *Making Connections within Mathematics*

Estimating Sums In Exercises 37–42, estimate the sum by rounding each fraction to the nearest $\frac{1}{2}$ and adding.

37. $\frac{5}{6} + \frac{3}{8}$ $\ 1\frac{1}{2}$

38. $\frac{2}{3} + \frac{5}{16}$ $\ 1$

39. $\frac{1}{10} + \frac{3}{4} + \frac{7}{8}$ $\ 2$

40. $\frac{7}{24} + \frac{3}{7} + \frac{13}{16}$ $\ 2$

41. $1\frac{3}{11} + 2\frac{9}{13}$ $\ 4$

42. $4\frac{4}{9} + 2\frac{1}{20}$ $\ 6\frac{1}{2}$

Exploration and Extension

P *Modeling Least Common Denominators* In Exercises 43–46, use the sample at the right to represent the sum with graph paper.

✪ **43.** $\frac{3}{4} + \frac{5}{9}$ $\ \frac{47}{36}$

✪ **44.** $\frac{1}{6} + \frac{1}{5}$ $\ \frac{11}{30}$

✪ **45.** $\frac{2}{5} + \frac{3}{10}$ $\ \frac{7}{10}$

✪ **46.** $\frac{1}{6} + \frac{1}{8}$ $\ \frac{7}{24}$

For use of graph paper, see Additional Answers.

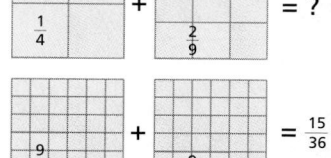

$\frac{1}{4}$ $\quad + \quad$ $\frac{2}{9}$ $\quad = \ ?$

$\frac{9}{36}$ $\quad + \quad$ $\frac{8}{36}$ $\quad = \ \frac{15}{36}$

✪ More difficult exercises
P Portfolio Opportunity

Answers

29. To get the next fraction, add 1 to the absolute values of both the numerator and the denominator and change the sign of the fraction to its opposite.

35. $\frac{11}{100} + \frac{7}{25} + \frac{7}{25} + \frac{9}{50} + \frac{3}{20} = \frac{11}{100} +$

$\frac{28}{100} + \frac{28}{100} + \frac{18}{100} + \frac{15}{100} = \frac{100}{100} = 1$

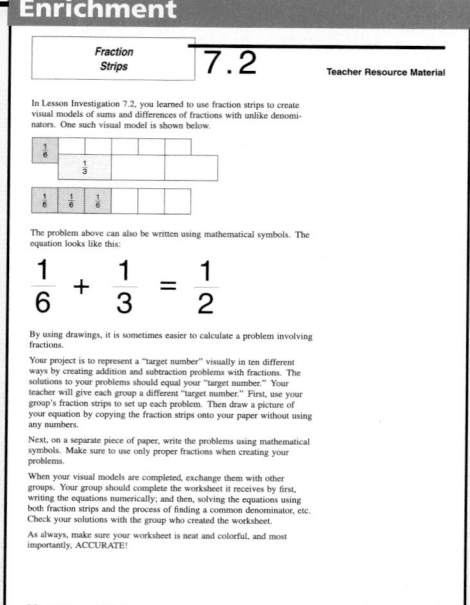

Fraction Strips **7.2** Teacher Resource Material

In Lesson Investigation 7.2, you learned to use fraction strips to create visual models of sums and differences of fractions with unlike denominators. One such visual model is shown below.

The problem above can also be written using mathematical symbols. The equation looks like this:

$$\frac{1}{6} + \frac{1}{3} = \frac{1}{2}$$

By using drawings, it is sometimes easier to calculate a problem involving fractions.

Your project is to represent a "target number" visually in ten different ways by creating addition and subtraction problems with fractions. The solutions to your problems should equal your "target number." Your teacher will give each group a different "target number." First, use your group's fraction strips to set up each problem. Then draw a picture of your equation by copying the fraction strips onto your paper without using any numbers.

Next, on a separate piece of paper, write the problems using mathematical symbols. Make sure to use only proper fractions when creating your problems.

When your visual models are completed, exchange them with other groups. Your group should complete the worksheet it receives by first, writing the equations numerically; and then, solving the equations using both fraction strips and the process of finding a common denominator, etc. Check your solutions with the group who created the worksheet.

As always, make sure your worksheet is neat and colorful, and most importantly, ACCURATE!

7.3 Exploring Fractions and Decimals

What you should learn:

Goal 1 How to add and subtract fractions by writing the fractions as decimals

Goal 2 How to use addition and subtraction of decimals to solve real-life problems

Why you should learn it:

You can use addition and subtraction of decimals to solve real-life problems, such as interpreting the results of a survey.

Goal 1 **Adding and Subtracting Decimals**

In Lessons 7.1 and 7.2, you studied ways to add and subtract fractions. Another way to add and subtract fractions is to rewrite the fractions as decimals or use geometric models. Which of the following ways of adding $\frac{1}{2}$ and $\frac{1}{4}$ do you prefer?

Adding as Fractions

$$\frac{1}{2} + \frac{1}{4} = \frac{1}{2} \cdot \frac{2}{2} + \frac{1}{4}$$
$$= \frac{2}{4} + \frac{1}{4}$$
$$= \frac{3}{4}$$

Adding as Decimals

$$\frac{1}{2} = 0.5 \text{ and } \frac{1}{4} = 0.25$$

$$\begin{array}{r} 0.5 \\ + 0.25 \\ \hline 0.75 \end{array}$$

Adding with Geometric Models

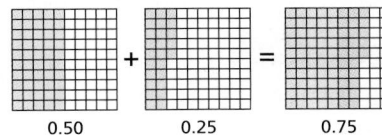

0.50   0.25   0.75

When you add or subtract fractions by first rewriting the fractions as decimals, remember that the resulting sums or differences may be only approximate.

Study Tip...

Example 1 asks you to round the result to 2 decimal places. To help avoid a round-off error, you should begin by rounding the numbers to 3 decimal places—one place more than is required in the final result. What would happen if you began by rounding the fractions to 0.31 and 0.63?

Example 1 **Adding and Subtracting Decimals**

Evaluate the expression by first rewriting in decimal form. Round the result to 2 decimal places.

a. $\frac{4}{13} + \frac{5}{8}$ **b.** $\frac{8}{11}x - \frac{3}{7}x$

Solution

a. $\frac{4}{13} + \frac{5}{8} \approx 0.308 + 0.625$ *Write as rounded decimals.*
$= 0.933$ *Add decimals.*
≈ 0.93 *Round to 2 decimal places.*

b. $\frac{8}{11}x - \frac{3}{7}x \approx 0.727x - 0.429x$ *Write as rounded decimals.*
$= 0.298x$ *Subtract decimals.*
$\approx 0.30x$ *Round to 2 decimal places.* ∎

7.3 • Exploring Fractions and Decimals **303**

▶ **PACING the Lesson**

Suggested Number of Days
Basic/Average 2 **Above Average** 1
Advanced 1

▶ **PLANNING the Lesson**

Lesson Plan 7.3, p. 53

ORGANIZER

Starters (reproduced below)
   Problem of the Day 7.3, p. 19
   Warm-Up Exercises 7.3, p. 19
Lesson Resources
   Color Transparencies
      Graph for Ex. 23–25, p. 29
   Math Log, p. 22
   Technology, p. 38
   Answer Masters 7.3, pp. 136, 137
   Extra Practice Copymaster 7.3, p. 53
   Reteaching Copymaster 7.3, p. 53
Special Populations
   Suggestions, Teacher's Edition, p. 292D

LESSON Notes

Ask students to verify that if the only factors of the denominator of a fraction are 2 and 5, then the decimal form of the fraction terminates; otherwise, the fraction is a repeating decimal.

Example 1

Have students compute the exact result of each part of the example using fractions and then compare their results with those presented in the example.
a. Exact result using sum of fractions:
   $\frac{97}{104} \approx 0.93$;
b. Exact result using sum of fractions:
   $\frac{23x}{77} \approx 0.30x$.

STARTER: Problem of the Day

Figure Analogies

is to   as   is to?

is to   as   is to? ▯

Also available as a copymaster, page 19

STARTER: Warm-Up Exercises

1. Write each fraction as a decimal.
a. $\frac{3}{4}$ **b.** $\frac{3}{8}$
c. $\frac{2}{5}$ **d.** $\frac{5}{16}$
a. 0.75, b. 0.375, c. 0.4, d. 0.3125
2. Write each fraction as a decimal.
a. $\frac{2}{3}$ **b.** $\frac{4}{9}$
c. $\frac{1}{11}$ **d.** $\frac{5}{27}$
a. $0.\overline{666}$, b. $0.44\overline{4}$, c. $0.0909\overline{09}$, d. $0.185\overline{185}$

Also available as a copymaster, page 19

It is convenient to be able to add fractions using decimals because of the widespread use of calculators.

Example 2

Ask students: What portion of the adults described themselves as something other than pretty or handsome?   776 out of 1000

Communicating about MATHEMATICS

Ask students to use a variety of models to represent $\frac{24}{7}$.

Writing Prompt
Have students explain why changing fractions to decimals and then adding may give only an approximate answer.

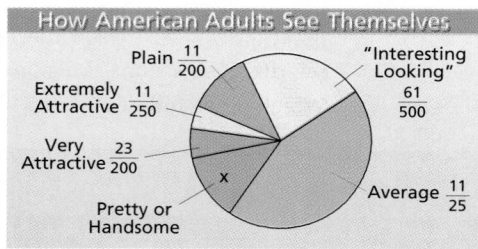
Real Life
Psychology

Psychologists study the ways people and animals think and relate to one another. An important part of psychology is studying the way people think about themselves.

Example 2   *Adding and Subtracting Decimals*

In a poll, adults were asked how they would describe their own physical appearance. The results are shown in the circle graph. What portion of the adults described themselves as "pretty or handsome"? (*Source: Cosmopolitan Magazine*)

How American Adults See Themselves

Plain $\frac{11}{200}$

Extremely Attractive $\frac{11}{250}$

Very Attractive $\frac{23}{200}$

Pretty or Handsome

x

"Interesting Looking" $\frac{61}{500}$

Average $\frac{11}{25}$

Solution   The fractions for the six parts have a sum of 1. To find the portion that answered "pretty or handsome," add the other five fractions and subtract the result from 1.

$$x = 1 - \left(\frac{11}{250} + \frac{23}{200} + \frac{11}{25} + \frac{61}{500} + \frac{11}{200}\right)$$
$$= 1 - (0.044 + 0.115 + 0.44 + 0.122 + 0.055)$$
$$= 1 - 0.776$$
$$= 0.224$$

This means that about 224 out of every 1000 adults consider themselves to be pretty or handsome. ∎

P   *Communicating* about MATHEMATICS

Cooperative Learning

▶ **SHARING IDEAS about the Lesson**

Modeling Fractions   Work with a partner. Explain how each model represents $\frac{7}{10}$. Describe other geometric models for this fraction. Explanations and descriptions vary.

A.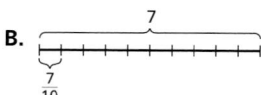
   0          $\frac{7}{10}$ 1

B.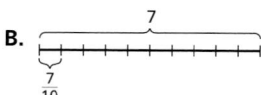
   $\frac{7}{10}$

C.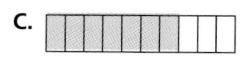

P Portfolio Opportunity

Technology

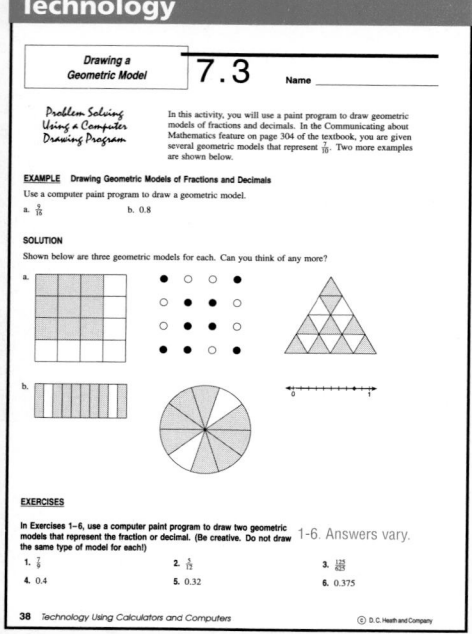

Drawing a Geometric Model   **7.3**   Name _____

OPTION: Extra Examples

Here is an additional example similar to Example 1 of the lesson.

1. Adding and Subtracting Decimals
Evaluate the following expression by first rewriting in decimal form. Round the result to 2 decimal places.

$$\frac{7}{9} - \frac{5}{12}$$

$$\frac{7}{9} - \frac{5}{12} \approx 0.778 - 0.417 \quad \text{Write as rounded decimals.}$$
$$\approx 0.361 \quad \text{Subtract decimals.}$$
$$\approx 0.36 \quad \text{Round to 2 decimal places.}$$

EXERCISES

Guided Practice

CHECK for Understanding

Explain each of the following steps.

$$\frac{7}{9} + \frac{11}{19} \approx 0.778 + 0.579$$
$$= 1.357 \quad \text{See below.}$$
$$\approx 1.36$$

Which is greater: $\frac{2}{3}$ or 0.67? Explain your reasoning. 0.67, it is $0.00\overline{3}$ greater.

Use a calculator to evaluate $\frac{2}{5} - \frac{10}{13}$. Round your results to two decimal places. -0.37

Write each fraction as a decimal rounded to three decimal places. Add the decimals and round the sum to two decimal places.

4. The sum of the fractions in the circle graph is 1. Use a calculator to solve for x. Round your result to two decimal places. 0.33

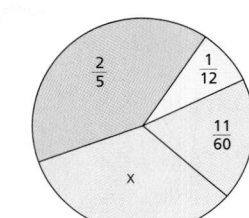

Independent Practice

Exercises 5–8, evaluate the expression.

5. $0.31 + 0.55$ 0.86 **6.** $1.823 + 0.021$ 1.844 **7.** $3.73 - 2.09$ 1.64 **8.** $2.009 - 1.793$ 0.216

Exercises 9 and 10, write the expression represented by the model. Then evaluate the expression by first converting to decimals. Round your result to two decimal places. See margin.

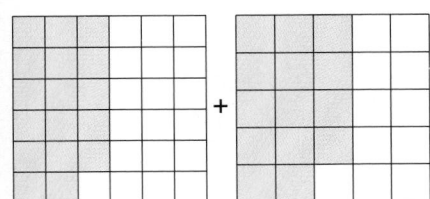   **10.**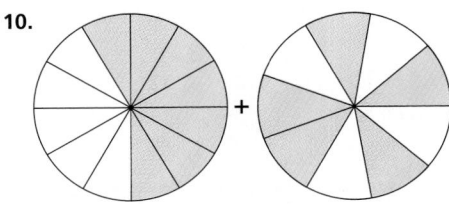

Modeling Fractions   In Exercises 11–14, sketch a geometric model of the fraction. (Use a different model for each exercise.) See Additional Answers.

11. $\frac{11}{16}$ **12.** $\frac{24}{50}$ **13.** 0.45 **14.** 0.625

Exercises 15–22, evaluate the expression by first rewriting in decimal form. Round your result to two decimal places. See margin.

15. $\frac{73}{111} + \frac{54}{109}$ **16.** $\frac{82}{89} - \frac{76}{127}$ **17.** $\frac{17}{35}y - \frac{14}{41}y$ **18.** $\frac{24}{31}n + \frac{7}{15}n$

19. $1 - \left(\frac{21}{56} + \frac{32}{99} + \frac{3}{25}\right)$ **20.** $2x - \left(\frac{4}{9}x + \frac{3}{7}x + \frac{11}{20}x\right)$

21. $2\frac{3}{4} + 3\frac{1}{8} - 1\frac{9}{10} + 4\frac{7}{10}$ **22.** $1\frac{5}{6} - 2\frac{3}{5} - \frac{17}{15} + 3\frac{5}{11}$

7.3 ▪ Exploring Fractions and Decimals   **305**

▶ **Ex. 23–25** Assign these as a group.

Integrated Review ────────

▶ **Ex. 31–36** These exercises, particularly those involving negative numbers, offer a good number sense workout.

Exploration and Extension

Ask students: Suppose the area of the circle were 3 square units. Would the answers to Ex. 37–39 change? Would the answer to Ex. 40 change?

┌──────────────────────────────────────┐
│ **Portfolio Opportunity: Math Log** │
│   │
│ In your own words, explain why adding │
│ or subtracting fractions by first rewrit- │
│ ing them as decimals may lead to results │
│ that are only approximate. When does │
│ this procedure give an exact result? │
└──────────────────────────────────────┘

Also available as a copymaster, page 22, Ex. 3

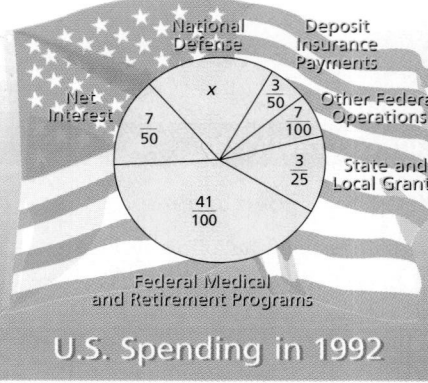

U.S. Spending in 1992

Government Spending In Exercises 23–25, use the circle graph, which shows how the United States federal government spent its money in 1992. (*Source: Office of Management and Budget*)

23. Find the sum of the portions for all categories other than national defense. 0.8

24. What portion was spent on the national defense? 0.2

25. Find the sum of the portions spent on state and local grants and "other federal operations." 0.19

26. *Error Analysis* You are asked to find the sum of $\frac{15}{31}$ and $\frac{18}{39}$ and to round the result to *two* decimal places. Which of the two solutions is better? Explain. b, it is more accurate

a. $\frac{15}{31} + \frac{18}{39} \approx 0.48 + 0.46$
$= 0.94$

b. $\frac{15}{31} + \frac{18}{39} \approx 0.484 + 0.462$
$= 0.946$
≈ 0.95

Integrated Review   *Making Connections within Mathematics*

Decimal Sense In Exercises 27–30, write each fraction as a decimal rounded to three decimal places.

27. $\frac{47}{99}$ 0.475

28. $\frac{63}{200}$ 0.315

29. $-\frac{12}{43}$ −0.279

30. $-\frac{79}{145}$ −0.545

Number Sense In Exercises 31–36, complete each statement with <, >, or =.

31. 0.9876 ? 0.9853 >

32. −0.4201 ? −0.4199 <

33. 1.0001 ? 1.1 <

34. $\frac{13}{21}$? 0.62 <

35. $-\frac{5}{13}$? −0.38 <

36. $\frac{6}{17}$? 0.353 <

Exploration and Extension

Area Models In Exercises 37–39, each of the geometric models is an area model. Each circle has an area of 1 square unit. Write the fraction and decimal that are represented by the shaded part of the model.

✪ 37.
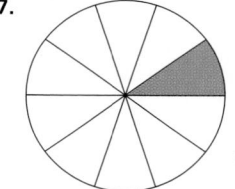
$\frac{1}{10}$, 0.1

✪ 38.
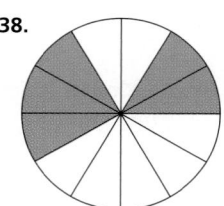
$\frac{5}{12}$, 0.41$\overline{6}$

✪ 39.
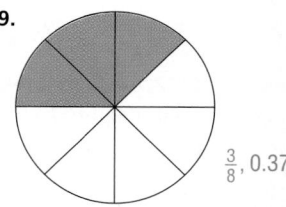
$\frac{3}{8}$, 0.375

✪ 40. Find the total area of the shaded parts in Exercises 37–39. 0.891$\overline{6}$ units²

P Portfolio Opportunity
✪ More difficult exercises

306   *Chapter 7 · Rational Numbers and Percents*

Mixed REVIEW

In Exercises 1–4, solve the equation. (7.2)

1. $a + \frac{2}{3} = \frac{4}{3}$ $\frac{2}{3}$

2. $y + \frac{1}{4} = \frac{3}{4}$ $\frac{1}{2}$

3. $\frac{1}{4}(4y + 8) = 16$ 14

4. $\frac{14}{9} = b + \frac{13}{9}$ $\frac{1}{9}$

In Exercises 5–8, write the fractions as decimals and solve the equation. Round your answer to two decimal places. (7.3) See margin.

5. $\frac{1}{4} + x = \frac{1}{8}$ -0.13

6. $\frac{1}{5}a = \frac{14}{5}$ 14

7. $y + \frac{1}{100} = \frac{1}{10}$ 0.09

8. $\frac{1}{20} = c + \frac{3}{16}$ -0.14

In Exercises 9–12, find the least common multiple. (6.4)

9. 2 and 7 14

10. 10 and 16 80

11. 3, 4, and 5 60

12. 4, 5, and 6 60

In Exercises 13–16, evaluate the expression. Then simplify, if possible. (7.2) $\frac{25}{25}, 1$

13. $\frac{1}{20} + \frac{1}{5} + \frac{1}{4}$ $\frac{10}{20}, \frac{1}{2}$

14. $\frac{2}{3} + \frac{4}{5} - \frac{1}{5}$ $\frac{19}{15}$

15. $\frac{99}{100} - \frac{1}{2} - \frac{6}{25}$ $\frac{25}{100}, \frac{1}{4}$

16. $\frac{4}{5} - \frac{1}{25} + \frac{6}{25}$

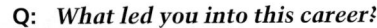
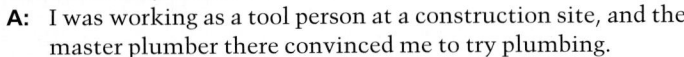

Career Interview

Plumber

Linda Savage is a master plumber. As the owner and operator of her own plumbing business, she works to keep the water and heating systems that people depend on safe and efficient.

Q: What led you into this career?
A: I was working as a tool person at a construction site, and the master plumber there convinced me to try plumbing.

Q: What special training did you have to take after high school?
A: I spent four years in apprenticeship and going to night school, and then after I passed the test to become a journeyman, I spent one more year working and going to night school in order to become a master plumber.

Q: What math did you take in school?
A: Algebra 1 and 2, geometry, and some trigonometry. Since then, I have had to learn lots of other math to get licensed.

Q: What would you like to tell kids who are in school about math?
A: Take as many math courses as you can, because most careers have lots of math, and many people are failing licensing tests because they didn't take enough.

Mixed Review **307**

► **PACING the Lesson**

Suggested Number of Days
Basic/Average 2   Above Average 1
Advanced 1

► **PLANNING the Lesson**

Lesson Plan 7.4, p. 54

ORGANIZER

Starters (reproduced below)
   Problem of the Day 7.4, p. 20
   Warm-Up Exercises 7.4, p. 20
Lesson Resources
   Math Log, p. 22
   Answer Masters 7.4, p. 139
   Extra Practice Copymaster 7.4, p. 54
   Reteaching Copymaster 7.4, p. 54
Special Populations
   Suggestions, Teacher's Edition, p. 292D

LESSON Notes

The rule for Multiplying Rational Numbers (fractions) is easy for students to remember and use. Have them record it in their journals.

Example 1

Demonstrate the area model for the multiplication of whole numbers. Then use the area model with fractions. This is a good way to motivate the rule for multiplying fractions.

7.4 Multiplication of Rational Numbers

What you should learn:

Goal 1 How to multiply rational numbers

Goal 2 How to use multiplication of rational numbers to solve real-life problems

Why you should learn it:

You can use multiplication of rational numbers to solve real-life problems, such as finding the floor area of a greenhouse.

Goal 1 **Multiplying Rational Numbers**

When adding or subtracting fractions, you have to consider whether they have like denominators or unlike denominators. In this lesson, you will learn that the rule for multiplying fractions applies whether the denominators are like or unlike.

> **Multiplying Rational Numbers**
>
> To multiply two rational numbers, $\frac{a}{b}$ and $\frac{c}{d}$, multiply the numerators and multiply the denominators.
>
> **Numerical Example**   **Variable Example**
> $\frac{1}{5} \cdot \frac{3}{4} = \frac{1 \cdot 3}{5 \cdot 4} = \frac{3}{20}$ $\frac{m}{n} \cdot \frac{r}{s} = \frac{m \cdot r}{n \cdot s} = \frac{mr}{ns}$

Example 1 *Multiplying Rational Numbers.*

a. $\frac{5}{8} \cdot \frac{-2}{3} = \frac{5 \cdot (-2)}{8 \cdot 3}$ *Multiply numerators and multiply denominators.*

$= \frac{-10}{24}$ *Simplify.*

$= \frac{2 \cdot (-5)}{2 \cdot 12}$ *Factor numerator and denominator.*

$= \frac{-5}{12}$ *Simplify fraction.*

b. $1\frac{2}{3} \cdot 3\frac{4}{5} = \frac{5}{3} \cdot \frac{19}{5}$ *Rewrite as improper fractions.*

$= \frac{5 \cdot 19}{3 \cdot 5}$ *Multiply.*

$= \frac{19}{3}$ *Simplify fraction.*

c. $\frac{6x}{5} \cdot 10 = \frac{6x}{5} \cdot \frac{10}{1}$ *Rewrite 10 as $\frac{10}{1}$.*

$= \frac{6x \cdot 10}{5 \cdot 1}$ *Multiply.*

$= \frac{6x \cdot 5 \cdot 2}{5}$ *Factor numerator.*

$= 12x$ *Simplify fraction.* ∎

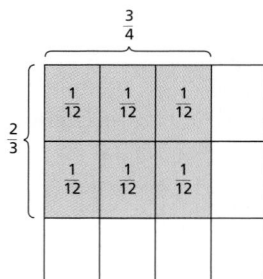

$\frac{3}{4}$

$\frac{2}{3}$ { [$\frac{1}{12}$ | $\frac{1}{12}$ | $\frac{1}{12}$] [$\frac{1}{12}$ | $\frac{1}{12}$ | $\frac{1}{12}$]]

This area model for multiplication shows that the product of $\frac{3}{4}$ and $\frac{2}{3}$ is $\frac{6}{12}$ or $\frac{1}{2}$.

Solving Real-Life Problems

Example 2 — *Finding the Area of a Region*

Real Life
Construction

The greenhouse shown at the left was built from prefabricated glass panels, each of which is $3\frac{1}{6}$ feet wide. What is the floor area of the greenhouse?

Solution The two sides of the greenhouse are each 3 panels wide. The front of the greenhouse is 4 panels wide.

$3\frac{1}{6}$ ft

$3\frac{1}{6}$ ft

$3\frac{1}{6}$ ft

$3\frac{1}{6}$ ft

$3\frac{1}{6}$ ft $3\frac{1}{6}$ ft $3\frac{1}{6}$ ft

$$\text{Width} = 3\left(3\frac{1}{6}\right) \qquad \text{Length} = 4\left(3\frac{1}{6}\right)$$
$$= 3\left(\frac{19}{6}\right) \qquad\qquad = 4\left(\frac{19}{6}\right)$$
$$= \frac{19}{2} \text{ feet} \qquad\qquad = \frac{38}{3} \text{ feet}$$

To find the area, multiply the width by the length.

$$\text{Area} = (\text{Width}) \times (\text{Length})$$
$$= \frac{19}{2} \times \frac{38}{3}$$
$$= \frac{19 \cdot 38}{2 \cdot 3}$$
$$= \frac{19 \cdot 2 \cdot 19}{2 \cdot 3}$$
$$= \frac{19^2}{3}$$
$$= \frac{361}{3} \text{ square feet}$$

This lean-to greenhouse is found in one corner of a rectangular patio whose outside dimensions are $20\frac{1}{2}$ feet by 24 feet.

The greenhouse has an area of $\frac{361}{3}$ or about 120.3 square feet. You can check this by reworking the problem with decimals. Using a width of 9.5 feet and a length of 12.667 feet, you obtain an area of (9.5)(12.667) or about 120.3 square feet. ■

P *Communicating about* **MATHEMATICS**

▷ **SHARING IDEAS about the Lesson**

Problem Solving In Example 2, find the area of the patio that is not covered by the greenhouse. Explain how you did it. $371\frac{2}{3}$ ft² $\quad(20\frac{1}{2} \times 24) - \frac{361}{3} = 492 - 120\frac{1}{3} = 371\frac{2}{3}$

Real-life measurements frequently result in mixed numbers. It is important for students to be able to multiply mixed numbers. This begins with the ability to change mixed numbers to improper fractions.

Example 2

Show how the mixed numbers were changed to improper fractions. Emphasize that the rule for multiplying fractions requires that the rational numbers have the form $\frac{a}{b}$, $b \neq 0$.

Communicating *about* **MATHEMATICS**

Have students measure the floor in your classroom and compute its area to the nearest square yard or square meter.

Writing Prompt
What do you know about $a \cdot b$ if a and b are both $\leq \frac{1}{2}$? Explain.

OPTION: Extra Examples

Here are additional examples similar to Example 1 of the lesson.

a. $1\frac{1}{8} \cdot 2\frac{2}{5} = \frac{9}{8} \cdot \frac{12}{5}$ Rewrite as improper fractions.

$\qquad = \frac{9 \cdot 12}{8 \cdot 5}$ Multiply numerators and denominators.

$\qquad = \frac{9 \cdot 4 \cdot 3}{4 \cdot 2 \cdot 5}$ Factor numerator and denominator.

$\qquad = \frac{27}{10}$ Simplify fraction.

b. $\frac{-7}{3x} \cdot \frac{6x^2}{5} = \frac{-7 \cdot 6x^2}{3x \cdot 5}$ Multiply numerators and denominators.

$\qquad = \frac{-7 \cdot 3 \cdot 2 \cdot x \cdot x}{3 \cdot x \cdot 5}$ Factor numerator and denominator.

$\qquad = -\frac{14x}{5}$ Simplify fraction.

EXERCISE Notes

EXERCISES

Guided Practice

▶ **CHECK for Understanding**

P **1.** *Writing* Explain in your own words how to multiply fractions. See page 308.

In Exercises 2–5, multiply. Then simplify, if possible.

2. $\frac{4}{7} \cdot \frac{3}{5}$ $\frac{12}{35}$

3. $\frac{4}{7} \cdot \frac{7}{4}$ 1

4. $\frac{5x}{9} \cdot \frac{2}{4x}$ $\frac{5}{18}$

5. $1\frac{3}{5} \cdot 2\frac{1}{2}$ 4

Area Models In Exercises 6–9, the large square is 1 unit by 1 unit. Find the dimensions and area of the green region.

6.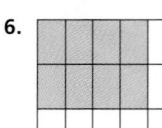
$\frac{8}{15}$ units^2
$\frac{2}{3}$ unit by $\frac{4}{5}$ unit

7.
$\frac{3}{7}$ units^2
$\frac{6}{7}$ unit by $\frac{3}{6}$ unit

8.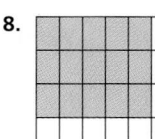
$\frac{5}{8}$ units^2
$\frac{3}{4}$ unit by $\frac{5}{6}$ unit

9.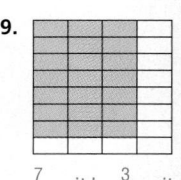
$\frac{7}{8}$ unit by $\frac{3}{4}$ unit

Independent Practice

In Exercises 10–17, multiply. Then simplify, if possible.

10. $\frac{1}{4} \cdot \frac{4}{5}$ $\frac{1}{5}$

11. $\frac{-2}{3} \cdot \frac{8}{9}$ $-\frac{16}{27}$

12. $\frac{-5}{6} \cdot \frac{-3}{4}$ $\frac{5}{8}$

13. $1\frac{2}{5} \cdot 2\frac{2}{7}$ $\frac{16}{5}$

14. $1\frac{1}{5} \cdot \left(-6\frac{2}{3}\right)$ -8

15. $-4\frac{1}{2} \cdot \left(-2\frac{5}{9}\right)$ $\frac{23}{2}$

16. $\frac{2}{3} \cdot \frac{-4}{7} \cdot \frac{4}{5}$ $-\frac{32}{105}$

17. $\frac{-8}{18} \cdot \frac{2}{3} \cdot \frac{-3}{8}$ $\frac{1}{9}$

In Exercises 18–25, multiply. Then simplify, if possible.

18. $\frac{5x}{6} \cdot 12$ $10x$

19. $7 \cdot \frac{8y}{3}$ $\frac{56y}{3}$

20. $\frac{-2x}{9} \cdot \frac{7}{4x}$ $-\frac{7}{18}$

21. $\frac{16z}{11} \cdot \frac{-11}{10z}$ $-\frac{8}{5}$

22. $\frac{-13t}{20} \cdot \frac{-1}{2}$ $\frac{13t}{40}$

23. $\frac{-5}{6} \cdot \frac{-6a}{15}$ $\frac{a}{3}$

24. $\frac{-16x^2}{9} \cdot \frac{9}{4x}$ $-4x$

25. $\frac{-6y^5}{7} \cdot \frac{-3}{14y^2}$ $\frac{9y^3}{49}$

Geometry In Exercises 26–28, find the area of the figure.

26.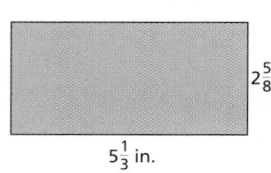
$2\frac{5}{8}$ in.
$5\frac{1}{3}$ in.
14 in.^{2}

27.
$1\frac{5}{9}$ in.
$2\frac{4}{7}$ in.
2 in.^{2}

28.
$2\frac{1}{8}$
$3\frac{2}{3}$ in.
$7\frac{19}{24}$ in.^{2}

▦ In Exercises 29–32, use a calculator to multiply. Round your result to three decimal places.

29. $\frac{9}{16} \cdot \frac{6}{13}$ 0.260

30. $\frac{17}{25} \cdot 2\frac{3}{4}$ 1.87

31. $\frac{23}{48} \cdot (-7)$ -3.354

32. $\frac{-21}{32} \cdot \frac{2}{5}$ -0.263

P Portfolio Opportuni

Extra Practice

Reteaching

Exercises 33–36, write each decimal as a fraction. Then multiply.

$\frac{3}{8}, \frac{7}{10}, \frac{21}{80}$

33. 0.25; 0.6 $\frac{1}{4}, \frac{2}{3}, \frac{1}{6}$ **34.** 0.3̄; 0.75 $\frac{1}{3}, \frac{3}{4}, \frac{1}{4}$ **35.** 0.2; 0.625 $\frac{1}{5}, \frac{5}{8}, \frac{1}{8}$ **36.** 0.375; 0.7

Dinosaurs   In Exercises 37–42, use the information given with the photograph to find the length of the dinosaur.

37. Torosaurus: Length is $\frac{1}{3}$ of Diplodocus   30 ft

38. Stegosaurus: Length is $\frac{2}{3}$ of Torosaurus   20 ft

39. Ankylosaurus: Length is $\frac{3}{4}$ of Stegosaurus   15 ft

40. Tyrannosaurus Rex: Length is $2\frac{2}{3}$ of Ankylosaurus

41. Ornitholestes: Length is $\frac{3}{20}$ of Tyrannosaurus Rex

42. Brachiosaurus: Length is $13\frac{1}{3}$ of Ornitholestes.

40. 40 ft   **41.** 6 ft   **42.** 80 ft

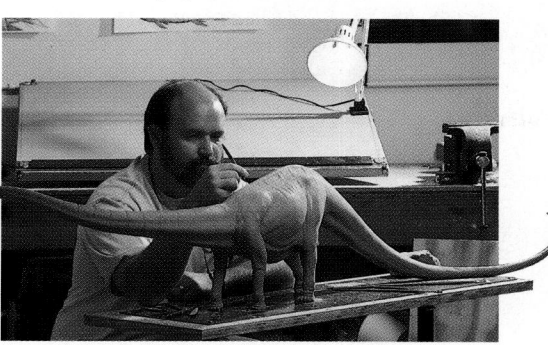

The longest known dinosaur was the Diplodocus measuring 90 feet.

Coins   In Exercises 43–46, represent the money shown as a fraction of a dollar.

43.  or $\frac{3}{25}$

44.   $\frac{36}{100}$ or $\frac{9}{25}$

45.   $\frac{30}{100}$ or $\frac{3}{10}$

46. $\frac{52}{100}$ or $\frac{13}{25}$

Integrated Review

Mental Math   In Exercises 47–52, solve the equation.

47. $4x = \frac{5}{6}$ $\frac{5}{24}$

48. $-9x = \frac{3}{7}$ $-\frac{1}{21}$

49. $-12x = \frac{-12}{19}$ $\frac{1}{19}$

50. $3x + 5x = \frac{4}{3}$ $\frac{1}{6}$

51. $13x = \frac{6}{11} + 8x$ $\frac{6}{55}$

52. $4x = 10x - \frac{12}{13}$ $\frac{2}{13}$

Making Connections within Mathematics

Exploration and Extension

The Number Line   In Exercises 53–55, use the number line below.

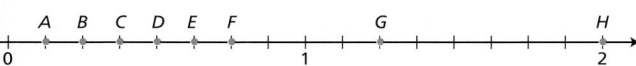

53. What point on the number line represents the product of D and F? C

54. What point on the number line represents the product of D and G? E

55. What point on the number line represents the product of H and A? B

More difficult exercises

7.4 • *Multiplication of Rational Numbers*   **311**

▶ Ex. 37–42
COOPERATIVE LEARNING
Assign these exercises as a group. The problems could be done as a cooperative group activity.

Integrated Review
These exercises provide a good review of solving multistep equations.

Exploration and Extension
These problems follow the same type of reasoning as is used in the Writing Prompt.

Portfolio Opportunity: Math Log
Reread exercises 37–42 in Section 7.4 of Windows to Algebra and Geometry. What word or phrase is used to indicate multiplication by a fraction?

Also available as a copymaster, page 22, Ex. 4

Short Quiz
Covers Lessons 7.3 and 7.4

Available as a copymaster, page 108

Alternative Assessment
Chapter 7 Group Assessment
A problem-solving exploration based on number properties.

Chapter 7 Individual Assessment
A similar follow-up activity for individual students. Adds incentive for the group activity and measures individual competence in the activity.

Available as copymasters, pages 71, 72

PACING the Lesson

Suggested Number of Days
Basic/Average 2 **Above Average** 1
Advanced 1

PLANNING the Lesson

Lesson Plan 7.5, p. 55

ORGANIZER

Starters (reproduced below)
 Problem of the Day 7.5, p. 20
 Warm-Up Exercises 7.5, p. 20
Lesson Resources
 Teaching Tools
  Graph paper, pp. T1, C2
 Math Log, p. 23
 Technology, p. 39
 Answer Masters 7.5, pp. 140, 141
 Extra Practice Copymaster 7.5, p. 55
 Reteaching Copymaster 7.5, p. 55
Special Populations
 Suggestions, Teacher's Edition, p. 292D

LESSON Notes

Many real-life situations involve the division of rational numbers. Rate comparisons are very common ("How many miles to the gallon does this car get?") Encourage students to put the rule for Dividing Rational Numbers in their journals.

Example 1

Addressing Misconceptions

Some students may ask: How is it that we can divide by multiplying (by the reciprocal of the divisor)? One explanation follows.

$$\frac{1}{5} \div \frac{3}{4} = \frac{\frac{1}{5}}{\frac{3}{4}} \cdot 1 = \frac{\frac{1}{5}}{\frac{3}{4}} \cdot \frac{\frac{4}{3}}{\frac{4}{3}}$$

$$= \frac{\frac{1}{5} \cdot \frac{4}{3}}{\frac{3}{4} \cdot \frac{4}{3}} = \frac{\frac{1}{5} \cdot \frac{4}{3}}{1} = \frac{1}{5} \cdot \frac{4}{3}$$

7.5 Division of Rational Numbers

What you should learn:

Goal 1 How to divide rational numbers

Goal 2 How to use division of rational numbers to solve real-life measurement problems

Why you should learn it:

You can use use division of rational numbers to solve real-life problems, such as finding the number of horses that can be grazed on a pasture.

Goal 1 Dividing Rational Numbers

Suppose you took 7 rides on a water slide in a half hour. How many rides could you take in an hour?

$$\frac{7 \text{ rides}}{\frac{1}{2} \text{ hour}} = \frac{14 \text{ rides}}{\text{hour}}$$

Dividing by $\frac{1}{2}$ produces the same result as multiplying by 2.

Dividing Rational Numbers

To divide by a fraction, multiply by its reciprocal.

Numerical Example	**Variable Example**
$\frac{1}{5} \div \frac{3}{4} = \frac{1}{5} \cdot \frac{4}{3} = \frac{4}{15}$	$\frac{a}{b} \div \frac{c}{d} = \frac{a}{b} \cdot \frac{d}{c} = \frac{ad}{bc}$

Example 1 *Dividing Rational Numbers*

a. $\frac{3}{4} \div 3 = \frac{3}{4} \cdot \frac{1}{3}$ *Reciprocal of 3 is $\frac{1}{3}$.*

  $= \frac{3 \cdot 1}{4 \cdot 3}$ *Multiply fractions.*

  $= \frac{1}{4}$ *Simplify fraction.*

b. $\frac{-2}{3} \div \frac{-4}{5} = \frac{-2}{3} \cdot \frac{5}{-4}$ *Reciprocal of $\frac{-4}{5}$ is $\frac{5}{-4}$.*

  $= \frac{-10}{-12}$ *Multiply fractions.*

  $= \frac{5}{6}$ *Simplify fraction.*

c. $3 \div 4\frac{1}{2} = 3 \div \frac{9}{2}$ *Write mixed number as fraction.*

  $= 3 \cdot \frac{2}{9}$ *Reciprocal of $\frac{9}{2}$ is $\frac{2}{9}$.*

  $= \frac{6}{9}$ *Multiply.*

  $= \frac{2}{3}$ *Simplify fraction.*

d. $\frac{x}{2} \div 3 = \frac{x}{2} \cdot \frac{1}{3}$ *Reciprocal of 3 is $\frac{1}{3}$.*

  $= \frac{x}{6}$ *Multiply fractions.*

Study Tip...
Note that negative fractions can be written in several ways. For instance,
$-\frac{4}{5}, \frac{-4}{5}$, and $\frac{4}{-5}$
are all equivalent.

STARTER: Problem of the Day

Figure Analogies

 is to  as

 is to?

Also available as a copymaster, page 20

STARTER: Warm-Up Exercises

1. Use your math journal to answer the following questions. What is a unit analysis? How does it provide a check of the solution of an equation?
Answers will vary.

2. Multiply.
a. $\frac{4}{7} \cdot \frac{3}{-8}$ **b.** $\frac{20}{27} \cdot -\frac{9}{12}$

a. $-\frac{3}{14}$, **b.** $-\frac{5}{9}$

Also available as a copymaster, page 20

Solving Real-Life Problems

Real Life
Ranching

Example 2 *Multiplying and Dividing Fractions*

You own a horse ranch. Your pasture is rectangular, with a width of $\frac{1}{2}$ mile and a length of $\frac{3}{4}$ mile. The recommended grazing area for each horse is $\frac{3}{2}$ acres. There are 640 acres in a square mile. What is the maximum number of horses you should have in your pasture?

Solution Your pasture has an area of $\frac{1}{2} \cdot \frac{3}{4}$, or $\frac{3}{8}$ square mile. To find the number of acres in your pasture, multiply by 640.

$$\frac{640 \text{ acres}}{1 \text{ square mile}} \cdot \left(\frac{3}{8} \text{ square mile}\right) = 240 \text{ acres}$$

To find the maximum number of horses, divide 240 acres by $\frac{3}{2}$ (acres per horse).

$$240 \text{ acres} \div \left(\frac{3}{2} \frac{\text{acres}}{\text{horses}}\right) = 240 \text{ acres} \cdot \frac{2}{3} \frac{\text{horses}}{\text{acres}}$$
$$= 240 \cdot \frac{2}{3} \text{ horses}$$
$$= 160 \text{ horses}$$

You can have up to 160 horses in your pasture. ■

In 1991, Americans owned about 4.9 million horses. Of the families who owned horses, the average number owned was 2.5.

Communicating about MATHEMATICS

Cooperative Learning

P ▶ **SHARING IDEAS about the Lesson**

Division Model Work with a partner. Divide the rectangle into squares, each of which has an area of $\frac{4}{25}$ square unit. How many small squares did you form? Show how to solve the problem both geometrically and algebraically.

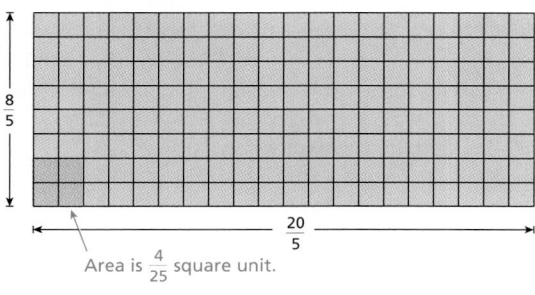

$\frac{8}{5}$

$\frac{20}{5}$

Area is $\frac{4}{25}$ square unit.

$\frac{0}{5}\big) \div \frac{4}{25}$

$\cdot \frac{25}{4}$

eometric solution,
dditional Answers.

Unit analysis often helps us formulate solutions and check answers for real-life problems.

Example 2

Notice how the unit analysis helps us see if the correct relationship has been formed. In particular, if we had written $\frac{3}{2} \div 240$, a unit analysis would show that a wrong relationship had been formed because our answer would have the unit $\frac{1}{\text{horses}}$.

Communicating about MATHEMATICS

Students should discuss their findings in class and record them in their math journals.

Writing Prompt
When I see $\frac{a}{b}$ I think . . .
When I see $a \div b$ I think . . .

OPTION: Extra Examples

Here are additional examples similar to Example 1 of the lesson.

a. $2\frac{2}{3} \div \frac{1}{6} = \frac{8}{3} \div \frac{1}{6}$ Write mixed number as fraction.

$= \frac{8}{3} \cdot 6$ Reciprocal of $\frac{1}{6}$ is 6.

$= 16$ Multiply.

b. $\frac{-2}{3} \div \frac{6}{x} = \frac{-2}{3} \cdot \frac{x}{6}$ Reciprocal of $\frac{6}{x}$ is $\frac{x}{6}$.

$= \frac{-2 \cdot x}{3 \cdot 6}$ Multiply fractions.

$= -\frac{x}{9}$ Simplify fraction.

Technology

| Multiplying and Dividing Rational Numbers | **7.4 & 7.5** Name _____ |

Problem Solving Using a Calculator   On page 42 of this supplement, you learned how to use the a b/c key on a scientific calculator to find the sum and difference of unlike fractions. In this activity, you will use the same key to multiply and divide rational numbers.

EXAMPLE Multiplying and Dividing Rational Numbers

Use a scientific calculator to evaluate the expression.

a. $\frac{-3}{8} \cdot \frac{9}{5}$ b. $2\frac{1}{7} \div \frac{21}{32}$ c. $-3\frac{3}{4} \div 1\frac{9}{16} \cdot \frac{-23}{3}$

SOLUTION

a. Enter the following keystrokes:
3 +/- a b/c 8 × 9 a b/c 5 =
The display should show $\frac{-27}{40}$.

b. Enter the following keystrokes:
2 a b/c 1 a b/c 7 ÷ 21 a b/c 32 =
The display should show $3\frac{1}{49}$.

c. Enter the following keystrokes:
3 +/- a b/c 3 a b/c 4 ÷ 1 a b/c 9 a b/c 16 × 23 +/- a b/c 3 =
The display should show $18\frac{2}{5}$.

EXERCISES

In Exercises 1–6, use a scientific calculator to evaluate the expression. If possible, write your answer as a mixed number and an improper fraction.

1. $\frac{5}{6} \cdot \frac{4}{11}$ $\frac{10}{33}$
2. $-2\frac{3}{4} \cdot 3\frac{3}{16}$ $-8\frac{49}{64} \cdot \frac{-561}{64}$
3. $\frac{-9}{2} \div \frac{7}{4} \cdot -2\frac{4}{7}$ $\frac{-18}{7}$
4. $6 \div \frac{10}{17}$ $\frac{17}{20}$
5. $\frac{7}{3} \cdot 3\frac{3}{5} \div 1$ $15\frac{13}{15} \frac{238}{15}$
6. $-1\frac{5}{16} \cdot \frac{8}{11} \cdot \frac{54}{7}$ -26

In Exercises 7–9, using only your calculator, find x.

7.   Area = x $x = \frac{77}{125}$ in.²
8.   Area = $6\frac{8}{10}$ cm² $x = 1\frac{4}{5}$ cm
9.   Area = 24 ft² $x = 4\frac{1}{2}$ ft

10. You and a classmate each use a calculator to evaluate $\frac{8}{9} \div \frac{4}{5}$. Your final answer is $\frac{40}{36}$ and your classmate's is 2.56. Which answer is correct? Why? Explain how each answer was obtained. See back of supplement.

© D. C. Heath and Company   *Technology Using Calculators and Computers* **39**

ASSIGNMENT GUIDE

Basic/Average:
  Day 1: Ex. 11–21 odd, 22, 23–31 odd
  Day 2: Ex. 33–43 odd, 45, 46, 49–55 odd
Above Average:
  Ex. 11–43 odd, 45, 46, 49–55 odd
Advanced: Ex. 11–43 odd, 45, 46, 49–55 odd
Selected Answers: Ex. 1–10, 11–51 odd

Guided Practice

▶ **Ex. 7–10** Have students work these in their groups and then share results.

Independent Practice

▶ **Ex. 14** Check for students' understanding of reciprocals in this problem.
▶ **Ex. 15–17** Have students check and correct these in their groups.
▶ **Ex. 18–21** Assign these as a group. For Ex. 18–21, encourage students to solve these using mental math and/or draw sketches of the problems. For example, for Ex. 18:

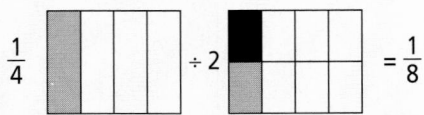

▶ **Ex. 23–26** These exercises should be assigned as a group.
▶ **Ex. 22, 27** These should be discussed as a summary of this page.

Answers

15. Multiply by the reciprocal of $\frac{3}{5}$, not by the reciprocal of $-\frac{3}{2}$.

$$-\frac{3}{2} \div \frac{3}{5} = -\frac{3}{2} \cdot \frac{5}{3}$$
$$= -\frac{5}{2}$$

16. The reciprocal of $2\frac{1}{2}$ is $\frac{2}{5}$, not $\frac{5}{2}$.

$$8 \div 2\frac{1}{2} = 8 \div \frac{5}{2}$$
$$= 8 \cdot \frac{2}{5}$$
$$= \frac{16}{5}$$

17. Multiply by the reciprocal of $\frac{1}{3}$, not by $\frac{1}{3}$.

$$\frac{1}{3} \div \frac{1}{3} = \frac{1}{3} \cdot 3$$
$$= 1$$

314 Chapter 7

EXERCISES

Guided Practice

▶ **CHECK for Understanding**

In Exercises 1–4, write the reciprocal.

1. $\frac{1}{5}$ 5

2. $-\frac{2}{3}$ $-\frac{3}{2}$

3. 7 $\frac{1}{7}$

4. $\frac{4}{t}$ $\frac{t}{4}$

Error Analysis   **In Exercises 5 and 6, describe the error. Then correct it.**

5. 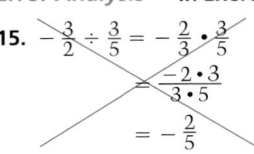 The reciprocal of 3 is $\frac{1}{3}$, not $\frac{3}{1}$.
$\frac{5}{6} \div 3 = \frac{5}{6} \cdot \frac{1}{3} = \frac{5 \cdot 1}{6 \cdot 3} = \frac{5}{18}$

6. 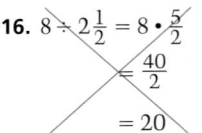 Multiply the denominators also not just the numerators.
$\frac{-4}{3} \div \frac{3}{2} = \frac{-4}{3} \cdot \frac{2}{3} = \frac{-4 \cdot 2}{3 \cdot 3} =$

In Exercises 7–10, simplify the expression.

7. $\frac{1}{2} \div \frac{5}{6}$ $\frac{3}{5}$

8. $6 \div \frac{4}{9}$ $\frac{27}{2}$

9. $\frac{n}{3} \div \frac{3}{2}$ $\frac{2n}{9}$

10. $3\frac{1}{2} \div \frac{4}{x}$ $\frac{7x}{8}$

Independent Practice

In Exercises 11–14, write the reciprocal.

11. $\frac{1}{4}$ 4

12. $\frac{3}{x}$ $\frac{x}{3}$

13. $\frac{7a}{5}$ $\frac{5}{7a}$

14. $-2\frac{2}{3}$ $-\frac{3}{8}$

Error Analysis   **In Exercises 15–17, describe the error. Then correct it.**   See margin.

15. $-\frac{3}{2} \div \frac{3}{5} = -\frac{2}{3} \cdot \frac{3}{5}$
$= \frac{-2 \cdot 3}{3 \cdot 5}$
$= -\frac{2}{5}$

16. $8 \div 2\frac{1}{2} = 8 \cdot \frac{5}{2}$
$= \frac{40}{2}$
$= 20$

17. $\frac{1}{3} \div \frac{1}{3} = \frac{1}{3} \cdot \frac{1}{3}$
$= \frac{1}{3 \cdot 3}$
$= \frac{1}{9}$

Mental Math   **In Exercises 18–21, simplify the expression.**

18. $\frac{1}{4} \div 2$ $\frac{1}{8}$

19. $\frac{1}{4} \div 3$ $\frac{1}{12}$

20. $\frac{1}{4} \div 4$ $\frac{1}{16}$

21. $\frac{1}{4} \div 5$ $\frac{1}{20}$

✪ **22.** *Finding a Pattern*   In Exercises 18–21, write each result as a decimal, rounded to two decimal places. Describe the pattern. What happens when you divide a number by larger and larger numbers? See margin, page 315.

In Exercises 23–26, simplify the expression.

23. $\frac{3}{2} \div \frac{1}{2}$ 3

24. $\frac{3}{2} \div \frac{1}{3}$ $\frac{9}{2}$

25. $\frac{3}{2} \div \frac{1}{4}$ 6

26. $\frac{3}{2} \div \frac{1}{5}$ $\frac{15}{2}$

✪ **27.** *Finding a Pattern*   In Exercises 23–26, write each result as a decimal. Describe the pattern. What happens when you divide a number by smaller and smaller numbers? See margin, page 315.

Extra Practice

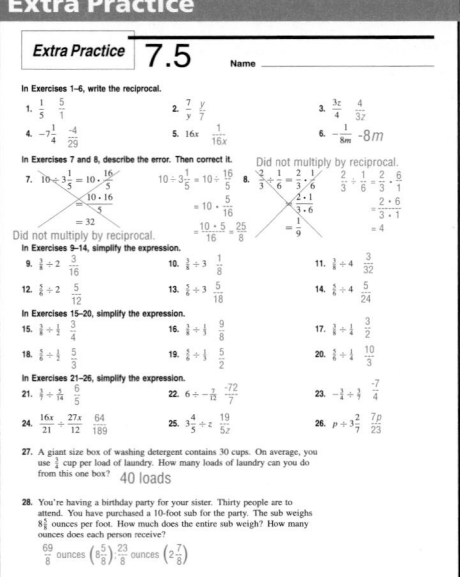

Reteaching

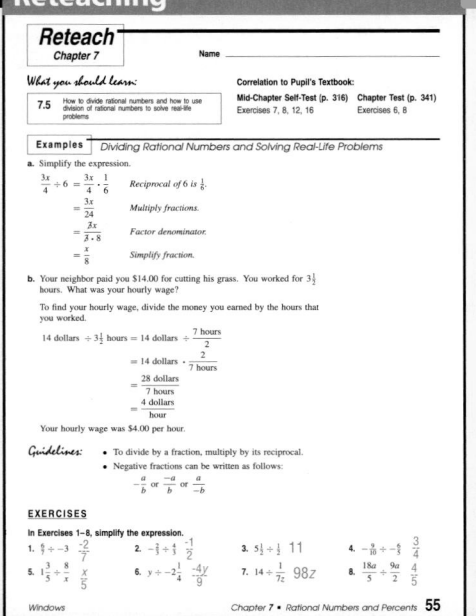

In Exercises 28–39, simplify the expression.

28. $\frac{3}{4} \div 2$ $\frac{3}{8}$

29. $3 \div \frac{-5}{6}$ $-\frac{18}{5}$

30. $\frac{-1}{2} \div \frac{1}{3}$ $-\frac{3}{2}$

31. $\frac{7}{4} \div \frac{1}{-4}$ -7

32. $3\frac{1}{2} \div \frac{3}{4}$ $\frac{14}{3}$

33. $\frac{4}{5} \div 1\frac{1}{2}$ $\frac{8}{15}$

34. $\frac{x}{2} \div (-4)$ $-\frac{x}{8}$

35. $\frac{-3}{5} \div \frac{9}{x}$ $-\frac{x}{15}$

36. $6\frac{2}{3} \div a$ $\frac{20}{3a}$

37. $n \div 1\frac{1}{4}$ $\frac{4n}{5}$

38. $\frac{1}{y} \div \frac{4}{y}$ $\frac{1}{4}$

39. $\frac{3b}{2} \div \frac{9b}{5}$ $\frac{5}{6}$

40. $2.40 per hour, multiply the answer by $1\frac{2}{3}$.

40. *Baby-sitting*   You baby-sat your three-year old sister and received $4.00 for working $1\frac{1}{3}$ hours. What was your hourly wage? Explain how to check your answer. See above.

41. *Baby-sitting*   You baby-sat your neighbor's son for $3\frac{3}{4}$ hours. You earned $12.00. What was your hourly wage? Explain how to check your answer. See below.

42. *Pizza*   You ordered 3 pizzas to be delivered when your friends come over. You think each person will eat $\frac{3}{8}$ of a pizza. How many people can you feed? 8

43. *Water Pitcher*   A pitcher holds $\frac{3}{4}$ gallon of water. If each water glass holds $\frac{1}{16}$ gallon, how many glasses can be filled? 12

41. $3.20 per hour, multiply the answer by $3\frac{3}{4}$.

Geometry   **In Exercises 44–47, write an equation that allows you to solve for x. Then solve the equation.**

44.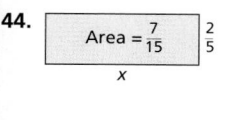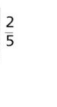

Area $= \frac{7}{15}$, $\frac{2}{5}$, x

$\frac{2}{5}x = \frac{7}{15}$, $1\frac{1}{6}$

45.

Area $= \frac{3}{40}$, $\frac{3}{8}$, x

$\frac{3}{8}x = \frac{3}{40}$, $\frac{1}{5}$

46.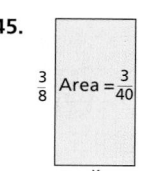

Area $= \frac{9}{8}$, x, $2\frac{1}{4}$

$\frac{1}{2}\left(\frac{9}{4}x\right) = \frac{9}{8}$, 1

47.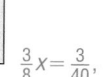

Area $= \frac{63}{4}$, $3\frac{1}{2}$, x

$\frac{7}{2}x = \frac{63}{4}$, $\frac{9}{2}$

Integrated Review

Making Connections within Mathematics

Unit Analysis   **In Exercises 48–51, determine the unit of measure of the quotient.**

48. $\dfrac{\text{miles}}{\left(\dfrac{\text{miles}}{\text{hour}}\right)}$ hours

49. $\left(\dfrac{\text{miles}}{\text{hour}}\right)$ (hours)   miles

50. $\left(\dfrac{\text{dollars}}{\text{pound}}\right)$ (pounds)   dollars

51. $\dfrac{\text{liters}}{\left(\dfrac{\text{liters}}{\text{minute}}\right)}$ minutes

---

Exploration and Extension

Number Sense   **In Exercises 52–55, use the restrictions for the numbers *a*, *b*, and *c* at the right. Complete the statement with $<$, $>$, $=$, or CBD (can't be determined). Give examples to illustrate your answer.**

52. $\frac{a}{b}$ [?] b $>$

53. $b \cdot c$ [?] c $<$

54. $c \div a$ [?] b CBD

55. $a \div a$ [?] $\frac{b}{b}$ $=$ For examples, see margin.

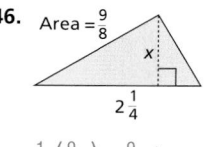

a is greater than 1.

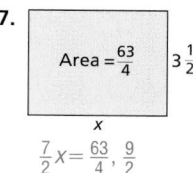

b is between 0 and 1.

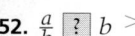
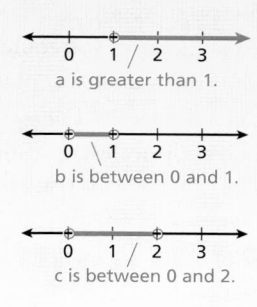

c is between 0 and 2.

▶ **Ex. 28–39** These exercises provide additional practice, combining work with integers and variable expressions.
▶ **Ex. 42, 43** These problems could be solved using a visual model.

Integrated Review

These exercises revisit unit analysis.

Exploration and Extension

COOPERATIVE LEARNING

Have students work these exercises in their groups and then report back to the entire class with the solutions.

Portfolio Opportunity: Math Log

Describe what happens when you divide a number by smaller and smaller negative numbers.

Also available as a copymaster, page 23, Ex. 5

Answers

22. 0.13, 0.08, 0.06, 0.05   Each denominator after the first is 4 more than the preceding denominator. The result gets smaller and smaller.

27. 3, 4.5, 6, 7.5   Each number after the first is $\frac{3}{2}$ or 1.5 more than the preceding number. The result gets larger and larger.

52. $\dfrac{\frac{3}{2}}{\frac{1}{2}} > \frac{1}{2}$, $\dfrac{\frac{3}{1}}{\frac{1}{4}} > \frac{1}{4}$

53. $\frac{1}{2} \cdot \frac{1}{3} < \frac{1}{3}$, $\frac{1}{4} \cdot \frac{5}{4} < \frac{5}{4}$

54. $\frac{1}{3} \div \frac{3}{2} < \frac{1}{2}$, $\frac{5}{4} \div 3 > \frac{1}{4}$

55. $\frac{3}{2} \div \frac{3}{2} = \dfrac{\frac{1}{2}}{\frac{1}{2}}$, $3 \div 3 = \dfrac{\frac{1}{4}}{\frac{1}{4}}$

Take this test as you would take a test in class. The answers to the exercises are given in the back of the book.

In Exercises 1–4, find the sum or difference and simplify, if possible. (7.1, 7.2)

1. $\frac{1}{11} + \frac{3}{11}$ $\frac{4}{11}$

2. $\frac{5}{6} - \frac{1}{6}$ $\frac{4}{6}, \frac{2}{3}$

3. $\frac{7}{10} + \frac{4}{25}$ $\frac{43}{50}$

4. $\frac{9}{10} - \frac{1}{2}$ $\frac{4}{10}, \frac{2}{5}$

In Exercises 5–8, find the product or quotient and simplify, if possible. (7.4, 7.5)

5. $-\frac{4}{7} \cdot \frac{7}{8}$ $-\frac{1}{2}$

6. $\frac{2}{3} \cdot \frac{3}{4} \cdot \frac{4}{5}$ $\frac{2}{5}$

7. $\frac{7}{10} \div 2$ $\frac{7}{20}$

8. $\frac{2}{5} \div \left(-\frac{6}{5}\right)$ $-\frac{1}{3}$

In Exercises 9–12, solve the equation. (7.1–7.5)

9. $\frac{4}{5} + a = \frac{1}{4}$ $-\frac{11}{20}$

10. $x - \frac{1}{5} = \frac{4}{5}$ 1

11. $\frac{1}{3}x = \frac{5}{6}$ $\frac{5}{2}$

12. $-4x = \frac{4}{5}$ $-\frac{1}{5}$

13. Find the perimeter and area of the rectangle. **(7.2, 7.4)**

$2\frac{2}{5}$ in.

$5\frac{1}{3}$ in.

$15\frac{7}{15}$ in., $12\frac{4}{5}$ in.²

14. The large square has an area of 1. Find the area of the blue region. **(7.4)**

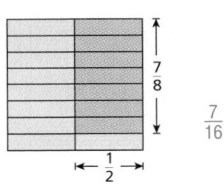

$\frac{7}{8}$

$\frac{1}{2}$

$\frac{7}{16}$ units²

15. A pair of unwashed jeans is 32 inches long. Washing shrinks the jeans to $\frac{7}{8}$ of their original length. How long are they after washing? **(7.4)**   28 in.

16. A piece of lumber is $8\frac{3}{4}$ feet long. The lumber is cut into 5 pieces of equal length. How long is each piece? **(7.5)** $1\frac{3}{4}$ ft.

In Exercises 17 and 18, use the following information. (7.1–7.4)

You are shopping for shoes and find a clearance rack with shoes that are $\frac{1}{3}$ to $\frac{1}{2}$ off the original price. The original price of the shoes is $30.

17. What is the most you could expect to pay? $20

18. What is the least you could expect to pay? $15

19. Which is larger: 0.72 or $\frac{8}{11}$? **(7.3)** $\frac{8}{11}$

20. Which of the following cannot be represented exactly with United States coins?   b

   a. One-fifth of $2.85

   b. One-fourth of $2.85

   c. One-third of $2.85

In 1990, about one fifth of all apparel stores in the United States were shoe stores (Source: U.S. Bureau of the Census)

316   *Chapter **7** ▪ Rational Numbers and Percents*

Partner Quiz

Chapter 7
Mid-Chapter Partner Quiz   (Use after Lesson 7.5)

Name _____

1. Write an expression for the geometric model and evaluate. (7.1)   1. $\frac{3}{8} + \frac{7}{8} - \frac{2}{8}$; 1

2. Find the sum. Then simplify. (7.2)
$\frac{1}{3} + \frac{5}{12} + \frac{3}{8}$ 2. $\frac{9}{8}$ or $1\frac{1}{8}$

3. Solve the equation. (7.2)
$\frac{2}{3} + c = \frac{1}{5}$ 3. $\frac{-7}{15}$

4. Evaluate the expression by first rewriting in decimal form. Round the result to three decimal places. (7.3)
$\frac{3}{7} + \frac{1}{6} - \frac{2}{9}$ 4. 0.373

5. The circle graph compares different uses of your allowance money. What portion of your allowance goes toward your college fund? Round your results to two decimal places. (7.3)   5. $\frac{1}{4}$

College Fund
"Mad Money"
Clothes
Stereo Fund
Entertainment

6. How does multiplying a negative number by a fraction less than 1 affect the size of the original number? (7.4)   6. It increases.

7. Find the area of the given figure. (7.4)   7. $11\frac{5}{8}$ or 11.625

$4\frac{1}{2}$ in.
$2\frac{1}{4}$ in.
$1\frac{1}{3}$ in.

8. Complete the statement. Division by $\frac{a}{b}$, $b \neq 0$, is the same as multiplication by $\boxed{?}$. (7.5)   8. $\frac{b}{a}$; $a \neq 0$

9. Describe the reciprocal of an integer. (7.5)   9. Descriptions vary slightly. Possible description: $\frac{1}{\text{integer}}$

10. It takes $\frac{1}{2}$ hour to mow $\frac{3}{4}$ of the lawn. How long does it take to mow the entire lawn? (7.4)   10. $\frac{7}{6}$ or $1\frac{1}{6}$ hr

50 *Alternative Assessment ▪*   © D.C. Heath and Company

Mid-Chapter Test

Mid-Chapter 7 Test **Form B**   Name _____
(Use after Lesson 7.5)   Date _____

In Exercises 1 and 2, find the sum or difference and simplify, if possible. (7.1, 7.2)

1. $\frac{8}{15} - \frac{9}{20}$ 1. $\frac{1}{12}$

2. $\frac{3}{14} + \frac{56}{35}$ 2. $\frac{71}{70}$ or $1\frac{1}{70}$

In Exercises 3 and 4, find the product or quotient and simplify, if possible. (7.4, 7.5)

3. $\frac{9}{10} \cdot \left(-\frac{5}{7}\right) \cdot \frac{3}{5}$ 3. $\frac{-27}{175}$

4. $\frac{2}{6} \div \left(-\frac{13}{42}\right)$ 4. $\frac{-7}{3}$

In Exercises 5 and 6, solve the equation. (7.2, 7.5)

5. $\frac{5}{9} + d = \frac{4}{15}$ 5. $d = \frac{-13}{45}$

6. $\frac{-3}{4}k = \frac{7}{12}$ 6. $k = \frac{-7}{9}$

7. Draw a rectangle that has a perimeter of $6\frac{1}{2}$. Find its area. (7.1, 7.2, 7.4)   7. Answers will vary.

8. Evaluate the expression by first rewriting in decimal form. Round your result to two decimal places. (7.3)
$2\frac{5}{8} + 3\frac{2}{7} - 1\frac{5}{16} + 4\frac{1}{8}$ 8. 8.41

9. A 6-foot submarine sandwich is cut into 18 equal pieces. How long is each piece? (7.5)   9. 4 inches or 1/3 foot

10. One store is selling running shoes originally priced at $54.99 a pair but marked "$\frac{1}{3}$ off." Another store is selling the shoes at the same price, but takes $\frac{1}{5}$ off the price of the first pair and $\frac{1}{4}$ off the first price of the second pair. Which is a better deal if you are buying two pairs of shoes? By how much? (7.4)   10. 2 pairs each at 1/5 off; $5.50

110 *Chapter 7 ▪ Rational Numbers and Percents*   © D.C. Heath and Company   *Windows*

Materials Needed: graph paper or grid paper

In this activity, you will use graph paper to investigate the concept of a portion of a region.

Example   *Finding Portions of Regions*

On a piece of graph paper, outline a square that is 5 units by 5 units. Then shade $\frac{1}{4}$ of the square.

Solution   There are many ways to shade one-fourth of the square. Three ways are shown below. Notice that the entire region has an area of 25 square units, and the shaded region has an area of $6\frac{1}{4}$ square units.

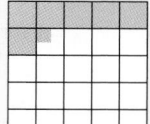 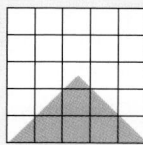 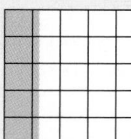

Exercises

In Exercises 1–3, what portion of the 10-by-10 rectangle is shaded blue?

1.  $\frac{1}{4}$

2. 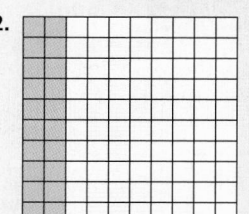 $\frac{1}{5}$

3. 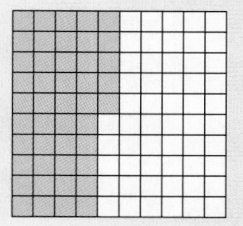 $\frac{9}{20}$

In Exercises 4–6, outline the indicated region on graph paper. Then shade the indicated number of unit squares. See margin.

4. 4×10 Rectangle
Shade 8 unit squares.

5. 5×5 Square
Shade 10 unit squares.

6. 5×9 Rectangle
Shade 9 unit squares.

7. In Exercises 4–6, what portion of each rectangle is shaded? $\frac{1}{5}, \frac{2}{5}, \frac{1}{5}$

8. Shade 8 unit squares on a piece of graph paper. Then draw a rectangle so that the shaded unit squares form one-third of the rectangle. See margin.

9. Shade 12 unit squares on a piece of graph paper. Then draw a rectangle so that the shaded unit squares form one third of the rectangle. See margin.

The goal of this investigation is to build intuition about percents. The last two exercises require a reversal in students' thinking. As a result of the investigation, a 10 x 10 grid can be used to introduce percents.

Materials
Teaching Tools
   Graph paper, pp. T1, C2

Answers

4.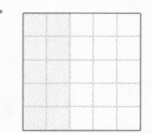

5.

6.

8.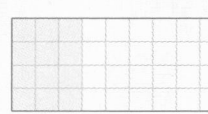

9.

PACING the Lesson

Suggested Number of Days
Basic/Average 2 **Above Average** 1
Advanced 1

PLANNING the Lesson

Lesson Plan 7.6, p. 56

ORGANIZER

Starters (reproduced below)
   Problem of the Day 7.6, p. 20
   Warm-Up Exercises 7.6, p. 20
Lesson Resources
   Teaching Tools
      Graph paper, pp. T1, C2
   Color Transparencies
      Symbols for Example 2, p. 29
   Math Log, p. 23
   Answer Masters 7.6, p. 142
   Extra Practice Copymaster 7.6, p. 56
   Reteaching Copymaster 7.6, p. 56
Special Populations
   Suggestions, Teacher's Edition, p. 292D

LESSON Notes

Percents are the most commonly used way to describe parts of a whole. Have students record the comparisons of the fraction, percent, and verbal forms in their math journals.

Example 1

Common-Error Alert!

Observe that the figure with the greatest percent of its area shaded need not have the largest shaded area.

7.6

Exploring Percents

 What you should learn:

Goal 1 How to write portions as percents

Goal 2 How to use percents to solve real-life problems

 Why you should learn it:

You can use percents to solve real-life problems, such as finding patterns in ancient writings.

> **Study Tip...**
> In Example 1, notice that rewriting each portion as a percent makes it easier to compare the portions. This is one of the main reasons for using percents.

Goal 1 **Writing Percents**

A **portion** is a fraction that compares the measure of part of a quantity to the measure of the whole quantity. For instance, if you own 12 T-shirts, 3 of which are black, then you can say that $\frac{3}{12}$ or $\frac{1}{4}$ of your T-shirts are black. For these portions, the denominators are 12 and 4. When the denominator is 100, the portion is called a **percent**.

> **Percent**
> A **percent** is a portion whose denominator is 100. The symbol % means *percent*. Here is an example.
>
> | Fraction Form | Percent Symbol Form | Verbal Form |
> |:---:|:---:|:---:|
> | $\frac{65}{100}$ | 65% | 65 percent |

Example 1 *Comparing Percents*

Which of the following has the greatest percent of its area shaded?

a. 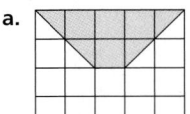 b. 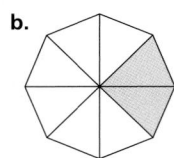 c.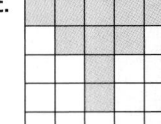

Solution

a. The portion of the region that is shaded is
$$\frac{6}{20} = \frac{6}{20} \cdot \frac{5}{5} = \frac{30}{100} = 30\%.$$

b. The portion of the region that is shaded is
$$\frac{2}{8} = \frac{1}{4} = \frac{1}{4} \cdot \frac{25}{25} = \frac{25}{100} = 25\%.$$

c. The portion of the region that is shaded is
$$\frac{10}{25} = \frac{10}{25} \cdot \frac{4}{4} = \frac{40}{100} = 40\%.$$

The third figure has the greatest percent of its area shaded. ∎

┌─ **STARTER: Problem of the Day** ─┐

What is the product?

$\frac{1}{2} \times \frac{2}{3} \times \frac{3}{4} \times \frac{4}{5} \times \ldots \times \frac{9}{10}$

0.1

Also available as a copymaster, page 20

┌─ **STARTER: Warm-Up Exercises** ─┐

1. Raise each fraction to higher terms as indicated.

a. $\frac{3}{4} = \frac{?}{100}$ **b.** $\frac{17}{25} = \frac{?}{100}$ **c.** $\frac{3}{8} = \frac{?}{96}$

a. 75, **b.** 68, **c.** 36

2. What fraction of each figure is shaded?
a. one half, **b.** one fourth, **c.** one half

a. 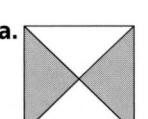 **b.** **c.**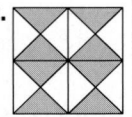

Also available as a copymaster, page 20

Goal 2 Solving Real-Life Problems

Example 2 *Writing Percents*

In the ancient Egyptian hieroglyph shown below, what percent of the symbols is the symbol for water, 〜〜〜 ?

Solution The hieroglyph contains 20 symbols, five of which are the symbol for water.

$$\text{Portion} = \frac{\text{Water symbols}}{\text{Total symbols}}$$

$$= \frac{5}{20}$$

The Rosetta Stone **For hundreds of years, no one could decode Egyptian hieroglyphics. This stone, called the Rosetta Stone, helped solve the mystery. It contains the same message in three languages.**

To rewrite this portion as a percent, multiply the numerator and denominator by 5.

$$\frac{5}{20} = \frac{5}{20} \cdot \frac{5}{5} \qquad \textit{Multiply by } \tfrac{5}{5}.$$

$$= \frac{25}{100} \qquad \textit{Fraction form}$$

$$= 25\% \qquad \textit{Percent form}$$

Thus, 25% of the symbols are symbols for water. ∎

Communicating about MATHEMATICS

▶ **SHARING IDEAS about the Lesson** See below.

Writing Percents What percent of each square is shaded blue? For which square is it easiest to find the percent? Why?

A. 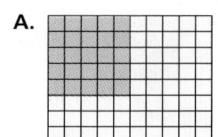 **B.** 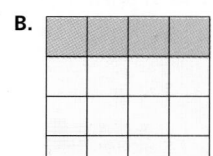 **C.**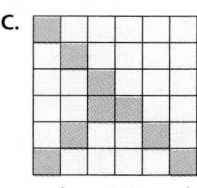

From these results, what common fraction is equal to 25%? $\frac{1}{4}$

A.–C. 25%, **A**, can visually divide the 100 small squares into fourths.

7.6 • Exploring Percents **319**

In any language, certain parts of speech (articles, verbs, prepositions, etc.) and certain words occur with greater frequency. This is often helpful in decoding and encoding languages.

Example 2

Hieroglyphics were used by ancient civilizations instead of an alphabet. A picture or symbol could represent a word, a syllable, or a sound. These pictures and symbols were frequently carved into wood and other hard materials.

Communicating about MATHEMATICS

Challenge
Express each fraction as a percent. (Hint: Use decimals.)
a. $\frac{3}{8}$ **b.** $\frac{5}{12}$
a. 37.5%, **b.** 41.666 %

Writing Prompt
Have students write about the different contexts in which they have heard of percents (school grades, sales, and so on). Refer also to Ex. 26 on page 321.

Here is an additional example similar to Example 1.

Comparing Percents
Which of the following has a greater percent of its area shaded?

a.  **b.** 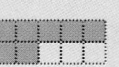 **c.**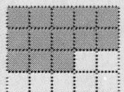

Solution
a. The portion of the region that is shaded is

$$\frac{3}{5} = \frac{3}{5} \cdot \frac{20}{20} = \frac{60}{100} = 60\%.$$

b. The portion of the region that is shaded is

$$\frac{7}{10} = \frac{7}{10} \cdot \frac{10}{10} = \frac{70}{100} = 70\%.$$

c. The portion of the region that is shaded is

$$\frac{13}{20} = \frac{13}{20} \cdot \frac{5}{5} = \frac{65}{100} = 65\%.$$

The second figure has the greatest percent of its area shaded.

ASSIGNMENT GUIDE

Basic/Average:
Day 1: Ex. 5–9, 11–21 odd
Day 2: Ex. 22–36

Above Average:
Ex. 5–9, 11–21 odd, 22–36

Advanced: Ex. 5–9, 11–21 odd, 22, 23, 25, 27–36

Selected Answers: Ex. 1–4, 5–31 odd

Guided Practice

These exercises summarize the key concepts of the lesson.

Independent Practice

▶ **Ex. 5, 6** Remind students that the shaded regions do not have to be adjacent in order to be included in the percent shaded.
▶ **Ex. 9** Have students explain their reasoning in this problem. Make sure that they understand the directive; they must find the percent of the shaded region in each figure and compare *percents*, not areas.
▶ **Ex. 14–17** Before changing each fraction to a percent, students should first reduce the fraction, as was shown in Example 1b.

EXERCISES

Guided Practice

▶ **CHECK for Understanding**

1. Copy and complete the table.

Fraction Form	Percent Symbol Form	Verbal Form
$\frac{24}{100}$	24%	24 percent
$\frac{83}{100}$	83%	83 percent
$\frac{49}{100}$	49%	49 percent

2. What percent of the figure is shaded? 50%

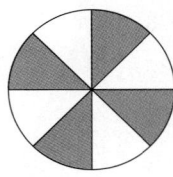

3. Write $\frac{9}{20}$ as a percent. 45%

P 4. *Modeling Percents* Draw two geometric models for 60%. Models vary.

Independent Practice

In Exercises 5–8, determine the percent of the figure that is shaded blue.

5. 36% **6.** 48% **7.** 34% **8.** 14%

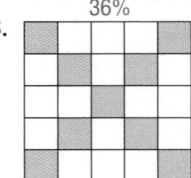 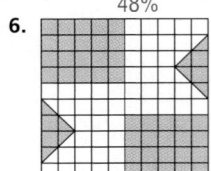 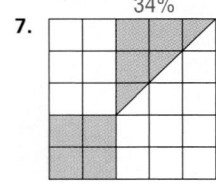 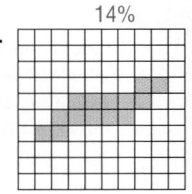

9. Which of the following has the least percent of its area shaded blue? d
Which has the greatest? a

a. **b.** **c.** **d.**

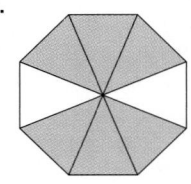  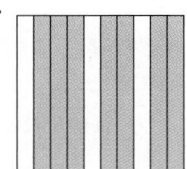 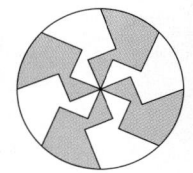

In Exercises 10–17, write each portion as a percent.

10. $\frac{1}{10}$ 10%   **11.** $\frac{1}{20}$ 5%   **12.** $\frac{31}{50}$ 62%   **13.** $\frac{7}{25}$ 28%

14. $\frac{24}{32}$ 75%   **15.** $\frac{18}{40}$ 45%   **16.** $\frac{45}{150}$ 30%   **17.** $\frac{180}{300}$ 60%

P *Modeling Percents* In Exercises 18–21, draw *two* geometric models for the percent. Models vary.

18. 25%   **19.** 20%   **20.** 80%   **21.** 100%

Extra Practice

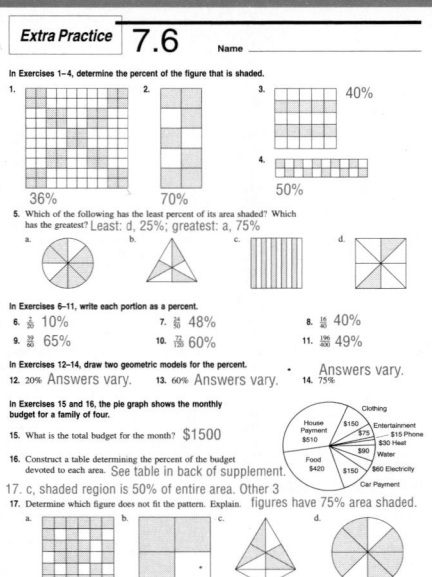

Extra Practice 7.6 Name _____

In Exercises 1–4, determine the percent of the figure that is shaded.

1. 2. 3. 40%
36% 70% 4. 50%

5. Which of the following has the least percent of its area shaded? Which has the greatest? Least: d, 25%; greatest: a, 75%
a. b. c. d.

In Exercises 6–11, write each portion as a percent.
6. $\frac{1}{10}$ 10%   7. $\frac{24}{50}$ 48%   8. $\frac{16}{40}$ 40%
9. $\frac{30}{40}$ 65%   10. $\frac{72}{120}$ 60%   11. $\frac{196}{400}$ 49%

In Exercises 12–14, draw two geometric models for the percent.
12. 20% Answers vary.   13. 60% Answers vary.   14. 75% Answers vary.

In Exercises 15 and 16, the pie graph shows the monthly budget for a family of four.
15. What is the total budget for the month? $1500
16. Construct a table determining the percent of the budget devoted to each area. See table in back of supplement.
17. c, shaded region is 50% of entire area. Other 3
17. Determine which figure does not fit the pattern. Explain. figures have 75% area shaded.
a. b. c. d.

56 Exploring Percents ▪ 7.6   Windows

Reteaching

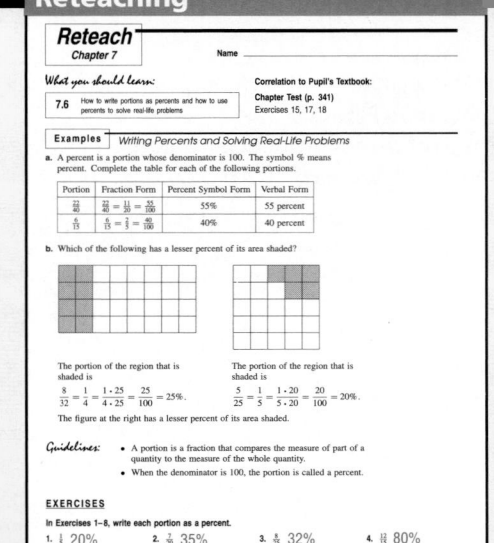

Reteach Chapter 7 Name _____

What you should learn:
7.6 How to write portions as percents and how to use percents to solve real-life problems

Correlation to Pupil's Textbook:
Chapter Test (p. 341)
Exercises 15, 17, 18

Examples *Writing Percents and Solving Real-Life Problems*

a. A percent is a portion whose denominator is 100. The symbol % means percent. Complete the table for each of the following portions.

Portion	Fraction Form	Percent Symbol Form	Verbal Form
$\frac{22}{40}$	$\frac{22}{40} = \frac{11}{20} = \frac{55}{100}$	55%	55 percent
$\frac{6}{15}$	$\frac{6}{15} = \frac{2}{5} = \frac{40}{100}$	40%	40 percent

b. Which of the following has a lesser percent of its area shaded?

The portion of the region that is shaded is
$\frac{8}{32} = \frac{1}{4} = \frac{1 \cdot 25}{4 \cdot 25} = \frac{25}{100} = 25\%.$

The portion of the region that is shaded is
$\frac{5}{25} = \frac{1}{5} = \frac{1 \cdot 20}{5 \cdot 20} = \frac{20}{100} = 20\%.$

The figure at the right has a lesser percent of its area shaded.

Guidelines: • A portion is a fraction that compares the measure of part of a quantity to the measure of the whole quantity.
• When the denominator is 100, the portion is called a percent.

EXERCISES

In Exercises 1–8, write each portion as a percent.
1. $\frac{1}{5}$ 20%   2. $\frac{7}{20}$ 35%   3. $\frac{8}{25}$ 32%   4. $\frac{8}{10}$ 80%
5. $\frac{12}{24}$ 50%   6. $\frac{12}{48}$ 25%   7. $\frac{2}{20}$ 10%   8. $\frac{150}{200}$ 75%

56 Chapter 7 ▪ Rational Numbers and Percents   Windows

Estimation In Exercises 22 and 23, use the map at the right. The blue regions on the map indicate water.

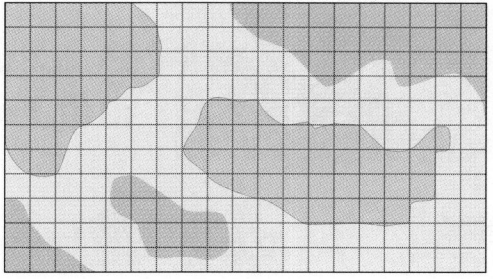

22. About what percent of the region shown on the map is water? 30%

23. Explain how to use your answer to Exercise 22 to estimate the percent of the region that is *not* water.
100%−30% = 70%

In Exercises 24 and 25, determine which figure does not fit the pattern. Explain, using percents. **24.** a, others each have 50% shaded. **25.** c, others each have 33.$\overline{3}$% shaded.

24. a.
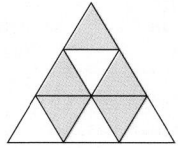
b.

c.
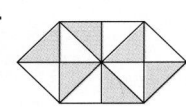
d.
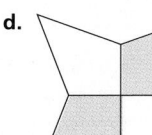

25. a.
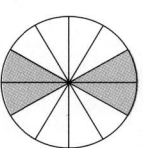
b.
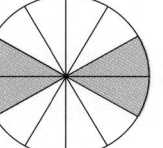
c.
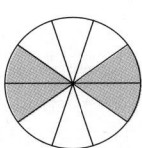
d.
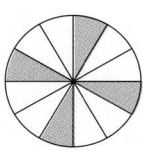

26. *Research Project* Find an advertisement or an article in a magazine or newspaper that uses percents. Then write a paragraph about how percent is used in the article or advertisement. Check students' work.

Integrated Review

Making Connections within Mathematics

Word Meanings In Exercises 27–32, match the "cent word" with its meaning.

a. Century
b. Centennial
c. Centavo
d. Centimeter
e. Centigrade
f. Centipede

27. 1/100th of a peso c
28. 100-base temperature scale e
29. 100 years a
30. 1/100th of a meter d
31. 100th anniverary b
32. Bug with "100 legs" f

Exploration and Extension

Estimating Percents In Exercises 33–36, estimate the percent of a typical school day that you perform each activity. Estimates vary.

33. Eat
✪ 34. Sleep
✪ 35. Attend school
✪ 36. Do homework

✪ More difficult exercises

7.6 • *Exploring Percents* **321**

▶ Ex. 22, 23

EXTENSION
Have students use a real map (or a globe) and estimate the percent of the map covered with water.

Integrated Review
These exercises help to emphasize the meaning of percent.

Exploration and Extension
Have students make sketches of their results.

Portfolio Opportunity: Math Log
What percent of a dollar are the following coins: penny, nickel, dime, quarter, half-dollar, silver dollar?

Also available as a copymaster, page 23, Ex. 6

Short Quiz
Covers Lessons 7.5 and 7.6

Available as a copymaster, page 111

Alternative Assessment
A journal entry activity that develops students' understanding of percents.

Available as a copymaster, page 27

PACING the Lesson

Suggested Number of Days
Basic/Average 2 **Above Average** 1
Advanced 1

PLANNING the Lesson

Lesson Plan 7.7, p. 57

ORGANIZER

Starters (reproduced below)
  Problem of the Day 7.7, p. 21
  Warm-Up Exercises 7.7, p. 21
Lesson Resources
  Color Transparencies
    Diagram for Ex. 53–56, p. 30
  Math Log, pp. 23, 24
  Answer Masters 7.7, pp. 143–145
  Extra Practice Copymaster 7.7, p. 57
  Reteaching Copymaster 7.7, p. 57
Special Populations
  Suggestions, Teacher's Edition, p. 292D

LESSON Notes

To describe real-life situations, we must be able to communicate effectively. Emphasize the importance of knowing a variety of ways to express the concept of percent.

Example 1

Record the rules for writing numbers in percent and decimal forms. Then ask students if there is a pattern in how the decimal point in the percent form is related to its position in the decimal form.

The decimal point is moved two places to the left.

Example 2

Ask students: On changing the number from the decimal form into the percent form, what effect on the position of the decimal point does multiplying by 100% have ?

The decimal point is moved two places to the right.

7.7 Percents, Decimals, and Fractions

What you should learn:

Goal 1 How to write percents as decimals and how to write decimals as percents

Goal 2 How to write fractions as percents and how to write percents as fractions

Why you should learn it:

Knowing how to interpret percents helps you understand data that is presented with circle graphs, such as a circle graph for the age distribution in the United States.

Need to Know

In Examples 1 and 2, notice that some percents are greater than 100%. Also notice that some percents are less than 1%.

Goal 1 Writing Percents as Decimals

In real life, percents are written in several different forms. For instance, a 35% discount at a store can be written in the following ways.

Percent Form	Verbal Form	Fraction Form	Decimal Form
35%	35 percent	$\frac{35}{100}$ or $\frac{7}{20}$	0.35

The first two forms are used for communication and the second two forms are used for computation.

Percent Form and Decimal Form

1. To write a percent as a decimal, remove the percent sign and divide by 100.
2. To write a decimal as a percent, multiply the decimal by 100%.

Example 1 *Rewriting Percents as Decimals*

When you are rewriting a percent in decimal form, remember that *percent* means *per hundred*.

a. $14\% = \frac{14}{100} = 0.14$ b. $0.5\% = \frac{0.5}{100} = 0.005$

c. $100\% = \frac{100}{100} = 1$ d. $125\% = \frac{125}{100} = 1.25$

e. $12.5\% = \frac{12.5}{100} = 0.125$ f. $33\frac{1}{3}\% \approx \frac{33.3}{100} = 0.333$

Example 2 *Rewriting Decimals as Percents*

To rewrite a decimal as a percent, multiply the decimal by 100%.

a. $0.28 = 0.28(100\%) = 28\%$
b. $0.346 = 0.346(100\%) = 34.6\%$
c. $0.9 = 0.9(100\%) = 90\%$
d. $2.3 = 2.3(100\%) = 230\%$
e. $1.045 = 1.045(100\%) = 104.5\%$
f. $0.001 = 0.001(100\%) = 0.1\%$

322 *Chapter 7 • Rational Numbers and Percents*

STARTER: Problem of the Day

Figure Analogies

[figure: is to ... as ... is to?]
[figure: is to ... as ... is to?]

Also available as a copymaster, page 21

STARTER: Warm-Up Exercises

1. Rewrite the fractions in decimal form.

a. $\frac{5}{6}$ b. $\frac{3}{4}$ c. $\frac{1}{3}$ d. $\frac{3}{8}$

a. 0.8333, b. 0.75, c. 0.333, d. 0.375

2. Multiply.

a. 0.313(10)   b. 0.82(100)
c. 0.0346(100)   d. 2.047(1000)
e. 0.304(10)   f. 0.003(100)

a. 3.13, b. 82, c. 3.46, d. 2,047, e. 3.04, f. 0.3

Also available as a copymaster, page 21

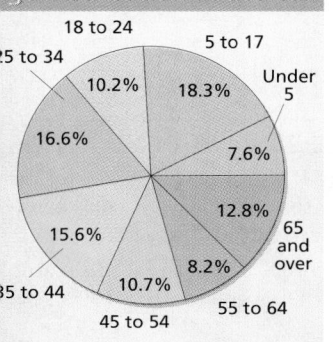

Age Distribution in the U.S.

18 to 24
25 to 34
5 to 17
10.2%
18.3%
16.6%
Under 5
7.6%
12.8%
15.6%
65 and over
8.2%
35 to 44
10.7%
55 to 64
45 to 54

The parts of a circle graph are often labeled with percents. This circle graph shows the age distribution in the United States in 1992. The sum of the percents in a circle graph is 100%. Check that the sum of the percents in this circle graph is 100%.

Goal 2 | **Writing Fractions as Percents**

To rewrite a fraction as a percent, first rewrite the fraction in decimal form. Then multiply by 100%. To rewrite a percent in fraction form, divide by 100%. Then simplify, if possible.

Example 3 | **Rewriting Fractions as Percents**

a. $\frac{7}{8} = 0.875 = 0.875(100\%) = 87.5\%$

b. $\frac{1}{3} \approx 0.333 = 0.333(100\%) = 33.3\%$

c. $\frac{12}{5} = 2.4 = 2.4(100\%) = 240\%$ ∎

Example 4 | **Rewriting Percents as Fractions**

a. $72\% = \frac{72}{100} = \frac{18}{25}$ | **b.** $125\% = \frac{125}{100} = \frac{5}{4}$ ∎

Commonly Used Percents		
$0 = 0\%$	$\frac{1}{10} = 0.1 = 10\%$	$\frac{1}{8} = 0.125 = 12.5\%$
$\frac{1}{6} \approx 0.167 = 16.7\%$	$\frac{1}{5} = 0.2 = 20\%$	$\frac{1}{4} = 0.25 = 25\%$
$\frac{3}{10} = 0.3 = 30\%$	$\frac{1}{3} \approx 0.333 = 33.3\%$	$\frac{3}{8} = 0.375 = 37.5\%$
$\frac{2}{5} = 0.4 = 40\%$	$\frac{1}{2} = 0.5 = 50\%$	$\frac{3}{5} = 0.6 = 60\%$
$\frac{5}{8} = 0.625 = 62.5\%$	$\frac{2}{3} \approx 0.667 = 66.7\%$	$\frac{7}{10} = 0.7 = 70\%$
$\frac{3}{4} = 0.75 = 75\%$	$\frac{4}{5} = 0.8 = 80\%$	$\frac{5}{6} \approx 0.883 = 83.3\%$
$\frac{7}{8} = 0.875 = 87.5\%$	$\frac{9}{10} = 0.9 = 90\%$	$1 = 100\%$

Communicating about **MATHEMATICS**

▶ **SHARING IDEAS about the Lesson**

Circle Graphs What percent of the circle graph is blue?

A.
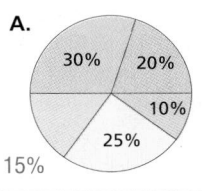
30%
20%
10%
25%
15%

B.
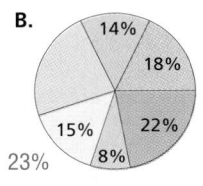
14%
18%
22%
8%
15%
23%

C.
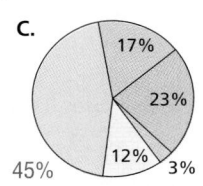
17%
23%
12%
3%
45%

7.7 · *Percents, Decimals, and Fractions* **323**

This section demonstrates how we can combine previously learned skills to enable us to change a number in fraction form into a percent, and vice versa.

Example 3

Sometimes we show the repeating part of $\frac{1}{3}$ and rewrite it in percent form as $33.\overline{3}\%$.

Example 4

Note that when we divide 72% by 100%, the % unit divides to 1:

$\frac{72\%}{100\%} = \frac{72}{100} = \frac{18}{25}$

ALTERNATE APPROACH

Using Tables You may want students to construct the Commonly Used Percents table on their own. Working in small groups, students could complete the percent side of the table and verify their results with members of their group.

Communicating about **MATHEMATICS**

Make another sketch of the circles, using fractions to represent parts of the whole. Then determine what portion of the circle graph is blue.

Writing Prompt
Expand upon Ex. 8 in Guided Practice. Give a real-life example of a percent that is greater than 100% and explain to a friend who was not in class today what this percent means.

ASSIGNMENT GUIDE

Basic/Average:
Day 1: Ex. 9–27 odd, 29–32, 33–47 odd
Day 2: Ex. 49–51 odd, 53–56, 61–69 odd

Above Average:
Ex. 9–27 odd, 33–51 odd, 57–60, 63–69 odd

Advanced: Ex. 9–27 odd, 33–51 odd, 57–60, 63–69 odd

Selected Answers: Ex. 1–8, 9–65 odd

Guided Practice

▶ **Ex. 1–4** Students should also be able to give the answers as fractions.

Independent Practice

▶ **Ex. 15, 16** Remind students to write the fractional part of the percent as a decimal before doing the percent conversion.
▶ **Ex. 17–24** Encourage students to use mental math in solving these problems.
▶ **Ex. 25–28** Some students may tend to ignore the need for a common form in comparing these quantities.
▶ **Ex. 29–32**
EXTENSION
Have students generate their own exercises of this type after researching. Each student could select a topic of personal interest (state demographics, sports, music, entertainment, and so on).

Guided Practice

▶ **CHECK for Understanding**

In Exercises 1–4, what portion of the figure is blue? Express your answer as a percent and as a decimal.

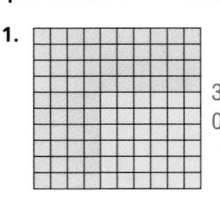

1. 36% 0.36

2. 44% 0.44

3. 12% 0.12

4.

5. See page 322. 0.48
6. See page 322. 4.5%
7. See page 323. 31.25%

5. Explain how to rewrite a percent as a decimal. Then rewrite 48% as a decimal.

6. Explain how to rewrite a decimal as a percent. Then rewrite 0.045 as a percent.

7. Explain how to rewrite a fraction as a percent. Then rewrite $\frac{5}{16}$ as a percent.

5.–7. See above.

8. *Problem Solving* Give a real-life example of a percent that is greater than 100%.
Examples vary.
A 150% increase in the price of some jewelry.

Independent Practice

In Exercises 9–16, rewrite the percent as a decimal.

9. 36% 0.36
10. 47% 0.47
11. 115% 1.15
12. 265% 2.65
13. 89.7% 0.897
14. 1.44% 0.0144
15. $14\frac{2}{3}\%$ ≈ 0.147
16. $36\frac{3}{4}\%$ 0.3675

In Exercises 17–24, rewrite the decimal as a percent.

17. 0.25 25%
18. 0.826 82.6%
19. 0.7 70%
20. 0.9453 94.53%
21. 1.4 140%
22. 3.083 308.3%
23. 0.009 0.9%
24. 0.055 5.5%

In Exercises 25–28, complete the statement with <, >, or =.

25. $\frac{3}{8}$? 3.75% >
26. $\frac{7}{16}$? 43.75% =
27. $\frac{1}{25}$? 4% =
28. $\frac{3}{50}$? 0.6% >

Estimation **In Exercises 29–32, match the percent with the portion of the American population that you think has the indicated characteristic.**

a. Over 85 years old   b. Female   c. Watch television   d. Under 10 years o

29. 51% b
30. 93% c
31. 15% d
32. 1% a

In Exercises 33–40, rewrite the percent as a fraction in simplest form.

33. 52% $\frac{13}{25}$
34. 75% $\frac{3}{4}$
35. 6% $\frac{3}{50}$
36. 8% $\frac{2}{25}$
37. 160% $\frac{8}{5}$
38. 248% $\frac{62}{25}$
39. 102% $\frac{51}{50}$
40. 95% $\frac{19}{20}$

Extra Practice

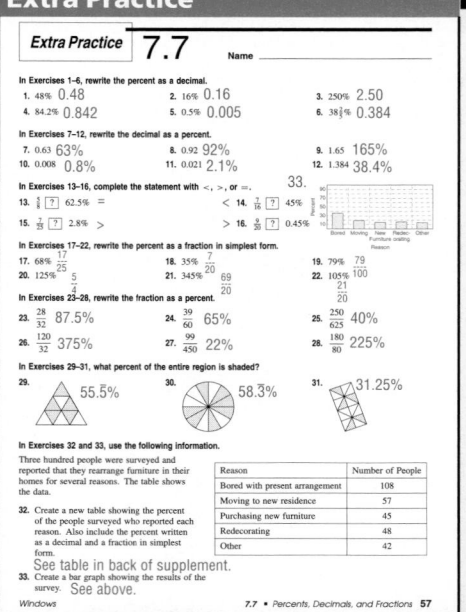

Extra Practice 7.7 Name _____

In Exercises 1–6, rewrite the percent as a decimal.
1. 48% 0.48   2. 16% 0.16   3. 250% 2.50
4. 84.2% 0.842   5. 0.5% 0.005   6. $38\frac{2}{5}\%$ 0.384

In Exercises 7–12, rewrite the decimal as a percent.
7. 0.63 63%   8. 0.92 92%   9. 1.65 165%
10. 0.008 0.8%   11. 0.021 2.1%   12. 1.384 38.4%

In Exercises 13–16, complete the statement with <, >, or =.
13. $\frac{5}{8}$? 62.5% =   14. $\frac{7}{16}$? 45% <
15. $\frac{1}{8}$? 2.8% >   16. $\frac{9}{20}$? 0.45% >

In Exercises 17–22, rewrite the percent as a fraction in simplest form.
17. 68% $\frac{17}{25}$ 18. 35% $\frac{7}{20}$ 19. 79% $\frac{79}{100}$
20. 125% $\frac{5}{4}$ 21. 345% $\frac{69}{20}$ 22. 105% $\frac{21}{20}$

In Exercises 23–28, rewrite the fraction as a percent.
23. $\frac{28}{32}$ 87.5%   24. $\frac{39}{60}$ 65%   25. $\frac{250}{625}$ 40%
26. $\frac{120}{32}$ 375%   27. $\frac{99}{450}$ 22%   28. $\frac{180}{80}$ 225%

In Exercises 29–31, what percent of the entire region is shaded?
29. 55.5%   30. 58.3%   31. 31.25%

In Exercises 32 and 33, use the following information.
Three hundred people were surveyed and reported that they rearrange furniture in their homes for several reasons. The table shows the data.

Reason	Number of People
Bored with present arrangement	108
Moving to new residence	57
Purchasing new furniture	45
Redecorating	48
Other	42

32. Create a new table showing the percent of the people surveyed who reported each reason. Also include the percent written as a decimal and a fraction in simplest form.
See table in back of supplement.
33. Create a bar graph showing the results of the survey. See above.

Windows   7.7 • *Percents, Decimals, and Fractions* **57**

Reteaching

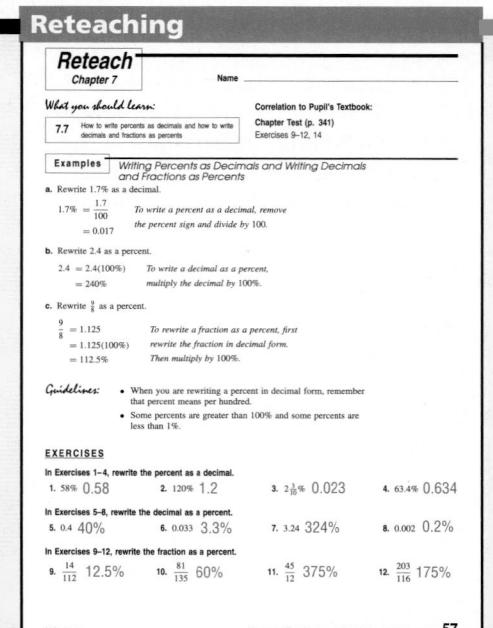

Reteach Chapter 7 Name _____

What you should learn:
7.7 How to write percents as decimals and how to write decimals and fractions as percents

Correlation to Pupil's Textbook:
Chapter Test (p. 341)
Exercises 9–12, 14

Examples *Writing Percents as Decimals and Writing Decimals and Fractions as Percents*

a. Rewrite 1.7% as a decimal.
$1.7\% = \frac{1.7}{100}$ *To write a percent as a decimal, remove the percent sign and divide by 100.*
$= 0.017$

b. Rewrite 2.4 as a percent.
$2.4 = 2.4(100\%)$ *To write a decimal as a percent,*
$= 240\%$ *multiply the decimal by 100%.*

c. Rewrite $\frac{9}{8}$ as a percent.
$\frac{9}{8} = 1.125$ *To rewrite a fraction as a percent, first*
$= 1.125(100\%)$ *rewrite the fraction in decimal form.*
$= 112.5\%$ *Then multiply by 100%.*

Guidelines:
• When you are rewriting a percent in decimal form, remember that percent means per hundred.
• Some percents are greater than 100% and some percents are less than 1%.

EXERCISES

In Exercises 1–4, rewrite the percent as a decimal.
1. 58% 0.58   2. 120% 1.2   3. $2\frac{3}{10}\%$ 0.023   4. 63.4% 0.634

In Exercises 5–8, rewrite the decimal as a percent.
5. 0.4 40%   6. 0.033 3.3%   7. 3.24 324%   8. 0.002 0.2%

In Exercises 9–12, rewrite the fraction as a percent.
9. $\frac{14}{112}$ 12.5%   10. $\frac{81}{135}$ 60%   11. $\frac{45}{12}$ 375%   12. $\frac{203}{116}$ 175%

Windows   Chapter 7 • *Rational Numbers and Percents* **57**

In Exercises 41–48, rewrite the fraction as a percent.

41. $\frac{13}{208}$ 6.25%   **42.** $\frac{52}{650}$ 8%   **43.** $\frac{78}{99} \approx 78.8\%$ **44.** $\frac{375}{450} \approx 83.3\%$

45. $\frac{104}{64}$ 162.5%   **46.** $\frac{429}{286}$ 150%   **47.** $\frac{180}{54} \approx 333.3\%$ **48.** $\frac{357}{252} \approx 141.7\%$

In Exercises 49–52, what percent of the entire region is blue?

49. 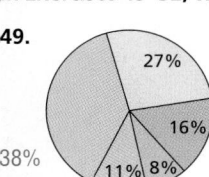   **50.** 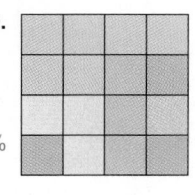   **51.** 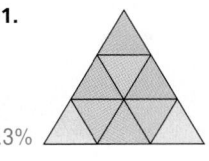   **52.**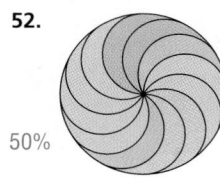

27%, 16%, 38%, 11%, 8%

37.5%   ≈ 33.3%   50%

Cameras   **In Exercises 53–56, use the circle graph at the right.** *(Source: Photo Marketing Association International)*

53. More than 3 out of every 20 American households purchased at least one new camera in 1990. What percent is this? 15%

54. Create a table showing each percent rewritten as a decimal and a fraction in simplest form.   See margin.

55. Show that the sum of the percents is 100%.   See below.

56. Which of the percents is three times as large as another?   12%

Shopping for Cameras

Types of cameras purchased in 1990:

35 mm point-and-shoot 49%

Camcorder 21%

110 13%

126, disc, and other 1%

Instant 4%

35 mm single lens reflex 12%

Test Grades   **In Exercises 57–60, use the table at the right that shows the grades on a math test.**

57. Create a table showing the fraction, decimal, and percent of the number of students receiving each letter grade.   See margin.

58. What percentage of students passed the test (got a D or better)?   95%

59. What percentage of students received a C or better?   87.5%

60. Create a bar graph showing the grade distribution.   See Additional Answers.

Grade	Number of Students
A	|||| |||| |||| |
B	|||| |||| ||||
C	||||
D	|||
F	||

Integrated Review

Making Connections within Mathematics

Estimation   **In Exercises 61–66, estimate the amount and tell how you estimated.**   For how estimated, see margin.

61. $\frac{1}{5}$ of 895   180   **62.** $\frac{4}{9}$ of 365   180   **63.** $\frac{2}{3}$ of $14.95 $10

64. 34% of $27.65 $9   **65.** 83% of 320   240   **66.** 37% of $49.29 $20 or $16

55. 49% + 21% + 13% + 12% + 4% + 1% = 100%

✪ More difficult exercises
Ⓟ Portfolio Opportunity

7.7 ▪ *Percents, Decimals, and Fractions*   **325**

▶ **Ex. 41–48**   Students need a calculator to complete these problems.

EXTENSION
Have students write story problems that relate to the fractions given.
▶ **Ex. 53–56**   Assign these as a group.
▶ **Ex. 57–60**   Assign these as a group.

Integrated Review

Student explanations that accompany their answers to these exercises may be more important than the numerical results.

Answers

54.

49%	0.49	$\frac{49}{100}$
21%	0.21	$\frac{21}{100}$
13%	0.13	$\frac{13}{100}$
12%	0.12	$\frac{3}{25}$
4%	0.04	$\frac{1}{25}$
1%	0.01	$\frac{1}{100}$

57.

A	$\frac{2}{5}$	0.4	40%
B	$\frac{7}{20}$	0.35	35%
C	$\frac{1}{8}$	0.125	12.5%
D	$\frac{3}{40}$	0.075	7.5%
F	$\frac{1}{20}$	0.05	5%

61.–66.   Estimates vary.

61. $\frac{1}{5}$ of 895 $\approx \frac{1}{5}$ of 900 = 180

62. $\frac{4}{9}$ of 365 $\approx \frac{1}{2}$ of 360 = 180

63. $\frac{2}{3}$ of $14.95 $\approx \frac{2}{3}$ of $15 = $10

64. 34% of $27.65 $\approx \frac{1}{3}$ of $27 = $9

65. 83% of 320 $\approx \frac{4}{5}$ of 300 = 240

66. 37% of $49.29 $\approx \frac{2}{5}$ of $50 = $20, or

37% of $49.29 $\approx \frac{1}{3}$ of $48 = $16

Exploration and Extension

These exercises assess a skill that is extremely important in data analysis.

Portfolio Opportunity: Math Log

1. Describe what the decimal forms of every percent between 0% and 1% have in common.

2. Describe what the decimal forms of every percent greater than 100% have in common.

Also available as copymasters, pages 23, 24, Ex. 7,8

Exploration and Extension

Estimation   **In Exercises 67–69, estimate the percent that is represented by each part of the circle graph. Which parts are easiest to estimate? Why?** See margin.

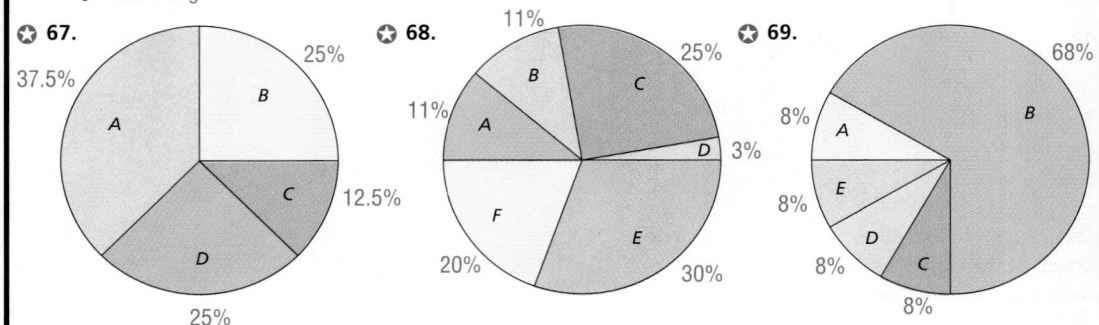

✪ **67.**
✪ **68.**
✪ **69.**

Mixed REVIEW

In Exercises 1–4, solve the equation. (7.2)

1. $\frac{1}{2} = \frac{1}{4} + r$ $\frac{1}{4}$

2. $1 = \frac{1}{6} + a$ $\frac{5}{6}$

3. $\frac{2}{5}z - 2 = \frac{1}{5}z$ 10

4. $-\frac{6}{7} + 3p = -\frac{1}{7}$ $\frac{5}{21}$

In Exercises 5–10, use mental math to solve the equation. (7.7)

5. $58\% + x = 67\%$ 9%

6. $32\% = b - 18\%$ 50%

7. $50\% - r = 25\%$ 25%

8. $84\% = 12\% + x$ 72%

9. $112\% = p - 24\%$ 136%

10. $42\% = 100\% - f$ 58%

In Exercises 11–16, solve the equation. (7.4, 7.5)

11. $\frac{1}{3}x = \frac{1}{2}$ $1\frac{1}{2}$

12. $\frac{1}{4} = \frac{1}{2}y$ $\frac{1}{2}$

13. $3b - \frac{1}{2} = \frac{1}{3}$ $\frac{5}{18}$

14. $\frac{2}{3} = 2d + \frac{1}{6}$ $\frac{1}{4}$

15. $\frac{10}{3} + 2x = \frac{1}{3}$ $-1\frac{1}{2}$

16. $\frac{5}{6} + 5y = \frac{5}{2}$ $\frac{1}{3}$

17. What does it mean when the weatherperson says, "There is a 50% chance of rain"?   It is equally likely to rain and not to rain.

In Exercises 18–20, write the verbal sentence as an equation and solve. (7.2, 7.4, 7.7)

18. x times $\frac{3}{4}$ is 18.75. $\frac{3}{4}x = 18.75,\ 25$

19. The product of $\frac{1}{4}$ and a is $\frac{2}{3}$. $\frac{1}{4}a = \frac{2}{3},\ 2\frac{2}{3}$

20. The sum of x and $\frac{1}{3}$ is $\frac{1}{2}$. $x + \frac{1}{3} = \frac{1}{2},\ \frac{1}{6}$

326   *Chapter 7* ▪ *Rational Numbers and Percents*   ✪ More difficult exercises

---

Answers

67. B and D, each is about $\frac{1}{4}$ of the circle graph.

68. C, it is about $\frac{1}{4}$ of the circle graph.

69. A, C, D, and E; three parts together are about $\frac{1}{4}$ of the circle graph and one part is about $\frac{1}{3}$ of $\frac{1}{4}$ of the circle graph.

7.8

Finding a Percent of a Number

 What you should learn:

Goal 1 How to find a percent of a number

Goal 2 How to use percents to solve real-life problems

 Why you should learn it:

Knowing how to find a percent of a number helps you solve real-life problems, such as finding how many people voted for a presidential candidate.

Goal 1 Finding a Percent of a Number

One way to find a percent of a number is to multiply the *decimal form* of the percent by the number.

Example 1 Finding Percents of Numbers

a. Find 36% of 825.   **b.** Find 150% of 38.

Solution

a. Begin by writing 36% as 0.36. Then multiply by 825.

$$0.36 \times 825 = 297$$

Thus, 36% of 825 is 297.

b. Begin by writing 150% as 1.5. Then multiply by 38.

$$1.5 \times 38 = 57$$

Thus, 150% of 38 is 57. ∎

Example 2 Finding a Percent of an Area

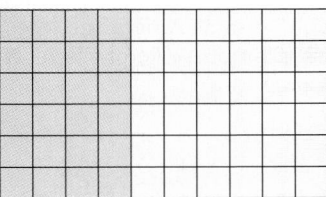

40% of 60 squares is 24 squares.

The rectangle at the left has 60 small squares. How many small squares are in 40% of the rectangle?

Solution   One way to answer this question is to shade 40% or $\frac{4}{10}$ of the rectangle and count the number of squares. Doing this, you can see that 40% of the rectangle consists of 24 squares. Another way to answer the question is to rewrite 40% as 0.4, then multiply by 60.

$$0.4 \times 60 = 24$$

Thus, 40% of 60 squares is 24 squares. ∎

With some common percents, you can use mental math to find the percent of a number. Here are two examples.

Study Tip...
$\frac{1}{3}$ of 100 is $33\frac{1}{3}$. So, $\frac{1}{3}$ of 100% is $33\frac{1}{3}$%.

Problem	Mental Math	Answer
50% of 30	One half of 30	15
$33\frac{1}{3}$% of 36	One third of 36	12

7.8 • Finding a Percent of a Number   **327**

▶**PACING** the Lesson

Suggested Number of Days
Basic/Average 0   **Above Average** 1
Advanced 1

▶**PLANNING** the Lesson

Lesson Plan 7.8, p. 58

ORGANIZER

Starters (reproduced below)
   Problem of the Day 7.8, p. 21
   Warm-Up Exercises 7.8, p. 21
Lesson Resources
   Teaching Tools
      Graph paper, pp. T1, C2
   Math Log, p. 24
   Answer Masters 7.8, pp. 147, 148
   Extra Practice Copymaster 7.8, p. 58
   Reteaching Copymaster 7.8, p. 58
   Enrichment Projects, pp. 37, 38
Special Populations
   Suggestions, Teacher's Edition, p. 292D

LESSON Notes

The convenience of using percent as a ratio of part to whole should become quite evident in this lesson. The close relationship between a percent and the corresponding decimal makes many everyday computations much easier, whether we use mental math or have the added convenience of a calculator.

Example 1

Emphasize that a *percent of a number* is a number value, not another percent.

Example 2

Ask which process students think is more effective for finding 40% of 60. Ask which process is easier to understand. Encourage students to discuss the options.

STARTER: Problem of the Day

Why are 1966 pennies worth almost twenty dollars?
It depends on how you read the question!
That many pennies are equivalent to $19.66, which is almost $20.

Also available as a copymaster, page 21

STARTER: Warm-Up Exercises

1. Multiply.
a. 0.3(638)   **b.** 0.05(46)   **c.** 1.32(516)
a. 191.4, **b.** 2.3, **c.** 681.12

2. Use mental math to evaluate the following.
a. one half of 78
b. one fourth of 120
c. one third of 36
d. three fourths of 200
a. 39, **b.** 30, **c.** 12, **d.** 150

Also available as a copymaster, page 21

Find out whether students are aware of other real-life situations in which percents are used to describe problems and to better understand them. Encourage students to look for sources in newspapers and magazines.

Example 3

Ask students: Do the given percents of the popular vote add to a sum of 100%? If not, what does this indicate? *Some ballots were invalid or were for other candidates.*

Communicating about MATHEMATICS

The models suggested here require students to convert 60% to a fraction ($\frac{3}{5}$). You may wish to explain to students that, in order for the model to work, the dimensions of each rectangle must be such that the area is a multiple of 5.

Writing Prompt

If you knew what 50% of a number was, explain how you would find 10% and 200% of the same number.

Real Life
Politics

In the United States, presidents are elected by electoral votes, not popular votes. For instance, in 1992, Bill Clinton received only 43% of the popular vote, but he received 68.8% of the electoral votes.

Goal 2 | **Solving Real-Life Problems**

Example 3 | *Finding Percents of Numbers*

In the 1992 election for the president of the United States, about 104,425,000 Americans voted. The total number of people who voted is called the *popular vote*. The percent of the popular vote received by the three main candidates is shown below. How many people voted for each of the three candidates?

Candidate	Political Party	Percent of Popular Vote
a. George Bush	Republican	37.4%
b. Bill Clinton	Democrat	43.0%
c. Ross Perot	Independent	18.9%

Solution

a. To find how many people voted for George Bush, rewrite 37.4% as 0.374, and multiply by the total popular vote.

$$0.374 \times 104,425,000 = 39,054,950 \quad \textit{Bush}$$

b. To find how many people voted for Bill Clinton, rewrite 43.0% as 0.43, and multiply by the total popular vote.

$$0.43 \times 104,425,000 = 44,902,750 \quad \textit{Clinton}$$

c. To find how many people voted for Ross Perot, rewrite 18.9% as 0.189, and multiply by the total popular vote.

$$0.189 \times 104,425,000 = 19,736,325 \quad \textit{Perot}$$

From these results, how can you tell that some Americans voted for candidates other than Bush, Clinton, or Perot? ■

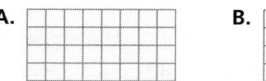
P *Communicating* about MATHEMATICS

▶ **SHARING IDEAS about the Lesson** See margin.

Using Area Models Copy the rectangles on graph paper. Then shade 60% of each rectangle. How many squares did you shade? Explain how to check your results.

A. **B.** **C.**

Answers

A

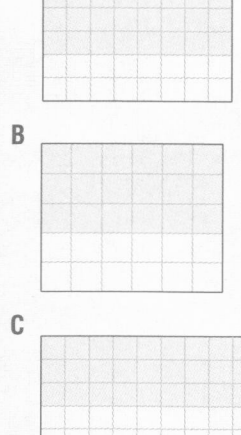

B

C

To check, divide the number of shaded squares by 40, 30, and 45, respectively.

OPTION: Extra Examples

Here are additional examples similar to Example 1.
Finding Percents of Numbers
a. Find 64% of 75.
b. Find 160% of 560.
Solution
a. Begin by writing 64% as 0.64. Then multiply by 75.
   $0.64 \times 75 = 48$.
Thus, 64% of 75 is 48.
b. Begin by writing 160% as 1.6. Then multiply by 560.
   $1.6 \times 560 = 896$
Thus, 160% of 560 is 896.

EXERCISES

Guided Practice

▶ CHECK for Understanding

1. *Writing* Explain in your own words how to find the percent of a number. See page 327.

2. Find 45% of 380. 171

3. *Mental Math* Use mental math to evaluate the expression.

a. 10% of 48
4.8

b. $33\frac{1}{3}$% of 96
32

c. 50% of 64
32

d. 200% of 23
46

Independent Practice

In Exercises 4–11, write the percent as a decimal. Then multiply to find the percent of the number.

4. 16% of 50 0.16, 8

5. 80% of 285 0.8, 228

6. 76% of 375 0.76, 285

7. 340% of 5 3.4, 17

8. 120% of 35 1.2, 42

9. 250% of 46 2.5, 115

10. 0.8% of 500 0.008, 4

11. 6.5% of 800
0.065, 52

In Exercises 12–15, match the percent phrase with the fraction phrase. Then find the percent of the number.

a. $\frac{1}{8}$ of 120

b. $\frac{1}{3}$ of 120

c. $\frac{3}{5}$ of 120

d. $\frac{1}{4}$ of 120

12. 25% of 120 d, 30

13. 60% of 120 c, 72

14. 12.5% of 120 a, 15

15. $33\frac{1}{3}$% of 120 b, 40

See Additional Answers.

In Exercises 16–18, copy the rectangle and shade the indicated number of squares.

16. 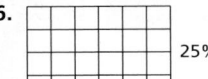 25%

17. $33\frac{1}{3}$ %

18. 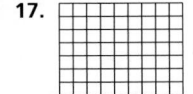 45%

In Exercises 19–22, use the percent key on a calculator to find the percent of the number. Round the result to 2 decimal places.

Sample (50% of 62): 50 % × 62 = or 62 × 50 INV %

19. 96% of 25 24

20. 185% of 40 74

21. 624% of 50 312

22. 1.5% of 800 12

Geometry In Exercises 23–26, use the rectangle at the right.

23. Find the perimeter and area of the rectangle. 46 in., 112 in.²

24. Draw a new rectangle whose dimensions are 150% of the given rectangle. Find the perimeter and area of the new rectangle.

25. Find 150% of the perimeter of the given rectangle. Is the result equal to the perimeter of the new rectangle? Why or why not?

26. Find 150% of the area of the given rectangle. Is the result equal to the area of the new rectangle? Why or why not? **24.–26.** See margin.

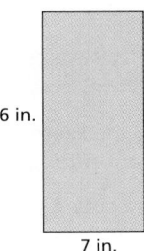
16 in.

7 in.

⊙ More difficult exercises

7.8 ▪ *Finding a Percent of a Number* **329**

Extra Practice

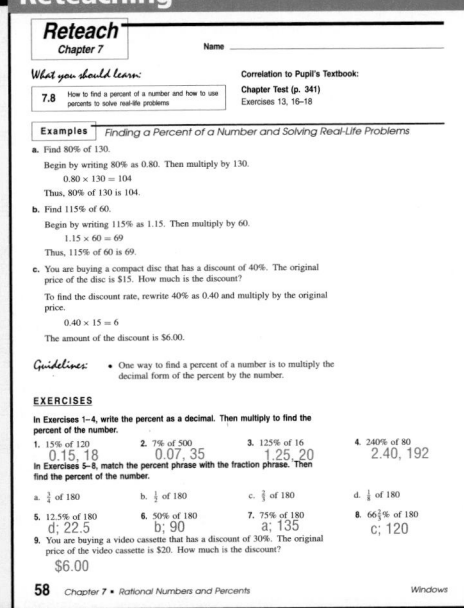

Reteaching

EXERCISE Notes

ASSIGNMENT GUIDE

*Basic/Average:
Day 1: Ex. 5–29 odd
Day 2: Ex. 30–39

Above Average:
Ex. 5–29 odd, 30–39

Advanced: Ex. 5–29 odd, 31–33, 37–39

Selected Answers: Ex. 1–3, 5–37 odd
*You may wish to omit this lesson for these students.

Guided Practice

▶ **Ex. 3** Ask students to explain their reasoning in answering these questions.

Independent Practice

▶ **Ex. 4–11** Students should estimate the answers to these exercises before using their calculators.

▶ **Ex. 12–15** Assign these as a group; since there are several ways to approach these problems, ask students to explain how they arrived at their answers.

▶ **Ex. 19–22** Discuss with students how they might work these exercises if they are using a graphing calculator (which doesn't have a percent key).

▶ **Ex. 23–26**

GROUP ACTIVITY
Assign this set of exercises as a group activity.

Answers

24.
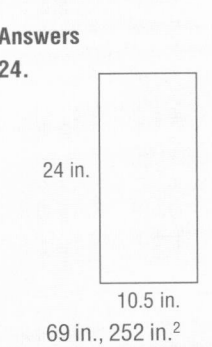
24 in.

10.5 in.

69 in., 252 in.²

25. 69 in., yes, $2(1.5 \times 16 + 1.5 \times 7)$
$= 1.5 \times 2(16 + 7)$

26. 168 in.², no, $(1.5 \times 16)(1.5 \times 7)$
$\neq 1.5(16 \times 7)$

Lesson 7.8 **329**

▶ **Ex. 30b** There are at least two ways to compute the answer: for example, $40 − 35\%$ of $40, or 65% of $40.

▶ **Ex. 31–33** Assign these as a group.

Portfolio Opportunity: Math Log

You go to the mall to buy a pair of tennis shoes. The original price was $58. They have been discounted at 25%. You have a coupon that allows an additional 10% off the sale price. Which calculation correctly determines the price you pay for the shoes? Explain your answer.

a. $0.10 \times 0.25 \times 58 = 1.45$

b. $0.90 \times 0.75 \times 58 = 39.15$

c. $(0.10 + 0.25) \times 58 = 0.35 \times 58 = 20.30$

Also available as a copymaster, page 24, Ex. 9

Short Quiz

Covers Lessons 7.7 and 7.8

Available as a copymaster, page 112

Alternative Assessment

A cooperative learning project that develops consumer awareness.

Available as copymasters, pages 27, 28

Geometry In Exercises 27–29, compare the width, length, and perimeter   See margin. of the blue rectangle with the large rectangle. For instance, in the sample, the width, length, and perimeter of the blue rectangle are each 50% of the width, length, and perimeter of the large rectangle.

Sample 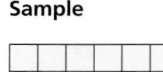   27. 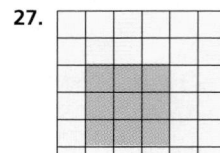   28. 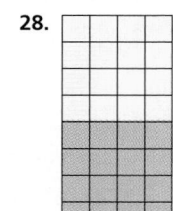   29.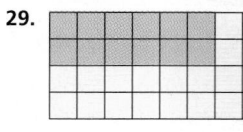

30. *Shopping*   You go to the mall to buy a sweater that has a discount of 35%. The original price of the sweater is $40.

   a. How much is the discount? That is, what is 35% of $40? $14
   b. How much do you have to pay for the sweater? $26

⊘ *Water Resources*   In Exercises 31–33, use the following information. Earth has about 326 million cubic miles of water. Of that, 3% is freshwater.

31. How many cubic miles of freshwater are on Earth?   9.78 million

32. How many cubic miles of salt water are on Earth?   316.22 million

33. A cubic mile of water contains about 9.5×10^{11} gallons. How many gallons of freshwater are on Earth? 9.291×10^{18}

Integrated Review

Number Sense   In Exercises 34–37, which item does not fit in the list? Explain.

34.	$\frac{3}{8}$	$1\frac{2}{8}$ ✓	37.5%	37.5 percent	$\frac{75}{200}$ Others = 0.375
35.	0.125 ✓	125%	$1\frac{1}{4}$	$\frac{5}{4}$	$\frac{125}{100}$ Others = 1.25
36.	4	16% of 25	10% of 40	40% ✓	4.0×10^{0} Others = 4
37.	4% of 150	0.06 ✓	75% of 8	6	$\frac{1}{2}$ of 12 Others = 6

Exploration and Extension

Patterns   In Exercises 38 and 39, evaluate each expression. Then describe the pattern and write the next three numbers in the sequence.   See margin.

⊘ 38. 1% of 500, 2% of 600, 3% of 700, 4% of 800, 5% of 900, 6% of 1000

⊘ 39. 25% of 4, 50% of 8, 75% of 12, 100% of 16, 125% of 20, 150% of 24

Answers

27. The width, length, and perimeter of the blue rectangle are each 50% of the width, length, and perimeter of the large rectangle.

28. The width of the blue rectangle is 100% of the width of the large rectangle, the length of the blue rectangle is 50% of the length of the large rectangle, and the perimeter of the blue rectangle is ≈ 66.7% of the perimeter of the large rectangle.

29. The width of the blue rectangle is 50% of the width of the large rectangle, the length of the blue rectangle is 75% of the length of the large rectangle, and the perimeter of the blue rectangle is ≈ 66.7% of the perimeter of the large rectangle.

38. 5, 12, 21, 32, 45, 60. To get the next number, add 7, add 9, add 11, etc., to the preceding number. 77, 96, 117.

39. 1, 4, 9, 16, 25, 36. To get the next number, name the next larger perfect square; or add 3, add 5, add 7, etc., to the preceding number. 49, 64, 81.

The interest paid in a savings account is a percent of the amount you deposit. For instance, if you deposit $50 in an account that pays 6% annual interest, then at the end of one year you will earn 6% of $50 or $3 in interest. Your new balance will then be $53. If you leave the money in the bank for a second year, then you will earn 6% of $53 or $3.18 in interest. The table shows the balances in your account during a 10-year period.

Year	Interest	Balance
1	$0.06 \cdot 50.00 = \$3.00$	$50.00 + 3.00 = \$53.00$
2	$0.06 \cdot 53.00 = \$3.18$	$53.00 + 3.18 = \$56.18$
3	$0.06 \cdot 56.18 = \$3.37$	$56.18 + 3.37 = \$59.55$
4	$0.06 \cdot 59.55 = \$3.57$	$59.55 + 3.57 = \$63.12$
5	$0.06 \cdot 63.12 = \$3.79$	$63.12 + 3.79 = \$66.91$
6	$0.06 \cdot 66.91 = \$4.01$	$66.91 + 4.01 = \$70.92$
7	$0.06 \cdot 70.92 = \$4.26$	$70.92 + 4.26 = \$75.18$
8	$0.06 \cdot 75.18 = \$4.51$	$75.18 + 4.51 = \$79.69$
9	$0.06 \cdot 79.69 = \$4.78$	$79.69 + 4.78 = \$84.47$
10	$0.06 \cdot 84.47 = \$5.07$	$84.47 + 5.07 = \$89.54$

X	Y1
1.00	53.00
2.00	56.18
3.00	59.55
4.00	63.12
5.00	66.91
6.00	70.93
7.00	75.18
8.00	79.69
9.00	84.47
10.00	89.54

The different balance in the 6th year occurs because of the way the balance is rounded.

A formula for finding the balance A after n years is

$$A = P(1 + r)^n$$

where P is the original deposit and r is the annual interest rate *in decimal form.* You can use a spreadsheet on a computer or a calculator to construct tables to find the balances listed above. For instance, the table at the right was made with a *TI-82* calculator.

Exercises

1. You have deposited $120 in a savings account that pays an annual interest rate of 7%. Construct a table that shows your balances after 1, 2, 3, 4, and 5 years.

Year	Balance
1	$128.40
2	$137.39
3	$147.01
4	$157.30
5	$168.31

In Exercises 2–5, use the formula given above to find the balance in your account after the indicated number of years.

	Deposit	Interest Rate	Number of Years	
2.	$80.00	7%	8 years	$137.45
3.	$800.00	6%	20 years	$2565.71
4.	$100.00	8%	100 years	$219,976.13
5.	$1000.00	8%	50 years	$46,901.61

Enter the following keystrokes on the TI-82 to make a table for the example.

50 [STO] P [ENTER]

0.06 [STO] R [ENTER]

[Y=] $P(1+R)^{\wedge}X$

[2nd] [TblSet] TblMin=0 ΔTbl=1

[2nd] [TABLE]

You can also use a spreadsheet to make the table. Enter the formula in cell B1 and fill down.

	A	B
1	1	$=50*(1+0.06)^{\wedge}A1$
2	2	
3	3	
4	4	

Refer to pages 40 and 41 in the Technology supplement for a graphing calculator program that calculates compound interest to be used with Lesson 7.9.

PACING the Lesson

Suggested Number of Days
Basic/Average 0   Above Average 1
Advanced 1

PLANNING the Lesson

Lesson Plan 7.9, p. 59

ORGANIZER

Starters (reproduced below)
 Problem of the Day 7.9, p. 21
 Warm-Up Exercises 7.9, p. 21
Lesson Resources
 Math Log, p. 24
 Technology, pp. 40, 41
 Answer Masters 7.9, p. 149
 Extra Practice Copymaster 7.9, p. 59
 Reteaching Copymaster 7.9, p. 59
Special Populations
 Suggestions, Teacher's Edition, p. 292D

LESSON Notes

Have students discuss as a class the particular tax rates imposed by your own state. Often, the tax rate varies for different types of purchased items.

Example 1

ALTERNATE APPROACH
Using the Distributive Property Instead of adding the sales tax to the purchase price to determine whether you have enough money to buy the necklace, you could multiply the cost by 1.06, or 1.08, and so on, to get the total cost. Ask students to explain why this is equivalent to the procedure presented in the text.

7.9 Problem Solving with Percents

What you should learn:

Goal 1 How to use percents to solve real-life consumer problems

Goal 2 How to use percents to help organize data

Why you should learn it:

You can use percents to solve real-life problems, such as calculating the sales tax on a purchase.

Real Life
Retail Business

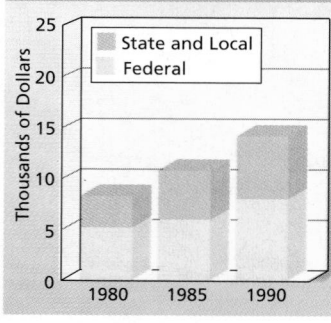

Tax Share Per Family

This stacked bar graph shows the average share per family of all taxes paid to federal, state, and local governments. (Source: U.S. Bureau of Census)

Goal 1 Using Percents in Real life

Most states charge a sales tax when you purchase certain types of items. To find the amount of the sales tax, change the percent to a decimal and multiply by the amount of the purchase. For instance, in a state that has a 6% sales tax, the tax on a $54.80 purchase is

$$0.06 \times 54.80 \approx \$3.29.$$

Here are some sales tax rates for different states.

State	Percent	State	Percent
California	6%	Ohio	5%
Connecticut	8%	Oregon	0%
Missouri	4.225%	Texas	6.25%
New Jersey	7%	Wyoming	3%

Example 1 *Finding Sales Tax Amounts*

You have $81.00 and want to buy a necklace that costs $76.95. In which of the states listed above would you have enough money to buy the necklace?

Solution

State	Sales Tax	Total Cost	Enough?
California	$0.06 \times 76.95 = \$4.62$	$81.57	No
Connecticut	$0.08 \times 76.95 = \$6.16$	$83.11	No
Missouri	$0.04225 \times 76.95 = \$3.25$	$80.20	Yes
New Jersey	$0.07 \times 76.95 = \$5.39$	$82.34	No
Ohio	$0.05 \times 76.95 = \$3.85$	$80.80	Yes
Oregon	None	$76.95	Yes
Texas	$0.0625 \times 76.95 = \$4.81$	$81.76	No
Wyoming	$0.03 \times 76.95 = \$2.31$	$79.26	Yes

You would have enough money to buy the necklace in Missouri, Ohio, Oregon, and Wyoming. ∎

Americans pay many types of taxes to the federal government, state governments, and local governments. Governments use taxes to provide services, such as roads and health care.

332   *Chapter 7 ▪ Rational Numbers and Percents*

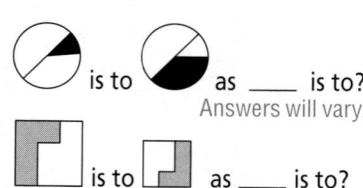

Goal 2 Using Percents to Organize Data

Example 2 **Organizing Data**

You are surveying 250 people. You ask them to read each common saying and state whether they believe it is true. Show how you could use percents to organize the results. *(Source: R.H. Bruskin)*

Saying	Number Answering True
a. *Beauty is only skin deep.*	205
b. *Don't put all your eggs in one basket.*	218
c. *Look before you leap.*	240
d. *The early bird catches the worm.*	188
e. *The grass is always greener on the other side of the fence.*	95
f. *What's good for the goose is good for the gander.*	143

Solution To find the percent who answered true, divide the number who answered true by the total number surveyed.

a. $\frac{205}{250} = 0.82 = 82\%$ **b.** $\frac{218}{250} = 0.872 = 87.2\%$

c. $\frac{240}{250} = 0.96 = 96\%$ **d.** $\frac{188}{250} = 0.752 = 75.2\%$

e. $\frac{95}{250} = 0.38 = 38\%$ **f.** $\frac{143}{250} = 0.572 = 57.2\%$

After calculating the percents, you could organize the results with a bar graph like the one shown below.

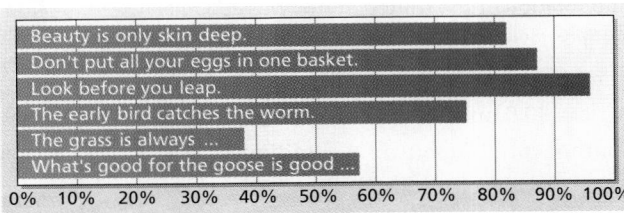

Beauty is only skin deep.	
Don't put all your eggs in one basket.	
Look before you leap.	
The early bird catches the worm.	
The grass is always ...	
What's good for the goose is good ...	

0% 10% 20% 30% 40% 50% 60% 70% 80% 90% 100% ■

Communicating about MATHEMATICS

▶ **SHARING IDEAS about the Lesson** See margin.

Interpreting a Survey If the survey in Example 2 had been taken with 400 people, how many do you think would have answered true to each saying? Explain.

7.9 ▪ *Problem Solving with Percents*   **333**

As we have seen, displaying the constituent parts of a given whole is frequently used to represent data. For this reason, percents are particularly convenient in collecting, organizing, and representing real-life data.

Example 2 —————

Addressing Misconceptions

Ask students to explain why the percents represented in this example need not add to 100%.
Respondents could reply more than once.

Communicating
about MATHEMATICS

Compare the results of the survey in Example 2 with the one taken in your class (or some subset of your school, if possible). Discuss the results.

Writing Prompt
Have students write about the things they understand (or don't understand) about percent.

Technology

Casio *fx-7700G*	Casio *fx-7700GE* , *fx-9700GE*
INTEREST	INTEREST
Fix 2	Fix 2
"PRINCIPAL"	"PRINCIPAL"
?→P	?→P
"INTEREST RATE"	"INTEREST RATE"
"IN DECIMAL FORM"	"IN DECIMAL FORM"
?→R	?→R
"TIMES COMPOUNDED"	"TIMES COMPOUNDED"
"PER YEAR"	"PER YEAR"
?→N	?→N
"NUMBER OF YEARS"	"NUMBER OF YEARS"
?→T	?→T
P(1+R÷N)x²(NT)→A	P(1+R÷N)^(NT)→A
A−P→I	A−P→I
"INTEREST EARNED"	"INTEREST EARNED"
I◢	I◢
"NEW BALANCE"	"NEW BALANCE"
A◢	A◢

EXERCISES

In Exercises 1–4, find the interest earned and the new balance using the given conditions.

1. Deposit of $256 at 3% interest, compounded once per year for 1 year
   Interest: $7.68; new balance: $263.68
2. Deposit of $256 at 6% interest, compounded twice per year for 1 year
   Interest: $15.59; new balance: $271.59
3. Deposit of $850 at 5.5% interest, compounded 4 times per year for 5 years
   Interest: $266.96; new balance: $1116.96
4. Deposit of $9825 at 8.1% interest, compounded 12 times per year for 10 years
   Interest: $12,200.67; new balance: $22,025.67
5. You have $1350 to invest in a new savings account. You are considering 7.5%:
   two different accounts. One account earns 7.5% compounded quarterly   Interest: $607.43
   and the other account earns 7.75% compounded semiannually. You are   Balance: $1957.43
   going to invest your money for 60 months. Which account would you   7.75%:
   choose? Why?   Interest: $624.44
     Balance: $1974.44
     Choose 7.75% account.
6. How much money do you have to invest in a savings account that earns
   5.25% interest compounded 12 times per year to have a balance of at least
   $2000 after six years? What if the interest is compounded 365 times per
   year? Answers vary slightly. Accept all answers where $P \geq \$1460.58$; and
       accept all answers where $P \geq \$1459.61$.
7. Explain the difference between simple interest and compound interest.
   Give an example of each.
   In a simple interest account, only the principal earns interest. In a compound interest account, the principal *and* any previously earned interest earns interest. Example will vary.

© D.C. Heath and Company   *Technology Using Calculators and Computers*   **41**

Answers to Communicating
a. 328, 82% of 400 = 0.82 × 400 = 328
b. 349, 87.2% of 400 = 0.872 × 400 = 348.8
   ≈ 349
c. 384, 96% of 400 = 0.96 × 400 = 384
d. 301, 75.2% of 400 = 0.752 × 400 = 300.8
   ≈ 301
e. 152, 38% of 400 = 0.38 × 400 = 152
f. 229, 57.2% of 400 = 0.572 × 400 = 228.8
   ≈ 229

ASSIGNMENT GUIDE

*Basic/Average:
Day 1: Ex. 5–7 odd, 9–14, 16, 17–22
Day 2: Ex. 23–26, 27–31 odd

Above Average:
Ex. 5, 7, 9–14, 16, 17–25 odd, 26, 27–31 odd

Advanced: Ex. 5, 7, 9–14, 16, 17–25 odd, 26, 27–31 odd

Selected Answers: Ex. 1–4, 5–29 odd
*You may wish to omit this lesson for these students.

Guided Practice
These exercises review the key concepts of the lesson.

Independent Practice
▶ **Ex. 5–8** For students who are ready, discuss using 104% of the item price versus adding the item price to 4% of the item price.
▶ **Ex. 9–14** Assign these as a group.
▶ **Ex. 15**
EXTENSION
Have students determine, using a calculator, the amount in the account after five years, assuming no additional money is withdrawn or added.

EXERCISES

Guided Practice

▶ **CHECK for Understanding**

1. **Sales Tax** The sales tax rate on a $19.79 item is 5.75%. What is the total cost of the item? $20.93

Restaurant Bill In Exercises 2 and 3, use the following information.

At a restaurant, the cost of the meal is $27.53. The sales tax is 5.75%.

2. What is your total cost, including the sales tax? $29.11

3. If you leave a 15% tip (of your total cost), how much will you leave for the tip? $4.37

4. In a survey of 175 adults, 104 of them said that they attend at least one movie per year. What percent does this represent? ≈59%

Independent Practice

In Exercises 5–8, the price of an item is given. Find the total cost of the item, including a 4% sales tax.

5. $4.65 $4.84
6. $10.39 $10.81
7. $50 $52
8. $463.87 $482.42

National Origins In Exercises 9–14, find the percent of the 1990 United States population that traced its origin to the given continent. In 1990, the total population of the United States was 250 million people. *(Source: Bureau of the Census)*

9. Europe, Australia: 177.3 million 70.92%
10. Africa: 30.0 million 12%
11. South/Central America: 22.4 million 8.96%
12. Asia, South Pacific: 7.3 million 2.92%
13. Native American: 2.0 million 0.8%
14. "American": 11.0 million 4.4%

In 1990, about 11 million Americans traced their origins by saying "I'm just American— a little bit of everything."

⊘ 15. **Starting a Savings Account** You deposit $350 into a savings account that pays 5.75% in simple interest. (This means that at the end of one year your savings account will earn 5.75% in interest.) If you make no other deposits or withdrawals during the year, how much money will be in the account after one year? $370.13

⊘ 16. **Developing a Budget** Members of a small town council determine that the town must decrease its operating cost by 17%. The present operating cost is $476,000. The council reduces the operating cost to $397,000. Is that enough? Explain. No, $(100 - 17)$% of $476,000 = 0.83 × $476,000 = $395,080 < $397,000

⊘ More difficult exercises

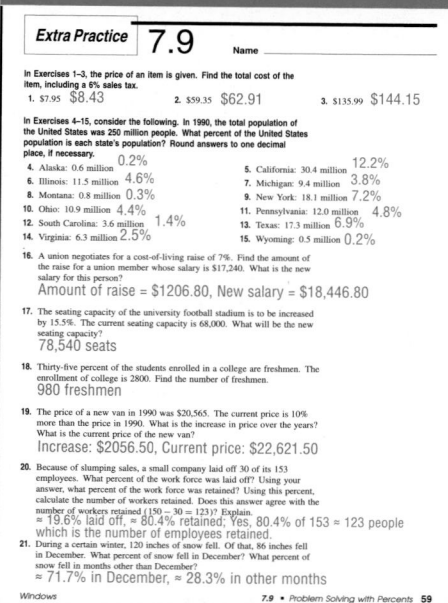

Extra Practice

Extra Practice 7.9 Name _____

In Exercises 1–3, the price of an item is given. Find the total cost of the item, including a 6% sales tax.
1. $7.95 **$8.43**
2. $59.35 **$62.91**
3. $135.99 **$144.15**

In Exercises 4–15, consider the following. In 1990, the total population of the United States was 250 million people. What percent of the United States population is each state's population? Round answers to one decimal place, if necessary.
4. Alaska: 0.6 million **0.2%**
5. California: 30.4 million **12.2%**
6. Illinois: 11.5 million **4.6%**
7. Michigan: 9.4 million **3.8%**
8. Montana: 0.8 million **0.3%**
9. New York: 18.1 million **7.2%**
10. Ohio: 10.9 million **4.4%**
11. Pennsylvania: 12.0 million **4.8%**
12. South Carolina: 3.6 million **1.4%**
13. Texas: 17.3 million **6.9%**
14. Virginia: 6.3 million **2.5%**
15. Wyoming: 0.5 million **0.2%**

16. A union negotiates for a cost-of-living raise of 7%. Find the amount of the raise for a union member whose salary is $17,240. What is the new salary for this person?
Amount of raise = $1206.80, New salary = $18,446.80

17. The seating capacity of the university football stadium is to be increased by 15.5%. The current seating capacity is 68,000. What will be the new seating capacity?
78,540 seats

18. Thirty-five percent of the students enrolled in a college are freshmen. The enrollment of college is 2800. Find the number of freshmen.
980 freshmen

19. The price of a new van in 1990 was $20,565. The current price is 10% more than the price in 1990. What is the increase in price over the years? What is the current price of the new van?
Increase: $2056.50, Current price: $22,621.50

20. Because of slumping sales, a small company laid off 30 of its 153 employees. What percent of the work force was laid off? Using your answer, what percent of the work force was retained? Using this percent, calculate the number of workers retained. Does this answer agree with the number of workers retained $(150 - 30 = 123)$? Explain.
≈ 19.6% laid off, ≈ 80.4% retained; Yes, 80.4% of 153 ≈ 123 people which is the number of employees retained.

21. During a certain winter, 120 inches of snow fell. Of that, 86 inches fell in December. What percent of snow fell in December? What percent of snow fell in months other than December?
≈ 71.7% in December, ≈ 28.3% in other months

Windows   7.9 ▪ Problem Solving with Percents **59**

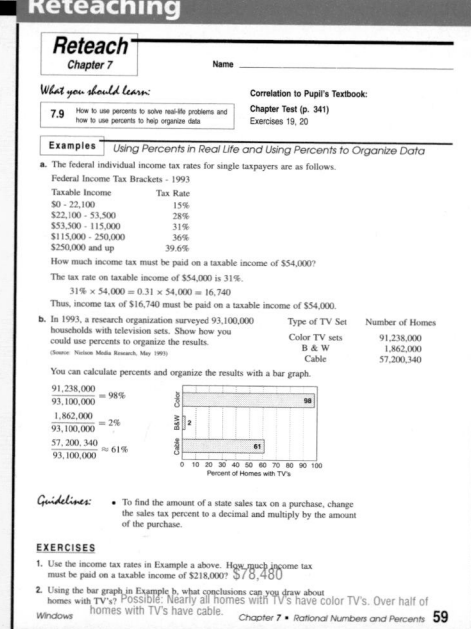

Reteaching

Reteach Chapter 7 Name _____

What you should learn:
7.9 How to use percents to solve real-life problems and how to use percents to help organize data

Correlation to Pupil's Textbook:
Chapter Test (p. 341)
Exercises 19, 20

Examples *Using Percents in Real Life and Using Percents to Organize Data*

a. The federal individual income tax rates for single taxpayers are as follows.

Federal Income Tax Brackets - 1993

Taxable Income	Tax Rate
$0 - 22,100	15%
$22,100 - 53,500	28%
$53,500 - 115,000	31%
$115,000 - 250,000	36%
$250,000 and up	39.6%

How much income tax must be paid on a taxable income of $54,000?

The tax rate on taxable income of $54,000 is 31%.

$31\% \times 54,000 = 0.31 \times 54,000 = 16,740$

Thus, income tax of $16,740 must be paid on a taxable income of $54,000.

b. In 1993, a research organization surveyed 93,100,000 households with television sets. Show how you could use percents to organize the results. *(Source: Nielsen Media Research, May 1993)*

Type of TV Set	Number of Homes
Color TV sets	91,238,000
B & W	1,862,000
Cable	57,200,340

You can calculate percents and organize the results with a bar graph.

$\frac{91,238,000}{93,100,000} ≈ 98\%$

$\frac{1,862,000}{93,100,000} ≈ 2\%$

$\frac{57,200,340}{93,100,000} ≈ 61\%$

Guidelines: • To find the amount of a state sales tax on a purchase, change the sales tax percent to a decimal and multiply by the amount of the purchase.

EXERCISES

1. Use the income tax rates in Example a above. How much income tax must be paid on a taxable income of $218,000? **$78,480**

2. Using the bar graph in Example b, what conclusions can you draw about homes with TV's? **Possible: Nearly all homes with TV's have color TV's. Over half of homes with TV's have cable.**

Windows   Chapter 7 ▪ Rational Numbers and Percents **59**

Payroll Taxes   **In Exercises 17–22, use the following.**

Your gross pay for one week is $650. To find your take-home pay, you must subtract each of the following taxes from your gross pay: Federal Income Tax: 18.1%, State Income Tax: 2.8%, Social Security Tax: 6.2%, Local Income Tax: 1%, and Medicare Tax: 1.5%.

17. What is your Federal income tax? $117.65

18. What is your state income tax? $18.20

19. What is your Social Security tax? $40.30

20. What is your local income tax? $6.50

21. What is your Medicare tax? $9.75

22. What is your take-home pay? $457.60

Newspaper Subscribers   **In Exercises 23–26, use the following.**

You work for a newspaper that has 60,200 subscriptions: 31,500 for the morning paper, 10,800 for the evening paper, and 17,900 for the Sunday paper.

23. What percent of your subscriptions are for the morning paper? $\approx$52.3%

24. What percent of your subscriptions are for the evening paper? $\approx$17.9%

25. What percent of your subscriptions are for the Sunday paper? $\approx$29.7%

26. *Estimation*   If the number of subscriptions increased to 72,000, how many do you think would be for the morning paper? Explain. $\approx$37,674; $\frac{31,500}{60,200} \times 72,000 \approx 37,674$

Integrated Review

Making Connections within Mathematics

Estimation   **In Exercises 27–30, use the following.**

In 1993, a survey was taken of 240 working mothers. The percent who said that the indicated condition was "very important" to them is given in the graph. *(Source: Kudos/Gallop poll)*

27. How many said that a guaranteed job was very important after returning from parental leave? $\approx$185

28. How many said that paid maternity leave was very important? $\approx$173

29. How many said that flexible working hours were very important? $\approx$151

30. How many said that a company that provided day care was very important? $\approx$139

What Working Moms Want

77% 72% 63% 58%

Parental leave (job guarantee) | Paid maternity leave | Flex time | Company-provided or -sponsored day care

Exploration and Extension

31. *Conducting a Survey*   Use the questions below to conduct a survey of at least 20 people. Organize your data using percents and a graph. Check students' work.

Almost every day:
a. do you eat breakfast?
b. do you talk on the phone?
c. do you watch television?
d. do you listen to music?
e. do you read part of a newspaper, magazine, or book?

P Portfolio Opportunity

7.9 • *Problem Solving with Percents*   **335**

► Ex. 17–22   Assign as a group.
► Ex. 23–26   Assign as a group.

Integrated Review

These exercises review some basic skills of data analysis.

Exploration and Extension

Assign this survey as a project to be completed outside of class within a given period of time.

Portfolio Opportunity: Math Log

Knowing the price of an item and the percent of sales tax, is it possible to find the total cost by multiplying the price by one quantity? Explain your answer.

Also available as a copymaster, page 24, Ex. 10

Alternate Assessment

A cooperative learning project that develops students' understanding of simple interest.

Also available as copymasters, page 28

Chapter SUMMARY

Some of the most frequently applied skills in mathematics are those used to compare the measure of part of a quantity to the measure of the whole quantity, for example, the amount of electricity produced from *gas* compared to the total amount of electricity produced. Quantitative comparisons of this kind can be expressed as fractions, as decimals, or as percents.

Lessons 7.1 and 7.2 presented the basic skills of adding and subtracting *fractions*. However, in actual real-life manipulation of fractions, especially with the use of calculators, the fractions are converted first to *decimals*, then added or subtracted, and the result rounded. This technique was presented in Lesson 7.3. Lessons 7.4 and 7.5 introduced techniques for multiplying and dividing rational numbers, including algebraic expressions. *Percents* were introduced in Lesson 7.6 and, in Lesson 7.7, fractions, decimals, and percents were shown in relation to one another. The two final lessons made it clear that real-life problem solving often uses all three methods of expressing quantitative comparisons.

7 Chapter Summary

What did you learn?

Skills
1. Add and subtract fractions
   - with like denominators. **(7.1)**
   - with unlike denominators. **(7.2)**
   - by writing decimals. **(7.3)**
2. Multiply fractions. **(7.4)**
3. Divide fractions. **(7.5)**
4. Perform operations with rational expressions that contain variables. **(7.1–7.5)**
5. Write a percent as a portion with a denominator of 100. **(7.6)**
6. Write percents in decimal form. **(7.7)**
   - Write decimals as percents. **(7.7)**
   - Write fractions as percents. **(7.7)**
   - Write percents as fractions. **(7.7)**
7. Find a percent of a number. **(7.8)**

Problem-Solving Strategies
8. Model and solve real-life problems. **(7.1–7.9)**
   - Use geometry to model operations with fractions, decimals, and percents **(7.1–7.9)**

Exploring Data
9. Use tables and graphs to solve problems. **(7.1–7.9)**
   - Interpret circle graphs. **(7.2, 7.3, 7.7)**

Why did you learn it?

You can use operations with fractions and percents to answer questions about real-life situations. For instance, in this chapter, you saw how subtraction of fractions can be used to compare running times in a 100-meter sprint, and how percents can be used to organize the results of a survey. You also saw how circle graphs can be used to represent parts of a whole, for instance, the different ways that electric power is produced.

How does it fit into the bigger picture of mathematics?

Numbers can be written in several different ways. For instance, the number $\frac{1}{4}$ can be written as $\frac{2}{8}$, or 0.25, or $\frac{25}{100}$, or as 25%. In this chapter, you learned that the "best" way to write a number depends on the way the number is being used. For instance, if you are advertising a clothing sale, you might choose 25% as the best way to describe your store's discount. However, when you are calculating the discount on a purchase, it is better to use the decimal form, 0.25, or the fraction form, $\frac{1}{4}$.

In Exercises 1–16, evaluate the expression. Then simplify, if possible. (7.1, 7.2, 7.4, 7.5)

1. $\frac{4}{9} + \frac{2}{9}$ $\frac{6}{9}, \frac{2}{3}$

2. $\frac{3}{10} - \frac{7}{10}$ $-\frac{4}{10}, -\frac{2}{5}$

3. $\frac{12}{13} - \frac{1}{2}$ $\frac{11}{26}$

4. $\frac{-5}{14} + \frac{-3}{4}$ $-\frac{31}{28}$

5. $-1\frac{3}{4} \cdot 2\frac{1}{4}$ $-\frac{63}{16}$

6. $\frac{-6}{7} \cdot \frac{-2}{5}$ $\frac{12}{35}$

7. $-8 \div \frac{-4}{5}$ 10

8. $3\frac{3}{4} \div \left(-2\frac{1}{2}\right)$ $-\frac{3}{2}$

9. $\frac{-5}{8t} + \frac{3}{8t}$ $-\frac{2}{8t}, -\frac{1}{4t}$

10. $\frac{-x}{6} + \frac{-5x}{6}$ $-\frac{6x}{6}, -x$

11. $\frac{-9}{xy} - \frac{4}{x}$ $\frac{-9-4y}{xy}$

12. $\frac{a}{3} + \frac{2a}{5}$ 11

13. $15 \cdot \frac{3m}{4}$ $\frac{45m}{4}$

14. $\frac{-36n^2}{7} \cdot \frac{7}{6n}$ $-6n$

15. $\frac{-8}{y} \div \frac{10}{y}$ $-\frac{4}{5}$

16. $\frac{-b^3}{6} \div \frac{-b}{3}$ $\frac{b^2}{2}$

In Exercises 17–28, solve the equation. (7.1, 7.2, 7.4, 7.5)

17. $x + \frac{3}{14} = \frac{9}{14}$ $\frac{3}{7}$

18. $y + \frac{5}{6} = \frac{1}{6}$ $-\frac{2}{3}$

19. $10z - \frac{11}{2} = \frac{1}{2}$ $\frac{3}{5}$

20. $a + \frac{4}{7} = \frac{-5}{14}$ $-\frac{13}{14}$

21. $b + \frac{3}{4} = \frac{2}{5}$ $-\frac{7}{20}$

22. $18t - \frac{9}{2} = \frac{-12}{8}$ $\frac{1}{6}$

23. $-7s = \frac{2}{5}$ $-\frac{2}{35}$

24. $2x = 6x - \frac{6}{10}$ $\frac{3}{20}$

25. $\frac{1}{14}y = \frac{5}{6}$ $\frac{35}{3}$

26. $25z + 5 = -8$ $-\frac{13}{25}$

27. $8y = 19 + 14y$ $-\frac{19}{6}$

28. $\frac{15}{9} = \frac{-1}{3}t - \frac{7}{2}$ $-\frac{31}{2}$

Geometry   In Exercises 29–31, find the perimeter of the figure. (7.1, 7.2)

29.
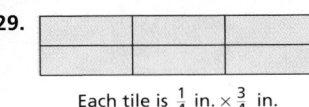
Each tile is $\frac{1}{4}$ in. $\times \frac{3}{4}$ in.

$5\frac{1}{2}$ in.

30.
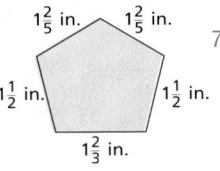
$1\frac{2}{5}$ in. $1\frac{2}{5}$ in.
$1\frac{1}{2}$ in. $1\frac{1}{2}$ in.
$1\frac{2}{3}$ in.

$7\frac{7}{15}$ in.

31.
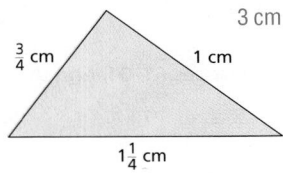
3 cm
$\frac{3}{4}$ cm   1 cm
$1\frac{1}{4}$ cm

Geometry   In Exercises 32–34, find the area of the figure. (7.4)

32.
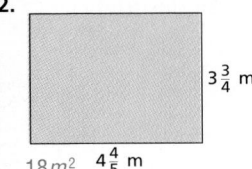
$3\frac{3}{4}$ m
$18m^2$ $4\frac{4}{5}$ m

33.
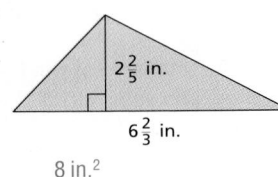
$2\frac{2}{5}$ in.
$6\frac{2}{3}$ in.
8 in.^{2}

34.
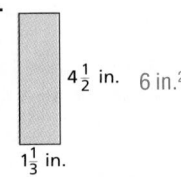
$4\frac{1}{2}$ in.   6 in.^{2}
$1\frac{1}{3}$ in.

In Exercises 35–46, use a calculator to evaluate the expression. Round your result to two decimal places. (7.3)

35. $\frac{3}{14} - \frac{9}{14}$ -0.43

36. $\frac{3}{7} + \frac{5}{7}$ 1.14

37. $-\frac{5}{9} + \frac{35}{89}$ -0.16

38. $\frac{7}{25} + \frac{13}{25}$ 0.8

39. $\frac{-8}{15} \cdot \frac{-7}{12}$ 0.31

40. $\frac{13}{19} \cdot \frac{-4}{5}$ -0.55

41. $\frac{16}{19} \div 5$ 0.17

42. $-\frac{48}{55} \div \frac{6}{11}$ -1.6

43. $\frac{65}{121} + \frac{99}{148}$ 1.21

44. $\frac{59}{252} - \frac{86}{133}$ -0.41

45. $\frac{12}{47}x - \frac{14}{15}x$ $-0.68x$

46. $\frac{43}{56}y + \frac{9}{13}y$ $1.46y$

47. Translate the following sentence to an equation. Then solve the equation. *The sum of one fourth and twice a number is equal to one half.* (7.2, 7.5)

$\frac{1}{4} + 2n = \frac{1}{2}, \frac{1}{8}$

⊗ **48.** Translate the following sentence to an equation. Then solve the equation. *The product of three eighths and a number is equal to one half.* (7.4, 7.5)

$\frac{3}{8}n = \frac{1}{2}, \frac{4}{3}$

⊗ More difficult exercises

Chapter REVIEW

Have students begin this Review in class and complete it as a homework assignment.

ASSIGNMENT GUIDE

*Basic/Average:
Ex. 9–23 odd, 30–33, 43–47, 49–63 odd, 65–68, 69–73 odd, 74–77, 79, 82, 83, 86–89

Above Average:
Ex. 9–23 odd, 30–33, 43–47, 49–63 odd, 65–68, 69–73 odd, 74–77, 79, 82, 83, 86–89

Advanced:
Ex. 9–23 odd, 30–33, 43–47, 49–63 odd, 65–68, 69–73 odd, 74–77, 79, 82, 83, 86–89

*For these students, you will need to limit assignments to cover only those lessons you chose to teach from this chapter.

Resources
Color Transparencies
   Graph for Ex. 74–77, p. 30
   Graph for Ex. 84, 85, p. 31
   Picture for Ex. 90–93, p. 31
Answer Masters, pp. 150–152

Chapter 7 Review   **337**

In Exercises 49–52, write the fraction that represents the portion of the figure's area that is blue. Then write the fraction as a percent. (7.1, 7.2, 7.4, 7.6, 7.7)

49.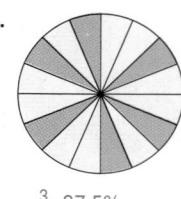

$\frac{3}{8}$, 37.5%

50.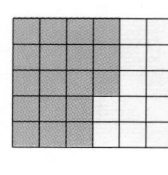

$\frac{3}{5}$, 60%

51.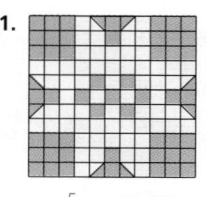

$\frac{5}{11}$, ≈ 45.5%

52.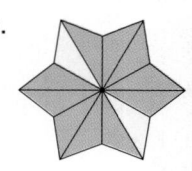

$\frac{5}{6}$, ≈ 83.3%

In Exercises 53–56, rewrite as a percent. (7.6, 7.7)

53. 0.745 74.5%　　　**54.** 0.029 2.9%　　　**55.** $\frac{7}{8}$ 87.5%　　　**56.** $\frac{27}{5}$ 540%

In Exercises 57–60, rewrite the percent as a fraction. Then simplify. (7.7)

57. 46% $\frac{46}{100}, \frac{23}{50}$　　　**58.** 88% $\frac{88}{100}, \frac{22}{25}$　　　**59.** 180% $\frac{180}{100}, \frac{9}{5}$　　　**60.** 104% $\frac{104}{100}, \frac{26}{25}$

In Exercises 61–64, find the percent of the number. (7.8)

61. 26% of 50 13　　　**62.** 78% of 150 117　　　**63.** 350% of 80 280　　　**64.** 520% of 105 546

Computation Sense　　In Exercises 65–68, match the operations. (7.7)

a. Divide by 20.　　**b.** Divide by 4.　　**c.** Divide by 8.　　**d.** Divide by 5.

65. Multiply by 25%. b　　**66.** Multiply by 5%. a　　**67.** Multiply by 20%. d　　**68.** Multiply by $12\frac{1}{2}$%.

Geometry　　In Exercises 69 and 70, find the total area of the figure. Then find the percent of the area that is red, blue, and yellow. (7.1–7.8) $3\frac{91}{192}$; ≈ 16.8%, ≈ 10.8%, ≈ 72.4%

69.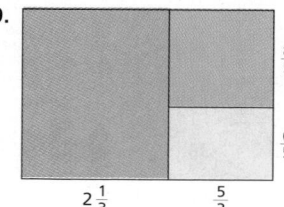

$\frac{8}{5}$

$\frac{6}{5}$

$2\frac{1}{3}$　　$\frac{5}{3}$

$11\frac{1}{5}$;

≈ 58.3%

≈ 23.8%

≈ 17.9%

70.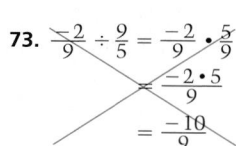

$\frac{7}{8}$

$\frac{1}{3}$

$1\frac{1}{8}$　　$\frac{7}{4}$

Error Analysis　　In Exercises 71–73, describe the error. Then correct it. (7.2, 7.5, 7.7) See margin.

71. $\frac{7}{20} - \frac{2}{10} = \frac{7-2}{20-10}$
$= \frac{5}{10}$
$= \frac{1}{2}$

72. $\frac{4}{5} + \frac{1}{3} = \frac{4+1}{15}$
$= \frac{5}{15}$
$= \frac{1}{3}$

73. $\frac{-2}{9} \div \frac{9}{5} = \frac{-2}{9} \cdot \frac{5}{9}$
$= \frac{-2 \cdot 5}{9}$
$= \frac{-10}{9}$

Answers

71. Subtract only the numerators, not the denominators too; and use a common denominator, which was not done.

$\frac{7}{20} - \frac{2}{10} = \frac{7}{20} - \frac{2}{10} \cdot \frac{2}{2}$
$= \frac{7}{20} - \frac{4}{20}$
$= \frac{3}{20}$

72. Multiply each numerator by the same number that the corresponding denominator was multiplied by; that was not done.

$\frac{4}{5} + \frac{1}{3} = \frac{4}{5} \cdot \frac{3}{3} + \frac{1}{3} \cdot \frac{5}{5}$
$= \frac{12}{15} + \frac{5}{15}$
$= \frac{17}{15}$

73. Multiply the denominators also, not just the numerators.

$\frac{-2}{9} \div \frac{9}{5} = \frac{-2}{9} \cdot \frac{5}{9}$
$= -\frac{10}{81}$

The Mail In Exercises 74–77, use the circle graph at the right, which shows the makeup of mail in the United States. *(Source: National Postal Museum)* **(7.1–7.2)**

What Makes Up Our Mail?

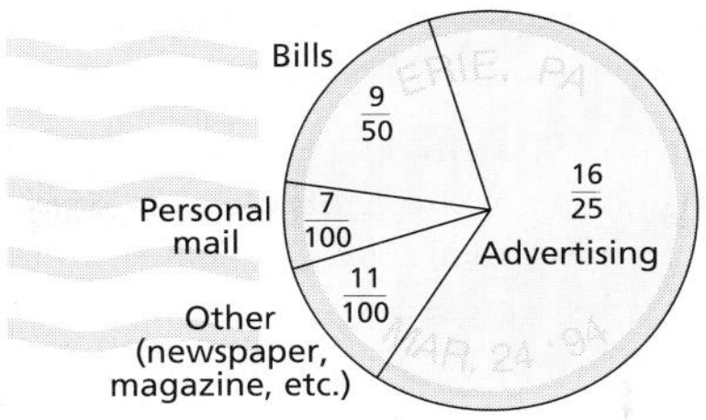

Bills $\frac{9}{50}$

Advertising $\frac{16}{25}$

Personal mail $\frac{7}{100}$

Other (newspaper, magazine, etc.) $\frac{11}{100}$

74. Find the sum of the portions representing personal mail and newspapers and magazines. $\frac{9}{50}$

75. Find the difference in the portions of mail that are advertising and bills. $\frac{23}{50}$

76. Which portions have a sum of $\frac{3}{4}$? Advertising and Other

77. What is the sum of the four portions? 1

78. **Sales Tax** You are buying a Navaho bracelet in New Mexico, where the sales tax is 4.75%. The price of the bracelet is $31.99. What is the total cost, including sales tax? **(7.9)** $33.51

79. **Loan Payment** You are borrowing $1200 from a bank. At the end of a year you will pay back all of the loan, plus an interest of 11.25%. How much will you owe at the end of the year? **(7.9)** $1335

80. **Test Scores** Your scores on five 100-point tests are 73%, 82%, 79%, 94%, and 98%. What is your average percent? **(7.9)** 85.2%

In Exercises 81 and 82, which number does not fit the list? Explain. (7.5)

81. $-\frac{1}{2}, \frac{-1}{2}, \frac{-1}{-2}, \checkmark \frac{-1}{-2}, \frac{1}{-2}$ Others $= -\frac{1}{2}$

⊙ 82. $\frac{-3}{8}, -\frac{3}{8}, \frac{3}{-8}, -\frac{-3}{8}, \checkmark \frac{-3}{-8}$ Others $= -\frac{3}{8}$

83. **National Forests and Parks** In a survey, 1500 people were asked whether national forests and parks should collect fees for various uses. Use percents and a graph to organize the results of the survey. (Some of those polled had no opinion.) **(7.9)**
(Source: Roper Organization) For graph, see Additional Answers.

	Should be free	Should pay a fee	
Logging	210	1155	14%, 77%
Hard-rock mining	210	1140	14%, 76%
Oil drilling	225	1095	15%, 73%
Ski area development	360	1005	24%, 67%
Livestock grazing	540	810	36%, 54%
Commercial fishing	585	765	39%, 51%
Game hunting	600	765	40%, 51%
Recreational fishing	1005	405	67%, 27%
Boating and yachting	1050	360	70%, 24%
Hiking	1275	180	85%, 12%

Hiking fees would be used to offset the expenses related to establishing, marking, and maintaining trails.

⊙ More difficult exercises

Real

Conne

Water Resources   **In Exercises 84 and 85, answer the questions about water resources in the United States. (7.9)** *(Source: World Book)*

84. In 1990, fifteen percent of the 250 million people living in the United States obtained their water from private wells. What number of people does this represent? 37.5 million

85. In 1990, there were about 70,000 public water-supply systems in the United States. Of these about 800 served 50,000 people or more. What percent of the public water-supply systems served 50,000 people or more? **(7.9)** ≈ 1.1%

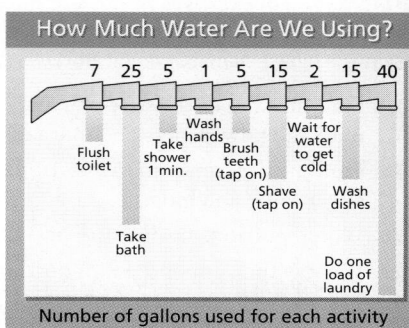

How Much Water Are We Using?

7 25 5 1 5 15 2 15 40

Flush toilet · Take shower 1 min. · Wash hands · Brush teeth (tap on) · Wait for water to get cold · Shave (tap on) · Wash dishes · Take bath · Do one load of laundry

Number of gallons used for each activity

Water Use   **In Exercises 86–88, use the following information. (7.9)**

Approximately 340 billion gallons of water are used in the United States each day. Twenty-two percent comes from groundwater (wells) and the rest comes from surface water (rivers and lakes). *(Source: U.S. Geological Survey)*

86. In a typical day, how many gallons of groundwater are used? 74.8 billion

87. What percent of water used in the United States comes from rivers and lakes? 78%

88. Two-thirds of the groundwater used in the United States is used to irrigate crops. Estimate this amount. 50 billion gallons

North American Waterfalls   **In Exercises 89–92, use the following information. (7.9)**

Bridal Veil Falls in California is 189 meters high.
Ribbon Falls in California is 491 meters high.
Nevada Falls in California is 181 meters high.
Multnomah Falls in Oregon is 165 meters high.

89. Niagara Falls, between New York and Ontario, is $\frac{2}{7}$ the height of Bridal Veil Falls. How high is Niagara Falls? 54 m

90. Yosemite Lower Falls in California is 20% of the height of Ribbon Falls. How high is Yosemite Lower Falls? 98.2 m

≈ 188.6 m

91. Multnomah Falls is part of a series of waterfalls. Multnomah Falls represents $\frac{7}{8}$ of the total height of the series. What is the total height of the series?

92. Nevada Falls in California is about 50% as high as Takakkaw Falls in British Columbia. How high is Takakkaw Falls? 362 m

In Exercises 1–4, find the sum or difference and simplify. (7.1, 7.2)

1. $\frac{1}{5} + \frac{3}{5}$ $\frac{4}{5}$

2. $\frac{11}{12}x - \frac{7}{12}x$ $\frac{1}{3}x$

3. $\frac{4}{5} + \frac{1}{10}$ $\frac{9}{10}$

4. $\frac{11}{18} - \frac{2}{3}$ $-\frac{1}{18}$

In Exercises 5–8, find the product or quotient and simplify. (7.4, 7.5)

5. $\frac{4}{5} \cdot \frac{1}{2}$ $\frac{2}{5}$

6. $\frac{4}{5} \div \frac{1}{2}$ $\frac{8}{5}$

7. $1\frac{1}{3} \times 1\frac{1}{2}$ 2

8. $-\frac{5s}{6} \div \frac{3s}{5}$ $-\frac{25}{18}$

9. Write $\frac{10}{25}$ as a percent. (7.6) 40%

10. Write 0.365 as a percent. (7.7) 36.5%

11. Write 24.5% as a decimal. (7.7) 0.245

12. Write 32% as a fraction and simplify. (7.7) $\frac{8}{25}$

13. Find 85% of 16. (7.8) 13.6

14. 12 is what percent of 48? (7.8) 25%

15. Find the total area of the figure below. Then find the percent of the area that is red, blue, and yellow. (7.1–7.8)

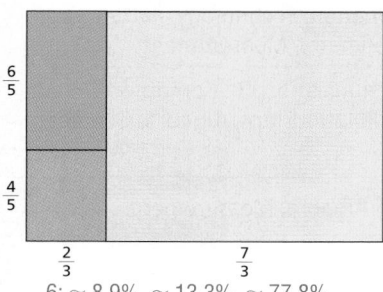

6; ≈ 8.9%, ≈ 13.3%, ≈ 77.8%

16. The circle graph shows the percents of types of books sold in the United States. If you owned a bookstore that sold 2546 books in a week, how many would you expect to be fiction? (7.9) 1502

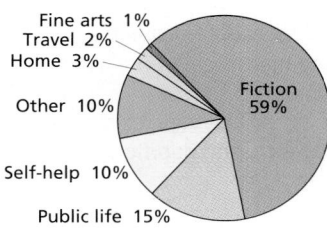

Fine arts 1%
Travel 2%
Home 3%
Other 10%
Fiction 59%
Self-help 10%
Public life 15%

In Exercises 17 and 18, use the following information. (7.9)

You are the manager of a clothing store. On one of your clearance racks, you have 65 shirts. Of these, 18 are T-shirts. Of the 18 T-shirts, 5 are blue and 8 are white.

17. What percent of the total number of shirts are T-shirts?

18. What percent of the total number of T-shirts are blue?

17. ≈ 27.7%   18. ≈ 27.8%

In Exercises 19 and 20, use the following information. (7.9)

In 1990, a survey was taken to determine the amount of television that American adults watch in a day. The results were: 1 hour or less (18.4%), between 1 and 5 hours (68.8%), between 5 and 10 hours (10.2%), between 10 and 15 hours (1.9%), and over 15 hours (0.7%). *(Source: Impact Resources, Inc.)*

19. Of 415 American adults, how many would you expect to watch television for 1 hour or less each day? 76

20. Of 824 American adults, how many would you expect to watch between 1 and 5 hours of television a day? 567

Sporting events, like the 1992 Barcelona Olympics, attract large audiences worldwide.

◄ Formal Assessment

Three **Chapter Tests.** Form A is of average difficulty, Form B is of average difficulty in multiple choice format, and Form C is more challenging.
Available as copymasters, pages 113–121

CHAPTER 8 GOALS

Lesson	Pages	Goals	Meeting the NCTM Standards
8.1	344–347	1. Find rates 2. Find ratios	Problem Solving, Communication, Connections, Number Relationships, Algebra, Geometry, Measurement
Lesson Investigation 8.2	348	Ratios	Number Relationships, Technology, Patterns and Functions
8.2	349–352	1. Solve proportions 2. Write proportions	Problem Solving, Connections, Number Relationships, Computation and Estimation, Technology, Patterns and Functions, Algebra, Geometry, Measurement
8.3	353–356	1. Use proportions to solve real-life problems 2. Use similar triangles to measure real-life objects indirectly	Problem Solving, Communication, Reasoning, Connections, Number Relationships, Algebra, Geometry, Measurement
Mixed Review	357	Review of arithmetic, algebra, and geometry	Number Relationships, Algebra, Measurement
Milestones	357	Arabian Legacy	Communication, Connections
8.4	358–361	1. Find what percent one number is of another 2. Solve a percent equation	Communication, Number Relationships, Algebra, Probability, Geometry
Mid-Chapter Self-Test	362	Diagnose student weaknesses and remediate with correlated Reteaching Copymasters	Assessment
8.5	363–366	1. Use percents to solve real-life problems 2. Use percents to find discounts	Problem Solving, Communication, Connections, Algebra, Statistics, Geometry, Measurement
8.6	367–371	1. Find a percent of increase 2. Find a percent of decrease	Problem Solving, Communication, Reasoning, Connections, Number Relationships, Computation and Estimation, Patterns and Functions, Statistics
Mixed Review	371	Review of arithmetic, algebra, and geometry	Number Relationships, Computation and Estimation, Algebra, Probability, Geometry
Lesson Investigation 8.7	372	Pascal's Triangle	Patterns and Functions
8.7	373–376	1. Use the Counting Principle 2. Use Pascal's Triangle to count the number of ways an event can happen	Communication, Connections, Computation and Estimation, Statistics, Probability
Using a Computer	377	Modeling Probability with a Computer	Number Relationships, Computation and Estimation, Technology, Statistics, Probability
8.8	378–381	1. Compare theoretical and experimental probabilities 2. Find the probability of a multi-stage event	Communication, Connections, Computation and Estimation, Statistics, Probability
Chapter Summary	382	A restatement of what has been learned, why it has been learned, and how it fits into the structure of mathematics	Communication, Connections
Chapter Review	383–386	Review of concepts and skills learned in the chapter	Problem Solving, Connections
Chapter Test	387	Diagnose student weaknesses and remediate with correlated Reteaching Copymasters	Assessment

RESOURCES ORGANIZER

Lesson Pages	8.1 344–347	8.2 349–352	8.3 353–356	8.4 358–361	8.5 363–366	8.6 367–371	8.7 373–376	8.8 378–381
Lesson Plans	60	61	62	63	64	65	66	67
Problem of the Day	22	22	22	23	23	23	24	24
Warm-Up Exercises	22	22	22	23	23	23	24	24
Color Transparencies	—	—	32	—	33, 34	—	—	34
Teaching Tools: Transparencies Copymasters	— —	— —	— —	— —	— —	T1, T2 C2, C3	— —	— —
Math Log	25	25	25	26	26	26, 27	27	27
Technology	44	45–47	—	—	48	—	49	—
Answer Masters	154, 155	156, 157	158	160	161	162, 163	165	166
Extra Practice Copymasters	60	61	62	63	64	65	66	67
Reteaching Copymasters	60	61	62	63	64	65	66	67
Enrichment Projects	—	—	39, 40	—	—	41, 42	—	43, 44
Alternative Assessment: Projects Partner Quizzes Group Assessment	29 — —	29 — —	29 — —	— 51 —	30 — —	— — —	— — 73, 74	30 — —
Formal Assessment Short Quizzes Tests	— —	122 —	— —	123 124, 125	— —	126 —	— —	127 128–136
Overhead Manipulatives Kit	—	—	—	—	—	—	—	—
Complete Solutions Manual	Includes step-by-step solutions for all exercises in the student text							
Computerized Test Bank	Creates customized tests that include graphics							
Interactive CD-ROM Project	Provides an interactive and interdisciplinary chapter project							

STARTERS

Problem of the Day

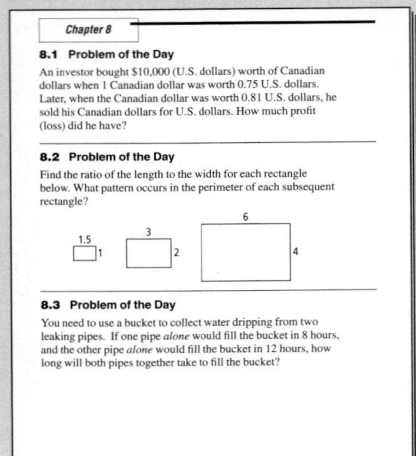

Chapter 8

8.1 Problem of the Day

An investor bought $10,000 (U.S. dollars) worth of Canadian dollars when 1 Canadian dollar was worth 0.75 U.S. dollars. Later, when the Canadian dollar was worth 0.81 U.S. dollars, he sold his Canadian dollars for U.S. dollars. How much profit (loss) did he have?

8.2 Problem of the Day

Find the ratio of the length to the width for each rectangle below. What pattern occurs in the perimeter of each subsequent rectangle?

8.3 Problem of the Day

You need to use a bucket to collect water dripping from two leaking pipes. If one pipe *alone* would fill the bucket in 8 hours, and the other pipe *alone* would fill the bucket in 12 hours, how long will both pipes together take to fill the bucket?

22 *Windows • Chapter 8* © D.C. Heath and Company

Warm-Up Exercises

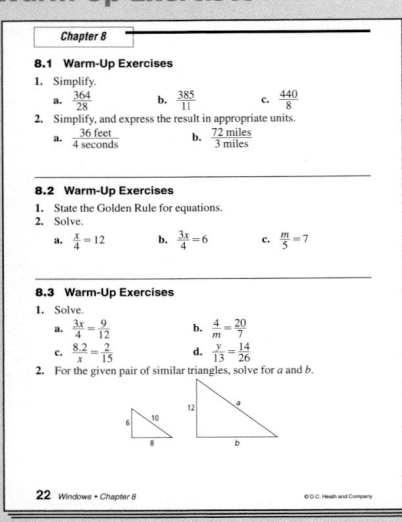

Chapter 8

8.1 Warm-Up Exercises

1. Simplify.

   a. $\frac{364}{28}$ b. $\frac{385}{11}$ c. $\frac{440}{8}$

2. Simplify, and express the result in appropriate units.

   a. $\frac{36 \text{ feet}}{4 \text{ seconds}}$ b. $\frac{72 \text{ miles}}{3 \text{ miles}}$

8.2 Warm-Up Exercises

1. State the Golden Rule for equations.
2. Solve.

   a. $\frac{x}{4} = 12$ b. $\frac{3x}{4} = 6$ c. $\frac{m}{5} = 7$

8.3 Warm-Up Exercises

1. Solve.

   a. $\frac{3x}{4} = \frac{9}{12}$ b. $\frac{4}{m} = \frac{20}{7}$

   c. $\frac{8.2}{x} = \frac{2}{15}$ d. $\frac{y}{13} = \frac{14}{26}$

2. For the given pair of similar triangles, solve for *a* and *b*.

22 *Windows • Chapter 8* © D.C. Heath and Company

FOR TEACHERS

Answer Masters

Answers for Lesson 8.1, pages 346 and 347

1. $\frac{a}{b}$ is a rate, read "*a* per *b*," if *a* and *b* have different units of measure; examples vary, 50 miles per hour is one. $\frac{a}{b}$ is a ratio, read "*a* to *b*," if *a* and *b* have the same units of measure; examples vary, 20 feet to 1 foot is one.

2. Rate, 25 mph
3. Ratio, 5 to 2
4. Ratio, 1 to 3
5. Rate, $9.33 per lb
6. $5 per hr
7. c
8. $\frac{4}{3}, \frac{5}{4}, \frac{9}{2}, \frac{9}{5}, \frac{2}{5}$
9. Ratio, 8 to 9
10. Rate, 8 meters per second
11. Rate, 22 points per game
12. Ratio, 3 to 5
13. $\frac{4 \text{ doctors}}{5 \text{ doctors}}$, it is a ratio because the units are the same.
14. $\frac{9 \text{ inspectors}}{10 \text{ inspectors}}$, it is a ratio because the units are the same.
15. $\frac{1600 \text{ miles}}{3 \text{ days}}$, it is a rate because the units are different.
16. $\frac{40 \text{ questions}}{60 \text{ minutes}}$, it is a rate because the units are different.
17. $\frac{24 \text{ in.}}{18 \text{ in.}} = \frac{4}{3}$
18. $\frac{2640 \text{ ft}}{5280 \text{ ft}} = \frac{1}{2}$
19. $\frac{120 \text{ sec}}{300 \text{ sec}} = \frac{2}{5}$
20. $\frac{3600 \text{ sec}}{3600 \text{ sec}} = \frac{1}{1}$
21. $\frac{640c}{400c} = \frac{8}{5}$
22. $\frac{8 \text{ qt}}{10 \text{ qt}} = \frac{4}{5}$
23. $\frac{200 \text{ cm}}{300 \text{ cm}} = \frac{2}{3}$
24. $\frac{2000 \text{ mL}}{50 \text{ mL}} = \frac{40}{1}$

154 *Windows Answer Masters* © D.C. Heath and Company

Lesson Plans

Lesson Plan 8.1
pages 344–347

Teacher's Name _____ Class _____ Date _____ Room _____

Goals 1. Find rates.
2. Find ratios.

State/Local Objectives _____

NCTM Curriculum Standards: Problem Solving, Communication, Connections, Number Relationships, Algebra, Geometry, Measurement

✔ **Check items you wish to use for this lesson.**

Introducing the Lesson
___ Problem of the Day copymaster page 22 or Teacher's Edition page 344
___ Warm-Up Exercises copymaster page 22 or Teacher's Edition page 344

Teaching the Lesson using the following:
___ Extra Examples, Teacher's Edition page 345
___ Notes for Substitute Teacher

Closing the Lesson
___ Communicating about Mathematics, Student's Edition page 345
___ Guided Practice Exercises, Student's Edition page 346

Homework Assignment, pages 346, 347
___ Basic/Average: Day 1: Ex. 9–25 odd
    Day 2: Ex. 27–31 odd, 43, 44
___ Above Average: Ex. 9–29 odd, 32, 40–44
___ Advanced: Ex. 9–29 odd, 32, 40–44

Reteaching the Lesson
___ Extra Practice Copymasters page 60
___ Reteaching Copymasters page 60
___ Math Log copymaster page 25 or Teacher's Edition page 347

Extending the Lesson
___ Writing, Teacher's Edition page 345
___ Enrichment, Teacher's Edition page 347
___ Alternate Assessment: Journal Entry, copymaster page 29
___ Technology Using Calculators and Computers copymaster page 44

Notes _____

60 *Windows* © D.C. Heath and Company

Teaching Tools

Name _____

C2 *Windows • Graph Paper* Use with Lessons 1.2, 1.4, 1.5, 2.1, 5.7, 6.2–6.4, 7.2, 7.5, 7.6, 7.8, 8.1

Teaching Tools includes:
Transparencies and Copymasters for classroom activities and study skills:

- Graph Paper
- Dot Paper (Geoboards)
- Algebra Tiles
- Number Counters
- Fraction Strips
- Models

REAL LIFE

Color Transparencies for Real-Life Applications

Color Transparencies for Real Life Applications • 33

Mid-Chapter Self-Test, Page 362, Exercise 17

Lesson 8.5, Page 365, Exercises 7–9

YEARLY INCOME FOR THE AVERAGE PAY PHONE

Calling cards, credit cards $1,170

Coin Revenue $1,050

Collect calls $488

Third-party calls $292

© D.C. Heath and Company Windows

Technology: Using Calculators and Computers

Constructing the Golden Rectangle **8.1** Teacher Demonstration Material

Exploration Using a Computer Drawing Program

If you have access to dynamic construction software such as *Cabri, The Geometer's Sketchpad,* or *Geometry Inventor,* there is an interesting demonstration you can do to help your students learn more about ratios. Specifically, you will show your students how to use the golden ratio to construct a golden rectangle. It is assumed that the user is familiar with the software.

The Golden Rectangle

A golden rectangle is a rectangle whose sides are in the golden ratio. (The golden ratio is $\frac{1 + \sqrt{5}}{2} \approx 1.618$.) For example, consider the rectangle shown at the right. The rectangle is a golden rectangle because the ratio $\frac{JL}{LM} = \frac{1 + \sqrt{5}}{2} \approx 1.618$. Have students approximate this by using a calculator to find $1 + \sqrt{5}$ and the resulting ratio.

Constructing The Golden Rectangle

Steps

1. Using the construction software, construct square *A B C D*.
2. Extend sides $\overline{BC}$ and $\overline{AD}$ by constructing $\overrightarrow{BC}$ and $\overrightarrow{AD}$.
3. Now construct point *E* on $\overrightarrow{BC}$ and a line through *E* that is perpendicular to $\overrightarrow{AD}$.
4. Then construct point *F*, the intersection of the line through *E* and $\overrightarrow{AD}$.
5. Finally, measure $\overline{BE}$ and $\overline{EF}$.

Comments

You may first want to see if the students can choose the golden rectangle on their own. To change the location of line $\overline{EF}$, click and drag on point *E*. Move point *E* until the majority of the class thinks the rectangle "looks good." The students will probably choose a rectangle that is close to the golden rectangle. (If possible, hide $\overline{CD}$ to help students choose the rectangle.)

Now find the ratio of BE to EF. If the ratio is ≈ 1.618, the rectangle is golden. If not, keep moving point *E* until it is. You have now constructed a golden rectangle.

Extension

In the first figure above, if $\overline{KN}$ is drawn so *J K N O* is a square, the ratio $\frac{LM}{MN} = \frac{2}{\sqrt{5} - 1} \approx 1.618$, the golden ratio. Thus, when this golden rectangle is divided into a square and a rectangle, the resulting rectangle *K L M N* is also a golden rectangle. Have students check if this observation is true using your construction. Encourage students to determine how to construct other golden rectangles within *A B E F*.

44 *Technology Using Calculators and Computers* © D.C. Heath and Company

Also Available:

- Complete Solutions Manual
- Overhead Manipulatives Kit
- Computerized Testing Program

- **Interactive CD-ROM Projects** Interactive projects for solving real-world problems using multimedia

- **Interactions: Real Math–Real Careers** A videodisc–based resource that connects math to real careers and on-the-job problem solving

- **PACKETS® Performance Assessment for Middle School Mathematics** A program that links assessment and instruction

ASSESSMENT

Alternative Assessment

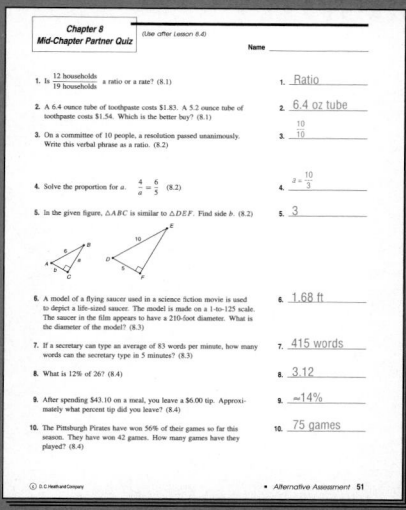

Alternative Assessment includes:
- Scoring Rubrics
- Portfolios
- Math Journals
- Projects
- Partner Quizzes
- Individual and Group Assessment

Formal Assessment

Formal Assessment includes:
- Short Quizzes (after every 2 lessons)
- Mid-Chapter Tests (2 forms)
- Chapter Tests (3 forms)
- Cumulative Tests (after every 3 Chapters)

MEETING INDIVIDUAL NEEDS

Extra Practice Copymasters

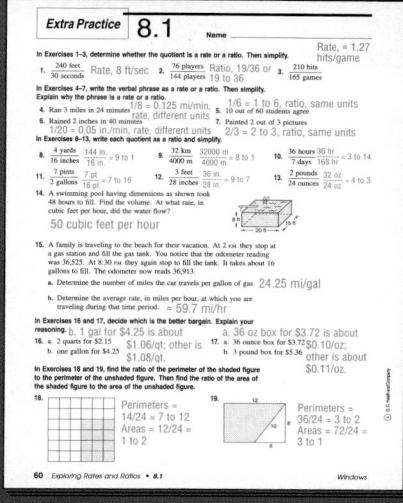

Reteaching Copymasters

Enrichment Projects

Math Log

Special Populations

Suggestions for providing equal access for:

Students Acquiring English Proficiency*

Some students may not be familiar with the customary measures used in Lessons 8.1 and 8.3. A poster that displays customary measures, their metric equivalents, and examples, may benefit these students.

Further explanation of the consumer topics in this chapter, such as discounts, may be needed.

Students with Various Learning Styles*

In Lessons 8.1 and 8.3, students who have trouble with memorization should be provided with a list of customary measures and their equivalents.

Allow students to confirm the results they obtain by using the counting principle and Pascal's Triangle in Lesson 8.7 by using colored cubes to find the different combinations. If colored cubes are not available, cut squares or circles from colored paper.

Underachieving Students*

In Lesson 8.1, maintain students' interest by developing ratios based on classroom statistics such as the ratio of students wearing sneakers to the entire class.

Bring in mail-order catalogs, and have students fill out order forms with a certain percent markdown. Have students make posters featuring the merchandise on sale, its original price, and its sale price after the markdown.

Gifted and Talented Students*

Have students work in pairs to find two uses of ratios or percents in the newspaper. For each use, they should write three problems using the information that they have found. Then have groups exchange problems and solve them.

*See page T19 for descriptions of these special populations.

Proportion, Percent, and Probability

PACING CHART

Lesson	Basic/ Average Course	Above Average Course	Advanced Course
8.1	2 days	1 day	1 day
8.2	2 days	1 day	1 day
8.3	2 days	1 day	1 day
8.4	2 days	1 day	1 day
8.5	2 days	1 day	1 day
8.6	0 days	2 days	1 day
8.7	2 days	1 day	1 day
8.8	0 days	2 days	1 day

About the Chapter

The previous chapter introduced students to the skills of manipulating fractions and to the three interchangeable forms used for comparing one quantity with another—fractions, decimals, and percents. These skills are developed further in the present chapter to include the technique of writing and solving proportions, a technique that is of immense importance in mathematics and in real-life situations.

For example, *similarity*, one of the most basic relationships in geometry, involves the concept of proportionality, and Lesson 8.2 illustrates how students can apply their newly learned skills to compute the side length of a triangle. Lesson 8.3 proceeds to demonstrate the indispensable role of proportions in everyday problem solving, most notably in the techniques of indirect measurement and estimation.

Lessons 8.4, 8.5, and 8.6 deal with a widely used application of proportion, namely, the writing and solving of percent equations and their use in such contexts as the display and interpretation of data in circle graphs, computing discounts, and analyzing quantitative changes in the world around us. The final two lessons take students further into probability (first introduced at the end of Chapter 5) with the Counting Principle.

The information superhighway of computer mail, cellular phones, and modems has been made possible by advances in fiber optics. These transparent glass fibers have revolutionized the fields of telecommunication and surgical medicine. A single glass fiber, whose diameter is 1.5×10^{-4} millimeters, can carry 2.5 trillion pages of data per second. In medicine, bundles of these flexible rods are used in laser surgery and in fiberscopes.

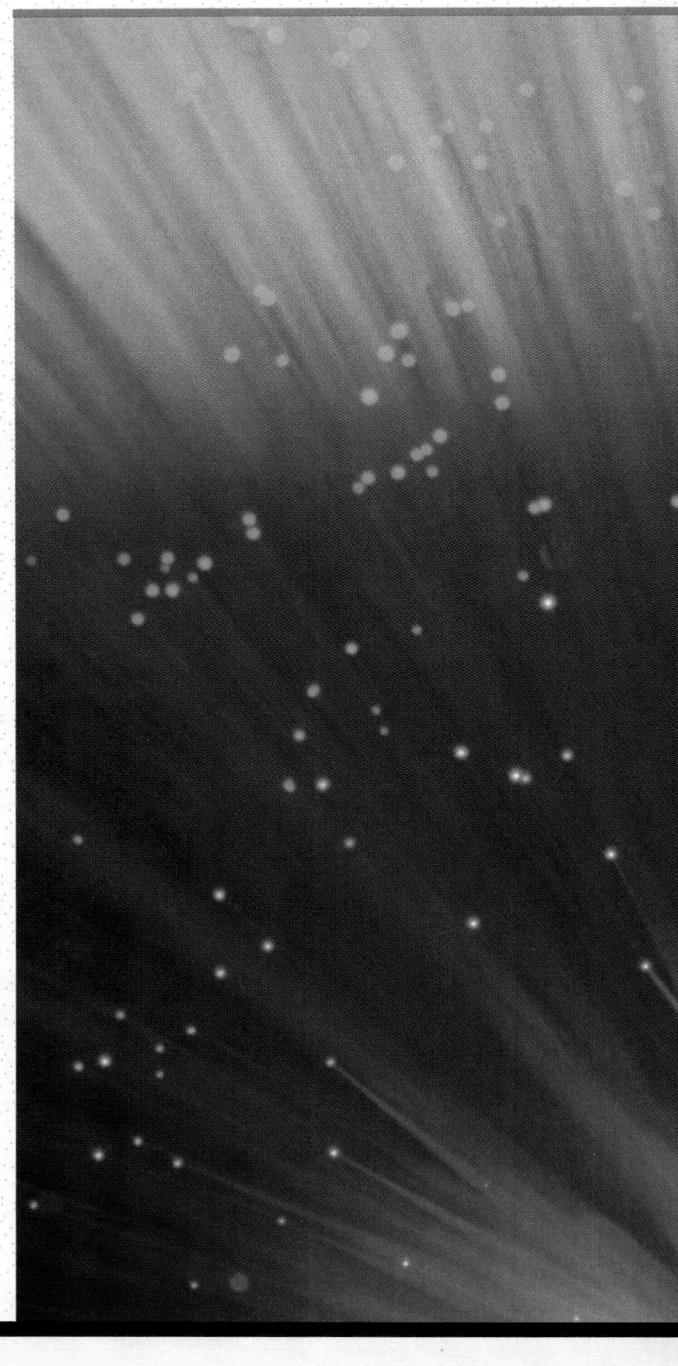

Real Life
Digital Communication

Actual Size:

Magnified Scale Model:

Miniaturization in the electronics industry has led to major advances in the computer and communications industries. Since 1988, telephone and cable television companies have begun replacing their nearly 3 billion kilometers of 2-millimeter copper wire cable lines with bundles of 600 silica glass fibers. The computer microchip shown in the scale drawing at the left is really a miniature computer capable of storing and processing up to 262,144 bits of computer information.

Scale drawings are just one real-life application of rates, ratios, and proportions that you will learn about in this chapter.

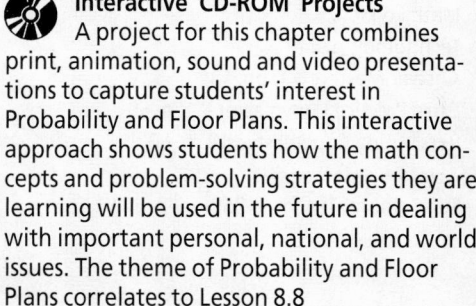

PACING the Lesson

Suggested Number of Days
Basic/Average 2   Above Average 1
Advanced 1

PLANNING the Lesson

Lesson Plan 8.1, p. 60

ORGANIZER

Starters (reproduced below)
  Problem of the Day 8.1, p. 22
  Warm-Up Exercises 8.1, p. 22
Lesson Resources
  Math Log, p. 25
  Technology, p. 44
  Answer Masters 8.1, pp. 154, 155
  Extra Practice Copymaster 8.1, p. 60
  Reteaching Copymaster 8.1, p. 60
Special Populations
  Suggestions, Teacher's Edition, p. 342D

LESSON Notes

Ask students to identify rates they encounter in their day-to-day situations. Have students record in their math journals that rates compare measures of *different* units.

Example 1

The term *speed* is a real-life word that indicates a rate. Challenge students to identify other real-life terms that indicate a rate.
Answers will vary; others include unit price, rate of growth, etc.

Example 2

Encourage students to observe pricing conventions at their local supermarkets. Supermarkets usually show the *unit price* of a food item on a label displayed on the front edge of the shelf, or on the package. Unit price expresses a rate (dollars per pound, dollars per ounce, and so on).

8.1 Exploring Rates and Ratios

What you should learn:

Goal 1 How to find rates

Goal 2 How to find ratios

Why you should learn it:

You can use rates and ratios to solve real-life problems, such as finding unit prices.

Real Life
Average Speed

Real Life
Unit Price

Goal 1   Finding Rates

If two quantities a and b have different units of measure, then the **rate** of a per b is $\frac{a}{b}$. Rates are used in almost all parts of real life. Here are two examples.

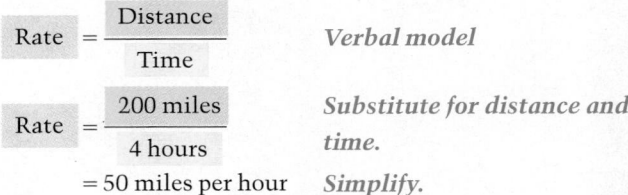

a	b	Rate
$21.00	3 hours	$\frac{21 \text{ dollars}}{3 \text{ hours}} = 7$ dollars per hour
240 miles	12 gallons	$\frac{240 \text{ miles}}{12 \text{ gallons}} = 20$ miles per gallon

Example 1   *Finding a Rate*

You drove 200 miles in 4 hours. What was your average speed?

Solution To find the rate, divide the distance by the time.

$$\text{Rate} = \frac{\text{Distance}}{\text{Time}} \qquad \textit{Verbal model}$$

$$\text{Rate} = \frac{200 \text{ miles}}{4 \text{ hours}} \qquad \textit{Substitute for distance and time.}$$

$$= 50 \text{ miles per hour} \qquad \textit{Simplify.}$$

Your rate (or average speed) was 50 miles per hour. ∎

Example 2   *Finding a Rate*

A 16-ounce box of breakfast cereal costs $2.89, and a 20-ounce box costs $3.49. Which is the better buy?

Solution

Price	Weight	Unit Price
$2.89	16 ounces	$\frac{\$2.89}{16 \text{ ounces}} \approx 0.181$ dollars per ounce
$3.49	20 ounces	$\frac{\$3.49}{20 \text{ ounces}} \approx 0.175$ dollars per ounce

Because the larger box has the smaller unit price, it follows that it is the better buy. ∎

STARTER: Problem of the Day

An investor bought $10,000 (U.S. dollars) worth of Canadian dollars when 1 Canadian dollar was worth 0.75 U.S. dollars. Later, when the Canadian dollar was worth 0.81 U.S. dollars, he sold his Canadian dollars for U.S. dollars. How much profit (loss) did he have?
$800 profit

Also available as a copymaster, page 22

STARTER: Warm-Up Exercises

1. Simplify.
  a. $\frac{364}{28}$ **b.** $\frac{385}{11}$ **c.** $\frac{440}{8}$
  a. 13, **b.** 35, **c.** 55
2. Simplify, and express the result in appropriate units.
  a. $\frac{36 \text{ feet}}{4 \text{ seconds}}$ **b.** $\frac{72 \text{ miles}}{3 \text{ miles}}$
  a. $\frac{9 \text{ feet}}{\text{second}}$, **b.** 24

Also available as a copymaster, page 22

The mechanical praying mantis at the right is 17 feet 4 inches long. It was built by Creative Presentations. This company built several huge insect robots for a traveling museum show called Backyard Monsters. *The company started by studying live insects.*

Real Life
Robotics

Goal 2 Finding Ratios

If two quantities a and b have the same units of measure, then the **ratio** of a to b is $\frac{a}{b}$.

Example 3 *Finding a Ratio*

To build the robot mantis shown above, Creative Presentations used a real praying mantis that was 4 inches long. What is the ratio of the robot mantis's length to the real mantis's length?

Solution To find a ratio, both quantities must have the same unit of measure. In inches, the length of the robot mantis is

$$17 \text{ feet} + 4 \text{ inches} = 17(12 \text{ inches}) + 4 \text{ inches} = 208 \text{ inches}.$$

The ratio of the robot's length to the real mantis's length is

$$\frac{\text{Robot's length}}{\text{Mantis's length}} = \frac{208 \text{ inches}}{4 \text{ inches}} = \frac{52}{1} \quad \text{or} \quad 52 \text{ to } 1.$$

The ratio of the robot mantis's length to the real mantis's length is 52 to 1. In other words, the robot is 52 times as long as the real mantis. ∎

> **Study Tip...**
> In Example 3, notice that both quantities were written in the same units of measure before dividing to find the ratio.

Communicating about MATHEMATICS

▶ **SHARING IDEAS about the Lesson**

Rate or Ratio? Decide whether the quotient is a rate or a ratio. Then simplify the quotient.

A. $\dfrac{10{,}000 \text{ people}}{4 \text{ years}}$	B. $\dfrac{10{,}000 \text{ people}}{4{,}000 \text{ people}}$	C. $\dfrac{\$6{,}000}{4 \text{ years}}$
Rate	Ratio	Rate

A. 2500 people per year **B.** 2.5 **C.** $1500 per year

Have students include in their journals that ratios compare measures of the *same* units. Thus, the quotient of such measures is a number value.

Example 3

Sometimes ratios are written using colons. For example, a ratio of 52 to 1 can be written as 52:1.

Communicating about MATHEMATICS

PROJECT
Have students look at magazines, science textbooks, and newspapers to discover uses of rates and ratios in real-life settings.

Writing Prompt
Describe any images that come to mind when you think of rates or ratios.

OPTION: Extra Examples

Here are additional examples similar to some of those of the lesson.

1. Finding a Rate
A 6.5-ounce jar of mustard costs 49¢ and a 9-ounce jar costs 69¢. Which is the better buy?
Solution

Price	Weight	Unit Price
49¢	6.5 ounces	$\dfrac{49¢}{6.5 \text{ ounces}} \approx 7.538$ cents per ounce
69¢	9 ounces	$\dfrac{69¢}{9 \text{ ounces}} \approx 7.667$ cents per ounce

Because the smaller jar has the smaller unit price, it follows that it is the better buy.

2. Finding a Ratio
An architect wants to represent the 30-foot length of a living room by a 5-inch segment. What is the ratio of the segment's length to the living room's length?
Solution
In inches, the length of the living room is 30 feet = 30(12 inches) = 360 inches.
The ratio of the segment's length to the living room's length is

$$\frac{\text{Segment's length}}{\text{Living room's length}} = \frac{5 \text{ inches}}{360 \text{ inches}} = \frac{1}{72}$$

The ratio of the segment's length to the living room's length is 1 to 72.

Technology

Constructing the Golden Rectangle	**8.1**	Teacher Demonstration Material

Exploration Using a Computer Drawing Program

If you have access to dynamic construction software such as *Cabri, The Geometer's Sketchpad,* or *Geometry Inventor,* there is an interesting demonstration you can do to help your students learn more about ratios. Specifically, you will show your students how to use the golden ratio to construct a golden rectangle. It is assumed that the user is familiar with the software.

The Golden Rectangle
A golden rectangle is a rectangle whose sides are in the golden ratio. (The golden ratio is $\frac{1 + \sqrt{5}}{2} \approx 1.618$.) For example, consider the rectangle shown at the right. The rectangle is a golden rectangle because the ratio $\frac{JL}{LM} = \frac{1 + \sqrt{5}}{2} \approx 1.618$. Have students approximate this by using a calculator to find $1 + \sqrt{5}$ and the resulting ratio.

Constructing The Golden Rectangle
Steps
1. Using the construction software, construct square $ABCD$.
2. Extend sides $\overline{BC}$ and $\overline{AD}$ by constructing $\overline{BC}$ and $\overline{AD}$.
3. Now construct point E on $\overline{BC}$ and a line through E that is perpendicular to $\overline{AD}$.
4. Then construct point F, the intersection of the line through E and $\overline{AD}$.
5. Finally, measure $\overline{BE}$ and $\overline{EF}$.

Comments
You may first want to see if the students can choose the golden rectangle on their own. To change the location of line $\overline{EF}$, click and drag on point E. Move point E until the majority of the class thinks the rectangle "looks good." The students will probably choose a rectangle that is close to the golden rectangle. (If possible, hide $\overline{CD}$ to help students choose the rectangle.)
Now find the ratio of BE to EF. If the ratio is ≈ 1.618, the rectangle is golden. If not, keep moving point E until it is. You have now constructed a golden rectangle.

Extension
In the first figure above, if $\overline{KN}$ is drawn so $JKNO$ is a square, the ratio $\frac{LM}{MN} = \frac{2}{\sqrt{5}-1} \approx 1.618$, the golden ratio. Thus, when this golden rectangle is divided into a square and a rectangle, the resulting rectangle $KLMN$ is also a golden rectangle. Have students check if this observation is true using your construction. Encourage students to determine how to construct other golden rectangles within $ABEF$.

44 *Technology Using Calculators and Computers* © D. C. Heath and Company

ASSIGNMENT GUIDE

Basic/Average:
Day 1: Ex. 9–25 odd
Day 2: Ex. 27–31 odd, 43, 44

Above Average:
Ex. 9–29 odd, 32, 40–44

Advanced: Ex. 9–29 odd, 32, 40–44

Selected Answers: Ex. 1–8, 9–41 odd

Guided Practice

▶ **Ex. 1** This exercise emphasizes an important distinction between rates and ratios. Be sure students understand the notion of *same* units of measure.
▶ **Ex. 8** Use this exercise as a one-minute small group in-class activity.

Independent Practice

▶ **Ex. 7–24** Remind students they must have similar units of measure to write the quotient as a ratio.

Answers

1. $\frac{a}{b}$ is a rate, read "*a* per *b*," if *a* and *b* have different units of measure; examples vary, 50 miles per hour is one. $\frac{a}{b}$ is a ratio, read "*a* to *b*," if *a* and *b* have the same units of measure; examples vary, 20 feet to 1 foot is one.

13. $\frac{4 \text{ doctors}}{5 \text{ doctors}}$, is a ratio because the units are the same.

14. $\frac{9 \text{ inspectors}}{10 \text{ inspectors}}$, is a ratio because the units are the same.

15. $\frac{1600 \text{ miles}}{3 \text{ days}}$, is a rate because the units are different.

16. $\frac{40 \text{ questions}}{60 \text{ minutes}}$, is a rate because the units are different.

17. $\frac{24 \text{ inches}}{18 \text{ inches}} = \frac{4}{3}$

18. $\frac{2640 \text{ feet}}{5280 \text{ feet}} = \frac{1}{2}$

19. $\frac{120 \text{ seconds}}{300 \text{ seconds}} = \frac{2}{5}$

20. $\frac{3600 \text{ seconds}}{3600 \text{ seconds}} = \frac{1}{1}$

21. $\frac{640¢}{40¢} = \frac{8}{5}$

22. $\frac{8 \text{ quarts}}{10 \text{ quarts}} = \frac{4}{5}$

23. $\frac{200 \text{ centimeters}}{300 \text{ centimeters}} = \frac{2}{3}$

24. $\frac{2000 \text{ milliliters}}{50 \text{ milliliters}} = \frac{40}{1}$

346 Chapter 8

Guided Practice

▶ **CHECK for Understanding**

P **1.** *Problem Solving* Explain the difference between a rate and a ratio. Give an example of each. See margin.

In Exercises 2–5, state whether the quotient is a rate or a ratio. Then simplify.

2. Rate, 25 miles per hour

5. Rate, $9.33 per pound

2. $\frac{100 \text{ miles}}{4 \text{ hours}}$

3. $\frac{10 \text{ inches}}{4 \text{ inches}}$ Ratio, 5 to 2

4. $\frac{8 \text{ balloons}}{24 \text{ balloons}}$ Ratio, 1 to 3

5. $\frac{\$27.99}{3 \text{ pounds}}$

6. You work for 12 hours and get paid $60. What is your rate of pay? Include units of measure in your answer. $5 per hour

7. Which of the following measures the rate at which an automobile uses gasoline? c

a. Miles per hour

b. Gallons per mile

c. Miles per gallon

8. Describe six ratios that compare the colors of the nine triangles below.

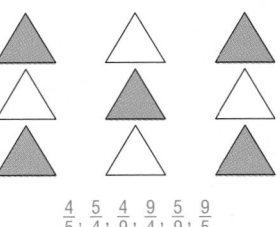

$$\frac{4}{5}, \frac{5}{4}, \frac{4}{9}, \frac{9}{4}, \frac{5}{9}, \frac{9}{5}$$

Independent Practice

In Exercises 9–12, determine whether the quotient is a rate or a ratio. Then simplify. 9. Ratio, 8 to 9 10. Rate, 8 meters per second

9. $\frac{16 \text{ students}}{18 \text{ students}}$

10. $\frac{120 \text{ meters}}{15 \text{ seconds}}$

11. $\frac{88 \text{ points}}{4 \text{ games}}$

12. $\frac{3 \text{ cars}}{5 \text{ cars}}$

11. Rate, 22 points per game 12. Ratio, 3 to 5

In Exercises 13–16, write the verbal phrase as a rate or a ratio. Explain why the phrase is a rate or a ratio. See margin.

13. Recommended by 4 out of 5 doctors

14. Approved by 9 out of 10 inspectors

15. Traveled 1600 miles in 3 days

16. Answered 40 questions in 60 minutes

In Exercises 17–24, write each quotient as a ratio and simplify. See margin.

17. $\frac{2 \text{ feet}}{18 \text{ inches}}$

18. $\frac{2640 \text{ feet}}{1 \text{ mile}}$

19. $\frac{2 \text{ minutes}}{300 \text{ seconds}}$

20. $\frac{1 \text{ hour}}{3600 \text{ seconds}}$

21. $\frac{640¢}{\$4}$

22. $\frac{2 \text{ gallons}}{10 \text{ quarts}}$

23. $\frac{200 \text{ centimeters}}{3 \text{ meters}}$

24. $\frac{2 \text{ liters}}{50 \text{ milliliters}}$

25. *Concert Tickets* A concert sold out in 6 hours. 9000 tickets were sold for the concert. At what rate did the tickets sell? 1500 tickets per hour

26. *Snowfall* The record for snowfall in a 24-hour period is 76 inches at Silver Lake, Colorado, on April 14–15, 1921. At what rate did the snow fall on that day? $3\frac{1}{6}$ inches per hour

---

Extra Practice

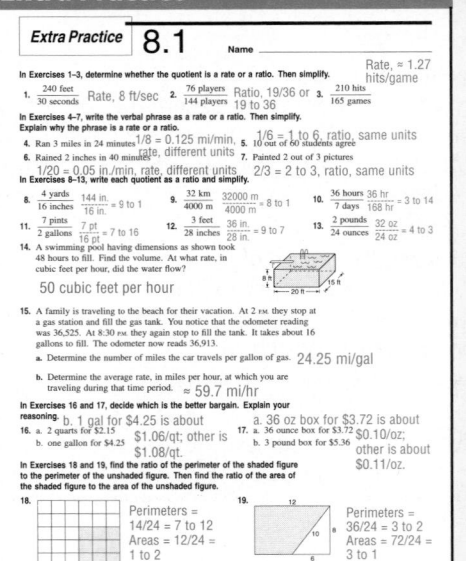

Reteaching

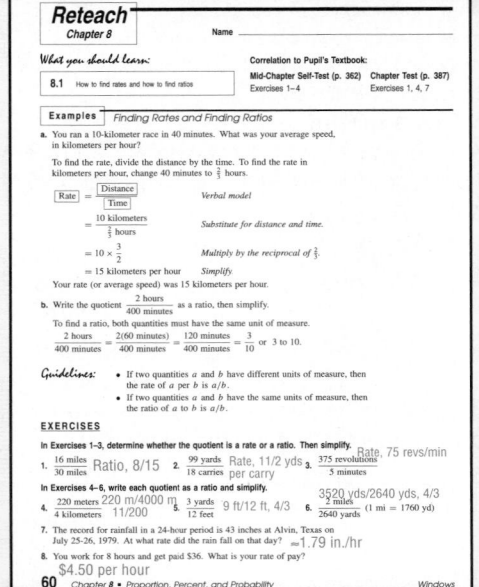

Unit Pricing   In Exercises 27–30, decide which is the better buy. Explain your reasoning.
For explanations, see margin.

27. a. 6 apples for $1.18   b
   b. 10 apples for $1.79

28. a. 12-ounce box for $2.69   b
   b. 18-ounce box for $3.99

29. a. 2 pounds, 4 ounces for $7.89   a
   b. 5 pounds, 2 ounces for $18.89

30. a. six 12-ounce cans for $2.69   a
   b. one half-gallon bottle for $4.59

31. *Ballooning*   It took 86 hours for Joe Kittinger to cross the Atlantic in his balloon, *Rosie O'Grady*. What was the average speed of the balloon?   ≈ 41.2 mph

Ex-USAF Colonel Joe Kittinger is the first man to complete a solo transatlantic crossing by balloon. Between September 14–18, 1984, he flew from Caribou, Maine, to Montenotte, Italy, approximately 3543 miles.

32. *Building a Model Railroad*   On an N-gauge model train set, a tank car is 3.75 inches long. An actual tank car is 50 feet long. What is the ratio of the length of the actual tank car to the length of the model tank car? $\frac{160}{1}$

Geometry   In Exercises 33–36, find the ratio of the blue figure's perimeter to the yellow figure's perimeter. Then find the ratio of the blue figure's area to the yellow figure's area. Which ratio is greater?

35. Ratio of perimeters
36. Ratio of areas

33.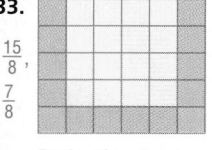

$\frac{15}{8}$,

$\frac{7}{8}$

Ratio of perimeters

✪ 34.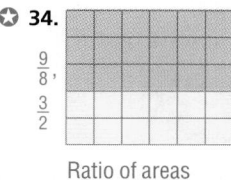

$\frac{9}{8}$,

$\frac{3}{2}$

Ratio of areas

✪ 35.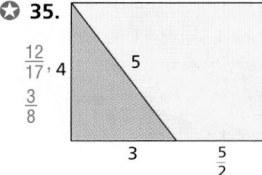

$\frac{12}{17}$, 4

$\frac{3}{8}$

5

3        $\frac{5}{2}$

✪ 36.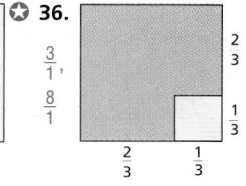

$\frac{3}{1}$,

$\frac{8}{1}$

2 $\frac{2}{3}$

1 $\frac{1}{3}$

$\frac{2}{3}$ $\frac{1}{3}$

Integrated Review

Making Connections within Mathematics

Measurement Sense   In Exercises 37–42, convert the measure as indicated.

37. 384 inches to feet   32 ft
38. 115 meters to centimeters   11,500 cm
39. 10,800 seconds to hours   3 hours
40. 584 cents to dollars $5.84
41. 10 pints to quarts   5 qt
42. 3 gallons to quarts   12 qt

Exploration and Extension

Geometry   In Exercises 43 and 44, refer to △ABC.

43. Find the following ratios. $\frac{5}{4}, \frac{5}{3}, \frac{3}{4}$
   a. c to a **b.** c to b **c.** b to a

44. Draw a second triangle, △DEF, that is larger than △ABC but whose sides have the same ratios.   Drawings vary.

A
c = 5
b = 3
C   a = 4   B

✪ More difficult exercises   **8.1** • *Exploring Rates and Ratios*   **347**

▶ **Ex. 31**   Students will need to read the caption with the photo to find the distance of 3543 miles.
▶ **Ex. 31, 32**   Ask students to use an answer format similar to Examples 1 and 3.
▶ **Ex. 33–36**   This exercise can be used as a small group in-class review to connect the concepts of area, perimeter, and ratio.

Integrated Review

▶ **Ex. 37–42**   Students may need some unit conversion review. These exercises could be used as a readiness check for the lesson.

Exploration and Extension

▶ **Ex. 43**   This exercise is a lead-in to future discussions of right triangle trigonometry ratios in geometry.

Portfolio Opportunity: Math Log

You bought a car with a 14-gallon tank that is advertised to get 25 miles per gallon. You begin a trip on a full tank of gas and after 300 miles you are on empty. What was the actual mileage for this trip?

Also available as a copymaster, page 25, Ex. 1

Alternative Assessment

A journal entry in which students research and record real-world ratios and rates.

Available as a copymaster, page 29

▶ **Enrichment**

Ask students to cut an advertisement from a newspaper and create one ratio and one rate problem that each describes the picture.

Answers
27. 17.9¢ per apple < 19.7¢ per apple
28. 22.2¢ per ounce < 22.4¢ per ounce
29. 21.9¢ per ounce < 23.0¢ per ounce
30. 3.7¢ per ounce < 7.2¢ per ounce

The purpose of this investigation is to explore the *golden rectangle* ratio. Golden rectangles have the property that the ratio of the length to the width is the *Golden Ratio* as described in Example 4.

Draw students' attention to the fact that, although in Lesson 8.1 the ratio of *a* to *b* was defined as $\frac{a}{b}$, ratios are sometimes expressed as single numbers, as in the solution to the example here. Students are expected to express also the answers to Ex. 3, 4 as single numbers.

Ask students to measure door frames and/or windows in your classroom. Students can check to see if the classroom architecture uses golden rectangles.

EXTENSION

Have students generate the Fibonacci numbers based on the pattern of 1,1, 2, 3, 5, ... Ask students how this number sequence relates to the Golden Ratio.

In this activity, you will find the length-to-width ratios of several rectangles.

Example   *Finding Ratios*

For each rectangle, find the ratio of the length to the width. Which rectangle do you think is most artistically pleasing to look at?

a. 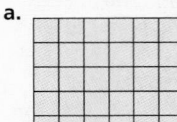   b. 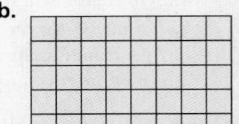   c.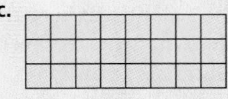

Solution

a. $\frac{6}{5} = 1.2$ **b.** $\frac{8}{5} = 1.6$ **c.** $\frac{8}{3} \approx 2.67$

For most people, the second rectangle is most pleasing. They find the first rectangle too square and the third too skinny.   ■

Exercises

Golden Ratio   **In Exercises 1–4, use the following rectangles.**

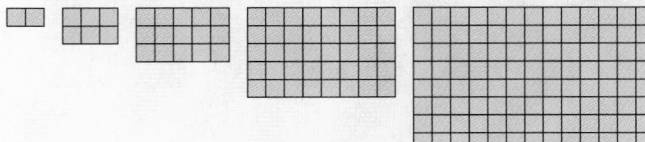

1. For each rectangle, find the ratio of its length to its width. $\frac{2}{1}, \frac{3}{2}, \frac{5}{3}, \frac{8}{5}, \frac{13}{8}$

2. Describe the patterns of the lengths and widths. What are the lengths and widths of the next three rectangles in the pattern?   See margin.

3. Use the results of Exercises 1 and 2 to complete the table.

Length	2	3	5	8	13	?	?	?	21, 34, 55
Width	1	2	3	5	8	?	?	?	13, 21, 34
Ratio	?	?	?	?	?	?	?	?	≈1.615, ≈1.619, ≈1.618

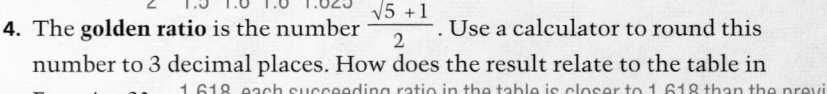

2   1.5 1.6̄ 1.6 1.625

4. The **golden ratio** is the number $\frac{\sqrt{5}+1}{2}$. Use a calculator to round this number to 3 decimal places. How does the result relate to the table in Exercise 3?   1.618, each succeeding ratio in the table is closer to 1.618 than the previous one.

Answer
2. Each length, after the first, is the sum of the preceding length and width, and each width, after the first, is the same as the preceding length; or each length, after the first two, is the sum of the two preceding lengths, and each width, after the first two, is the sum of the two preceding widths. Lengths: 21, 34, 55; widths: 13, 21, 34.

8.2

Solving Proportions

What you should learn:

 Goal 1
How to solve proportions

 Goal 2
How to write proportions for similar triangles

Why you should learn it:

You can use proportions to solve problems in geometry, such as finding the lengths of the sides of similar triangles.

Goal 1 **Solving Proportions**

An equation that equates two ratios is a **proportion.** For instance, if the ratio $\frac{a}{b}$ is equal to the ratio $\frac{c}{d}$, then the proportion is

$$\frac{a}{b} = \frac{c}{d}. \qquad \textit{Proportion}$$

This is read as "a is to b as c is to d."

Example 1 ___ **Solving a Proportion**

Solve the proportion for x: $\frac{x}{2} = \frac{3}{4}$.

Solution

$\frac{x}{2} = \frac{3}{4}$	*Rewrite original proportion.*
$2 \cdot \frac{x}{2} = 2 \cdot \frac{3}{4}$	*Multiply each side by 2.*
$x = \frac{6}{4}$	*Simplify.*
$x = \frac{3}{2}$	*Simplify.*

The solution is $x = \frac{3}{2}$. Check this in the original proportion. ∎

Cross Product Property

You can solve or check a proportion by using the **Cross Product Property,** which states that

if $\frac{a}{b} = \frac{c}{d}$, then $ad = bc$.

For instance, you can check the solution of Example 1 as follows.

$$\frac{x}{2} \overset{?}{=} \frac{3}{4}$$

$$\frac{\frac{3}{2}}{2} \overset{?}{=} \frac{3}{4}$$

$$\frac{3}{2} \cdot 4 \overset{?}{=} 2 \cdot 3$$

$$6 = 6 \checkmark$$

Example 2 ___ **Solving a Proportion**

Solve the proportion for m: $\frac{3}{m} = \frac{5}{8}$.

Solution To solve this proportion, you can use the **Reciprocal Property**, which states that if $\frac{a}{b} = \frac{c}{d}$, then $\frac{b}{a} = \frac{d}{c}$.

$\frac{3}{m} = \frac{5}{8}$	*Rewrite original proportion.*
$\frac{m}{3} = \frac{8}{5}$	*Reciprocal Property*
$3 \cdot \frac{m}{3} = 3 \cdot \frac{8}{5}$	*Multiply each side by 3.*
$m = \frac{24}{5}$	*Simplify.*

The solution is $m = \frac{24}{5}$. Check this in the original proportion. Try using the Cross Product Property to solve this proportion. Which method do you prefer? ∎

8.2 • Solving Proportions **349**

You may wish to sketch other examples of similar triangles. Explain that $\frac{a}{d} = \frac{b}{e} = \frac{c}{f}$ is shorthand for three separate equations, $\frac{a}{d} = \frac{b}{e}$, $\frac{a}{d} = \frac{c}{f}$, and $\frac{b}{e} = \frac{c}{f}$.

Example 3

Common-Error Alert!

Be sure that the geometric figures have the same orientation before you attempt to identify corresponding parts of the triangles.

Communicating
about MATHEMATICS

Have students rewrite each of these proportions as a proportion statement.

a. $\frac{3}{8} = \frac{m}{16}$ **b.** $\frac{7}{x} = \frac{16}{28}$

a. 3 is to 8 as m is to 16. **b.** 7 is to x as 16 is to 28.

Writing Prompt
Explain two different approaches you can use to solve proportions.

Technology

| Solving Proportions | 8.2 | Name _____ |

Problem Solving Using a Calculator In this problem-solving activity, you will learn various ways to use a scientific calculator to solve the proportion $\frac{x}{8} = \frac{x}{5}$.

EXAMPLE Solving a Proportion
Use a scientific calculator to solve the proportion.
a. $\frac{x}{15} = \frac{14.4}{27}$ b. $\frac{63}{x} = \frac{100.5}{80.4}$

SOLUTION
a. When the variable is in the numerator, enter the following keystrokes:
14.4 × 15 ÷ 27 =
The display should show 8. Thus, $x = 8$. Could the keystrokes be entered differently?
b. When the variable is in the denominator, enter the following keystrokes:
100.5 ÷ (80.4 × 63) = 1/x
The display should show 50.4. Thus, $x = 50.4$. Why is 1/x entered?
After solving the proportion, you should always check your solution. One way to check your solution is to determine whether the ratios on both sides of the proportion are equal. If they are, then your solution is correct. For example, in Part a, substitute 8 for x and find the ratio $\frac{8}{15}$. Then determine the ratio $\frac{14.4}{27}$. Because both ratios are equal to 0.53, you know the solution is correct.

EXERCISES
In Exercises 1–8, use a scientific calculator to solve the proportion. Check your solution.
                                                          $z = 7.875$
1. $\frac{x}{64} = \frac{25}{16}$ $x = 100$ 2. $\frac{y}{12} = \frac{1.8}{5.4}$ $y = 4$ 3. $\frac{35}{20} = \frac{t}{35}$ $t = 61.25$ 4. $\frac{7}{8} = \frac{z}{9}$
5. $\frac{13}{m} = \frac{104}{24}$ $m = 3$ 6. $\frac{10}{r} = \frac{14.4}{103.68}$ $r = 72$ 7. $\frac{11.5}{2.3} = \frac{28}{n}$ $n = 5.6$ 8. $\frac{1}{8} = \frac{2.5}{w}$
                                                          $w = 20$
9. You run 0.25 miles in 1.5 minutes. Assuming you keep the same pace, how long will it take you to run 5 miles? 30 minutes
10. Explain how the Reciprocal Property makes it possible to solve Example b using the method in Example a. See back of supplement.
11. Using the Cross Product Property, explain another way in which you can check your solution. Check that $ad = bc$.

© D.C. Heath and Company   Technology Using Calculators and Computers 45

Two triangles are **similar** if they have the same angle measures. If two triangles are similar, then the ratios of **corresponding sides** are equal. For instance, the following triangles are similar because each has a 30° angle, a 60° angle, and a 90° angle. Because the ratios of corresponding sides are equal, it follows that

$$\frac{a}{d} = \frac{b}{e} = \frac{c}{f}.$$

Need to Know
Similar triangles have the same shape but not necessarily the same size. When two angles have the same measure, they are marked with the same symbols.

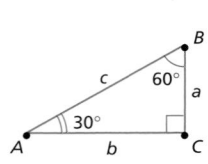

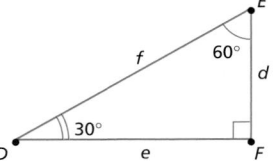

Connections
Geometry

Example 3   *Writing a Proportion*

The triangles at the left are *similar*. Find a.

Solution Begin by writing a proportion that involves a. Then solve the proportion.

$\frac{a}{d} = \frac{c}{f}$ *Ratios of corresponding sides are equal.*

$\frac{a}{3} = \frac{10}{5}$ *Substitute for c, d, and f.*

$3 \cdot \frac{a}{3} = 3 \cdot \frac{10}{5}$ *Multiply each side by 3.*

$a = 6$ *Simplify.*

Try using this approach to find b. Note that each side of $\triangle ABC$ is twice as long as the corresponding side of $\triangle DEF$. ∎

A. $\frac{x}{5} = \frac{3}{30}$, $\frac{1}{2}$

B. $\frac{4}{n} = \frac{12}{30}$, 10

C. $\frac{5}{3} = \frac{m}{5}$, $8\frac{1}{3}$

D. $\frac{4}{7} = \frac{6}{y}$, $10\frac{1}{2}$

Communicating *about* MATHEMATICS

▶ **SHARING IDEAS about the Lesson**

Writing Proportions Write a proportion for each statement. Then solve the proportion.

A. x is to 5 as 3 is to 30.   **B.** 4 is to n as 12 is to 30.
C. 5 is to 3 as m is to 5.   **D.** 4 is to 7 as 6 is to y.

OPTION: Extra Examples

Here are additional examples similar to some of those of the lesson.

Solving a Proportion

1. Solve the proportion for x: $\frac{15}{8} = \frac{x}{5}$.

Solution

$\frac{15}{8} = \frac{x}{5}$ Rewrite original proportion.

$5 \cdot \frac{15}{8} = 5 \cdot \frac{x}{5}$ Multiply each side by 5.

$\frac{75}{8} = x$ Simplify.

The solution is $x = \frac{75}{8}$. Check this in the original proportion.

2. Solve the proportion for n: $\frac{9}{20} = \frac{4}{n}$.

Solution

To solve this proportion, you can use the Reciprocal Property, which states that if $\frac{a}{b} = \frac{c}{d}$, then $\frac{b}{a} = \frac{d}{c}$.

$\frac{9}{20} = \frac{4}{n}$ Rewrite original proportion.

$\frac{20}{9} = \frac{n}{4}$ Reciprocal Property.

$4 \cdot \frac{20}{9} = 4 \cdot \frac{n}{4}$ Multiply each side by 4.

$\frac{80}{9} = n$ Simplify.

The solution is $\frac{80}{9} = n$. Check this in the original proportion.

EXERCISES

Guided Practice

CHECK for Understanding

No, $\frac{2,000}{80,000} \neq \frac{3,000}{100,000}$

1. Think about It A person paid $2000 in property tax on an $80,000 house. In the same neighborhood, another person paid $3000 tax on a $100,000 house. Is that fair? Explain how a proportion could be used to answer the question.

Answers vary.

2. Problem Solving Proportions are often used to measure fairness or equity in real life. Exercise 1 gives one example. Describe some others.

In Exercises 3–6, solve the proportion. Explain how to check your answers.

3. $\frac{b}{3} = \frac{4}{12}$ 1

4. $\frac{9}{x} = \frac{3}{5}$ 15

5. $\frac{2}{3} = \frac{m}{36}$ 24

6. $\frac{7}{18} = \frac{21}{y}$ 54

Substitute an answer for the variable and simplify where possible.

In Exercises 7 and 8, state whether the triangles are similar. If they are, write three of the proportions that compare their sides.

7.
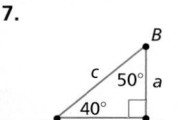 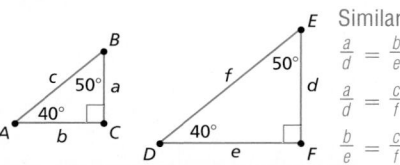
Similar
$\frac{a}{d} = \frac{b}{e}$,
$\frac{a}{d} = \frac{c}{f}$,
$\frac{b}{e} = \frac{c}{f}$

8.
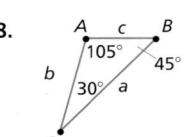 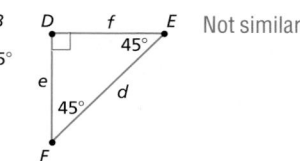
Not similar

Independent Practice

In Exercises 9–12, decide whether the proportion is true. Explain.

9. $\frac{1}{4} \overset{?}{=} \frac{3}{12}$ Yes
$1 \times 12 = 4 \times 3$

10. $\frac{6}{16} \overset{?}{=} \frac{3}{7}$ No
$6 \times 7 \neq 16 \times 3$

11. $\frac{4}{9} \overset{?}{=} \frac{16}{36}$ Yes
$4 \times 36 = 9 \times 16$

12. $\frac{9}{7} = \frac{18}{15}$ No
$9 \times 15 \neq 7 \times 18$

In Exercises 13–20, solve the proportion. Check your solution.

13. $\frac{x}{3} = \frac{4}{9}$ $\frac{4}{3}$

14. $\frac{y}{5} = \frac{8}{5}$ 8

15. $\frac{5}{7} = \frac{z}{2}$ $\frac{10}{7}$

16. $\frac{5}{12} = \frac{t}{2}$ $\frac{5}{6}$

17. $\frac{8}{m} = \frac{2}{5}$ 20

18. $\frac{9}{x} = \frac{15}{2}$ $\frac{6}{5}$

19. $\frac{2}{3} = \frac{12}{b}$ 18

20. $\frac{2.8}{y} = \frac{11}{2.5}$ $\frac{7}{11}$

In Exercises 21–26, write the sentence as a proportion. Then solve. See margin.

21. x is to 6 as 8 is to 9.

22. y is to 5 as 6 is to 17.

23. 3 is to 8 as m is to 24.

24. 2 is to 5 as 10 is to n.

25. 5 is to 6 as 12 is to s.

26. 2 is to t as 4 is to 13.

In Exercises 27–30, use a calculator to solve the proportion. Round your result to 2 decimal places.

Sample $\frac{3}{4} = \frac{x}{8}$: 3 ☒ 8 ÷ 4 =

27. $\frac{14}{15} = \frac{x}{25}$ 23.33

28. $\frac{y}{32} = \frac{16}{27}$ 18.96

29. $\frac{p}{21} = \frac{8}{42}$ 4

30. $\frac{14}{15} = \frac{x}{36}$ 33.6

ASSIGNMENT GUIDE

Basic/Average:
Day 1: Ex. 9–23 odd, 27–33
Day 2: Ex. 34–37, 39

Above Average:
Ex. 9–10 odd, 25–28, 31–34, 36, 38, 39

Advanced: Ex. 9–19 odd, 25–28, 31–34, 36, 38, 39

Selected Answers: Ex. 1–8, 9–37 odd

Guided Practice

▶ **Ex. 3–6** Remind students they can use the Cross Product Property illustrated on page 349.
▶ **Ex. 7, 8** These exercises are based on the definition that two triangles are similar if they have the same angle measurements.

Independent Practice

▶ **Ex. 9–30** Remind students to use the Cross Product Property and to show their work. For example, Ex. 28 might look like this:

$\frac{y}{32} = \frac{16}{27}$

$27y = 16 \bullet 32$ Cross multiply.

$27y = 512$ Use a calculator.

$y = \frac{512}{27}$ Divide by 27.

$y \approx 18.96$ Use a calculator and round to two decimal places.

Answers

21. $\frac{x}{6} = \frac{8}{9}$, $\frac{16}{3}$

22. $\frac{y}{5} = \frac{6}{17}$, $\frac{30}{17}$

23. $\frac{3}{8} = \frac{m}{24}$, 9

24. $\frac{2}{5} = \frac{10}{n}$, 25

25. $\frac{5}{6} = \frac{12}{s}$, $\frac{72}{5}$

26. $\frac{2}{t} = \frac{4}{13}$, $\frac{13}{2}$

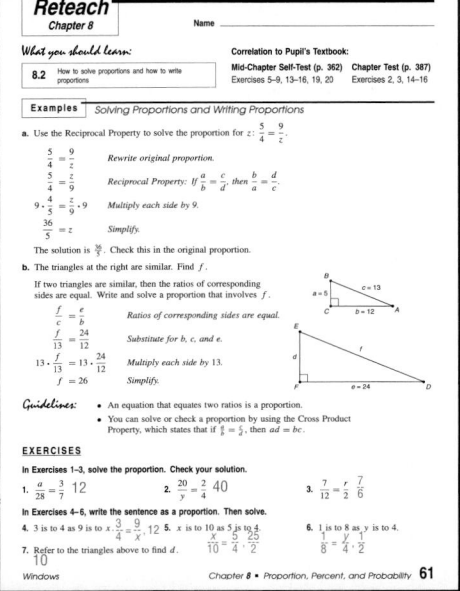

► **Ex. 31–34** Students may not be familiar with congruence markings. Be sure to explain this convention for them.
► **Ex. 36** You can use this as an in-class small-group quiz.

Integrated Review

These exercises review the skill of looking for a pattern.

Exploration and Extension

► **Ex. 39** You can use the reduction/enlargement feature of a copier to actually illustrate the idea expressed in this exercise. You may wish to use a student photograph and perform actual measurements.

Portfolio Opportunity: Math Log

Explain what is wrong with this exercise. Then correct it.

$$\frac{3}{x} = \frac{1}{2} + \frac{2}{3}$$

$$\frac{x}{3} = \frac{2}{1} + \frac{3}{2}$$

$$\frac{x}{3} = \frac{4}{2} + \frac{3}{2}$$

$$\frac{x}{3} = \frac{7}{2}$$

$$x = \frac{21}{2}$$

Also available as a copymaster, page 25, Ex. 2

Short Quiz

Covers Lessons 8.1 and 8.2

Available as a copymaster, page 122

Alternative Assessment

A class demonstration that develops students' skill at using proportions.

Available as a copymaster, page 29

Geometry **In Exercises 31–34, find the missing lengths of the sides of the similar triangles.**

31.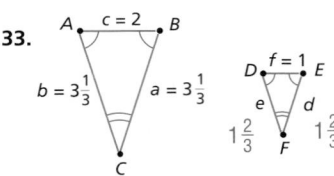

32.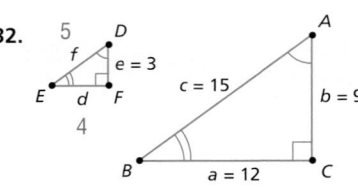

33.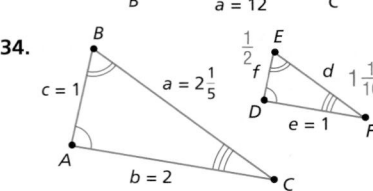

34.

35. *Yogurt Shop* You work for a frozen yogurt shop. You sell yogurt cones at an average rate of 170 every 3 hours. The shop is open for 12 hours. About how many will be sold on a given day? 680

✪ 36. *Canoe Racing* Two canoes are competing in a 20-mile race. Canoe 1 is traveling at a rate of 4 miles every 25 minutes. Canoe 2 is traveling at a rate of 3 miles every 20 minutes.

    a. How many minutes did it take each canoe to complete the race? 1:125, 2:$133\frac{1}{3}$

    b. How many hours did it take for each canoe to complete the race? 1:$2\frac{1}{12}$, 2:$2\frac{2}{9}$

    c. How fast (in miles per hour) were the canoes traveling? 1:$9\frac{3}{5}$ mph, 2:9 mph

    d. Which canoe won the race? 1

The only American canoeist to have won two Olympic gold medals is Greg Barton, who won the singles and doubles 1000-meter kayak races in 1988.

Integrated Review   *Making Connections within Mathematics*

Sequence **In Exercises 37 and 38, solve each proportion. Describe the pattern and find the next 2 numbers of the sequence.** See margin.

37. $\frac{1}{x} = \frac{2}{3}, \frac{2}{x} = \frac{3}{4}, \frac{3}{x} = \frac{4}{5}, \frac{4}{x} = \frac{5}{6}$

38. $\frac{x}{7} = \frac{1}{2}, \frac{x}{6} = \frac{1}{3}, \frac{x}{5} = \frac{1}{4}, \frac{x}{4} = \frac{1}{5}$

Exploration and Extension

✪ 39. *Photography Enlargements* You have a 3-inch by 5-inch post card
P   that contains a photograph of a triangle. You enlarge the post card so that it is 6 inches by 10 inches. Is the enlarged triangle similar to the original? Explain your reasoning and illustrate your answer with a drawing. Yes; the lengths of the sides of the triangle are doubled, while the measures of the angles remain the same. Check students' drawings.

✪ More difficult exercises
P Portfolio Opportunity

352   *Chapter 8 ▪ Proportion, Percent, and Probability*

Answers

37. $\frac{3}{2}, \frac{8}{3}, \frac{15}{4}, \frac{24}{5}$. To get the next number, add 5, add 7, add 9, etc., to the numerator of the preceding number and add 1 to the denominator. $\frac{35}{6}, \frac{48}{7}$

38. $\frac{7}{2}, \frac{6}{3}$ or 2, $\frac{5}{4}, \frac{4}{5}$. To get the next number, subtract 1 from the numerator of the preceding number and add 1 to the denominator. $\frac{3}{6}$ or $\frac{1}{2}, \frac{2}{7}$

8.3

Problem Solving Using Proportions

What you should learn:

How to use proportions to solve real-life problems

Goal 2
How to use similar triangles to measure objects indirectly

Why you should learn it:

You can use proportions to solve real-life problems, such as finding the dimensions of an airplane from a scale model.

Real Life
Aircraft

Goal 1 **Solving Real-Life Problems**

Proportions are used in architecture and manufacturing to construct scale models. For instance, if you are drawing house plans that have a 1-foot-to-$\frac{1}{8}$-inch scale, then the ratio of the actual house dimensions to the dimensions on the plans is

$$\frac{1 \text{ foot}}{\frac{1}{8} \text{ inch}} = \frac{12 \text{ inches}}{\frac{1}{8} \text{ inch}} \quad \textit{Rewrite 1 foot as 12 inches.}$$
$$= 12 \cdot \frac{8}{1} \quad \textit{Multiply by reciprocal of denominator.}$$
$$= 96. \quad \textit{Simplify.}$$

This means that each dimension of the actual house is 96 times as large as the corresponding dimension in the house plans.

Example 1 *Finding Dimensions*

You have purchased a scale model of a Boeing 767, as shown at the left. The model is constructed on a 1-to-250 scale. The wing span on the model is $7\frac{1}{2}$ inches. What is the wing span on an actual 767?

Solution

Verbal Model

Model wing span	=	1
767 wing span		250

Labels
Model wing span = 7.5   (inches)
767 wing span = x (inches)

Algebraic Model

$$\frac{7.5}{x} = \frac{1}{250} \quad \textit{Proportion}$$
$$\frac{x}{7.5} = 250 \quad \textit{Reciprocal Property}$$
$$7.5 \cdot \frac{x}{7.5} = 7.5 \cdot 250 \quad \textit{Multiply each side by 7.5.}$$
$$x = 1875 \quad \textit{Simplify.}$$

The wing span of the 767 is 1875 inches. To convert this measurement to feet, divide by 12 to obtain a wing span of $156\frac{1}{4}$ feet. ■

8.3 • *Problem Solving Using Proportions*   **353**

▶**PACING** the Lesson

Suggested Number of Days
Basic/Average 2   **Above Average** 1
Advanced 1

▶**PLANNING** the Lesson

Lesson Plan 8.3, p. 62

ORGANIZER

Starters (reproduced below)
   Problem of the Day 8.3, p. 22
   Warm-Up Exercises 8.3, p. 22
Lesson Resources
   Color Transparencies
     Diagram for Goal 2, p. 32
     Picture for Example 2, p. 32
   Math Log, p. 25
   Answer Masters 8.3, p. 158
   Extra Practice Copymaster 8.3, p. 62
   Reteaching Copymaster 8.3, p. 62
   Enrichment Projects, pp. 39, 40
Special Populations
   Suggestions, Teacher's Edition, p. 342D

LESSON Notes

Scale drawings are common in map making, construction, art, and design. Poll students to see if anyone collects scale models (cars, dolls, etc.) as a hobby, and encourage discussion where appropriate.

Example 1

Have students apply the Cross Product Property of Lesson 8.2 to the algebraic model in the solution.

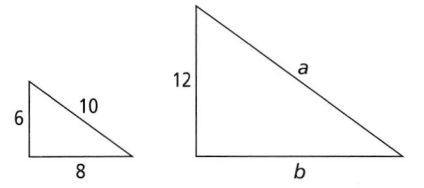

Indirect measurements are needed frequently in real-life construction problems. Note that we are able to measure the lengths of the shadows and the height of the post directly using appropriate measurement tools (e.g., tape measures).

Example 2

At another time of day, the Transco Tower would have a shadow of different length. Ask students whether this would affect our ability to determine its height and have them explain their answers.
It does not; the post shadow would change proportionally.

Communicating about MATHEMATICS

CLASS ACTIVITY

Ask students to bring samples of the models they collect. Try to determine the scale factors of the models.

Writing Prompt

Describe how you feel about solving proportion problems.

Real Life
Architecture

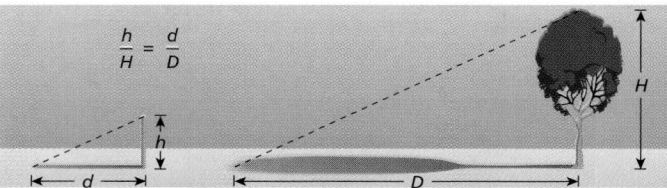

In Lesson 8.2, you learned that the ratios of corresponding sides of similar triangles are equal. This property of similar triangles can be used to indirectly measure the heights of trees or buildings. For instance, in the drawing below, the ratio of the post's height to the tree's height is equal to the ratio of the post's shadow to the tree's shadow. Knowing the post's height and the lengths of the two shadows (at the same time of day) allows you to find the tree's height.

$$\frac{h}{H} = \frac{d}{D}$$

Example 2   *Finding the Height of a Building*

To estimate the height of the Transco Tower in Houston, Texas, you measure its shadow to be 55 meters. The shadow of a 5-meter post is 1 meter. How tall is the Transco Tower?

Solution

Verbal Model

$$\frac{\text{Transco Tower Height}}{\text{Post Height}} = \frac{\text{Transco Tower shadow}}{\text{Post shadow}}$$

Labels   Transco Tower height = x (meters)
Post height = 5   (meters)
Transco Tower shadow = 55   (meters)
Post shadow = 1   (meter)

You are asked to complete the solution below. ■

Communicating about MATHEMATICS

▶ **SHARING IDEAS about the Lesson**

Extending the Example Example 2 contains only a partial solution. Use the verbal model and labels to write the algebraic model. Then solve the algebraic model to find the height of the Transco Tower in Houston. $\frac{x}{5} = \frac{55}{1}$, 275 m

EXERCISES

Guided Practice

▶ CHECK for Understanding

Flagpole Height   **In Exercises 1–4, use the following information.**

A flagpole is casting a 15-foot shadow. You are five feet tall and cast a 3-foot shadow. What is the height of the flagpole?

1. Sketch a diagram of the given information. Check students' diagrams.

2. Which of the following verbal models is correct? b

a. $\dfrac{\text{Flagpole height}}{\text{Your height}} = \dfrac{\text{Your shadow}}{\text{Flagpole shadow}}$

b. $\dfrac{\text{Flagpole height}}{\text{Your height}} = \dfrac{\text{Flagpole shadow}}{\text{Your shadow}}$

3. Write an algebraic model for the problem. Let h represent the height of the flagpole. $\dfrac{h}{5} = \dfrac{15}{3}$

4. Solve the algebraic model to find the height of the flagpole. 25 ft

Independent Practice

Heartbeat Rate   **In Exercises 5 and 6, use the following information.**

A typical heartbeat rate (or pulse) is 72 beats per minute. When exercising, this rate increases.

5. Assume you have the typical heartbeat rate. If you take your pulse for 10 seconds, how many beats would you feel? 12

6. After jogging one-half hour, you take your pulse for 6 seconds. You feel 11 beats. What is your heartbeat rate in beats per minute? 110

Estimation   **In Exercises 7 and 8, use the following information.**

In 1993, an average of about 8800 Americans per day became teenagers.

7. About how many Americans became teenagers in April? 264,000

8. About how many Americans became teenagers in 1993? 3,212,000

9. *Estimation*   If you sleep 220,000 hours by age 70, about how many hours will you have slept by age 40? 125,714

The President's Council on Physical Fitness and Sports recommends 30 minutes of continuous exercise at least 3 times a week.

10. *Estimation*   If you pay $1500 in property tax for a $90,000 house, about how much would you pay for a $110,000 house? $1833

8.3 ▪ *Problem Solving Using Proportions*   **355**

EXERCISE Notes

ASSIGNMENT GUIDE

Basic/Average:
  Day 1: Ex. 7–9, 11–13, 17–20
  Day 2: Ex. 5, 6, 14–16, 21, 22

Above Average:
Ex. 7–9, 11–16, 21, 22

Advanced: Ex. 7–9, 11–16, 21, 22

Selected Answers: Ex. 1–4, 5–19 odd

Guided Practice

Use these exercises during the last ten minutes of class to check students' understanding. Let students think and work alone during the first five minutes and then share ideas during the last five minutes.

Independent Practice

▶ **Ex. 5, 6** As a follow-up to these exercises, ask students to do a 10-second resting pulse-rate check on themselves in class to see if they are "typical."

356 *Chapter 8*

▶ **Ex. 11–16** For these exercises, students should refer to Example 2 on page 354.

Refer to Example 2 on page 354.

Integrated Review

These exercises review the Cross Product Property introduced in the previous lesson.

Exploration and Extension

▶ **Ex. 21–24** Before assigning these exercises, you may need to review the meaning of the word *congruent*.

Portfolio Opportunity: Math Log

A model of a building has a 1-inch-to-20-foot scale. The ratio used to determine the dimensions of the building is NOT $\frac{1}{20}$. Explain why and give the correct ratio.

Also available as a copymaster, page 25, Ex. 3

Alternative Assessment

A cooperative learning project that develops students' estimation skills using proportions.

Available as a copymaster, page 29

Computer Screens **In Exercises 11–13, use the following information.**

Computer screens are partitioned into pixels. Consider a rectangular computer screen that is $8\frac{1}{2}$ inches by 10 inches and has 5184 pixels per square inch. How many pixels are on the entire screen?

12. $\frac{p}{5184} = \frac{8\frac{1}{2} \times 10}{1}$

✪ **11.** Which of the following verbal models is correct? a

a. $\dfrac{\text{Pixels on screen}}{\text{Pixels in 1 in.}^2} = \dfrac{\text{Area of screen}}{1 \text{ in.}^2}$

b. $\dfrac{\text{Pixels on screen}}{\text{Pixels in 1 in.}^2} = \dfrac{10 \text{ inches}}{8\frac{1}{2} \text{ inches}}$

✪ **12.** Assign labels to the correct verbal model and write an algebraic model. See above.

✪ **13.** Solve the algebraic model to find the number of pixels on the computer screen. 440,640

Magnification **In Exercises 14–16, use the following information.**

An amoeba, a one-celled organism, has been magnified 250 times by a microscope and photographed. In the photo, the amoeba is 25 millimeters wide. What is the actual width of the amoeba?

✪ **14.** Which of the following verbal models is correct? a

a. $\dfrac{\text{Photo amoeba width}}{\text{Actual amoeba width}} = \dfrac{250}{1}$

b. $\dfrac{\text{Photo amoeba width}}{1 \text{ millimeter}} = \dfrac{\text{Actual amoeba width}}{250 \text{ millimeters}}$

✪ **15.** Assign labels to the verbal model and write an algebraic model. $\frac{25}{w} = \frac{250}{1}$

✪ **16.** Solve the algebraic model to find the width of the amoeba. 0.1mm

---

Integrated Review **Making Connections within Mathematics**

Mental Math **In Exercises 17–20, use mental math to solve the proportion.**

17. $\frac{1}{2} = \frac{x}{8}$ 4

18. $\frac{m}{6} = 40$ 240

19. $\frac{5}{n} = \frac{10}{25}$ 12.5

20. $\frac{2}{3} = \frac{8}{b}$ 12

Exploration and Extension

P *Geometry* **In Exercises 21–24, draw each figure. Then divide the figure into four congruent figures, each of which is similar to the larger figure. A sample is shown at the right.**
See Additional Answers.

Two geometric figures are **congruent** if they have exactly the same size and shape. Two figures are **similar** if they have the same shape.

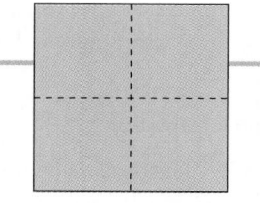

This square is divided into 4 congruent squares.

✪ **21.**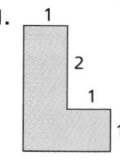

✪ **22.**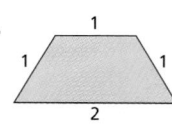

✪ **23.**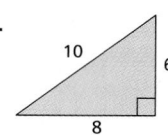

✪ **24.**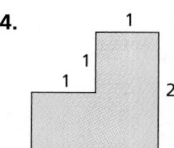

✪ More difficult exercises
P Portfolio Opportunity

Enrichment

Ask the students to bring to class a map (national, state, or local) that uses the legend "1 inch = ___ miles." They can then use their maps to estimate the distance between two cities using measurement or proportion. Ask students how their computations compare with the red or black road mileages listed on the map.

Mixed REVIEW

In Exercises 1–9, solve the equation. Check your solution. (4.2, 4.4, 4.5)

1. $4(x + 2) = 12$ 1

2. $3y = 4y - 7$ 7

3. $a + \frac{5}{3} = 2a - \frac{1}{3}$ 2

4. $\frac{1}{12}p - \frac{1}{12} = \frac{5}{12}$ 6

5. $5 + 2(q - 3) = 0$ $\frac{1}{2}$

6. $0.2s - 5.4 = 0$ 27

7. $1 = \frac{1}{2}(p - 1)$ 3

8. $\frac{1}{4}x + \frac{1}{4}x = 3$ 6

9. $\frac{1}{3}p - 2 = 2$ 12

In Exercises 10–13, write the percent in decimal form. (7.6–7.8)

10. 52%   0.52

11. 83%   0.83

12. 146%   1.46

13. 206%   2.06

In Exercises 14–17, determine whether the quotient is a rate or a ratio. Then simplify. (8.1)

14. $\frac{16 \text{ yards}}{2 \text{ jumps}}$ Rate

15. $\frac{28 \text{ points}}{4 \text{ quarters}}$ Rate

16. $\frac{2 \text{ animals}}{20 \text{ animals}}$ Ratio $\frac{1}{10}$

17. $\frac{4 \text{ feet}}{10 \text{ seconds}}$ Rate

8 yd per jump   7 points per quarter   2 feet per 5 seconds

Milestones
THE ARABIAN LEGACY

...0   600   800   1000   1200   1400   1600   1800   2000

l of Rome   Mohammed born   First printed book, China   Printing Press   Electric Battery   Satellite Intelsat
476   570   868   1450   1786   1965

By the ninth century, years of conflict had destroyed many European centers of learning. By contrast, from about 800 through 1100 the Arabic influence extended from Baghdad, Iraq, its center, westward to Europe and Africa, northward to Turkey and Russia, and eastward to India and China. Arabic scholars translated thousands of ancient Latin, Greek, Hebrew, and Hindu texts into Arabic, thus preserving them from total destruction.

The most famous Arabic author, Mohammed ibn-Musa al-Khowarizmi (?825), wrote a treatise on equations called *Hisab Al-jabr* meaning the "science of restoration or reunion." (In Spain, barbers, who were the bone setters of the day, called themselves "algebristi.") The person responsible for the mathematical term *algebra* was Leonardo of Pisa, also known as Fibonacci (1180–1250). While a child, he learned mathematics through Arabic texts. When he translated *Hisab Al-jabr* into Latin, it became translated as the "science of equations."

*painting from 1494
s Laila and Majnun,
ian heroine and
at school.*

- *Fibonacci is most famous for his sequence 1, 1, 2, 3, 5, 8, . . . (see page 41). Find the quotient, or ratio, of successive terms for the first 10 terms. That is, find $1 \div 1$, $2 \div 1$, $3 \div 2$, etc.*
  1, 2, 1.5, 1.6, 1.6, 1.625, ≈ 1.615, ≈ 1.619, ≈ 1.618
- *What pattern do you notice in these ratios? (See page 348.)*
  They approach the Golden Ratio.

Milestones
Theme: *The Liber Abaci*

Fibonacci's book *The Liber Abaci,* written in 1202, contains many famous arithmetic problems. Here are two of them. (Both problems are taken from pages 170 and 171 of *Great Moments in Mathematics Before 1650* by Howard Eves published by the Mathematical Association of America, 1983.) Variations of these problems have appeared in mathematics textbooks throughout the ages.

(Arithmetic solutions are given for each problem. You may wish to have students tell you how they solved these problems.)

1. A man entered an orchard through seven gates, and there took a certain number of apples. When he left the orchard he gave the guard at the first gate half the apples that he had and one apple more. To the second guard he gave half his remaining apples and one apple more. He did the same to each of the remaining five guards, and left the orchard with one apple. How many apples did he gather in the orchard?

Work backwards: The man left gate 7 with 1 apple, gate 6 with 2(1 + 1) = 4; gate 5 with 2(4 + 1) = 10, gate 4 with 2(10 + 1) = 22, and so on. So he entered gate 1 with 2(190 + 1) = 382 apples.

2. A certain king sent 30 men into his orchard to plant trees. If they could plant 1000 trees in 9 days, in how many days would 36 men plant 4400 trees?

If 30 men take 9 days to plant 1000 trees, then 1 man takes 9 days to plant $33\frac{1}{3}$ trees. So, 1 man takes 1 day to plant $3\frac{19}{27}$ trees, 36 men take one day to plant $133\frac{1}{3}$ trees, and finally, 36 men take $(4400 \div 133\frac{1}{3} = 33)$ days to plant 4400 trees.

Library Skills

Have students use library resources to research other famous problems found in the *Liber Abaci*. Students should also note its role, as well as Fibonacci's role, in the history of mathematical thought.

358 *Chapter 8*

Suggested Number of Days
Basic/Average 2 **Above Average** 1
Advanced 1

► **PLANNING the Lesson**

Lesson Plan 8.4, p. 63

ORGANIZER

Starters (reproduced below)
    Problem of the Day 8.4, p. 23
    Warm-Up Exercises 8.4, p. 23
Lesson Resources
    Math Log, p. 26
    Answer Masters 8.4, p. 160
    Extra Practice Copymaster 8.4, p. 63
    Reteaching Copymaster 8.4, p. 63
Special Populations
    Suggestions, Teacher's Edition, p. 342D

LESSON Notes

Students should copy the Percent Equation
into their math journals. The statement "*a* is *p*
percent of *b*" can be restated as "*a* of *b* is *p*
percent." Remind students that *percent*
means "per 100."

Example 1

Point out to students that, in the original
equation, we could have first multiplied both
sides of the equation by 100 to get
$100 \times \frac{17}{20} = p$, and then simplified the left side
by dividing 20 into 100 to get $5(17) = p$ or
$85 = p$.

EXTENSION
Have students study the margin model of
85% of 20, and then have them model 106%
of 50.

8.4 Solving Percent Equations

What you should learn:

Goal 1 How to find what
percent one number
is of another

Goal 2 How to solve a percent equation

Why you should learn it:

You can use percents to describe
real-life situations, such as finding your correct percent on a
quiz.

Goal 1 **Finding Percents**

In Chapter 7, you learned that percents can be written in
different forms. For instance, 25% can be written as

    25%, $\frac{25}{100}$,   0.25,   or   25 percent.

The most common use of percents is to compare one quantity
to another. For instance, because 3 is one-fourth of 12, you can
say that 3 is 25% of 12.

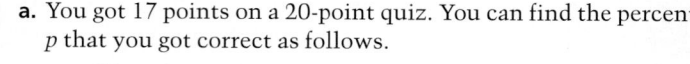

The Percent Equation
The statement "*a* is *p* percent of *b*" is equivalent to the equation

$$\frac{a}{b} = \frac{p}{100}.$$ *Percent equation*

In this equation, *b* is the **base** and *a* is the number that is compared to the base.

Example 1 *Finding Percents*

a. You got 17 points on a 20-point quiz. You can find the percent
p that you got correct as follows.

    $\frac{17}{20} = \frac{p}{100}$ *Write percent equation.*
    $0.85 = \frac{p}{100}$ *Divide to obtain decimal form.*
    $85 = p$ *Multiply each side by 100.*

You got 85% correct. One way to describe this is to say that
17 is 85% of 20.

b. On a 50-point quiz, you got 48 points plus 5 bonus points.
You can find the percent *p* that you got correct as follows.

    $\frac{53}{50} = \frac{p}{100}$ *Write percent equation.*
    $1.06 = \frac{p}{100}$ *Divide to obtain decimal form.*
    $106 = p$ *Multiply each side by 100.*

You got 106% correct. One way to describe this is to say that
53 is 106% of 50. ■

*One way to see that 17 is 85% of
20 is to use a grid with 100
squares. Divide the grid into
twenty 1-by-5 rectangles. Then
shade 17 of the rectangles and
count the number of small squares
that have been shaded.*

358   *Chapter 8* • *Proportion, Percent, and Probability*

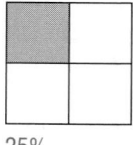 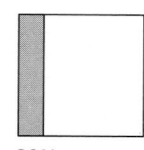 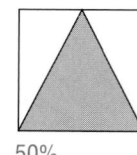

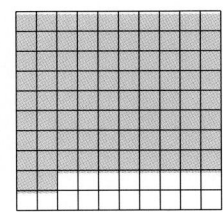

If each small square represents 2.5 people, then 82 squares must represent 82(2.5) or 205 people.

25%	25%	25%	25%
$8.83	$8.83	$8.83	$8.83

3(8.83) = $26.49

4(8.83) = $35.32

Geometric models like these can help you solve percent problems.

Goal 2 — Solving Percent Equations

There are three basic types of percent problems. Each can be solved by substituting the two given quantities into the percent equation and solving for the third quantity.

Question	Given	Percent equation
a is what percent of b?	a and b	Solve for p.
What is p percent of b?	p and b	Solve for a.
a is p percent of what?	a and p	Solve for b.

Example 2 — Solving Percent Equations

a. You ask 250 people whether they prefer blue jeans or another color of jeans and 82% say they prefer blue jeans. You can find the number a of people who prefer blue jeans as follows.

$$\frac{a}{250} = \frac{82}{100} \qquad \textit{Write in fraction form.}$$

$$\frac{a}{250} = 0.82 \qquad \textit{Write in decimal form.}$$

$$a = 250 \cdot 0.82 \qquad \textit{Multiply each side by 250.}$$

$$a = 205 \qquad \textit{Simplify.}$$

Thus, 205 people said they prefer blue jeans.

b. You paid $26.49, which is 75% of the full price, for a sweater. You can find the full price b as follows.

$$\frac{26.49}{b} = \frac{75}{100} \qquad \textit{Write in fraction form.}$$

$$\frac{b}{26.49} = \frac{100}{75} \qquad \textit{Write reciprocal of each side.}$$

$$b = 26.49 \cdot \frac{100}{75} \qquad \textit{Multiply each side by 26.49.}$$

$$b = 35.32 \qquad \textit{Simplify.}$$

The full price of the sweater is $35.32. ∎

P Communicating about MATHEMATICS

▶ SHARING IDEAS about the Lesson

Using Percents Your aunt works in a clothing store. She tells you that a quick way to find p% of b is to change p% to decimal form and multiply by b. Is she correct? Explain your reasoning to your partner. Yes, explanations vary.

Cooperative Learning

OPTION: Extra Examples

Here are additional examples similar to Example 1.

Finding Percents

a. You got 19 points on a 25-point quiz. You can find the percent p that you got correct as follows.

$$\frac{19}{25} = \frac{p}{100} \qquad \text{Write percent equation.}$$

$$0.76 = \frac{p}{100} \qquad \text{Divide to obtain decimal form.}$$

$$76 = p \qquad \text{Multiply each side by 100.}$$

You got 76% correct. One way to describe this is to say that 19 is 76% of 25.

b. On a 40-point quiz, you got 38 points plus 6 bonus points. You can find the percent p that you got correct as follows.

$$\frac{44}{40} = \frac{p}{100} \qquad \text{Write percent equation.}$$

$$1.1 = \frac{p}{100} \qquad \text{Divide to obtain decimal form.}$$

$$110 = p \qquad \text{Multiply each side by 100.}$$

You got 110% correct. One way to describe this is to say that 44 is 110% of 40.

ALTERNATE APPROACH

Pictorial You can use an arrangement of two parallel line segments to help students write percent equations. The upper line represents percents while the lower line represents numbers. The statement "a is p percent of b" can be represented as follows.

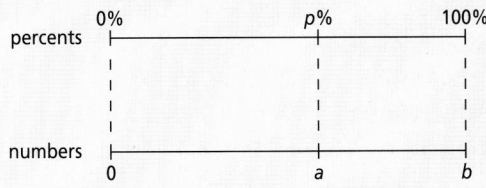

Once students have established the location of the three elements in the statement, they can write correct proportion statements (or percent equations) in several ways, according to which pair of arrows they choose.

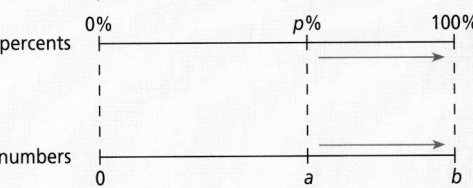

Right arrows suggest $\frac{p}{100} = \frac{a}{b}$ (Left arrows would suggest $\frac{100}{p} = \frac{b}{a}$.)

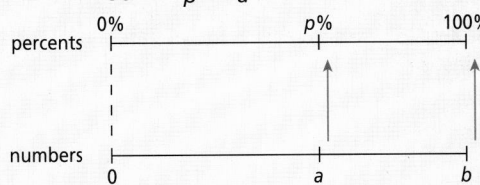

Up arrows suggest $\frac{a}{p} = \frac{b}{100}$ (Down arrows would suggest $\frac{p}{a} = \frac{100}{b}$.)

Example 2

Students could use the Alternate Approach described above to set up the percent equation in this example. 82% is located on the upper line, 250 (the total number of people) is located on the lower line opposite 100%, and the unknown number a is located on the lower line opposite 82%.

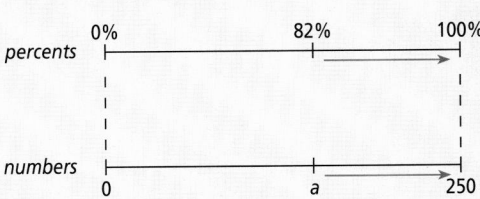

The right arrows suggest the equation $\frac{82}{100} = \frac{a}{250}$.

Communicating about MATHEMATICS

Have students work this exercise together.

Writing Prompt
Reflect on your participation in class today and complete the statement: I discovered today that I . . .

ASSIGNMENT GUIDE

Basic/Average:
Day 1: Ex. 7–19 odd, 21, 22, 26, 27, 31–37 odd
Day 2: Ex. 23–25, 28–30, 39–41

Above Average:
Ex. 11–27 odd, 28–30, 33, 37, 39–41

Advanced: Ex. 11–27 odd, 28–30, 33, 37, 39–41

Selected Answers: Ex. 1–6, 7–37 odd

Guided Practice

▶ **Ex. 1–6** These exercises allow students to think about and practice the process for solving percent equations. Use this as an in-class summary activity.

Independent Practice

▶ **Ex. 7–16** Encourage students to use a solution format similar to the one shown in Example 1, page 358. They may want to solve the proportion by using cross products.
▶ **Ex. 7–20** Use these as an in-class activity.
▶ **Ex. 23–25** Be sure to model a solution to these exercises before assigning them for homework.
▶ **Ex. 26** Assign this as an in-class summary question.

Guided Practice

▶ CHECK **for Understanding**

P In Exercises 1 and 2, describe the strategy that was used to solve the problem. See margin.

1. **Problem:** What is 65% of 160?
   Solution: $\frac{a}{160} = \frac{65}{100}$
   $\frac{a}{160} = 0.65$
   $a = 104$

2. **Problem:** 50 is what percent of 40?
   Solution: $\frac{50}{40} = \frac{p}{100}$
   $1.25 = \frac{p}{100}$
   $125 = p$

In Exercises 3–5, identify the base. Then write and solve the percent equation.

25, 80%
3. 20 is what percent of 25?

50, 8
4. What is 16% of 50?

what, 120
5. 90 is 75% of what?

6. Is fifteen 250% of six? Explain your reasoning. Yes, $\frac{15}{6} = \frac{250}{100}$

Independent Practice

In Exercises 7–16, solve the percent equation. Round your answer to 2 decimal places.

7. 22 is what percent of 30? 73.33%
8. What is 33 percent of 165? 54.45
9. What is 2% of 360? 7.2
10. 66 is 120 percent of what number? 55
11. 34 is 50% of what number? 68
12. 45 is what percent of 20? 225%
13. What is 110 percent of 110? 121
14. 6.06 is 20.2% of what number? 30
15. 71.5 is what percent of 90? 79.44%
16. What is 25.5% of 270? 68.85

Mental Math In Exercises 17–20, use mental math to solve the percent equation.

17. 100 is 200 percent of what number? 50
18. What is 50% of 200? 100
19. 100 is 100% of what number? 100
20. 5 is what percent of 15? $33\frac{1}{3}\%$

Error Analysis In Exercises 21 and 22, find and correct the error.

21. **Problem:** 45 is what percent of 150?
   Percent Equation: $\frac{150}{45} = \frac{p}{100}$ $\frac{45}{150} = \frac{p}{100}$

22. **Problem:** What is 24 percent of 50?
   Percent Equation: $\frac{24}{50} = \frac{p}{100}$ $\frac{a}{50} = \frac{24}{100}$

P *Geometric Modeling* In Exercises 23–25, solve the percent equation. Then sketch a geometric model that illustrates your solution. For sketches, see Additional Answers.

✪ 23. $\frac{13}{25} = \frac{p}{100}$ 52%

✪ 24. $\frac{a}{20} = \frac{85}{100}$ 17

✪ 25. $\frac{3}{b} = \frac{60}{100}$ 5

✪ More difficult exercises
P Portfolio Opportunity

360 *Chapter 8 • Proportion, Percent, and Probability*

Extra Practice

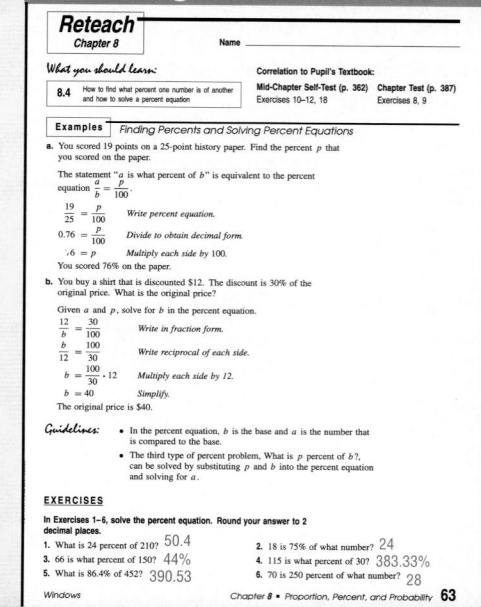

Extra Practice **8.4** Name _____

In exercises 1–10, solve the percent equation. Round your answer to 2 decimal places.

1. 16 is what percent of 500? 3.2%
2. What is 27 percent of 320? 86.4
3. What is 46% of 86? 39.56
4. 234 is 36 percent of what number? 650
5. 27 is 125% of what number? 21.6
6. 456 is $33\frac{1}{3}$% of what number? 1368
7. What is 365% of 430? 1569.5
8. 2.52 is 18% of what number? 14
9. 92 is what percent of 86? 106.98%
10. What is 36% of 125? 45

In Exercises 11–14, use mental math to solve the percent equation.

11. 20 is 20% of what number? 100
12. What is 75% of 400? 300
13. 6 is what percent of 60? 10%
14. 300 is 200% of what number? 150

In Exercises 15 and 16, find and correct the error. Then solve.

15. Problem: 25 is what percent of 675?
   Percent equation $\frac{a}{675} = \frac{25}{100}$ $\frac{25}{675} = \frac{p}{100}$, p = 3.70%

16. Problem: What is 52% of 162?
   Percent equation $\frac{100}{162} = \frac{p}{52}$ $\frac{a}{162} = \frac{52}{100}$, a = 84.24

In Exercises 17–19, solve the percent equation. Then sketch a geometric model that illustrates your solution.

17. $\frac{125}{500} = \frac{p}{100}$
   p = 25%

18. $\frac{a}{25} = \frac{80}{100}$
   a = 20

19. $\frac{36}{b} = \frac{45}{100}$
   b = 80

Each □ = 5   Each □ = ┼   Each □ = 0.6

20. The annual auto insurance premium for a policyholder is normally $739. However, after having an automobile accident, the policyholder was charged an additional 32%. What is the new annual premium?
   $975.48

21. Suppose you buy a motorbike that costs $1450 plus 6% sales tax. Find the amount of sales tax, and the total bill.
   Sales tax = $87, total bill = $1537

22. A customer left $20 for a meal that cost $16.95. How much was the tip? What percent of the cost of the meal is the amount of the tip?
   Tip = $3.05 ≈ 18.0% tip rate (17.99%)

23. The monthly salary of an employee is $1000 plus a 7% commission on her total sales. How much must the employee sell in order to obtain a monthly salary of $3500?
   ≈ $35,714.29

Windows 8.4 • Solving Percent Equations **63**

Reteaching

Reteach Chapter 8 Name _____

What you should learn:

8.4 How to find what percent one number is of another and how to solve a percent equation

Correlation to Pupil's Textbook:
Mid-Chapter Self-Test (p. 362) Chapter Test (p. 387)
Exercises 10–12, 18   Exercises 8, 9

Examples *Finding Percents and Solving Percent Equations*

a. You scored 19 points on a 25-point history paper. Find the percent p that you scored on the paper.

The statement "a is what percent of b" is equivalent to the percent equation $\frac{a}{b} = \frac{p}{100}$.

$\frac{19}{25} = \frac{p}{100}$ Write percent equation.

$0.76 = \frac{p}{100}$ Divide to obtain decimal form.

$76 = p$ Multiply each side by 100.

You scored 76% on the paper.

b. You buy a shirt that is discounted $12. The discount is 30% of the original price. What is the original price?

Given a and p, solve for b in the percent equation.

$\frac{12}{b} = \frac{30}{100}$ Write in fraction form.

$\frac{b}{12} = \frac{100}{30}$ Write reciprocal of each side.

$b = \frac{100}{30} \cdot 12$ Multiply each side by 12.

$b = 40$ Simplify.

The original price is $40.

Guidelines: • In the percent equation, b is the base and a is the number that is compared to the base.
• The third type of percent problem, What is p percent of b?, can be solved by substituting p and b into the percent equation and solving for a.

EXERCISES

In Exercises 1–6, solve the percent equation. Round your answer to 2 decimal places.

1. What is 24 percent of 210? 50.4
2. 18 is 75% of what number? 24
3. 66 is what percent of 150? 44%
4. 115 is what percent of 30? 383.33%
5. What is 86.4% of 452? 390.53
6. 70 is 250 percent of what number? 28

Windows Chapter 8 • Proportion, Percent, and Probability **63**

Answers

1. Write the percent equation, divide to obtain decimal form, multiply each side by 160.
2. Write the percent equation, divide to obtain decimal form, multiply each side by 100.

No, $\frac{31}{35} \approx 89\%$

26. *Test Scores*   On a 35-question exam, you needed to get 90% of the questions correct to earn an *A*. You answered 31 questions correctly. Did you earn an *A*? Explain.

28. *Kicking Field Goals*   During the regular season, a field goal kicker made 75% of the field goals he attempted. He made 24 field goals. How many did he attempt?   32

Winning a Grammy   **In Exercises 29 and 30, use the following information.**

When the Grammy Awards began in 1958, there were 28 categories in which to win an award. In 1993, there were 81 categories.
(Source: National Academy of Recording Arts and Sciences)

29. The number of awards given in 1958 is what percent of the number of awards given in 1993? $\approx 34.6\%$

30. The number of awards given in 1993 is what percent of the number of awards given in 1958? $\approx 289.3\%$

27. *Sales Tax*   You buy a new Sega Genesis game. You pay $54.99 for the game plus $2.75 in sales tax. What is the sales tax percent?   5%

Linda Ronstadt is a multiple-category grammy winner: country vocal (1975), pop vocal (1976), country duo or group (1987), best Mexican/American (1988 and 1992), pop duo or group (1989 and 1990), and best tropical Latin (1992).

Integrated Review

Making Connections within Mathematics

Decimal Sense   **In Exercises 31–34, write the percent as a decimal.**

31. 62% 0.62   **32.** 21% 0.21   **33.** 18.24% 0.1824   **34.** 98.04% 0.9804

Percents   **In Exercises 35–38, write the decimal as a percent.**

35. 0.1234 12.34%   **36.** 0.1001 10.01%   **37.** 0.9432 94.32%   **38.** 0.7693 76.93%

Exploration and Extension

Geometric Probability   **In Exercises 39–41, a pebble is tossed and lands on the region. The pebble is equally likely to land anywhere on the region. What is the probability that the pebble will land on the green region? Give your answer in percent form.**

39.
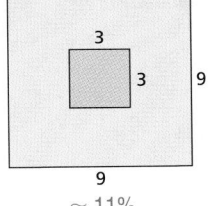
$\approx 11\%$

40.
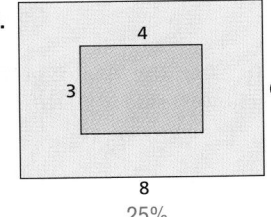
25%

41.
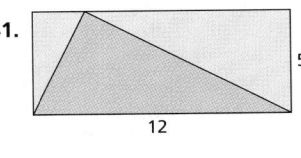
50%

8.4 • Solving Percent Equations   **361**

Mid-Chapter SELF-TEST

Take this test as you would take a test in class. The answers to the exercises are given in the back of the book.

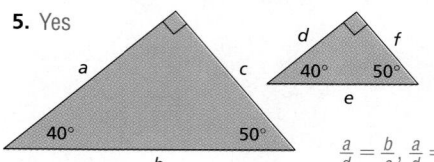

In Exercises 1–4, is the quotient a rate or ratio? Simplify. (8.1)

1. $\frac{100 \text{ meters}}{18 \text{ seconds}}$ Rate   *50 meters per 9 seconds*

2. $\frac{18 \text{ lures}}{6 \text{ fishermen}}$ Rate   *3 lures per fisherman*

3. $\frac{42 \text{ pounds}}{3 \text{ pounds}}$ Ratio $\frac{14}{1}$

4. $\frac{5 \text{ days}}{1 \text{ week}}$ Rate   *5 days per week*

In Exercises 5 and 6, state whether the two triangles are similar. If they are, write three different proportions that compare the side lengths. (8.2)

5. Yes

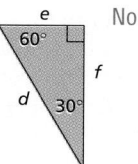

$\frac{a}{d} = \frac{b}{e}, \frac{a}{d} = \frac{c}{f}, \frac{b}{e} = \frac{c}{f}$

6. No

In Exercises 7–9, decide whether the equation is true. (8.2)

7. $\frac{2}{11} \overset{?}{=} \frac{10}{55}$ Yes

8. $\frac{250}{350} \overset{?}{=} \frac{2}{3}$ No

9. $\frac{5}{7} \overset{?}{=} \frac{25}{35}$ Yes

In Exercises 10–12, solve the percent equation. (8.4)

10. What is 35% of 18? 6.3

11. 36 is what percent of 150? 24%

12. 18 is 150% of what? 12

In Exercises 13–16, solve the proportion. Check your solution. (8.2)

13. $\frac{x}{4} = \frac{8}{2}$ 16

14. $\frac{3}{7} = \frac{a}{9}$ $\frac{27}{7}$

15. $\frac{18}{b} = \frac{25}{36}$ 25.92

16. $\frac{y}{3} = \frac{10}{2}$ 15

17. You are visiting the Gateway Arch in St. Louis, Missouri. To find out how tall the monument is, you measure the length of the shadow as 60 feet. At the same time, your own shadow is $\frac{1}{2}$ foot long. If you are $5\frac{1}{4}$-feet tall, how tall is the Gateway Arch? (8.2) 630 ft

18. While in St. Louis, you decide to take a tour through an automobile manufacturing plant. Your tour guide tells you that 29% of the cars are manufactured with a driver's side airbag. If 47,000 cars are manufactured, how many have an airbag? (8.4) 13,630

The Gateway Arch in St. Louis, Missouri, is the nation's tallest monument.

In Exercises 19 and 20, $\triangle ABC$ is similar to $\triangle DEF$. The lengths of the sides of $\triangle ABC$ are $a = 8$, $b = 10$, and $c = 12$. The shortest side of $\triangle DEF$ is $d = 9$. (8.2)

19. In $\triangle DEF$, find the longest side. $13\frac{1}{2}$

20. In $\triangle DEF$, find the third side. $11\frac{1}{4}$

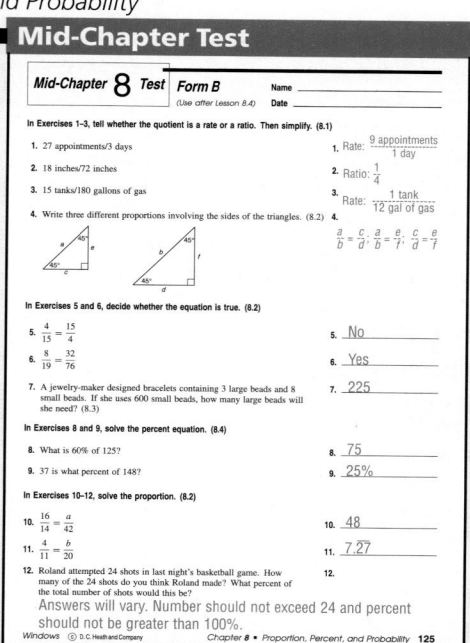

Mid-Chapter Test

8.5

Problem Solving Using Percents

What you should learn:

Goal 1 How to use percents to solve real-life problems

Goal 2 How to use percents to find discounts

Why you should learn it:

You can use percents to solve real-life problems, such as finding a discount.

Real Life
Education

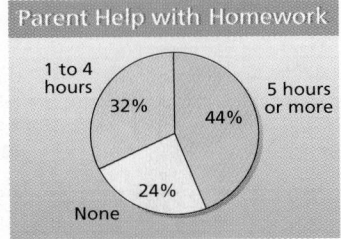

Parent Help with Homework

1 to 4 hours 32%
5 hours or more 44%
24%
None

Goal 1 **Solving Real-Life Problems**

Knowing how to use percents is important in almost every part of real life. In this lesson, you will see how the problem-solving plan can be used to solve real-life problems involving percents.

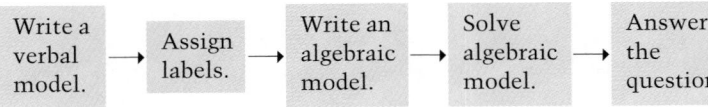

| Write a verbal model. | → | Assign labels. | → | Write an algebraic model. | → | Solve algebraic model. | → | Answer the question |

Example 1 *Using a Problem-Solving Plan*

In a survey, parents of elementary school children were asked how many hours per week they spent helping their children with homework. The results are shown in the circle graph at the left. Eighty-eight said they spent 1 to 4 hours. How many parents were surveyed? How many said "none"? How many said "5 hours or more"? (*Source: 20/20 Research*)

Solution

Verbal Model

$$\frac{\text{Number spending 1-4 hours}}{\text{Number surveyed}} = \frac{\text{Percent}}{100}$$

Labels

Number spending 1–4 hours = 88   (people)
Number surveyed = b (people)
Percent = 32   (percent)

Algebraic Model

$\frac{88}{b} = \frac{32}{100}$ *Percent equation*

$\frac{b}{88} = \frac{100}{32}$ *Reciprocal Property*

$b = 88 \cdot \frac{100}{32}$ *Multiply each side by 88.*

$b = 275$ *Simplify.*

There were 275 parents surveyed. To find the number who said "none," find 24% of 275. To find the number who said "5 hours or more," find 44% of 275.

$0.24 \cdot 275 = 66$ *"None"*
$0.44 \cdot 275 = 121$ *"5 hours or more"* ∎

► **PACING** the Lesson

Suggested Number of Days
Basic/Average 2   **Above Average** 1
Advanced 1

► **PLANNING** the Lesson

Lesson Plan 8.5, p. 64

ORGANIZER

Starters (reproduced below)
   Problem of the Day 8.5, p. 23
   Warm-Up Exercises 8.5, p. 23
Lesson Resources
   Color Transparencies
      Diagram for Ex. 7–9, p. 33
      Diagrams for Ex. 15, 16, p. 34
   Math Log, p. 26
   Technology, p. 48
   Answer Masters 8.5, p. 161
   Extra Practice Copymaster 8.5, p. 64
   Reteaching Copymaster 8.5, p. 64
Special Populations
   Suggestions, Teacher's Edition, p. 342D

LESSON Notes

Remind students that it is important to check their answer to see if it is reasonable. (Refer to the problem-solving plan in their journals for Lesson 2.8.)

Example 1

Ask students to explain why the sum of the percents shown on the circle graph should add to 100.

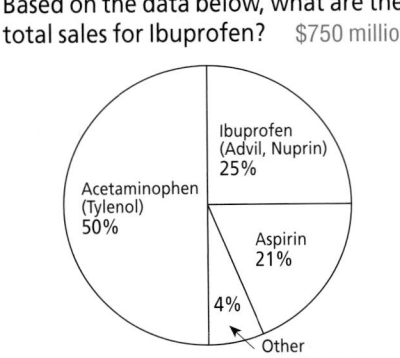

MATH JOURNAL

The discount formula should be included in students' math journals for future reference. Note that the parallel-segments guide for setting up percent equations (see teaching notes on page 359) is applicable also here.

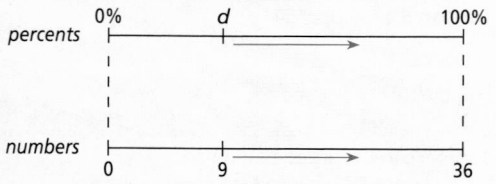

The right arrows suggest the equation $\frac{d}{100} = \frac{9}{36}$, where d is the discount percent.

Common-Error Alert!

Be sure that students recognize the difference between the discount (a number value) and the discount percent. In particular, in using the parallel-segments guide, actual cash discounts are placed on the lower line; discount *percents* are placed on the upper line.

Example 2

Using the parallel-segments guide for writing percent equations, we locate the elements of the proportion as follows:

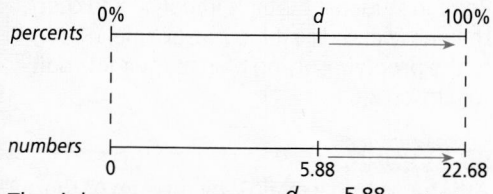

The right arrows suggest $\frac{d}{100} = \frac{5.88}{22.68}$, which gives $d = 100\left(\frac{5.88}{22.68}\right)$ or $d \approx 25.9\%$.

Communicating about MATHEMATICS

EXTENSION

Have students use the parallel-segments guide for writing percent equations to uncover the manager's mistake.

Writing Prompt

Have students create their own realistic discount problem (see Ex. 14). The solution of each student's problem can be assigned to a small group or to the entire class.

Real Life
Consumers

When an item is "on sale" the difference between the regular price and the sale price is called the **discount**.

| Discount | = | Regular Price | − | Sale Price |

To find the **discount percent**, use the regular price as the base. For instance, if a $36 book is on sale for $27, then the discount is $9, and the discount percent is

$$\frac{\text{Discount}}{\text{Regular Price}} = \frac{9}{36} \qquad \text{\textit{Divide discount by regular price.}}$$

$$= 0.25 \qquad \text{\textit{Rewrite in decimal form.}}$$

$$= 25\%. \qquad \text{\textit{Rewrite in percent form.}}$$

Example 2 Finding a Discount

Last week you bought a sweatshirt for $16.80. The store had a sign that stated that the price had been discounted 35%. This week you visit the store again and discover that the regular price is $22.68. Did you really get a 35% discount?

Solution The discount is

$$22.68 - 16.80 = \$5.88. \qquad \text{\textit{Discount}}$$

Then use the formula to find the discount percent.

$$\frac{5.88}{22.68} \approx 0.259 \qquad \text{\textit{Divide discount by regular price.}}$$

$$= 25.9\% \qquad \text{\textit{Write in percent form.}}$$

The discount was only 25.9%, not 35%. ∎

Communicating about MATHEMATICS

▶ **SHARING IDEAS about the Lesson**

What Is Wrong? After seeing the regular price, you asked the store manager why the sweatshirt was listed as having a 35% discount. The manager tells you that 35% of $16.80 is $5.88, and the regular price is

$$\$16.80 + \$5.88 = \$22.68.$$

The base is the regular price, not the sale price.

P What is wrong with the manager's mathematics?

364 Chapter **8** ▪ Proportion, Percent, and Probability   **P** Portfolio Opportunity

---

Technology

| Paying Your Restaurant Check | **8.5** | Name _____ |

Problem Solving Using a Spreadsheet

In this activity, you will use a spreadsheet program to create a table that lists the tax, tip, and total amount due for a given meal total. It is assumed that the user is familiar with the software.

The partial table shown below lists the meal total, meal tax rate, meal tax amount, tip rate, tip amount, and total amount due. (A meal tax rate of 6% and a tip rate of 15% is assumed.) The formulas in Row 3 show how to calculate the meal tax amount, tip amount, and final amount due.

	A	B	C	D	E	F
1			Tax, Tip and Total Amount Due Table			
2	Meal Total	Meal Tax Rate	Meal Tax Amount	Tip Rate	Tip Amount	Total Amount Due
3	10.00	6%	=A3*B3	15%	=A3*D3	=A3+C3+E3
4	=A3+1	6%	0.66	15%	1.65	13.31
5	12.00	6%	0.72	15%	1.80	14.52
:						
42	49.00	6%	2.94	15%	7.35	59.29
43	50.00	6%	3.00	15%	7.50	60.50

EXERCISES

1. Use a spreadsheet to complete the table. See students' work.

In Exercises 2–5, use the table to find the meal tax amount, tip amount, and total amount due for the given meal total.

2. $17.00
Meal tax: $1.02
Tip: $2.55
Total: $20.57

3. $23.00
Meal tax: $1.38
Tip: $3.45
Total: $27.83

4. $39.00
Meal tax: $2.34
Tip: $5.85
Total: $47.19

5. $45.00
Meal tax: $2.70
Tip: $6.75
Total: $54.45

6. Modify the spreadsheet so that the table lists the meal totals by increases of 50 cents (instead of a dollar) and use your state's meal tax rate. To modify spreadsheet, change formula in Cell A4 to =A3 + 0.5. Then change % in Column B to your state's tax rate.

In Exercises 7–10, use the modified table to find the meal tax amount, tip amount, and total amount due for the given meal total.

7. $27.50   **8.** $14.00   **9.** $31.50   **10.** $29.50

11. Using the modified table as a guide, estimate the meal tax amount, tip amount, and total amount due for a meal total of $26.85.

7-11. Answers depend on state meal tax rate in Column B.

48 Technology Using Calculators and Computers   © D.C. Heath and Company

EXERCISES

Guided Practice

▶ **CHECK for Understanding**

1. *Shoe Sale*   You pay $38.15 for a pair of tennis shoes. The discount was $16.35.
   a. What is the original price? $54.50
   b. Based on the *original price,* what is the discount percent? 30%

2. *Shoe Sale*   You are shopping for shoes and see the sign at the right. Explain how you could find the original price of the shoes. See above.

2. $100\% - 25\% = 75\% = \frac{75}{100}$, $\frac{29.99}{b} = \frac{75}{100}$, solve for b. ($39.99$)

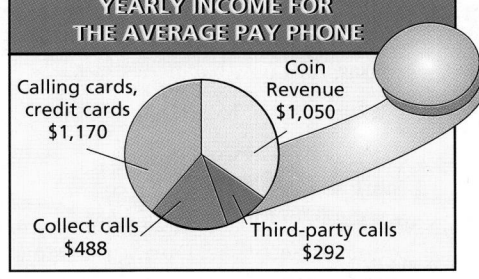

Independent Practice

Music   **In Exercises 3 and 4, use the following.**

You take a survey in your classroom about favorite types of music. The circle graph shows the percent of students in each type. Nine students said that country was their favorite.

3. How many students were surveyed? 45

4. How many students said
   a. pop? 18
   b. rhythm and blues? 14
   c. easy listening? 4

5. *Spanish*   In 1992, about 410,000 Americans took a course in Spanish. This represented 41% of those who took a language course. How many took a language course?
   (*Source: Modern Language Association*)   1,000,000

6. *French*   In 1992, 27.4% of the Americans who took a language course took a course in French. Use the result of Exercise 5 to find the number of Americans who took a course in French.   274,000

Pay Phones   **In Exercises 7–9, use the following.**

The circle graph shows the categories and the amounts of money that make up the yearly income for the average pay phone. Coin revenue makes up 35% of the yearly income.
(*Source: USA Today*)

7. What is the yearly income for the average pay phone? $3000

8. Describe another way to find the yearly income.   Solve $0.35x = 1050$.

9. Find the percent of yearly income of
   a. calling and credit cards.   39%
   b. collect calls.   ≈16%
   c. third-party calls.   ≈10%

8.5 ▪ Problem Solving Using Percents   **365**

EXERCISE Notes

ASSIGNMENT GUIDE
Basic/Average:
   Day 1: Ex. 3–5, 10–13, 17–23 odd
   Day 2: Ex. 6–9, 14–16, 25, 26
Above Average:
Ex. 5, 7–15, 22–26
Advanced: Ex. 5, 7–15, 22–26
Selected Answers: Ex. 1, 2, 3–23 odd

Guided Practice

It's important that students understand that the discount percent uses the original or regular price as its base.

Independent Practice

▶ **Ex. 3, 4**   Survey your students regarding their favorite music. Use the survey to create posterboard results that can be placed on a wall in the classroom.

Extra Practice

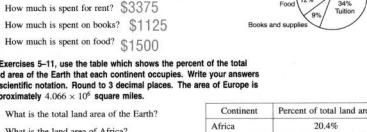

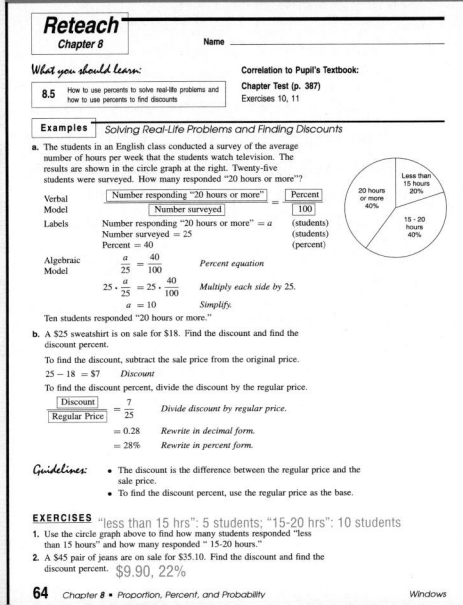

Lesson 8.5   **365**

▶ **Ex. 10–13** Survey your students regarding the location of radios in their homes. Display the results of the survey on the bulletin board.

Exploration and Extension

You may wish to show students how the (1.035) part of the savings balance formula is derived, as follows.

If the annual interest rate *percent* is 3.5, then the annual interest on *each* dollar is $3.5 \div 100 = 0.035$ and the annual interest on 470 dollars is 470(0.035) dollars. So,

$$\begin{align}
\text{Savings balance (\$)} &= 470 + 470(0.035) \\
&= 470(1 + 0.035) \\
&= 470(1.035)
\end{align}$$

Where Is Your Radio? In Exercises 10–13, use the following information.

The table shows the numbers, in millions, of radios in specific locations in American households. The percent of radios in bathrooms is about 4.3%.

Location	Number of Radios
Bedrooms	172.3
Living rooms	63.3
Kitchens	46.2
Bathrooms	14.7
Dining rooms	13.3
Other	33.2

10. How many radios do Americans own? 343 million
11. Find the percent of radios in bedrooms. ≈50.2%
12. Find the percent of radios in living rooms. ≈18.5%
13. Find the percent of radios in kitchens. ≈13.5%

14. *Discount* You buy a pair of rollerblades. The sign at the sporting goods store stated that the price of rollerblades had been discounted 25%. The discount was $21.40. What was the regular price of the rollerblades? $85.60

Geometry In Exercises 15 and 16, the blue region's percent of the total area is given.

15. The blue region has an area of 16 square units. What is the area of the entire region? ≈23.5 units²

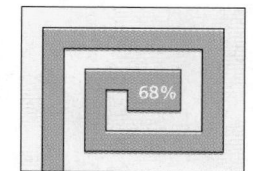

16. The yellow region has an area of 16 square units. What is the area of the entire region? ≈31.4 units²

Integrated Review   *Making Connections within Mathematics*

Proportions In Exercises 17–24, solve the proportion.

17. $\frac{95}{x} = \frac{20}{100}$ 475

18. $\frac{50}{100} = \frac{84}{y}$ 168

19. $\frac{n}{90} = \frac{60}{100}$ 54

20. $\frac{m}{40} = \frac{80}{100}$ 32

21. $\frac{9}{60} = \frac{x}{100}$ 15

22. $\frac{y}{100} = \frac{3}{5}$ 60

23. $\frac{45}{50} = \frac{s}{100}$ 90

24. $\frac{36}{90} = \frac{t}{100}$ 40

Exploration and Extension

✪ 25. *Banking* You deposit $470 into a savings account. At the end of one year, your account will earn interest at the rate of 3.5%. A shortcut for finding your new balance is

$$470(1.035) = \text{balance.} \quad 1(470) + 0.035(470) = 1.035(470)$$

Use the Distributive Property to explain how you could obtain this shortcut.

✪ 26. *Banking* In Exercise 25, suppose that you leave the money in the account for two years. During that time, you make no additional deposits or withdrawals. What is your balance at the end of two years? $503.48

8.6

Exploring Percent of Increase or Decrease

What you should learn:

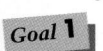 **Goal 1** How to find a percent of increase

 Goal 2 How to find a percent of decrease

Why you should learn it:

You can use percents to show how real-life quantities increase or decrease over time.

Goal 1 **Finding a Percent of Increase**

A **percent of increase** or **percent of decrease** tells how much a quantity has changed. For instance, the enrollments at Roosevelt Middle School for 1992 and 1994 are shown below.

1992 Enrollment: 400   **1994 Enrollment:** 420

From 1992 to 1994, the enrollment *increased* by 20 students. The percent of increase is

Percent increase $= \frac{20}{400} = 0.05 = 5\%$.

Percent of Increase or Decrease

The percent of change of a quantity is given by

$$\frac{\text{Actual change}}{\text{Original amount}}.$$

This percent is a **percent of increase** if the quantity increased and it is a **percent of decrease** if the quantity decreased.

Real Life
Technology

Example 1 *Finding a Percent of Increase*

The bar graph shows the number of computers that were in use in public schools from 1985 through 1991. Find the percent of increase from 1990 to 1991. *(Source: Market Data Retrieval)*

Solution There were 2.2 million in 1991 and 2 million in 1990. This means that the actual increase was 0.2 million computers. To find the percent of increase, find the ratio of 0.2 million (the increase) to 2 million.

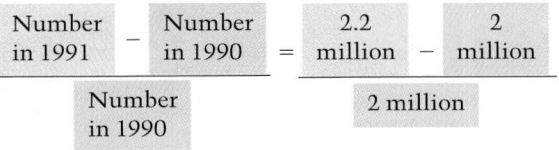

Classroom Computers

$$= \frac{0.2 \text{ million}}{2 \text{ million}} = 0.1 = 10\%$$

The percent of increase is 10%. ∎

Example 2

Using the TO and FROM values in this example, we would write:

% Change $= \frac{\text{TO} - \text{FROM}}{\text{FROM}} = \frac{\$0.14 - \$0.16}{\$0.16}$

$= \frac{-\$0.02}{\$0.16} = -0.125$ or 12.5% *decrease*

Communicating about MATHEMATICS

Have students identify real-life situations in which percents of increase or decrease are involved. Discuss these situations as a class.

Writing Prompt
List any questions you have about the work you are doing with percents.

Real Life
Communication

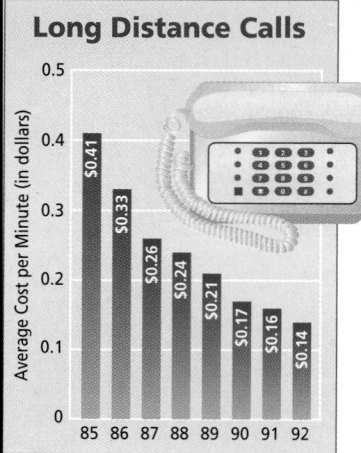

Long Distance Calls

Average Cost per Minute (in dollars)

Values: $0.41 (85), $0.33 (86), $0.26 (87), $0.24 (88), $0.21 (89), $0.17 (90), $0.16 (91), $0.14 (92)

Goal 2 **Finding a Percent of Decrease**

Example 2 *Finding a Percent of Decrease*

The bar graph at the left shows the averge cost per minute for long distance calls from 1985 through 1992. Find the percent of decrease from 1991 to 1992. *(Source: Federal Communications Commission)*

Solution The average cost in 1991 was $0.16, and the average cost in 1992 was $0.14. This means that the actual decrease was $0.02. To find the percent of decrease, find the ratio of $0.02 to $0.16.

$$\frac{\text{Average Cost in 1991} - \text{Average Cost in 1992}}{\text{Average Cost in 1991}} = \frac{\$0.16 - \$0.14}{\$0.16}$$

$$= \frac{\$0.02}{\$0.16}$$

$$= 0.125$$

$$= 12.5\%$$

The percent of decrease was 12.5%. ∎

When you are finding percents of increase or decrease over time, notice that the earlier number is always the base. For instance, in Example 1, the 1990 number is the base because it is earlier than the 1991 number. In Example 2, the 1991 number is the base because it is earlier than the 1992 number.

Communicating about MATHEMATICS

▶ **SHARING IDEAS about the Lesson**

Finding Percents of Decrease Use the data in the graph in Example 2 to find the percents of decrease over pairs of consecutive years. Then copy and complete the table. When did the greatest decrease occur? When did the greatest percent of decrease occur? 85–86, 86–87

	8¢	7¢	2¢	3¢	4¢	1¢	2
Years	85–86	86–87	87–88	88–89	89–90	90–91	91–
Decrease	?	?	?	?	?	?	
Percent	?	?	?	?	?	?	
	≈ 19.5	≈ 21.2	≈ 7.7	12.5	≈ 19.0	≈ 5.9	12

EXERCISES

Guided Practice

▶ CHECK for Understanding

1. *Computers* In Example 1 on page 367, find the percent of increase in the number of computers from 1985 to 1991. 175%

2. *Long-Distance Rates* In Example 2 on page 368, find the percent of decrease in the average cost per minute for long-distance telephone calls from 1985 to 1992.
≈ 65.9%

In Exercises 3 and 4, state whether the quantities represent a percent of increase or a percent of decrease. Then find the percent.

3. Yesterday: $16.35
Today: $18.21
Increase, ≈ 11.4%

4. May: 1056 units
June: 972 units
Decrease, ≈ 8.0%

Independent Practice

In Exercises 5–10, decide whether the change is an increase or a decrease and find the percent. I = Increase, D = Decrease

5. Before: 10, After: 12 I, 20%
6. Before: 15, After: 12 D, 20%
7. Before: 75, After: 60 D, 20%
8. Before: 110, After: 143 I, 30%
9. Before: 90, After: 200 I, ≈ 122.2%
10. Before: 260, After: 160 D, ≈ 38.5%

In Exercises 11–14, decide whether the change is an increase or a decrease and find the percent.

11. 1994: $171.33 Increase, ≈ 17.7%
1995: $201.59

12. Regular Price: $31.99 Decrease, ≈ 30.0%
Sale Price: $22.39

13. Beginning Balance: $521.43 Decrease, ≈ 20.7%
End Balance: $413.68

14. Opening Price: $18.77 Increase, ≈ 2.1%
Closing Price: $19.17

Finding a Pattern In Exercises 15–18, use percents to describe the sequence's pattern. Then list the next three terms. For descriptions, see margin.

15. 1, 2, 4, 8, [?] [?] [?] 16, 32, 64
16. 4096, 1024, 256, 64, [?] [?] [?] 16, 4, 1
17. 15625, 3125, 625, 125, [?] [?] [?] 25, 5, 1
18. 1, 3, 9, 27, [?] [?] [?] 81, 243, 729

Reasoning In Exercises 19–22, decide whether the statement is true or false. Explain.

19. Two times a number is a 100% increase of the number. True, $2n = n + n$

20. Half a number is a 50% decrease of the number. True, $\frac{1}{2}n = n - \frac{1}{2}n$

21. A 20% decrease of 80 is 60. False, $80 - 0.20(80) = 64 \neq 60$

22. A 25% increase of 100 is 125. True, $100 + 0.25(100) = 125$

✪ More difficult exercises

8.6 • Exploring Percent of Increase or Decrease   **369**

EXERCISE Notes

ASSIGNMENT GUIDE

*Basic/Average:
Day 1: Ex. 5–25 odd, 31–35 odd
Day 2: Ex. 26–30, 37–39

Above Average:
Day 1: Ex. 5–25 odd, 31–35 odd
Day 2: Ex. 26–30, 37–39

Advanced: Ex. 5–27 odd, 28, 33–39 odd

Selected Answers: Ex. 1–4, 5–35 odd

*You may wish to omit this lesson for these students.

Guided Practice

Use these exercises as an in-class small group summary. Be sure to emphasize how students are to determine the *base* for the percent increase or decrease.

Independent Practice

▶ **Ex. 19–22** Use these exercises as an in-class small-group activity accompanied by student reasoning leading to conjectures.

Answers

15. Each number after the first is 200% of the preceding number.

16. Each number after the first is 25% of the preceding number.

17. Each number after the first is 20% of the preceding number.

18. Each number after the first is 300% of the preceding number.

▶ **Ex. 27–28** Sources for problems such as these can be located in magazines or newspapers such as *USA Today.*

Ask students to find out salaries at local fast food restaurants. If the salaries have changed recently, have students compute the percent increase or decrease.

Integrated Review

▶ **Ex. 33–36** These exercises review the skills presented in Lesson 8.2.

P *Problem Solving*   **In Exercises 23 and 24, describe a real-life situation that involves the given increase or decrease.**   Answers vary.

23. An increase of 15%

24. A decrease of 30%

25. Copy and complete the table.

Original Number	New Number	Percent Change	
45	72	?	60% Increase
45	18	?	60% Decrease
400	?	25% Increase	500
400	?	25% Decrease	300

26. *Production*   In August, a small company produced 32,562 units. In September, the company produced 28,894 units. Find the percent decrease from August to September. ≈ 11.3%

27. *County Population*   Riverside County, California, had a large percent increase in population between 1980 and 1990. The 1980 population was 663,199 and the 1990 population was 1,170,413. Find the percent increase of population. *(Source: U.S. Bureau of Census)* ≈ 76.5%

28. *Shoe Profits*   The graph at the right shows the net profits (in millions of dollars) of Reebok for 1988 to 1994. Approximate the percent of change of net profit for each year. *(Source: Reebok International, Ltd.)* I = Increase, D = Decrease: ≈ 27.7% I, ≈ 0.6% I, ≈ 33.0% I, ≈ 0.9% D, ≈ 0.9% D, ≈ 1.7% I

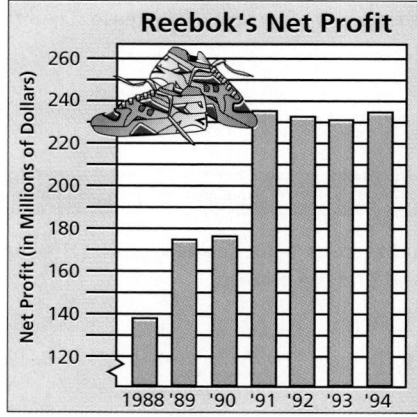

Reebok's Net Profit

Salary Increase   **In Exercises 29 and 30, use the following information.**

Your older sister tells you that she and a co-worker each received an annual salary increase. Your sister's salary was increased from $24,000 to $25,800 and her co-worker's salary was increased from $27,000 to $28,944.

✪ **29.** Find the percent of increase in your sister's salary and her co-worker's salary. 7.5%, 7.2%

✪ **30.** Who received the larger raise? Who received the larger percent raise? Co-worker, sister

Integrated Review   *Making Connections within Mathematics*

31. *Estimation*   Which percent best approximates the increase in the United States population each year? a

a. 1%   b. 10%   c. 25%   d. 50%

32. *Estimation*   Which percent best approximates the decrease in the value of a dollar each year? a

a. 6%   b. 26%   c. 46%   d. 66%

33. What is 75% of 240? 180

34. 72 is what percent of 180? 40%

35. 2.8 is 50% of what number? 5.6

36. 234.5 is 35% of what number? 670

✪ More difficult exercises
P Portfolio Opportunity

370   *Chapter **8** ▪ Proportion, Percent, and Probability*

Geometry   In Exercises 37–40, use graph paper or dot paper to draw the indicated figure. Each small square in the figure has an area of one square unit.   See Additional Answers.

37. Draw a figure whose area is 25% less than the area of the figure at the right.

38. Draw a figure whose area is $66\frac{2}{3}\%$ less than the area of the figure at the right.

39. Draw a figure whose area is 75% greater than the area of the figure at the right.

40. Draw a figure whose area is $33\frac{1}{3}\%$ greater than the area of the figure at the right.

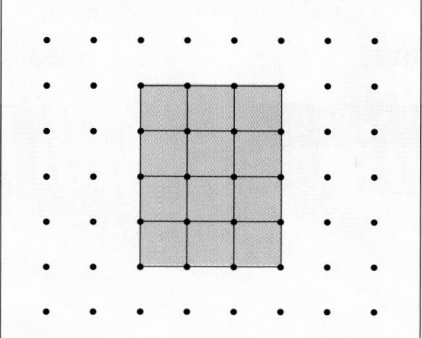

Mixed REVIEW

In Exercises 1–4, use the spinner at the right. All the divisions are the same size. (5.8)

1. Find the probability that the spinner will stop on red. $\frac{3}{8}$

2. Find the probability that the spinner will stop on blue. $\frac{1}{4}$

3. Find the probability that the spinner will stop on green. $\frac{1}{4}$

4. Find the probability that the spinner will stop on yellow. $\frac{1}{8}$

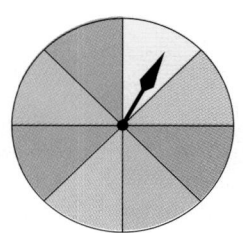

In Exercises 5–8, evaluate the expression when $a = -8$ and $b = 2$. (3.1)

5. $|ab|$ 16

6. $|a^2|$ 64

7. $|a| - |b|$ 6

8. $|a - b|$ 10

9. On a number line, plot the integers 4, -3, -2, and 0. (3.1) See margin.

10. Order the numbers $\frac{1}{2}$, $\frac{1}{3}$, $\frac{5}{8}$, $\frac{3}{7}$, and $\frac{4}{9}$ from least to greatest. (6.5, 7.7) $\frac{1}{3}, \frac{3}{7}, \frac{4}{9}, \frac{1}{2}, \frac{5}{8}$

11. What is the average of -1.02, -0.98, -1.01, -1, and -1.04? (3.6) -1.01

In Exercises 12–15, simplify the expression, if possible. Then evaluate the expression when $x = 5$ and $y = -4$. (3.3)

12. $3x + 2y + x$ $4x + 2y$, 12

13. $4x - 5y$ 40

14. $xy - 2y$ -12

15. $10x + 20y + 2x$ $12x + 20y$, -20

In Exercises 16–19, solve the percent problem. (8.4)

16. What is 35% of 80? 28

17. 32 is 45% of what number? $71\frac{1}{9}$

18. 190 is what percent of 310? $\approx 61.3\%$

19. What is 116% of 92? 106.72

8.6 • *Exploring Percent of Increase or Decrease*   **371**

Answer to Mixed Review

9.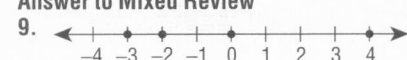

You can use the table in Ex. 3 to find the future value of a sum of money that *doubles itself* every day. Have students predict the amount of money available on the thirtieth day if the initial sum is just a penny.
2^{29} pennies ($\approx$ 5.4 million dollars!)

EXTENSION
Have students examine and predict patterns in the diagonal rows for Pascal's Triangle.

In this activity, you will explore the patterns in Pascal's Triangle. This triangle is named after the French mathematician Blaise Pascal (1623–1662).

Example *Exploring Pascal's Triangle*

Describe the pattern of the numbers in Pascal's Triangle. Then use the pattern to write the 8th row.

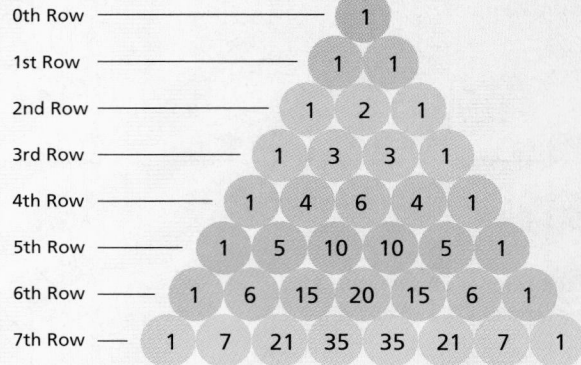

Solution The pattern of the numbers is as follows: The first and last numbers in each row are always 1, and every other number is the sum of the two numbers that lie directly above it. (For instance, 7 is the sum of 1 and 6. Similarly, 21 is the sum of 6 and 15.) Using this pattern, you can write the 8th row as follows.

1+7 7+21 21+35 35+35 35+21 21+7 7+1

1   8   28   56   70   56   28   8   1   ∎

Exercises   1, 9, 36, 84, 126, 126, 84, 36, 9, 1 | **2.** 1, 10, 45, 120, 210, 252, 210, 120, 45, 10, 1

1. Write the 9th row of Pascal's Triangle.

2. Write the 10th row of Pascal's Triangle.

3. Find the sum of the numbers in each of the first 8 rows of Pascal's Triangle. Then copy and complete the table.

Row	0	1	2	3	4	5	6	7
Sum	?	?	?	?	?	?	?	?

1   4   16   64
2   8   32   128

4. Describe the pattern in the table. Use your pattern to predict the sum of the 8th row. Then find the sum to confirm your prediction.
Each sum after the first is twice the preceding sum, 256.

8.7

The Counting Principle and Probability

What you should learn:

Goal 1 How to the Counting Principle

Goal 2 How to use Pascal's Triangle to count the number of ways an event can happen

Why you should learn it:

You can use the counting principle to solve real-life problems, such as finding the number of different committees that can be chosen from a group.

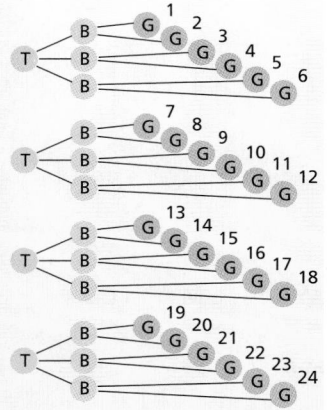

This tree diagram shows that 1 teacher, 1 boy, and 1 girl can be chosen from 4 teachers, 3 boys, and 2 girls in 24 different ways.

Goal 1 — Using the Counting Principle

Suppose there are 30 people in your class, and each person has exactly 5 books. Then the total number of books is 30 • 5 or 150 books. This is an example of the **Counting Principle.**

> **The Counting Principle**
>
> If one event can occur in *m* ways and another event can occur in *n* ways, then the two events can occur in *mn* ways.

Example 1 — *Forming a Committee*

The math club in your school has 5 officers: 3 boys and 2 girls. You are forming a committee of two officers to visit the math club at another school. You want the committee to have 1 boy and 1 girl. How many different committees are possible? Donna is one of the officers. What is the probability that she will be on the committee?

Solution With small numbers like this, you can find the sample space by listing the different committees.

Six different committees are possible. You can check this with the Counting Principle. Because you can choose a boy in 3 ways and a girl in 2 ways, it follows that you can choose 1 boy and 1 girl in 3 • 2 or 6 ways. If each committee is equally likely, then the probability that Donna will be chosen is

$$\frac{\text{Number of committees Donna is on}}{\text{Total number of committees}} = \frac{3}{6} = \frac{1}{2}.$$ ∎

The Counting Principle can be applied to three or more events. For instance, suppose your school has 4 math teachers, and the committee is to consist of 1 math teacher, 1 boy, and 1 girl. Then the number of possible committees is 4 • 3 • 2 or 24, as shown by the tree diagram at the left.

▶ **PACING the Lesson**

Suggested Number of Days
Basic/Average 2 **Above Average** 1
Advanced 1

▶ **PLANNING the Lesson**

Lesson Plan 8.7, p. 66

ORGANIZER

Starters (reproduced below)
  Problem of the Day 8.7, p. 24
  Warm-Up Exercises 8.7, p. 24
Lesson Resources
  Math Log, p. 27
  Technology, p. 49
  Answer Masters 8.7, p. 165
  Extra Practice Copymaster 8.7, p. 66
  Reteaching Copymaster 8.7, p. 66
Special Populations
  Suggestions, Teacher's Edition, p. 342D

LESSON Notes

The Counting Principle is useful in a variety of mathematical settings, including statistics and probability. This important principle is an appropriate journal entry.

Example 1

Explain to students that the *sample space* referred to at the beginning of the solution is defined as "the set of all possible outcomes" (see page 229).

Use a tree diagram to represent a two-person committee consisting of 1 boy and 1 girl chosen from 3 boys and 2 girls.

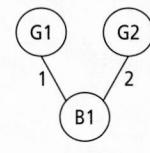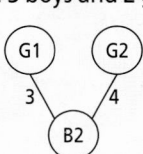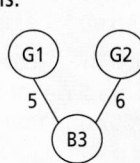

| **STARTER: Problem of the Day** |

More than one answer is possible.
One answer is shown.

■ Fill each square with a number, 1 through 9.
■ Numbers can be used more than once.
■ Numbers in each row should add up to the total on the right. ■ Numbers in each column should add up to the total at the bottom. ■ Numbers in diagonals through the center dot should add up to the total in the upper and lower right-hand corners.

				12
2	3	7	1	13
2	2	1	6	11
8	3	7	4	22
7	7	7	6	27
19	15	22	17	17

Also available as a copymaster, page 24

| **STARTER: Warm-Up Exercises** |

1. You have three shirts that go especially well with two different pairs of slacks. Using these items, how many outfits can you put together? 6
2. Create a diagram that shows the makeup of your outfits in **1.** Answers will vary. Sample is shown.

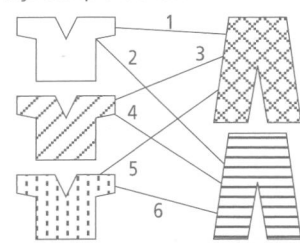

Also available as a copymaster, page 24

The Investigation on page 372 shows Pascal's Triangle. Display this special triangle on an overhead transparency for easy reference.

Example 2

To help your students understand how the committees can be formed, assign a number to each of the 5 officers in the club. Then form committees of two people using pairs of numbers to indicate who sits on a given committee. The following display will allow most students to see why there are 10 possible committees of two people.

Point out that the *n*th row of Pascal's Triangle provides information about forming subgroups from a group of *n* people.

Communicating
about MATHEMATICS

EXTENSION
For each problem, assume there are exactly 3 girls among the people from whom the committees are formed. Choose a committee for each situation, A, B, and C, that has exactly 1 girl and the rest boys.   A. 9, B. 9, C. 12

Writing Prompt
Complete the statement: The method of counting that I feel most confident with is....

Real Life
Social Studies

Almost all organizations such as schools, corporations, and governments use committees to help make decisions for the organization.

Goal 2 — Using Pascal's Triangle

Example 2   *Forming a Committee*

After finding the number of ways that 1 boy and 1 girl can be chosen to form the committee in Example 1, someone in the math club objects. The person thinks that *any* two of the officers should be able to be on the committee—even if the two are both boys or both girls. How many ways can you choose 2 committee members out of the 5 officers?

Solution   As in Example 1, you can find the sample space by listing the different committees.

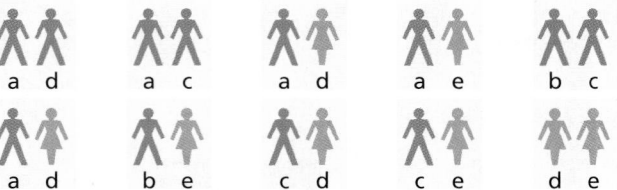

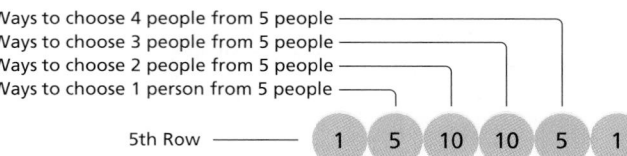

Ten committees are possible.

You can use the 5th row of Pascal's Triangle (see page 372) to find the number of ways you can choose 2 people from a group of 5 people.

Ways to choose 4 people from 5 people
Ways to choose 3 people from 5 people
Ways to choose 2 people from 5 people
Ways to choose 1 person from 5 people

5th Row ———   1   5   10   10   5   1

Communicating *about* MATHEMATICS

Cooperative Learning

▶ **SHARING IDEAS about the Lesson** For lists, see margin.

Using Pascal's Triangle Work with a partner. Use Pascal's Triangle to find the number of committees that can be formed. Then verify your answer by actually listing the different committees.

A. Choose a committee of 2 from 6 people. 15
B. Choose a committee of 3 from 6 people. 20
C. Choose a committee of 2 from 7 people. 21

Technology

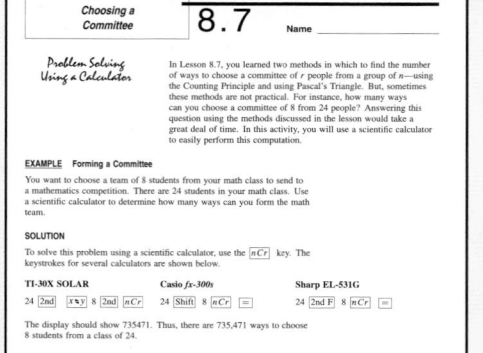

| Choosing a Committee | **8.7** | Name _____ |

Problem Solving Using a Calculator

In Lesson 8.7, you learned two methods in which to find the number of ways to choose a committee of *r* people from a group of *n*—using the Counting Principle and using Pascal's Triangle. But, sometimes these methods are not practical. For instance, how many ways can you choose a committee of 8 from 24 people? Answering this question using the methods discussed in the lesson would take a great deal of time. In this activity, you will use a scientific calculator to easily perform this computation.

EXAMPLE   Forming a Committee

You want to choose a team of 8 students from your math class to send to a mathematics competition. There are 24 students in your math class. Use a scientific calculator to determine how many ways you can form the math team.

SOLUTION

To solve this problem using a scientific calculator, use the |nCr| key. The keystrokes for several calculators are shown below.

TI-30X SOLAR   **Casio fx-300s**   **Sharp EL-531G**

24 |2nd| |xʸ| 8 |2nd| |nCr| 24 |Shift| 8 |nCr| |=| 24 |2nd F| 8 |nCr| |=|

The display should show 735471. Thus, there are 735,471 ways to choose 8 students from a class of 24.

EXERCISES

In Exercises 1–6, use a scientific calculator to find the number of ways to choose the committee.

1. Choose 2 from a group of 6. 15
2. Choose 3 from a group of 6. 20
3. Choose 11 from a group of 14. 364
4. Choose 9 from a group of 21. 293,930
5. Choose 6 from a group of 30. 593,775
6. Choose 5 from a group of 25. 53,130

7. As the winner of a contest, you win the choice of any 3 CD's from the most recent top 40 list. How many ways can you choose the 3 CD's? 9880
8. A donut shop offers a selection of 20 different donuts. How many ways can you buy a dozen donuts from the shop? 125,970
9. Solving for *r* in the following statement yields *two* possible solutions. Use your calculator to find them.
   The number of ways to choose *r* people from a group of 24 is 134,596. 6 and 18

EXERCISES

Guided Practice

1. *Counting Principle*   You have two pair of cutoffs and 4 T-shirts. Use the Counting Principle to determine how many different outfits you can wear by choosing 1 pair of cutoffs and 1 T-shirt. 8

2. *Counting Principle*   The diagram at the right shows how many ways you can order four books on a shelf. Explain how to use the Counting Principle to find the number of ways you can order the books. 24, see margin.

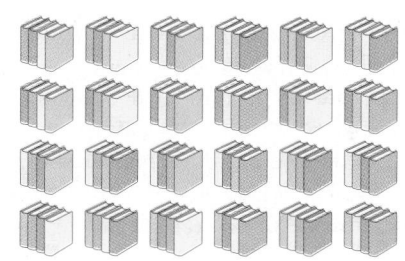

3. *Using a Tree Diagram*   You are writing a three-digit number. The first digit must be 1 or 7, the second digit must be 3, 6, or 9, and the number must be divisible by 5. Use a tree diagram to find how many numbers are possible. 12, see margin.

4. *Using Pascal's Triangle*   The diagram at the right shows how many ways you can choose two sweaters from a group of 7 sweaters. Explain how to use Pascal's Triangle to find how many ways you can choose two sweaters from 7 sweaters.
21, go to the 7th row and count in 2 places from the 1.

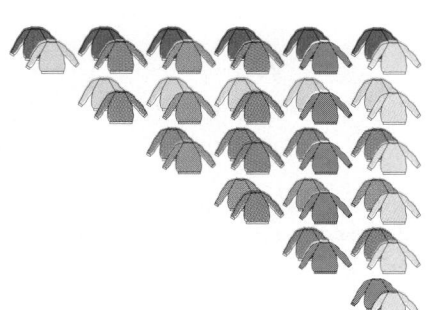

Independent Practice

5. *Yogurt Sundae*   A yogurt shop has 6 flavors of yogurt and 5 toppings. Each sundae consists of 1 yogurt flavor and 1 topping. Use the Counting Principle to find how many different sundaes are possible. Then confirm your answer by listing the different sundaes. 30

6. *Menu Choices*   The menu at the right shows the choices of side dishes that come with each dinner. You are to choose 1 vegetable and 1 rice or potato. Use the Counting Principle to find how many different choices you have. Then confirm your answer by listing the different choices. 20

7. *Probability*   In Exercise 6, suppose you are asked to make the choices for someone else's dinner. Without knowing their preferences, what is the probability that you will chose exactly the items they want? $\frac{1}{20}$

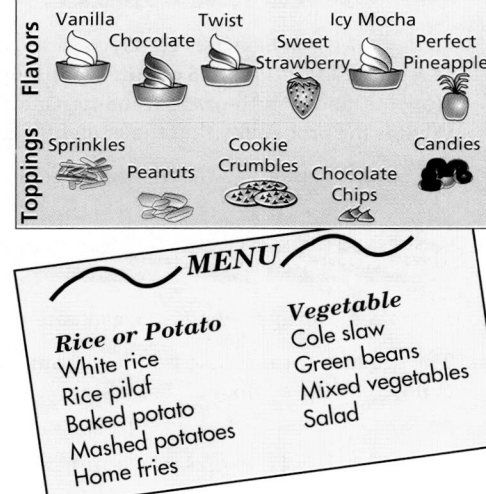

8.7 ▪ *The Counting Principle and Probability*   **375**

EXERCISE Notes

ASSIGNMENT GUIDE
Basic/Average:
   Day 1: Ex. 5–11 odd, 12–17
   Day 2: Ex. 6–10 even, 18–24
Above Average:
   Ex. 5–11 odd, 12–15, 18–24
Advanced: Ex. 5–11 odd, 12–15, 18–24
Selected Answers: Ex. 1–4, 5–19 odd

Guided Practice

Use these exercises as an in-class ten-minute summary activity. They review three counting techniques: the counting principle, tree diagrams, and Pascal's Triangle.

Answers

2. You can choose a book for the first position in 4 ways, then you can choose a book for the second position in 3 ways, then you can choose a book for the third position in 2 ways, then you can choose a book for the fourth position in only 1 way. 4 • 3 • 2 • 1 = 24

3.

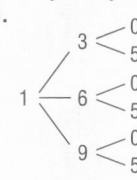

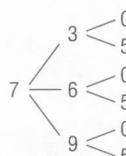

Lesson 8.7   **375**

Independent Practice

▶ **Ex. 9** You can connect this exercise to Ex. 20–24 as students discover that the number of ways to arrange *n* objects is *n*-factorial.
▶ **Ex. 12–15** Before assigning these exercises, be sure to review the Communicating feature on page 375.

Integrated Review

For these exercises, remind students that the probability of an event *E* is

$\frac{\text{Number of outcomes in } E}{\text{Number of outcomes in } S}$, where *S* is the total sample space.

Exploration and Extension

TECHNOLOGY
Show students the factorial key on a calculator. Allow them to explore large factorials such as 35! or 65! They may have questions regarding printout notation for these large numbers. Ask whether they can find 99! Ask: What seems to be the limit of the calculator for this function?

Portfolio Opportunity: Math Log

You can use the Counting Principle to answer the question in Example 2 of Section 8.7: Any one of 5 officers can be chosen for the committee and then any of the 4 remaining officers can be chosen. By the Counting Principle, multiply 4 and 5. However, the result must be divided by 2. Explain why.

Also available as a copymaster, page 27, Ex. 7

Alternative Assessment

Chapter 8 Group Assessment
An exploration using two methods of determining the possible outcomes of an event.

Chapter 8 Individual Assessment
An opportunity for each student to apply what was discussed in the group activity.

Available as copymasters, pages 73, 74

Answers
8. There are 2 ways to answer each question, so the Counting Principle is used.
9. To get the next number, multiply the preceding number by 3, by 4, by 5, etc.: 5040.

✪ **8.** *Taking a Test*   You are taking a test with 8 questions. Each question must be answered true or false. Which of the following represents the number of ways you can answer the 8 questions? Explain. a, see margin.
  a. $2 \cdot 2 \cdot 2 \cdot 2 \cdot 2 \cdot 2 \cdot 2 \cdot 2 = 2^8$ **b.** $2 + 2 + 2 + 2 + 2 + 2 + 2 + 2 = 8(2)$

✪ **9.** *Standing in Line*   In how many different orders can 2 people stand 2, 6, 24
  in line? In how many different orders can 3 people stand in line? In   See margin.
  how many different orders can 4 people stand in line? Describe the pattern. Find the number of orders that 7 people can stand in line.

10. *Shopping*   You are buying a sweatshirt. You have a choice of a pullover, button-down, or hooded sweatshirt. Each style comes in red, white, blue, gray, green, or purple.
  a. How many different sweatshirts can you choose from? 18
  b. Verify your answer with a tree diagram. See Additional Answers.

11. *Board Game*   You are playing a board game and must spin each of four spinners. How many different arrangements can the spinners show? 120

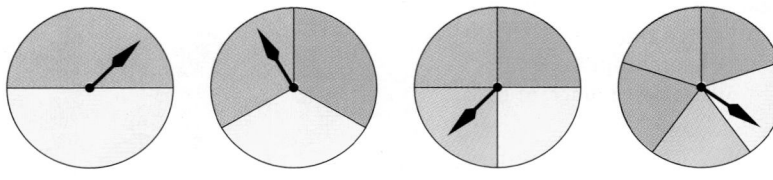

Pascal's Triangle   **In Exercises 12–15, use Pascal's Triangle to find the number of ways to choose the following.**

12. Choose 3 books from 7 books. 35
13. Choose 4 pencils from 8 pencils. 70
14. Choose 5 CDs from 6 CDs. 6
15. Choose 3 photos from 9 photos. 84

Integrated Review   *Making Connections within Mathematics*

Probability   **In Exercises 16–19, consider a school bus that has 3 seventh-grade students, 5 eighth-grade students, 4 ninth-grade students, and 6 tenth-grade students. One of the students is chosen. What is the probability that the student is in the indicated grade?**

16. Seventh grade $\frac{1}{6}$ **17.** Eighth grade $\frac{5}{18}$ **18.** Ninth grade $\frac{2}{9}$ **19.** Tenth grade $\frac{1}{3}$

Exploration and Extension

Factorials   **In Exercises 20–23, evaluate the factorial.**

The product of the whole numbers from 1 to *n* is called ***n*-factorial** and is denoted by the symbol *n*!. For instance, $3! = 3 \cdot 2 \cdot 1 = 6$.

✪ **20.** 4! 24   ✪ **21.** 5! 120   ✪ **22.** 6! 720   ✪ **23.** 7! 5040

✪ **24.** In Exercise 11, express the number of arrangements as a factorial. Explain.
          $5!, 2 \cdot 3 \cdot 4 \cdot 5 = 1 \cdot 2 \cdot 3 \cdot 4 \cdot 5 = 5!$

376   *Chapter 8 • Proportion, Percent, and Probability*   ✪ More difficult exercises

---

▶ **Enrichment**

Use the following exercises to allow further student exploration of factorials. Using mental math, evaluate.

1. $\frac{8!}{7!}$ **2.** $\frac{200!}{199!}$ **3.** 5!   **4.** $\frac{11!}{9!}$
Using a calculator, evaluate.
5. 11!   **6.** 4! × 3!   **7.** 10 × 9!   **8.** 10!
State whether the statement is true or false and explain your reasoning.

  9. $4! \times 2! = 4! + 4!$ **10.** $\frac{10!}{5!} = 2!$
11. $6! \times 12! = 12!$

There are two basic ways to compute the probability of an event: experimental and theoretical. The experimental approach often involves a **simulation,** which is an experiment that models a real-life situation.

Example   *Using a Computer Simulation*

You are making a long distance telephone call to a friend. You remember your friend's number, but all you remember about the 3-digit area code is that the first digit is 2. If you randomly choose the second and third digits, what is the probability that the area code is correct? (The actual area code is 206.)

Solution   One way to answer this question is to use a computer simulation, as shown below. Each time the program is run, it selects 1000 random numbers, each of the form 2??. The program then counts the number of times the area code 206 was chosen. To test the simulation, we ran the program 100 times. The results are shown in the line plot. The exercises below ask you to analyze these results.

```
BASIC PROGRAM
10 RANDOMIZE
20 FOR I = 1 TO 1000
30 N = 200 + FIX(100*RND)
40 IF N = 206 THEN C = C + 1
50 NEXT
60 PRINT "AREA CODE 206
WAS CHOSEN" C "TIMES."
70 END
```

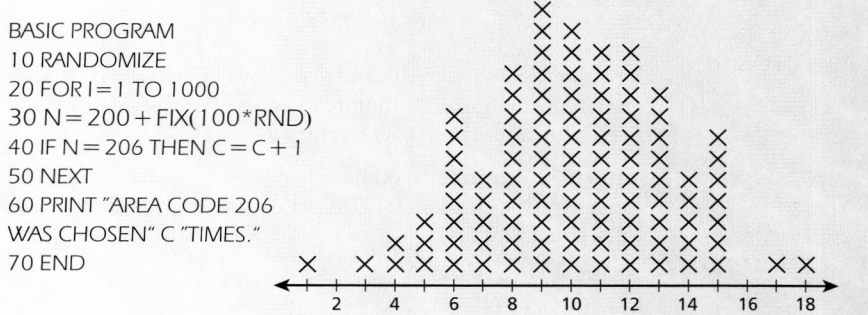

Exercises

1. For each of the 100 times the program was run, it selected 1000 numbers. How many numbers did it select all together? 100,000

2. Use the line plot to determine how many times the program selected the correct area code. 1007

3. Use the results of Exercises 1 and 2 to find the experimental probability that the correct area code is selected. $\frac{1007}{100,000} = 0.01007$

TECHNOLOGY Notes

Before running this program with the class, check that the program is compatible with the version of BASIC on your computer. Some older versions of BASIC do not define the RANDOMIZE command. If this is the case, refer to the software manual to find the commands used to randomly generate whole numbers less than 100.

If an overhead graphing calculator is available, you could use the random number generator to simulate the experiment in class. Students could tally results and generate their own line plot similar to the one shown.

EXTENSION

A non-technology simulation could be used with a spinner. Use a circle divided into ten similar sectors and spin a paper clip from its center. Have students record the results.

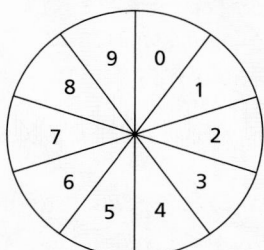

▶ **PLANNING the Lesson**

Lesson Plan 8.8, p. 67

ORGANIZER

Starters (reproduced below)
Problem of the Day 8.8, p. 24
Warm-Up Exercises 8.8, p. 24

Lesson Resources
Color Transparencies
Diagrams for Communicating about
Mathematics, p. 34
Math Log, p. 27
Answer Masters 8.8, p. 166
Extra Practice Copymaster 8.8, p. 67
Reteaching Copymaster 8.8, p. 67
Enrichment Projects, pp. 43, 44

Special Populations
Suggestions, Teacher's Edition, p. 292D

LESSON Notes

Review the Counting Principle with your
students. Then give them the formula for the
probability of an event, *E*, where *E* is a subset
of the sample space *S* (the set of all possible
outcomes). The Counting Principle is
frequently needed to determine the sample
space.

Example 1

Have students find the probability of dialing
the correct area code if the 2nd and 3rd digits
are even.
Probability is 0.04. Since 0.04 is 4(0.01), you are
four times more likely to pick the correct area code
if the unknown digits are both even.

8.8 Probability and Simulations

What you should learn:

Goal 1 Compare theoretical
and experimental
probabilities

Goal 2 How to find the probability of a multistage
event

Why you should learn it:
You can use probability to solve
real-life problems, such as finding the likelihood of dialing a
correct telephone number.

Real Life
Telephone Area Codes

```
200 201 202 203 204 205 206 207
208 209 210 211 212 213 214 215
216 217 218 219 220 221 222 223
224 225 226 227 228 229 230 231
232 233 234 235 236 237 238 239
240 241 242 243 244 245 246 247
248 249 250 251 252 253 254 255
256 257 258 259 260 261 262 263
264 265 266 267 268 269 270 271
272 273 274 275 276 277 278 279
280 281 282 283 284 285 286 287
288 289 290 291 292 293 294 295
296 297 298 299
```

*There are 100 3-digit area codes
that begin with 2. The ones shown
in blue have even second and third
digits.*

Goal 1 Comparing Probabilities

In the *Lesson Investigation* on page
377, you used a computer to *simulate* choosing an area code.

Using a computer is only one
way to simulate an event.
There are many other ways.
For instance, you could use
pieces of paper. Can you see
how?

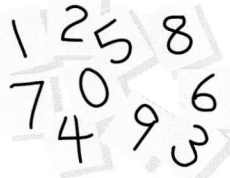

*Describe a simulation for
Example 1 that uses 10
pieces of paper*

Example 1 *Theoretical and Experimental
Probabilities*

Consider the question discussed on page 377. Show how you
can use the Counting Principle to compute the possibility that a
randomly chosen area code is correct.

Solution You have 10 choices for the second digit and 10
choices for the third digit. Thus, the number of different area
codes you could dial is

$$\begin{array}{c}\text{Choices}\\\text{for 2nd}\\\text{digit}\end{array} \cdot \begin{array}{c}\text{Choices}\\\text{for 3rd}\\\text{digit}\end{array} = 10 \cdot 10 = 100.$$

Because only one of these area codes is correct, the probability
that you will dial the correct area code is

$$\text{Probability} = \frac{1}{100} = 0.01.$$

This theoretical probability is close to the result that was obtained with the computer simulation on page 377. ∎

Suppose that you remembered that the second and third digits
are both even numbers. Would you be twice as likely to dial the
correct area code or four times as likely?

┌ STARTER: Problem of the Day ┐

The list below shows the high and low
temperatures for the region around
Chicago, Illinois, in July. What is the
probability of randomly selecting a city
listed that has a high in the 90's and a
low below 74?

Superior	81/60	Davenport	92/73
Marquette	83/65	Vincennes	93/74
Green Bay	88/69	E. St.Louis	93/74
Traverse City	86/67	Springfield	94/74
Cedar Rapids	92/71	Fort Wayne	91/70
Madison	90/70	New Buffalo	91/70
Detroit	91/72	Chicago	92/73

$\frac{7}{14} = 50\%$

Also available as a copymaster, page 24

┌ STARTER: Warm-Up Exercises ┐

1. What are "equally likely" events?
2. What is the probability that the spinner shown below will land on a shaded
region?

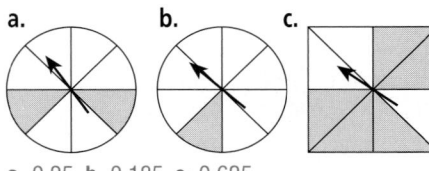

a. 0.25, b. 0.125, c. 0.625

3. From a group of 8 people—4 girls, 2
boys, and 2 teachers—how many 3-
member committees can be formed
consisting of a teacher, a girl, and a boy?
16

Also available as a copymaster, page 24

Real Life
License Plates

In 1990, there were about 143 million automobiles in the United States. Of these, 17 million were in California. (Source: Federal Highway Commission)

Goal 2 — **The Probability of a Multistage Event**

Example 2 — *Finding a Probability*

You live in a state whose automobile license plates have 3 letters followed by 3 digits.

a. How many different license plate "numbers" are possible?

b. Your license number is DBX-281. If one of the possible license-plate numbers is chosen at random, what is the probability that the number is yours?

Solution

a. For each of the three letters, there are 26 choices. For each of the three digits, there are 10 choices. Thus, the number of different license plate numbers is

$$26 \cdot 26 \cdot 26 \cdot 10 \cdot 10 \cdot 10 = 26^3 \cdot 10^3$$
$$= 17,576,000.$$

b. Because there are 17,576,000 different license numbers, the probability that yours is chosen is

$$\text{Probability} = \frac{1}{17,576,000}.$$

In other words, there is only 1 chance in over 17 million that your number will be chosen! ■

Communicating about MATHEMATICS

▶ **SHARING IDEAS about the Lesson**

Finding Probabilities Your automobile license number has three letters followed by three digits. In each of the following cases, you have forgotten one or more of the letters or digits. If you choose the letters and numbers at random, what is the probability that you will be correct?

A. $\frac{1}{26}$ Welcome to America's A?Q-568 Winter Wonderland

B. M??-420 Home of the Rockies $\frac{1}{676}$

C. $\frac{1}{10}$ Settle Down in BLT-30? The Sunset State

D. A Tropical Paradise S?N-4?3 In Your Own Back $\frac{1}{260}$

Example 1 involved a two-stage event because we had to consider two independent choices to get the desired outcome. In Example 2, we have a multistage event (consisting of 6 stages) because the license plate is made from six independent choices. Independent choices are those that are not affected by previous choices made.

Example 2
EXTENSION
Have students work the following problem. You have a personalized license plate: MATHPRO. If personalized plates use only the letters of the alphabet and must have exactly seven letters, what is the probability that a plate selected at random is yours?
$\frac{1}{8031810176}$

Communicating about MATHEMATICS

EXTENSION
Have students work the following problem. In some states, commercial vehicles have special license-plate numbers. For example, in one state whose license plates have 3 letters followed by 3 digits, all rental cars begin with the letter R, followed by another letter and 4 digits.
a. How many rental-car license plates could there be in this state?
b. Of all the rental cars in this state, what is the probability that the one you rent will have the plate "RC0001"?
a. 260,000, **b.** $\frac{1}{260,000}$

Writing Prompt
What I liked best about the math in this chapter is....

ASSIGNMENT GUIDE

*Basic/Average:
Day 1: Ex. 5, 6, 7–23 odd
Day 2: Ex. 25–37 odd

Above Average:
Day 1: Ex. 5, 6, 7–23 odd
Day 2: Ex. 25–37 odd

Advanced: Ex. 5, 6, 7–23 odd, 25–37 odd

Selected Answers: Ex. 1–4, 5–31 odd

*You may wish to omit this lesson for these students.

Guided Practice

Use these exercises as a ten-minute summary activity.

Independent Practice

▶ **Ex. 5, 6** Use these exercises as an in-class small-group activity. This will help students work Ex.13–17 and Ex. 19–24 during their homework.
▶ **Ex. 18** This is an excellent in-class follow-up activity for the next day. Use it to verify results from Ex.13–17.

EXERCISES

Guided Practice

▶ **CHECK for Understanding**

Choosing a Committee **In Exercises 1–4, use the following information.**

The math class in your school has five officers: 3 boys and 2 girls. To form a committee of two officers, you select two names at random. (The possible committees are listed in Example 2 on page 374.)

1. How many committees are possible? 10
2. What is the probability the committee will consist of one boy and one girl? $\frac{3}{5}$
3. What is the probability the committee will consist of two boys? $\frac{3}{10}$
4. What is the probability the committee will consist of two girls? $\frac{1}{10}$

Independent Practice

Spinning Spinners **In Exercises 5 and 6, use the following information.**

Each of the spinners at the right is spun once. On the first, the arrow is equally likely to land on any letter and on the second, the arrow is equally likely to land on any number.

5. How many outcomes are possible? 40
⭐ 6. Explain how to find the probability that the first spinner will land on A *and* the second will land on 1. See margin.

In Exercises 7–12, find the probability of each outcome.

7. *C* and 6 $\frac{1}{40}$ 8. *E* and 5 $\frac{1}{40}$
9. A vowel and 4 $\frac{1}{20}$ 10. A vowel and an even number $\frac{1}{5}$
11. A consonant and 2 $\frac{3}{40}$ 12. A consonant and an odd number $\frac{3}{10}$

Tossing a Coin and Rolling a Die **In Exercises 13–17, a coin is tossed, then a six-sided die is rolled. Find the probability of the indicated outcome.**

13. Heads and 5 $\frac{1}{12}$ 14. Tails and 1 $\frac{1}{12}$
15. Tails and an even number $\frac{1}{4}$
16. Heads and a prime number $\frac{1}{4}$
17. Heads and a number less than 3 $\frac{1}{6}$
P 18. *Simulation* Toss a coin and roll a six-sided die 40 times. Use the results to find the experimental probabilities for each of the outcomes in Exercises 13–17. Answers vary.

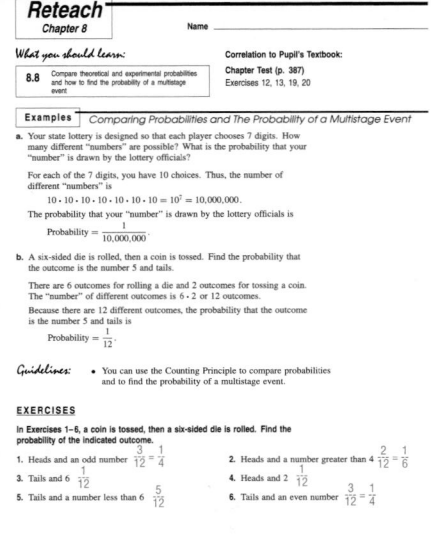

⭐ More difficult exercises
P Portfolio Opportunity

Answer

6. $\boxed{\text{Choices for 1st spinner}} \cdot \boxed{\text{Choices for 2nd spinner}} = 5 \cdot 8 = 40$

Because there are 40 different outcomes, the probability of A and 1 occurring together is $\frac{1}{40}$.

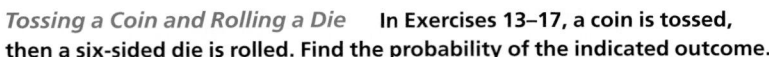

Extra Practice

Extra Practice 8.8 Name _____

In Exercises 1–4, two six-sided dice are rolled.
1. How many outcomes are possible? 36

2. List the outcomes that are possible using a tree diagram.

3. If the numbers that are rolled are added together, what is the smallest sum and the largest sum possible? Smallest: 2, largest: 12

4. Find the probability of rolling the following sums:
   a. 2 1/36   b. 6, 9, or 10 1/3   c. 7 1/6
   d. An even number 1/2   e. At most 11 35/36   f. At least 7 7/12

5. Roll two six-sided dice 50 times and record the results. Find the experimental probabilities for each of the outcomes in Exercise 4. Compare the results to the theoretical probabilities. Write a short paragraph explaining your results. Answers vary.

In Exercises 6–8, a six question true-false exam was given.
6. How many ways could the exam be answered?
   64 ways
7. If you guessed on each question, what is the probability that you have a perfect score? 1/64
8. If you answered the first and third question correctly and guessed on the remaining questions, what is the probability that you have a perfect score? 1/16

In Exercises 9–11, you are on a game show. You have the chance to win a car. All that you have to do is to guess correctly the actual price of the car. The price is a five digit number. The diagram gives the choices for each digit.
9. How many possible prices of the car exist?
   720 ways
10. What is the probability of choosing the correct price on your initial guess? 1/720
11. If you know the first two digits, what is the probability of winning? 1/120

Windows   8.8 • Probability and Simulations **67**

Reteaching

Reteach Chapter 8 Name _____

What you should learn:
8.8 Compare theoretical and experimental probabilities and how to find the probability of a multistage event

Correlation to Pupil's Textbook:
Chapter Test (p. 387)
Exercises 12, 13, 19, 20

Examples *Comparing Probabilities and The Probability of a Multistage Event*

a. Your state lottery is designed so that each player chooses 7 digits. How many different "numbers" are possible? What is the probability that your "number" is drawn by the lottery officials?

For each of the 7 digits, you have 10 choices. Thus, the number of different "numbers" is
$10 \cdot 10 \cdot 10 \cdot 10 \cdot 10 \cdot 10 \cdot 10 = 10^7 = 10,000,000$.
The probability that your "number" is drawn by the lottery officials is
Probability $= \frac{1}{10,000,000}$.

b. A six-sided die is rolled, then a coin is tossed. Find the probability that the outcome is the number 5 and tails.

There are 6 outcomes for rolling a die and 2 outcomes for tossing a coin. The "number" of different outcomes is $6 \cdot 2$ or 12 outcomes.

Because there are 12 different outcomes, the probability that the outcome is the number 5 and tails is
Probability $= \frac{1}{12}$.

Guidelines: • You can use the Counting Principle to compare probabilities and to find the probability of a multistage event.

EXERCISES

In Exercises 1–6, a coin is tossed, then a six-sided die is rolled. Find the probability of the indicated outcome.
1. Heads and an odd number $\frac{3}{12} = \frac{1}{4}$ 2. Heads and a number greater than 4 $\frac{2}{12} = \frac{1}{6}$
3. Tails and 6 $\frac{1}{12}$ 4. Heads and 2 $\frac{1}{12}$
5. Tails and a number less than 6 $\frac{5}{12}$ 6. Tails and an even number $\frac{3}{12} = \frac{1}{4}$

Windows   Chapter 8 • Proportion, Percent, and Probability **67**

Rolling a Die and Choosing a Card   In Exercises 19–24, a die is rolled, then a card is chosen from a deck of standard playing cards. Find the probability of each outcome.

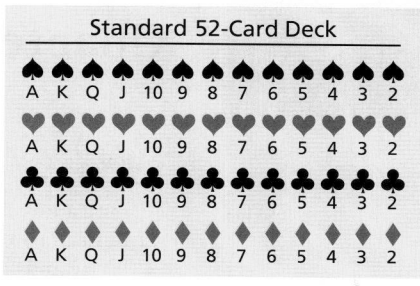

Standard 52-Card Deck

19. A six and an ace of hearts $\frac{1}{312}$
20. A three and a ten of diamonds $\frac{1}{312}$
21. A two and a king $\frac{1}{78}$
22. A five and a club $\frac{1}{24}$
23. An odd number and a queen $\frac{1}{26}$
24. An even number and a spade $\frac{1}{8}$

Social Security Number   In Exercises 25–28, digits are chosen at random to complete the Social Security Number, as indicated. Find the probability that the number will be 256-18-9342.

25. 256-1?-9342 $\frac{1}{10}$
26. 256-??-9342 $\frac{1}{100}$
27. ???-18-9342 $\frac{1}{1000}$
28. 256-18-???? $\frac{1}{10,000}$

Integrated Review   *Making Connections within Mathematics*

Estimation   In Exercises 29–32, use the graph at the right to estimate the probability that a grandparent, chosen at random, is of the indicated age. The graph shows the ages of grandparents in the United States in 1993. *(Source: Doublebase Mediamark Research, Inc.)*

29. 44 or under $\frac{7}{94}$
30. Between 45 and 54 $\frac{21}{94}$
31. Between 55 and 64 $\frac{15}{47}$
32. 65 or over $\frac{18}{47}$

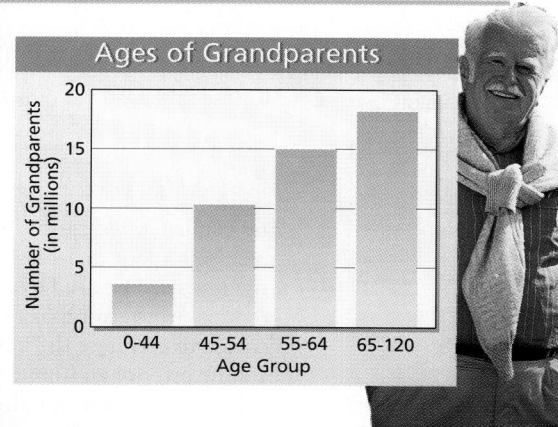

Ages of Grandparents

Exploration and Extension

Spinning a Spinner   In Exercises 33–38, each spinner is spun once. Find the probability of the indicated result.

33. Blue, *A*, 4 $\frac{1}{120}$
34. Green, a vowel, 3 $\frac{1}{60}$
35. Yellow, *C*, an odd number $\frac{1}{40}$
36. Orange, a consonant, 1 $\frac{1}{40}$
37. Green, a consonant, an even number $\frac{3}{40}$
38. Yellow, a vowel, a number less than 5 $\frac{1}{15}$

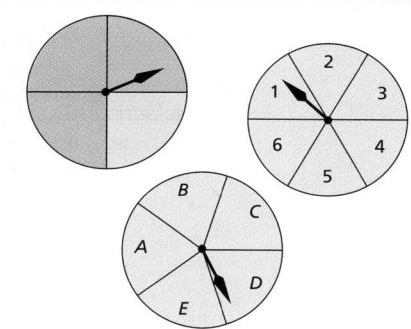

8.8 • *Probability and Simulations*   **381**

▶ **Exploration and Extension**

▶ **Ex. 33–38**   Discuss solution techniques to these exercises before assigning them.

Portfolio Opportunity: Math Log

Your class is organizing a raffle to earn money for a class trip. For $1, each participant may select any three-digit number from 000 to 999. No two participants may have the same number. There is no winner if a number is drawn which no one has selected.

a. What is the probability of winning if you select 1 number?

b. What is the probability of winning if you select 2, 3, or 4 numbers?

c. What happens to the percent of increase in your probability of winning with each additional number purchase?

Also available as a copymaster, page 27, Ex. 8

Short Quiz

Covers Lessons 8.7 and 8.8

Available as a copymaster, page 127

Alternative Assessment

A class coin-tossing experiment that develops understanding of the connection between theoretical and experimental probabilities.

Available as a copymaster, page 30

Enrichment

PROJECT
Have students find a bar graph from a local source similar to the type illustrated in Ex. 29–32. Ask them to create a probability exercise based on the bar graph that they have found.

Chapter SUMMARY

This chapter brought students beyond the simple manipulation of fractions and rational expressions to one of the most important and far-reaching applications of those skills, the technique of writing and solving proportions. Students were shown some of the major applications of proportions in mathematics and the real world of surveying, economics, demographics, and so on. They learned to apply proportion in geometry to compute side lengths in similar triangles. They were then introduced to the general techniques of indirect measurement and estimation. Lessons 8.4–8.6 were devoted to the topic of percent equations, their application to consumer discount, and their convenience as a means of representing and interpreting real-life data and rates of change. Finally, in Lessons 8.7 and 8.8, students were introduced to the Counting Principle and its use in computing probabilities.

8 Chapter Summary

What did you learn?

Skills

1. Find a rate of one quantity per another quantity. **(8.1)**
2. Find a ratio of one quantity to another. **(8.1)**
3. Write and solve a proportion. **(8.2)**
   - Use similar triangles to write a proportion. **(8.2, 8.3)**
4. Solve a percent equation.
   - a is what percent of b? **(8.4)**
   - What is p percent of b? **(8.4)**
   - a is p percent of what? **(8.4)**
5. Use percents to solve discount problems. **(8.5)**
6. Find a percent of increase or decrease. **(8.6)**
7. Find the theoretical probability of an event
   - by using the Counting Principle. **(8.7)**
   - by using simulations as experimental models. **(8.8)**
8. Use Pascal's Triangle to find the number of ways an event can occur. **(8.7)**

Problem-Solving Strategies

9. Model and solve real-life problems. **(8.1–8.8)**

Exploring Data

10. Use tables and graphs to solve problems. **(8.1–8.8)**

Why did you learn it?

You can use rates, ratios, proportions, percents, and probabilities to answer questions about real-life situations. For instance, in this chapter, you saw how rates can be used to compare unit prices and determine which of two products is a better bargain. You also saw how ratios and proportions can be used to estimate the height of a building, how percents can be used to find the price of an item that is on sale, and how probability can be used to find the likelihood of dialing a forgotten area code.

How does it fit into the bigger picture of mathematics?

In this chapter, you learned that when you are using rational numbers to model a real-life situation, it is important to know the units of measure. For instance, if a is measured in miles and b is measured in hours, then the rate $\frac{a}{b}$ is measured in miles per hour. You also learned that when a and b have the same units of measure, then the ratio $\frac{a}{b}$ has no units of measure. Percents and probabilities are examples of ratios. Knowing this can help you check the units in your answers. For instance, 25% of 8 *dollars* is $0.25 \cdot 8$ or 2 *dollars*. Multiplying 8 dollars by 0.25 doesn't change the units of measure because 0.25 has no units of measure.

Chapter REVIEW

Have students begin this Review in class and complete it as a homework assignment.

■ **Exercises 1–6, match the term with its description. (8.1–8.7)**

a. Ratio **b.** Counting Principle **c.** Rate

d. Reciprocal Property **e.** Percent Equation **f.** Proportion

1. An equation that relates two ratios ᶠ

2. If one event can occur in m ways and another can occur in n ways, then the two can occur in mn ways. ᵇ

3. $\frac{a}{b} = \frac{p}{100}$ ᵉ **4.** If $\frac{a}{b} = \frac{c}{d}$, then $\frac{b}{a} = \frac{d}{c}$. ᵈ

5. $\frac{a}{b}$ where a and b have the same units of measure ᵃ

6. $\frac{a}{b}$ where a and b have different units of measure ᶜ

ASSIGNMENT GUIDE

*Basic/Average:
Ex. 1–6, 7–29 odd, 34–36, 37–40, 58, 59, 63–71 odd, 72–76

Above Average:
Ex. 1–6, 7–29 odd, 34–36, 37–40, 43–57 odd, 58, 59, 63–71 odd, 72–76

Advanced:
Ex. 1–6, 7–29 odd, 34–36, 37–40, 43–57 odd, 58, 59, 63–71 odd, 72–76

*For these students, you will need to limit assignments to cover only those lessons you chose to teach from this chapter.

Resources
Color Transparencies
Diagram for Ex. 42–53, p. 35
Diagram for Ex. 58, 59, p. 35
Answer Masters, pp. 167, 168

■ **Exercises 7–10, decide whether the quotient is a rate or a ratio. Then simplify. (8.1)**

7. $\frac{51 \text{ shoes}}{9 \text{ shoes}}$ Ratio, $\frac{17}{3}$ **8.** $\frac{25 \text{ boys}}{30 \text{ girls}}$ Rate, $\frac{5 \text{ boys}}{6 \text{ girls}}$ **9.** $\frac{184 \text{ miles}}{4 \text{ hours}}$ Rate, $\frac{46 \text{ miles}}{1 \text{ hour}}$ **10.** $\frac{14 \text{ bikes}}{70 \text{ bikes}}$ Ratio, $\frac{1}{5}$

■ **Exercises 11–14, write the verbal phrase as a rate or a ratio. State whether the result is a rate or a ratio. (8.1)**

11. 27 out of 50 people surveyed $\frac{27}{50}$, ratio **12.** 5 out of 6 students participating $\frac{5}{6}$, ratio

13. Jogged 13 miles in 2 days $\frac{13 \text{ miles}}{2 \text{ days}}$, rate **14.** Solved 75 problems in 2 days $\frac{75 \text{ problems}}{2 \text{ days}}$, rate

■ **Exercises 15–22, solve the proportion. Check your solution. (8.2)**

15. $\frac{x}{4} = \frac{5}{8}$ $\frac{5}{2}$ **16.** $\frac{7}{9} = \frac{y}{3}$ $\frac{7}{3}$ **17.** $\frac{2}{z} = \frac{11}{6}$ $\frac{12}{11}$ **18.** $\frac{5}{2} = \frac{13}{a}$ $\frac{26}{5}$

19. $\frac{b}{8} = \frac{7}{11}$ $\frac{56}{11}$ **20.** $\frac{4}{15} = \frac{s}{2}$ $\frac{8}{15}$ **21.** $\frac{10}{3} = \frac{12}{t}$ $\frac{18}{5}$ **22.** $\frac{6}{7} = \frac{9}{x}$ $\frac{21}{2}$

■ **Exercises 23 and 24, the triangles are similar. Solve for x. (8.2)**

23.

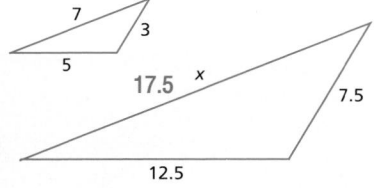

24.

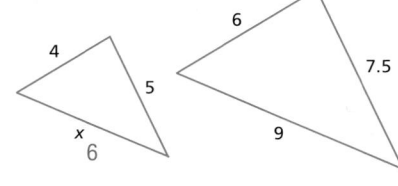

■ **Exercises 25–30, solve the percent equation. (8.4)**

25. 35 is what percent of 40? 87.5% **26.** What is 68 percent of 22? 14.96

27. 44 is 25% of what number? 176 **28.** 55 is what percent of 25? 220%

29. What is 86 percent of 7.5? 6.45 **30.** 86.4 is 64% of what number? 135

■ **Exercises 31–33, decide whether the change represents a percent increase or a percent decrease. Then find the percent. (8.6)**

31. Before: 15, After: 21 Increase, 40% **32.** Before: 112, After: 56 Decrease, 50% **33.** Before: 250, After: 325 Increase, 30%

In Exercises 34–36, decide whether the two quantities represent a percent of increase or a percent of decrease and find the percent. (8.6)

34. Monday: 845 people   Next day: 169 people   Decrease, 80%

35. Beginning Balance: $740.20   Ending Balance: $777.21   Increase, 5%

36. Regular Price: $65.50   Sale Price: $45.85   Decrease, 30%

Error Analysis   **In Exercises 37–39, find and correct the error. (8.2, 8.4, 8.5)**

⭐ **37.**
$$\frac{1}{8} = \frac{a}{2}$$
$$\frac{8}{1} = \frac{a}{2}$$
$$2 \cdot \frac{8}{1} = \frac{a}{2} \cdot 2$$
$$16 = a$$

$$\frac{1}{8} = \frac{a}{2}$$
$$2 \cdot \frac{1}{8} = 2 \cdot \frac{a}{2}$$
$$\frac{2}{8} = a$$
$$\frac{1}{4} = a$$

⭐ **38.** Sale price: $35
Discount: 25%
Regular price:
$$35 + x(0.25) = x$$
$$35 + 35(0.25) = \$43.75$$

⭐ **39.** Problem:
55 is 44% of what?
Percent equation:
$$\frac{a}{55} = \frac{44}{100} \quad \frac{55}{b} = \frac{44}{100}$$

40. What percent of 120 is 25% of 25%? **(8.6)**   6.25%

41. What percent of 120 is 50% of 50%? **(8.6)**   25%

Tossing Two Dice   **In Exercises 42–53, use the following information.**

When two 6-sided dice are tossed, 36 different outcomes can occur. These outcomes are shown at the right. Use the table to find the probability that the indicated total is tossed.

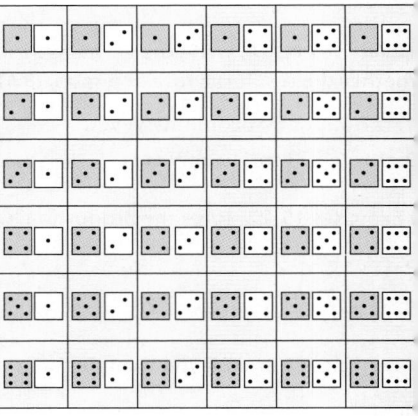

42. A total of 2 $\frac{1}{36}$

43. A total of 3 $\frac{1}{18}$

44. A total of 4 $\frac{1}{12}$

45. A total of 5 $\frac{1}{9}$

46. A total of 6 $\frac{5}{36}$

47. A total of 7 $\frac{1}{6}$

48. A total of 8 $\frac{5}{36}$

49. A total of 9 $\frac{1}{9}$

50. A total of 10 $\frac{1}{12}$

51. A total of 11 $\frac{1}{18}$

52. A total of 12 $\frac{1}{36}$

53. Graph your results.
See margin.

Computer Passwords   **In Exercises 54–57, use the following information.**

Each of the computer passwords below consists of 5 letters followed by 3 digits. You randomly choose letters or digits to complete each password. What is the probability that you will obtain the correct password? **(8.8)**

54. M L K ? P 1 2 ? $\frac{1}{260}$

55. N ? A C ? 4 8 7 $\frac{1}{676}$

56. ? Z X W A ? ? 7 $\frac{1}{2600}$

57. B ? F ? H ? 3 ? $\frac{1}{67,600}$

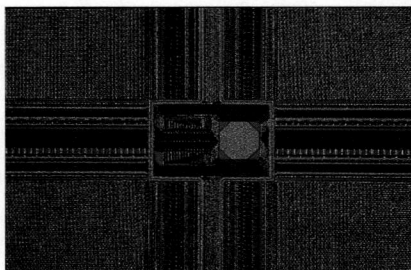

The horizontal and vertical decoder bands on computer microchips act like coordinate axes dividing the memory cells into 4 quadrants.

Answer
53.

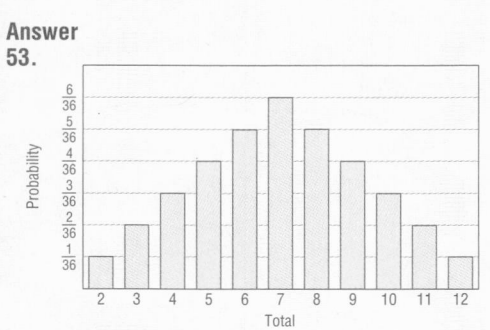

Playing Basketball **In Exercises 58 and 59, use the diagram at the right. In the diagram, the sun is creating two similar triangles. (8.2, 8.3)**

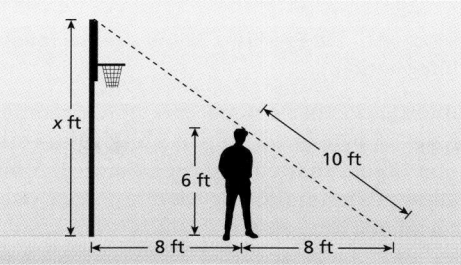

58. Explain why the following proportion is valid.

$$\frac{x}{8+8} = \frac{6}{8}$$ Ratios of corresponding sides are equal.

59. What is the height of the backboard? 12 ft

In Exercises 60–62, rewrite the quotient as a ratio. Then simplify. (8.1)

60. $\frac{2 \text{ feet}}{10 \text{ inches}}$ $\frac{24}{10}, \frac{12}{5}$

61. $\frac{8 \text{ ounces}}{2 \text{ pounds}}$ $\frac{8}{32}, \frac{1}{4}$

62. $\frac{60 \text{ centimeters}}{2 \text{ meters}}$ $\frac{60}{200}, \frac{3}{10}$

63. *Discount* A sign in a store states that all baseball hats are 45% off. The regular price is $15.00. What is the sale price of the hat? **(8.5)** $8.25

64. *Discount* A sign in a store states that all baseball hats are 45% off. The discount is $9.36. What was the regular price of the hat? **(8.5)** $20.80

65. *Beach Volleyball* Using the caption at the right, find the percent increase in the number of volleyball players from 1989 to 1992. **(8.6)** ≈28.2%

In 1989, 10.3 million Americans played beach volleyball. In 1992, 13.2 million Americans played beach volleyball. (Source: Sporting Goods Manufacturers Association)

Pascal's Triangle **In Exercises 66 and 67, use Pascal's Triangle to find the number of teams that can be formed. Then verify your answer by actually listing the different teams. (8.7)**

66. Choose a team of 3 from 5 people. 10, see below

67. Choose a team of 5 from 6 people. 6, see below

Estimation **In Exercises 68–71, use the graph at the right, which shows by percents what happened to the 242 million automobile tires that were discarded in 1990 in the United States.** *(Source: National Solid Wastes Management Associates)*

68. About how many tires were exported? 12 million

69. About how many tires were recycled?

70. About how many tires were burned for energy? **69.** 17 million **70.** 25 million

71. If you randomly selected a discarded tire in 1990, what is the probability that it was dumped in a landfill or dumped illegally? $\frac{39}{50}$

66. abc, abd, abe, acd, ace, ade, bcd, bce, bde, cde

67. abcde, abcdf, abcef, abdef, acdef, bcdef

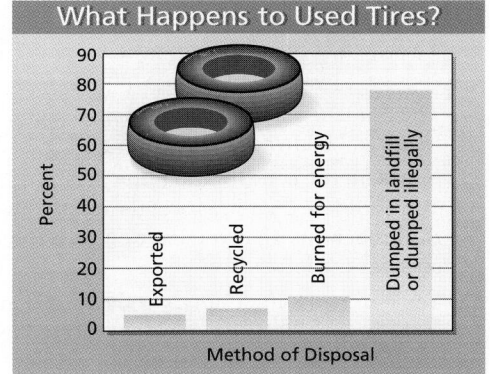

Modems **In Exercises 72–76, use the following information.**

Information in a computer is stored in units called bytes. A byte is made up of 8 bits. A bit is the smallest unit of information that can be stored. A modem allows two computers to communicate over a telephone line. Rate, units are different

⭐ **72.** Some modems can transfer data at 14,400 bits per second. Is that a rate or a ratio? Explain.

⭐ **73.** How many bits of information are there in 36 bytes? 288

⭐ **74.** How many bytes are needed to store 776 bits? 97

⭐ **75.** A 10,000-byte file, which could be four pages of text, is to be transferred over a 1200-bit-per-second modem. How many seconds will the transfer take? $66\frac{2}{3}$

⭐ **76.** A 10,000-byte file is transferred over a 9600-bit-per-second modem. How many seconds will the transfer take? $8\frac{1}{3}$

Binary Codes **In Exercises 77–82, use the following information.**

Binary codes use the numbers zero and one in different combinations to represent symbols such as letters, numbers, and punctuation. The diagram at the right shows how many different codes are possible with one, two, three, or four digits.

77. The *Baudot binary system* uses 5 digits. How many codes are possible in this system? 32

78. The *BCD binary system* uses 6 digits. How many codes are possible in this system? 64

79. The *ASCII binary system* uses 7 digits. How many codes are possible in this system? 128

80. The *EBCDIC binary system* uses 8 digits. How many codes are possible in this system? 256

81. In ASCII, the code for the letter A is "1000001." You enter a 7-digit binary code at random. What is the probability that you have entered the ASCII code for the letter A? $\frac{1}{128}$

82. You enter an 8-digit binary code at random. What is the probability that you have entered the EBCDIC code for the letter A? $\frac{1}{256}$

A modem converts digital signals from a sending computer into analog signals that can travel over telephone lines. A modem attached to a receiving computer converts the analog signals back to digital signals.

Possible 1-Digit Codes
0, 1

Possible 2-Digit Codes
00, 01, 10, 11

Possible 3-Digit Codes
000, 001, 010, 011,
100, 101, 110, 111

Possible 4-Digit Codes
0000, 0001, 0010, 0011, 0100, 0101
0110, 0111, 1000, 1001, 1010, 1011
1100, 1101, 1110, 1111

⭐ More difficult exercises

In Exercises 1–4, use the similar triangles at the right. (8.1, 8.2)

1. Find the ratio of a to d. $\frac{2}{3}$
2. Solve for f. 7.5
3. Solve for e. 6
4. Find the ratio of b to e. $\frac{2}{3}$

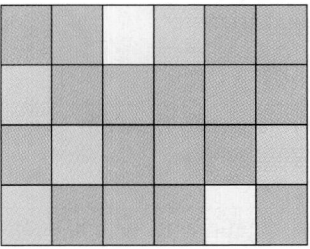

In Exercises 5 and 6, find the percent increase or decrease. (8.4, 8.6)

5. Before: 76   After: 95   25% increase
6. Before: $15.00   After: $9.00   40% decrease
7. You rent a car for 5 days for $195. What is the daily rental rate? (8.3) $39 per
8. What is 82% of 115? (8.5) 94.3
9. 56 is what percent of 70? (8.5) 80%

In Exercises 10–13, use the rectangle at the right. Each small rectangle is the same size. (8.5, 8.8)

10. What percent of the large rectangle is red? 37.5%
11. What percent of the large rectangle is yellow? $\approx 8.3\%$
12. If one of the small rectangles is chosen at random, what is the probability that it will be green? $\frac{5}{24}$
13. If one of the small rectangles is chosen at random, what is the probability that it will not be red? $\frac{5}{8}$

In Exercises 14–20, use the given information.

Shadows   A building is casting a 100-foot shadow at the same time that a 5-foot post is casting a 1-foot shadow. (8.2, 8.3)

14. Draw a diagram that shows the building, the post, and the two shadows.   See margin.
15. Write a proportion that involves the height of the building, the height of the post, and the lengths of the two shadows. $\frac{h}{5} = \frac{100}{1}$
16. Solve the proportion to find the height of the building. 500 ft

Committees   A two-person committee is to be chosen from 3 seventh-grade students and 3 eighth-grade students. The committee must have one student from each grade. (8.7) See below.

17. List the different committees that are possible.
18. Use the Counting Principle to confirm your list.
$3 \cdot 3 = 9$

Birth Rates   In 1990, about 10,500 women gave birth in the United States. Of these, 217 women gave birth to twins and 5 women gave birth to triplets. (8.8)

19. Estimate the chance of having twins. $\frac{1}{50}$
20. Estimate the chance of having triplets. $\frac{1}{2100}$

17. AX, AY, AZ, BX, BY, BZ, CX, CY, CZ

Chapter Test

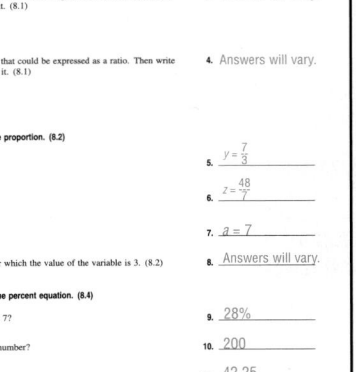

Answer
14.

Not drawn to scale

◀ **Formal Assessment**

Three **Chapter Tests.** Form A is of average difficulty, Form B is of average difficulty in multiple choice format, and Form C is more challenging.
Available as copymasters, pages 128–136

CHAPTER 9 GOALS

Lesson	Pages	Goals	Meeting the NCTM Standards
9.1	390–393	1. Solve equations whose solutions are square roots 2. Use square roots to solve real-life problems	Problem Solving, Communication, Connections, Computation and Estimation, Technology, Patterns and Functions, Algebra, Geometry, Measurement
Using a Calculator	394	Approximating Square Roots	Computation and Estimation, Technology
9.2	395–398	1. Classify real numbers as rational or irrational 2. Represent real numbers with a number line	Communication, Reasoning, Connections, Number Relationships, Computation and Estimation, Technology
Lesson Investigation 9.3	399	Exploring Right Triangles	Algebra, Geometry
9.3	400–403	1. Use the Pythagorean Theorem 2. Solve a right triangle	Problem Solving, Communication, Reasoning, Connections, Computation and Estimation, Algebra, Geometry, Measurement
Mixed Review	404	Review of arithmetic, algebra, and geometry	Computation and Estimation, Algebra, Geometry, Measurement
Career Interview	404	Solar Consultant and Construction Contractor	Connections
9.4	405–408	1. Use properties of triangles to solve real-life problems 2. Use the Pythagorean Theorem to measure indirectly	Problem Solving, Communication, Connections, Patterns and Functions, Geometry, Measurement
Mid-Chapter Self-Test	409	Diagnose student weaknesses and remediate with correlated Reteaching Copymasters	Assessment
Lesson Investigation 9.5	410	Plotting Irrational Numbers	Number Relationships
9.5	411–415	1. Graph an inequality 2. Write equivalent inequalities	Problem Solving, Communication, Connections, Number Relationships, Technology, Algebra
Mixed Review	415	Review of arithmetic, algebra, and geometry	Problem Solving, Number Relationships, Algebra, Probability
9.6	416–419	1. Use properties of inequalities 2. Use multiplication and division to solve an inequality	Problem Solving, Communication, Reasoning, Connections, Number Relationships, Algebra, Statistics
9.7	420–423	1. Solve multi-step inequalities 2. Use multi-step inequalities to solve real-life problems	Problem Solving, Communication, Reasoning, Connections, Algebra, Geometry, Measurement
Lesson Investigation 9.8	424	Exploring Triangles	Patterns and Functions, Algebra, Geometry, Measurement
9.8	425–428	1. Use the Triangle Inequality 2. Use the Triangle Inequality to solve real-life problems	Communication, Reasoning, Connections, Patterns and Functions, Algebra, Geometry, Measurement
Chapter Summary	429	A restatement of what has been learned, why it has been learned, and how it fits into the structure of mathematics	Communication, Connections
Chapter Review	430–432	Review of concepts and skills learned in the chapter	Problem Solving, Connections
Chapter Test	433	Diagnose student weaknesses and remediate with correlated Reteaching Copymasters	Assessment

RESOURCES ORGANIZER

Lesson Pages	9.1 390–393	9.2 395–398	9.3 400–403	9.4 405–408	9.5 411–415	9.6 416–419	9.7 420–423	9.8 425–428
Lesson Plans	68	69	70	71	72	73	74	75
Problem of the Day	25	25	25	26	26	26	27	27
Warm-Up Exercises	25	25	25	26	26	26	27	27
Color Transparencies	36	—	—	37	38	38	39	—
Teaching Tools: Transparencies Copymasters	T1, T8 C2, C10	T6 C8	T12 C18	— —	T6 C8	T6 C8	— —	T12 C18
Math Log	28	28	28, 29	29	29	30	30	30
Technology	—	—	51	52	—	—	53	54
Answer Masters	170, 171	172–174	175, 176	178	179, 180	182, 183	184, 185	186
Extra Practice Copymasters	68	69	70	71	72	73	74	75
Reteaching Copymasters	68	69	70	71	72	73	74	75
Enrichment Projects	45, 46	—	47, 48	—	—	—	—	—
Alternative Assessment: Projects Partner Quizzes Group Assessment	— — —	31 — —	31 — —	32 52 —	— — —	— — —	32 — —	— — 75, 76
Formal Assessment: Short Quizzes Tests	— —	137 —	— —	138 139, 140	— —	141 —	— —	142 143–151
Overhead Manipulatives Kit	—	—	—	—	—	—	—	—
Complete Solutions Manual	Includes step-by-step solutions for all exercises in the student text							
Computerized Test Bank	Creates customized tests that include graphics							
Interactive CD-ROM Project	Provides an interactive and interdisciplinary chapter project							

STARTERS

Problem of the Day

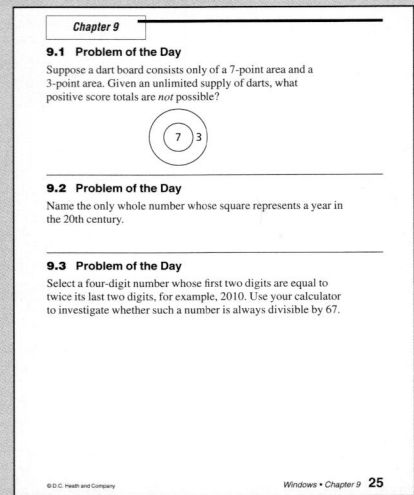

Chapter 9

9.1 Problem of the Day
Suppose a dart board consists only of a 7-point area and a 3-point area. Given an unlimited supply of darts, what positive score totals are *not* possible?

9.2 Problem of the Day
Name the only whole number whose square represents a year in the 20th century.

9.3 Problem of the Day
Select a four-digit number whose first two digits are equal to twice its last two digits, for example, 2010. Use your calculator to investigate whether such a number is always divisible by 67.

© D.C. Heath and Company   *Windows • Chapter 9* **25**

Warm-Up Exercises

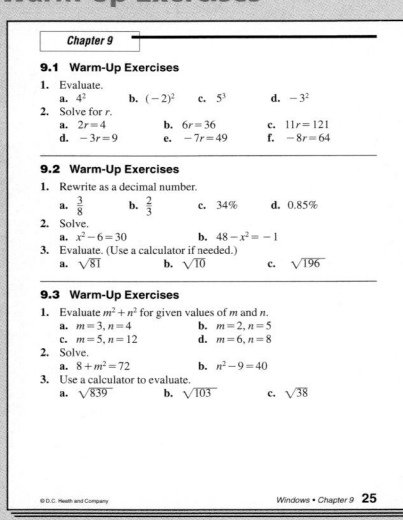

Chapter 9

9.1 Warm-Up Exercises
1. Evaluate.
   a. 4^2 b. $(-2)^2$ c. 5^3 d. -3^2
2. Solve for r.
   a. $2r = 4$ b. $6r = 36$ c. $11r = 121$
   d. $-3r = 9$ e. $-7r = 49$ f. $-8r = 64$

9.2 Warm-Up Exercises
1. Rewrite as a decimal number.
   a. $\frac{3}{8}$ b. $\frac{2}{3}$ c. 34%   d. 0.85%
2. Solve.
   a. $x^2 - 6 = 30$ b. $48 - x^2 = -1$
3. Evaluate. (Use a calculator if needed.)
   a. $\sqrt{81}$ b. $\sqrt{10}$ c. $\sqrt{196}$

9.3 Warm-Up Exercises
1. Evaluate $m^2 + n^2$ for given values of m and n.
   a. $m = 3, n = 4$ b. $m = 2, n = 5$
   c. $m = 5, n = 12$ d. $m = 6, n = 8$
2. Solve.
   a. $8 + m^2 = 72$ b. $n^2 - 9 = 40$
3. Use a calculator to evaluate.
   a. $\sqrt{839}$ b. $\sqrt{103}$ c. $\sqrt{38}$

© D.C. Heath and Company   *Windows • Chapter 9* **25**

FOR TEACHERS

Answer Masters

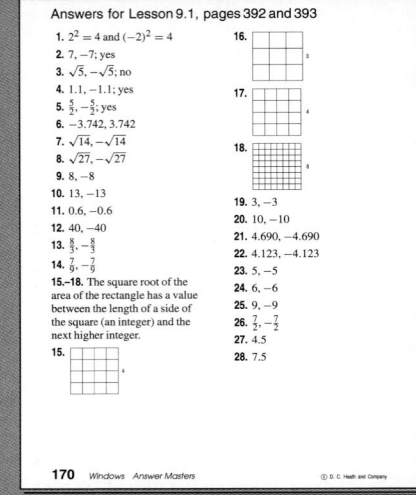

Answers for Lesson 9.1, pages 392 and 393

1. $2^2 = 4$ and $(-2)^2 = 4$
2. $7, -7$; yes
3. $\sqrt{5}, -\sqrt{5}$; no
4. $1.1, -1.1$; yes
5. $\frac{5}{2}, -\frac{5}{2}$; yes
6. $-3.742, 3.742$
7. $\sqrt{14}, -\sqrt{14}$
8. $\sqrt{27}, -\sqrt{27}$
9. $8, -8$
10. $13, -13$
11. $0.6, -0.6$
12. $40, -40$
13. $\frac{8}{3}, -\frac{8}{3}$
14. $\frac{7}{9}, -\frac{7}{9}$
15.–18. The square root of the area of the rectangle has a value between the length of a side of the square (an integer) and the next higher integer.
15.
16.
17.
18.
19. $3, -3$
20. $10, -10$
21. $4.690, -4.690$
22. $4.123, -4.123$
23. $5, -5$
24. $6, -6$
25. $9, -9$
26. $\frac{7}{2}, -\frac{7}{2}$
27. 4.5
28. 7.5

170   *Windows   Answer Masters*   © D.C. Heath and Company

Lesson Plans

Lesson Plan 9.1
pages 390–393

Teacher's Name _____ Class _____ Date _____ Room _____

Goals 1. Solve equations whose solutions are square roots.
2. Use square roots to solve real-life problems.

State/Local Objectives _____

NCTM Curriculum Standards: Problem Solving, Communication, Connections, Computation and Estimation, Technology, Patterns and Functions, Algebra, Geometry, Measurement

✔ **Check items you wish to use for this lesson.**

Introducing the Lesson
___ Problem of the Day copymaster page 25 or Teacher's Edition page 390
___ Warm-Up Exercises copymaster page 25 or Teacher's Edition page 390

Teaching the Lesson using the following:
___ Common-Error Alert, Teacher's Edition page 390
___ Extra Examples, Teacher's Edition page 391
___ Color Transparencies: chapter opener and picture for Example 2, page 36
___ Teaching Tools: graph paper and coordinate plane, pages T1, T8, C2, C10
___ Notes for Substitute Teacher

Closing the Lesson
___ Communicating about Mathematics, Student's Edition page 391
___ Guided Practice Exercises, Student's Edition page 392

Homework Assignment, pages 392, 393
___ Basic/Average: Day 1: Ex. 3–33 odd
       Day 2: Ex. 35–39, 41–43
___ Above Average: Ex. 11–21 odd, 27–37 odd, 38, 39, 41–43
___ Advanced: Ex. 11–21 odd, 27–37 odd, 38, 39, 41–43

Reteaching the Lesson
___ Extra Practice Copymasters page 68
___ Reteaching Copymasters page 68
___ Math Log copymaster page 28 or Teacher's Edition page 393

Extending the Lesson
___ Writing, Teacher's Edition page 391
___ Enrichment, Teacher's Edition page 393
___ Enrichment Projects copymasters pages 45, 46

Notes _____

68   *Windows*   © D.C. Heath and Company

Teaching Tools

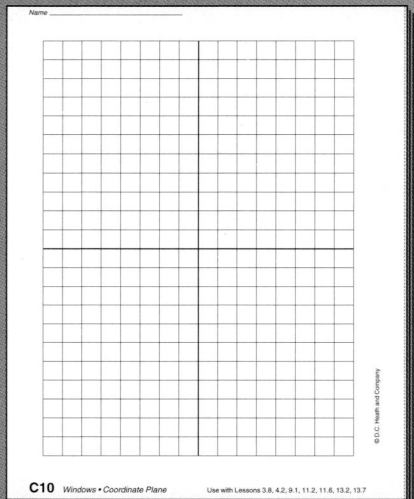

Name _____

C10   *Windows • Coordinate Plane*   Use with Lessons 3.8, 4.2, 9.1, 11.2, 11.6, 13.2, 13.7

© D.C. Heath and Company

Teaching Tools includes:
Transparencies and Copymasters for classroom activities and study skills:
- Graph Paper
- Dot Paper (Geoboards)
- Algebra Tiles
- Number Counters
- Fraction Strips
- Models

REAL LIFE
Color Transparencies for Real-Life Applications

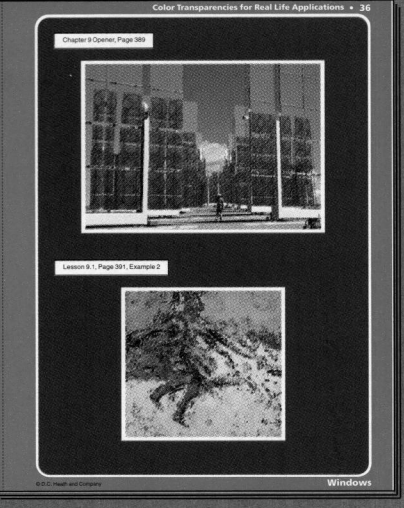

Color Transparencies for Real Life Applications • 36

Chapter 9 Opener, Page 389

Lesson 9.1, Page 391, Example 2

© D.C. Heath and Company   **Windows**

Technology: Using Calculators and Computers

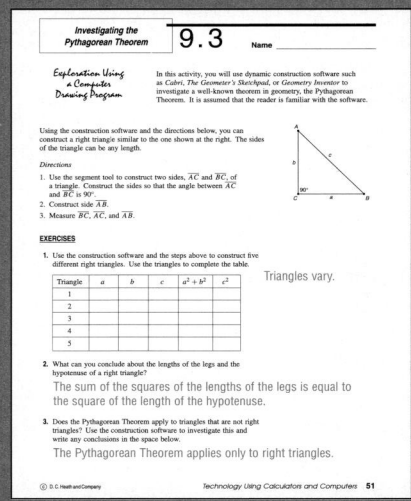

Investigating the Pythagorean Theorem   **9.3**   Name _____

Exploration Using a Computer Drawing Program

In this activity, you will use dynamic construction software such as Cabri, The Geometer's Sketchpad, or Geometry Inventor to investigate a well-known theorem in geometry, the Pythagorean Theorem. It is assumed that the reader is familiar with the software.

Using the construction software and the directions below, you can construct a right triangle similar to the one shown at the right. The sides of the triangle can be any length.

Directions
1. Use the segment tool to construct two sides, $\overline{AC}$ and $\overline{BC}$, of a triangle. Construct the sides so that the angle between $\overline{AC}$ and $\overline{BC}$ is 90°.
2. Construct side $\overline{AB}$.
3. Measure $\overline{BC}$, $\overline{AC}$, and $\overline{AB}$.

EXERCISES
1. Use the construction software and the steps above to construct five different right triangles. Use the triangles to complete the table.

Triangle	a	b	c	$a^2 + b^2$	c^2
1					
2					
3					
4					
5					

Triangles vary.

2. What can you conclude about the lengths of the legs and the hypotenuse of a right triangle?
   The sum of the squares of the lengths of the legs is equal to the square of the length of the hypotenuse.

3. Does the Pythagorean Theorem apply to triangles that are not right triangles? Use the construction software to investigate this and write any conclusions in the space below.
   The Pythagorean Theorem applies only to right triangles.

© D.C. Heath and Company   *Technology Using Calculators and Computers* **51**

Also Available:

- Complete Solutions Manual
- Overhead Manipulatives Kit
- Computerized Testing Program

- **Interactive CD-ROM Projects**
  Interactive projects for solving real-world problems using multimedia

- **Interactions: Real Math–Real Careers**
  A videodisc–based resource that connects math to real careers and on-the-job problem solving

- **PACKETS® Performance Assessment for Middle School Mathematics**
  A program that links assessment and instruction

ASSESSMENT

Alternative Assessment

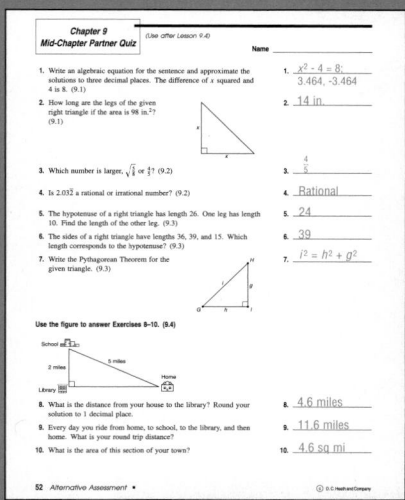

Alternative Assessment includes:
- Scoring Rubrics
- Portfolios
- Math Journals
- Projects
- Partner Quizzes
- Individual and Group Assessment

Formal Assessment

Formal Assessment includes:
- Short Quizzes (after every 2 lessons)
- Mid-Chapter Tests (2 forms)
- Chapter Tests (3 forms)
- Cumulative Tests (after every 3 Chapters)

MEETING INDIVIDUAL NEEDS

Extra Practice Copymasters

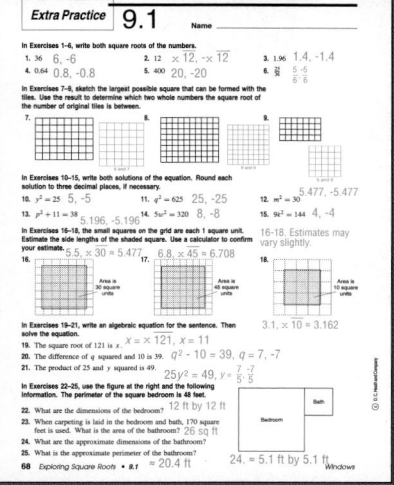

Reteaching Copymasters

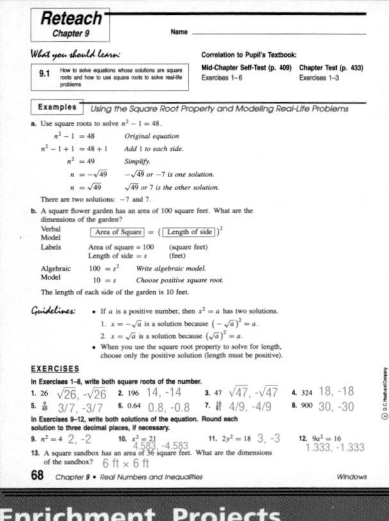

Enrichment Projects

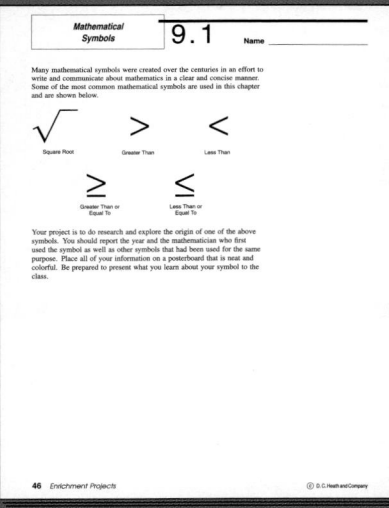

Math Log

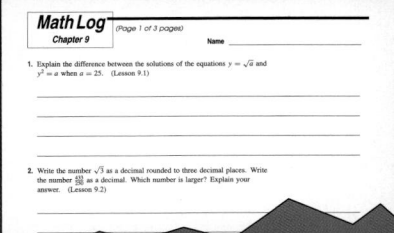

Special Populations

Suggestions for providing equal access for:

Students Acquiring English Proficiency*

The word problems in Lesson 9.4 may need further explanation. These students will benefit from working in groups of students with mixed reading skills to complete the exercises.

The use of the word *leg* in reference to a right triangle may be confusing to these students. Other terms that may need explaining include *terminating, hypotenuse,* and *theorem.*

Students with Various Learning Styles*

Incorporate the use of geoboards as much as possible throughout this chapter, especially in Lesson Investigations 9.3 and 9.8.

Remind students what the signs $>$, $\geq$, $<$, and $\leq$ mean in Lesson 9.5. Explain that the pointed end always points to the smaller number.

*Underachieving Students

In Lesson 9.2, some students may find the concept of nonrepeating decimals confusing if they rely solely on their calculators to find the decimal equivalents of irrational numbers. A discussion of how calculators truncate a nonrepeating decimal, and a simple example done by hand showing a nonrepeating decimal, will help to illustrate this concept.

Some students may become frustrated with the number of rules and steps involved with solving a multistep inequality in Lesson 9.7. Working in cooperative groups where students take turns performing the steps may benefit these students.

Gifted and Talented Students*

Briefly discuss with students roots other than square roots. Explain that 8 is called a perfect cube because $2 \cdot 2 \cdot 2 = 8$ and 2 is called the cube root (or third root) of 8. Have students find other perfect cubes and their cube roots. Have students extend the activity by finding fourth roots.

*See page T19 for descriptions of these special populations.

CHAPTER 9 OVERVIEW

Real Numbers and Inequalities

PACING CHART

Lesson	Basic/ Average Course	Above Average Course	Advanced Course
9.1	2 days	1 day	1 day
9.2	2 days	1 day	1 day
9.3	2 days	1 day	1 day
9.4	2 days	1 day	1 day
9.5	0 days	1 day	1 day
9.6	0 days	1 day	1 day
9.7	0 days	1 day	1 day
9.8	0 days	1 day	1 day

About the Chapter

Lesson 9.1 introduces students to the square root property in the context of solving an equation in x^2. Students are thereby taken a step beyond the skills taught in Chapter 4 in their ability to solve equations and, consequently, in their readiness to model and solve real-life problems. Also, since many square roots are irrational, students' understanding of the number line is expanded, in Lesson 9.2, to include both rational and irrational numbers.

In Lessons 9.3 and 9.4, students are introduced to one of the major topics of geometry—the Pythagorean Theorem, and to its use as a powerful tool in problem solving by indirect measurement.

Bearing in mind that the main thrust of this course is to empower students to model the real world, it is opportune at this point of the course to recognize that real-world problems cannot always be modeled with equations but require appropriate *inequalities*. Lessons 9.5, 9.6, and 9.7 are therefore concerned with the graphing, writing, and solving of inequalities more complex than those presented in Chapter 2 (Lesson 2.9). Finally, in Lesson 9.8, connections with geometry are maintained by applying inequalities to the side-lengths of a triangle.

LESSONS

Solar photovoltaic generators of electricity, like the one shown here in California, have an efficiency rating of about 15% and currently cost between 25¢ and 35¢ per electrical unit. This is double the cost of nuclear power plants and 5 to 10 times more costly than traditional power plants.

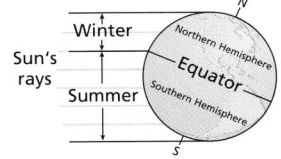

Real Life
Solar Energy

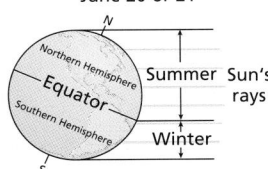

December 21 or 22

June 20 or 21

Seasonal changes affect the efficiency of solar panels. The closer to the vertical that the sun's rays strike the panel, the more solar energy they can produce. Since the Earth's axis is tilted 23.4° from the vertical, countries near the equator have the best potential for developing solar energy year round. As you move north or south from the equator, the sun's intensity decreases during the winter. In the United States, the only year-round solar energy plants are located in the Southwest.

The distance from the sun to Earth changes seasonally. (It is actually the least during our winter.) A verbal model for this information is 1.47×10^8 km is less than the distance to the sun is less than 1.52×10^8 km.

In this chapter you will learn to write inequalities and find all their real-number solutions.

389

Using the Page

In 1991, Southern California Edison and Texas Instruments reported that they had developed an inexpensive rooftop unit for the production of solar energy. With this technology, it is estimated that electricity will be produced at rates cheaper than nuclear power and comparable to electricity from coal-fired generators.

Have students investigate this new panel and its current stage of development. Ask students to report on any other new developments made in solar technology. Some students may be interested in investigating solar-powered cars.

Multimedia Resources

Interactive CD-ROM Projects A project for this chapter combines print, animation, sound and video presentations to capture students' interest in Air Traffic Controller. This interactive approach shows students how the math concepts and problem-solving strategies they are learning will be used in the future in dealing with important personal, national, and world issues.

The theme of Air Traffic Controller correlates to Lesson 9.3.

Interactions: Real Math—Real Life The theme of this chapter, Digital communications, correlates with an episode of **Interactions** which is a videodisc-based multimedia resource that connects middle school math topics with real-life careers. In each of the twelve episodes, students go on-site with a variety of professionals to witness real-life applications of the math they are studying. Students see math concepts and problem-solving strategies in a context that helps them connect what they are studying to the world outside the classroom. **Interactions** was developed by the Foundation for Advancements in Science and Education (FASE) and is published by D.C. Heath and Company.

The theme of Digital Communications is continued throughout the chapter on pages 356, 357, 365–368, 377, and 386.

Performance Assessment Resource

The PACKETS® Program: Performance Assessment for Middle School Mathematics was developed by Educational Testing Service and is published by D.C. Heath. **PACKETS** helps you assess your students' performances as they learn. You can use a wide variety of **PACKETS** Activity Units with this chapter because, in every activity, students will use ideas from all topic areas of mathematics. However, you can use the chart on page T16 to help you choose the **PACKETS** Activity Unit(s) that may fit best with this chapter.

► **PLANNING the Lesson**

Lesson Plan 9.1, p. 68

ORGANIZER

Starters (reproduced below)
Problem of the Day 9.1, p. 25
Warm-Up Exercises 9.1, p. 25
Lesson Resources
Color Transparencies,
Chapter opener, p. 36
Picture for Example 2, p. 36
Teaching Tools,
Graph paper, pp. T1, C2
Coordinate plane, pp. T8, C10
Math Log, p. 28
Answer Masters 9.1, pp. 170, 171
Extra Practice Copymaster 9.1, p. 68
Reteaching Copymaster 9.1, p. 68
Enrichment Projects, pp. 45, 46
Special Populations
Suggestions, Teacher's Edition, p. 388D

LESSON Notes

Common-Error Alert!

Students should be reminded of the special meaning of the square root sign ($\sqrt{}$) that involves only the positive value whose square is the radicand of the expression. In this context, $\sqrt{16}$ is 4, not -4, even though $-4 \cdot -4 = 16$. Finding the possible square root of a positive number is not the same as finding the value of x that satisfies the equation $x^2 = a$. In the latter case, there are two solutions, one positive and one negative.
Students should include the Square Root Property in their journals.

Example 1

Again, distinguish between the two situations: the solutions of $x^2 = 25$, and the value of $\sqrt{25}$ (in part **a**). The first expression is an equation that can be solved using the Square Root Property. There are two solutions. The second is a computation determined by the special convention requiring only the positive value whose square is 25.
The solutions to parts **a** and **b** are integer solutions. They are also referred to as exact solutions. An equation such as $x^2 = 10$ does not have an integer solution, but its exact solution is given by $\sqrt{10}$ and $-\sqrt{10}$ (no approximation of the square root is obtained).

9.1 Exploring Square Roots

What you should learn:

Goal 1 How to solve equations whose solutions are square roots

Goal 2 How to use square roots to solve real-life problems

Why you should learn it:

You can use square roots to solve real-life problems, such as finding the dimensions of a painting.

Need to Know

If a is a perfect square, then the two solutions of $x^2 = a$ can be written without using a square root symbol. For instance, the two solutions of $x^2 = 1.44$ are -1.2 and 1.2.

If a is not a perfect square, then the two solutions of $x^2 = a$ should be written with square root symbols. For instance, the two solutions of $x^2 = 10$ are $-\sqrt{10}$ and $\sqrt{10}$.

Goal 1 — Using the Square Root Property

The square at the right has an area of 16 square units. Because each side has a length of x units, it follows that

$$x^2 = 16.$$

There are two numbers whose square is 16: -4 and 4. Because length must be positive, each side of the square has a length of 4 units.

x — Area is 16 square units — x

Square Root Property

If a is a positive number, then $x^2 = a$ has two solutions.

1. $x = -\sqrt{a}$ is a solution because $(-\sqrt{a})^2 = a$.
2. $x = \sqrt{a}$ is a solution because $(\sqrt{a})^2 = a$.

Example 1 *Using Square Roots to Solve Equations*

a. $t^2 = 25$ *Original equation*

$t = -\sqrt{25}$ $-\sqrt{25}$ *or* -5 *is one solution.*

$t = \sqrt{25}$ $\sqrt{25}$ *or 5 is the other solution.*

There are two solutions: -5 and 5. You can check these by observing that $(-5)^2 = 25$ and $5^2 = 25$.

b. $x^2 + 2 = 11$ *Original equation*

$x^2 + 2 - 2 = 11 - 2$ *Subtract 2 from each side.*

$x^2 = 9$ *Simplify.*

$t = -\sqrt{9}$ $-\sqrt{9}$ *or* -3 *is one solution.*

$t = \sqrt{9}$ $\sqrt{9}$ *or 3 is the other solution.*

There are two solutions: -3 and 3. You can check these by observing that $(-3)^2 + 2 = 11$ and $3^2 + 2 = 11$. ∎

STARTER: Problem of the Day

Suppose a dartboard consists only of a 7-point area and a 3-point area. Given an unlimited supply of darts, what positive score totals are *not* possible?

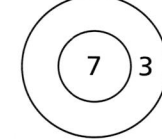

1, 2, 4, 5, 8, and 11

Also available as a copymaster, page 25

STARTER: Warm-Up Exercises

1. Evaluate
   a. 4^2 **b.** $(-2)^2$ **c.** 5^3 **d.** -3^2
   a. 16, b. 4, c. 125, d. -9
2. Solve for r.
   a. $2r = 4$ **b.** $6r = 36$ **c.** $11r = 121$
   d. $-3r = 9$ **e.** $-7r = 49$ **f.** $-8r = 64$
   a. 2, b. 6, c. 11, d. -3, e. -7, f. -8

Also available as a copymaster, page 25

Modeling Real-Life Problems

Real Life
Art

"Falling Star" was painted by
Robert Orduño, a native American
artist. It depicts the story from
Sioux mythology of Wohp̄e, the
only daughter of the Great Spirit
Wakan Tanka, failing from the sky.

Example 2 *Finding the Dimensions of a Painting*

The square painting, "Falling Star," has an area of 3600 square inches. What are the dimensions of the painting?

Solution

Verbal Model

$$\text{Area of Square} = \left(\text{length of side} \right)^2$$

Labels

Area of square = 3600   (square inches)
Length of side = s (inches)

Algebraic Model

$3600 = s^2$ *Write algebraic model.*
$60 = s$ *Choose positive square root.*

The length of each side of the painting is 60 inches. You can check this by squaring 60 to obtain 60^2 or 3600.

In Example 2, notice that s^2 is in *square* inches, which means that s is measured in inches. Here are two other examples.

1. If a square parking lot has an area of 120 *square meters*, then the length of each side of the parking lot is $\sqrt{120}$ *meters* or about 10.95 meters.

2. If a square book cover has an area of 400 *square centimeters*, then the length of each side of the cover is 20 *centimeters*.

Communicating about MATHEMATICS

▷ **SHARING IDEAS about the Lesson**

Estimation The small squares of the graph paper are each 1 square unit. Estimate the side lengths of each larger square. Explain your reasoning. Check your estimate with a calculator.

A. 4.7
B. 3.2
C. 7.5

A.
Area is 22 square units.

B.
Area is 10 square units.

C.
Area is 56 square units.

Estimates and explanations vary.

Many real-life applications of square roots can be found in building and construction occupations. Scientists also use square roots in the measurements of natural phenomena.

Example 2

Call attention to the square (the geometric figure) and the algebraic relationships among its sides. It is no coincidence that x^2 is read "x squared." Have students identify square objects in your classroom. Have them measure the sides of these objects. This provides additional opportunities for students to grasp the relationship between a square and the length of its sides.

Communicating about MATHEMATICS

Have students create the equation associated with each (geometric) square.

Writing Prompt
Write a mathematical bumper sticker using "square roots" in its slogan.

OPTION: Extra Examples

Here is an additional example similar to Example 1.
Using Square Roots to Solve Equations

$8n^2 = 128$ Original equation
$n^2 = 16$ Divide each side by 8.
$n = -\sqrt{16}$ $-\sqrt{16}$ or -4 is one solution.

$n = \sqrt{16}$ $\sqrt{16}$ or 4 is the other solution.
There are two solutions: -4 and 4. You can check these by observing that $8(-4)^2 = 128$ and $8(4)^2 = 128$.

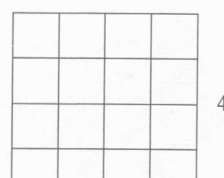
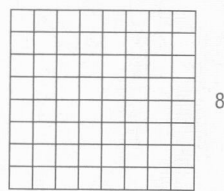
EXERCISES

Guided Practice

▶ **CHECK for Understanding**

1. Explain why $r^2 = 4$ has two solutions. $2^2 = 4$ and $(-2)^2 = 4$

In Exercises 2–5, write both square roots of the number. State whether the number is a perfect square.

2. 49 $7, -7$; yes
3. 5 $\sqrt{5}, -\sqrt{5}$; no
4. 1.21 $1.1, -1.1$; yes
5. $\frac{25}{4}$ $\frac{5}{2}, -\frac{5}{2}$; yes

6. Solve the equation $x^2 = 14$. Use a calculator to approximate the solutions to three decimal places. $3.742, -3.742$

Independent Practice

In Exercises 7–14, write both square roots of the number.

7. 14 $\sqrt{14}, -\sqrt{14}$
8. 27 $\sqrt{27}, -\sqrt{27}$
9. 64 $8, -8$
10. 169 $13, -13$
11. 0.36 $0.6, -0.6$
12. 1600 $40, -40$
13. $\frac{64}{9}$ $\frac{8}{3}, -\frac{8}{3}$
14. $\frac{49}{81}$ $\frac{7}{9}, -\frac{7}{9}$

P In Exercises 15–18, sketch the largest possible square that can be formed with the tiles. (You won't be able to use all the tiles.) How does the result help estimate the square root of a number? See margin.

15.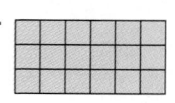
16.
17.
18.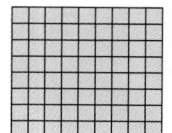

In Exercises 19–26, write both solutions of the equation. Round each solution to three decimal places, if necessary.

19. $t^2 = 9$ $3, -3$
20. $x^2 = 100$ $10, -10$
21. $p^2 = 22$ $4.690, -4.690$
22. $r^2 = 17$ $4.123, -4.12$
23. $b^2 + 2 = 27$ $5, -5$
24. $y^2 - 6 = 30$ $6, -6$
25. $3a^2 = 243$ $9, -9$
26. $4s^2 = 49$ $\frac{7}{2}, -\frac{7}{2}$

Estimation In Exercises 27–30, the small squares of the graph paper are each 1 square unit. Estimate the side lengths of the blue square. Use a calculator to confirm your estimate.

27.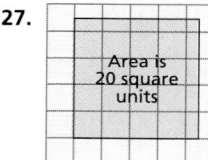
Area is 20 square units
4.5

28.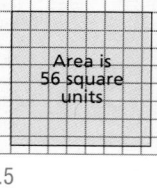
Area is 56 square units
7.5

29.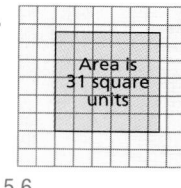
Area is 31 square units
5.6

30.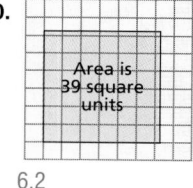
Area is 39 square units
6.2

392 Chapter **9** ▪ Real Numbers and Inequalities   P Portfolio Opportunity

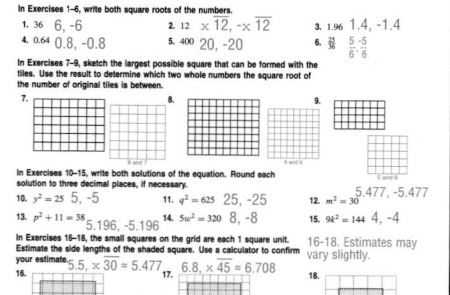

33. $a^2 + 6 = 14$, $\sqrt{8}$ and $-\sqrt{8}$ **34.** $3r^2 = 27$, 3 and -3

In Exercises 31–34, write an algebraic equation for the sentence. Then solve the equation.

31. The positive square root of 25 is x. $\sqrt{25} = x$, 5

32. y squared is 47. $y^2 = 47$, $\sqrt{47}$ and $-\sqrt{47}$

33. The sum of a squared and 6 is 14. See above.

34. The product of 3 and r squared is 27. See above.

On a Clear Day　In Exercises 35 and 36, use the following information.

On a clear day, the distance, d, in miles that you can see out to the ocean is approximated by the equation $d^2 = \frac{3}{2}h$, where h is the height in feet of your eyes above ground level.

35. You are standing on an observation deck overlooking the Atlantic Ocean. Your eyes are 10 feet above sea level. How far can you see on a clear day? ≈ 3.87 mi

36. You climb to the top of the observation tower where your eyes are 30 feet above sea level. How far can you see on a clear day? ≈ 6.71 mi

The apparent boundary of the earth and sky is called the horizon. The horizon seems nearer to an observer at ground level.

37. *Falling Objects*　The time, t, in seconds it takes an object to fall when dropped can be modeled by $-16t^2 + s = 0$, where s is the height in feet from which the object is dropped. If a ball is dropped from a height of 20 feet, how long does it take before it hits the ground? ≈ 1.12 seconds

38. *Surface Area*　The surface area of a cube is the sum of the areas of its faces. How long is each edge if the surface area is 216 square centimeters? 6 cm

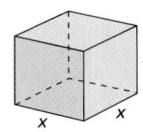

Integrated Review

39. *Estimation*　Which number best estimates 4.5^2? c

a. 9　　**b.** 16　　**c.** 20　　**d.** 25

Making Connections within Mathematics

40. *Estimation*　Which number best estimates $\left(\frac{7}{16}\right)^2$? a

a. $\frac{1}{4}$　**b.** $\frac{3}{4}$　**c.** $\frac{7}{8}$　**d.** $\frac{49}{16}$

Exploration and Extension

41. *Coordinate Patterns*　Copy and complete the table.

1.7　2　2.2　2.4　2.6　2.8　3　3.2

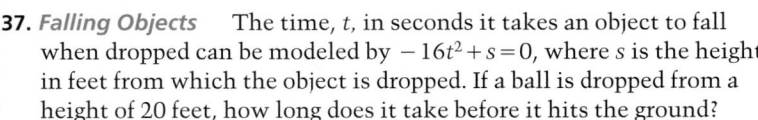

x	0	1	2	3	4	5	6	7	8	9	10
$y = \sqrt{x}$	0	1	1.4	?	?	?	?	?	?	?	?

42. Plot the data in the table in a coordinate plane. Describe the pattern.

43. Create another table for $y = -\sqrt{x}$. Plot the results in a coordinate plane and describe the pattern.
42., 43. See margin.

☼ More difficult exercises

9.1 • *Exploring Square Roots* **393**

▶ **Ex. 35, 36**　For these exercises, ask students if they have ever looked at the horizon line where the sky seems to meet the ocean.

Integrated Review

▶ **Ex. 39**　Help students understand that $4.5^2 = (4.5)^2$.

Exploration and Extension

Have students use a graphing calculator to demonstrate the graphs of $y_1 = \sqrt{x}$ and $y_2 = -\sqrt{x}$ and to verify the numerical approximations.

Portfolio Opportunity: Math Log

Explain the difference between the solutions of the equations $y = \sqrt{a}$ and $y^2 = a$ when $a = 25$.

Also available as a copymaster, page 28, Ex. 1

Answers
42.

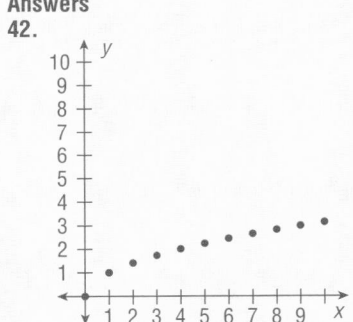

The value of y gradually increases.

43.

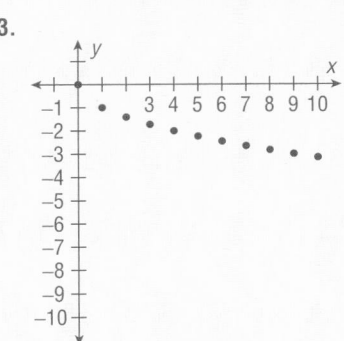

The value of y gradually decreases.

USING A CALCULATOR
Approximating Square Roots

By its definition, you know that when you square a square root of a number, you obtain the original number. For instance, 7 is a square root of 49 because $7^2 = 49$.

The number $\sqrt{49}$ can be written exactly as a decimal because 49 is a perfect square. However, many square roots cannot be written as exact decimals. For instance, no matter how many decimal places you list for $\sqrt{50}$, you will not obtain a number whose square is *exactly* 50.

Number of Decimal Places	Decimal Approximation	Check by Squaring
1	$\sqrt{50} \approx 7.1$	$(7.1)^2 = 50.41$
2	$\sqrt{50} \approx 7.07$	$(7.07)^2 = 49.9849$
3	$\sqrt{50} \approx 7.071$	$(7.071)^2 = 49.999041$
4	$\sqrt{50} \approx 7.0711$	$(7.0711)^2 = 50.00045521$
5	$\sqrt{50} \approx 7.07107$	$(7.07107)^2 = 50.0000309449$

Example *Approximating Square Roots*

Use a calculator to evaluate the square root. Round your result to three decimal places, if necessary.

a. $\sqrt{2.25}$ **b.** $\sqrt{2.2}$

Solution

a. Because 2.25 is a perfect square, you can write
$$\sqrt{2.25} = 1.5. \quad Check: 1.5^2 = 2.25$$

b. The number 2.2 is not a perfect square, so you must approximate its square root.
$$\sqrt{2.2} \approx 1.483 \quad Check: 1.483^2 = 2.199289 \approx 2.2 \quad \blacksquare$$

Exercises

In Exercises 1–8, use a calculator to decide whether the square root can be written exactly as a decimal. If it can, write the exact decimal. If it can't, round the decimal to three places.

1. $\sqrt{1.21}$ 1.1 **2.** $\sqrt{1.25}$ 1.118 **3.** $\sqrt{17}$ 4.123 **4.** $\sqrt{81}$ 9

5. $\sqrt{10,000}$ 100 **6.** $\sqrt{500}$ 22.361 **7.** $\sqrt{12.96}$ 3.6 **8.** $\sqrt{12.95}$ 3.599

9. Make a table like that above that shows how you can obtain better and better approximations of $\sqrt{30}$ by listing more and more decimal places. See margin.

Answer

9.

Number of Decimal Places	Decimal Approximation	Check by Squaring
1	$\sqrt{30} \approx 5.5$	$(5.5)^2 = 30.25$
2	$\sqrt{30} \approx 5.48$	$(5.48)^2 = 30.0304$
3	$\sqrt{30} \approx 5.477$	$(5.477)^2 = 29.997529$
4	$\sqrt{30} \approx 5.4772$	$(5.4772)^2 = 29.9997$
5	$\sqrt{30} \approx 5.47723$	$(5.47723)^2 = 30.0000$

9.2

The Real Number System

► **PACING** the Lesson

Suggested Number of Days
Basic/Average 2   **Above Average** 1
Advanced 1

► **PLANNING** the Lesson

Lesson Plan 9.2, p. 69

What you should learn:

Goal 1 How to classify real numbers as rational or irrational

Goal 2 How to represent real numbers with a number line

Why you should learn it:
Many numbers that occur in real-life problems are not rational. Some real-life problems can be modeled only with irrational numbers.

Goal 1   Classifying Real Numbers

In Lesson 6.6, you learned that a *rational number* is a number that can be written as the quotient (or ratio) of two integers. *Irrational numbers* are numbers that cannot be written as the quotient of two integers. Together, the sets of all rational numbers and irrational numbers make up the set of **real numbers.** The decimal form of a rational number either terminates or repeats. The decimal form of an irrational number does not terminate and does not repeat.

Number	Type	Decimal Form	Decimal Type
$\frac{3}{4}$	Rational	$\frac{3}{4} = 0.75$	Terminating
$\frac{1}{11}$	Rational	$\frac{1}{11} = 0.0909\ldots = 0.\overline{09}$	Repeating
$\sqrt{3}$	Irrational	$\sqrt{3} = 1.7320508\ldots$	Nonrepeating

Example 1 describes a real-life length that is irrational.

Real Life
Floor Covering

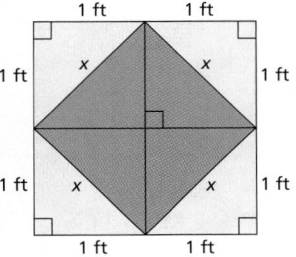

Example 1   *Measuring Sides of Triangles*

You are designing floor tiles that are right triangles. Eight of the tiles can be used to form a square that is 2 feet by 2 feet, as shown at the left. What are the lengths of the sides of each tile? Can these lengths be written exactly as decimals?

Solution   The blue square is formed by 4 tiles. The large square is formed by 8 tiles and has an area of 4 square feet. This means that the blue square must have an area of 2 square feet.

$$\text{Area of blue square} = x^2$$

$$2 = x^2$$

By solving this equation, you can conclude that x is equal to $\sqrt{2}$. Thus, each tile has side lengths of 1 foot, 1 foot, and $\sqrt{2}$ feet. A length of 1 foot can be represented exactly as a decimal, but a length of $\sqrt{2}$ feet cannot. Rounding to two decimal places, you can approximate $\sqrt{2}$ feet as

$$\sqrt{2} \approx 1.41 \text{ feet.}$$

9.2 ▪ The Real Number System   **395**

ORGANIZER

Starters (reproduced below)
 Problem of the Day 9.2, p. 25
 Warm-Up Exercises 9.2, p. 25
Lesson Resources
 Teaching Tools
  Number lines, pp. T6, C8
 Math Log, p. 28
 Answer Masters 9.2, pp. 172–174
 Extra Practice Copymaster 9.2, p. 69
 Reteaching Copymaster 9.2, p. 69
Special Populations
 Suggestions, Teacher's Edition, p. 388D

LESSON Notes

Addressing Misconceptions

Review rational numbers by looking at examples of rational numbers that terminate and those that repeat. Students may recognize the number π, which is an irrational number but does not involve radicals. Then describe a variety of irrational numbers. Have students recall that irrational numbers such as $\sqrt{3}$ and $\sqrt{5}$ neither terminate nor repeat.

Example 1

Point out to students that it can be shown that $\sqrt{2}$ cannot be written in the form $\frac{a}{b}$, but the proof is beyond the scope of this text. For now, we must accept that $\sqrt{2}$ is irrational.

Because we cannot write $-\sqrt{2}$ and $\sqrt{3}$ as rational numbers, we must approximate their values using decimals and plot these locations on the number line.

Example 2

The decimal expansion of each number allows us to compare place values to determine which number is larger. For example, $\sqrt{5} < \frac{9}{4}$ because $\sqrt{5} \approx 2.236$ and $\frac{9}{4} = 2.25$.

Communicating about MATHEMATICS

Have students use their results to order the seven numbers from smallest to largest.

Writing Prompt
Assign Ex. 45 on page 398 as a weekend essay/journal question to be collected later.

396 *Chapter 9*

Real numbers can be plotted on a number line. For example, the number line below shows the points that correspond to the real numbers $-\frac{3}{2}$, $\sqrt{2}$, -0.5, $\sqrt{3}$, and $\frac{8}{3}$.

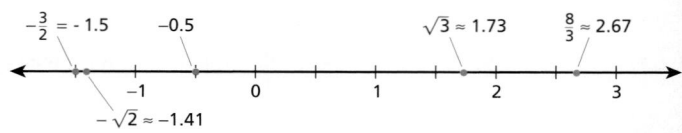

$-\frac{3}{2} = -1.5$ -0.5 $\sqrt{3} \approx 1.73$ $\frac{8}{3} \approx 2.67$

$-\sqrt{2} \approx -1.41$

To plot a real number on a number line, you could first write the number in decimal form.

Example 2   *Comparing Numbers on a Number Line*

Plot each pair of numbers. Then complete the statement with $<$, $>$, or $=$.

a. $\sqrt{5}$ $\boxed{?}$ $\frac{9}{4}$ **b.** $-\sqrt{7}$ $\boxed{?}$ $-\frac{8}{3}$ **c.** $\sqrt{\frac{9}{4}}$ $\boxed{?}$ $\frac{3}{2}$

Solution

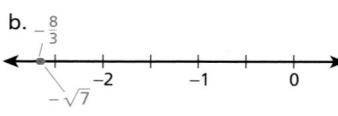

a.

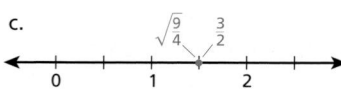

b. $-\frac{8}{3}$

$-\sqrt{7}$

c.

a. Begin by writing each number as a decimal.
$$\sqrt{5} \approx 2.236 \qquad \text{and} \qquad \frac{9}{4} = 2.25$$

Then, plot the numbers, as shown at the left. Because $\sqrt{5}$ is to the left of $\frac{9}{4}$, it follows that $\sqrt{5} < \frac{9}{4}$.

b. Begin by writing each number as a decimal: $-\sqrt{7} \approx -2.646$ and $-\frac{8}{3} \approx -2.667$. After plotting the numbers on a number line, you can conclude that $-\sqrt{7} > -\frac{8}{3}$.

c. You could begin by writing each number as a decimal. In this case, however, you may notice that $\frac{9}{4}$ is a perfect square.

Because $\left(\frac{3}{2}\right)^2 = \frac{9}{4}$, it follows that $\sqrt{\frac{9}{4}} = \frac{3}{2}$.

Communicating about MATHEMATICS

▶ **SHARING IDEAS about the Lesson**

Comparing Numbers Use a calculator to plot the set of numbers on a number line. See margin.

$$\left\{ \sqrt{\frac{3}{2}}, \, 0.83, \, -1, \, \sqrt{2}, \, -\frac{5}{4}, \, -\sqrt{3}, \, -\frac{6}{11} \right\}$$

Answer to Communicating

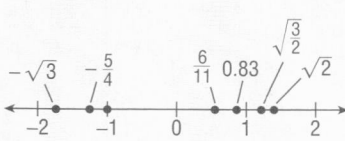

$-\sqrt{3}$ $-\frac{5}{4}$ $\frac{6}{11}$ 0.83 $\sqrt{\frac{3}{2}}$ $\sqrt{2}$

EXERCISES

Guided Practice

▶ **CHECK for Understanding**

1. *Writing*   In your own words, state the definition of a rational number. See page 395.

2. *Writing*   In your own words, explain how the decimal form of a rational number differs from the decimal form of an irrational number. See page 395.

3. State whether the number is rational. Explain your reasoning.
   a. 0.123   **b.** 0.$\overline{123}$ **c.** 0.123714356…

   a. Yes, the decimal terminates.
   b. Yes, the decimal repeats.
   c. No, the decimal neither terminates nor repeats.

In Exercises 4–7, state whether the number is rational or irrational.

4. $\frac{8}{2}$ Rational   5. $\sqrt{5}$ Irrational   6. $\sqrt{9}$ Rational   7. $-\sqrt{\frac{16}{9}}$ Rational

8. Plot the set of numbers on a number line. $\left\{0, \frac{1}{2}, -\frac{5}{3}, -2.1, -\sqrt{4}, \sqrt{6}, -\sqrt{8}, 3\right\}$
   See margin.

Independent Practice

Number Sense   **In Exercises 9–16, determine whether the number is rational or irrational. Explain your reasoning.** For explanations, see margin.

9. $\frac{11}{5}$ Rational   10. $-\frac{21}{16}$ Rational   11. $\sqrt{10}$ Irrational   12. $-\sqrt{15}$ Irrational

13. $\sqrt{1.44}$ Rational   14. $-\sqrt{\frac{100}{36}}$ Rational   15. $-\sqrt{\frac{3}{2}}$ Irrational   16. $\sqrt{\frac{9}{6}}$ Irrational

Logical Reasoning   **In Exercises 17–20, complete the statement using *always, sometimes,* or *never*. Explain.** For explanations, see margin.

17. A real number is ? a rational number. sometimes

18. An irrational number is ? a real number. always

19. A negative integer is ? an irrational number. never

20. The square root of a number is ? an irrational number. sometimes

In Exercises 21–24, evaluate the expression for $a = 2$, $b = 4$, and $c = 9$. Is the result rational? Explain. For explanations, see margin.

21. $\sqrt{a} + \sqrt{b}$ $\sqrt{2}+2$, no   22. $\sqrt{b} - \sqrt{c}$ -1, yes   23. $\sqrt{c} \cdot \sqrt{b}$ 6, yes   24. $\sqrt{b} \div \sqrt{a}$ $\frac{2}{\sqrt{2}}$, no

In Exercises 25–30, match the number with its graph.

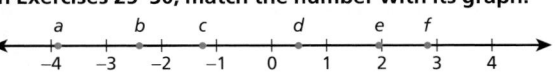

25. $\sqrt{8}$ f   26. $-\sqrt{15}$ a   27. $\frac{-\sqrt{144}}{5}$ b   28. 0.49 d   29. $\sqrt{3.8}$ e   30. $-\sqrt{\frac{25}{16}}$ c

✪ More difficult exercises
🄿 Portfolio Opportunity

9.2 ▪ *The Real Number System*   **397**

EXERCISE Notes

ASSIGNMENT GUIDE
Basic/Average:
  Day 1: Ex. 9–35 odd
  Day 2: Ex. 37–45 odd, 46, 47–51 odd
Above Average: Ex. 14–20, 21–45 odd, 46–49
Advanced: Ex. 14–20, 21–45 odd, 46–49
Selected Answers: Ex. 1–8, 9–45 odd

Guided Practice
▶ **Ex. 2**   Use this exercise to stress a fundamental distinction between rational and irrational numbers.
▶ **Ex. 8**   For this exercise, students could express each number using decimal notation.

Independent Practice
▶ **Ex. 9–20**   Before assigning these exercises, complete Ex. 46 in class.
▶ **Ex. 25–42**   For these exercises, recommend that students use a calculator.

Answers
8.

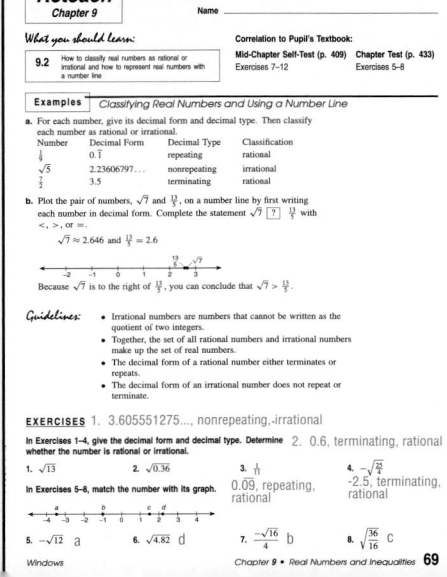

9., 10. It is the quotient of two integers.
11., 12. Its decimal form neither terminates nor repeats.
13. Its decimal form terminates.
14. It is the quotient of two integers.
15., 16. Its decimal form neither terminates nor repeats.
17., 18. Real numbers consist of rational numbers and irrational numbers.
19. All integers are rational numbers.
20. $\sqrt{9}$ is rational and $\sqrt{10}$ is irrational. (Examples vary.)
21. Decimal neither terminates nor repeats.
22., 23. Can be represented as the quotient of two integers.
24. Decimal neither terminates nor repeats.

Lesson 9.2   **397**

▶ **Ex. 45** See the suggestion in Writing Prompt, page 396.

Integrated Review

▶ **Ex. 46** Use this exercise for a 10-minute in-class overview of the different classifications of numbers.

Exploration and Extension

Using an overhead graphing calculator, graph $y = \sqrt{x}$ and check the table values for 7, 30, 50, 70, 110, and 150. Share these values with the students *after* they have made mental math estimations.

Portfolio Opportunity: Math Log

Write the number $\sqrt{3}$ as a decimal rounded to three decimal places. Write the number $\frac{433}{250}$ as a decimal. Which number is larger? Explain your answer.

Also available as a copymaster, page 28, Ex. 2

Short Quiz

Covers Lessons 9.1 and 9.2

Available as a copymaster, page 137

Alternative Assessment

A cooperative learning project that develops students' ability to compare different types of numbers.

Available as a copymaster, page 31

In Exercises 31–36, plot the number on a number line. See margin.

31. $-\frac{7}{2}$ **32.** $\frac{11}{3}$ **33.** $\sqrt{12}$

34. $-\sqrt{0.81}$ **35.** $\frac{\sqrt{3}}{2}$ **36.** $-\frac{\sqrt{30}}{3}$

In Exercises 37–42, complete the statement with <, >, or =.

37. $\sqrt{3}$? $\frac{23}{13}$ <

38. $-\sqrt{0.16}$? $-\frac{16}{41}$ <

39. $\sqrt{2.25}$? $\frac{3.6}{2.4}$ =

40. $\sqrt{\frac{49}{64}}$? $\frac{98}{112}$ =

41. $-\sqrt{2}$? $-\frac{\sqrt{19}}{3}$ >

42. $-\frac{25}{3}$? $-\frac{\sqrt{275}}{2}$ <

✪ℙ **43.** *Geometry*   Decide whether the side lengths of the shaded square can be written exactly as decimals. Explain.

✪ℙ **44.** *Carpentry*   You are helping rebuild a stairway in an apartment building. One of the boards needs to be $\sqrt{56}$ feet long. How accurately do you think the board should be measured? Explain your reasoning. **43.**, **44.** See margin.

✪ℙ **45.** *Think About It*   There are an *infinite* number of rational numbers. Do you think there are an infinite number of irrational numbers? Write a paragraph explaining your answer. Check students' work.

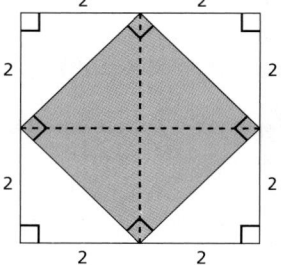

Integrated Review   *Making Connections within Mathematics*

ℙ **46.** *Venn Diagram*   Copy the table. In your copy of the table, use check marks to indicate all the labels that describe the numbers. The Venn diagram can help you make your decisions. See Additional Answers.

	Natural	Whole	Integers	Rational	Irrational	Real
-5						
$\frac{15}{12}$						
$\sqrt{9}$						
$-\sqrt{\frac{6}{5}}$						
$\sqrt{11}$						
0						

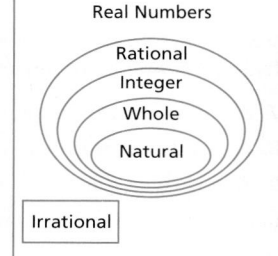

Exploration and Extension

Estimating Square Roots   **In Exercises 47–52, estimate the square root.** For example, $\sqrt{10}$ is greater than 3.1 (because $3.1^2 = 9.61$), but less than 3.2 (because $3.2^2 = 10.24$). Use a calculator to check your estimate.

✪ **47.** $\sqrt{7}$ 2.6

✪ **48.** $\sqrt{30}$ 5.5

✪ **49.** $\sqrt{50}$ 7.1

✪ **50.** $\sqrt{70}$ 8.4

✪ **51.** $\sqrt{110}$ 10.5

✪ **52.** $\sqrt{150}$ 12.2

✪ More difficult exercises
ℙ Portfolio Opportunity

▶ **Enrichment**

Have students find two solutions to the equation $x^2 = x$.   0, 1

Answers
31.–36.

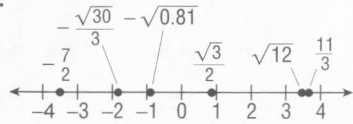

43. No. The area of the shaded square is half the area of the larger square, or 8. So each side length of the shaded square is $\sqrt{8}$. $\sqrt{8}$ is an irrational number, so its decimal form neither terminates nor repeats.

44. To the nearest quarter of an inch.
$\sqrt{56}$ ft ≈ 7.4833 ft ≈ 89.7998 in. $\approx 89\frac{3}{4}$ in.

Materials Needed: metric dot paper, metric ruler

Example *Exploring Right Triangles*

Use metric dot paper to draw a right triangle. Label the sides a, b, and c. Draw a square along each of the sides. Compare the areas of the squares. What can you conclude?

Solution Draw a right triangle, as shown below at the left. Next, draw a square along each side. From the dot pattern, you know that $a = 2$ centimeters and $b = 3$ centimeters. Using a metric ruler, you can approximate the length of the third side to be $c \approx 3.6$ centimeters. The areas of the squares are

$$a^2 = 2^2 = 4, \quad b^2 = 3^2 = 9, \quad \text{and} \quad c^2 \approx 3.6^2 = 12.96.$$

For this triangle, $a^2 + b^2$ is close to the approximation of c^2.

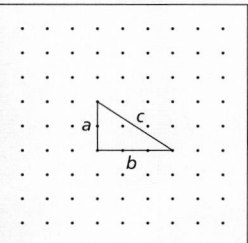
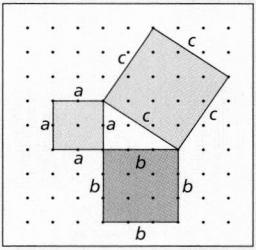

Exercises

In Exercises 1 and 2, copy the triangle and squares on metric dot paper. Compare the values of a^2, b^2, and c^2.

1.

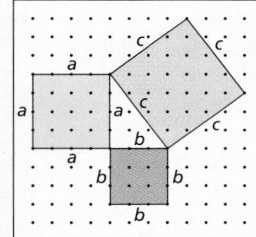

$a^2 = 16$,
$b^2 = 9$,
$c^2 = 5^2 = 25$;
$a^2 + b^2 = c^2$

2.

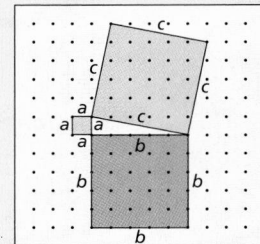

$a^2 = 1$,
$b^2 = 25$,
$c^2 = 5.1^2 = 26.01$;
$a^2 + b^2 \approx c^2$

3. Repeat the procedure described in the example for several other triangles. What can you conclude? Check students' work. $a^2 + b^2 \approx c^2$

INVESTIGATION Notes

Materials
Teaching Tools
  Dot paper, pp. T2, C3
  Ruler, pp. T12, C18

Use this investigation to help students visually explore the nature of the Pythagorean Theorem.

EXTENSION
Have students draw a right triangle, $\triangle ABC$, on graph paper. They can cut out the squares of sides a and b, respectively, and use pieces of these squares to cover the square of side c. They can thus verify if $a^2 + b^2$ does, in fact, equal c^2.

PACING the Lesson

Suggested Number of Days
Basic/Average 2   Above Average 1
Advanced 1

PLANNING the Lesson

Lesson Plan 9.3, p. 70

ORGANIZER

Starters (reproduced below)
Problem of the Day 9.3, p. 25
Warm-Up Exercises 9.3, p. 25
Lesson Resources
Teaching Tools, ruler, pp. T12, C18
Math Log, pp. 28, 29
Technology, p. 51
Answer Masters 9.3, pp. 175, 176
Extra Practice Copymaster 9.3, p. 70
Reteaching Copymaster 9.3, p. 70
Enrichment Projects, pp. 47, 48
Special Populations
Suggestions, Teacher's Edition, p. 388D

LESSON Notes

The Pythagorean Theorem was used by the ancient Egyptians to survey the Nile and build the pyramids. It is one of the most celebrated theorems in all of mathematics. Students should record this important relationship in their math journals.

Example 1

It may be interesting for students to look at local maps to see if any of the roads or streets in their community form right angles.

9.3 The Pythagorean Theorem

What you should learn:

 Goal 1 How to use the Pythagorean Theorem

Goal 2 How to solve a right triangle

Why you should learn it:

You can use the Pythagorean Theorem to solve real-life problems, such as finding a driving distance.

Goal 1   Using the Pythagorean Theorem

A right triangle is a triangle that has a right angle (one whose measure is 90°). The sides that form the right angle are the **legs** of the triangle, and the other side is the **hypotenuse.** The small square in the corner indicates which angle is the right angle.

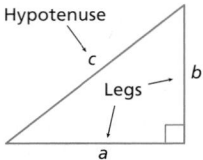

In the Lesson Investigation on page 399, you may have discovered a rule that is true of all right triangles. The rule is called the **Pythagorean Theorem,** and it is named after the Greek mathematician Pythagoras (about 585–500 B.C.).

> **Pythagorean Theorem**
>
> For any right triangle, the sum of the squares of the lengths of the legs, a and b, equals the square of the length of the hypotenuse, c.
>
> $a^2 + b^2 = c^2$ *Pythagorean Theorem*

Real Life
Distance

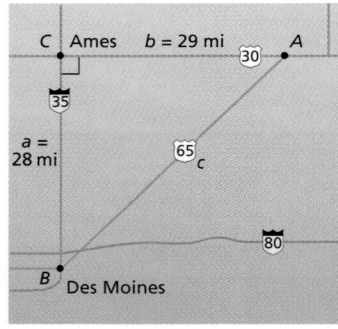

Example 1   *Finding a Hypotenuse Length*

From the Highway 65 junction, you drive on Highway 30 to Ames, Iowa. Then, you turn south and drive on Highway 35 to Des Moines. How many miles of driving would you have saved if you had driven on Highway 65 to Des Moines?

Solution On the map, $\triangle ABC$ is a right triangle.

$$\begin{aligned}
a^2 + b^2 &= c^2 && \textit{Pythagorean Theorem} \\
28^2 + 29^2 &= c^2 && \textit{Substitute for a and b.} \\
1625 &= c^2 && \textit{Simplify.} \\
\sqrt{1625} &= c && \textit{Square Root Property} \\
40.3 &\approx c && \textit{Use a calculator.}
\end{aligned}$$

The distance along Highway 65 is about 40.3 miles. You would have saved $(28 + 29) - 40.3$ or about 16.7 miles.

400   *Chapter 9 • Real Numbers and Inequalities*

Goal 2 Solving a Right Triangle

Using the lengths of two sides of a right triangle to find the length of the third side is called **solving a right triangle.** For instance, in Example 1 you used the lengths of the legs to find the length of the hypotenuse. Example 2 shows how to use the lengths of the hypotenuse and one of the legs to find the length of the other leg.

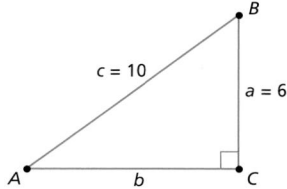

Connections
Geometry

Example 2 Solving a Right Triangle

a. In $\triangle ABC$, $c = 10$ and $a = 6$. You can use the Pythagorean Theorem to find the length of the other leg.

$$a^2 + b^2 = c^2 \quad \textit{Pythagorean Theorem}$$
$$6^2 + b^2 = 10^2 \quad \textit{Substitute for a and c.}$$
$$36 + b^2 = 100 \quad \textit{Simplify.}$$
$$b^2 = 64 \quad \textit{Subtract 36 from each side.}$$
$$b = 8 \quad \textit{Square Root Property}$$

The length of the other leg is 8.

b. $\triangle DEF$, is **isosceles,** which means that its legs have the same length. The hypotenuse has a length of 8. You can use the Pythagorean Theorem to find the length of each leg.

$$d^2 + e^2 = f^2 \quad \textit{Pythagorean Theorem}$$
$$d^2 + d^2 = 8^2 \quad \textit{Substitute d for e and 8 for f.}$$
$$2d^2 = 64 \quad \textit{Simplify.}$$
$$d^2 = 32 \quad \textit{Divide each side by 2.}$$
$$d = \sqrt{32} \quad \textit{Square Root Property}$$
$$d \approx 5.66 \quad \textit{Use a calculator.}$$

Each leg has a length of about 5.66 units. ∎

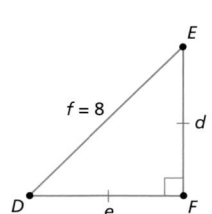

Cooperative Learning

Communicating about MATHEMATICS

▶ **SHARING IDEAS about the Lesson**

Pythagorean Triples A set of three natural numbers that represent the lengths of the sides of a right triangle is called a **Pythagorean Triple.** For instance, in Example 2a, the natural numbers 6, 8, and 10 form a Pythagorean Triple. With your partner, find other examples of Pythagorean Triples. Answers vary.

P Portfolio Opportunity

9.3 ▪ *The Pythagorean Theorem* **401**

Vocabulary Alert!
Have students include the phrase "solving a right triangle" with its definition in their math journals.

Example 2
Remind students that they have already solved equations similar to these in Lesson 1.3.

Communicating about MATHEMATICS

INVESTIGATION
The numbers 6, 8, 10 are Pythagorean Triples. Ask students whether multiples of these numbers also are Pythagorean Triples. Yes Have students test their conjecture with other triples.

Writing Prompt
Explain what is most important to understand about the Pythagorean Theorem.

Lesson 9.3 **401**

ASSIGNMENT GUIDE

Basic/Average:
  Day 1: Ex. 5–8, 9–25 odd, 30
  Day 2: Ex. 27–29, 31–35, 39–42
Above Average: Ex. 5–8, 13–16, 25–29, 32,
    37–42
Advanced: Ex. 5–8, 13–16, 25–29, 32, 37–42
Selected Answers: Ex. 1–4, 5–37 odd

Guided Practice

▶ **Ex. 2** In this exercise, students may not remember that the sum of the degree measures of the angles of a triangle is 180.
▶ **Ex. 3, 4** Use these exercises as a closing in-class small-group activity.
See also the note on Exploration and Extension on page 403.

Independent Practice

▶ **Ex. 5–8** For these exercises, ask students to explain their reasoning.
▶ **Ex. 9–14** Encourage students to draw a diagram.
▶ **Ex. 15–22** Students can use graph paper or dot paper to actually draw and approximate lengths. This could be done as a 10-minute in-class activity.

Guided Practice

▶ **CHECK for Understanding**

1. Draw a right triangle. Label its legs m and n and its hypotenuse t. How are the legs and hypotenuse related by the Pythagorean Theorem? $m^2 + n^2 = t^2$

2. Can a right triangle have an obtuse angle? Explain. No, explanations vary.

P In Exercises 3 and 4, a and b are the lengths of the legs of a right triangle and c is the length of the hypotenuse. Draw the right triangle on graph paper and estimate the missing length. Then use the Pythagorean Theorem to confirm your estimate.

3. $a = 3, b = \boxed{?}, c = 5$ 4

4. $a = 6, b = 7, c = \boxed{?}$ 9.2

Independent Practice

Logical Reasoning In Exercises 5–8, decide whether the statement is *sometimes*, *always*, or *never* true.

✪ 5. The Pythagorean Theorem can be applied to a triangle that is not a right triangle. Never

✪ 6. The hypotenuse is the longest side of a right triangle. Always

✪ 7. The legs of a right triangle are the same length. Sometimes

✪ 8. In a right triangle, if a and b are integers, then c is an integer. Sometimes

In Exercises 9–14, a and b are the lengths of the legs of a right triangle, and c is the length of the hypotenuse. Find the missing length.

9. $a = 7, b = 11$ ≈ 13.04 10. $a = 16, c = 34$ 30   11. $b = 12, c = 15$ 9

12. $a = 6, c = 16.16$ ≈ 15.00 13. $b = 42, c = 43.17$ ≈ 9.98 14. $a = 18, b = 28$ ≈ 33.29

In Exercises 15–22, if possible, draw a right triangle whose sides have the given lengths. Only 15, 16, and 20 are possible. See Additional Answers.

15. 8, 15, 17   16. 5, 12, 13   17. 9, 38, 41   18. 13, 36, 40

19. 7, 24, 26   20. 20, 21, 29   21. 30, 180, 181   22. 12, 35, 38

In Exercises 23–26, find the length of the third side.

23.

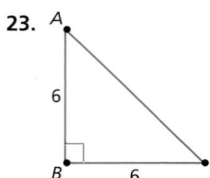

24.

25.

26.

≈8.49   7   36   ≈10.30

402 Chapter 9 ▪ Real Numbers and Inequalities

✪ More difficult exercis
P Portfolio Opportunity

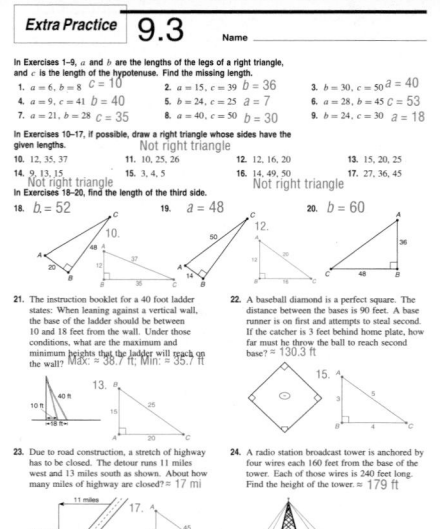
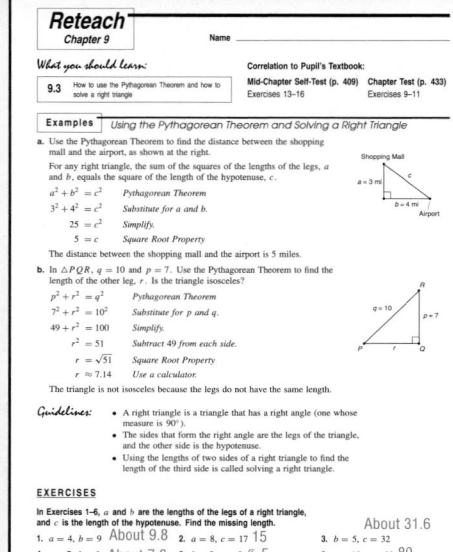

Volleyball   **In Exercises 27–29, use the following infor-**
mation.

You are setting up a volleyball net. To stay each pole, you use two ropes and two stakes as shown at the right.

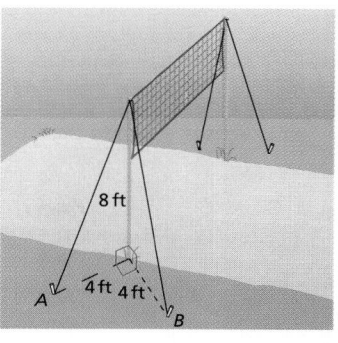

27. How long is each piece of rope? ≈ 8.944 ft

28. Estimate the total length of the rope needed to stay both poles. ≈ 35.78 ft

29. What is the distance between the stakes marked *A* and *B*? ≈ 5.66 ft

30. *Visiting Friends*   You ride your bike to your friend's house. You take the back roads as shown on the map at the right. How many miles would you have saved if you had traveled through town? ≈ 3.78

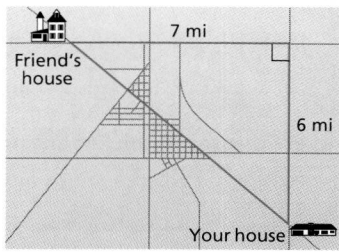

Drawing Right Triangles   **In Exercises 31 and 32, you are given the lengths of two sides of a right triangle. Draw two *different* sizes of right triangles that have these side lengths and find the length of the third side.**

31. 8, 10   **32.** 5, 6   For drawings, see Additional Answers.

3rd sides: 6, ≈12.8   3rd sides: ≈3.3, ≈7.8

Integrated Review   *Making Connections within Mathematics*

Coordinate Graphing   **In Exercises 33–38, plot the points in a coordinate plane. Decide whether the points can be connected to form a right triangle. If they can, find the lengths of the sides of the right triangle.** For plots, see Additional Answers.

33. (1, 2), (−3, 2), (−3, −5) Yes; 4, 7, ≈ 8.06   **34.** (0, 1), (4, 1), (2, 2) No

35. (2, 0), (−2, 0), (0, 1) No   **36.** (−3, 1), (−3, −3), (3, −3) Yes; 4, 6, ≈ 7.21

37. (5, 1), (5, 4), (2, 3) No   **38.** (4, 0), (−5, 0), (−5, −5) Yes; 5, 9, ≈10.30

Exploration and Extension

Area of a Trapezoid   **In Exercises 39–42, use the diagram at the right and the following information.**

The area of a trapezoid is $A = \frac{1}{2}(b_1 + b_2) \cdot h$.

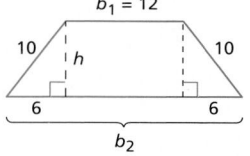

39. Find the base length, b_2. 24 units

40. Find the height, *h*. 8 units

41. Use the formula given above to find the area of the trapezoid. 144 units²

42. Find the area of the trapezoid in another way and compare your result to the area found in Exercise 41. 2(24) + 96 = 144 units²

9.3 ▪ *The Pythagorean Theorem*   **403**

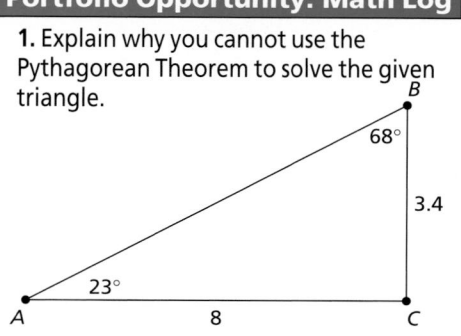
Lesson 9.3 **403**

In Exercises 1–4, find the side length of the square with the given area. (9.1)

1. 68 square units
 ≈ 8.25 units

2. 121 square units
 11 units

3. 31.36 square units
 5.6 units

4. 53.29 square units
 7.3 units

In Exercises 5–8, solve the right triangle. (9.3)

5.
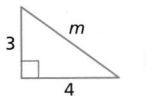

6.
≈ 8.94

7.
131.22 ≈ 92.79

8.
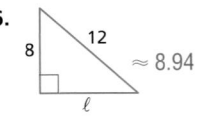

In Exercises 9–12, solve the inequality. (2.9)

9. $x + 2 \geq 9$ $x \geq 7$

10. $2p < 14$ $p < 7$

11. $5n > 8$ $n > \frac{8}{5}$

12. $y - 7 \leq 4$ $y \leq 11$

In Exercises 13–16, find the greatest common factor. (6.3)

13. 24 and 39   3

14. 88 and 60   4

15. $100x$ and $222y$ 2

16. 9, 12, 15   3

Career Interview

Solar Consultant and Construction Contractor

Michael A. Coca owns his own company, San Miguel Sun Dwellings, where he teaches others how to improve their homes with solar energy.

Q: What types of math do you use on your job?

A: In order to determine the best way to improve the heating system of a house or business, heat-load analysis must be performed. This requires estimating how many square feet of different materials will be needed and drawing a one-dimensional scaled model of the construction.

Q: What led you to this career?

A: It was exciting to be at the beginning of a new technology. I wanted to use what I learned to help people with the basic necessities of life, particularly shelter.

Q: What would you like to tell kids who are in school?

A: Education is not just about learning math, English, science, and social studies. It is about learning how to live. Many of you have a vision of how you want to live when you grow up—you want to own a home, have a family, own a car, etc. In order to make that vision a reality, you must learn what it takes to get there.

9.4

Problem Solving Using the Pythagorean Theorem

 What you should learn:

How to use properties of triangles to solve real-life problems

Goal 2
How to use the Pythagorean Theorem to measure indirectly

Why you should learn it:

You can use properties of triangles to solve real-life problems, such as finding the area of a park.

 *Real Life*
City Planning

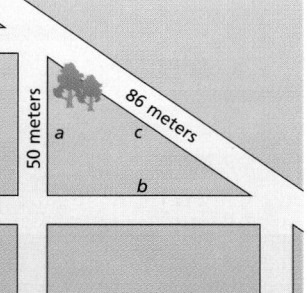

Goal 1 Modeling Real-Life Problems

You have now studied four properties of triangles.

- *Perimeter* The perimeter of a triangle is the sum of the lengths of its sides.
- *Area* The area of a triangle is one-half the product of its base and its height.
- *Similar Triangles* The ratios of corresponding sides of similar triangles are equal.
- *Pythagorean Theorem* In a right triangle, the sum of the squares of the lengths of the legs is equal to the square of the length of the hypotenuse.

In many real-life problems, you may need to use two or more of these properties to solve the problem.

Example 1 *Finding Area and Perimeter*

You are planning a city park as shown at the left. The park has the shape of a right triangle. You have measured one of the legs to be 50 meters and have measured the hypotenuse to be 86 meters. Do you need to take additional measurements to determine the perimeter and area of the park?

Solution Using the two measurements you already have, you can use the Pythagorean Theorem to find the length of the other leg.

$$a^2 + b^2 = c^2 \qquad \textit{Pythagorean Theorem}$$
$$50^2 + b^2 = 86^2 \qquad \textit{Substitute for a and c.}$$
$$2500 + b^2 = 7396 \qquad \textit{Simplify.}$$
$$b^2 = 4896 \qquad \textit{Subtract 2500 from each side.}$$
$$b = \sqrt{4896} \qquad \textit{Square Root Property}$$
$$b \approx 70 \qquad \textit{Use a calculator.}$$

Thus the perimeter of the park is about $50 + 86 + 70$ or 206 meters, and the approximate area is

$$\text{Area} = \tfrac{1}{2}ab = \tfrac{1}{2}(50)(70) = 1750 \text{ square meters.} \qquad \blacksquare$$

9.4 • *Problem Solving Using the Pythagorean Theorem* **405**

▶ **PACING** the Lesson

Suggested Number of Days
Basic/Average 2 **Above Average** 1
Advanced 1

▶ **PLANNING** the Lesson

Lesson Plan 9.4, p. 71

ORGANIZER

Starters (reproduced below)
   Problem of the Day 9.4, p. 26
   Warm-Up Exercises 9.4, p. 26
Lesson Resources
   Color Transparencies,
      Picture for Example 2, p. 37
      Diagram for Ex. 1, 2, p. 37
   Math Log, p. 29
   Technology, p. 52
   Answer Masters 9.4, p. 178
   Extra Practice Copymaster 9.4, p. 71
   Reteaching Copymaster 9.4, p. 71
Special Populations
   Suggestions, Teacher's Edition, p. 388D

LESSON Notes

Ask students to restate the four properties of triangles using labeled diagrams. Then have them describe situations in which we would use these relationships.

Example 1

Point out that the leg of 50 meters and the hypotenuse of 86 meters were measured *directly*. Ask students to indicate how, in real life, these measurements might have been made. The measure of the other leg and the area of the triangle were obtained *indirectly* using measurements of the other parts of the triangle and right triangle relationships.

STARTER: Problem of the Day
Find the product of the only set of three consecutive prime numbers that differ by 2. $3 \times 5 \times 7 = 105$

Also available as a copymaster, page 26

STARTER: Warm-Up Exercises
1. Solve for *m*. **a.** $m^2 = 121$ **b.** $m^2 = 225$ **c.** $m^2 = 1.96$ **a.** ± 11, **b.** ± 15, **c.** ± 1.4 **2.** Compute. **a.** $3^2 + 8^2$ **b.** $17^2 + 6^2$ **c.** $23^2 + 42^2$ **a.** 73, **b.** 325, **c.** 2293

Also available as a copymaster, page 26

Real Life
Street Maintenance

This huge sinkhole appeared in Atlanta, Georgia in June 1993. The sinkhole was over a hundred feet wide.

Goal 2 — Indirect Measurement

In Lesson 8.3, you learned how to use ratios of corresponding sides of similar triangles to indirectly measure the height of a tree or a building. The Pythagorean Theorem can also be used to measure objects indirectly.

Example 2 — *Using the Pythagorean Theorem*

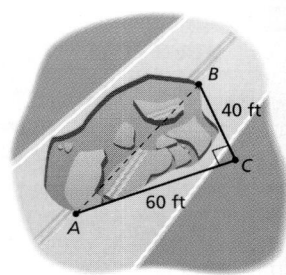

You work on a street maintenance crew for a city. Part of the street has caved in, as shown at the right. You don't have any ropes or tape measures that are long enough to stretch across the hole. Explain how you could measure the distance across the hole indirectly.

Solution Here is one way to solve the problem. Mark the vertices of a right triangle whose hypotenuse is the distance across the hole. Measure the legs of the right triangle, as shown in the figure. Then, use the Pythagorean Theorem to find the length of the hypotenuse.

$$a^2 + b^2 = c^2 \qquad \textit{Pythagorean Theorem}$$
$$40^2 + 60^2 = c^2 \qquad \textit{Substitute for a and b.}$$
$$1600 + 3600 = c^2 \qquad \textit{Simplify.}$$
$$5200 = c^2 \qquad \textit{Simplify.}$$
$$\sqrt{5200} = c \qquad \textit{Square Root Property}$$
$$72.1 \approx c \qquad \textit{Use a calculator.}$$

The distance across the hole is about 72.1 feet.

P ## *Communicating* about MATHEMATICS

▷ **SHARING IDEAS about the Lesson**

Indirect Measurement The three strawberries on this page form the vertices of a right triangle. Use a ruler to measure the two legs. Then *indirectly* find the length of the hypotenuse. Then measure the hypotenuse *directly* to check your result. See margin.

Answer to Communicating

AC	BC	AB computed	AB measured
$6\frac{1}{4}$ in.	$5\frac{3}{8}$ in.	≈ 8.243 in.	$8\frac{1}{4}$ in.
15.8 cm	13.6 cm	≈ 20.847 cm	20.9 cm

EXERCISES

Guided Practice

CHECK for Understanding

. **Drawing Triangles** Draw sketches to illustrate the four properties of triangles that you have studied in this course. *Check students' work.*

. **Playground** You are designing a neighborhood playground that has the shape of a right triangle, as shown at the right. You have measured one of the legs to be 45 meters and the hypotenuse to be 75 meters. Do you need to take additional measurements to determine the perimeter and the area of the playground? Explain. *No*
For explanation, see margin.

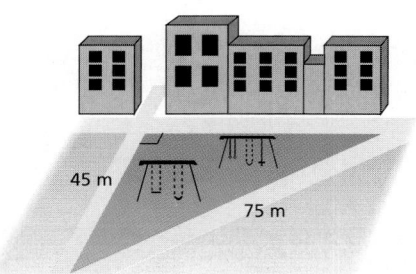

45 m
75 m

Independent Practice

Exercises 3–6, find the perimeter and area of the figure.

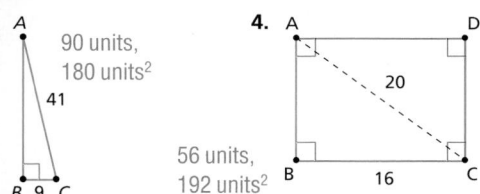

. **A** 90 units, 180 units² 41 B 9 C

4. A D 20 56 units, 192 units² B 16 C

5. 8 units, 4 units² A D √8 B C

6. 36 units, 54 units² A 10 D 5 3 B E C

. **Walking in the City** Your apartment is 6 blocks from your friend's apartment and 8 blocks from your cousin's apartment, as shown at the right. Each block is 500 feet long. You are walking from your friend's apartment to your cousin's apartment. Is the walk at least one mile? Explain your reasoning. *No; For explanation, see margin.*

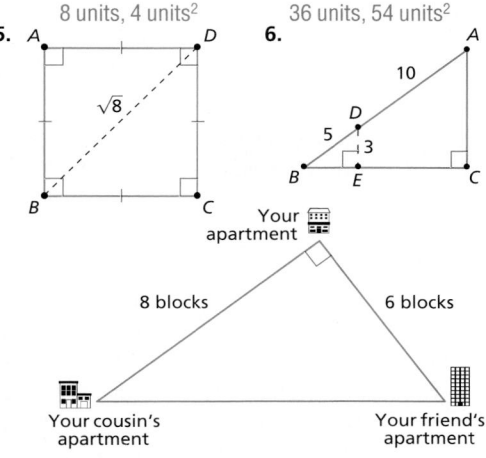

Your apartment
8 blocks
6 blocks
Your cousin's apartment
Your friend's apartment

. **Camping** You are setting up a camping tent, as shown below. What is the tallest that a person could be to stand in the tent? Explain your reasoning. *6 ft*
For explanation, see margin.

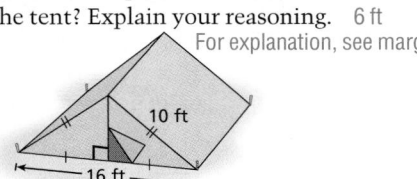

10 ft
16 ft

9. Tree Height How tall is the tree shown below? Explain your reasoning. *12 ft,* $\frac{21}{t} = \frac{16+12}{16}$,

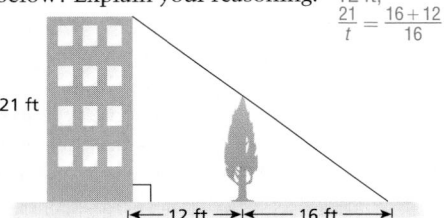

21 ft
12 ft 16 ft

9.4 ▪ Problem Solving Using the Pythagorean Theorem **407**

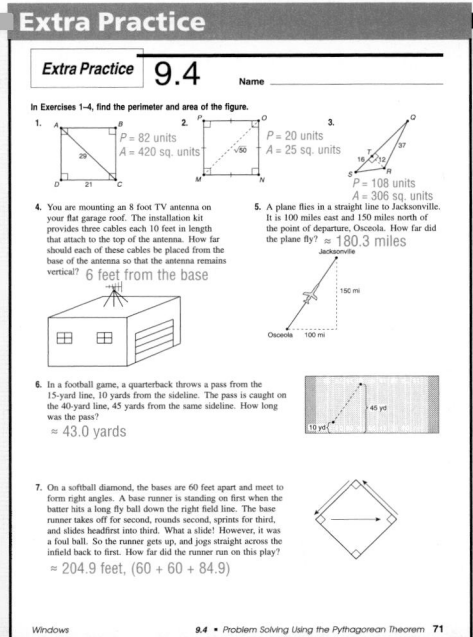

▶ **Ex. 12–14** Assign these as an in-class small-group activity. Encourage the investigation of multiples of other types of triples such as 5, 12, 13 or 8, 15, 17.

Exploration and Extension

Before assigning these exercises, discuss the word *converse* with students.
▶ **Ex. 16–19** Encourage the use of calculators for these exercises.

Portfolio Opportunity: Math Log

Explain how to find the perimeter of the right triangle $\triangle ABC$. What is the perimeter of $\triangle ABC$?

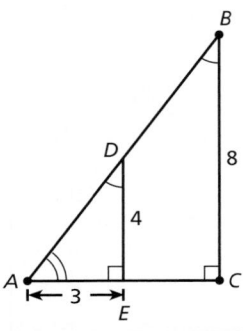

Also available as a copymaster, page 29, Ex. 5

Short Quiz

Covers Lessons 9.3 and 9.4

Available as a copymaster, page 138

Alternative Assessment

A cooperative learning project that develops students' understanding of map scales.

Available as a copymaster, page 32

Answer
12. To get the next set of Pythagorean Triples, name the next consecutive multiples of the three numbers.

---

10. *Flying a Kite* You are flying a kite. You have let out 2000 feet of string. The sun is directly overhead and is casting a shadow that is 1325 feet from you. How high is the kite? ≈1498 ft

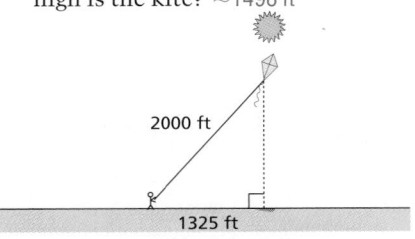

2000 ft

1325 ft

11. *Swimming* It takes you 10 seconds to swim the length of the pond shown below. How fast (in feet per second) did you swim? $2\frac{1}{2}$ ft per second

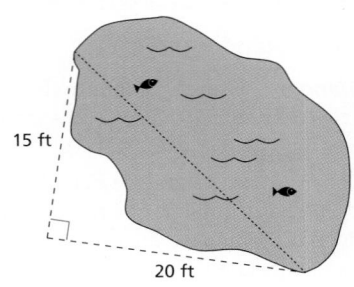

15 ft

20 ft

Integrated Review

Making Connections within Mathematics

Pythagorean Triples In Exercises 12–14, use the table at the right that shows some Pythagorean Triples.

12. Describe the pattern. See margin.

13. Find the next 3 Pythagorean Triples of the table.

P 14. *Think about It* If the table were extended indefinitely, would it contain all the possible Pythagorean Triples? If not, list some triples that would not appear in the table.
No. 5, 12, 13; 8, 15, 17

a	b	c	$a^2 + b^2 = c^2$
3	4	5	$3^2 + 4^2 = 5^2$
6	8	10	$6^2 + 8^2 = 10^2$
9	12	15	$9^2 + 12^2 = 15^2$
12	16	20	$12^2 + 16^2 = 20^2$
15	20	25	
18	24	30	
21	28	35	

Exploration and Extension

✪ **15.** *The Converse of the Pythagorean Theorem* The ancient Egyptians used a rope with equally spaced knots, as shown at the right. When the rope was held tight as shown, they concluded that the triangle was a right triangle. Which of the following results were they using? Explain your reasoning.

  a. **Pythagorean Theorem** In a right triangle, the sum of the squares of the leg lengths is equal to the square of the hypotenuse length.

  b. **Converse of the Pythagorean Theorem** In a triangle, if the sum of the squares of two side lengths is equal to the square of the third side length, then the triangle is a right triangle.
  b; $3^2 + 4^2 = 5^2$, so the triangle is a right triangle.

Converse of the Pythagorean Theorem In Exercises 16–19, you are given the lengths of the sides of a triangle. From the given information, can you find the area of the triangle? Explain your reasoning.

✪ **16.** 4, 5, 6 No, not a right triangle
✪ **17.** 5, 12, 13 Yes, is a right triangle; 30 units^2
✪ **18.** 6, 8, 10 Yes, is a right triangle; 24 units^2
✪ **19.** 5, 7, 9 No, not a right triangle

✪ More difficult exercises
P Portfolio Opportunity

▶ **Enrichment**

Have students use a library search to locate historical information about the Pythagorean Theorem. Have them research such questions as: How was the theorem named? Where did it originate? Why is it so useful? How many proofs of the theorem exist? Which president of the United States was a mathematician who wrote an original proof of this famous theorem?

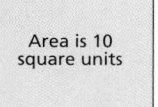
Take this test as you would take a test in class. The answers to the exercises are given in the back of the book.

In Exercises 1–4, find both square roots of the number. (9.1)

1. 16 $4, -4$

2. 121 $11, -11$

3. 0.49 $0.7, -0.7$

4. 0.36 $0.6, -0.6$

In Exercises 5 and 6, find the side lengths of the squares. (9.1)

5.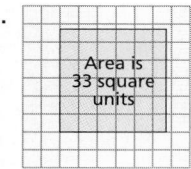
Area is 10 square units   ≈3.16 units

6.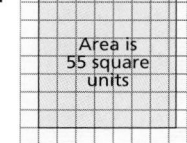
Area is 79.21 square units   8.9 units

In Exercises 7 and 8, the small squares are each 1 square unit. Estimate the side lengths of the larger square. (9.1)

7.
Area is 33 square units   ≈5.7 units

8.
Area is 55 square units   ≈7.4 units

In Exercises 9–12, explain whether the number is rational or irrational. (9.2) For explanations, see margin.

9. $\sqrt{250}$ Irrational

10. $\sqrt{25}$ Rational

11. $\sqrt{2.5}$ Irrational

12. $\sqrt{0.25}$ Rational

In Exercises 13–16, solve the triangle. Round your result to 2 decimal places. (9.3)

13.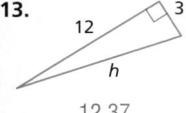
12 3 h
12.37

14.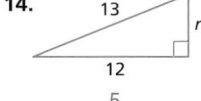
13 r 12 5

15.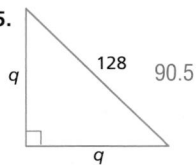
q 128 90.51 q

16.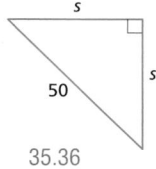
s 50 s 35.36

In Exercises 17–19, use the following information. (9.4)

You are building a bookshelf in the corner of your room, as shown to the right. The walls intersect at a right angle.

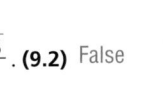
20 inches
29 inches
ℓ

17. What is the length of ℓ? 21 in.

18. What is the perimeter of the shelf? 70 in.

19. What is the area of the shelf? 210 in.²

20. *True or False?* $\sqrt{5}$ is rational because it can be written as $\dfrac{\sqrt{5}}{1}$. **(9.2)** False

---

Partner Quiz

Chapter 9
Mid-Chapter Partner Quiz   *(Use after Lesson 9.4)*
Name

1. Write an algebraic equation for the sentence and approximate the solutions to three decimal places. The difference of x squared and 4 is 8. (9.1)
   1. $x^2 - 4 = 8$; 3.464, -3.464

2. How long are the legs of the given right triangle if the area is 98 in.²? (9.1)
   2. 14 in.

3. Which number is larger, $\sqrt{\frac{5}{8}}$ or $\frac{4}{5}$? (9.2)
   3. $\frac{4}{5}$

4. Is $2.03\overline{2}$ a rational or irrational number? (9.2)
   4. Rational

5. The hypotenuse of a right triangle has length 26. One leg has length 10. Find the length of the other leg. (9.3)
   5. 24

6. The sides of a right triangle have lengths 36, 39, and 15. Which length corresponds to the hypotenuse? (9.3)
   6. 39

7. Write the Pythagorean Theorem for the given triangle. (9.3)
   7. $i^2 = h^2 + g^2$

Use the figure to answer Exercises 8–10. (9.4)

School   5 miles   Home
2 miles
Library

8. What is the distance from your house to the library? Round your solution to 1 decimal place.
   8. 4.6 miles

9. Every day you ride from home, to school, to the library, and then home. What is your round trip distance?
   9. 11.6 miles

10. What is the area of this section of your town?
    10. 4.6 sq mi

52 *Alternative Assessment* •   © D.C. Heath and Company

Mid-Chapter Test

Mid-Chapter 9 Test Form B   Name
(Use after Lesson 9.4)   Date

In Exercises 1 and 2, find both square roots of the number. (9.1)

1. 256
   1. +16, -16

2. 0.09
   2. +0.3, -0.3

3. Find the side lengths of the square. Round your result to three decimal places. (9.1)
   Area is 47.5 square units
   3. 6.892 units

In Exercises 4 and 5, decide whether the number is rational or irrational. (9.2)

4. $\sqrt{50}$
   4. Irrational

5. $\sqrt{2.25}$
   5. Rational

In Exercises 6 and 7, solve the triangle. Round your result to three decimal places. (9.3)

6.
   10 6 m
   6. $m = 8$

7.
   9 10 n
   7. $n = 13.454$

8. A wooden plank placed 50 cm from an apartment building touches an apartment window 1.2 m (120 cm) from the ground. What is the length of the plank? (9.4)
   8. 1.3 m or 130 cm

140 *Chapter 9 • Real Numbers and Inequalities*   © D.C. Heath and Company *Windows*

Answers

9. Its decimal form neither terminates nor repeats.
10. Its decimal form terminates.
11. Its decimal form neither terminates nor repeats.
12. Its decimal form terminates.

◀ Alternative Assessment

A **Partner Quiz** assesses students' achievement and provides them with an opportunity to communicate about mathematics.
Available as a copymaster, page 52

◀ Formal Assessment

Two **Mid-Chapter Tests** of average difficulty.
Available as copymasters, pages 139, 140

Materials

Teaching Tools
  Graph paper, pp. T1, C2
  Ruler, pp. T12, C18

This investigation helps students answer the question: How do I plot or *exactly* locate an irrational number —a non-repeating, non-terminating decimal—on a number line? The Pythagorean Theorem helps to supply the answer.

Students may need instruction on the proper use of a compass.

Ask students to verify the predicted exact length located graphically by using a calculator check. For example: on a calculator, $\sqrt{20} \approx 4.472$. Did $\sqrt{20}$ graphically fall between 4 and 5? Yes.

EXTENSION

Ask students to determine a 2-digit number in which plotting the square root using the technique of this investigation results in integer values for the legs.
Example: 80, since $4^2 + 8^2 = 16 + 64 = 80$

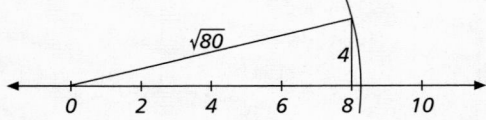

Answers
3.

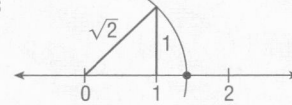

4.

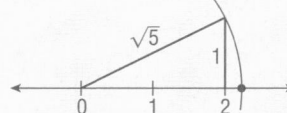

5.

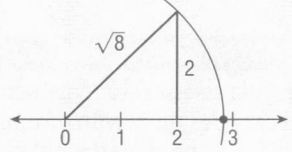

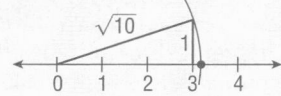

Materials Needed: compass, straightedge, graph paper

Example   *Plotting Irrational Numbers*

Plot the irrational number $\sqrt{20}$ on a number line.

Solution   One way to plot the number is to use a calculator to approximate $\sqrt{20}$ as 4.5. Another way to plot the number is to use a compass, straightedge, and graph paper. Begin by drawing a right triangle whose legs have lengths of 2 and 4. By the Pythagorean Theorem, you can conclude that the hypotenuse has a length of $\sqrt{20}$. As shown in the figure below, draw a number line along the leg whose length is 4. Then use a compass to copy the hypotenuse's length onto the number line. Because the hypotenuse has a length of $\sqrt{20}$, you can conclude that the copied segment also has a length of $\sqrt{20}$.

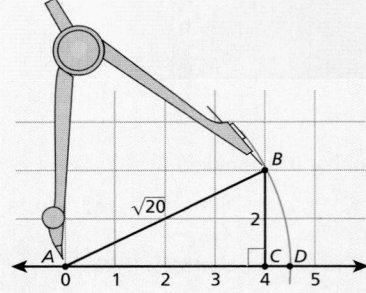

Exercises

In Exercises 1 and 2, state the irrational number that has been plotted on the number line.

1.

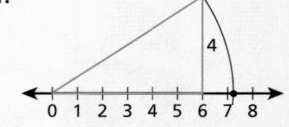

$\sqrt{52}$

2.

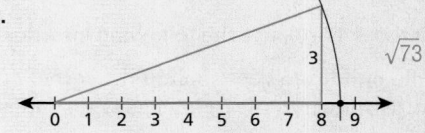

$\sqrt{73}$

P In Exercises 3–6, use a compass and straightedge to plot the irrational number on a number line. See margin.

3. $\sqrt{2}$ **4.** $\sqrt{5}$ **5.** $\sqrt{8}$ **6.** $\sqrt{10}$

9.5

Graphing Inequalities

 Goal 1 How to graph an inequality

 Goal 2 How to write equivalent inequalities

What you should learn:

Why you should learn it:

You can use inequalities to model and solve real-life problems, such as describing the size of an oil spill.

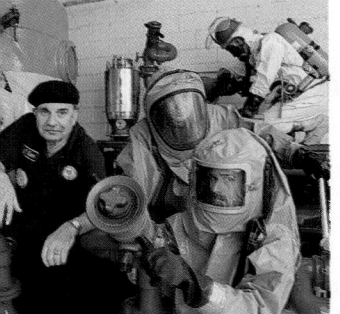

David Usher (second from left) is shown with his crew. His company, Marine Pollution Control, travels around the world helping to clean up after environmental accidents, such as oil spills.

Goal 1 Graphing Inequalities

In Lesson 2.9, you learned how to solve simple inequalities. Here is an example.

$$x + 3 > 1 \qquad \text{\textit{Original inequality}}$$
$$x + 3 - 3 > 1 - 3 \qquad \text{\textit{Subtract 3 from each side.}}$$
$$x > -2 \qquad \text{\textit{Simplify.}}$$

The solution of this inequality is the set of all real numbers that are greater than -2. To graph this inequality on a number line, plot the number -2 with an open dot to show that -2 is not included. Then shade the part of the number line that is to the right of -2, as shown below.

Open dot

Inequalities are used to describe many types of real-life situations. For instance, the number of gallons in an ocean oil spill would have to be greater than zero.

There are four basic types of simple inequalities. Example 1 shows a sample of each type.

Example 1 *Graphing Inequalities on a Number Line*

Verbal Phrase	Inequality	Graph
a. All real numbers less than 2	$x < 2$	Open
b. All real numbers greater than -3	$x > -3$	Open
c. All real numbers less than or equal to -1	$x \le -1$	Closed
d. All real numbers greater than or equal to 0	$x \ge 0$	Closed

■

9.5 ▪ Graphing Inequalities **411**

▶ **PACING the Lesson**

Suggested Number of Days
Basic/Average 0   **Above Average** 1
Advanced 1

▶ **PLANNING the Lesson**

Lesson Plan 9.5, p. 72

ORGANIZER

Starters (reproduced below)
   Problem of the Day 9.5, p. 26
   Warm-Up Exercises 9.5, p. 26
Lesson Resources
   Color Transparencies
      Picture for Ex. 37, p. 38
   Teaching Tools, number lines, pp. T6, C8
   Math Log, p. 29
   Answer Masters 9.5, pp. 179, 180
   Extra Practice Copymaster 9.5, p. 72
   Reteaching Copymaster 9.5, p. 72
Special Populations
   Suggestions, Teacher's Edition, p. 388D

LESSON Notes

Challenge students to describe other situations in which inequalities can be used. Discuss the differences between graphs of equations such as $x = 3$, and of inequalities such as $x > 3$.

Example 1

Ask students to give the verbal phrases that describe the following inequalities. Encourage them to use the phrase "all real numbers that—"
a. $x < -4$ **b.** $x \ge -6$ **c.** $x > 4$ **d.** $x \le 8$

It is customary to write inequalities with the variable on the left side of the statement. We call this the *standard form* of an inequality. However, when we solve inequalities, it may be convenient to solve for the variable on the right side. Consequently, students need to be able to write equivalent inequalities to express results in standard form.

Example 2

Have students graph each equivalent inequality.

Have students write verbal sentences for each inequality.

Writing Prompt

In your own words, explain the meaning of "greater than" or "less than." Why do you think the symbols $>$ and $<$ are used in math books for these relationships?

Answers to Communicating

A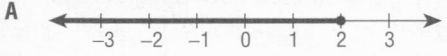

B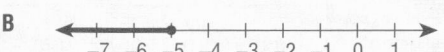

C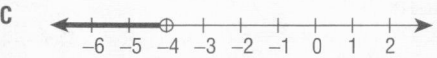

Answers

9.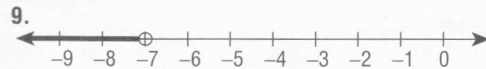

10.

11.

12.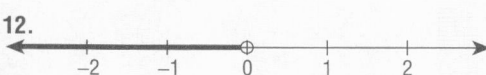

13.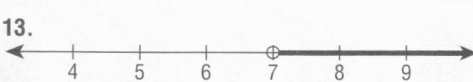

14.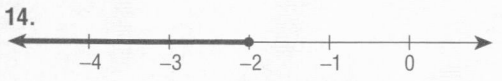

Each of the inequalities in Example 1 is written with the variable on the left. They can also be written with the variable on the right. For instance, $x < 2$ is equivalent to $2 > x$.

The graph of the inequality $x < 2$ is all real numbers that are less than 2.

The graph of the inequality $2 > x$ is all real numbers that 2 is greater than.

To write an inequality that is equivalent to $x < 2$, move each number and letter to the other side, and reverse the inequality.

$$x < 2 \implies 2 > x$$

Example 2   *Writing Equivalent Inequalities*

For each of the following, write an equivalent inequality. State the inequality verbally.

a. $y > -3$ **b.** $0 \leq m$ **c.** $4 \geq t$

Solution

a. The inequality $y > -3$ is equivalent to
$-3 < y$.
Either inequality can be written verbally as "the set of all real numbers that are greater than -3."

b. The inequality $0 \leq m$ is equivalent to
$m \geq 0$.
Either inequality can be written verbally as "the set of all real numbers that are greater than or equal to 0."

c. The inequality $4 \geq t$ is equivalent to
$t \leq 4$.
Either inequality can be written verbally as "the set of all real numbers that are less than or equal to 4." ∎

Study Tip

One way to check that two inequalities are equivalent is to be sure that the inequality symbols "point" toward the same number or variable. For instance, in the inequalities $x < 2$ and $2 > x$, the inequality symbols point to x.

Similarly, in inequalities $y > -3$ and $-3 < y$, the inequality symbols point to -3.

Communicating about MATHEMATICS

▶ **SHARING IDEAS about the Lesson**

Solving Inequalities   Solve each inequality. Then graph the solutions. For graphs, see margin.

A. $3 + b \leq 5$ **B.** $-3 \geq x + 2$ **C.** $y - 4 < -8$

$b \leq 2$ $x \leq -5$ $y < -4$

OPTION: Extra Examples

Here are additional examples similar to Example 1.

Graphing Inequalities on a Number Line

Verbal Phrase	Inequality	Graph
a. All real numbers less than -1	$x < -1$	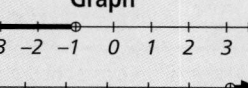
b. All real numbers greater than 3	$x > 3$	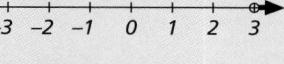
c. All real numbers less than or equal to 1	$x \leq 1$	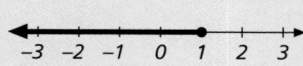
d. All real numbers greater than or equal to -2	$x \geq -2$	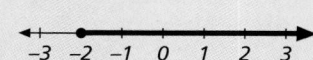

EXERCISES

Guided Practice

▶ **CHECK for Understanding**

In Exercises 1–4, match the inequality with its graph.

a.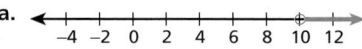
a number line from −4 to 12

b. a number line from −6 to 1

c. a number line from −4 to 12

d. a number line from −6 to 1

1. $x < 10$ c   **2.** $x \geq -4$ d   **3.** $x \leq -4$ b   **4.** $x > 10$ a

In Exercises 5–8, write two equivalent inequalities for the phrase.

5. All real numbers less than 15 $x < 15, \; 15 > x$

6. All real numbers greater than or equal to 0 $x \geq 0, \; 0 \leq x$

7. All real numbers greater than -3 $x > -3, \; -3 < x$

8. All real numbers less than or equal to -11 $x \leq -11, \; -11 \geq x$

In Exercises 9 and 10, solve the inequality. Then graph the solution.

9. $x + 5 < -2$ $x < -7$ **10.** $x - 5 \geq -2$ $x \geq 3$

For graphs, see margin, page 412.

Independent Practice

In Exercises 11–14, graph the inequality. See margin, page 412.

11. $x \geq 1$ **12.** $x < 0$ **13.** $x > 7$ **14.** $x \leq -2$

In Exercises 15–18, write the inequality represented by the graph.

15. number line from −15 to 15 $x \geq -5$

16. number line from −8 to 8 $x < 4$

17. number line from −4 to 4 $x \leq -1$

18. number line from −4 to 3 $x \geq 2$

In Exercises 19–22, write the inequality given by the verbal phrase. Then graph the inequality. For graphs, see margin.

19. All real numbers greater than $\sqrt{2}$ $x > \sqrt{2}$

20. All real numbers less than or equal to $\sqrt{5}$ $x \leq \sqrt{5}$

21. All real numbers less than $-\sqrt{3}$ $x < -\sqrt{3}$

22. All real numbers greater than or equal to $-\sqrt{6}$ $x \geq -\sqrt{6}$

In Exercises 23–28, solve the inequality. Then graph the solution.

23. $x + 3 \geq 2$ $x \geq -1$ **24.** $5 > y + 2$ $y < 3$ **25.** $-3 < n - 4$ $n > 1$

26. $t - 1 \leq 7$ $t \leq 8$ **27.** $z + 7 > -2$ $z > -9$ **28.** $-5 \geq w - 4$ $w \leq -1$

For graphs, see margin.

P Portfolio Opportunity

9.5 ▪ *Graphing Inequalities*   **413**

Lesson 9.5   **413**

Integrated Review ─────────

The next lesson involves *solving* inequalities. Use these exercises to do a mental math review of similar skills from Chapters 2 and 4.

In Exercises 29–32, write an equivalent inequality. Then write the inequality verbally. For verbal inequalities, see margin.

29. $x \le -20$ $-20 \ge x$ **30.** $y > -3$ $-3 < y$ **31.** $s < 17$ $17 > s$ **32.** $m \ge 13$ $13 \le m$

In Exercises 33–36, write an algebraic model for the verbal phrase. Then solve. $x - 5 < -19, x < -14$

✪ **33.** t plus 17 is greater than 24. $t + 17 > 24, t > 7$ ✪ **34.** x minus 5 is less than -19.

✪ **35.** The sum of n and 5 is less than or equal to -9. $n + 5 \le -9, n \le -14$ ✪ **36.** The difference of m and 10 is greater than or equal to 12. $m - 10 \ge 12, m \ge 22$

✪ **37.** *Solar Energy* The fastest speed attained by the *Sunraycer*, a solely solar-powered vehicle, is 48.71 miles per hour. Let S represent the speed of the *Sunraycer*. Which of the following best describes the *Sunraycer's* speed? Explain your reasoning. d, 0 mph and 48.71 mph

   a. $0 < S$ and $S < 48.71$ were both
   b. $0 < S$ and $S \le 48.71$ attained by
   c. $0 \le S$ and $S < 48.71$ the *Sunraycer*.
   d. $0 \le S$ and $S \le 48.71$

38. The sun is about 93 million miles from Earth. In 1977, *Voyager I* was launched from Earth and moved out in the solar system (away from the sun). Let d represent the distance between *Voyager I* and the sun. Write an inequality that describes the values of d. $d \ge 93,000,000$

On June 24, 1988, at Mesa, Arizona, Molly Brennan, shown here outside the Lincoln Memorial, drove the Sunraycer at a record speed.

39. *Temperatures* The lowest possible temperature is $-453°F$. Let T represent the temperature of an object. Write an inequality that describes the possible values of T. $T \ge -453$

40. *Mammal Weights* The largest mammals are blue whales that can weigh up to 450,000 pounds. Let w be the weight of a mammal. Write two inequalities that describe the possible values of w. $0 < w$ and $w \le 450,000$

P *Choosing the Better Graph* **In Exercises 41 and 42, match the statement with the graph that you think is a better representation. Explain.**

  a.   **b**

        0   5   10   15   0   5   10   15

✪ **41.** At least 5 students attended the party. b   ✪ **42.** The temperature is at least 5 degrees.
A number of students must be a whole number.   A number of degrees can be any real number. a

| **Integrated Review** | *Making Connections within Mathematics* |

Mental Math **In Exercises 43–48, use mental math to solve the equation.**

43. $x - 19 = 40$ 59   **44.** $y - 12 = -3$ 9   **45.** $t + 9 = 21$ 12

46. $s + 31 = 66$ 35   **47.** $r - 19 = -1$ 18   **48.** $n + 16 = -4$ -20

✪ More difficult exercises
P Portfolio Opportunity

Answers
29. The set of all real numbers that are less than or equal to -20.
30. The set of all real numbers that are greater than -3.
31. The set of all real numbers that are less than 17.
32. The set of all real numbers that are greater than or equal to 13.

Compound Inequalities In Exercises 49–52, match the compound inequality with its graph. State the inequality verbally.

Sample: The statement *All real numbers greater than 0 and less than 3* is a **compound inequality**. It can be written as $0 < x < 3$ and its graph is

For verbal inequalities, see margin.

a.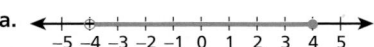

b.

c.

d.

49. $-4 < x < 4$ d   ⭐ **50.** $-4 < x \leq 4$ a   ⭐ **51.** $-4 \leq x < 4$ b   ⭐ **52.** $-4 \leq x \leq 4$ c

---

Mixed REVIEW

In Exercises 1–5, use the diagram at the right.
(8.3, 9.3, 9.4)

1. Find x, the height of the building. 400 ft

2. Find y, the distance from the top of the building to the end of the building's shadow. ≈404.5 ft

3. Find the distance from the top of the pole to the end of its shadow. ≈10.1 ft

4. Write a proportion involving x, 60, and 10. $\frac{x}{10} = \frac{60}{1.5}$

5. Write a proportion involving y, 60, and 1.5. $\frac{y}{10.1} = \frac{60}{1.5}$

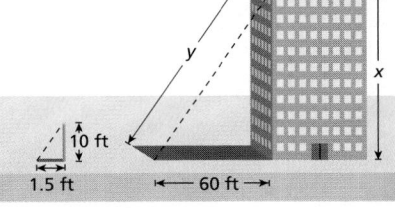

4., 5. Proportions vary.

In Exercises 6–9, solve the inequality and graph the solution on a number line. (2.9, 9.5)
For graphs, see margin.

6. $x + 2 > 12$ $x > 10$ **7.** $0 > x - 2$ $x < 2$ **8.** $2x \leq 10$ $x \leq 5$ **9.** $4x \geq x - 9$ $x \geq -3$

In Exercises 10–15, write the prime factorization of the number. (6.2)

10. 70 $2 \cdot 5 \cdot 7$ **11.** 360 $2^3 \cdot 3^2 \cdot 5$ **12.** 270 $2 \cdot 3^3 \cdot 5$

13. 189 $3^3 \cdot 7$ **14.** 369 $3^2 \cdot 41$ **15.** 368 $2^4 \cdot 23$

In Exercises 16–20, take the word REARRANGE and write each letter on a separate piece of paper. Put the pieces in a bag. What is the percent probability that you choose the indicated letter? (8.8)

16. R ≈33.3%   **17.** N ≈11.1%   **18.** G ≈11.1%

19. A or E ≈44.4%   **20.** a letter other than R ≈66.7%

Provide a model for these exercises before assigning them. Discuss the word *between* with students. For example, all real numbers *between* 2 and 6 can be written as $2 < x < 6$ and graphed as below.

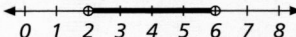

Portfolio Opportunity: Math Log

Looking only at the graph of an inequality, how can you determine if the endpoint is a solution?

Also available as a copymaster, page 29, Ex. 6

Answers
49. The set of all real numbers greater than -4 and less than 4.
50. The set of all real numbers greater than -4 and less than or equal to 4.
51. The set of all real numbers greater than or equal to -4 and less than 4.
52. The set of all real numbers greater than or equal to -4 and less than or equal to 4.

Answers to Mixed Review

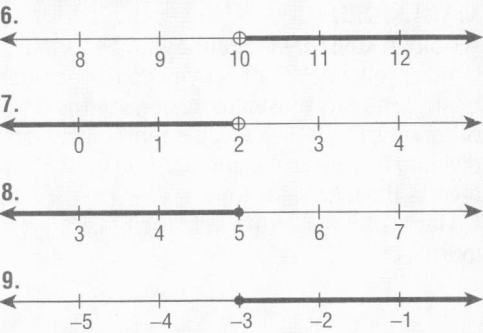

6.

7.

8.

9.

▶ Enrichment

Ask students to explore the words "at least" and "at most." They could write inequalities to represent phrases such as the following:

I ate at least five pieces of pizza. $x \geq 5$

At most, Jessica has four sweatshirts. $x \leq 4$

I have at least $9.00 in my wallet. $x \geq 9$

At most, 50 students will make the track team. $x \leq 50$

Ask the students to explain the difference between "at least" and "more than."

LESSON Notes

Lesson Investigation
ALTERNATE APPROACH
Looking for a Pattern Another approach to understanding the solutions to $-2x < 4$ is as follows:
Determine the truth of the sequence of statements below.

$-2(-4) < 4$?, No
$-2(-3) < 4$?, No
$-2(-2) < 4$?, No
$-2(-1) < 4$?, Yes
$-2(0) < 4$?, Yes
$-2(1) < 4$?, Yes

Point out to students that, because of the negative coefficient of x, the *smaller* initial values of x in the sequence above make the statement false (the expression on the left side is *greater than* that on the right). When the x value *increases* to -2, the expressions become equal. So, any *greater* values of x will make the expression on the left side *less than* that on the right. In fact, for all values of x *greater than* -2, the statement is true. This may help students understand the need to reverse the inequality sign for inequalities of this kind.

MATH JOURNAL
A Golden Rule for Inequalities can be formulated as follows: Whatever you do to one side of an inequality must also be done to the other side, EXCEPT that when multiplying or dividing by a negative number, you must reverse the inequality sign.

Have students write this in their math journals.

What you should learn:

How to use properties of inequalities

How to use multiplication and division to solve an inequality

Why you should learn it:

You can use inequalities to model and solve real-life problems, such as finding real-estate commissions.

Goal 1 **Using Properties of Inequalities**

In this lesson, you will learn that there is an important difference between solving an equation and solving an inequality. You can discover this difference in the following investigation.

LESSON INVESTIGATION

■ Investigating Solutions of Inequalities

Group Activity Consider the inequality $-2x < 4$. You can check whether a number is a solution of the inequality by substituting the number for x. For instance, $x = 1$ is a solution because $-2(1)$ is equal to -2, which is less than 4. On the other hand, $x = -3$ is *not* a solution because $-2(-3)$ is equal to 6, which is not less than 4. Use a guess, check, and revise strategy to discover the solution of this inequality. Can you obtain your solution by dividing each side of the inequality by -2?

In the above investigation, you may have discovered that the solution of $-2x < 4$ is $x > -2$. To obtain this solution, you can divide each side of the original equation by -2, *provided* you reverse the direction of the inequality symbol.

$$-2x < 4 \qquad \textit{Original inequality}$$
$$\frac{-2x}{-2} > \frac{4}{-2} \qquad \textit{Divide each side by } -2 \textit{ and reverse inequality.}$$
$$x > -2 \qquad \textit{Simplify.}$$

Properties of Inequalities

1. Adding or subtracting the same number on each side of an inequality produces an equivalent inequality.
2. Multiplying or dividing each side of an inequality by the same *positive* number produces an equivalent inequality.
3. Multiplying or dividing each side of an inequality by the same *negative* number and *reversing the direction of the inequality symbol* produces an equivalent inequality.

Goal 2 Solving Inequalities

Example 1 Solving Inequalities

a.

$$-\tfrac{1}{2}x \geq 6 \qquad \textit{Original inequality}$$

$$-2 \cdot \left(-\tfrac{1}{2}\right)x \leq -2 \cdot 6 \qquad \textit{Multiply each side by } -2 \textit{ and reverse inequality.}$$

$$x \leq -12 \qquad \textit{Simplify.}$$

The solution is $x \leq -12$, which is the set of all real numbers that are less than or equal to -12.

b.

$$12 < 3m \qquad \textit{Original inequality}$$

$$\tfrac{12}{3} < \tfrac{3m}{3} \qquad \textit{Divide each side by 3.}$$

$$4 < m \qquad \textit{Simplify.}$$

The solution is $4 < m$ or $m > 4$, which is the set of all real numbers that are greater than 4. ■

Example 2 Solving an Inequality

Real Life
Real Estate

You are a real-estate agent and earn a 5% commission for each house you sell. What range of house prices will earn you a commission of at least $4000?

Solution Let H represent the price of the house. Then your commission is 5% of H, or $0.05H$.

$$0.05H \geq 4000 \qquad \textit{Commission is at least \$4000.}$$

$$\tfrac{0.05H}{0.05} \geq \tfrac{4000}{0.05} \qquad \textit{Divide each side by 0.05.}$$

$$H \geq 80{,}000 \qquad \textit{Simplify.}$$

The price of the house you sell must be at least $80,000. ■

Communicating about MATHEMATICS

▶ **SHARING IDEAS about the Lesson**

Answers vary.

It's Up to You Compare the following strategies used to solve the inequality $2 > -x$. Which do you prefer? Why?

A. Divide each side by -1 and reverse inequality.

B. Add x to each side, then subtract 2 from each side.

The list of Properties of Inequalities provides us with more options for solving a variety of inequalities. (See Communicating about Mathematics below.)

Example 1

Have students graph each inequality in the solution to this example.

Example 2

You may wish to point out to students that the phrase "range of house prices" is a reminder that the solution of an inequality is a *set* of values, not a single value.

Communicating about MATHEMATICS

EXTENSION
Have students use two approaches similar to **A** and **B** to solve $3 - 2x > 11$. Ask students which strategy they prefer.

Writing Prompt
Describe any places where you became stuck when solving inequalities. What helped you to get unstuck?

OPTION: Extra Examples

Here are additional examples similar to Example 1.

Solving Inequalities

a. $4x \leq -20$ Original inequality

$\tfrac{4x}{4} \leq \tfrac{-20}{4}$ Divide each side by 4.

$x \leq -5$ Simplify.

The solution is $x \leq -5$, which is the set of all real numbers that are less than or equal to -5.

b. $42 > -6n$ Original inequality

$\tfrac{42}{-6} < \tfrac{-6n}{-6}$ Divide each side by -6 and reverse the inequality.

$-7 < n$ Simplify.

The solution is $-7 < n$ or $n > -7$, which is the set of all real numbers that are greater than -7.

EXERCISE Notes

EXERCISES

Guided Practice

▶ **CHECK for Understanding**

In Exercises 1–4, use $<$, $>$, $\le$, or $\ge$ to complete the inequality.

1. $4 > -x$

 $-4 \;?\; x <$

2. $-3 \ge -t$

 $3 \;?\; t \le$

3. $3y > 15$

 $y \;?\; 5 >$

4. $-2 \ge -\frac{1}{2}a$

 $4 \;?\; a \le$

In Exercises 5–8, will the strategy require reversing the direction of the inequality?

5. Multiply both sides by -1. Yes

6. Divide both sides by 4. No

7. Multiply both sides by $\frac{1}{4}$. No

8. Divide both sides by -5. Yes

In Exercises 9–12, solve the inequality.

9. $4b > 24$ $b > 6$

10. $-\frac{1}{4}x \le 14$ $x \ge -56$

11. $-5 < 0.2h$ $h > -25$

12. $36 \ge -\frac{1}{2}f$ $f \ge -72$

Independent Practice

P **Error Analysis** In Exercises 13–15, describe the error. See margin.

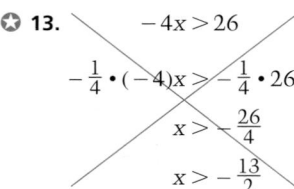

✪ **13.**
$$-4x > 26$$
$$-\frac{1}{4} \cdot (-4)x > -\frac{1}{4} \cdot 26$$
$$x > -\frac{26}{4}$$
$$x > -\frac{13}{2}$$

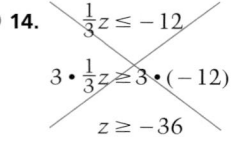

✪ **14.**
$$\frac{1}{3}z \le -12$$
$$3 \cdot \frac{1}{3}z \ge 3 \cdot (-12)$$
$$z \ge -36$$

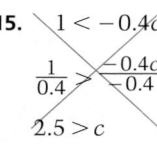

✪ **15.**
$$1 < -0.4c$$
$$\frac{1}{0.4} > \frac{-0.4c}{-0.4}$$
$$2.5 > c$$

In Exercises 16–19, match the solution of the inequality to its graph.

a.
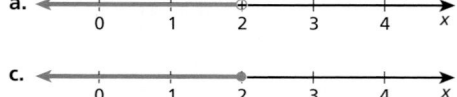

b.
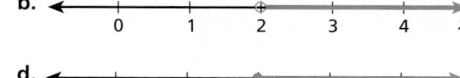

c.

d.

16. $0.7x \le 1.4$ c

17. $-1 > -\frac{1}{2}x$ b

18. $\frac{1}{8} \le \frac{1}{16}x$ d

19. $-3x > -6$ a

In Exercises 20–35, solve the inequality. Then graph the solution. For graphs, see Additional Answers.

20. $3m < 4$ $m < \frac{4}{3}$

21. $2n \ge 5$ $n \ge \frac{5}{2}$

22. $\frac{x}{2} \le 8$ $x \le 16$

23. $\frac{y}{9} > 4$ $y > 36$

24. $35 \ge -5b$ $b \ge -7$

25. $\frac{1}{2} < -2a$ $a < -\frac{1}{4}$

26. $-\frac{1}{2}z > 5$ $z < -10$

27. $-\frac{1}{5}p \le 2$ $p \ge -10$

28. $-\frac{3}{4}a \le -6$ $a \ge 8$

29. $14 > -\frac{1}{3}n$ $n > -42$

30. $4 < 0.8r$ $r > 5$

31. $1.2x \ge 3.6$ $x \ge 3$

32. $\frac{a}{6} > -2$ $a > -12$

33. $\frac{3}{5}y \le -6$ $y \le -10$

34. $-1.4m \ge -5.6$ $m \le 4$

35. $-\frac{3}{2} < -\frac{1}{4}x$ $x < 6$

✪ More difficult exercises
P Portfolio Opportunity

Extra Practice

Extra Practice **9.6**

Name _____

1. Symbol not reversed when multiplying by positive number.
In Exercises 1–3, describe the error. Then solve the inequality correctly.

1. $5x < -32$ $\frac{1}{5} \cdot 5x \le \frac{1}{5} \cdot (-32)$ $x \le -\frac{32}{5}$
~~$\frac{1}{5} \cdot 5x \ge \frac{1}{5} \cdot (-32)$~~   ~~$x \ge -\frac{32}{5}$~~

2. $-\frac{1}{2}z < -5$ $-2 \cdot (-\frac{1}{2})z < -2 \cdot (-5)$ $z < 10$
~~$-2 \cdot (-\frac{1}{2})z < -2 \cdot (-5)$~~   ~~$z > 10$~~
Symbol reversed when multiplying by negative number.

In Exercises 3–6, match the solution of the inequality to its graph.

a.   b.   c.   d.

3. $-\frac{1}{3}z < -4$ c
4. $6x < -12$ b
5. $\frac{1}{2} \ge -\frac{1}{16}z$ a
6. $0.3w \le -1.8$ d

In Exercises 7–18, solve the inequality. Then graph its solution. For graphs, see back of supplement.

7. $5n < 12$ $n < \frac{12}{5}$
8. $-3m < 11$ $m > -\frac{11}{3}$
9. $\frac{x}{4} \ge 6$ $x \ge 24$
10. $25 \ge 15k$ $\frac{5}{3} \ge k$
11. $\frac{3}{8} < -4c$ $-\frac{3}{32} > c$
12. $-\frac{1}{4} \le \frac{3}{4}w$ $-\frac{3}{5} \le w$
13. $-\frac{2}{5}p \le 10$ $p \ge -25$
14. $19 \ge -6m$ $-\frac{19}{6} \le m$
15. $15 < 0.4p$ $3.75 < p$
16. $\frac{a}{12} < -6$ $a < -72$
17. $14d < -21$ $d < -\frac{3}{2}$
18. $-3.2w < 1.28$ $w > -0.4$

19. You are recycling aluminum cans to save enough money to buy a new portable CD player which costs \$120.75. The recycling center is paying 35¢ per pound of aluminum. How many pounds of aluminum cans do you need to recycle to have at least \$120.75?
At least 345 pounds
20. You and your family are traveling to the mountains for a weekend vacation. The last sign you saw said that your destination is still 255 miles away. Your parents say that you'll be there in at most $4\frac{1}{2}$ hours. How fast will your family have to travel to arrive in at most $4\frac{1}{2}$ hours?
At least 56.6 mph
21. Your family has added a new room to your home. You've budgeted \$450 for carpeting. The room has a floor area of 30 square yards. What is the most you can spend per square yard if the cost of the carpeting is not more than \$450?
\$15.00 per square yard
22. You're taping some of your favorite singles onto a 90 minute blank cassette. On average each of your favorite singles is 4 minutes 30 seconds. What is the greatest number of singles that can be recorded without cutting any song short?
20 singles

Windows 9.6 • Solving Inequalities: Multiplying and Dividing **73**

Reteaching

Reteach Chapter 9

Name _____

What you should learn:
 9.6 How to use properties of inequalities and how to use multiplication and division to solve an inequality

Correlation to Pupil's Textbook:
Chapter Test (p. 433)
Exercises 15, 17

Examples *Using Properties of Inequalities and Solving Inequalities*

a. Use the properties of inequalities to solve $8 \ge -4x$.

$8 \ge -4x$ *Original inequality*
$\frac{8}{-4} \le \frac{-4x}{-4}$ *Divide each side by -4 and reverse the direction of the inequality symbol.*
$-2 \le x$ *Simplify.*

The solution is $-2 \le x$, which is the set of all real numbers that are greater than or equal to -2.

b. You are paid \$2.50 per hour to babysit. How many hours of babysitting will earn you at least \$35?

Let n represent the number of hours. Then your total pay is \$2.50n.

$2.50n \ge 35$ *Pay is at least \$35.*
$\frac{2.50n}{2.50} \ge \frac{35}{2.50}$ *Divide each side by 2.50.*
$n \ge 14$ *Simplify.*

You will earn at least \$35 if you babysit at least 14 hours.

Guidelines:
 • Adding or subtracting the same number on each side of an inequality produces an equivalent inequality.
 • Multiplying or dividing each side of an inequality by the same positive number produces an equivalent inequality.
 • Multiplying or dividing each side of an inequality by the same negative number and reversing the direction of the inequality symbol produces an equivalent inequality.

EXERCISES

In Exercises 1–8, solve the inequality. Then graph the solution.

1. $6y \ge -18$ $y \ge -3$
2. $\frac{x}{3} < -1$ $x < -3$
3. $-70 > 7a$ $-10 > a$
4. $-3n \le 15$ $n \ge -5$
5. $2 \ge \frac{-1}{4}z$ $-8 \le z$
6. $3.5x > 10.5$ $x > 3$
7. $\frac{-3}{8} < \frac{-3}{4}b$ $\frac{1}{2} > b$
8. $\frac{t}{-2} \le 3$ $t \ge -6$

Windows Chapter 9 • Real Numbers and Inequalities **73**

36. Fundraiser You are selling sandwiches as a fundraiser for the softball team. You make a profit of 75¢ for each sandwich sold and the team needs to raise at least $300.00. How many sandwiches must be sold? Number ≥ 400

37. Buying a Video The movie video you want to buy costs $26.95. You earn $3 an hour baby-sitting. What is the least number of hours you need to baby-sit to earn enough money to buy the video? 9

38. Walking Speed You want to walk 2 miles in less than 40 minutes. What must your speed be in miles per hour? Speed > 3 mph

39. Riding Speed Your top bicycling speed is 40 kilometers per hour. What is the least amount of time it would take you to ride 60 kilometers? $1\frac{1}{2}$ hours

Integrated Review

Making Connections within Mathematics

Logical Reasoning In Exercises 40–43, decide whether the statement can be determined from the bar graph. Explain. *(Source: American Hotel and Motel Association)*

40. Some visitors come for more than one reason. Yes

41. *About* the same number of people come for business reasons as come to visit friends. Yes

42. *Exactly* the same number of people come for business reasons as come to visit friends. No

43. Some people who come for holiday travel also come for business or to visit friends. No

40.–43. For explanations, see margin.

Why Overseas Visitors Come to the USA

Travel holiday	56%
Business	25%
Visiting friends	25%
Convention	8%
Studying	4%

Exploration and Extension

44. Game Strategy With a partner, set up and play the following game. After playing the game, describe a playing strategy. See margin.

Setup: Write the numbers 1 to 9 on pieces of paper. Lay the pieces faceup on a table.

Object: Obtain three numbers whose sum is 15.

Rules: Players take turns choosing numbers, one number at a time.

End: The game ends when one player has chosen three numbers whose sum is 15.

45. Complete the magic square so that the sum of 3 horizontal, vertical, or diagonal numbers is 15.

46. Does the magic square in Exercise 45 influence your strategy for the game in Exercise 44? Explain. Yes, see answer to Exercise 44.

		6
	5	
4		

2, 7   8, 1
9, 1 or 3, 7

3, 8   9, 2

9.6 ▪ *Solving Inequalities: Multiplying and Dividing* **419**

Solving Multi-Step Inequalities

▶ PACING the Lesson

Suggested Number of Days
Basic/Average 0 **Above Average** 1
Advanced 1

▶ PLANNING the Lesson

Lesson Plan 9.7, p. 74

ORGANIZER

Starters (reproduced below)
  Problem of the Day 9.7, p. 27
  Warm-Up Exercises 9.7, p. 27
Lesson Resources
  Color Transparencies
    Picture for Example 2, p. 39
  Math Log, p. 30
  Technology, p. 53
  Answer Masters 9.7, pp. 184, 185
  Extra Practice Copymaster 9.7, p. 74
  Reteaching Copymaster 9.7, p. 74
Special Populations
  Suggestions, Teacher's Edition, p. 388D

LESSON Notes

You may wish to stress the general similarity of solving multistep inequalities and solving multistep equations. Students will probably find such comparisons helpful.

Example 1

Ask students if the solution steps would be different if we were asked to solve $2x + 1 = 4$. Solution steps would be the same.

Example 2

Ask students: Would the solution steps be different if we were asked to solve $-\frac{1}{3}m - 5 = 2$? If so, where does the difference arise? Yes; in the reversal of the relationship symbol.
Have students graph the solution.

What you should learn:

Goal 1 How to solve multi-step inequalities

Goal 2 How to use multi-step inequalities to solve real-life problems

Why you should learn it:

You can use inequalities to model and solve real-life problems, such as problems that deal with nutrition.

Goal 1 **Solving Multi-step Inequalities**

In Lessons 9.5 and 9.6, you used properties of inequalities to solve inequalities that can be solved with one step. You can use these same properties to solve inequalities that require two or more steps. Remember that if you multiply or divide by a negative number, you must reverse the direction of the inequality symbol.

Example 1 *Solving a Multi-step Inequality*

Solve $2x + 1 \leq 4$.

Solution

$2x + 1 \leq 4$	*Rewrite original inequality.*
$2x + 1 - 1 \leq 4 - 1$	*Subtract 1 from each side.*
$2x \leq 3$	*Simplify.*
$\frac{2x}{2} \leq \frac{3}{2}$	*Divide each side by 2.*
$x \leq \frac{3}{2}$	*Simplify.*

The solution is all real numbers that are less than or equal to $\frac{3}{2}$. A graph of the solution is shown at the left. ■

Example 2 *Solving a Multi-step Inequality*

Solve $-\frac{1}{3}m - 5 > 2$.

Solution

$-\frac{1}{3}m - 5 > 2$	*Rewrite original inequality.*
$-\frac{1}{3}m - 5 + 5 > 2 + 5$	*Add 5 to each side.*
$-\frac{1}{3}m > 7$	*Simplify.*
$(-3)\left(-\frac{1}{3}\right)m < (-3)(7)$	*Multiply each side by -3 and reverse the inequality.*
$m < -21$	*Simplify.*

The solution is all real numbers that are less than -21. ■

Study Tip...
You can check a solution of an inequality by substituting several numbers into the original inequality. For instance, when checking the solution in Example 1, numbers that are less than $\frac{3}{2}$ should yield true statements and numbers that are greater than $\frac{3}{2}$ should yield false statements.

STARTER: Problem of the Day

Suppose you select one button on the telephone pad at random. State the probability that you select
a. A prime number;
b. The letter J;
c. An even number;
d. The pound sign (#);
e. The letter Z.

a. $\frac{1}{3}$, b. $\frac{1}{12}$, c. $\frac{5}{12}$, d. $\frac{1}{12}$,
e. 0

	ABC	DEF
1	2	3
GHI	JKL	MNO
4	5	6
PRS	TUV	WXY
7	8	9
*	OPER	#
	0	

Also available as a copymaster, page 27

STARTER: Warm-Up Exercises

1. Solve.
 a. $x + 3 < 42$ **b.** $3 - x > 15$ **c.** $x - 18 \geq 19$
 a. $x < 39$, b. $x < -12$, c. $x \geq 37$
2. Solve.
 a. $-\frac{2}{3}x > 18$ **b.** $\frac{5}{6}x \leq 30$
 a. $x < -27$, b. $x \leq 36$
3. Solve.
 a. $2x + 1 = 4$ **b.** $-\frac{1}{3}m - 5 = 2$
 a. $x = \frac{3}{2}$, b. $m = -21$

Also available as a copymaster, page 27

Goal 2 Solving Real-Life Problems

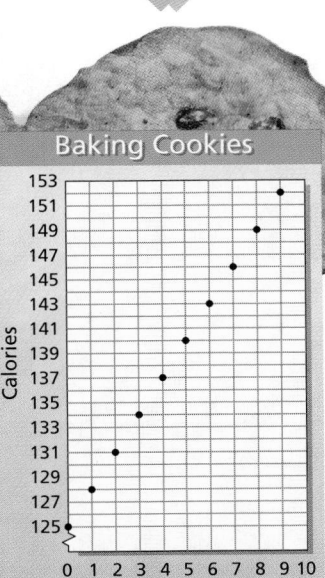

Baking Cookies

| Example 3 | Solving an Inequality |

You are baking a batch of 36 oatmeal chip cookies. Without the chips, the recipe has 4500 calories. You want each cookie to have less than 150 calories. Each chocolate chip has 3 calories. How many chips can you have in each cookie?

Solution Without any chocolate chips, each cookie would have $\frac{1}{36}$ (4500) or 125 calories.

Verbal Model $125 + 3 \cdot$ [Chips per cookie] < 150

Labels   Number of chocolate chips per cookie $= n$ (chips)

Algebraic Model
$$125 + 3 \cdot n < 150$$
$$3n < 25$$
$$n < 8\tfrac{1}{3}$$

You can use up to 8 chocolate chips per cookie. ∎

You can also solve Example 3 with a table or with a graph. With either the table or the graph, notice that the number of calories exceeds 150 when the number of chocolate chips is greater than 8.

Number of Chips	0	1	2	3	4
Calories	125	128	131	134	137

Number of Chips	5	6	7	8	9
Calories	140	143	146	149	152

Communicating about MATHEMATICS

▶ **SHARING IDEAS about the Lesson**

Nutrition Work with a partner to plan a "macaroni and cheese" school lunch that is to contain at least 20 grams of protein. Without the macaroni and cheese, the lunch has 6 grams of protein. The macaroni and cheese has 2 grams of protein per ounce. What size servings of macaroni and cheese should you plan?   At least 7 ounces

---

Many real-life situations can be described using multistep inequalities. Challenge students to identify examples.

Example 3

You may wish to point out that, even when solving this problem using the table and graph, you can still use the verbal model to help compute the table values and the points on the graph.

Communicating about MATHEMATICS

Encourage students to solve the problem using all three methods presented in Example 3 of the lesson.

Writing Prompt
Complete the sentence: If I could change one thing about this chapter it would be …

OPTION: Extra Examples

Here is an additional example similar to Example 1.
Solving a Multistep Inequality.
Solve $\frac{1}{2}x - 9 > -1$.

Solution

$\frac{1}{2}x - 9 \geq -1$	Rewrite original inequality.
$\frac{1}{2}x - 9 + 9 \geq -1 + 9$	Add 9 to each side.
$x \geq 8$	Simplify
$2 \cdot \frac{1}{2}x \geq 2 \cdot 8$	Multiply each side by 2.
$x \geq 16$	Simplify.

The solution is all real numbers that are greater than or equal to 16. A graph of the solution is shown below.

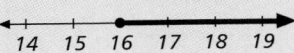

14 15 16 17 18 19

Technology

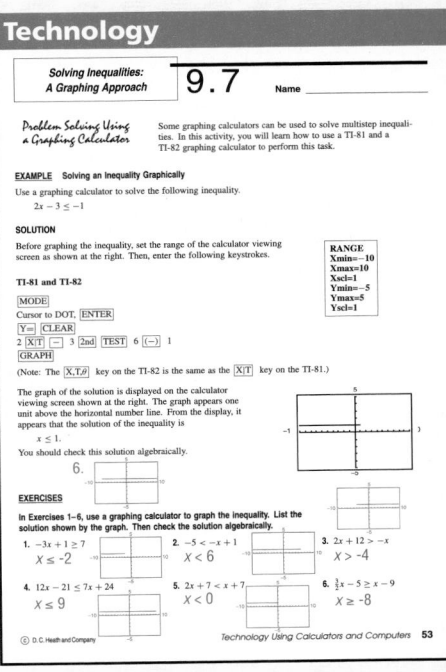

EXERCISE Notes

ASSIGNMENT GUIDE

*Basic/Average:
Day 1: Ex. 6, 8, 9–21 odd, 27–31 odd
Day 2: Ex. 28–34 even, 38–40

Above Average: Ex. 6, 8, 9–21 odd, 27–31 odd, 30–34 even, 38–40

Advanced: Ex. 6, 8, 9–21 odd, 27–31 odd, 30–34 even, 38–40

Selected Answers: Ex. 1–5, 7–37 odd

*You may wish to omit this lesson for these students.

Guided Practice

Use these exercises as an in-class 10-minute closing activity. Tour the classroom and check the written format of student solutions. Encourage students to write reasons for their steps.

Independent Practice

▶ **Ex. 9–12** These exercises can be difficult for students. Assign them as part of an in-class think/share activity for pairs of students.
▶ **Ex. 17–25** Encourage students to use a solution format similar to the model provided in Examples 1 and 2, page 420.

Answers
1. Add 2 to each side, divide each side by 3.
2. Subtract 2 from each side, multiply each side by -5 and reverse the inequality.
3. Substitute several numbers into the orginal inequality, some that you think will yield true statements and some that you think will yield false statements. You try to get false statements as well as true ones, and your check cannot be complete.

4.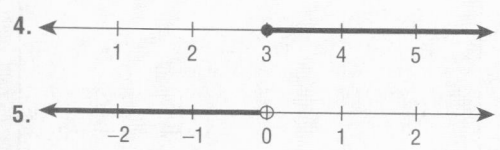

5.

6. The direction of the inequality symbol was not reversed, as it should have been.
7. The direction of the inequality symbol was reversed, but it should not have been.
8. The left side becomes $-\frac{1}{4}x$, not $\frac{1}{4}x$; so each side should be multiplied by -4, not 4.

422 Chapter 9

Guided Practice

▶ **CHECK for Understanding**

Reasoning In Exercises 1 and 2, solve the inequality. **Explain your steps.** For explanations, see margin.

1. $3x - 2 \le 13$ $x \le 5$

2. $4 < -\frac{1}{5}y + 2$ $y < -10$

Ⓟ **3.** *Writing* In your own words, explain how to check a solution of an inequality. How is it different from checking a solution of an equation? See margin.

In Exercises 4 and 5, solve the inequality. Then graph the solution on a number line.

4. $-18 + 4y \ge -6y + 12$ $y \ge 3$

5. $2(z + 1) < -3z + 2$ $z < 0$

For graphs, see margin.

Independent Practice

Ⓟ *Error Analysis* In Exercises 6–8, describe the error. Then correct it. See margin.

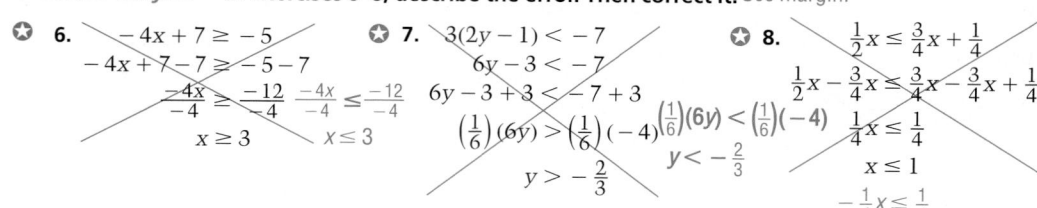

Logical Reasoning In Exercises 9–12, decide whether the statement is sometimes, always, or never true.

✪ **9.** If $-5x + 9 \le -11$, then $x = 3$. Never

✪ **10.** If $7y - 20 \ge 2y + 15$, then $y = 7$. Sometimes

✪ **11.** If $4(2a - 1) < 8$, then $a < 1$. Sometimes

✪ **12.** If $2(-3b - 6) > 9b - 3$, then $b < \frac{3}{5}$. Always

In Exercises 13–16, match the inequality with its solution.

a. $x < -2$ **b.** $x < 2$ **c.** $x > -2$ **d.** $x > 2$

13. $2x + 13 > 9$ c

14. $-7x - 8 > 5x + 16$ a

15. $6 < 6(3 - x)$ b

16. $2(8 - 5x) < 4 - 4x$ d

In Exercises 17–25, solve the inequality.

17. $-11x + 3 < -30$ $x > 3$

18. $\frac{1}{5}y + 12 \le 8$ $y \le -20$

19. $5a + 6 \ge 14a - 9$ $a \le \frac{5}{3}$

20. $8b - 9 < 2b - 13$ $b < -\frac{2}{3}$

21. $\frac{3}{4}m \le \frac{1}{4}m + 2$ $m \le 4$

22. $-\frac{1}{5}x > \frac{4}{5}x + 3$ $x < -3$

23. $2(x + 1) \ge 3x - 2$ $x \le 4$

24. $4x + 1 \le 2(x + 2)$ $x \le \frac{3}{2}$

25. $-4x + 3 \ge -5x$ $x \ge -3$

422 Chapter **9** • Real Numbers and Inequalities

✪ More difficult exercises
Ⓟ Portfolio Opportunity

Extra Practice

Reteaching

Consecutive Integers In Exercises 26–28, let n, $n + 1$, and $n + 2$ be consecutive integers. Write the inequality that represents the verbal sentence. Then solve the inequality.

26. The sum of 2 consecutive integers is less than or equal to 7. $n+n+1 \leq 7, n \leq 3$

27. The sum of 3 consecutive integers is more than 18. $n+n+1+n+2 > 18, n > 5$

28. The sum of 3 consecutive integers is less than 20. $n+n+1+n+2 < 20, n < 5\frac{2}{3}$

Geometry In Exercises 29 and 30, describe the possible values of x.

29. The area of the rectangle is at least 28 square centimeters. $x \leq -4$

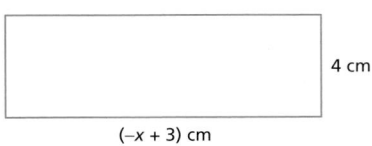

4 cm

$(-x + 3)$ cm

30. The perimeter of the triangle is less than or equal to 36 feet.

$x \geq 3$ (Also $x < 5\frac{1}{2}$, so that the length of the base is positive.)

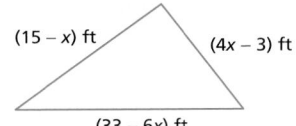

$(15 - x)$ ft $(4x - 3)$ ft

$(33 - 6x)$ ft

31. *Night Work* You are a food server at a restaurant. You earn $4 an hour, plus tips. One night, you earned $15 in tips and your total earnings were less than $43. Describe the number of hours you could have worked. Less than 7

32. *Carnival* You are going to a carnival. It costs $10 to enter and $0.25 each for tickets for games and rides. You don't want to spend more than $20. Write an inequality that describes the number of tickets you can buy. $10 + 0.25t \leq 20, t \leq 40$

33. Create a table showing the results of Exercise 32.

34. *Riding a Bike* You rode your bike on a trail that is over 12 miles long. Your average speed was 15 miles per hour. Write an inequality that represents the time (in hours) that you rode your bike. Solve the inequality. $15t > 12, t > \frac{4}{5}$

33. See Additional Answers.

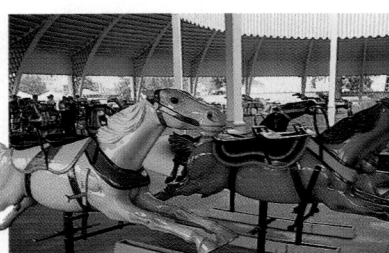

In a racing derby, the four horses in a row compete against each other. One of these very rare carousels is in Sandusky, Ohio; the other is in Rye, New York.

Integrated Review

Making Connections within Mathematics

Ordered Pairs In Exercises 35–38, decide whether the ordered pair is a solution to the inequality. If not, find an ordered pair that *is* a solution. Ordered pairs vary.

35. $x + 3y \leq 6$; $(0, 2)$ Yes

36. $2x - y > -4$; $(-2, 1)$ No, $(0,0)$

37. $4x - 5y \leq 21$; $(3, -2)$ No, $(0, 0)$

38. $-3x + 9y < 1$; $(-3, -1)$ Yes

Exploration and Extension

39. *Equation Sense* In a coordinate plane, graph all ordered pairs, (x, y), for which the following is true: x and y are positive integers and $xy \leq 8$.

✪ **40.** *Equation Sense* In a coordinate plane, graph all ordered pairs, (x, y), for which the following is true: x and y are positive integers and $x + y \leq 8$.

39., 40. See Additional Answers.

9.7 • *Solving Multi-Step Inequalities*   **423**

The purpose of this investigation is to allow students to discover an inequality connection in geometry—the Triangle Inequality. This concept is established in Lesson 9.8

EXTENSION
Ask the students to try to draw a triangle with lengths of 3, 4, and 10. Do the lengths form a triangle? Why or why not?

LESSON INVESTIGATION 9.8
Exploring Triangles

Materials Needed: paper, ruler

| Example | *Exploring Triangles* |

Draw a large triangle on a piece of paper. Then use a ruler to measure the lengths of the sides of the triangle. Compare the sum of the lengths of any two of the sides with the length of the third side.

Solution Begin by drawing a triangle. Then, use the ruler to measure the lengths of the sides of the triangle. In $\triangle ABC$ below, the lengths of the sides are about 6 inches, 4.75 inches, and 5.25 inches. You can compare the sum of the lengths of any two sides with the length of the third side, as follows.

Two Sides	Sum of Lengths of Two Sides	Length of 3rd Side
$\overline{AB}$, $\overline{AC}$	$4.75 + 6 = 10.75$ inches	$a = 5.25$ inches
$\overline{AB}$, $\overline{BC}$	$4.75 + 5.25 = 10$ inches	$b = 6$ inches
$\overline{AC}$, $\overline{BC}$	$6 + 5.25 = 11.25$ inches	$c = 4.75$ inches

In the table, notice that the sides of $\triangle ABC$ are denoted by $\overline{AB}$, $\overline{AC}$, and $\overline{BC}$, and the lengths of the sides are denoted by c, b, and a.

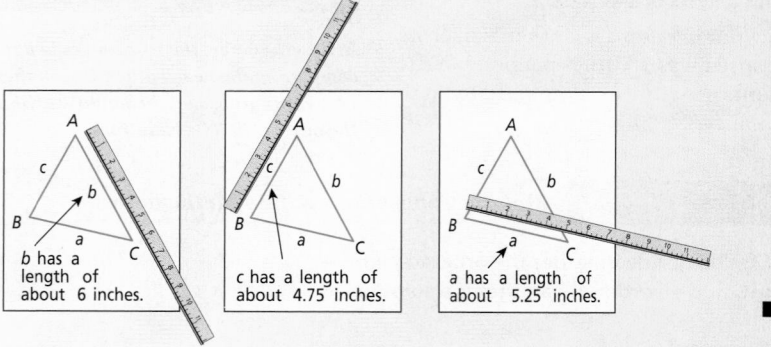

b has a length of about 6 inches. *c has a length of about 4.75 inches.* *a has a length of about 5.25 inches.*

∎

Exercises
Check students' work.
1. Repeat the procedure shown in the example with two other triangles.
2. Compare your results with others in your class. Did anyone in the class find a triangle that has one side that is longer than the sum of the lengths of the other two sides? What can you conclude? No, see below.
3. Let a, b, and c be the lengths of the sides of a triangle. Write three inequalities that compare a, b, and c. $a + b > c, a + c > b, b + c > a$

2. The sum of the lengths of any two sides of a triangle is greater than the length of the third side.

9.8

The Triangle Inequality

 What you should learn:

Goal 1 How to use the Triangle Inequality

Goal 2 How to use the Triangle Inequality to solve real-life problems

 Why you should learn it:

You can use the Triangle Inequality to solve real-life problems, such as finding bounds on the distance between two locations.

Goal 1 **Using the Triangle Inequality**

In the *Lesson Investigation* on page 424, you may have discovered that the sum of the lengths of two sides of a triangle is always greater than the length of the third side. This result is called the **Triangle Inequality.**

> **The Triangle Inequality**
> The sum of the lengths of any two sides of a triangle is greater than the length of the third side.

In any triangle, the Triangle Inequality produces three inequalities. For instance, in $\triangle DEF$ at the right, you can write the following inequalities.

$$d + e > f$$
$$d + f > e$$
$$e + f > d$$

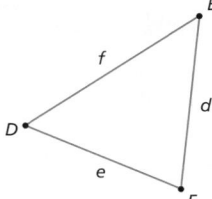

Example 1 *Using the Triangle Inequality*

Real Life
Travel

You have moved to a new city, and are told that your apartment is 5 miles from your school and 6 miles from the restaurant where you have a part-time job. You are also told that your apartment, school, and restaurant do not lie on a straight line. Without knowing any other information, what can you say about the distance between your school and the restaurant?

Solution Begin by drawing a diagram, as shown at the left. Because your apartment, school, and restaurant do not lie on a line, they must form the vertices of a triangle. From the triangle, you can write the following inequalities:

$$5 + x > 6 \quad \text{and} \quad 5 + 6 > x.$$

By solving these two inequalities, you can determine that the distance between your school and restaurant is *more than 1 mile* ($x > 1$) and *less than 11 miles* ($x < 11$). ■

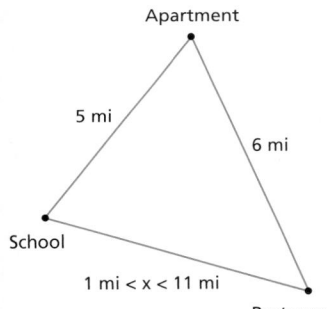

9.8 • The Triangle Inequality **425**

▶ **PACING the Lesson**

Suggested Number of Days
Basic/Average 0 **Above Average** 1
Advanced 1

▶ **PLANNING the Lesson**

Lesson Plan 9.8, p. 75

ORGANIZER

Starters (reproduced below)
  Problem of the Day 9.8, p. 27
  Warm-Up Exercises 9.8, p. 27
Lesson Resources
  Teaching Tools
   Ruler, pp. T12, C18
  Math Log, p. 30
  Technology, pp. 54, 55
  Answer Masters 9.8, p. 186
  Extra Practice Copymaster 9.8, p. 75
  Reteaching Copymaster 9.8, p. 75
Special Populations
  Suggestions, Teacher's Edition, p. 388D

LESSON Notes

The Triangle Inequality should be added to students' math journals. Discuss the findings of the investigation on page 424.

Example 1

Have students verify the solution by checking out values of $x \le 1$ and values of $x \ge 11$. Have them show that these values (outside the range represented by the solution) do *not* satisfy the Triangle Inequality.

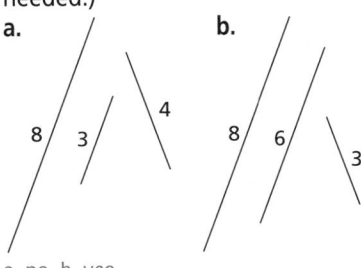

Have students identify situations in which triangles are used. Ask whether there are uses of the Triangle Inequality in these situations.

Example 2

Ask students what measurements would work for the stained glass window in this example.

Real Life
Art

Stained glass windows are made up of pieces of colored glass held together by strips of lead. Sunlight enhances the design effects.

Example 2 *Using the Triangle Inequality*

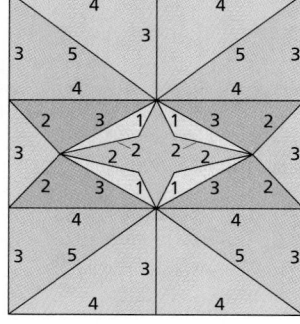

You are creating a design for a large stained-glass window. To begin, you draw a pattern and label the lengths (in feet) of each piece of glass. When a friend of yours looks at the plans, she says that there is something wrong with the measurements. How can she tell?

Solution There are four different sizes of triangles in the pattern. The smallest one must be mislabeled.

From the Triangle Inequality, it is possible to have a triangle whose sides are 3, 4, and 5. It is also possible to have a triangle whose sides are 2, 3, and 4, and one whose sides are 2, 2, and 3. It is *not,* however, possible to have a triangle whose sides have lengths of 1, 2, and 3 because the sum of the lengths of two sides would be equal to the length of the third side. This is not possible because the Triangle Inequality states that the sum of the lengths of any two sides must be *greater than* the length of the third side. ∎

Communicating **about MATHEMATICS**

▶ **SHARING IDEAS about the Lesson**

Using the Triangle Inequality Which of the following triangles must have at least one of its lengths listed incorrectly? Explain your reasoning. C, $85 + 53 \not> 138$

A.
50
50
71

B.
100
82
60

C.
138
53
85

Technology

Investigating the Triangle Inequality **9.8** Name _____

Exploration Using a Computer Drawing Program

In this activity, you will use dynamic construction software such as *Cabri, The Geometer's Sketchpad,* or *Geometry Inventor* to investigate the Triangle Inequality. Follow the directions given below to complete the investigation. It is assumed the user is familiar with the software.

Directions
1. Construct a random triangle, △ABC.
2. Measure the length of each side. That is, find *a, b,* and *c.*
3. To change the side lengths of △ABC, simply click and drag on *A, B,* or *C.*

EXERCISES

1. Use the construction software and the directions listed above to construct five different triangles. Use the triangles to complete the table. Triangles vary.

Triangle	a	b	c	a+b	b+c	a+c
1						
2						
3						
4						
5						

2. What can you conclude about the sum of the lengths of any two sides of a triangle? Include inequalities in your conclusion.
   The sum of the lengths of two sides of a triangle is greater than the length of the third side. For example, in △ABC, the following are true. a + b > c, b + c > a, a + c > b
3. Now change △ABC so that the length of $\overline{AB}$ is 7 inches and the length of $\overline{BC}$ is 3 inches. Investigate to find the possible lengths of $\overline{AC}$. Write your solution as an inequality.
   4 inches < AC < 10 inches

EXERCISES

Guided Practice

▶ **CHECK for Understanding**   No, see margin.

1. Can lengths of 5 cm, 6 cm, and 11 cm be sides of a triangle? Explain your answer with a sketch.

2. Which of the following are true statements about the lengths of the sides of $\triangle RST$? Explain.

   a. $r + s \geq t$ **b.** $r > s + t$ **c.** $r + s > t$ c, by the Triangle Inequality

3. Which of the following cannot be the side lengths of a triangle? Explain.   b, $4 + 6 \not> 10$

   a. 3, 4, 6   **b.** 4, 6, 10   **c.** 5, 7, 11

In Exercises 4–6, the measures of two sides of a triangle are given. What can you say about the measure of the third side?

4. 3 and 5   Greater than 2, less than 8

5. 9 and 11   Greater than 2, less than 20

6. 16 and 20   Greater than 4, less than 36

Independent Practice

In Exercises 7–10, can the side lengths be correct? Explain.

7.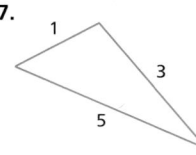

8.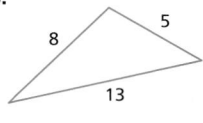

9.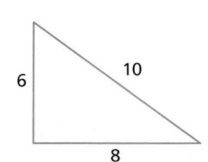

10.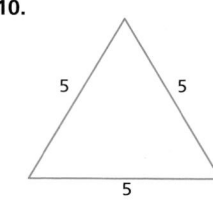

No, $1 + 3 \not> 5$

No, $8 + 5 \not> 13$

Yes; $6 + 8 > 10$, $6 + 10 > 8$, $8 + 10 > 6$

Yes, $5 + 5 > 5$

11. Copy and complete the table.

Measure of Side 1	Measure of Side 2	Measure of Side 3 is greater than	Measure of Side 3 is less than	
3 cm	8 cm	?	?	5 cm, 11 cm
9 in.	16 in.	?	?	7 in., 25 in.
10 ft	21 ft	?	?	11 ft, 31 ft
30 m	45 m	?	?	15 m, 75 m
100 cm	225 cm	?	?	125 cm, 325 cm

In Exercises 12–17, can the numbers be side lengths of a triangle?

12. $\frac{5}{2}, \frac{7}{2}, \frac{9}{2}$ Yes

13. $\sqrt{2}, \sqrt{3}, \sqrt{10}$ No

14. 3.25, 6.79, 10.1   No

15. 4.06, 13.58, 17.21   Yes

16. $\sqrt{15}, \sqrt{20}, \sqrt{65}$ Yes

17. $\frac{1}{8}, \frac{1}{4}, \frac{1}{2}$ No

9.8 ▪ *The Triangle Inequality*   **427**

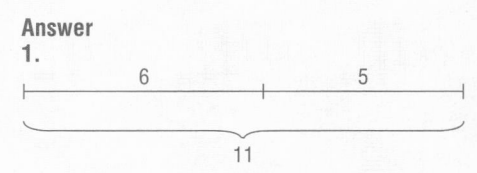

Extra Practice

Extra Practice 9.8   Name _____

In Exercises 1–4, can the side lengths be correct? Explain.
1. No, $2 + 5 \not> 8$ 2.
3. No, $8 + 10 \not> 18$ 4. Yes   Yes

5. Copy and complete the table.

Measure of side 1	Measure of side 2	Measure of side 3 is greater than	Measure of side 3 is less than
4 in.	10 in.	6 in.	14 in.
9 cm	17 cm	8 cm	26 cm
12 ft	20 ft	8 ft	32 ft
45 m	75 m	30 m	120 m
125 yd	170 yd	45 yd	295 yd

In Exercises 6–11, can the numbers be side lengths of a triangle?
6. $\frac{1}{2}, \frac{1}{3}, \frac{1}{4}$ Yes   7. $\sqrt{2}, \sqrt{3}, \sqrt{10}$ Yes   8. 3.24, 6.98, 10.18 Yes
9. $\sqrt{22}, 5, \sqrt{90}$ Yes   10. $\frac{1}{3}, \frac{1}{4}, \frac{1}{8}$ No   11. 10.29, 12.89, 23.18 No

In Exercises 12–15, use the figure at the right to complete the statement.
12. $a + c > \boxed{?}$ $e + d$ 13. $a + \boxed{?} > e$ b
14. $e + d + c > \boxed{?}$ a   15. $b + c > \boxed{?}$ d

16. You are given a 14-inch piece of rope. Your instructions are to cut the rope and form a triangle. The only restriction is that you can only cut the rope into lengths that are integers. List the side lengths of all the possible triangles that could be formed.   2 in., 6 in., 6 in.; 3 in., 5 in., 6 in.; 4 in., 4 in., 6 in.; 4 in., 5 in., 5 in.
17. Is it possible to form a triangle with side lengths of
   a. three consecutive integers?   Yes, except for lengths 1, 2, 3.
   b. three consecutive even integers?   Yes, except for lengths 2, 4, 6.
   c. three consecutive odd integers?   Yes, except for lengths 1, 3, 5.
   Explain your results.
18. You have purchased a triangular piece of land and are planning to build a fence along the entire perimeter. You already have measurements from two sides which are 310 feet and 275 feet. What are the possible lengths for the third side? How much fencing will you purchase to ensure that you have enough fencing to enclose the entire area? How much fencing could you possibly have remaining after you complete the job?   35 ft < 3rd side < 585 ft; at least 1170 ft; < 550 ft

Windows   *9.8* ▪ The Triangle Inequality   **75**

Reteaching

Reteach Chapter 9   Name _____

What you should learn: **Correlation to Pupil's Textbook:**
9.8   How to use the Triangle Inequality   Chapter Test (p. 433)   Exercise 18

Examples   *Using the Triangle Inequality*

a. For triangle PQR shown at the right, use the Triangle Inequality to write three inequalities.

The sum of the lengths of any two sides of a triangle is greater than the length of the third side. In $\triangle PQR$, you can write

   $p + q > r$
   $q + r > p$
   $p + r > q$.

b. The measures of two sides of a triangle are 12 and 15. What can you say about the measure of the third side?

Begin by drawing a diagram with the sides 12, 15 and x. From the triangle, you can write the following inequalities:

   $12 + x > 15$ and $12 + 15 > x$.

By solving these two inequalities, you can determine that the measure of the third side is more than 3 ($x > 3$) and less than 27 ($x < 27$).

Guidelines: • The sum of the lengths of any two sides of a triangle is greater than the length of the third side.

EXERCISES

In Exercises 1–4, use the figure at the right to complete the statement.
1. $s + q > \boxed{?}$ t   2. $r < p + \boxed{?}$ +t   q
3. $r < \boxed{?} + p$ s   4. $p + q + r > \boxed{?}$ t

In Exercises 5–7, the measures of two sides of a triangle are given. What can you say about the measure of the third side?
5. 9 and 14 $x > 5$ and $x < 23$
6. 10 and 18 $x > 8$ and $x < 28$
7. 7 and 11 $x > 4$ and $x < 18$

Windows   Chapter 9 ▪ Real Numbers and Inequalities   **75**

▶ **Ex. 25** Use this as an in-class think/share activity for pairs of students.

Integrated Review

These exercises provide excellent practice in multistep inequalities.

Exploration and Extension

Using either pencils or straws, allow students to do the exercises as an in-class lab activity.

Portfolio Opportunity: Math Log

If one side of a triangle has length 6 cm, and the second side is twice the length of the third side, what can be said about the lengths of the unknown sides?

Also available as a copymaster, page 30. Ex. 9

Short Quiz

Covers Lessons 9.7 and 9.8

Available as a copymaster, page 142

Alternative Assessment

Chapter 9 Group Assessment
A problem-solving grid activity that develops critical thinking about the Pythagorean Theorem.

Chapter 9 Individual Assessment
A similar follow-up activity for individual students. Adds incentive for the group activity and measures individual competence in the activity.

Available as copymasters, pages 75, 76

In Exercises 18–21, use the figure at the right to complete the statement.

18. $b + d > \boxed{?}$ e

19. $a + b + \boxed{?} > e$ c

20. $a < d + \boxed{?}$ c

21. $b + \boxed{?} + e > c$ a

In Exercises 22 and 23, decide whether the string can be folded at the indicated points to form a triangle. Explain.

✪ 22.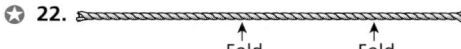
      Fold   Fold

✪ 23.
      Fold   Fold

See margin.

✪ P 24. *Using Scissors*   The blades on your scissors are both 3.75 inches long. The two tips of the blades and the pin that holds the scissors together can form a triangle. When a triangle is formed, how far apart can the tips of the blades be? Explain your reasoning.   Less than $7\frac{1}{2}$ in., by the Triangle Inequality

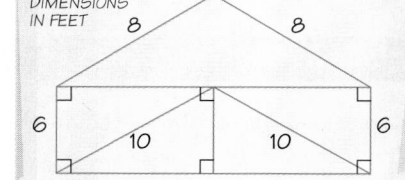

✪ P 25. *Engineering*   Engineers often use triangles to support structures that they build. After receiving the following partial blueprint design for a project, you discover that a mistake has been made. What is it?   See below.

✪ 26. *Finding Perimeters*   A triangle has side lengths of 11 centimeters and 14 centimeters. The perimeter of the triangle must be between what two numbers?   28 and 50

DIMENSIONS IN FEET   8   8
6   10   10   6

25.   If the 6's and 10's are correct, the 8's are incorrect.

Integrated Review   *Making Connections within Mathematics*

Inequalities   **In Exercises 27–30, solve the inequality.**

27. $2x + 17 > 33$ $x > 8$

28. $21 - 3x \le 36$ $x \ge -5$

29. $4x + 2 < 3x + 7$ $x < 5$

30. $6x - 3 \ge 2x + 25$ $x \ge 7$

31. *Geometry*   The triangle at the right is a right triangle. Find the perimeter of the triangle.   30

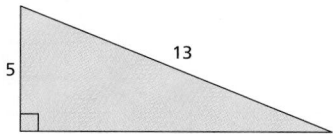
13
5

Exploration and Extension

P *Creating Triangles*   **In Exercises 32–34, you have 5 pencils whose lengths are 3 inches, 4 inches, 5 inches, 8 inches, and 10 inches.**

✪ 32. How many different sizes of triangles can you make with the pencils?   5

✪ 33. How many of the triangles are right triangles?   1

✪ 34. How many of the triangles have a perimeter that is divisible by 3?   2

✪ More difficult exercises
P Portfolio Opportunity

Answers
22. Yes, the sum of the two shorter lengths is greater than the longest length.
23. No, the sum of the two shorter lengths is not greater than the longest length.

9

Chapter Summary

What did you learn?

Why did you learn it?

Not all of the numbers that occur in real-life situations are rational. For instance, you learned that if a right triangle has legs that are each 1-foot long, then the hypotenuse has a length of $\sqrt{2}$ feet or about 1.41 feet. In this chapter, you also learned that many real-life situations are better modeled by inequalities rather than equations. For instance, if you earn a commission of 5%, then the range of house prices H that will earn a commission of at least $4000 is modeled by the inequality $0.05H \geq 4000$ or $H \geq 80,000$.

How does it fit into the bigger picture of mathematics?

Throughout history, people have developed different types of numbers to model different types of real-life situations. Thousands of years ago, primitive people needed only natural numbers such as 1, 2, 3, and 4. As civilization became more and more complicated, people needed rational numbers to measure half of a field or two-thirds of a sack of grain. Later, negative numbers and irrational numbers were needed to measure things such as temperatures below zero and lengths of hypotenuses of triangles. The study of different types of *real numbers* will help you prepare for future classes and occupations.

COOPERATIVE LEARNING
Encourage students to study together. Emphasize the importance of teaching a classmate how to perform a skill or how to recall a procedure. When students work together, everyone wins. The students receiving help get additional instruction, and the students giving help gain a deeper understanding of the skills and concepts involved.

Chapter SUMMARY

Students were introduced at the start of this chapter to the square root property, specifically in the context of solving a simple quadratic equation. Choosing this context took students a step beyond the skills taught in Chapter 4 by further developing their ability to solve equations and to model and solve real-life problems. Since many square roots are irrational, students' understanding of the number line was then expanded to include both rational and irrational numbers.

In Lessons 9.3 and 9.4, students were introduced to the Pythagorean Theorem and to its use as a powerful tool in problem solving.

Recognizing that real-world problems cannot always be modeled with equations but require appropriate inequalities, Lessons 9.5, 9.6, and 9.7 were concerned with the graphing, writing, and solving of inequalities more complex than those presented in Chapter 2. Finally, Lesson 9.8 applied inequalities to the side-lengths of a triangle.

Have students begin this Review in class and complete it as a homework assignment.

ASSIGNMENT GUIDE

*Basic/Average: Ex. 5–11 odd, 17–25 odd, 33–49 odd, 52–58, 59–65 odd

Above Average: Ex. 5–11 odd, 17–25 odd, 33–49 odd, 52–58, 59–65 odd

Advanced: Ex. 5–11 odd, 17–25 odd, 33–49 odd, 52–58, 59–65 odd

*For these students, you will need to limit assignments to cover only those lessons you chose to teach from this chapter.

Resources
Answer Masters, pp. 187, 188

Answers
21. The set of all real numbers less than or equal to -5.
22. The set of all real numbers greater than 13.
23. The set of all real numbers less than 13.
24. The set of all real numbers greater than or equal to -27.
25. The set of all real numbers greater than or equal to 8.
26. The set of all real numbers greater than 20.
27. The set of all real numbers less than $-\frac{1}{9}$.
28. The set of all real numbers less than or equal to $-\frac{5}{2}$.

29.
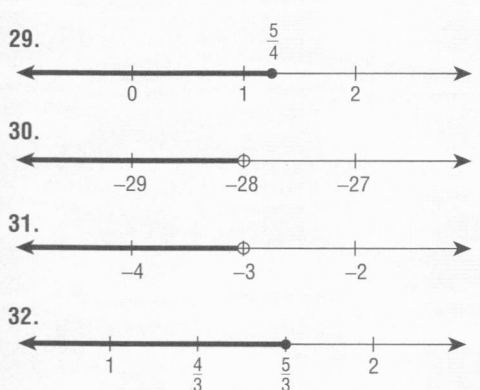

30.

31.

32.
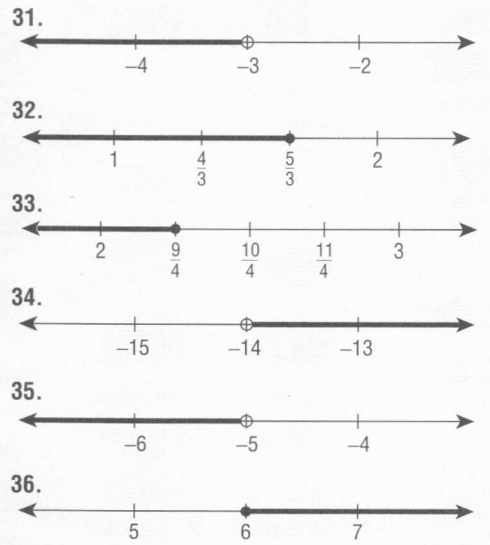

33.

34.

35.

36.

37.

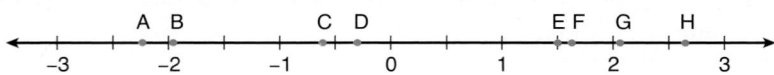

In Exercises 1–8, solve the equation. (9.1)

1. $x^2 = 49$ $7, -7$
2. $y^2 = 144$ $12, -12$
3. $35 = s^2$ $\sqrt{35}, -\sqrt{35}$
4. $t^2 = 19$ $\sqrt{19}, -\sqrt{19}$
5. $a^2 + 4 = 20$ $4, -4$
6. $46 = b^2 - 18$ $8, -8$
7. $5m^2 = 605$ $11, -11$
8. $5n^2 = 25$ $\sqrt{5}, -\sqrt{5}$

In Exercises 9–16, state whether the number is rational or irrational. Then match the number with its location on the number line. (9.2)

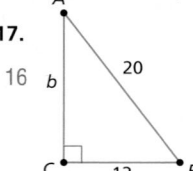

9. $\frac{13}{8}$ Rational, *F*
10. $-\frac{49}{25}$ Rational, *B*
11. $-\sqrt{5}$ Irrational, *A*
12. $\sqrt{7}$ Irrational, *H*

13. $\sqrt{2.25}$ Rational, *E*
14. $-\sqrt{0.09}$ Rational, *D*
15. $-\sqrt{\frac{3}{8}}$ Irrational, *C*
16. $\sqrt{\frac{17}{4}}$ Irrational, *G*

In Exercises 17–20, solve the right triangle. (9.3)

17.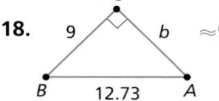
18. ≈ 9.00
19. ≈ 8.06
20.

In Exercises 21–28, solve the inequality. Then write the solution in verbal form. (9.5, 9.6) For verbal forms, see margin.

21. $x + 12 \le 7$ $x \le -5$
22. $-3 < y - 16$ $y > 13$
23. $4 > m - 9$ $m < 13$
24. $n + 8 \ge -19$ $n \ge -27$
25. $5z \ge 40$ $z \ge 8$
26. $\frac{x}{-2} < -10$ $x > 20$
27. $-6p > \frac{2}{3}$ $p < -\frac{1}{9}$
28. $-\frac{1}{4} \ge \frac{1}{10}q$ $q \le -\frac{5}{2}$

In Exercises 29–37, solve the inequality. Then graph the solution on a number line. (9.7) For graphs, see margin.

29. $4x + 8 \le 13$ $x \le \frac{5}{4}$
30. $-\frac{1}{7}y + 5 > 9$ $y < -28$
31. $5x + 18 < -x$ $x < -3$
32. $-6x + 12 \ge 3x - 3$ $x \le \frac{5}{3}$
33. $-45 \le 4(-x - 9)$ $x \le \frac{9}{4}$
34. $-\frac{1}{4}(2x + 8) < 5$ $x > -14$
35. $3(-7 - x) > 19 + 5x$ $x < -5$
36. $6(8 - 2x) \le 3(x - 14)$ $x \ge 6$
37. $-3y + 4 \ge 2y - 6$ $y \le 2$

In Exercises 38–41, decide whether the triangle can have the given side lengths. Explain. (9.3, 9.8)

38.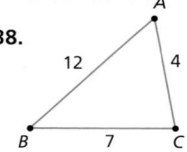
No, $4 + 7 \ne 12$
39.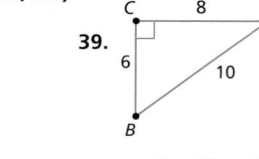
Yes, $6^2 + 8^2 = 10^2$
40.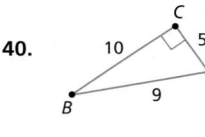
No, $5^2 + 10^2 \ne 9^2$
41.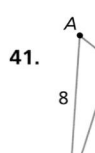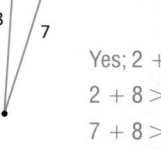
Yes; $2 + 7$
$2 + 8 > 7,$
$7 + 8 > 2$

In Exercises 42–49, write an algebraic model for the sentence. Then solve. (9.1, 9.5–9.7)

42. The sum of b^2 and 11 is 75.　$b^2 + 11 = 75; 8, -8$

43. The product of 5 and t^2 is 125.　$5t^2 = 125; 5, -5$

44. a plus 16 is less than 3.　$a + 16 < 3, a < -13$

45. x minus 7 is greater than 11.　$x - 7 > 11, x > 18$

46. y divided by -6 is greater than or equal to -8.　$\frac{y}{-6} \geq -8, y \leq 48$

47. -4 times m is less than or equal to 52.　$-4m \leq 52, m \geq -13$

48. The difference of $9z$ and 14 is greater than 49.　$9z - 14 > 49, z > 7$

49. The product of 2 and $(5 - x)$ is less than $(x + 11)$.　$2(5 - x) < x + 11, x > -\frac{1}{3}$

50. Explain why there are two solutions to $x^2 = 9$. **(9.1)**　$3^2 = 9$ and $(-3)^2 = 9$

51. *Monopoly*　The board for a Monopoly game is square and has an area of 380.25 square inches. Write an equation that models the area of the board. Then solve to find its side length. **(9.1)**　$x^2 = 380.25, 19.5$ in.

52. *Geometry*　The rectangle at the right has a perimeter that is at most 32 feet. Write an inequality that models this condition. Then solve the inequality. **(9.7)**　$2(4x - 3) + 2(x + 9) \leq 32, x \leq 2$

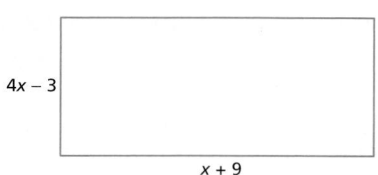

53. *Geometry*　A triangle has side lengths 9 and 16. The perimeter of the triangle must be between what 2 numbers? **(9.8)**　32 and 50

In Exercises 54–56, find the length of the unlabeled side of the triangle. (9.3)

54.
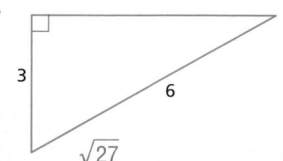

55.
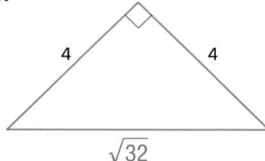

56.
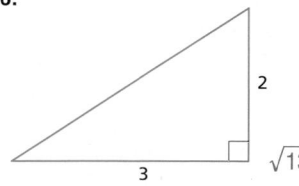

Bowling　**In Exercises 57 and 58, use the following information.**

You and a friend go bowling. Your friend brings her own bowling shoes. You need to rent shoes, which costs \$1.25. Each game costs \$1.75. Your friend says she can spend at most \$7.00. You can spend at most \$10.00. **(9.5–9.7)**

57. Which of the following is the correct model for your friend's expenses? Solve the correct model and interpret the result.　d, $x \leq 4$, she can play at most 4 games

　a. $1.25x + 1.75 \leq 7$　　**b.** $1.75x + 1.25 \leq 7$　　**c.** $1.25x \leq 7$　　**d.** $1.75x \leq 7$

58. Which of the following is the correct model for your expenses? Solve the correct model and interpret the result.　b, $x \leq 5$, you can play at most 5 games

　a. $1.25x + 1.75 \leq 10$　　**b.** $1.75x + 1.25 \leq 10$　　**c.** $1.25x \leq 10$　　**d.** $1.75x \leq 10$

❂ More difficult exercises

Solar Energy Facts   In Exercises 59–61, solve for *a*, *b*, or *c* to obtain the solar energy fact.

a.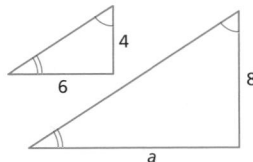

b.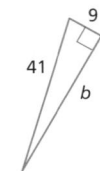

c.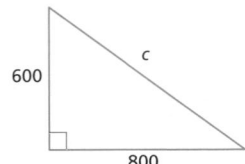

✪ **59.** Every *b* minutes, the sun delivers as much energy to the earth's surface as all the people on earth use in one year.   40

✪ **60.** The amount of solar energy falling on an area of 1 square yard on a sunny day is approximately *c* watts.   1000

✪ **61.** The solar energy that falls on the earth in *a* weeks is the equivalent of the world's entire initial reserves of coal and gas.   12

62. $T \leq 6870$

✪ **62.** *The Odeillo Solar Oven*   The Odeillo Solar Oven's mirror reflects the sun's rays into a solar furnace. Temperatures inside the furnace can reach up to 6870°F. Let *T* represent the temperature inside the furnace. Write an inequality for *T*.

✪ **63.** *The Odeillo Solar Oven*   The huge mirror actually consists of 9500 smaller square mirrors. The side length of each small mirror is about 18 inches. Approximate the total area of the mirror. Write your answer in square inches *and* square feet. 3,078,000 in.²; 21,375 ft²

Types of Solar Energy   In Exercises 64 and 65, use the following information.

There are two basic types of solar energy systems: photovoltaic systems and solar thermal systems. Photovoltaic systems convert sunlight directly into electricity by means of solar cells. These systems are quiet, require no fuel, and generate no pollution. Solar thermal systems do not generate electricity directly. Instead, they use the heat from the sun's rays to run generators that produce electricity.

✪ **64.** What type of solar energy system do you think solar-powered calculators use? Explain.

✪ **65.** What type of solar energy system does the Odeillo Solar Oven use? Explain.   Solar thermal, the furnace is the generator.

64. Photovoltaic, there is no generator.

The Odeillo Solar Oven, built in France in the 1960s, is one of the most successful solar furnaces. It is also the largest solar-powered electric plant in Europe.

Solar collectors are painted black since black absorbs sunlight more effectively. The glass covers protect the panels from the weather.

✪ More difficult exercises

1. List both square roots of 225. (**9.1**)   15, -15
2. Solve the equation $a^2 + 3 = 39$. (**9.1**)   6, -6
3. A square has an area of 65.61 square units. What is the length of each side? (**9.1**)   8.1 units
4. A right triangle has sides of 5 inches and 12 inches. Name two possibilities for the length of the third side. (**9.3**)   13 in., ≈10.91 in.

In Exercises 5–8, match each number with its location on the number line. (9.2)

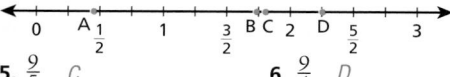

5. $\frac{9}{5}$ C
6. $\frac{9}{4}$ D
7. $\sqrt{3}$ B
8. $\sqrt{0.2}$ A

In Exercises 9–11, solve the triangle. (9.3)

9.

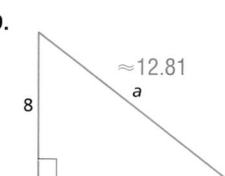

10.

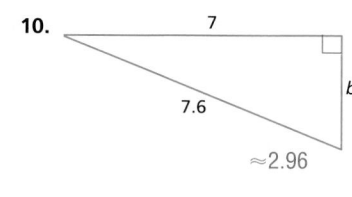

11.

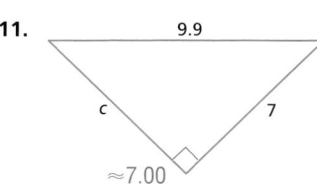

In Exercises 12–14, graph the inequality on a number line. (9.5)   See margin.

12. $x \geq -4$
13. $x < 12$
14. $x > 5$

In Exercises 15–17, solve the inequality. (9.6, 9.7)

15. $-x < 2$ $x > -2$
16. $-8r + 16 \leq 8$ $r \geq 1$
17. $-2p \geq 5$ $p \leq -\frac{5}{2}$

18. The measures of two sides of a triangle are 4 cm and 9 cm. What can you say about the measure of the third side? (**9.8**)
    Greater than 5 cm, less than 13 cm

In Exercises 19–21, use the following. (9.4)

You have a summer job of painting houses. You want to place a 20-foot ladder to the bottom of a window, as shown in the diagram at the right.

19. How far away from the house do you need to put the bottom of the ladder?   12 ft
20. If you wanted to move the ladder just above the top of the window, how far away from the house would you have to put the bottom of the ladder?   ≈6.24 ft
21. To maintain balance, you don't want the bottom of the ladder to be closer than 5 feet from the house. What is the highest that the top of the ladder can be?   ≈19.36 ft

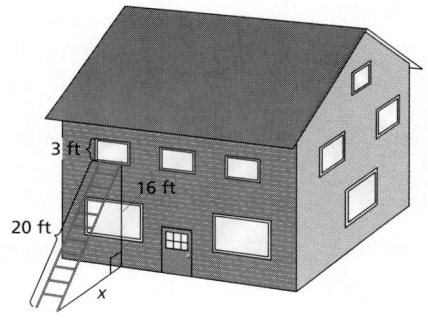

Chapter Test

Resources
Color Transparencies
   Diagram for Ex. 19–21, p. 39

Answers

12.

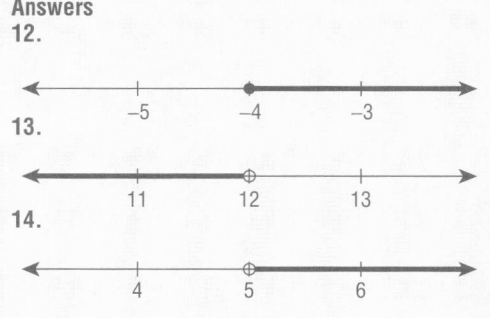

13.

14.

◀ Formal Assessment

Three **Chapter Tests.** Form A is of average difficulty, Form B is of average difficulty in multiple choice format, and Form C is more challenging.
Available as copymasters, pages 143–151

Cumulative REVIEW ■ Chapters 7–9

In Exercises 1–4, simplify the expression. (7.1–7.2)

1. $\frac{2}{7} + \frac{4}{7}$ $\frac{6}{7}$

2. $\frac{16x}{4} - \frac{14x}{4}$ $\frac{x}{2}$

3. $\frac{1}{4} + \frac{1}{6}$ $\frac{5}{12}$

4. $\frac{5}{8} - \frac{17}{32}$ $\frac{3}{32}$

In Exercises 5–8, use a calculator to evaluate the expression. Round the result to 2 decimal places. (7.3)

5. $\frac{64}{71} + \frac{57}{90}$ 1.53

6. $\frac{104}{115}x - \frac{21}{37}x$ 0.34x

7. $1 - \left(\frac{3}{20} + \frac{7}{31}\right)$ 0.62

8. $\frac{26}{9}t + \frac{85}{200}t$ 3.31t

In Exercises 9–12, simplify the expression. (7.4–7.5)

9. $\frac{5}{12} \cdot \frac{10}{3}$ $\frac{25}{18}$

10. $\frac{5}{2} \div \frac{1}{5}$ $\frac{25}{2}$

11. $\frac{7n}{4} \cdot 16$ 28n

12. $-\frac{6}{10} \div \frac{z}{5}$ $-\frac{3}{z}$

In Exercises 13 and 14, find the perimeter and area of the figure. (7.1–7.5)

13.

5 $\frac{5}{6}$ in.

4 $\frac{1}{4}$ in.

$20\frac{1}{6}$ in., $24\frac{19}{24}$ in.²

14.

6 $\frac{7}{8}$ in.

6 $\frac{7}{8}$ in.

14. $27\frac{1}{2}$ in., $47\frac{17}{64}$ in.²

In Exercises 15–18, write the portion as a percent. (7.6)

15. $\frac{3}{10}$ 30%

16. $\frac{18}{25}$ 72%

17. $\frac{140}{175}$ 80%

18. $\frac{100}{250}$ 40%

19. *Geometry*   What portion of the figure at the right is shaded blue? Express your answer as a fraction, percent, and decimal. **(7.7)** $\frac{3}{5}$, 60%, 0.6

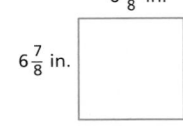

20. *Simple Interest*   You deposit $632 in a savings account that pays 4.82% in simple interest. If you make no other deposits or withdrawals during the year, how much money will be in the account after one year? **(7.8–7.9)** $662.46

In Exercises 21–24, decide whether the quotient is a rate or a ratio. Then simplify. (8.1)

21. $\frac{84 \text{ gallons}}{3 \text{ minutes}}$ Rate, 28 gal per min

22. $\frac{5 \text{ houses}}{3 \text{ houses}}$ Ratio, $\frac{5}{3}$

23. $\frac{16 \text{ feet}}{24 \text{ inches}}$ Ratio, $\frac{8}{1}$

24. $\frac{63 \text{ meters}}{1.5 \text{ seconds}}$ Rate 42 m per sec

25. *Property Tax*   If you pay $2100 in property tax for a $105,000 house, how much property tax would you pay for a $140,000 house? **(8.3)** $2800

In Exercises 26–29, solve the proportion. (8.2)

26. $\frac{3}{18} = \frac{t}{30}$ 5

27. $\frac{12}{16} = \frac{27}{n}$ 36

28. $\frac{1}{m} = \frac{1.5}{6}$ 4

29. $\frac{x}{55} = \frac{5}{8}$ $\frac{275}{8}$

In Exercises 30–35, solve the percent equation. (8.4)

30. 63 is what percent of 90?   70%

31. What is 85% of 40?   34

32. 80 is 50% of what number?   160

33. 95 is what percent of 125?   76%

34. What is 52.5% of 230?   120.75

35. 105 is 150% of what number?   70

434   *Chapter 9 • Real Numbers and Inequalities*

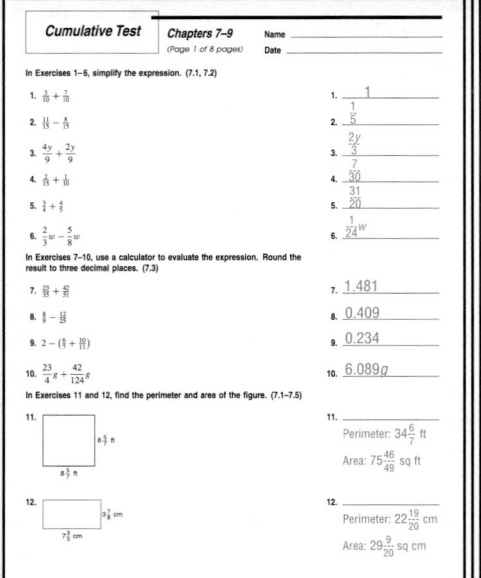

Favorite Movies **In Exercises 36–40, use the following.**
(8.5)

You take a survey about favorite types of movies. The circle graph shows the results of your survey. Eighteen people said that science fiction movies were their favorite.

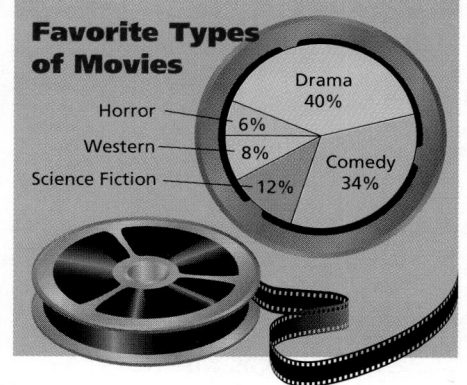

Favorite Types of Movies

Drama 40%
Horror 6%
Western 8%
Comedy 34%
Science Fiction 12%

36. How many people were surveyed? 150
37. How many people said drama? 60
38. How many people said comedy? 51
39. How many people said western? 12
40. How many people said horror? 9

In Exercises 41 and 42, decide whether the change is an increase or decrease. Then find the percent. (8.6)

41. 1995: 207,100 units Increase,
　　　 1996: 215,025 units ≈3.83%

42. Regular Price: $39.99 Decrease,
　　　 Sale Price: $25.99 ≈35.01%

Canadian Zip Codes **In Exercises 43–45, use the following. (8.7–8.8)**

In Canada, each zip code begins with a letter, then alternates between numbers and letters. How many zip codes have the indicated form?

43. L2R 1?0 26
44. H?C 4?9 260
45. L2R ??? 2600

46. Plot the set of numbers on a number line. **(9.2)** See margin.

$$\left\{ \frac{12}{15}, \ -\sqrt{3} \ , \ -\sqrt{\frac{81}{121}} \ , \ \frac{\sqrt{68}}{4} \ , \ -\frac{14}{29}, \ \sqrt{5.76} \ \right\}$$

In Exercises 47–49, solve the right triangle. (9.3)

47. 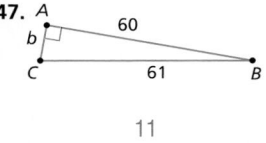 11

48. 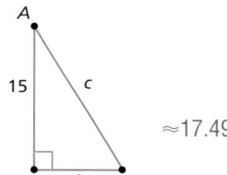 ≈17.49

49. 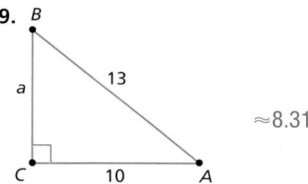 ≈8.31

In Exercises 50–53, solve the inequality. Then graph the solution. (9.4–9.8) For graphs, see margin.

50. $a + 12 < 7$　$a < -5$　**51.** $b - 19 \geq -5$　$b \geq 14$　**52.** $-4 \geq -6m$　$m \geq \frac{2}{3}$　**53.** $\frac{-n}{8} > \frac{2}{3}$　$n < -\frac{16}{3}$

In Exercises 54–56, decide whether the numbers can be the lengths of three sides of a triangle. (9.8)

54. 5, 9, 13　Yes
55. $\frac{6}{17}, \frac{1}{4}, \frac{3}{8}$　Yes
56. 4, 7, $\sqrt{128}$　No

 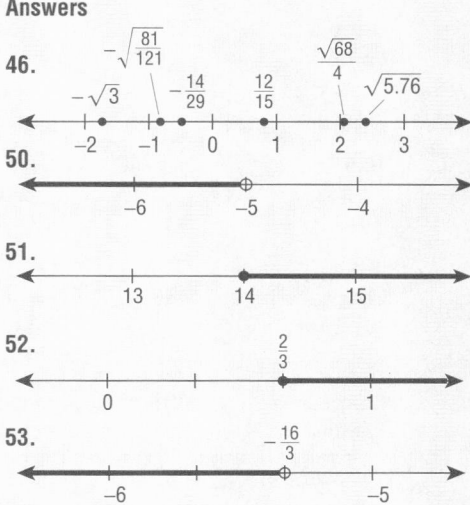

CHAPTER 10 GOALS

CHAPTER 10 · OVERVIEW

Lesson Pages	10.1 439–442	10.2 443–446	10.3 448–451	10.4 453–456	10.5 457–460	10.6 462–466	10.7 467–470	10.8 472–475	10.9 477–480
Lesson Plans	76	77	78	79	80	81	82	83	84
Problem of the Day	28	28	28	29	29	29	30	30	30
Warm-Up Exercises	28	28	28	29	29	29	30	30	30
Color Transparencies	—	40	40, 41	41, 42	42	43	44	—	44
Teaching Tools: Transparencies	—	T12	T3	T9	T2, T13	T2, T12, T14	T2	T1, T12,	T9, T12
Copymasters	—	C18	C4	C11	C3, C19	C3, C18, C20	C3, C21	C2, C18	C11, C18
Math Log	31	31	31	32	32	32	33	33	33
Technology	—	—	57	58	59	—	—	60	61
Answer Masters	192, 193	194	195	197	198–200	201, 202	204	205, 206	207–209
Extra Practice	76	77	78	79	80	81	82	83	84
Reteaching Copymasters	76	77	78	79	80	81	82	83	84
Enrichment Projects	—	—	—	49, 50	51–53	—	—	—	54, 55
Alternative Assessment: Projects	33	—	—	34	34	—	—	—	—
Partner Quizzes	—	—	—	—	53	—	—	—	—
Group Assessment	—	—	—	—	—	—	77, 78	—	—
Formal Assessment Short Quizzes	—	160	—	161	—	164	—	165	—
Tests	—	—	—	—	162, 163	—	—	—	166–174
Overhead Manipulatives Kit	—	—	—	—	—	—	—	—	—
Complete Solutions Manual	Includes step-by-step solutions for all exercises in the student text								
Computerized Test Bank	Creates customized tests that include graphics								
Interactive CD-ROM Project	Provides an interactive and interdisciplinary chapter project								

STARTERS

Problem of the Day

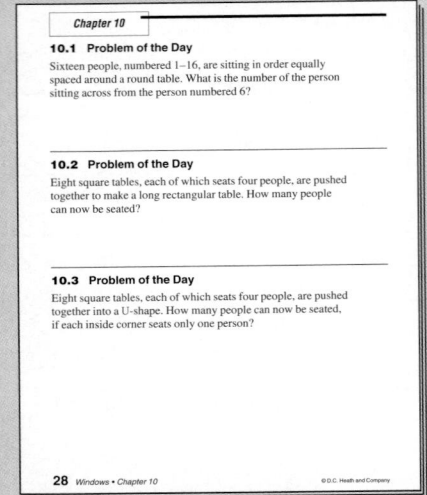

Warm-Up Exercises

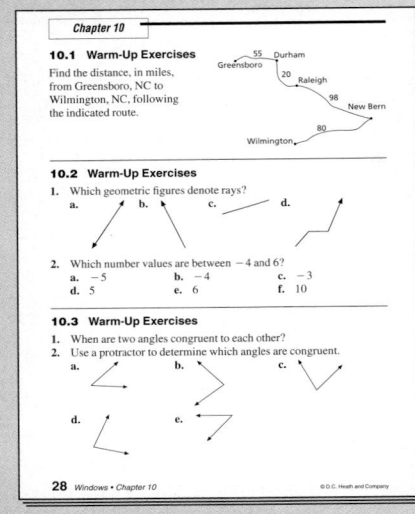

FOR TEACHERS

Answer Masters

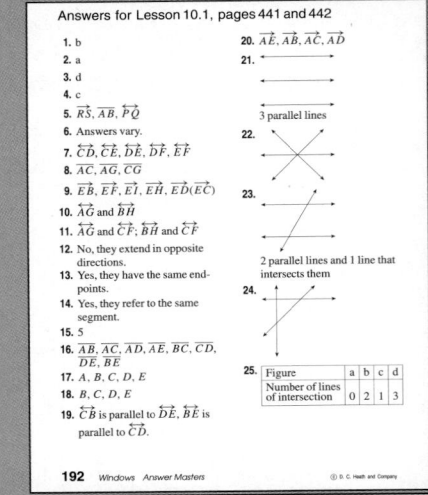

Lesson Plans

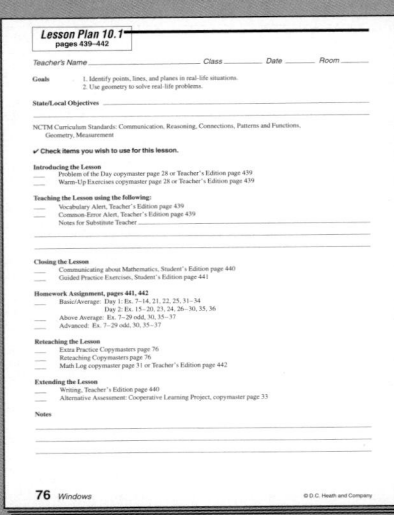

Teaching Tools

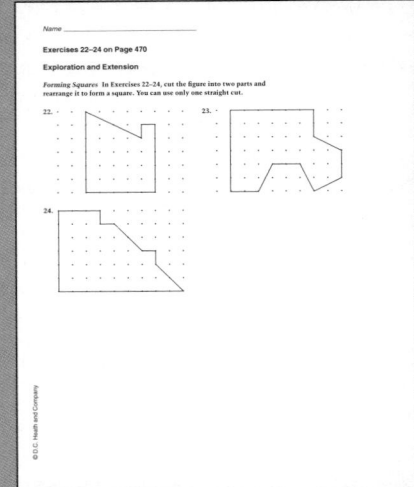

Teaching Tools includes:
Transparencies and Copymasters for classroom activities and study skills:

- Graph Paper
- Dot Paper (Geoboards)
- Algebra Tiles
- Number Counters
- Fraction Strips
- Models

REAL LIFE

Color Transparencies for Real-Life Applications

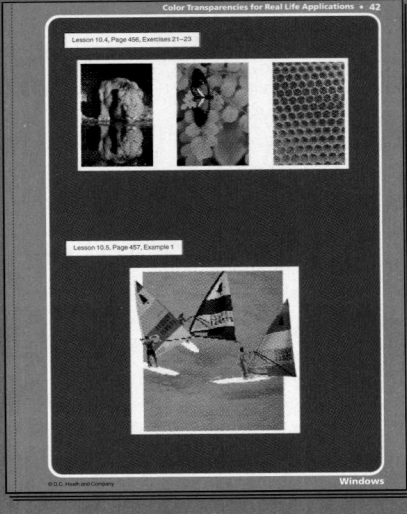

Technology: Using Calculators and Computers

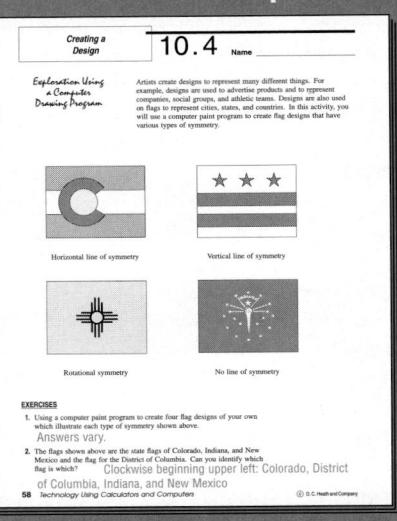

Also Available:

- Complete Solutions Manual
- Overhead Manipulatives Kit
- Computerized Testing Program

- **Interactive CD-ROM Projects**
  Interactive projects for solving real-world problems using multimedia

- **Interactions: Real Math–Real Careers**
  A videodisc–based resource that connects math to real careers and on-the-job problem solving

- **PACKETS® Performance Assessment for Middle School Mathematics**
  A program that links assessment and instruction in real-life settings

ASSESSMENT

Alternative Assessment

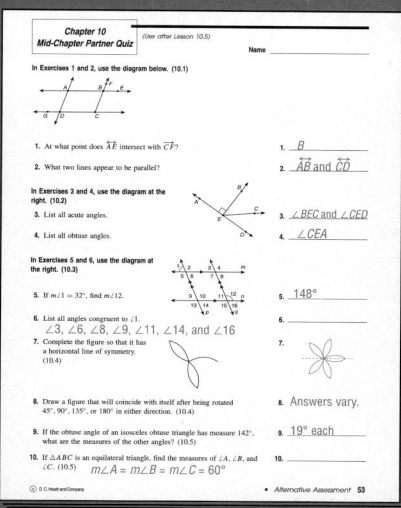

Alternative Assessment includes:

- Scoring Rubrics
- Portfolios
- Math Journals
- Projects
- Partner Quizzes
- Individual and Group Assessment

Formal Assessment

Formal Assessment includes:

- Short Quizzes (after every 2 lessons)
- Mid-Chapter Tests (2 forms)
- Chapter Tests (3 forms)
- Cumulative Tests (after every 3 Chapters)

MEETING INDIVIDUAL NEEDS

Extra Practice Copymasters

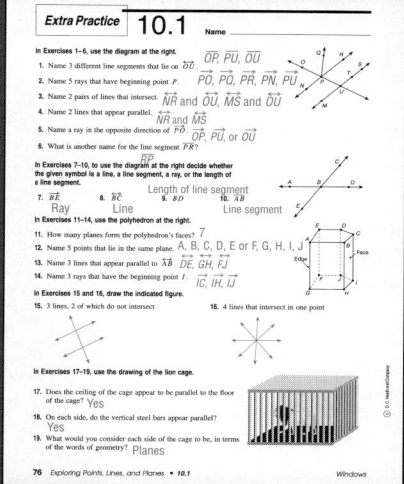

Reteaching Copymasters

Enrichment Projects

Math Log

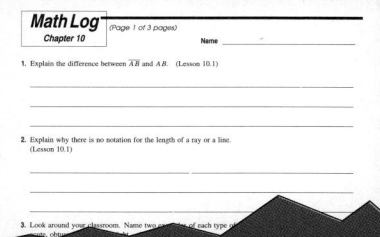

Special Populations

Suggestions for providing equal access for:

Students Acquiring English Proficiency*

To assist these students in learning the names of the shapes used in this chapter, provide them with pictures and/or cutouts of the various figures. Have them draw and label each figure and find examples of each in common classroom objects.

Students with Various Learning Styles*

Do not be overly concerned if students experience difficulty memorizing new vocabulary words. It is more important that they grasp the geometric concepts and applications. Let students make posters illustrating things that tend to confuse them, for example, parallel and perpendicular lines.

In Lesson 10.4, try to find actual physical objects that illustrate the different types of symmetry.

Underachieving Students*

Some students may have difficulty using a protractor and compass. Cooperative learning activities will help these students while encouraging interactions with classmates.

In Lessons 10.5 and 10.6, have students use geoboards to make the different triangles and quadrilaterals that are defined.

*Gifted and Talented Students

After students complete the Exploration and Extension exercises in Lesson 10.6, challenge students to use all the tangram pieces to make different objects such as a plane, a rocket, and a bird.

Have students work in groups to extend the Exploration and Extension in Lesson 10.7 by drawing figures that can be cut into two parts and rearranged to form a square. Groups can then exchange papers and check one another's work.

* See page T19 for descriptions of these special populations.

CHAPTER

10

Geometry Concepts and Spatial Thinking

PACING CHART

Lesson	Basic/ Average Course	Above Average Course	Advanced Course
10.1	2 days	1 day	1 day
10.2	2 days	1 day	1 day
10.3	2 days	1 day	1 day
10.4	2 days	1 day	1 day
10.5	2 days	1 day	1 day
10.6	2 days	2 days	1 day
10.7	0 days	1 day	1 day
10.8	2 days	2 days	1 day
10.9	0 days	1 day	1 day

About the Chapter

This is the first of three chapters in which students are introduced informally to many of the important concepts in geometry through simple, hands-on methods—measurement with ruler and protractor, models, paper-cutting, dot- and graph paper, simple computer software, and so on. Students will begin to learn the language of geometry, the recognition and classification of figures, and the use of some simple reasoning based on the properties of geometric figures.

In Lessons 10.1 and 10.2, students learn the terminology for points, lines, planes, and angles. Lesson 10.3 uses the properties of parallel lines to afford students an opportunity for simple reasoning. Lesson 10.4 introduces students to one of the properties used to classify figures—symmetry. The basics of classification are developed further in Lesson 10.5 and 10.6, first with triangles and then with quadrilaterals. In Lessons 10.7 and 10.8, polygons are used as the context in which students learn about congruence of figures and about angle relationships, and these two concepts are developed further in Lesson 10.9.

Breath-held divers have been recorded at depths of about −278 feet (feet below sea level). With the aid of SCUBA (Self Contained Underwater Breathing Apparatus) gear, divers have reached depths of −437 feet. By contrast, mammals like seals have been found at depths of about −1970 feet and sperm whales at about −3270 feet.

Real Life

Deep Sea Missions

Cathode Ray Display

Ships use sonar (SOund NAvigation and Ranging) to track icebergs, whales, and schools of fish. Sound pulses are sent out in all directions. When they encounter a large object, the sound wave bounces back as an echo. A cathode ray screen displays the echo as a blip of light.

The cathode ray display is a coordinate system. Angle measures are read along the outer rim. Distances from the center (the location of the ship) are read from the concentric circles. The measuring of angles and distances is just one of the real-life spatial relationships that you will encounter in this chapter.

Using the Page

Light travels more slowly in water than it does in air. For this reason, light waves travelling in straight lines bend at the border of air and water. How light travels through different media is another example of a real-life spatial relationship.

One experiment you can try with your students is to place a coin in the center of a small dish. Place the dish so that students can't see the coin but can see the far inside edge of the dish at eye level. Fill the dish with water until students can see the coin without craning their necks. Challenge students to create a different experiment that demonstrates how light waves behave in water or in glass.

Multimedia Resources

Interactive CD-ROM Projects
A project for this chapter combines print, animation, sound and video presentations to capture students' interest in Tiling. This interactive approach shows students how the math concepts and problem-solving strategies they are learning will be used in the future in dealing with important personal, national, and world issues.

The theme of Tiling correlates to examples and exercises on pages 468 and 470.

Interactions: Real Math—Real Life
The theme of this chapter, Deep Sea Missions, correlates with an episode of **Interactions** which is a videodisc-based multimedia resource that connects middle school math topics with real-life careers. In each of the twelve episodes, students go on-site with a variety of professionals to witness real-life applications of the math they are studying. Students see math concepts and problem-solving strategies in a context that helps them connect what they are studying to the world outside the classroom. **Interactions** was developed by the Foundation for Advancements in Science and Education (FASE) and is published by D.C. Heath and Company.

The theme of Deep Sea Missions is continued throughout the chapter on pages 452 and 484.

Performance Assessment Resource

The PACKETS® Program: Performance Assessment for Middle School Mathematics was developed by Educational Testing Service and is published by D.C. Heath. **PACKETS** helps you assess your students' performances as they learn. You can use a wide variety of **PACKETS** Activity Units with this chapter because, in every activity, students will use ideas from all topic areas of mathematics. However, you can use the chart on page T16 to help you choose the **PACKETS** Activity Unit(s) that may fit best with this chapter.

This is an investigation in three dimensions. Since we live in a 3-D world, this investigation gives students the opportunity to investigate geometric properties in an environment that they are familiar with. In the investigation, the marshmallows represent points and toothpicks represent the segments.

Materials Needed: toothpicks, small marshmallows

Example **Exploring Three-Dimensional Objects**

Use toothpicks and small marshmallows to build some three-dimensional objects. Each toothpick must have a marshmallow at each end, and each marshmallow must have at least 3 toothpicks stuck into it. After you have created the objects, count the number of marshmallows and toothpicks used. Then count the number of positions that the object can be turned so that the object can be set on a table.

Solution Two objects are shown below. The first uses 8 marshmallows and 12 toothpicks. This object can be placed on a table in 6 different positions. With each position, 4 marshmallows are on the table. The second object uses 5 marshmallows and 8 toothpicks. This object can be placed on a table in 5 different positions. With four of the positions, 3 marshmallows are on the table. With the fifth position, 4 marshmallows are on the table.

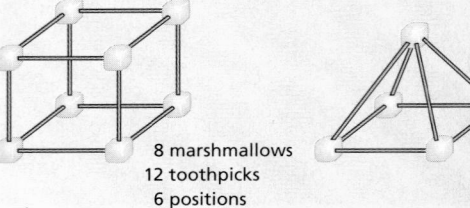

8 marshmallows
12 toothpicks
6 positions

5 marshmallows
8 toothpicks
5 positions

Exercises

Answer the following questions in groups. Before answering the questions, each member of your group should build at least two objects that are different from those shown above.

1. What is the fewest number of marshmallows used by a person in your group to form another object? Is this the fewest possible? The fewest possible is 4.

2. What is the fewest number of toothpicks used by a person in your group to form an object? Is this the fewest possible? The fewest possible is 6.

3. Using exactly 6 marshmallows, can you build two objects that do not look alike? Yes, for figures see margin.

4. Name the shapes that are formed by the bottom of each object you have made as it rests on a table. Answers vary, but include triangles, squares, etc.

Answer
3.

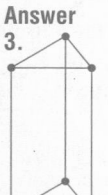 

10.1

Exploring Points, Lines, and Planes

 What you should learn:

Goal 1 How to identify points, lines, and planes in real-life situations

Goal 2 How to use geometry figures to solve real-life problems

 Why you should learn it:

You can use geometry to solve real-life problems, such as planning a trip through several cities.

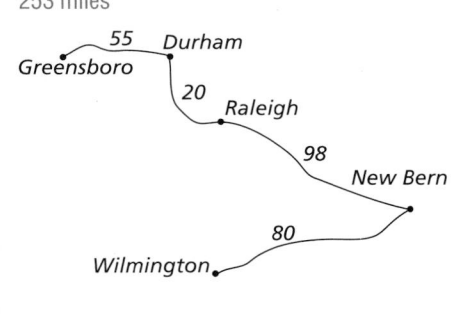
Goal 1 **Identifying Points, Lines, and Planes**

In Chapters 10, 11, and 12, you will learn how geometry can be used to model real-life situations. To become skilled in geometry, you must learn the meaning of the *words* of geometry and you must learn how to use the *properties* of geometry.

Pictured at the right are **points,** a **line,** a **ray,** a **line segment,** and a **plane.** You can't actually draw a line, ray, or plane because each extends forever in at least one direction. A line extends forever in two directions, a ray extends forever in only one direction, and a plane extends forever in many directions.

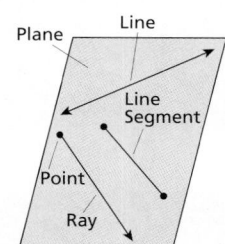

The **length** of a line segment $\overline{AB}$ is denoted by AB. Notice the difference between the symbols used to denote lines, rays, line segments, and lengths of line segments.

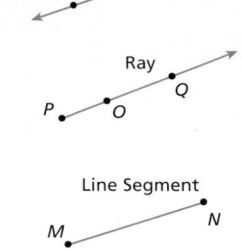

Name	Symbol
Line	$\overleftrightarrow{RS}, \overleftrightarrow{SR}, \overleftrightarrow{RT}$
Ray	$\overrightarrow{PQ}, \overrightarrow{PO}$
Line segment	$\overline{MN}, \overline{NM}$
Line segment length	MN, NM

Example 1 *Exploring Parallel Lines*

Two lines are **parallel** if they lie in the same plane and do not **intersect.** Which streets on the map at the left are parallel?

Solution Elm Street, Maple Street, and Pine Street are parallel. Main Street and State Street are also parallel. No other pair of streets are parallel because they intersect. In fact, the word *intersection* is used in everyday language to indicate the place where two streets or roads meet. ∎

10.1 • *Exploring Points, Lines, and Planes* **439**

▶ **PACING the Lesson**

Suggested Number of Days
Basic/Average 2 **Above Average** 1
Advanced 1

▶ **PLANNING the Lesson**

Lesson Plan 10.1, p. 76

ORGANIZER

Starters (reproduced below)
Problem of the Day 10.1, p. 28
Warm-Up Exercises 10.1, p. 28
Lesson Resources
Math Log, p. 31
Answer Masters 10.1, pp. 192, 193
Extra Practice Copymaster 10.1, p. 76
Reteaching Copymaster 10.1, p. 76
Special Populations
Suggestions, Teacher's Edition, p. 436D

LESSON Notes

Vocabulary Alert!

The boldface words should be entered into students' mathematics journals. Discuss each term and provide several examples or illustrations of each. You may want to have students construct physical models of selected geometric objects after the discussion. Or you may wish to provide opportunities for students to practice how the various objects are drawn.

Common-Error Alert!

When naming rays, the order in which points are named is important. Make sure that students recognize that the vertex must be stated first. When naming lines and line segments, the order in which points are named is not important.

Example 1

Emphasize that the map is a model of a plane on which the streets lie. Students might want to look at local maps to see how frequently parallel streets occur in their communities.

Geometric ideas such as points, line segments, and lines, are seen in many real-life situations. Challenge students to identify everyday settings in which these geometric objects are found.

Example 2

Ask students to repeat this activity using local towns and cities near their communities.

Communicating about MATHEMATICS

Students might enjoy looking at different routes among the major cities in their state.

Writing Prompt
Give examples of physical models that could represent a point, a segment, a ray, and a plane.

Real Life
Trip Planning

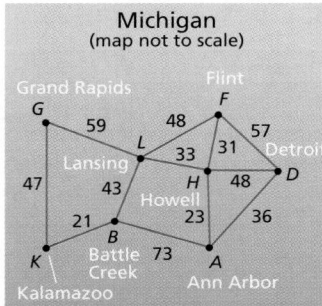

The University of Michigan, located in Ann Arbor, was established in 1817.

Example 2 | *Using Line Segments*

You are planning a trip through eight cities in Michigan: Kalamazoo, Grand Rapids, Lansing, Howell, Flint, Ann Arbor, Battle Creek, and Detroit. You want to travel on the roads shown on the map at the left. Beginning and ending in Detroit, what is the least number of miles you can drive?

Solution Four possible routes are shown below. To find the distance along each route, add the lengths of the line segments that make up the route. For instance, the distance along Route 1 is

$$48 + 23 + 73 + 21 + 47 + 59 + 48 + 57 = 376 \text{ miles.}$$

In the *Communicating* feature below, you are asked to find the distances along the other routes.

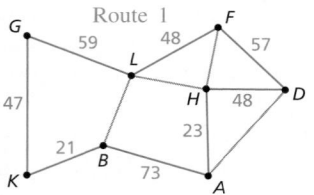
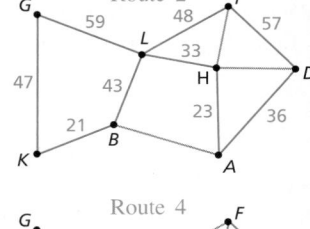
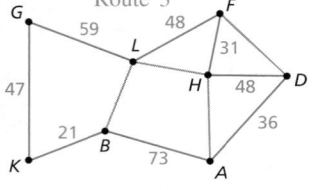
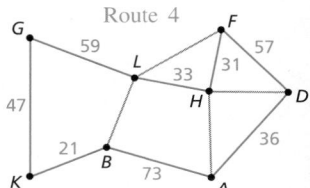

367 mi, 363 mi, 357 mi; 4; no, two consecutive "spokes" from Howell must be traveled and there are only these four most efficient routes to take.

Communicating about MATHEMATICS

▶ **SHARING IDEAS about the Lesson**

Comparing Distances In Example 2, find the distances you would travel along Routes 2, 3, and 4. Which of these four routes is the shortest? Is there another route that is shorter than the four routes shown? Explain your reasoning.

EXERCISES

Guided Practice

▶ **CHECK for Understanding**

In Exercises 1–4, match the figure with its term.

a.
A ●————————● B

b.
S ←●————————●→ R

c.

d.
←●————————●→
  P   Q

1. Ray b   **2.** Line Segment a   **3.** Line d $\overleftrightarrow{}$ **4.** Plane c

5. Write the symbol for each figure in Exercises 1–3. $\overrightarrow{RS}$, $\overline{AB}$, $\overleftrightarrow{PQ}$

6. *The Shape of Things*   Describe examples of parallel lines and intersecting lines in your classroom. Answers vary.

Independent Practice

In Exercises 7–14, use the diagram at the right.

9. $\overrightarrow{EB}$, $\overrightarrow{EF}$, $\overrightarrow{EI}$, $\overrightarrow{EH}$, $\overrightarrow{ED}$ ($\overrightarrow{EC}$)

7. Write four other names for the line $\overleftrightarrow{CF}$. $\overleftrightarrow{CD}$, $\overleftrightarrow{CE}$, $\overleftrightarrow{DE}$, $\overleftrightarrow{DF}$, $\overleftrightarrow{EF}$

8. Name 3 different line segments that lie on $\overleftrightarrow{AG}$. $\overline{AC}$, $\overline{AG}$, $\overline{CG}$

9. Name 5 rays that have the same beginning point. See above.

10. Name 2 lines that appear parallel. $\overleftrightarrow{AG}$ and $\overleftrightarrow{BH}$

11. Name 2 pairs of lines that intersect. $\overleftrightarrow{AG}$ and $\overleftrightarrow{CF}$, $\overleftrightarrow{BH}$ and $\overleftrightarrow{CF}$

12. Are $\overrightarrow{EB}$ and $\overrightarrow{BE}$ the same ray? Explain. No, they extend in opposite directions.

13. Are $\overline{EI}$ and $\overline{IE}$ the same line segment? Explain. Yes, they have the same endpoints.

14. Do DC and CD represent the same length? Explain. Yes, they refer to the same segment.

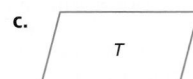

In Exercises 15–20, use the pyramid at the right.

A **pyramid** is a space figure whose base is a polygon and whose other faces are triangles that share a common vertex.

15. How many planes form the pyramid's faces? 5

16. Name the line segments that form the pyramid's edges. See below.

17. Name the points that form the pyramid's vertices. A, B, C, D, E

18. Name four points that lie in the same plane. B, C, D, E

19. Which line is parallel to $\overleftrightarrow{DE}$? to $\overleftrightarrow{CD}$? $\overleftrightarrow{CB}$, $\overleftrightarrow{BE}$

20. Name four rays that have the same beginning point.

16. $\overline{AB}$, $\overline{AC}$, $\overline{AD}$, $\overline{AE}$, $\overline{BC}$, $\overline{CD}$, $\overline{DE}$, $\overline{BE}$

20. $\overrightarrow{AB}$, $\overrightarrow{AC}$, $\overrightarrow{AD}$, $\overrightarrow{AE}$

In Exercises 21–24, draw the indicated figure.
See Additional Answers.

21. 3 lines that do not intersect   ✪ **22.** 3 lines that intersect in 1 point

23. 3 lines that intersect in 2 points   ✪ **24.** 3 lines that intersect in 3 points

✪ More difficult exercises
Ⓟ Portfolio Opportunity

10.1 • Exploring Points, Lines, and Planes   **441**

EXERCISE Notes

ASSIGNMENT GUIDE
Basic/Average:
 Day 1: Ex. 7–14, 21, 22, 25, 31–34
 Day 2: Ex. 15–20, 23, 24, 26–30, 35, 36
Above Average: Ex. 7–29 odd, 30, 35–37
Advanced: Ex. 7–29 odd, 30, 35–37
Selected Answers: Ex. 1–6, 7–35 odd

Guided Practice

▶ **Ex. 5** $\overrightarrow{RS}$ should be denoted with a right-pointing arrow even though the model shows the ray continuing in the left direction.
▶ **Ex. 6**
EXTENSION
Have students describe examples of parallel and intersecting lines on a playing field (soccer, baseball, etc.).

Independent Practice

▶ **Ex. 8** Point out to students that $\overline{AC}$ and $\overline{CA}$ are not different segments.
▶ **Ex. 12–14** Make sure that students understand the difference in the responses to these three questions.
▶ **Ex. 15–20** You can help the discussion of these exercises by having models of pyramids available for students to handle.
▶ **Ex. 21–24** Pieces of uncooked spaghetti can be used on an overhead projector to model the responses to these exercises.

Extra Practice

Extra Practice 10.1   Name _____

In Exercises 1–6, use the diagram at the right.
1. Name 3 different line segments that lie on $\overleftrightarrow{OU}$. $\overline{OP}$, $\overline{PU}$, $\overline{OU}$
2. Name 5 rays that have beginning point P. $\overrightarrow{PO}$, $\overrightarrow{PQ}$, $\overrightarrow{PR}$, $\overrightarrow{PN}$, $\overrightarrow{PU}$
3. Name 2 pairs of lines that intersect. $\overleftrightarrow{NR}$ and $\overleftrightarrow{OU}$, $\overleftrightarrow{MS}$ and $\overleftrightarrow{OU}$
4. Name 2 lines that appear parallel. $\overleftrightarrow{NR}$ and $\overleftrightarrow{MS}$
5. Name a ray in the opposite direction of $\overrightarrow{PO}$. $\overrightarrow{OP}$, $\overrightarrow{PU}$, or $\overrightarrow{OU}$
6. What is another name for the line segment $\overline{PR}$? $\overline{RP}$

In Exercises 7–10, use the diagram at the right decide whether the given symbol is a line, a line segment, a ray, or the length of a line segment.
7. $\overline{BE}$ Ray   **8.** $\overleftrightarrow{BC}$ Line   **9.** BD Length of line segment   **10.** $\overline{AB}$ Line segment

In Exercises 11–14, use the polyhedron at the right.
11. How many planes form the polyhedron's faces? 7
12. Name 5 points that lie in the same plane. A, B, C, D, E or F, G, H, I, J
13. Name 3 lines that appear parallel to $\overleftrightarrow{AB}$. $\overleftrightarrow{DE}$, $\overleftrightarrow{GH}$, $\overleftrightarrow{FJ}$
14. Name 3 rays that have beginning point I. $\overrightarrow{IC}$, $\overrightarrow{IH}$, $\overrightarrow{IJ}$

In Exercises 15 and 16, draw the indicated figure.
15. 3 lines, 2 of which do not intersect   **16.** 4 lines that intersect in one point

In Exercises 17–19, use the drawing of the lion cage.
17. Does the ceiling of the cage appear to be parallel to the floor of the cage? Yes
18. On each side, do the vertical steel bars appear parallel? Yes
19. What would you consider each side of the cage to be, in terms of the words of geometry? Planes

76 *Exploring Points, Lines, and Planes • 10.1*   Windows

Reteaching

Reteach Chapter 10   Name _____

What you should learn:
10.1 How to identify points, lines, and planes in real-life situations and how to use geometry to solve real-life problems

Correlation to Pupil's Textbook:
Mid-Chapter Self-Test (p. 461) Chapter Test (p. 485)
Exercises 1–4   Exercises 9, 10

Examples *Identifying Points, Lines, and Planes and Solving Real-Life Problems*

a. Use the diagram at the right for each of the following.
Name the points. P, Q, R, S, T
Name three line segments on $\overline{TR}$. $\overline{QT}$, $\overline{QR}$, $\overline{RT}$
Name two lines that appear parallel. $\overleftrightarrow{PQ}$ and $\overleftrightarrow{RS}$
Name two rays that have the same beginning point R. $\overrightarrow{RQ}$ and $\overrightarrow{RS}$

b. You are planning a delivery route through 4 cities. You must start at city A and stop first at city B. Your next stop is either city C or city D, but you must stop at both cities before returning to city A. Which of the two routes shown in the diagrams at the right is the shortest?

To find the distance along each route, add the lengths of the line segments that make up the route.
The distance along Route 1 is $4 + 20 + 15 + 13 = 52$ miles.
The distance along Route 2 is $4 + 10 + 15 + 18 = 47$ miles.
Route 2 is the shortest route.

Guidelines:
• The length of the line segment $\overline{KL}$ is denoted by KL.
• Two lines are parallel if they lie in the same plane and do not intersect.

EXERCISES

In Exercises 1–4, use the diagram at the right.
1. Write two other names for the line $\overleftrightarrow{EC}$. $\overleftrightarrow{AC}$, $\overleftrightarrow{AE}$
2. Name 4 rays that have the same beginning point. $\overrightarrow{EA}$, $\overrightarrow{EB}$, $\overrightarrow{EC}$, $\overrightarrow{ED}$
3. Name a point of intersection of two lines. E
4. Name 3 different line segments that lie on $\overleftrightarrow{DB}$. $\overline{DE}$, $\overline{EB}$, $\overline{DB}$

76 *Chapter 10 • Geometry Concepts and Spatial Thinking*   Windows

Lesson 10.1 **441**

▶ **Ex. 25** Use cardboard dividers from packaging to help students visualize these 3-D images.

▶ **Ex. 26–30** Assign these exercises as a group.

▶ **Ex. 31–35** Assign these as a group. Have students extend the patterns and try to generalize their results.

Exploration and Extension

EXTENSION
Have students investigate how many different nets can be folded into a cube. Here are some examples.

Portfolio Opportunity: Math Log

1. Explain the difference between $\overline{AB}$ and AB.
2. Explain why there is no notation for the length of a ray or a line.

Also available as a copymaster, page 31, Ex. 1, 2

Alternative Assessment

A cooperative learning project that develops students' construction techniques and introduces the concept of proof.

Available as a copymaster, page 33

25. *Visualizing Planes*   Each figure shows three planes. Explain how the planes differ. See margin.

a. 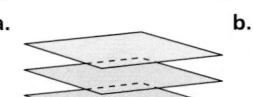   b. 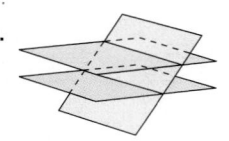   c. 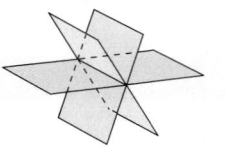   d.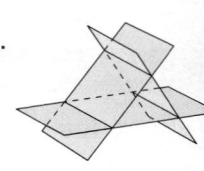

Architecture   **In Exercises 26–30, use the building at the right.**

Each window in the building is 10 feet wide and 7 feet high. The front doors of the building are 10 feet wide and 10 feet high. The space between the windows is 3 feet, and the space between the windows and the edges of the building is 3 feet.

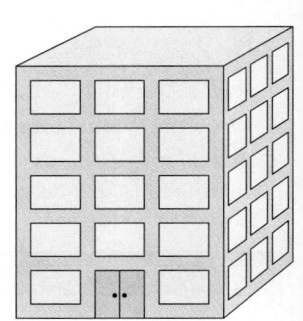

26. Describe some windows that lie in the same plane.
27. Is the base of every window parallel to the base of every other window? Explain.   **26., 27.** See margin
28. What are the dimensions of the building's base? 42 ft by 42 ft
29. How tall is the building? 53 ft
30. What percent of the front of the building is glass? ≈ 44%

Integrated Review   *Making Connections within Mathematics*

Drawing Lines   **In Exercises 31–34, copy the points on a piece of paper.** See Additional Answers.
Then draw and name all the lines that pass through pairs of points.

31. 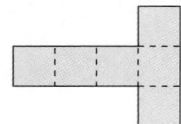   **32.** *A*   **33.** *A* *B*   **34.** *B*

(points A, B; C, B — figures)

35. *Patterns*   Describe how the pattern for the number of lines found in Exercises 31–34 are related to Pascal's triangle (page 372). See margin.

Exploration and Extension

Folding Cubes   **In Exercises 36 and 37, use the nets (patterns) shown below.**

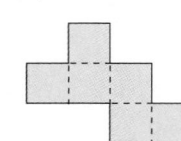

✪ **36.** Use graph paper to draw, cut, and fold each net to form a cube. Check students' work.
✪ **37.** Find a different net that you can cut and fold to form a cube. Answers vary.

Answers
25.

Figure	a	b	c	d
Number of lines of intersection	0	2	1	3

26. All of the windows on each wall lie in the same plane.
27. No, only the bases of windows on the same wall (and not side by side) or on opposite walls of the building are parallel.
35. To get the next number, add 2, add 3, add 4, etc., to the preceding number. The numbers are found in the third diagonal column of Pascal's triangle.

10.2 Angles: Naming, Measuring, Drawing

PACING the Lesson
Suggested Number of Days
Basic/Average 2 Above Average 1
Advanced 1

PLANNING the Lesson
Lesson Plan 10.2, p. 77

What you should learn:

Goal 1 How to identify angles as acute, right, obtuse, or straight

Goal 2 How to use angle measures to analyze real-life situations

Why you should learn it:

You can use angles to solve real-life problems, such as finding angles that produce certain types of reflections in mirrors.

Babylonian Geometry   The concept of degree measure began with the ancient Babylonians in northern Africa. They divided a full circle into 360 degrees.

Goal 1   Identifying Angles

An **angle** consists of two rays that begin at the same point. The rays are the **sides** of the angle, and the point is the **vertex** of the angle. The angle at the right can be denoted by

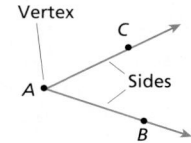

Vertex

Sides

$\angle BAC$, $\angle CAB$, or $\angle A$.

The **measure** of $\angle A$ is denoted by $m\angle A$. A **protractor** can be used to approximate the measure of an angle. An **acute angle** measures between 0° and 90°. A **right angle** measures 90°. An **obtuse angle** measures between 90° and 180°. A **straight angle** measures 180°. Two lines or line segments that meet at a right angle are **perpendicular.**

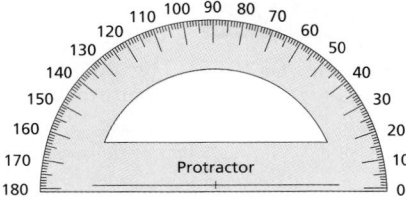

Protractor

LESSON INVESTIGATION

■ Investigating Angle Measures

Group Activity Use a scrap of paper to fold an obtuse angle and an acute angle, as shown below. Use a protractor to measure each of your angles.

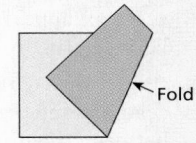

←Fold

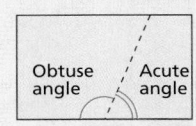

Obtuse angle   Acute angle

Two angles are **congruent** if they have the same measure. Are any of the angles folded by your group congruent?

10.2 • *Angles: Naming, Measuring, Drawing*   **443**

LESSON Notes

Vocabulary Alert!
Have students record the boldface words in the lesson in their mathematics journals. Discuss the terms and provide examples or illustrations of angles.

Lesson Investigation
Give students an opportunity to measure lots of different angles using a protractor. Have them label their measurements. Each member of the group should fold a scrap of paper as shown in the pupil text and compare results.

Historical Note
Babylonian tablets can be identified by their cuneiform (wedge-shaped) characters. This tablet, dating from before 1000 B.C., can be found in the British Museum. Its rows and columns contain sixteen different examples from geometry together with their solutions. The tablet is like an ancient Solution Key, illustrating methods of describing the geometric properties of figures, and of finding their areas and volumes. Exercise 4 on the lower left, is solved by *drawing a diagram.*

STARTER: Problem of the Day

Eight square tables, each of which seats four people, are pushed together to make a long rectangular table. How many people can now be seated?
$8 \times 2 + 2 = 18$

Also available as a copymaster, p. 28

STARTER: Warm-Up Exercises

1. Which geometric figures denote rays?
   b.
   a.   b.   c.   d.

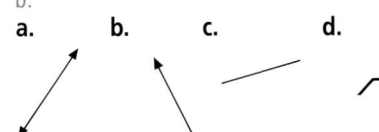

2. Which number values are between −4 and 6?
   a. −5   b. −4   c. −3
   d. 5   e. 6   f. 10   c., d.

Also available as a copymaster, p. 28

Have students identify examples or illustrations of angles found in their classroom. If possible, measure them and note which angle measures occur most often.

If kaleidoscopes are available, discuss how they seem to work and how they are related to this example.

Communicating about MATHEMATICS

ALTERNATE APPROACH
Revisit the example. Instead of first arranging the mirrors so that a special polygon is formed, select the angle measure between the mirrors and then determine the type of polygon created in the mirrors. Have students discuss how this approach affects their investigation.

Writing Prompt
Are all acute angles congruent? Are all right angles congruent? Are all obtuse angles congruent? Explain and give examples.

Real Life
Mirrors

The property of mirrors that is illustrated in Example 1 is used to build kaleidoscopes.

Goal 2 **Measuring Angles in Real Life**

Example 1 *Measuring Angles*

Draw a line on a piece of paper. Then tape two mirrors together and place the mirrors on the paper so that a segment appears to form a hexagon and an octagon. Measure the angles between the two mirrors.

Solution
As shown at the right, there is an acute angle that will make a segment appear to form a hexagon. Once you can see a hexagon, trace the angle between the two mirrors and use a protractor to measure the angle. You will find that the angle measures 60°.

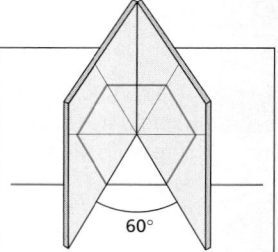

As shown at the right, there is an acute angle that will make a segment appear to form an octagon. Once you can see an octagon, trace the angle between the two mirrors and use a protractor to measure the angle. You will find that the angle measures 45°.

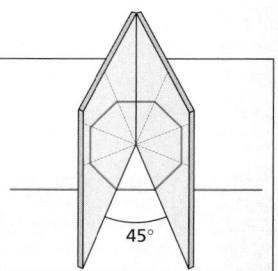

Communicating about MATHEMATICS

Cooperative Learning

▶ **SHARING IDEAS about the Lesson**

Measuring Angles Work with a partner.

A. Adjust the two taped mirrors in Example 1 so that a segment appears to form a pentagon. What is the angle between the mirrors? 72°

B. Adjust the two taped mirrors in Example 1 so that a segment appears to form a square. What is the angle between the mirrors? 90°

C. Can you form other polygons with the mirrors? If so, what angle is associated with each polygon?

Answers may include heptagon—$51\frac{3}{7}°$, nonagon—40°, decagon—36°.

EXERCISES

Guided Practice

▶ **CHECK for Understanding**

In Exercises 1–4, use the figure at the right.

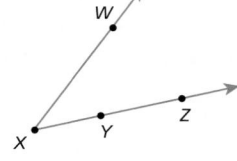

1. Name the vertex of $\angle WXZ$. X
2. Name the sides of $\angle WXZ$. $\overrightarrow{XW}$, $\overrightarrow{XZ}$
3. State other names for $\angle WXZ$. $\angle X$, $\angle WXY$, $\angle ZXW$, $\angle YXW$
4. Which appears to have the greater measure: $\angle WXZ$ or $\angle WYZ$?
   $\angle WYZ$

In Exercises 5–8, use a protractor to measure the angle. Is the angle acute, obtuse, right, or straight?

5.
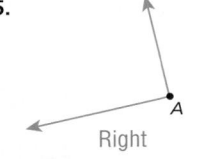
Right

6.
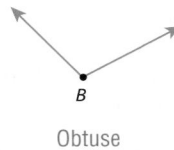
Obtuse

7.
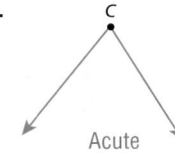
Acute

8.
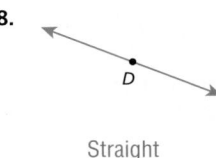
Straight

Independent Practice

In Exercises 9–14, use the figure at the right.

10.–13. For lists, see margin.

9. List four other names for $\angle B$. $\angle ABC$, $\angle DBC$, $\angle CBA$, $\angle CBD$
10. How many acute angles are in the figure? List them. 7
11. How many obtuse angles are in the figure? List them. 2
12. How many right angles are in the figure? List them. 3
13. How many straight angles are in the figure? List them. 2
14. Identify the vertex and sides of $\angle CDE$. Explain why you can't simply name the angle as $\angle D$. Vertex: D, sides: $\overrightarrow{DC}$, $\overrightarrow{DE}$; there are 6 angles with the vertex D.

In Exercises 15–18, without using a protractor, match the angle with its measure.

a. 45° **b.** 90° **c.** 180° **d.** 135°

15.
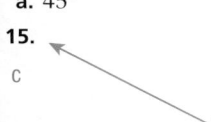
c

16.
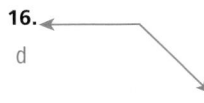
d

17.

b

18.

a

In Exercises 19–22, use a protractor to draw an angle with the indicated measure. Check students' work.

19. 30° 20. 90° 21. 125° 22. 135°

❂ More difficult exercises

ASSIGNMENT GUIDE

Basic/Average:
  Day 1: Ex. 9–28, 36–38
  Day 2: Ex. 29–35, 39, 40
Above Average: Ex. 9–14, 15–35 odd, 37–40
Advanced: Ex. 9–14, 15–35 odd, 37–40
Selected Answers: Ex. 1–8, 9–39 odd

Guided Practice

▶ **Ex. 2** Sides should be named as rays. However, many students may name them as segments.
▶ **Ex. 5–8** Students may need help with placing the protractor properly.

Independent Practice

▶ **Ex. 15–18** Have students think of a right angle as a benchmark. The right angle is a corner of a piece of paper. Students can ask themselves: Is the given angle smaller, larger, or about the same as the benchmark?

Answers
10. $\angle A$, $\angle ADE$, $\angle EDC$, $\angle BDC$, $\angle B$, $\angle BCD$, $\angle DCE$
11. $\angle ADC$, $\angle EDB$
12. $\angle AED$, $\angle CED$, $\angle ACB$
13. $\angle AEC$, $\angle ADB$

Lesson 10.2 **445**

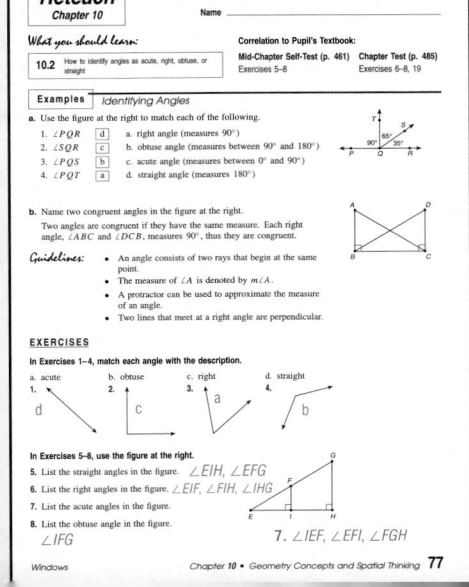

▶ **Ex. 28** Students can use tracing paper to confirm their answers to these exercises.

Integrated Review

▶ **Ex. 36–38**

Common-Error Alert!

Some students may solve for *x* in these exercises but forget to substitute in order to compute the measure of each angle.

Exploration and Extension

This problem could be used as an investigation for the next lesson.

Portfolio Opportunity: Math Log

Look around your classroom. Name two examples of each type of angle: acute, obtuse, right, and straight.

Also available as a copymaster, page 31, Ex. 3

Short Quiz

Covers Lessons 10.1 and 10.2

Available as a copymaster, page 160

In Exercises 23–26, use a protractor to measure the angle.

23. 35° **24.** 100° **25.** 155° **26.** 70°

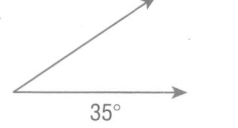 

27. *Writing* In your own words, explain what it means for two angles to be congruent. They have the same measure.

28. Which of the following angles are congruent? b and d

a.   **b.**   **c.**   **d.**

Clock Faces **In Exercises 29–32, determine what type of angle (acute, right, obtuse, or straight) the hands of a clock make at the given time.**

29. 6:00 P.M. Straight
30. 9:00 A.M. Right
31. 4:00 A.M. Obtuse
32. 10:00 P.M. Acute

Birds in Flight **In Exercises 33–35, measure the angle from the wingtip to the beak to the other wingtip. Name the type of angle formed.**

33.  Acute
34. Obtuse
35.  Right

---

Integrated Review   *Making Connections within Mathematics*

Algebra **In Exercises 36–38, use the fact that the two angles are congruent to solve for *x*. Then find the measures of the angles.**

36. $5x - 20°$, $3x + 34°$ 27°, 115°

37. $35° - x$, $2x + 15°$ $6\frac{2}{3}°$, $28\frac{1}{3}°$

38. $2x - 1°$, $x + 47°$ 48°, 95°

39. *Estimation* Which of the following is the best estimate for the angle of the tip of a star on a United States flag? b
  a. 5° **b.** 36° **c.** 90° **d.** 120°

Exploration and Extension

40. *Intersecting Lines* Use a straightedge to draw two lines that intersect to form two acute angles and two obtuse angles. Are the acute angles congruent? Are the obtuse angles congruent? Explain. See margin.

✪ More difficult exercises
P Portfolio Opportunity

Answer
40.

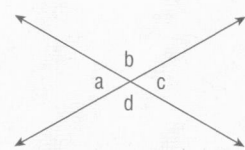

Yes, yes. $a + b = 180°$ and $a + d = 180°$, so $b = d$;
$a + b = 180°$ and $c + b = 180°$, so $a = c$.

Materials Needed: ruled paper, straightedge, colored pencils, scissors

Example   *Exploring Parallel Lines*

Use a pencil and straightedge to darken three lines on a piece of ruled paper. Then, use the pencil and straightedge to draw two other parallel lines, one on each side of the straightedge, as shown below. Draw these lines at a slant—not at right angles to rules on the paper. On another piece of paper, carefully trace one of the quadrilaterals formed by the parallel lines. Cut out the quadrilateral and use it to compare the angles formed by the parallel lines. What can you conclude?

Solution   By moving the quadrilateral around on the paper, you can determine that ∠1, ∠2, and ∠3 have the same measure, which means they are congruent. You can also determine that ∠4, ∠5, and ∠6 have the same measure, which means that they are also congruent. ■

Exercises

1. Try the investigation described in the example. Make the slanted parallel lines meet the horizontal lines at any angle except a right angle. The five lines should form 24 angles. Use colored pencils to indicate angles that are congruent. Check students' work.

2. In the quadrilateral that you cut out, are any of the four angles congruent? How can you tell? Yes, opposite angles are congruent; measure them.

3. Draw two parallel lines. Then draw a third line that intersects each of the first two lines at a slant. How many angles are formed by the three lines? Use colored pencils to classify the angles into congruent groups. Check students' work.

INVESTIGATION Notes

Students informally investigate the relationship between parallel lines and the angles they form with a transversal. Students intuitively recognize that the alternate interior angles are congruent, even though students' vocabulary may not communicate the relationships precisely.

What you should learn:

 Goal 1 How to identify angles formed when
two parallel lines
intersect a third line

 **Goal 2** How to use a property
of parallel lines to
solve real-life prob-
lems

Why you should learn it:

You can use a property of parallel lines to solve real-life problems, such as measuring angles
in construction projects.

Goal 1 ## Using a Property of Parallel Lines

In the *Investigation* on page 447, you may have discovered that
when two parallel lines are intersected by a third line, several
pairs of congruent angles are formed. To describe the results, it
helps to classify pairs of angles as **vertical angles** and **corresponding angles.**

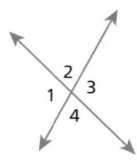 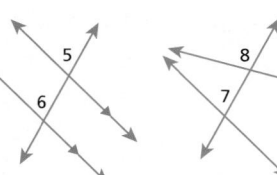

Vertical angles:
∠1 and ∠3, ∠2 and ∠4

Corresponding angles:
∠5 and ∠6, ∠7 and ∠8

Vertical Angles and a Property of Parallel Lines
1. Vertical angles are congruent.
2. When two *parallel* lines are intersected by a third line, the corresponding angles are congruent. (If the lines are not parallel,
   then the corresponding angles are not congruent.)

Example 1   *Identifying Congruent Angles*

In the diagram at the left, identify all congruent vertical angles
and all congruent corresponding angles.

Solution   The three lines form four sets of vertical angles.

∠1 ≅ ∠4,   ∠2 ≅ ∠3   *Vertical angles*
∠5 ≅ ∠8,   ∠6 ≅ ∠7   *Vertical angles*

The symbol ≅ means "is congruent to." Because m and n are
parallel, the three lines also form four sets of congruent corresponding angles.

∠1 ≅ ∠5,   ∠2 ≅ ∠6   *Corresponding angles*
∠3 ≅ ∠7,   ∠4 ≅ ∠8   *Corresponding angles*

*The red arrowheads indicate that
the lines m and n are parallel.*

448   *Chapter 10 ▪ Geometry Concepts and Spatial Thinking*

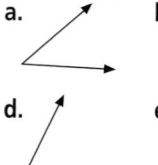 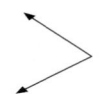 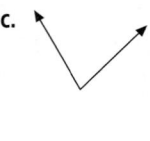

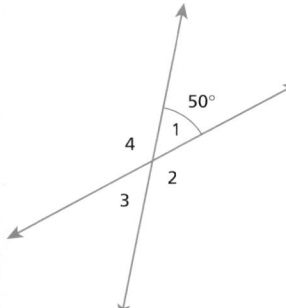

Goal 2 Solving Real-Life Problems

Example 2 — Finding Angle Measures

In the diagram at the left, $m\angle 1 = 50°$. Find the measures of the other three angles.

Solution Because $\angle 1$ and $\angle 3$ are vertical angles, they are congruent and must have the same measure. Thus, $m\angle 3 = 50°$.

Because $\angle 1$ and $\angle 2$ combined form a straight angle, you know that the sum of their measures is 180°. Thus,

$$m\angle 2 = 180° - m\angle 1 = 180° - 50° = 130°.$$

Because $\angle 2$ and $\angle 4$ are vertical angles, they are congruent and you can conclude that $m\angle 4 = 130°$.

Example 3 — Identifying Congruent Angles

Real Life
Construction

In the photo at the left, the lower man is sitting on a pair of cross beams. Draw a diagram of the beams and label the congruent angles.

Solution The beams form two pairs of parallel lines, as shown at the right. By using vertical angles and a property of parallel lines, you can conclude that

$$\angle 1 \cong \angle 3.$$

Using similar reasoning, you can also conclude that

$$\angle 2 \cong \angle 4.$$

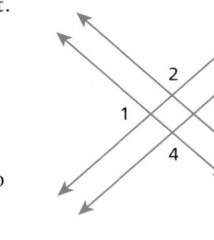

In the *Communicating* feature below, you are asked to explain how you can use vertical angles and a property of parallel lines to make these conclusions. ■

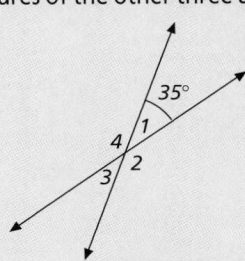

Communicating about MATHEMATICS

▶ **SHARING IDEAS about the Lesson**

Extending the Example In Example 3, explain why $\angle 1 \cong \angle 3$ and $\angle 2 \cong \angle 4$. If $m\angle 1 = 84°$, what are the measures of the other three angles? *$m\angle 2 = 96°$, $m\angle 3 = 84°$, $m\angle 4 = 96°$*

For explanation, see Additional Answers.

10.3 • Exploring Parallel Lines **449**

The examples illustrate how we can use our knowledge of vertical and corresponding angle pairs to deduce the measures of other angles.

Example 2

Students could have reasoned differently. Because $\angle 1$ and $\angle 2$ combine to form a straight angle, $m\angle 2 = 180° - 50° = 130°$. Because $\angle 2$ and $\angle 3$ form a straight angle, $m\angle 3 = 180° - 130° = 50°$. Similarly, $m\angle 4 = 180° - 50° = 130°$.

Example 3

The two pairs of parallel lines form 16 angles. For the diagram below, have students deduce how $\angle 5$ and $\angle 6$ are related to $\angle 1$, $\angle 2$, $\angle 3$, and $\angle 4$.

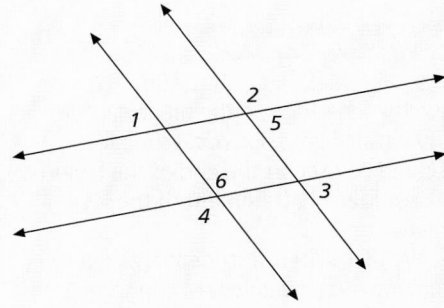

$\angle 6 \cong \angle 4$, $\angle 6 \cong \angle 2$, $\angle 5 \cong \angle 1$, and $\angle 5 \cong \angle 3$

Communicating about MATHEMATICS

Ask students to find the measures of all of the remaining (unlabeled) angles.

Writing Prompt
Your friend claims that either two lines are parallel or they intersect. Is your friend correct? Explain.

Technology

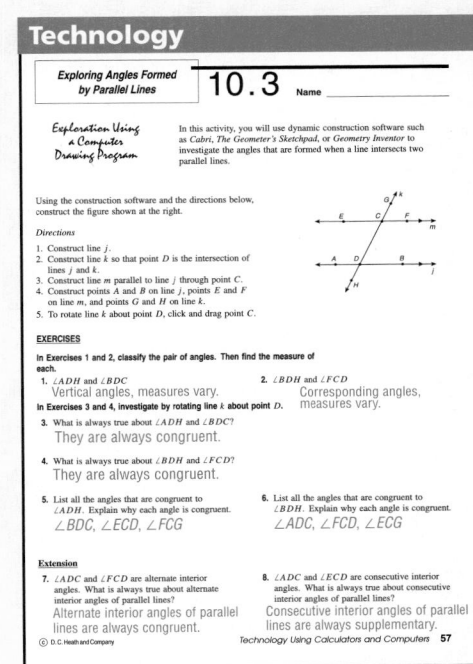

OPTION: Extra Examples

Here is an additional example similar to Example 2.

Finding Angle Measures
In the given diagram, $m\angle 1 = 35°$. Find the measures of the other three angles.

Solution
Because $\angle 1$ and $\angle 3$ are vertical angles, they are congruent and must have the same measure. Thus, $m\angle 3 = 35°$.

Because $\angle 1$ and $\angle 2$ combined form a straight angle, you know that the sum of their measures is 180°. Thus, $m\angle 2 = 180° - m\angle 1 = 180° - 35° = 145.°$

Because $\angle 2$ and $\angle 4$ are vertical angles, they are congruent, and you can conclude that $m\angle 4 = 145°$.

Lesson 10.3 **449**

ASSIGNMENT GUIDE

Basic/Average:
Day 1: Ex. 9–18, 23–26
Day 2: Ex. 20–22, 27–34

Above Average: Ex. 9–21 odd, 27, 28–32 even, 33, 34

Advanced: Ex. 9–21 odd, 27, 28–32 even, 33, 34

Selected Answers: Ex. 1–8, 9–31 odd

Guided Practice

These exercises could be assigned to groups and then discussed with the whole class. For Ex. 7 and 8, encourage students to draw sketches.

Independent Practice

▶ **Ex. 9–16** Make sure that students observe the markings on the diagram that identify parallel lines. Exercises similar to these could be used at the end of the lesson to assess students' attainment of the lesson objectives.

▶ **Ex. 17, 18** When a student is asked to explain why certain angles are congruent, "eyesight" should not be accepted as an answer!

Guided Practice

▶ **CHECK for Understanding**

In Exercises 1–6, use the figure at the right.

1. Which two lines are parallel? *m* and *n*
2. Name four pairs of vertical angles. See above.
3. Name four pairs of corresponding angles. See above.
4. What is the measure of ∠2? Explain your reasoning. 55°
5. What is the measure of ∠4? Explain your reasoning. 55°
6. What is the measure of ∠8? Explain your reasoning. 55°
7. Two lines intersect to form four angles. One of the angles measures 45°. What do the other three angles measure? Explain your reasoning. 45°, 135°, 135°

2. ∠1 and ∠3, ∠2 and ∠4, ∠5 and ∠7, ∠6 and ∠8
3. ∠1 and ∠5, ∠2 and ∠6, ∠3 and ∠7, ∠4 and ∠8

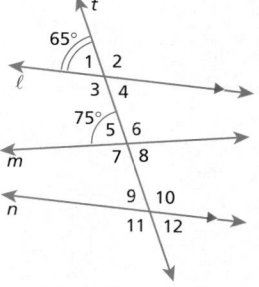

4.–6. For explanations, see margin.

8. Draw two parallel lines. Then draw a line that intersects one of the lines to form a 60° angle. Of the eight angles that are formed, how many measure 60°? 4

7. Vertical angles are congruent and the sum of the measures of pairs of angles is 180°.

Independent Practice

In Exercises 9–16, use the figure at the right.

9. Which two lines are parallel? *l* and *n*
✪ 10. Explain why ∠4 is not congruent to ∠8. *l* and *m* are not parallel.
11. List all angles whose measure is 65°. ∠1, ∠4, ∠9, ∠12
12. List all angles whose measure is 75°. ∠5, ∠8
13. List all angles whose measure is 115°. ∠2, ∠3, ∠10, ∠11
14. List all angles whose measure is 105°. ∠6, ∠7
15. Name two corresponding angles that have different measures. One example: ∠1 and ∠5
16. Name two corresponding angles that have the same measure. One example: ∠1 and ∠9

Parallelogram Grids **In Exercises 17 and 18, explain why the indicated angles are congruent.** See margin.

✪ 17.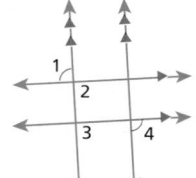

✪ 18.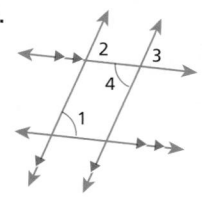

What Do You See? **In Exercises 19 and 20, draw and label the figure. List the lines that appear parallel.** See margin.

19.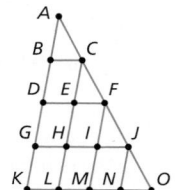

20.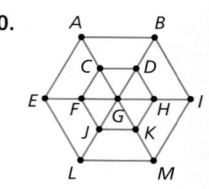

Extra Practice

Extra Practice **10.3** Name
In Exercises 1–5, use the figure at the right.
2. No, *l* & *p* not parallel, corresponding angles not congruent.
1. Which two lines are parallel? *m* ‖ *n*
2. Is ∠12 congruent to ∠8? Why or why not? ∠12, ∠10
3. List all angles whose measure is 55°. ∠12, ∠10
4. List all angles whose measure is 85°. ∠2, ∠4, ∠8, ∠6
5. Name two corresponding angles that have the same measure. ∠1 & ∠5, ∠4 & ∠8, ∠2 & ∠6, ∠3 & ∠7
6. Explain why the indicated angles are congruent.
∠1 ≅ ∠2 Corresponding angles of ‖ lines ≅ or
∠1 ≅ ∠6 Corresponding angles of ‖ lines ≅
∠2 ≅ ∠3 Vertical angles ≅ or
∠3 ≅ ∠4 Corresponding angles of ‖ lines ≅
∠4 ≅ ∠5 Corresponding angles of ‖ lines ≅
∠4 ≅ ∠5 Vertical angles ≅
∠5 ≅ ∠6 Corresponding angles of ‖ lines ≅

In Exercises 7–9, use the diagram of the city streets and the information. The north side of Morgan Road and the east side of Ryan Street meet to form a 75° angle. The west side of Danver Drive and the north side of Morgan Road meet to form a 105° angle.
7. Draw and label a diagram of the streets. Identify the location of mailbox, bus stop and fire hydrant.
8. Present a case to explain why Danver Drive and Ryan Street are parallel. Accept all reasonable answers. See back of supplement for more details.
9. Find measures of the angles (or intersection) at which the mailbox, bus stop and fire hydrant are placed. Fire hydrant, bus stop, mailbox all placed at 75° angles.
10. Chef Carlo Vincento wishes to decorate his world famous strawberry pie with fresh strawberries. He wishes to place the strawberries at the intersections of the parallel lines of whipped cream. However, for cosmetic appearances, the strawberries are only to be placed at congruent angles to the initial strawberry. Place a dot at every congruent angle to the one marked on the figure. See diagram above.

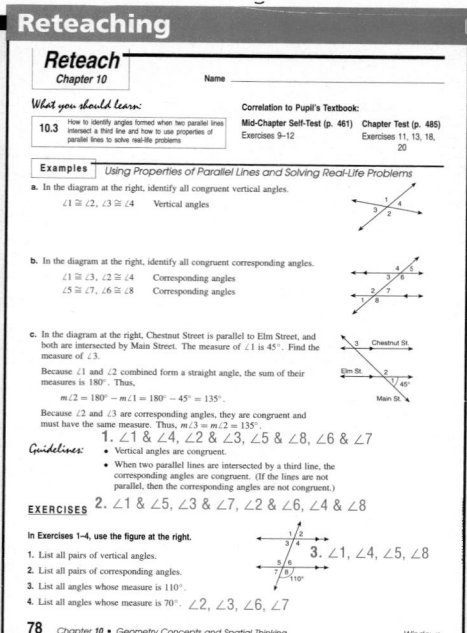

78 Exploring Parallel Lines ▪ 10.3 Windows

Reteaching

Reteach Chapter 10 Name

What you should learn:

	Correlation to Pupil's Textbook:
10.3 How to identify angles formed when two parallel lines intersect a third line and how to use properties of parallel lines to solve real-life problems	**Mid-Chapter Self-Test (p. 461)** Chapter Test (p. 485) Exercises 9–12 Exercises 11, 13, 18, 20

Examples *Using Properties of Parallel Lines and Solving Real-Life Problems*

a. In the diagram at the right, identify all congruent vertical angles.
∠1 ≅ ∠2, ∠3 ≅ ∠4 Vertical angles

b. In the diagram at the right, identify all congruent corresponding angles.
∠1 ≅ ∠3, ∠2 ≅ ∠4 Corresponding angles
∠5 ≅ ∠7, ∠6 ≅ ∠8 Corresponding angles

c. In the diagram at the right, Chestnut Street is parallel to Elm Street, and both are intersected by Main Street. The measure of ∠1 is 45°. Find the measure of ∠3.
Because ∠1 and ∠2 combined form a straight angle, the sum of their measures is 180°. Thus,
$m\angle2 = 180° - m\angle1 = 180° - 45° = 135°.$
Because ∠2 and ∠3 are corresponding angles, they are congruent and must have the same measure. Thus, $m\angle3 = m\angle2 = 135°.$

Guidelines:
• Vertical angles are congruent.
• When two parallel lines are intersected by a third line, the corresponding angles are congruent. (If the lines are not parallel, then the corresponding angles are not congruent.)

EXERCISES

In Exercises 1–4, use the figure at the right.
1. List all pairs of vertical angles.
2. List all pairs of corresponding angles.
3. List all angles whose measure is 110°.
4. List all angles whose measure is 70°. ∠2, ∠3, ∠6, ∠7

1. ∠1 & ∠4, ∠2 & ∠3, ∠5 & ∠8, ∠6 & ∠7
2. ∠1 & ∠5, ∠3 & ∠7, ∠2 & ∠6, ∠4 & ∠8
3. ∠1, ∠4, ∠5, ∠8

78 Chapter 10 ▪ Geometry Concepts and Spatial Thinking Windows

Answers

4. When two parallel lines are intersected by a third line, the corresponding angles are congruent; so ∠6 ≅ ∠2.
5. Vertical angles are congruent; so ∠2 ≅ ∠4.
6. Vertical angles are congruent; so ∠6 ≅ ∠8.
17. ∠1 ≅ ∠2, ∠2 ≅ ∠3, and ∠3 ≅ ∠4; so ∠1 ≅ ∠4.
18. ∠1 ≅ ∠2, ∠2 ≅ ∠3, and ∠3 ≅ ∠4; so ∠1 ≅ ∠4.
19. $\overleftrightarrow{BC}, \overleftrightarrow{DF}, \overleftrightarrow{GJ},$ and $\overleftrightarrow{KO}$; $\overleftrightarrow{AK}, \overleftrightarrow{CL}, \overleftrightarrow{FM},$ and $\overleftrightarrow{JN}$
20. $\overleftrightarrow{AB}, \overleftrightarrow{CD}, \overleftrightarrow{EI}, \overleftrightarrow{JK},$ and $\overleftrightarrow{LM}$; $\overleftrightarrow{AE}, \overleftrightarrow{CF}, \overleftrightarrow{BL}, \overleftrightarrow{HK},$ and $\overleftrightarrow{IM}$; $\overleftrightarrow{BI}, \overleftrightarrow{DH}, \overleftrightarrow{AM}, \overleftrightarrow{FJ},$ and $\overleftrightarrow{EL}.$

21. *Systematic Counting*   How many triangles are in the figure in Exercise 19?   10

22. *Systematic Counting*   How many trapezoids are in the figure in Exercise 19?   20

Walking   **In Exercises 23–25, use the map at the right and the information below.**

You live on 4th Street, which runs parallel to 5th and 6th Streets. The route you follow from your house to your friend's house is shown on the map. The turn from 4th Street onto Cherry Street is 117° and from Lake Street onto 6th Street is 34°.   Check students'

23. Draw and label a diagram of the streets.   work.

24. Identify all the congruent angles.   **24., 25.**   See margin.

25. Find the measures of all the angles.

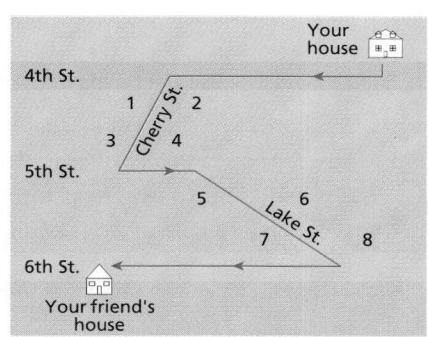

26. *Great Britain*   Draw a diagram of the flag of Great Britain shown at the right. Is it true that every line segment in the flag is parallel to the top of the flag, the right side of the flag, or one of its two diagonals?   Yes

27. Use a protractor to measure several of the angles in Great Britain's flag. How many different angle measures are there? Explain your reasoning.
4; angles are 35°, 55°, 90°, and 180°.

World Flags   **Great Britain's flag, known as the British Union Jack, was adopted in 1801.**

Integrated Review

Making Connections within Mathematics

Triangular Grid   **In Exercises 28–32, draw the grid on triangular dot paper. Then outline the indicated figure.**
Check students' work.

28. Trapezoid

29. Hexagon

30. Pentagon

31. Two similar triangles

32. Two parallelograms that have different shapes

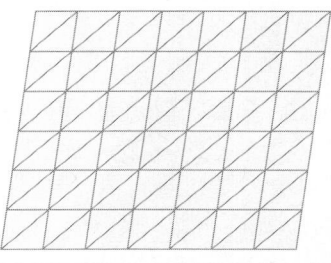

Exploration and Extension

Alternate Interior Angles   **In Exercises 33 and 34, use the figure at the right. In the figure, ∠3 and ∠6 are called alternate interior angles.**

33. Explain why ∠3 is congruent to ∠6.   See below.

34. Name another set of alternate interior angles.

33. ∠3 ≅ ∠2 and ∠2 ≅ ∠6

∠4 and ∠5

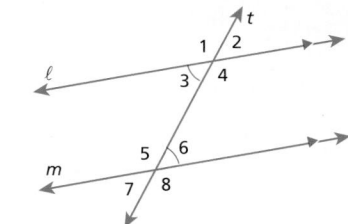

P Portfolio Opportunity

▶ **Ex. 23–25**   Assign these exercises as a group.
▶ **Ex. 26, 27**   Assign these also as a group.

Integrated Review ———————

These exercises assess students' ability to visualize geometric properties. Note that dot paper is available in the Teaching Tools supplement. Refer to the Lesson Resources list on page 448.

Exploration and Extension

These exercises preview some subskills of deductive proof that students will study in geometry.

Portfolio Opportunity: Math Log

In the figure, mark an angle that is congruent to ∠1, and give a reason for your selection. Continue this process until you have shown that ∠1 is congruent to ∠2.

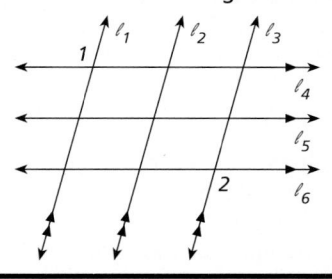

Also available as a copymaster, page 31, Ex. 4

Enrichment

Ask the social studies teacher to plan an interdisciplinary unit on flags. Students could design their own flags and/or study the geometry of real flags.

Answers
24. ∠2 ≅ ∠3, ∠1 ≅ ∠4, ∠6 ≅ ∠7, ∠5 ≅ ∠8
25. m∠2 = m∠3 = 117°, m∠1 = m∠4 = 63°, m∠6 = m∠7 = 34°, m∠5 = m∠8 = 146°

Milestones

Theme: Time and Location

The invention of the compass, the mechanical clock, and the sextant in the 1700's made navigation a science. How, then, did Stone-Age Polynesians, who had no written language, colonize such a vast area without measuring instruments? Part of the answer is that they had developed their own latitude and longitude systems by drawing the position at various times of day and night of the sun, stars, and planets in relationship to *etaks,* or reference islands.

1. Greenwich Mean Time (GMT) places Greenwich, England (0° longitude) at the center of the 0 time zone, which runs from 7.5° west to 7.5° east. When it is noon at Greenwich, what time would it be in Atlanta, Georgia, whose longitude reading is about 88° west?

(88 − 7.5) ÷ 15 ≈ 5, so there is a 5 hour time difference between Greenwich and Atlanta. Since the sun rises in the east and moves west throughout the day, Atlanta's local time is 5 hours earlier than GMT. When it is noon in Greenwich, it is 7 AM in Atlanta.

2. Consult an atlas or other reference. Determine what time zone you live in. Suppose you want to phone a cousin who lives in Honolulu and also a cousin who lives in Moscow. If your local time is 6 PM, should you wait to call them?

Answers vary. For example, when it is 6 PM. in New York, it is 8 hours later, or 2 AM the next day, in Moscow. It is 5 hours earlier, or 1 PM in Honolulu. So, you could probably call your cousin in Honolulu immediately, but you should wait before calling your cousin in Russia.

Library Skills

Have students use library resources to research the history of time measurement, including various calendars, geological time clocks, etc. Some students may wish to share their findings with the class.

Mixed REVIEW

See margin.

In Exercises 1–4, plot and label the points in the same coordinate plane. (3.8)

1. $A(3, 3)$ **2.** $B(3, -1)$ **3.** $C(-1, -1)$ **4.** $D(-1, 3)$

In Exercises 5–8, use the points in Exercises 1–4. (10.1, 10.2)

5. By connecting the points, what types of polygons can you form? Triangles and a square

6. Use the points to identify parallel lines. $\overleftrightarrow{AB}$ and $\overleftrightarrow{CD}$, $\overleftrightarrow{AD}$ and $\overleftrightarrow{BC}$

7. Use the points to identify perpendicular lines. See margin.

8. What is the length of AC? (Round your answer to 2 decimal places.) 5.66

In Exercises 9–13, use the figure at the right. (10.3) ∠8, ∠14

9. Name two angles that are corresponding angles to ∠6.

10. Name two sets of vertical angles. Example: ∠1 and ∠6, ∠2 and ∠5

11. If $m\angle 1 = 45°$, what is $m\angle 2$? 135°

12. If $m\angle 13 = 135°$, what is $m\angle 4$? 135°

13. What is the relationship between ∠1 and ∠6? Vertical congruent angles

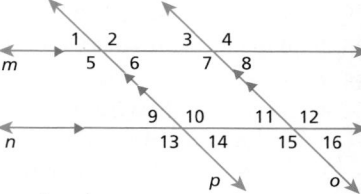

Milestones — NAVIGATION

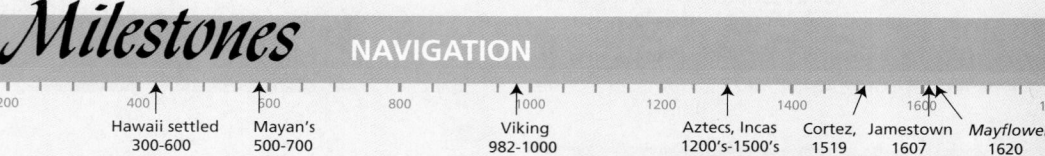

| 200 | 400 | 600 | 800 | 1000 | 1200 | 1400 | 1600 | 18 |

Hawaii settled 300-600   Mayan's 500-700   Viking 982-1000   Aztecs, Incas 1200's-1500's   Cortez, 1519   Jamestown 1607   *Mayflower* 1620

Hawaii, the Aloha State, entered the union as the 50th state on August 21, 1959.

Before oceanography became a science in the 1700's, navigators had u daytime observations of the sun to determine their east-west location (longitude) and the nighttime observations of the stars and planets to determine their north-south locations (latitude).

When Captain James Cook set out in the 1760's and 1770's to chart the Pacific, imagine his surprise at finding a vast triangular empire bordered by Hawaii, New Zealand, and Easter Island, off Chile. These Pacific Islands had all been settled by descendants of stone-age Melanesians and Micronesians who dominated the Pacific.

• *If it takes 24 hours for the Earth to rotate 360° from east to west, th how many minutes is 1° of longitude?* 4 minutes

• *The world is divided into 24 time zones, 1 hour apart. How many degrees of longitude wide is one time zone?* 15°

Answers to Mixed Review

1.–4.

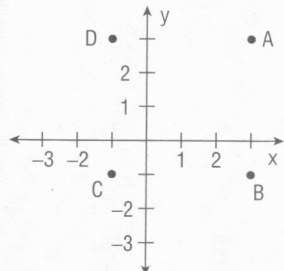

7. $\overleftrightarrow{AB}$ and $\overleftrightarrow{BC}$, $\overleftrightarrow{BC}$ and $\overleftrightarrow{CD}$, $\overleftrightarrow{CD}$ and $\overleftrightarrow{DA}$, $\overleftrightarrow{DA}$ and $\overleftrightarrow{AB}$

10.4 Symmetry

What you should learn:

Goal 1 How to identify line symmetry

Goal 2 How to identify rotational symmetry

Why you should learn it:

You can use symmetry to describe objects that occur in nature, such as the radiance of the sun.

Goal 1 Identifying Line Symmetry

A figure has **line symmetry** if it can be divided by a line into two parts, each of which is the mirror image of the other.

Example 1   Identifying Line Symmetry

Identify the lines of symmetry in the figures.

a.
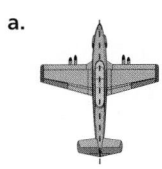

b.
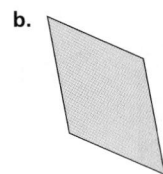

c.
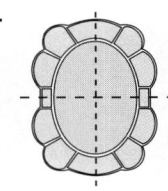

Solution

a. This figure has a vertical line of symmetry.

b. This figure has no line of symmetry.

c. This figure has a vertical line of symmetry *and* a horizontal line of symmetry. ∎

LESSON INVESTIGATION

■ **Investigating Line Symmetry**

Group Activity With a partner, fold a sheet of paper, as shown in Diagram 1 or 2 below. Cut a design out of one or more edges of the folded paper. Predict the pattern when the paper is unfolded. Did symmetry help you make a prediction? Explain.

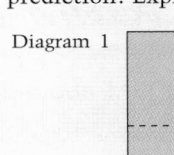
Cut out

A •

B •
Cut out

Cut designs in one or more edges of the folded paper.

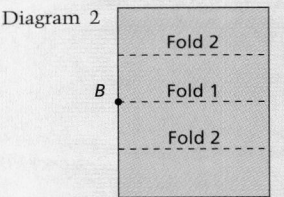
Diagram 1

Diagram 2

▶ PACING the Lesson

Suggested Number of Days
Basic/Average 2   **Above Average** 1
Advanced 1

▶ PLANNING the Lesson

Lesson Plan 10.4, p. 79

ORGANIZER

Starters (reproduced below)
 Problem of the Day 10.4, p. 29
 Warm-Up Exercises 10.4, p. 29
Lesson Resources
 Color Transparencies
  Picture for Example 2, p. 41
  Pictures for Ex. 21, 22, p. 42
 Teaching Tools
  Coordinate planes, pp. T9, C11
 Math Log, p. 32
 Technology, p. 58
 Answer Masters 10.4, p. 197
 Extra Practice Copymaster 10.4, p. 79
 Reteaching Copymaster 10.4, p. 79
 Enrichment Projects, pp. 49, 50
Special Populations
 Suggestions, Teacher's Edition, p. 436D

LESSON Notes

Line symmetry is used frequently in the design of buildings, art, and clothing.

Example 1

Point out that the "mirror image" referred to is the part of the figure that lies on one side of the fold in the paper.

Lesson Investigation

As a project, have students investigate how paper dolls are created using folds of paper. Students find the paper folding activities to be a lot of fun.

On the dot grid below, the horizontal or vertical distance from one dot to the next is 1 unit. Determine the perimeter of the figure.   44 units

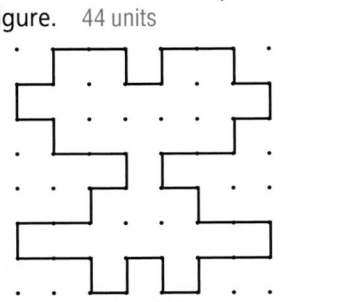

Also available as a copymaster, p. 29

Fold a sheet of paper in half. Cut out a triangle as shown below. Describe what figure you see when you open out the sheet of paper.   An isosceles triangle

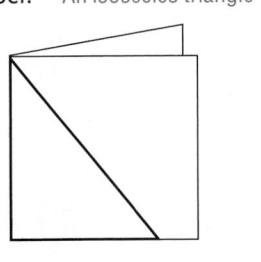

Also available as a copymaster, p. 29

Figures with rotational symmetry are used frequently in the design of clothing logos and company logos. It is important to note that figures with line symmetry may also have rotational symmetry. Finally, discuss with students what clockwise and counterclockwise motions are, and what it means for figures to coincide.

Example 2

Call students' attention to the point around which the figures are rotated. Ask them to investigate whether other points can work. No

Communicating about MATHEMATICS

Ask students to discuss how tracing paper can be used to demonstrate line and rotational symmetries.

Writing Prompt
Have students write answers for Ex. 1 and 2 of Guided Practice in their journals.

Many objects in nature have line symmetry or rotational symmetry. What types of symmetry does this photograph of the sun have?

A figure has **rotational symmetry** if it coincides with itself after rotating 180° or less, either clockwise or counterclockwise, about a point.

Example 2   *Identifying Rotational Symmetry*

Identify any rotational symmetry in the figures.

a. 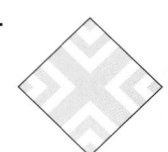   b.    c.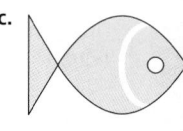

Solution

a. This figure has rotational symmetry. It will coincide with itself after being rotated 90° or 180° in either direction.

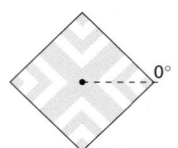 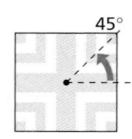 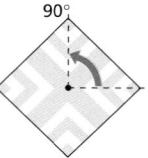

b. This figure has rotational symmetry. It will coincide with itself after being rotated 60°, 120°, or 180° in either direction.

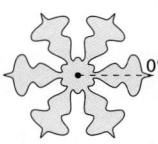 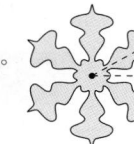 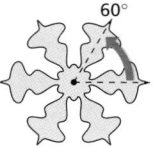

c. This figure has no rotational symmetry. (It does have line symmetry about a horizontal line.)

Communicating about MATHEMATICS

▶ **SHARING IDEAS about the Lesson**

Point Symmetry Trace the object in the photograph at the upper left. Then rotate the tracing and place it on the photograph. Can you find a rotation for which the tracing coincides with the original photo? What can you conclude?

The photo has rotational symmetry.

454   *Chapter **10** ▪ Geometry Concepts and Spatial Thinking*

Technology

| Creating a Design | **10.4** Name _____ |

Exploration Using a Computer Drawing Program

Artists create designs to represent many different things. For example, designs are used to advertise products and to represent companies, social groups, and athletic teams. Designs are also used on flags to represent cities, states, and countries. In this activity, you will use a computer paint program to create flag designs that have various types of symmetry.

Horizontal line of symmetry   Vertical line of symmetry

Rotational symmetry   No line of symmetry

EXERCISES

1. Using a computer paint program to create four flag designs of your own which illustrate each type of symmetry shown above.
   Answers vary.

2. The flags shown above are the state flags of Colorado, Indiana, and New Mexico and the flag for the District of Columbia. Can you identify which flag is which?   Clockwise beginning upper left: Colorado, District of Columbia, Indiana, and New Mexico

58   *Technology Using Calculators and Computers*   © D.C. Heath and Company

EXERCISES

Guided Practice

▶ **CHECK for Understanding**

1. *The Shape of Things*   Name several objects in your classroom that have line symmetry.   Answers vary.

P **2.** *The Shape of Things*   Name several objects in your classroom that have rotational symmetry.   Answers vary.

In Exercises 3–6, identify any symmetry of the figure.

3.

1 line of symmetry

4.

4 lines of symmetry; rotational symmetry at 45°, 90°, 135°, and 180° in either direction

5.

1 line of symmetry

6.

3 lines of symmetry, rotational symmetry at 120° in either direction

Independent Practice

In Exercises 7–10, identify any symmetry of the figure.

8. 5 lines of symmetry, rotational symmetry at 72° and 144° in either direction

7.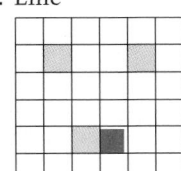

8.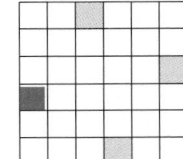

9.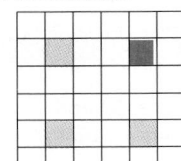

1 line of symmetry

10.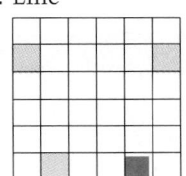

1 line of symmetry

7. Rotational symmetry at 60°, 120°, and 180° in either direction

In Exercises 11–14, draw, if possible, a figure that has the given characteristics.
All are possible. Check students' work.

11. Exactly one line of symmetry

⭐ **12.** Exactly two lines of symmetry

13. Line, but not rotational, symmetry

⭐ **14.** Rotational, but not line, symmetry

In Exercises 15–18, copy the figure. Then shade one square so that the figure has the indicated symmetry.

15. Line

16. Rotational

17. Rotational

18. Line

19. *Experimenting with Symmetry*   Can you draw a figure that has a vertical and horizontal line of symmetry but does not have rotational symmetry?   No

⭐ **20.** *Experimenting with Symmetry*   Can you draw a figure that has a vertical line of symmetry and rotational symmetry but does not have a horizontal line of symmetry?   Yes, see figure in Exercise 6.

⭐ More difficult exercises
P Portfolio Opportunity

10.4 • Symmetry   **455**

EXERCISE Notes

ASSIGNMENT GUIDE

Basic/Average:
   Day 1: Ex. 7–14, 15–25 odd
   Day 2: Ex. 20, 27, 28–31
Above Average: Ex. 7–29 odd, 30, 31
Advanced: Ex. 7–29 odd, 30, 31
Selected Answers: Ex. 1–6, 7–29 odd

Guided Practice

▶ **Ex. 1, 2**   Have students respond to these exercises in their journal.

▶ **Ex. 4**   Students may not see all four lines of symmetry, nor the eight-fold rotational symmetry of this star. Make a copy of this figure in advance in order to demonstrate the types of symmetry.

Independent Practice

▶ **Ex. 11–14**   Some students have greater success with these problems if they have been provided with dot or grid paper, while other students feel restricted by the dots or grids. Make alternative types of paper available to those students who need it.

▶ **Ex. 15–18**
EXTENSION
Look for crosswords with symmetry and make a bulletin board display or a poster.
Resource: NCTM Student Math Notes, September 1994.

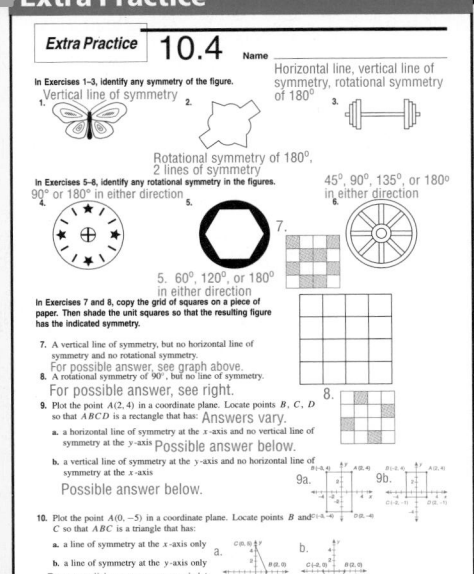

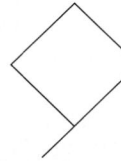
Symmetry in Nature   **In Exercises 21–23, identify any type of symmetry.** See margin.

21.

22.

23.

Letter Symmetry   **In Exercises 24–26, trace the figure and find out what word is spelled using the indicated line of symmetry. (Hint: You can also use a mirror to solve the problems.)**

24. ~~BOX~~
BOX

25. ~~DECK~~
DECK

26. ~~CHOICE~~
CHOICE

⊕ **27.** *Try It Yourself*   List as many words as you can that have the type of symmetry used in Exercises 24–26. Try to write an entire sentence using such words. Answers vary. Examples: BOOK, DICE; HE DIED.

Integrated Review

28. *Coordinate Geometry*   Plot the point $A(4, 3)$ in a coordinate plane. Locate the points B, C, and D so that $ABCD$ is a rectangle that has the x-axis and y-axis as lines of symmetry.
B or D $(4, -3)$, $C(-4, -3)$, D or B $(-4, 3)$

Making Connections within Mathematics

29. *Coordinate Geometry*   Plot the points $A(2, 1)$ and $B(-2, 3)$ in a coordinate plane. Locate the points C and D so that quadrilateral $ABCD$ is a parallelogram that has rotational symmetry about the origin, but no line symmetry. $C(-2, -1)$, $D(2, -3)$

Exploration and Extension

Symmetric Polygons   **In Exercises 30 and 31, cut and label a 3-inch by 5-inch index card as shown.**

⊕ **30.** How many different polygons can be formed by placing the two triangles side by side so that their sides coincide? 6

⊕ **31.** Identify the type of symmetry of each polygon formed in Exercise 30. 2 triangles: both have 1 line of symmetry; 4 quadrilaterals: 2 have rotational symmetry at 180°, 1 has 2 lines of symmetry, 1 has 1 line of symmetry

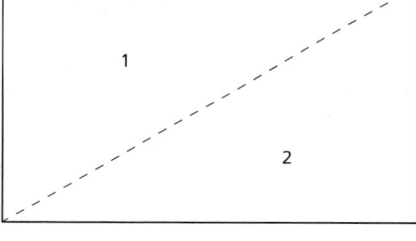

Enrichment

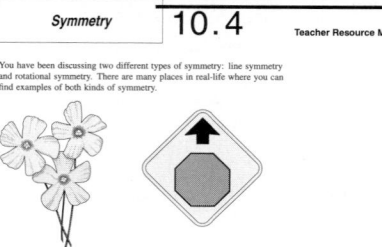

| Symmetry | 10.4 | Teacher Resource Material |

You have been discussing two different types of symmetry: line symmetry and rotational symmetry. There are many places in real-life where you can find examples of both kinds of symmetry.

Your project has two parts. Part 1 is to analyze the alphabet. On a piece of posterboard, classify letters that have (a) line symmetry, (b) rotational symmetry, (c) both types of symmetry, or (d) neither type of symmetry.

Part 2 is to find 3–5 examples of symmetry in your community. Your examples could be road or business signs. Certain types of leaves might also provide examples of symmetry. If possible, include examples which illustrate the different types of symmetry. Your findings should be reported either on the back of the posterboard you used above, or on a separate piece. Make your displays neat and colorful.

10.5

Exploring Triangles

 Goal 1 How to identify triangles by their sides

 Goal 2 How to identify triangles by their angles

What you should learn:

Why you should learn it:

Triangles occur in a wide variety of real-life situations. Being able to identify types of triangles helps you communicate ideas about real-life situations.

The sails of these windsurfboards are scalene triangles—all three sides of each sail have different lengths.

Goal 1 — Identifying Triangles by Their Sides

LESSON INVESTIGATION

■ **Investigating Types of Triangles**

Partner Activity Use the sheet of triangles provided by your teacher. Cut the triangles out. Then sort the triangles into two piles so that every triangle in one pile has a certain property and every triangle in the other pile does not have the property. Ask your partner to describe the property. Then, reverse roles and ask your partner to sort the triangles and see whether you can describe your partner's property.

Can you and your partner discover other properties that allow you to sort the triangles into two piles?

Triangles are classified by their sides into three categories. For a **scalene** triangle, all sides have different lengths. For an **isosceles** triangle, at least two sides have the same length. For an **equilateral** triangle, all three sides have the same length.

Example 1 *Classifying Triangles*

Classify each triangle according to its sides.

a. 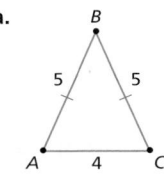 b.   c.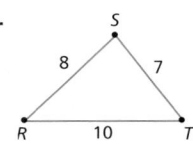

Solution

a. △*ABC* is isosceles because it has two sides of length 5.

b. △*DEF* is equilateral because each side has a length of 6.

c. △*RST* is scalene—all three sides have different lengths. ■

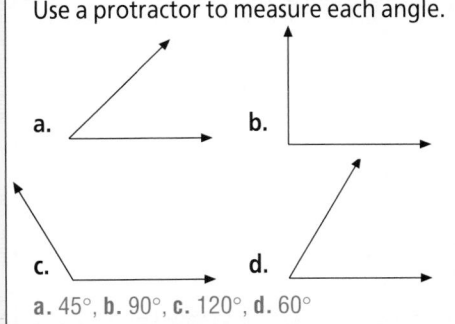

Repeat the Lesson Investigation sorting activity as follows. Have students work in small groups to measure the angles of the triangles in the two piles. Discuss observations about the classification of triangles by angles and sides.

Example 2

In the diagrams, ask students to measure ∠C and side $\overline{AB}$. Ask students: As ∠C increases, how is $\overline{AB}$ affected?

Communicating about MATHEMATICS

EXTENSION

Have students repeat the activity using a 4 × 4 and a 5 × 5 square.

Writing Prompt

In your own words, explain the difference between equilateral and equiangular.

Triangles are classified by their angles into four categories. A triangle is **acute** if all three angles are acute. An acute triangle is **equiangular** if all three angles have the same measure. A triangle is **obtuse** if one of its angles is obtuse. A triangle is **right** if one of its angles is a right angle.

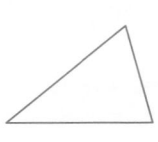 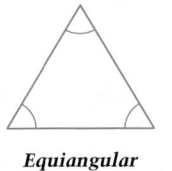 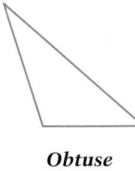 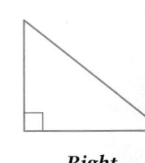

Acute	*Equiangular*	*Obtuse*	*Right*
Triangle	*Triangle*	*Triangle*	*Triangle*

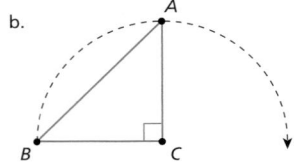

Real Life
Mechanics

Example 2 *Comparing Sides and Angles*

The diagram at the left shows part of an engine. Point C is the center of a circle. Point B stays in the same position on the circle, and point A moves clockwise around the circle. How does $\triangle ABC$ change as point A moves around the circle?

Solution

a. In this position, each angle of $\triangle ABC$ is acute, so $\triangle ABC$ is acute.

b. In this position, $\angle C$ is a right angle, so $\triangle ABC$ is a right triangle.

c. In this position, $\angle C$ is obtuse, so $\triangle ABC$ is obtuse.

a.

b.

c.

8; 3 isosceles right,
2 isosceles acute,
2 scalene obtuse,
1 scalene right

Communicating about MATHEMATICS

▶ **SHARING IDEAS about the Lesson**

Classifying Triangles On a sheet of square dot paper, outline several 9-dot squares. How many *different* (noncongruent) triangles can you draw? Classify each triangle by its sides and angles.

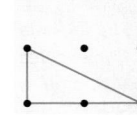

Technology

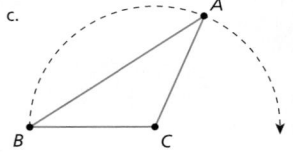

Exploring Triangles: Can You Draw It?	10.5	Name

Exploration Using a Computer Drawing Program

In this activity, you will use construction software to investigate what types of triangles can be drawn.

EXERCISES

In Exercises 1–12, determine whether it is possible to construct the triangle.
If it is, sketch an example. If it isn't, then write an explanation.

1. An acute scalene triangle
Possible, sketches vary.

2. An obtuse scalene triangle
Possible, sketches vary.

3. A right scalene triangle
Possible, sketches vary.

4. An equiangular scalene triangle
Not possible; In any scalene triangle, each angle measure is different (in any equiangular triangle, all 3 sides have same length).

5. An acute isosceles triangle
Possible, sketches vary.

6. An obtuse isosceles triangle
Possible, sketches vary.

7. A right isosceles triangle
Possible, sketches vary.

8. An equiangular isosceles triangle
Possible; sketches vary. (Note: The triangle will be equilateral as well as isosceles.)

9. An acute equilateral triangle
Possible, sketches vary.

10. An obtuse equilateral triangle
Not possible; Each angle measure in an equilateral triangle is 60°.

11. A right equilateral triangle
Not possible; Each angle measure in an equilateral triangle is 60°.

12. An equiangular equilateral triangle
Possible, sketches vary.

EXERCISES

Guided Practice

▶ **CHECK for Understanding**   For explanations, see Additional Answers.

In Exercises 1–8, match each triangle with all words that describe it. Explain.

a. Isosceles   **b.** Equiangular   **c.** Scalene   **d.** Obtuse
e. Equilateral   **f.** Right   **g.** Acute

1.
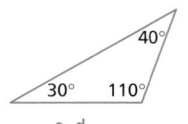
c, d

2.
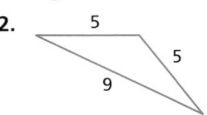
a, d

3.

c, f

4.
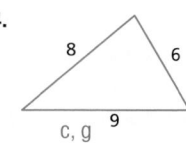
c, g

5.
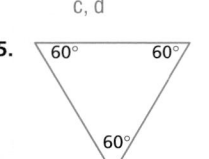
a, b, e, g

6.
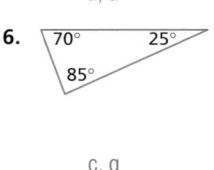
c, g

7.
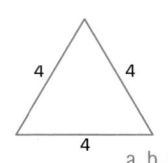
a, b, e, g

8.
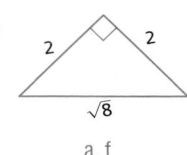
a, f

Independent Practice

Sketching Triangles   **In Exercises 9–14, sketch the indicated type of triangle. Then label it with appropriate side or angle measures.** Check students' work.

9. Obtuse   **10.** Acute   **11.** Right scalene

12. Right isosceles   **13.** Acute isosceles   **14.** Obtuse scalene

In Exercises 15–20, classify the triangle according to its sides and angles.

15.

Scalene right

16.
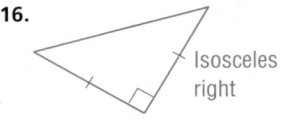
Isosceles right

17.
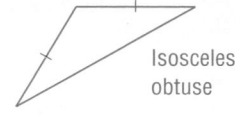
Isosceles obtuse

18.
Scalene acute

19.
Scalene obtuse

20.
Isosceles acute

In Exercises 21–26, use a protractor to draw △ABC with the given angle measures. Then classify the triangle according to its sides and angles. See Additional Answers.

21. $m\angle A = 60°, m\angle B = 60°, m\angle C = 60°$ **22.** $m\angle A = 70°, m\angle B = 70°, m\angle C = 40°$

23. $m\angle A = 50°, m\angle B = 60°, m\angle C = 70°$ **24.** $m\angle A = 30°, m\angle B = 60°, m\angle C = 90°$

25. $m\angle A = 45°, m\angle B = 45°, m\angle C = 90°$ **26.** $m\angle A = 120°, m\angle B = 40°, m\angle C = 20°$

10.5 · Exploring Triangles   **459**

Lesson 10.5 **459**

EXERCISE Notes

ASSIGNMENT GUIDE

Basic/Average:
Day 1: Ex. 9–25 odd, 27–33
Day 2: Ex. 34, 35, 37–39 odd, 40–43
Above Average: Ex. 9–39 odd, 40–43
Advanced: Ex. 9–39 odd, 40–43
Selected Answers: Ex. 1–8, 9–39 odd

Guided Practice
Have students complete these exercises in groups. Remind them that each triangle can be named according to its sides and according to its angles.

Independent Practice
▶ **Ex. 9–14**   You may wish to have students use protractor and ruler, or have them estimate measurements.
▶ **Ex. 21–26**   Compare students' results from these exercises. The triangles drawn by students for each exercise should be similar, and students should discover this fact on their own.

▶ **Ex. 27–30** Remind students to use the Pythagorean Theorem.
▶ **Ex. 33** These models can be made with coffee stirrers (or better, flexible straws) and pins.

Integrated Review

These exercises preview important basics of coordinate geometry.

Exploration and Extension

Explain that in each problem students should consider just one of each named figure. For example, in Ex. 40, they should consider one triangle and one line segment.

Portfolio Opportunity: Math Log

Complete the statement with always, sometimes, or never. Explain your reasoning.
a. An equilateral triangle is ⬚?⬚ acute.
b. An obtuse triangle is ⬚?⬚ isosceles.
c. A scalene triangle is ⬚?⬚ equiangular.

Also available as a copymaster, page 32, Ex. 6

Alternative Assessment

A construction project that develops students' construction skills.

Available as a copymaster, page 34

In Exercises 27–30, find the triangle's perimeter and area. Then classify the triangle according to its sides and angles. (The area of each small square on the grid is 1 square unit.)

27. 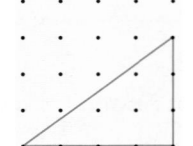   28.    29.   30.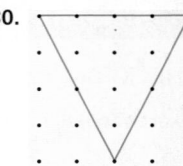

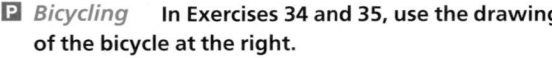

✪ **31.** Explain the relationship between an equilateral triangle and an equiangular triangle.

✪ **32.** *Think about It*   Can a right triangle be equilateral? Explain your reasoning.

✪ **33.** *The Shape of Things*   The figures at the
Ⓟ   right are made with popsicle sticks and brads. Is the triangle rigid, or can you adjust its sticks to form a different shape of triangle? Is the rectangle rigid, or can you adjust its sticks to form a different shape of quadrilateral?

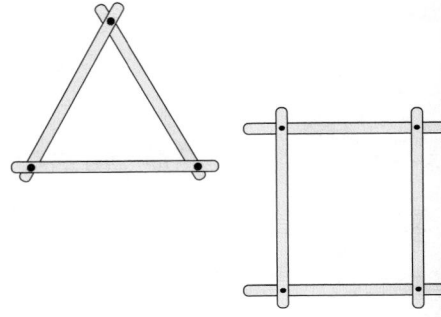

Ⓟ *Bicycling*   **In Exercises 34 and 35, use the drawing of the bicycle at the right.**

34. Sketch the frame of the bicycle. Then label the frame with points and identify all of the triangles formed by the bicycle's frame.

✪ **35.** *The Shape of Things*   Based on your answers to Exercise 33, why do you think triangles are used in bicycle construction instead of quadrilaterals?
Triangles will not collapse.

Integrated Review
Making Connections within Mathematics

Coordinate Geometry   **In Exercises 36–39, plot the points on a coordinate plane. Then classify △ABC by its sides and angles.** See Additional Answers.

36. $A(3, 0)$, $B(3, -3)$, $C(0, -3)$
37. $A(0, 1)$, $B(4, -1)$, $C(-4, -1)$
38. $A(-1, -5)$, $B(-5, -5)$, $C(-4, 2)$
39. $A(-1, 3)$, $B(2, 3)$, $C(2, -3)$

Exploration and Extension

Ⓟ *Intersections*   **In Exercises 40–43, sketch all possible intersections of the given figures.** See Additional Answers.

✪ **40.** Triangle and line segment   ✪ **41.** Two triangles
✪ **42.** Triangle and rectangle   ✪ **43.** Triangle and hexagon

460   Chapter **10** · Geometry Concepts and Spatial Thinking

✪ More difficult exercises
Ⓟ Portfolio Opportunity

Answers

27. ≈10.24 units, $4\frac{1}{2}$ units²; isosceles right

28. 12 units, 6 units²; scalene right
29. ≈9.66 units, 4 units²; isosceles right
30. ≈12.94 units, 8 units²; isosceles acute
31. An equilateral triangle is equiangular and vice versa.
32. No, the side opposite the right angle must be longer than the other two sides.
33. The triangle is rigid. You can adjust the rectangle's sticks to form a different shape of quadrilateral.
34.

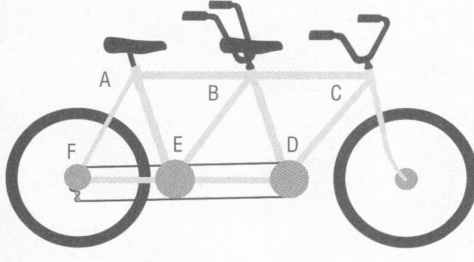

△AEF, △EAB, △BDE, △BDC

Take this test as you would take a test in class. The answers to the exercises are given in the back of the book.

In Exercises 1–4, use the cube at the right. (10.1)

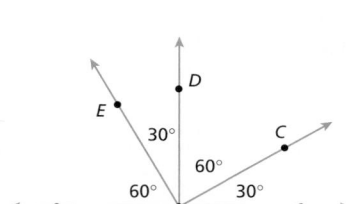

1. Name another point that lies in the same plane as M, N, and P. S

2. Name two lines that are parallel to $\overleftrightarrow{SR}$. $\overleftrightarrow{PQ}$, $\overleftrightarrow{NO}$

3. Name the point of intersection of $\overline{SP}$ and $\overline{PQ}$. P

4. Does the ray $\overrightarrow{NP}$ point up or down? Up

In Exercises 5–8, use the figure at the right. (10.2)

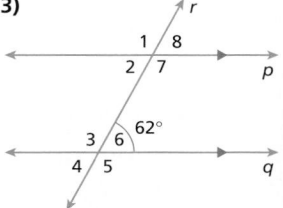

5. Name the right angles. $\angle DAB$, $\angle DAF$, $\angle CAE$

6. Name the acute angles. $\angle FAE$, $\angle EAD$, $\angle DAC$, $\angle CAB$

7. Name the obtuse angles. $\angle FAC$, $\angle EAB$

8. Name the straight angle. $\angle FAB$

In Exercises 9–12, use the figure at the right. (10.3)

In Exercises 9–11, use the words *vertical* or *corresponding*.

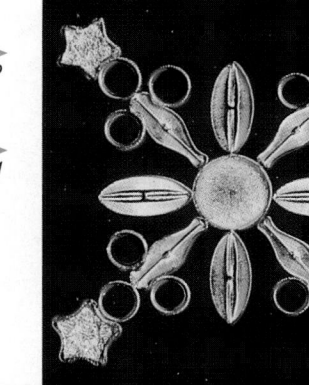

9. $\angle 1$ and $\angle 7$ are ⬚ angles. Vertical

10. $\angle 1$ and $\angle 3$ are ⬚ angles. Corresponding

11. $\angle 2$ and $\angle 4$ are ⬚ angles. Corresponding

12. Find the measure of each angle.
See margin.

Line p and line q are parallel.

In Exercises 13–15, identify any symmetry of the figure. (10.4) See margin.

13.

14.

15.

This microscopic diatom has both line and rotational symmetries.

In Exercises 16–19, classify the triangle by its sides and by its angles. (10.5)

16.
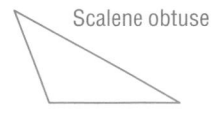
Scalene obtuse

17.

See below.

18.

Scalene right

19.
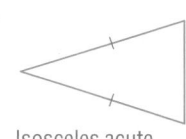
Isosceles acute

20. If a triangle is obtuse, does it have to be scalene? Illustrate your answer with a sketch. No; for sketch, see margin.

17. Equilateral, acute, equiangular, isosceles

Mid-Chapter Self-Test **461**

Answers

12. $m\angle 2 = m\angle 4 = m\angle 6 = m\angle 8 = 62°$
$m\angle 1 = m\angle 3 = m\angle 5 = m\angle 7 = 118°$
13. 6 lines of symmetry; rotational symmetry at 60°, 120°, and 180° in either direction
14. 5 lines of symmetry; rotational symmetry at 72° and 144° in either direction
15. 1 line of symmetry
20.
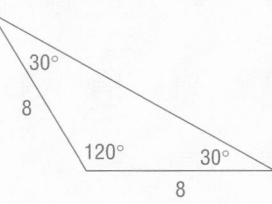

◀ **Alternative Assessment**

A **Partner Quiz** assesses students' achievement and provides them with an opportunity to communicate about mathematics.
Available as a copymaster, page 53

◀ **Formal Assessment**

Two **Mid-Chapter Tests** of average difficulty.
Available as copymasters, pages 162, 163

Mid-Chapter Self-Test **461**

PLANNING the Lesson

Lesson Plan 10.6, p. 81

ORGANIZER

Starters (reproduced below)
Problem of the Day 10.6, p. 29
Warm-Up Exercises 10.6, p. 29

Lesson Resources
Color Transparencies
Picture for Example 1, p. 43
Teaching Tools
Dot paper, pp. T2, C3
Protractor, pp. T12, C18
Tangram, pp. T14, C20
Math Log, p. 32
Answer Masters 10.6, pp. 201, 202
Extra Practice Copymaster 10.6, p. 81
Reteaching Copymaster 10.6, p. 81

Special Populations
Suggestions, Teacher's Edition, p. 436D

LESSON Notes

Lesson Investigation
In order to describe the variety of quadrilaterals that they construct, students should refer to the list of quadrilaterals at the bottom of the pupil page. Have students sketch their own illustrations of each type of quadrilateral.

10.6 Exploring Quadrilaterals

What you should learn:

Goal 1 How to identify quadrilaterals

Goal 2 How to identify quadrilaterals in real-life situations

Why you should learn it:

Being able to identify different types of quadrilaterals helps you communicate ideas about real-life situations.

3 sizes of squares, 1 size of nonsquare rectangle, 2 nonspecial parallelograms, 2 nonspecial trapezoids, 1 isosceles trapezoid, 1 kite, 4 nonspecial quadrilaterals (2 nonconvex)

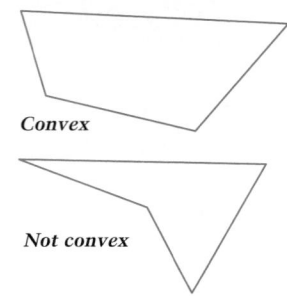

Convex

Not convex

Quadrilaterals can be convex or not convex. (See page 37 for a definition of convex.)

Goal 1   Identifying Quadrilaterals

LESSON INVESTIGATION

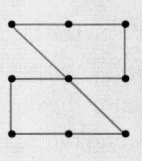

■ **Investigating Types of Quadrilaterals**

Group Activity How many different sizes of quadrilaterals can you draw on a 9-dot square? (The two quadrilaterals at the right are not considered different.) Discuss your results with other members of your group. What types of quadrilaterals were you able to draw? See answer at left.

In the above investigation, you may have used some of the following terms to classify quadrilaterals.

Parallelogram: A quadrilateral with opposite sides parallel
Rectangle: A parallelogram with 4 right angles
Square: A rectangle with sides of equal length
Rhombus: A parallelogram with sides of equal length
Trapezoid: A quadrilateral with only one pair of parallel sides
Kite: A quadrilateral that is not a parallelogram, but has two pair of sides of equal length
Scalene quadrilateral: All sides have different lengths.

A trapezoid is **isosceles** if its nonparallel sides have the same length. The figures below show several types of quadrilaterals.

 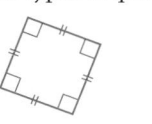

Parallelogram   *Rectangle*   *Square*   *Rhombus*

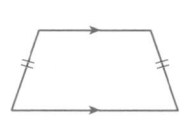 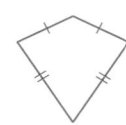 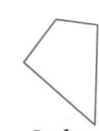

Trapezoid   *Isosceles trapezoid*   *Kite*   *Scalene*

STARTER: Problem of the Day

On the dot grid below, the horizontal or vertical distance from one dot to the next is 1 unit. Determine the area of the figure.   29 square units

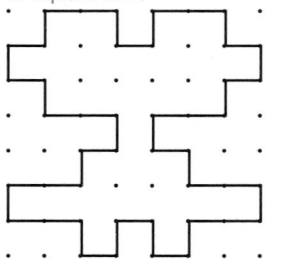

Also available as a copymaster, p. 29

STARTER: Warm-Up Exercises

1. How are a square and a rectangle alike? How are they different?
2. Sketch a parallelogram that is not a rectangle.
3. What kinds of geometric figures can you identify in the following diagram?

1. They are parallelograms with four right angles. A square has four congruent sides.
2. Check students' work.
3. Triangle, rectangle, trapezoid

Also available as a copymaster, p. 29

The photo at the left was scanned into a computer. Then a computer design program was used to alter the shape of the photo.

Real Life
Photography

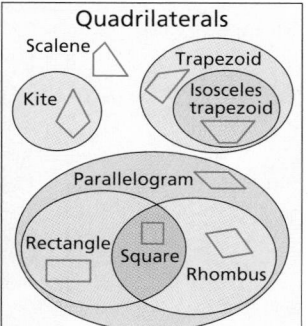

Example 1   *Classifying Quadrilaterals*

Each of the photographs shown above is a quadrilateral. Name *all* types of quadrilaterals that each photograph appears to be.

Solution   The first photograph appears to have opposite sides that are parallel, which would make it a parallelogram. Moreover, it appears to have 4 right angles, which makes it a rectangle.

The second photograph also appears to have opposite sides that are parallel, which would make it a parallelogram. Moreover, it appears to have 4 right angles, which would make it a rectangle, *and* sides of equal length, which would make it a square and a rhombus.

The third photograph appears to have opposite sides that are parallel, which would make it a parallelogram. ∎

Communicating about MATHEMATICS

Cooperative Learning

▶ **SHARING IDEAS about the Lesson**

Interpreting Venn Diagrams The Venn diagram above shows that every square is a rectangle. Work with a partner. Use the diagram to write several other statements of the form "Every [?] is a [?] ." Answers vary.

Common-Error Alert!

The classification of quadrilaterals can often be misunderstood, especially where one quadrilateral fits into several categories.

Example 1 ————————

Provide quadrilaterals of other shapes and have students classify them. Or ask them to draw quadrilaterals that satisfy given specifications. For example, have them draw a quadrilateral that is both a rhombus and a rectangle.

Communicating about MATHEMATICS

Before starting this activity, you may wish to provide students with additional practice in reading and interpreting Venn diagrams. Begin by classifying common objects in the classroom.

Writing Prompt
Using two names from the list of quadrilaterals on page 462 of the pupil text, complete the following.
A _____ and a _____ are alike because . . .

EXERCISES

Guided Practice

▶ **CHECK for Understanding**

1. Name all quadrilaterals that:
   1. For clarifications, see margin.
   a. Parallelograms   c. Trapezoids

   a. have 2 pair of parallel sides.
   b. have no parallel sides. Kites, nonspecial quadrila
   c. have exactly one pair of parallel sides.
   d. have 4 congruent sides. Rhombuses
   e. have no congruent sides.
      Scalene quadrilaterals
   f. have at least one pair of congruent sides.
      Kites, isosceles trapezoids, parallelograms

P **2.** *Writing* In your own words, state how to determine whether a quadrilateral is convex or not convex. Draw examples of convex and nonconvex quadrilaterals. Answers vary. Check students' work.

P **3.** Explain the difference between a kite and a rhombus.

P **4.** Explain the difference between a square and a rectangle.
A square is a rectangle with sides of equal length.
3. A rhombus is a parallelogram and a kite is not.

Independent Practice

In Exercises 5–12, identify the quadrilateral from its appearance. Use the name that *best* describes the quadrilateral.

Parallelogram

5. Trapezoid 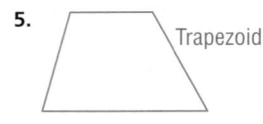 **6.** Kite 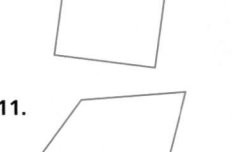 **7.** Square  **8.**

9. Rhombus 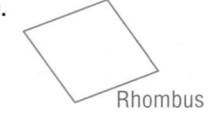 **10.** Isosceles trapezoid 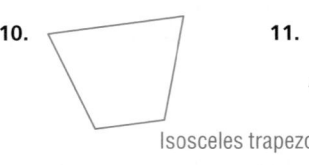 **11.** Scalene quadrilateral 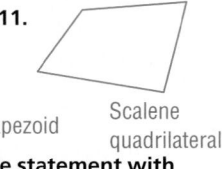 **12.** Rectangle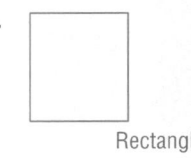

Logical Reasoning In Exercises 13–16, complete the statement with *always*, *sometimes*, or *never*. **Explain.** For explanations, see margin.

⭐ **13.** A quadrilateral is ⟨?⟩ a parallelogram. sometimes
⭐ **14.** A rectangle is ⟨?⟩ a rhombus. sometimes
⭐ **15.** A trapezoid is ⟨?⟩ a convex quadrilateral. always
⭐ **16.** A rhombus is ⟨?⟩ a square. sometimes

In Exercises 17–20, find the values of *x* and *y*.

17. Isosceles trapezoid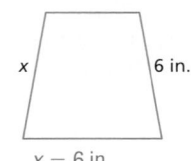
x   6 in.
x = 6 in.

18. Square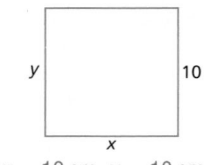
y   10 cm
x
x = 10 cm, *y* = 10 cm

19. Parallelogram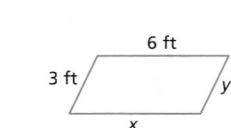
6 ft
3 ft   *y*
x
x = 6 ft, *y* = 3 ft

20. Kite   *x* = 5 m, *y* =
x   5 m
y   11 m

⭐ More difficult exercises
P Portfolio Opportunity

464 Chapter **10** • Geometry Concepts and Spatial Thinking

Answers

1.a. Parallelograms that include rectangles, squares, and rhombuses
c. Trapezoids that include isosceles trapezoids
d. Rhombuses that include squares
e. Scalene quadrilaterals that include some trapezoids that are not isosceles
f. Isosceles trapezoids and some trapezoids that are not isosceles; and parallelgrams that include rectangles, squares, and rhombuses
13. A parallelogram is only one type of quadrilateral.
14. A square is the only type of rectangle that is also a rhombus.
15. A segment joining any two interior points lies completely within a trapezoid.
16. A square is only one type of rhombus.

464 Chapter 10

Drawing Figures   **In Exercises 21–24, use the description to sketch the figure. If it is not possible, write *not possible*.**

21. A parallelogram with 2 pair of congruent sides   Draw any parallelogram.

22. A quadrilateral with one pair of congruent sides and one pair of parallel sides   Draw any isosceles trapezoid.

23. A parallelogram with no congruent sides   Not possible

24. A quadrilateral with no congruent sides   Draw any scalene quadrilateral.

Symmetry   **In Exercises 25–32, match the quadrilateral with the description of its symmetry. Use each description that applies. Make a sketch to support your answers.**

  a. No symmetry
             b. Exactly 1 line of symmetry

  c. Exactly 2 lines of symmetry
      d. Exactly 3 lines of symmetry

  e. Exactly 4 lines of symmetry
      f. Rotational symmetry

25. Parallelogram f   **26.** Rectangle c, f   **27.** Square e, f   **28.** Rhombus c, f

29. Trapezoid a   **30.** Isosceles trapezoid b   **31.** Kite b   **32.** Scalene quadrilateral a

Making a Conjecture   **In Exercises 33–36, use a straightedge and protractor.**
33., 34. Check students' work.

33. Draw any convex quadrilateral and measure its angles.

34. Repeat Exercise 33 using three different quadrilaterals. Record the sum of the measures of the angles for each quadrilateral.

35. Use the results of Exercises 33 and 34 to write a conjecture about the sum of the measures of the angles of any convex quadrilateral.

36. Use your conjecture to find $m\angle A$ for the quadrilateral at the right. 100°
35. The sum of the measures of the angles of any convex quadrilateral is 360°.

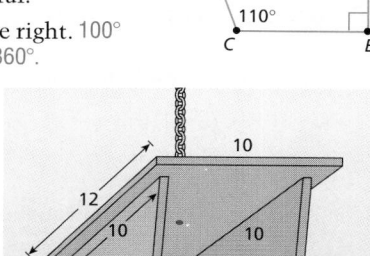

Bird Feeder   **In Exercises 37–40, use the drawing of a bird feeder at the right.** 37.–39. See margin.

37. Draw each piece of wood that is used to build the bird feeder.

38. Identify each piece of wood that you sketched in Exercise 37.

39. Identify all pieces of wood that are congruent.

40. Design your own bird feeder. Sketch and identify the pieces of wood that you use.   Answers vary.

Integrated Review

Making Connections within Mathematics

Coordinate Geometry   **In Exercises 41–44, plot the points in a coordinate plane. Then identify the quadrilateral *ABCD*.**   For plots, see Additional Answers.

41. $A(0, 0)$, $B(2, 3)$, $C(8, 0)$, $D(2, -3)$ **42.** $A(-2, 3)$, $B(2, 3)$, $C(5, -2)$, $D(-5, -2)$

43. $A(0, 0)$, $B(3, 3)$, $C(9, 3)$, $D(6, 0)$ **44.** $A(2, 2)$, $B(2, -2)$, $C(-2, -2)$, $D(-2, 2)$
  41. Kite   **42.** Isosceles trapezoid   **43.** Parallelogram **44.** Square

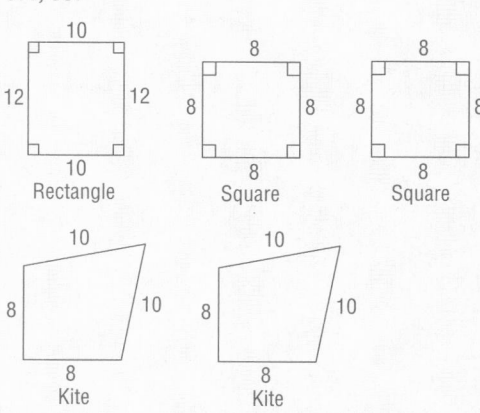

▶ **Ex. 21–24** The answers to these problems should be shared as a class by having several volunteers put their sketches for each problem on the board.

▶ **Ex. 25–32** Assign these exercises as a group, then summarize the results, for example, that "none of the figures had three lines of symmetry, two had exactly one line of symmetry," and so on.

▶ **Ex. 33–36** Assign these as a group.

▶ **Ex. 37–39** Assign these also as a group.

▶ **Ex. 40**

EXTENSION
This exercise could be done as an interdisciplinary activity.

Integrated Review

When a quadrilateral has been centered about the origin (Ex. 44), ask students to make observations about the ordered pairs (in order to detect patterns that result due to symmetry).

Answers
37., 38.

Rectangle   Square   Square

Kite   Kite

39. The 2 side walls that are kites, the back wall and bottom that are squares

COOPERATIVE LEARNING
These problems could be used as a cooperative learning activity. Students enjoy manipulating the tangram pieces to make new shapes.

Portfolio Opportunity: Math Log

In your own words, describe the difference between a parallelogram and a trapezoid.

Also available as a copymaster, page 32, Ex. 7

Short Quiz

Covers Lessons 10.5 and 10.6

Available as a copymaster, page 164

Answers

45.

46.

47.

48.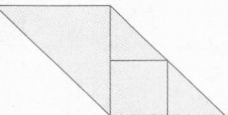

49.

50.

51.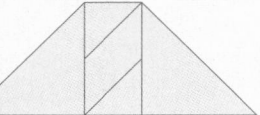

52.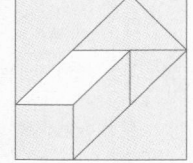

466 Chapter 10

Exploration and Extension

Tangrams **In Exercises 45–52, use the tangram pieces at the right to construct the quadrilateral.** See margin.

✪ **45.** Use 3 tangram pieces to make a square.

✪ **46.** Use 3 tangram pieces to make an isosceles trapezoid.

✪ **47.** Use 4 tangram pieces to make a nonsquare rectangle.

✪ **48.** Use 4 tangram pieces to make a nonrectangular parallelogram.

✪ **49.** Use 4 tangram pieces to make a nonisosceles trapezoid.

✪ **50.** Use 5 tangram pieces to make a square.

✪ **51.** Use 5 tangram pieces to make an isosceles trapezoid.

✪ **52.** Use 7 tangram pieces to make the figure at the right.

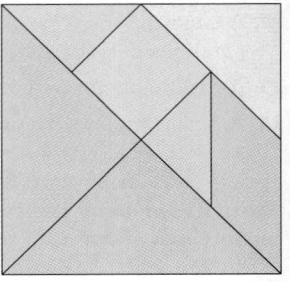

Chinese Tangrams *A tangram is a square that has been cut into a square, a parallelogram, and 5 triangles. Tangram puzzles were invented by the Chinese more than 1000 years ago.*

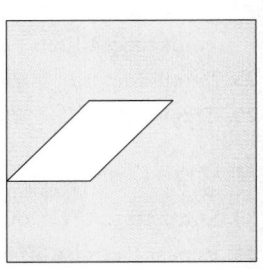

Mixed REVIEW

For plots, see Additional Answers.

In Exercises 1–3, plot the points and identify quadrilateral *BDCA*. (10.6)

1. $A(0, 2)$, $B(-2, 0)$
$C(1, 1)$, $D(0, -3)$
Scalene quadrilateral

2. $A(-2, -1)$, $B(-1, 1)$
$C(4, -1)$, $D(3, 1)$
Isosceles trapezoid

3. $A(0, 5)$, $B(2, 4)$
$C(-2, 4)$, $D(0, 0)$
Kite

In Exercises 4–9, solve the equation. (4.2, 7.2)

4. $2b - 2 = -2b$ $\frac{1}{2}$

5. $62p - 203 = 111 - 38p$ 3.14

6. $2a + 4.04 = 16.08$ 6.02

7. $\frac{1}{4}(3r - 1) = \frac{1}{4}$ $\frac{2}{3}$

8. $p^2 + 4 = 40$ $6, -6$

9. $q - \frac{1}{2} = \frac{1}{3}$ $\frac{5}{6}$

In Exercises 10–14, rewrite the number in scientific notation. (6.8)

10. 2100
2.1×10^3

11. 0.00092
9.2×10^{-4}

12. 16,000,000
1.6×10^7

13. 0.00000046
4.6×10^{-7}

14. 92.4×10^{18}
9.24×10^{19}

In Exercises 15–20, simplify the expression. (7.2, 7.4, 7.5)

15. $\frac{1}{5} + \frac{2}{5}$ $\frac{3}{5}$

16. $\frac{4}{9} - \frac{2}{9}$ $\frac{2}{9}$

17. $\frac{4}{9} + \frac{1}{3}$ $\frac{7}{9}$

18. $\frac{4}{5} - \frac{3}{4}$ $\frac{1}{20}$

19. $\frac{3}{8} \times \frac{1}{2}$ $\frac{3}{16}$

20. $\frac{3}{10} \div \frac{9}{2}$ $\frac{1}{15}$

10.7

Polygons and Congruence

PACING the Lesson
Suggested Number of Days
Basic/Average 0   Above Average 1
Advanced 1

PLANNING the Lesson
Lesson Plan 10.7, p. 82

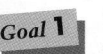 *What you should learn:*

 Goal 1 How to recognize congruent polygons

Goal 2 How to identify regular polygons

Why you should learn it:

Congruent polygons can be used to create real-life floor tiles.

Islamic Art   *This Morroccan mosaic is a prime example of the geometric tiling patterns found in Islamic art and architecture.*

Goal 1   **Recognizing Congruent Polygons**

Two polygons are **congruent** if they are exactly the same size and shape. To decide whether two polygons are congruent, you can trace each on paper, cut one out, and try to move the cut polygon so that it lies exactly on top of the other polygon.

LESSON INVESTIGATION

■ Investigating Congruent Polygons

Group Activity Use dot paper to draw a hexagon or octagon whose sides have the same lengths and whose angles have the same measures. In how many ways can you divide the hexagon or octagon into congruent polygons? The sample below shows an equilateral triangle divided into congruent polygons in four different ways.

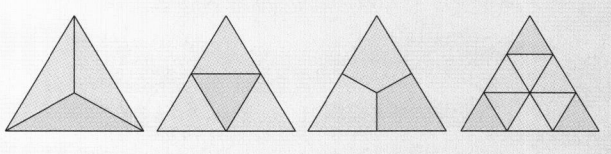

See margin.

Example 1   *Identifying Congruent Polygons*

Which of the quadrilaterals are congruent?

a. 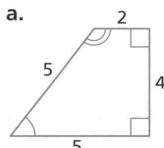   b. 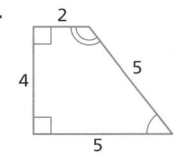   c.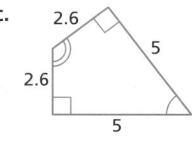

Solution   The first two quadrilaterals are congruent. Try confirming this with tracing paper.

The third quadrilateral is not congruent to either of the first two. One reason for this is that its sides don't have the same lengths as the sides of either of the first two quadrilaterals. ■

10.7 ▪ Polygons and Congruence   **467**

ORGANIZER

Starters (reproduced below)
Problem of the Day 10.7, p. 30
Warm-Up Exercises 10.7, p. 30
Lesson Resources
Color Transparencies
Picture for Example 1, p. 44
Teaching Tools
Dot paper, pp. T2, C3
Diagrams for Ex. 22–24, p. C21
Math Log, p. 33
Answer Masters 10.7, p. 204
Extra Practice Copymaster 10.7, p. 82
Reteaching Copymaster 10.7, p. 82
Special Populations
Suggestions, Teacher's Edition, p. 436D

LESSON Notes

Congruence in manufactured items guarantees that replacement parts are built to desired specifications. Ask students if there are any congruent objects in their classroom.

Lesson Investigation
Discuss why dot paper makes it easy to determine if congruent polygons have been constructed.

Example 1

Ask students to draw a fourth quadrilateral that *is* congruent to quadrilateral **c.**

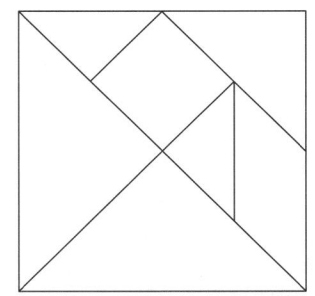
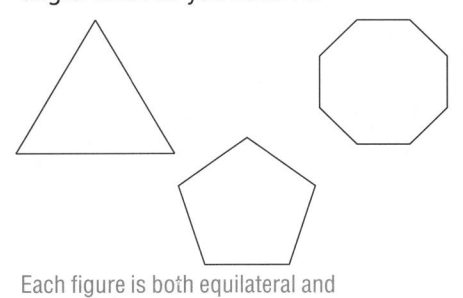
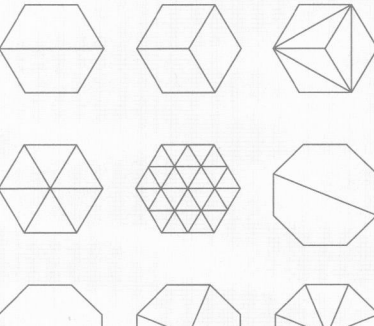

Regular polygons are often used in commercial and fashion design. Have students determine if there are examples of regular polygons in their classroom.

Example 2

Ask students to identify the other name for a regular triangle and a regular quadrilateral.
Equilateral triangle, square

Communicating
about MATHEMATICS

Ask students: Are there real-life examples of mixed tiling patterns? Have students look for examples in art, magazines, and so on.

Writing Prompt
Make a list of congruent polygons that can be seen in
a. the classroom,
b. the school lunch room,
c. the kitchen in your home.

A polygon is **regular** if each of its sides has the same length *and* each of its angles has the same measure. Four examples are shown below.

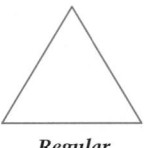  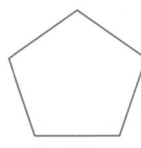 

| Regular Triangle | Regular Quadrilateral | Regular Pentagon | Regular Hexagon |

 *Real Life*
Tiling Design

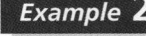

Example 2   *Tiling with Regular Polygons*

Which of the above regular polygons could be used to tile a floor with no gaps or overlapping tiles?

Solution   You can solve this problem experimentally by tracing several polygons of each shape and trying to fit the polygons together. After doing this, you can discover that regular triangles, quadrilaterals, and hexagons can be used as tiles, but the regular pentagons cannot be used.

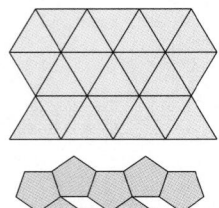   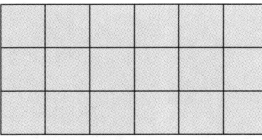

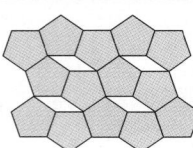   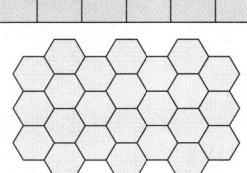

Color and shading can be used to create illusions of space and form. In this design, the tilted tiles appear to radiate from a center point.

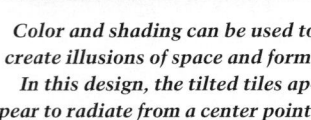
P   ## Communicating *about* MATHEMATICS

▶ **SHARING IDEAS about the Lesson**

Extending the Example In Example 2, suppose you could mix different types of regular polygons to tile the floor. Draw some possible patterns. Answers vary, see margin.

Answer to Communicating

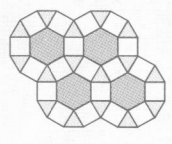 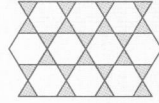

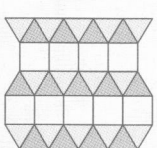

EXERCISES

Guided Practice

CHECK for Understanding

1. Explain how you can tell whether two polygons are congruent.   See top of page 467.

In Exercises 2 and 3, two polygons are congruent. Which are they?

2. a. 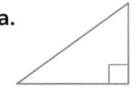 b.  c.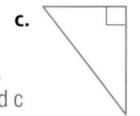

a and c

3. a. 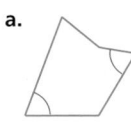 b.  c.

b and c

4. Name each polygon. Is the polygon regular?

a.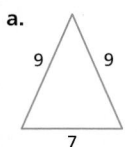

9   9

7

Isosceles triangle, no

b.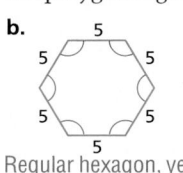

5   5
5   5
5   5
5

Regular hexagon, yes

c.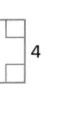

8
4   4
8

Rectangle, no

d.

6
6   6
6

Rhombus, no

Independent Practice

In Exercises 5–8, match the quadrilateral with a congruent quadrilateral.

a.  b. 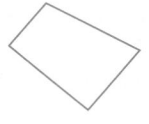 c. 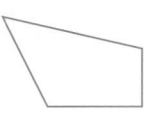 d.

5.
d

6.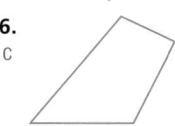
c

7.
a

8.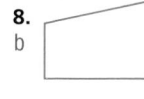
b

In Exercises 9 and 10, use the words congruent, equilateral, equiangular, and regular to describe the polygons.   See margin.

9. a.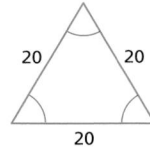

20   20
20

b.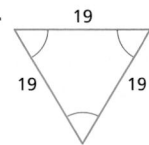

19
19   19

c.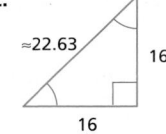

≈22.63
16
16

d.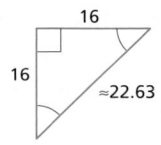

16
16   ≈22.63

10. a.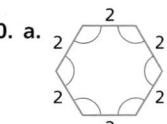

2
2   2
2   2
2

b.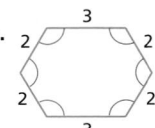

3
2   2
2   2
3

c.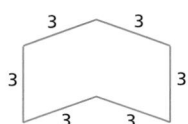

3   3
3   3
3   3

d.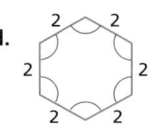

2   2
2   2
2   2

Extra Practice

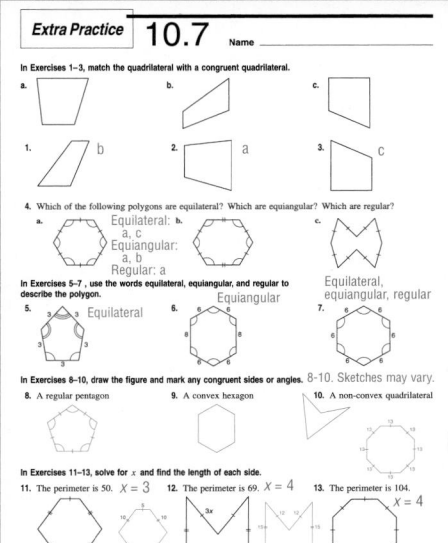

Reteaching

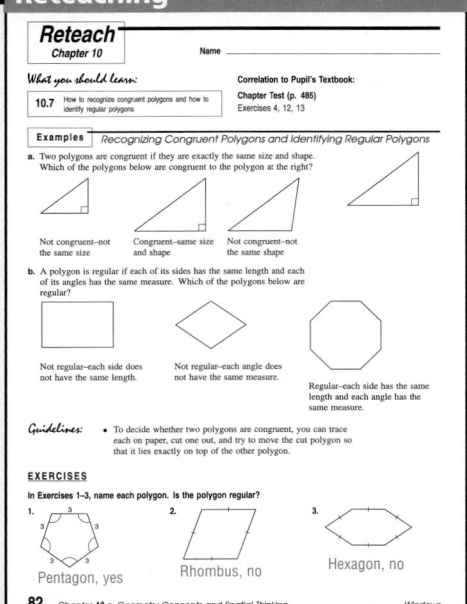

ASSIGNMENT GUIDE

*Basic/Average:
Day 1: Ex. 5–15
Day 2: Ex. 16–24

Above Average: Ex. 5–9, 11, 13, 16–18, 19, 21, 23, 24

Advanced: Ex. 5–9, 11, 13, 16–18, 19, 21, 23, 24

Selected Answers: Ex. 1–4, 5–21 odd

*You may wish to omit this lesson for these students.

Guided Practice

▶ Ex. 4c, d

Addressing Misconceptions

Students may judge these figures too quickly and incorrectly—a polygon can be equilateral without being equiangular, and vice versa.

Independent Practice

▶ Ex. 9, 10   Check for the completeness of students' answers.

Answers

9. a. Equilateral, equiangular, regular
   b. Equilateral, equiangular, regular
   c. Congruent to *d*
   d. Congruent to *c*

10. a. Equilateral, equiangular, regular, congruent to *d*
    b. Equiangular
    c. Equilateral
    d. Equilateral, equiangular, regular, congruent to *a*

In Exercises 11–14, trace the figure. Then divide the figure into congruent regular triangles. Use as few triangles as possible.

✪ **11.**    ✪ **12.** 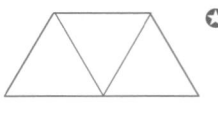   ✪ **13.**    ✪ **14.**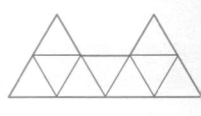

✪ **15.** *Think about It* Discuss the relationship between equilateral, equiangular, and regular. If a polygon is equilateral, must it be equiangular? Explain. See margin.

Polygon Puzzle **In Exercises 16–18, use the figure at the right.**

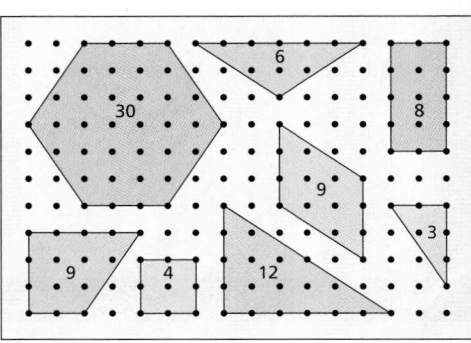

✪ **16.** The eight polygons at the right can be rearranged to form a square. What is the area of the square? What are the dimensions of the square? 81 units², 9 units by 9 units

✪ **17.** Which of the polygons are equilateral? Which are equiangular? square; square, rectangle

✪ **18.** Trace the eight figures on dot paper. Then rearrange the figures to form a square. (*Hint:* The result of Exercise 16 can help you.) See margin.

Integrated Review   *Making Connections within Mathematics*

Perimeter **In Exercises 19–21, solve for *x* and find the length of each side.**

19. The perimeter is 90.
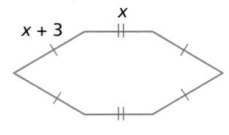
13; 13, 13, 16, 16, 16, 16

20. The perimeter is 42.
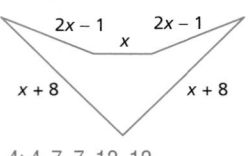
4; 4, 7, 7, 12, 12

21. The perimeter is 62.
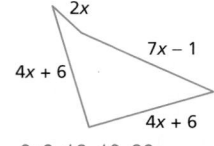
3; 6, 18, 18, 20

Exploration and Extension

Forming Squares **In Exercises 22–24, copy the figure. Then cut the figure into two parts and rearrange it to form a square. You can use only one straight cut.**

✪ **22.** 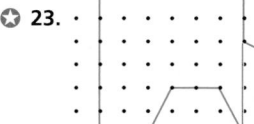   ✪ **23.**   ✪ **24.**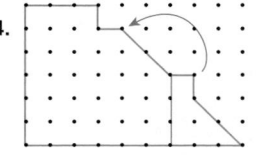

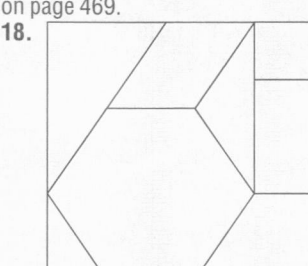

Materials Needed: paper, straightedge, scissors

Example   *Exploring Angles of Triangles*

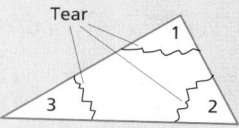

Tear

Draw a large triangle on a piece of paper. Cut the triangle out and tear off its three corners. Explain how you can use the three corners to confirm that the sum of the three angle measures is 180°.

Solution   You can arrange the three corners as shown at the right. If you place the corners carefully, you will see that they form a straight angle. This implies that the sum of the three angle measures is 180°. ∎

Exercises

1. Work in a group to complete the table. Use the procedure described in Example 2 on page 204.

Polygon	Number of Sides	Number of Angles	Number of Triangles	Sum of Angle Measures	Measure of Each Angle in a Regular Polygon
Triangle	3	3	1	1(180°) = 180°	60°
Quadrilateral	4	4	2	2(180°) = 360°	90°
Pentagon	5	? 5	? 3	3 (180°) ? = 540°	? 108°
Hexagon	6	? 6	? 4	4 (180°) ? = 720°	? 120°
Heptagon	7	? 7	? 5	5 (180°) ? = 900°	? $128\frac{4}{7}°$
Octagon	8	? 8	? 6	6 (180°) ? = 1080°	? 135°
Nonagon	9	? 9	? 7	7 (180°) ? = 1260°	? 140°
Decagon	10	? 10	? 8	8 (180°) ? = 1440°	? 144°
n-gon	n	?	?	?	?
		n	$n-2$	$(n-2)180°$	$\frac{(n-2)\,180°}{n}$

2. Describe the pattern for the sum of the measures of the angles of a polygon. Use your result to find the sum of the measures of the angles of a 12-sided polygon.   To get the next sum, add 180° to the previous sum. 1800°

3. Describe the pattern for the measure of each angle of a regular polygon. Use your result to find the measure of each angle of a regular 12-sided polygon.   To get the 2nd measure, find $\frac{2}{4}$ of 180°; to get the 3rd measure, find $\frac{3}{5}$ of 180°; to get the 4th measure, find $\frac{4}{6}$ of 180°; etc. 150°

EXTENSION
Have students graph the results of their investigation. Many kinds of graphs or scatter plots can be done (see below). These graphs reinforce the idea of looking for graphical relationships and the need to choose appropriate scales and labels for the axes.

Possible graphs
1. Plot the number of sides versus the number of angles.
2. Plot the number of sides versus the number of triangles formed.
3. Plot the number of sides versus the sum of the interior angles.
4. Plot the number of sides versus the measure of each interior angle in a regular polygon.

    Note that in each graph, the number of sides is the independent variable. The other data *depend* on the number of sides.

▶ **PLANNING the Lesson**

Lesson Plan 10.8, p. 83

ORGANIZER

Starters (reproduced below)
Problem of the Day 10.8, p. 30
Warm-Up Exercises 10.8, p. 30

Lesson Resources
Teaching Tools
Protractor, pp. T12, C18
Graph paper, pp. T1, C2
Math Log, p. 33
Technology, p. 60
Answer Masters 10.8, pp. 205, 206
Extra Practice Copymaster 10.8, p. 83
Reteaching Copymaster 10.8, p. 83

Special Populations
Suggestions, Teacher's Edition, p. 436D

LESSON Notes

Point out that an interior angle and the corresponding exterior angle together form a straight angle.

Lesson Investigation
Students will enjoy working in groups to complete this activity. Encourage students to repeat the activity using a variety of polygons.

Example 1

Refer students to the table completed in the investigation on page 471. The data for a *quadrilateral* shows the sum of its interior angle measures to be 360°. This is referred to in the solution of Example 1.

10.8 Angles of Polygons

What you should learn:

Goal 1 How to find the measures of the angles of a polygon

Goal 2 How to find the measure of each angle of a regular polygon

Why you should learn it:

You can use the measures of the angles of a polygon to solve real-life problems, such as analyzing the design of a star.

The sum of the exterior angle measures is 360°. Yes. Explanations vary.

Goal 1 **Measuring the Angles of a Polygon**

The angles of a polygon are called **interior angles.** Polygons also have **exterior angles,** as shown below.

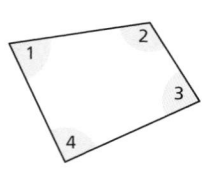

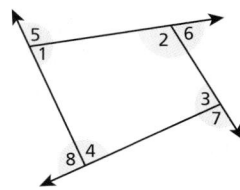

∠1, ∠2, ∠3, and ∠4 are interior angles of this polygon.

∠5, ∠6, ∠7, and ∠8 are exterior angles of this polygon.

LESSON INVESTIGATION

■ **Investigating Exterior Angles of a Polygon**
Group Activity Draw a polygon on a piece of paper and extend the sides to form one exterior angle at each vertex. Then cut out the exterior angles and tape them together. Discuss your result. Do you think the result is true of *any* polygon? Explain your reasoning. See answers at left.

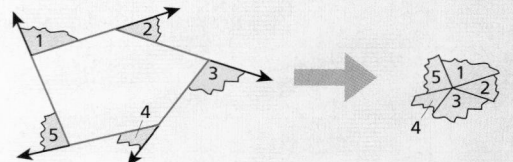

Example 1 *Measuring the Angles of a Polygon*

Find the measures of the angles of the polygon at the left.

Solution You are given that $m\angle 1 = 90°$, $m\angle 2 = 120°$, and $m\angle 3 = 70°$. Because the sum of the interior angles is 360°, it follows that $m\angle 4 = 360° - (90° + 120° + 70°)$ or 80°. Explain how you can find the measure of each exterior angle. ∎

┌─ **STARTER: Problem of the Day** ─┐

The lengths of two sides of a triangle are *x* cm and 2*x* cm respectively. What inequality can you write that expresses the length of the third side?
x < third side < 3*x*

Also available as a copymaster, p. 30

┌─ **STARTER: Warm-Up Exercises** ─┐

In the given figure, $\overleftrightarrow{AB} \parallel \overleftrightarrow{CD}$, and *m* intersects them. If $m\angle 4 = 60°$, find the measure of all the other labeled angles.

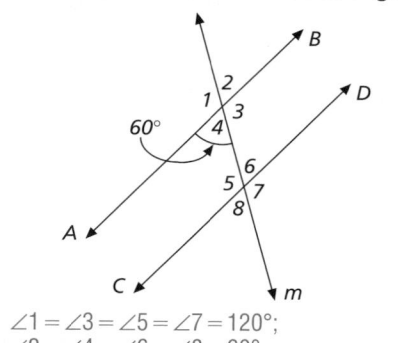

∠1 = ∠3 = ∠5 = ∠7 = 120°;
∠2 = ∠4 = ∠6 = ∠8 = 60°

Also available as a copymaster, p. 30

Mosaic star designs often contain both "regular" and "irregular" stars.

Measuring Angles in a Regular Polygon

Angle Measures of a Polygon

Consider a polygon with *n* sides.

1. The sum of the interior angle measures is $(n - 2)(180°)$.

2. For a regular polygon, each interior angle measures $\frac{(n-2)(180°)}{n}$.

3. The sum of the exterior angle measures is 360°.

4. For a regular polygon, each exterior angle measures $\frac{360°}{n}$.

Real Life
Design

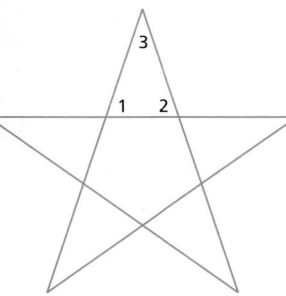

Example 2   *Measuring Angles in a Regular Polygon*

You are designing a flag that uses "regular" five-pointed stars. Sketch a five-pointed star. Then explain how to determine the measures of its angles.

Solution   A sketch of a five-pointed star is shown at the left. Notice that the star is built around a regular pentagon.

Each exterior angle of the regular pentagon has a measure of

$$\frac{360°}{5} = 72°. \qquad\qquad m\angle 1, m\angle 2$$

Because the measures of $\angle 1$ and $\angle 2$ are the same, it follows that the measure of $\angle 3$ is

$$180° - (m\angle 1 + m\angle 2) = 180° - 144° = 36°. \qquad m\angle 3$$

The measures of the other angles of the star can be found in a similar way. ∎

P

Communicating about MATHEMATICS

▶ **SHARING IDEAS about the Lesson**

Designing Stars See margin.

A. Draw a six-pointed "regular" star and label its angles. Explain how to find the measures of its angles.

B. Draw a seven-pointed "regular" star and label its angles. Explain how to find the measures of its angles.

C. Draw an eight-pointed "regular" star and label its angles. Explain how to find the measures of its angles.

Have students complete a table similar to the one shown below. They should use the information contained in the box at the top of page 473 of the pupil text (Angle Measures of a Polygon). Completing the table may be helpful in better understanding the angle measures of polygons.

Interior Angle Measures of Regular Polygons		
# Sides	Angle Sum	Each Angle
3	180°	60°
4	360°	90°
5	540°	108°
6	720°	120°
7	900°	128.6°
8	1080°	135°
n	$180(n-2)°$	$\frac{180(n-2)°}{n}$

Example 2

Ask students: What type of symmetry does the five-pointed star have?   Line and rotational symmetry

Communicating about MATHEMATICS

Have students explain why all the triangles that form the "points" of an *n*-pointed star ($n = 5, 6, 7$, etc.) are congruent.

Writing Prompt
Describe geometrically any road signs that you passed on the way to school today.

Answers to Communicating

A.   **B.**   **C.**

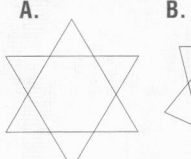 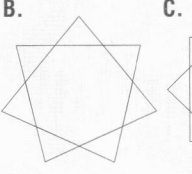

A.–C.

Number of vertex angles in star	Each exterior angle of regular convex polygon	Each vertex angle of star
6	$\frac{360°}{6} = 60°$	$180° - 2(60°) = 60°$
7	$\frac{360°}{7} = 51\frac{3}{7}°$	$180° - 2\left(51\frac{3}{7}°\right) = 77\frac{1}{7}°$
8	$\frac{360°}{8} = 45°$	$180° - 2(45°) = 90°$

Technology

Exploring Interior and Exterior Angles of Polygons   **10.8**   Teacher Demonstration Material

Exploration Using a Computer Drawing Program

In this activity, you will use dynamic construction software such as *Cabri, The Geometer's Sketchpad,* or *Geometry Inventor* to demonstrate that the formulas used to find the sum of the measures of the interior and exterior angles of polygons work for any convex polygon. It is assumed that the user is familiar with the software.

Interior Angles of Polygons

In this part of the demonstration, you will show students that the sum of the measures of the interior angles of any convex *n*-gon is $(n − 2)(180°)$.

Begin by letting your students choose *any* convex polygon and, using the formula, have them determine the sum of the interior angles. Then use the software to construct the polygon and measure each interior angle. Instruct your students to use a calculator to find the sum of the measured angles. The sum will equal the value of the formula. (Answers may vary slightly due to rounding.)

Complete this part of the demonstration by showing that the formula works for any convex polygon. You can do this by altering the constructed polygon and measuring the interior angles again and by constructing other types of polygons.

Exterior Angles of Polygons

In this part of the demonstration, you will show students that the sum of the measures of the exterior angles of any convex *n*-gon is 360°.

Again, begin by letting your students choose *any* convex polygon. Then use the software to construct the polygon, extend its sides, and measure each exterior angle. Instruct your students to use a calculator to find the sum of the measured angles. The sum will equal 360°. (Again, answers may vary slightly due to rounding.)

Complete the demonstration by showing that the sum of the measures of the exterior angles of any convex polygon is 360°. You can do this by altering the constructed polygon and measuring the exterior angles again and by constructing other types of polygons.

After completing the demonstration, your students should be convinced that the formulas listed on page 473 of the textbook can be used to determine the sum of the interior and exterior angle measures for any convex polygon; however, they may want to try this activity on their own.

60 *Technology Using Calculators and Computers*   Ⓒ D. C. Heath and Company

EXERCISE Notes

ASSIGNMENT GUIDE

*Basic/Average:
Day 1: Ex. 5–8, 9–17 odd, 23, 24
Day 2: Ex. 19–22, 25–29

Above Average:
Day 1: Ex. 5–8, 9–17 odd, 23, 24
Day 2: Ex. 19–22, 25–29

Advanced: Ex. 8, 9–23 odd, 24–29

Selected Answers: Ex. 1–4, 5–27 odd

*You may wish to omit this lesson for these students.

Guided Practice

Use this as a five-minute in-class activity for students working in pairs.

Independent Practice

▶ **Ex. 9–11** Encourage students to copy the diagram onto their homework paper before trying to determine the angle measures.
▶ **Ex. 12–14** Calculators would be helpful for these exercises.
▶ **Ex. 15–18** One exercise of this type should be modeled during the lesson.

Answers

1.

60° \ 120°

2.

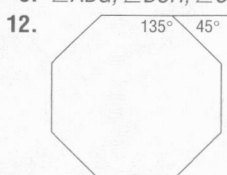
60°

5. ∠ABC, ∠BCD, ∠CDE, ∠DEA, ∠EAB; 540°
6. ∠ABG, ∠BCH, ∠CDI, ∠DEJ, ∠EAF; 360°

12.
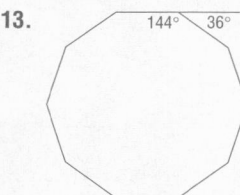
135° 45°

13.
144° 36°

14.
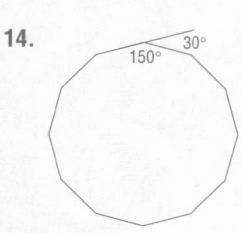
30°
150°

474 Chapter 10

EXERCISES

Guided Practice

▶ **CHECK for Understanding**   **1., 2.** See margin.
1. Draw a triangle with a 60° exterior angle.   2. Draw a quadrilateral with a 60° interior angle.

In Exercises 3 and 4, find the measure of each labeled angle.

3. Hexagon (vertical line of symmetry)

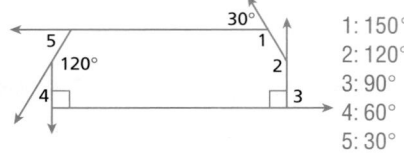

1: 150°
2: 120°
3: 90°
4: 60°
5: 30°

4. Regular hexagon.

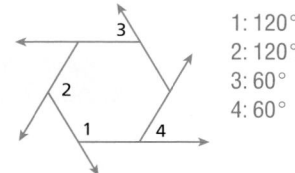

1: 120°
2: 120°
3: 60°
4: 60°

Independent Practice

In Exercises 5–8, use the pentagon at the right.

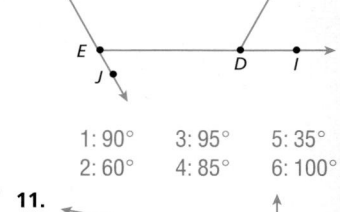

5. Name the interior angles of the pentagon. What is the sum of their measures? **5., 6.** See margin.
6. Name the indicated exterior angles of the pentagon. What is the sum of their measures?
7. Does the pentagon appear to be regular? No
8. If $m\angle ABG = 35°$, what is $m\angle ABC$? 145°

In Exercises 9–11, find the measures of the labeled angles.

9.
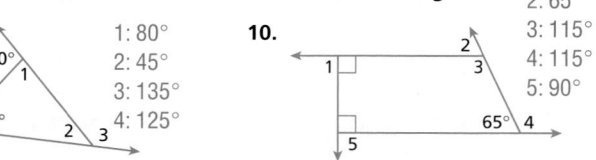
100°
55°
4 2 3

1: 80°
2: 45°
3: 135°
4: 125°

10.
1: 90°
2: 65°
3: 115°
4: 115°
5: 90°

11.
1: 90°
2: 60°
3: 95°
4: 85°
5: 35°
6: 100°

In Exercises 12–14, find the measure of each interior and exterior angle of the regular polygon. Illustrate your results with a sketch.   For sketches, see margin.

12. Regular octagon 135°, 45°   **13.** Regular decagon 144°, 36°   **14.** Regular 12-gon 150°, 30°

Algebra   In Exercises 15–18, find the measure of each interior angle.

15.
$x + 30°$
$x + 30°$ x
40°, 70°, 70°

16.
x $x - 5°$
$x - 5°$ $x + 10°$
85°, 85°, 90°, 100°

17.
$5x + 8°$
$5x + 8°$ $5x + 8°$
$6x - 12°$
$6x - 12°$
Each is 108°

18.
$4x + 8°$
$4x - 2°$
$4x + 5°$ $5x - 4°$
$3x$ $4x - 7°$
90°, 113°, 118°, 125°, 128°, 146°

474   Chapter **10** ▪ Geometry Concepts and Spatial Thinking

---

Extra Practice

Extra Practice 10.8 Name _____

In Exercises 1–3, find the measure of ∠x.

1. 40°   2. 90°   3. 110°

In Exercises 4–6, you are given the measure of each interior angle of a regular polygon. How many sides does the polygon have?
4. 108° 5   5. 140° 9   6. 150° 12

In Exercises 7–9, you are given the measure of each exterior angle of a regular polygon. How many sides does the polygon have?
7. 40° 9   8. 60° 6   9. 120° 3

In Exercises 10–12, you are given the number of sides of a regular polygon. Find the measure of each interior and exterior angle.
10. 10 144°, 36°   11. 6 120°, 60°   12. 18 160°, 20°

In Exercises 13 and 14, you are shown part of a convex n-gon. The pattern of congruent angles continues around the polygon. Find n. (Hint: If the sum of the exterior angles is 360°, how many sides are there?)
13. 8   14. 10

In Exercises 15 and 16, find the measure of each angle.
15. 68°, 88°, 108°, 128°, 148°
Angle increases 20° clockwise
16. 82.5°, 97.5°, 112.5°, 127.5°, 142.5°, 157.5°
Angle increases 15° clockwise

Windows   10.8 ▪ Angles of Polygons **83**

Reteaching

Reteach Chapter 10   Name _____

What you should learn:
| 10.8 | How to find the measures of the angles of a polygon and how to find the measure of each angle of a regular polygon |

Correlation to Pupil's Textbook:
Chapter Test (p. 485)
Exercises 15, 16

Examples Measuring the Angles of a Polygon and Measuring Angles in a Regular Polygon

a. Find the measures of ∠1 and ∠2 for the polygon shown at the right.

For a polygon with *n* sides, the sum of the measures of the interior angles is (*n* − 2)(180°). For *n* = 3, the sum of the angles is 180°.
You are given that $m\angle 3 = 40°$ and $m\angle 5 = 110°$. It follows that
$m\angle 1 = 180° - (40° + 110°)$
$= 180° - 150°$
$= 30°.$
Because ∠1 and ∠2 combine to form a straight angle,
$m\angle 1 + m\angle 2 = 180°$
$30° + m\angle 2 = 180°$
$m\angle 2 = 150°.$

b. Find the sum of the measures of the interior angles of a regular hexagon. Then find the measure of each interior angle.
For a polygon with *n* sides, the sum of the interior angle measures is (*n* − 2)(180°). For *n* = 6, the sum of the angles is 4(180°) = 720°. For a regular polygon, each interior angle measures $\frac{(n-2)180°}{n}$.
For *n* = 6, each interior angle measures $\frac{4(180°)}{6} = 120°.$

c. Find the sum of the measures of the exterior angles of a regular hexagon. Then find the measure of each exterior angle.
The sum of the exterior angle measures of any polygon is 360°. For a regular polygon, each exterior angle measures $\frac{360°}{n}$.
For *n* = 6, each exterior angle measures $\frac{360°}{6} = 60°.$

Guidelines: • The angles of a polygon are called interior angles.
• Polygons also have exterior angles, each of which combines with an interior angle to form a straight angle.

EXERCISE
Find the measures of ∠4 and ∠6 in Example a above. $m\angle 4 = 140°, m\angle 6 = 70°$

Windows   Chapter 10 ▪ Geometry Concepts and Spatial Thinking **83**

Sunrooms   In Exercises 19–22, use the photo at the right.

19. Sketch the glass panes and describe their shapes. **19., 20.** See margin.

20. Which panes appear congruent?

21. Find the angle measures of the glass triangle. 27°, 63°, 90°

22. The ceiling meets the left wall of the sunroom at an angle of 117°. Find the angle measures of the glass trapezoid. 63°, 90°, 90°, 117°

23. *Error Analysis*   The polygon below has a vertical line of symmetry and exactly one of the angle measures is incorrect. Which measure is incorrect? What should it be? Top one, 140°

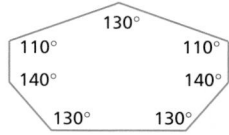

24. The square at the right is composed of 1 square, 4 equilateral triangles, and 4 isosceles triangles. What is the measure of the angles of each isosceles triangle? 150°, 15°, 15°

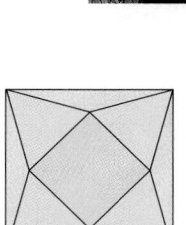

Integrated Review   *Making Connections within Mathematics*

25. *Making a Table* . Copy and complete the table.

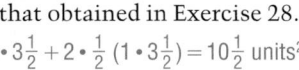

Regular Polygon	Triangle	Square	Pentagon	Hexagon	Heptagon	Octagon
	60°	90°	108°	120°	128⁴⁄₇°	135°
Interior Angle Measure	?	?	?	?	?	?

26. *Making a Scatter Plot*   Use the data in Exercise 25 to make a scatter plot. See margin.

27. *Interpreting a Scatter Plot*   Use the scatter plot to estimate the interior angle measure of a regular nonagon (9 sides). Confirm your result. 140°

Exploration and Extension

28. *Estimation*   Copy the hexagon at the right onto graph paper. Each small square has an area of 1 square unit. Estimate the area of the hexagon. $10\frac{1}{2}$ units²

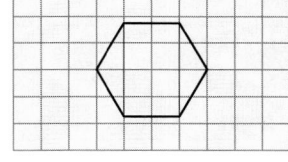

29. Show how to divide the hexagon into a rectangle and 2 triangles. Use these polygons to estimate the area of the hexagon. Compare the result to that obtained in Exercise 28.

$$2 \cdot 3\frac{1}{2} + 2 \cdot \frac{1}{2}\left(1 \cdot 3\frac{1}{2}\right) = 10\frac{1}{2} \text{ units}^2$$

✪ More difficult exercises

10.8 • Angles of Polygons   **475**

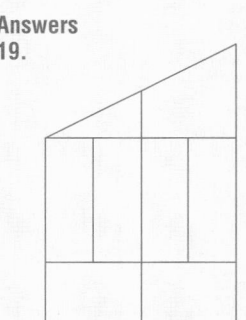

▶ **Ex. 19–21**   If a drafting course is taught in your school, ask the teacher to share copies of blueprints with your class.
▶ **Ex. 24**   Encourage students to make a rough sketch of the figure before beginning to compute angle measures.

Integrated Review

These problems are an extension of the investigation on page 471.

Exploration and Extension

These estimation exercises could be done as a group activity in class.

Portfolio Opportunity: Math Log

Determine if the following descriptions are possible. Explain your reasoning.
a. Regular octagon with an interior angle of 135°
b. Regular hexagon with an interior angle of 120°
c. Pentagon in which the sum of the interior angles is 720°

Also available as a copymaster, page 33, Ex. 9

Short Quiz

Covers Lessons 10.7 and 10.8

Available as a copymaster, page 165

Answers
19.

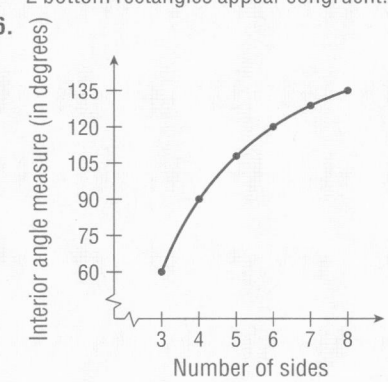

20. The 4 tall rectangles appear congruent and the 2 bottom rectangles appear congruent.

26.

TECHNOLOGY Notes

This program is an excellent way to get students thinking informally about the angle and side relationships of right triangles.

Students can also investigate the side and angle relationships of obtuse and acute triangles. For each triangle, have students increase the measure of the right angle from 90° to 130° by clicking and dragging on the upper vertex. Then have them copy and complete the table for this set of triangles and describe the pattern. Have students repeat these steps, decreasing the measure of the 130°angle to 60°. What can they conclude?

Some computer programs are able to measure lengths and angles. If you have access to such a program, try using it to duplicate the activity described in the following example.

Example   *Measuring Angles of Triangles*

Use a computer drawing program to draw the nine right triangles shown below. For each triangle, measure the upper angle. Describe the pattern.

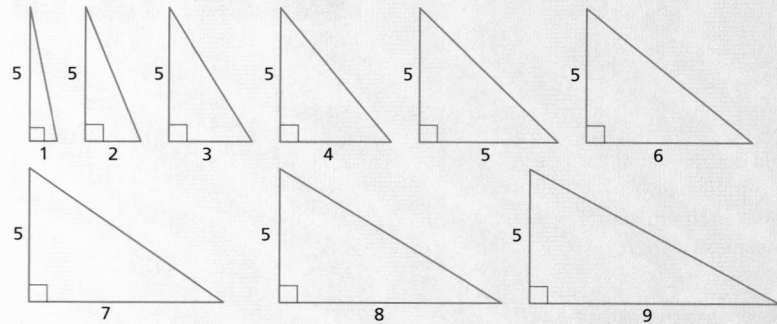

Solution   Using a computer drawing program, you can obtain the measures shown in the table.

Height	5	5	5	5	5	5	5	5	5
Base	1	2	3	4	5	6	7	8	9
Angle	11.2°	21.8°	31.0°	38.7°	45.0°	50.2°	54.5°	58.0°	60.9°

From the table, you can see that as the base increases, the measure of the upper angle increases. ∎

Exercise

Use a computer drawing program to draw nine right triangles. Let the height of each triangle be 6, and let the bases vary from 1 to 9. Measure the upper angle of each triangle and complete the table. How does this table compare to that given in the example.

Height	6	6	6	6	6	6	6	6	6
Base	1	2	3	4	5	6	7	8	9
Angle	?	?	?	?	?	?	?	?	?

9.5°, 18.4°, 26.6°, 33.7°, 39.8°, 45°, 49.4°, 53.1°, 56.3°; corresponding measures of the angles are smaller.

10.9

Angle and Side Relationships

Goal 1

Angles and Sides of Triangles

What you should learn:

 Goal 1 How to compare side lengths and angle measures of a triangle

 Goal 2 How to find the angle measures of an isosceles triangle

Why you should learn it:

You can use the measures of the angles and sides of a triangle to solve real-life problems, such as analyzing the angles in a house of cards.

▌triangle: ≈132°, ≈20°, ≈28°;
▌triangle: ≈122°, ≈29°, ≈29°;
°–80° triangle: 5 cm, 6.7 cm, 7.7 cm;
°–100° triangle: 5 cm, 12.7 cm, 14.4 cm;
°–110° triangle: 5 cm, 5 cm, 8.2 cm;
clusions, see two
ces above Example 1.

LESSON INVESTIGATION

■ **Investigating Lengths and Angle Measures**

Group Activity Use a ruler and compass to draw triangles with the following side lengths.

    5 cm, 7 cm, 11 cm;   8 cm, 8 cm, 14 cm

Use a protractor to measure each angle.
Next, use a protractor and straightedge to draw triangles with the following angle measures.

    40°, 60°, 80°;   20°, 60°, 100°;   35°, 35°, 110°

Use a ruler to measure the length of each side. What conclusions can you make about the relationships between side lengths and angle measures?

You may have discovered the following relationships between the side lengths and the angle measures of a triangle.

Angle and Side Relationships

1. In a triangle, the longest side is opposite the largest angle and the shortest side is opposite the smallest angle.
2. In an isosceles triangle, the angles opposite the sides of the same lengths have equal measures.

Example 1 — Comparing Sides and Angles

In the triangle at the left, without using a ruler, state which side is longest and which is shortest.

Solution The largest angle is $\angle A$. This implies that the longest side is $\overline{BC}$. The smallest angle is $\angle B$. This implies that the shortest side is $\overline{AC}$. ■

(Triangle: A at top 62°, C at lower left 60°, B at lower right 58°)

P Portfolio Opportunity

10.9 • Angle and Side Relationships   **477**

▶ **PACING the Lesson**

Suggested Number of Days
Basic/Average 0   **Above Average** 1
Advanced 1

▶ **PLANNING the Lesson**

Lesson Plan 10.9, p. 84

ORGANIZER

Starters (reproduced below)
  Problem of the Day 10.9, p. 30
  Warm-Up Exercises 10.9, p. 30
Lesson Resources
  Color Transparencies
    Picture for Example 3, p. 44
  Teaching Tools
    Protractor, pp. T12, C18
    Coordinate planes, T9, C11
  Math Log, p. 33
  Technology, p. 61
  Answer Masters 10.9, pp. 207–209
  Extra Practice Copymaster 10.9, p. 84
  Reteaching Copymaster 10.9, p. 84
  Enrichment Projects, pp. 54, 55
Special Populations
  Suggestions, Teacher's Edition, p. 436D

LESSON Notes

Triangles can be found in many different structures, including buildings, bridges, and machinery. Knowing something about the properties of triangles and their parts often helps us use triangles more effectively and efficiently.

Lesson Investigation
ALTERNATE APPROACH
Constructing Triangles Take some time to show students how to use the compass to draw triangles of specified side lengths. This activity could then be extended to exploring a larger, more varied collection of triangles in which more attention could be given to *constructing* triangles.

At the conclusion of the lesson investigation, have students record in their journals the relationships between side lengths and angle measures.

Example 1

For each of the triangles below, have students state, without using a protractor, which angle measure is largest and which is smallest.

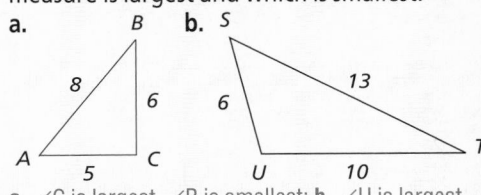

a. $\angle C$ is largest, $\angle B$ is smallest; **b.** $\angle U$ is largest, $\angle T$ is smallest.

Review with your students the definition of an isosceles triangle. Then pose the following questions.

a. Can an acute triangle also be an isosceles triangle?   Yes

b. Can an obtuse triangle also be an isosceles triangle?   Yes

c. Can a right triangle also be an isosceles triangle?   Yes

Have students support their answers with sketches.

Example 2

Reinforce the conclusion of this example by asking students if the acute angles of *all* right isosceles triangles measure 45°. Not every student will realize that this is so.

Example 3

PROJECT

Have students look at magazine illustrations or pictures of the frameworks of houses, office buildings, etc. Students should pay special attention to the roofs of these structures. Ask them what special triangles they can identify.   Isosceles and right triangles occur frequently.

Communicating about MATHEMATICS

Let students create their own matching exercises for other classmates to complete. This is a good activity for small groups.

Writing Prompt
In this chapter, I have enjoyed studying ... because ...

Technology

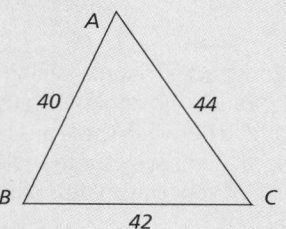

Exploring Angle and Side Relationships   **10.9**   Name _____

Exploration Using a Computer Drawing Program   In this activity, you will use construction software to investigate the relationships between the angles and the sides of various triangles.

EXERCISES

1. Using the construction software, construct △ABC as indicated in the table. Then measure the angles and sides to complete the table.

△ABC	m∠A	m∠B	m∠C	AB	BC	AC
Right						
Acute						
Obtuse						

   See students' work.

2. Draw a sketch of each triangle you created. Label the side lengths and angle measures.   See students' work.
3. For each triangle in Exercise 1, order the angles and sides from smallest to largest. Use the names of the angles and sides (not their measures).

	Angles	Sides
Right triangle:		
Acute triangle:	See students' work.	
Obtuse triangle:		

4. What relationships do you notice between the angles and sides of triangles in Exercises 1 and 2? The longest side is opposite the largest angle and the shortest side is opposite the smallest angle.
5. Using the construction software, construct an *isosceles* triangle, △ABC, as indicated in the table. Then measure the angles and sides to complete the table.

△ABC	m∠A	m∠B	m∠C	AB	BC	AC
Right						
Acute						
Obtuse						

   See students' work.

6. Draw a sketch of each triangle you created. Label the side lengths and angle measures.   See students' work.
7. What relationships do you notice between the angles and sides of triangles in Exercise 4? Sides opposite angles of equal measure are same length.

© D.C. Heath and Company   *Technology Using Calculators and Computers* **61**

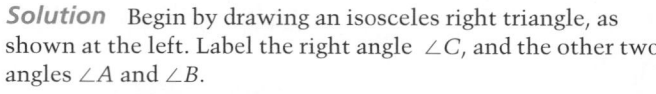

Goal **2**   **Comparing Angles in Isosceles Triangles**

Example 2   *Analyzing an Isosceles Right Triangle*

In an isosceles right triangle, what is the measure of each angle?

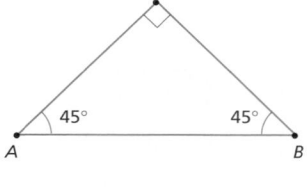

Solution   Begin by drawing an isosceles right triangle, as shown at the left. Label the right angle ∠C, and the other two angles ∠A and ∠B.

Because ∠A and ∠B are opposite the sides that are the same length, they must have equal measures. That is, $m\angle A = m\angle B$. Because $m\angle A + m\angle B = 90°$, you can conclude that

$$m\angle A = 45° \quad \text{and} \quad m\angle B = 45°.$$ ∎

Example 3   *Measuring Angles*

You are building a house of cards, as shown at the left. Each triangle formed by the cards has exactly one angle that measures 30°. What are the measures of the other two angles?

Solution   Because each triangle has two sides formed by cards of the same size, it follows that each triangle is isosceles. Thus, each triangle has two angles that have the same measure. The sum of these two angles is

$$180° - 30° = 150°.$$

Thus, each of the two "same-size" angles must measure $\frac{1}{2}(150°)$ or 75°.   ∎

Communicating about MATHEMATICS

▶ **SHARING IDEAS about the Lesson**

Matching Triangles   The angle measures and side lengths of three triangles are given below. Match the angle measures with the side lengths and explain your reasoning.

A. 30°, 60°, 90°   **B.** 50°, 50°, 80°   **C.** 30°, 30°, 120°

1. 10, 10, 17.3   C   **2.** 5, 8.66, 10   A   **3.** 10, 10, 12.9   B

For explanation, see margin, page 479.

◤ **OPTION: Extra Examples**

Here is an additional example similar to Example 1.

Comparing Sides and Angles
In the triangle given, state which angle is largest and which is smallest, without using a protractor.

```
        A
       /\
      /  \
    40    44
    /      \
   B_____C
       42
```

Solution
The longest side is $\overline{AC}$. This implies that the largest angle is ∠B. The shortest side is $\overline{AB}$. This implies that the smallest angle is ∠C.

EXERCISES

Guided Practice

▶ **CHECK for Understanding**

1. Discuss the angle and side relationships of   See margin.
   a. a scalene triangle.   b. an isosceles triangle.   c. a regular triangle.

2. *Writing*   In your own words, explain why an isosceles right triangle must have two 45° angles.   See margin.

In Exercises 3–6, identify the smallest angle, largest angle, shortest side, and longest side.

3.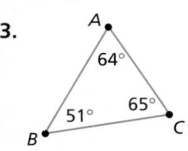
∠B, ∠C, $\overline{AC}$, $\overline{AB}$

4.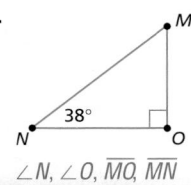
∠N, ∠O, $\overline{MO}$, $\overline{MN}$

5.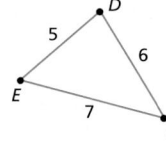
∠F, ∠D, $\overline{DE}$, $\overline{EF}$

6.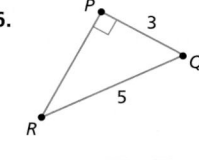
∠R, ∠P, $\overline{PQ}$, $\overline{QR}$

Independent Practice

In Exercises 7–12, use the figure at the right. List the angle measures of the triangle. Then name its shortest and longest sides.

7. △DEF   **7.** 40°, 60°, 80°; $\overline{EF}$, $\overline{DE}$
8. △FGH   45°, 55°, 80°; $\overline{FH}$, $\overline{GH}$
9. △ADG   **9.** 15°, 60°, 105°; $\overline{AD}$, $\overline{AG}$
10. △DFG   35°, 45°, 100°; $\overline{FG}$, $\overline{DG}$
11. △CGH   **11.** 45°, 60°, 75°, $\overline{CG}$, $\overline{CH}$
12. △DGH   35°, 55°, 90°; $\overline{GH}$, $\overline{DH}$

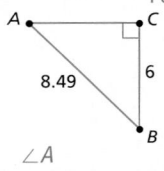
$AB = AC = BC = 12$

13. What is the longest side of a right triangle? Explain.   The hypotenuse, it is opposite the largest angle.

In Exercises 14–17, name the smallest angle of the right triangle. Explain.   For explanations, see Additional Answers.

14.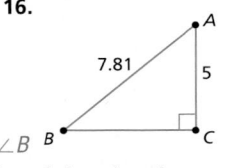
∠A

15.
∠A

16.
∠B

17.
∠B

In Exercises 18–21, name the shortest and longest sides of the triangle. Explain.   For explanations, see Additional Answers.

18.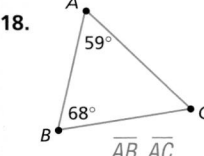
$\overline{AB}$, $\overline{AC}$

19.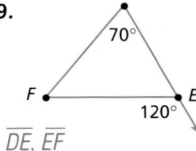
$\overline{DE}$, $\overline{EF}$

20.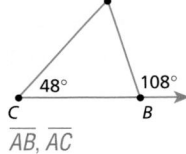
$\overline{AB}$, $\overline{AC}$

21.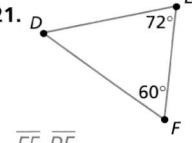
$\overline{EF}$, $\overline{DF}$

P Portfolio Opportunity

10.9 • Angle and Side Relationships   **479**

Extra Practice

Extra Practice 10.9   Name _____

In Exercises 1–3, state the shortest and longest sides of the triangle.
1. $\overline{MK}$ shortest $\overline{LK}$ longest
2. $\overline{AB}$ shortest $\overline{AC}$ longest
3. $\overline{XZ}$ shortest $\overline{YZ}$ longest

In Exercises 4–6, state the smallest and largest angles of the triangle.
4.   ∠C smallest, m∠A = m∠B largest
5.   ∠G smallest, ∠F largest
6.   ∠H smallest, ∠I largest

In Exercises 7 and 8, order the sides from shortest to longest.
7. $\overline{AC}$, $\overline{AB}$, $\overline{BC}$, $\overline{DC}$, $\overline{BD}$
8. $\overline{KM}$, $\overline{KL}$, $\overline{LM}$, $\overline{LN}$, $\overline{NM}$

In Exercises 9 and 10, solve for x. Then name the smallest angle, the largest angle, the shortest side and the longest side of the triangle.
9.   x = 15, ∠B smallest, ∠A largest, $\overline{AC}$ smallest, $\overline{BC}$ longest
10.   x = 10, ∠F smallest, ∠FED largest, $\overline{DE}$ smallest, $\overline{DF}$ largest

In Exercises 11–13, match the angle measures with the approximate side lengths. Explain your reasoning. See back of supplement for explanations.
a. 40°, 50°, 90°   b. 60°, 60°, 60°   c. 30°, 75°, 75°
11. 2, 2, 2 b   12. 5, 8, 8 c   13. 7, 9, 11.4 a

14. Buck Springs is 60 miles N30°E of Angel Falls. San José is 40 miles due east of Angel Falls. Buck Springs is also N10°W of San José. Use a protractor and straight edge to sketch a diagram of the three towns. Then determine which two towns are the furthest apart and which two are the nearest. The distance between Buck Springs and San José must be between our last two values? Furthest: Angel Falls & Buck Springs; closest: Angel Falls & San José; distance: 40 < d < 60

84   Angle and Side Relationships • 10.9   Windows

Reteaching

Reteach Chapter 10   Name _____

What you should learn: How to compare side lengths and angle measures of a triangle and how to find the angle measures of an isosceles triangle

Correlation to Pupil's Textbook: Chapter Test (p. 485)   Exercise 17

Examples   *Angles and Sides of Triangles and Comparing Angles in Isosceles Triangles*

a. In the triangle at the right, without using a protractor, state which angle is the largest and which is the smallest.
   In a triangle, the longest side is opposite the largest angle. The longest side is $\overline{PR}$. This implies that the largest angle is ∠Q.
   Also, in a triangle, the shortest side is opposite the smallest angle. The shortest side is $\overline{PQ}$; therefore, the smallest angle is ∠R.

b. In the triangle at the right, name two angles that have equal measures.
   In an isosceles triangle, the angles opposite the sides of the same lengths have equal measures. Since sides $\overline{AB}$ and $\overline{AC}$ have the same length, 7, ∠B and ∠C have the same measure.

Guidelines: • In a triangle, the longest side is opposite the largest angle and the shortest side is opposite the smallest angle.
   • In an isosceles triangle, the angles opposite the sides of the same lengths have equal measures.

EXERCISES

In Exercises 1–3, identify the smallest angle, largest angle, shortest side, and longest side.
1. c ∠R, ∠Q, $\overline{PQ}$, $\overline{PR}$ 2. ∠Z, ∠Y, $\overline{XY}$, $\overline{XZ}$ 3. c ∠E, ∠C, $\overline{CD}$, $\overline{DE}$

In Exercises 4–6, use the figure at the right to find the measure of the angle.
4. m∠JKN 75°
5. m∠JML 75°
6. m∠NJK 30°

84   Chapter 10 • Geometry Concepts and Spatial Thinking   Windows

---

EXERCISE Notes

ASSIGNMENT GUIDE

*Basic/Average:
   Day 1: Ex. 7–25 odd
   Day 2: Ex. 27–29 odd, 31, 32, 33–39 odd
Above Average: Ex. 7–29 odd, 32, 33–39 odd
Advanced: Ex. 7–29 odd, 32, 33–39 odd
Selected Answers: Ex. 1–6, 7–35 odd
*You may wish to omit this lesson for these students.

Guided Practice

These exercises assess students' understanding of the lesson goals. The exercises can be completed independently or as a group process.

Independent Practice

▶ **Ex. 7–12** Students should make a copy of the diagram before beginning work on this group of problems.
▶ **Ex. 14–17** Students should use the Pythagorean Theorem rather than eyesight for these exercises.

Answer to Communicating
In Exercise 2, no two sides are the same length; so no two angles have the same measure; so A matches with Exercise 2. The longest side in Exercise 1 is more than 70% longer than the shorter sides, while the longest side in Exercise 3 is less than 33% longer than the shorter sides; so the largest angle in Exercise 1 is larger than the largest angle in Exercise 3; so C matches with Exercise 1. Then B matches with Exercise 3.

Answers
1. a. The longest side is opposite the largest angle and the shortest side is opposite the smallest angle.
   b. The angles opposite the sides of the same lengths have equal measures.
   c. All three angles are congruent and all three sides are congruent.

2. An isosceles right triangle has a 90° angle and two angles of equal measure.
$$180° − 90° = 90°, \frac{90°}{2} = 45°$$

Lesson 10.9   **479**

► Ex. 22–25

Common-Error Alert!

Students may be tempted to set the sum of *all* angle expressions equal to 180° without checking the relationship among these angles. For Ex. 23 and 24, this would be incorrect.

► Ex. 26–30

COOPERATIVE LEARNING

Assign all these exercises to groups, and have groups record an explanation for the decisions they make.

Integrated Review

► Ex. 35, 36   You may need to explain to students that these questions relate to the slopes of the graphs.

Exploration and Extension

These exercises further develop students' preparedness for simple coordinate geometry.

Portfolio Opportunity: Math Log

In △ABC, it is given that $m\angle A = 40°$ and $AB > BC$. What can you conclude about $m\angle B$? Explain your answer.

Also available as a copymaster, page 33, Ex. 10

Algebra   **In Exercises 22–25, solve for x. Then name the smallest angle, the largest angle, the shortest side, and the longest side of the triangle.** See margin.

22. 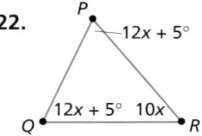   **23.** 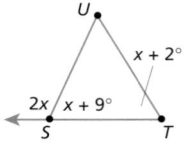   **24.** 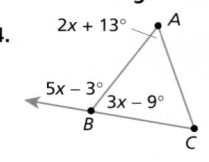   **25.**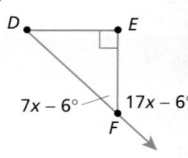

In Exercises 26–30, match the angle measures with the approximate side lengths. Explain your reasoning.   For explanations, see Additional Answers.

a. 40°, 70°, 70°   b. 30°, 60°, 90°   c. 60°, 60°, 60°   d. 45°, 45°, 90°   e. 25°, 25°, 130°

✪ **26.** 5, 5, 7.1   d   ✪ **27.** 5, 5, 5   c   ✪ **28.** 5, 5, 9.1   e   ✪ **29.** 3, 5.2, 6   b   ✪ **30.** 5, 5, 3.4   a

Walking to the Library   **In Exercises 31 and 32, use the following information.**

You and a friend are on a walk, as shown at the right. From your point of view, the angle between your friend and the library is 55°. From your friend's point of view, the angle between you and the library is 62°.

31. What is the third angle of the triangle?   63°

32. Who has farther to walk to the library, you or your friend? Explain your reasoning.   You, the longer side is opposite the larger angle.

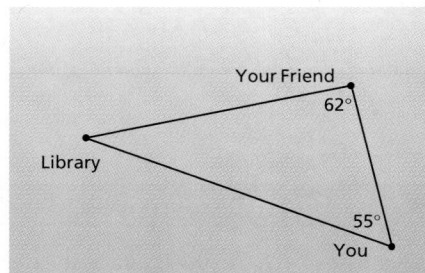

Integrated Review

Making Connections within Mathematics

Movie Attendance   **In Exercises 33–36, use the line graph at the right, which shows the percent of Americans who went to the movies every week.** *(Source: Motion Picture Association of America)*

33. Approximate the percent in 1955.   24%

34. Approximate the change from 1946 to 1993.   46%

35. During which decade (50's, 60's, 70's, or 80's) did the greatest decrease occur? Explain.   See below.

36. During which decade (50's, 60's, 70's, or 80's) was the percent most stable? Explain.
70's or 80's, there was less than a 2% change.

35. 50's, there was about a 25% decrease.

Going to the Movies Every Week
Percent of Americans who went to the movies every week

55.8%

ADMIT ONE

9.3%

60%
50%
40%
30%
20%
10%

'46 '50   '60   '70   '80   '90 '93
Year

Exploration and Extension

Coordinate Geometry   **In Exercises 37–40, draw △ABC in a coordinate plane. Find the lengths of its sides. Then name its smallest and largest angles.**   See Additional Answers.

✪ **37.** $A(4, 0), B(0, 0), C(0, -4)$ ✪ **38.** $A(5, 4), B(5, -2), C(3, -2)$

✪ **39.** $A(-2, -1), B(-2, -3), C(4, -3)$ ✪ **40.** $A(0, 2), B(3, -4), C(-3, -4)$

Enrichment

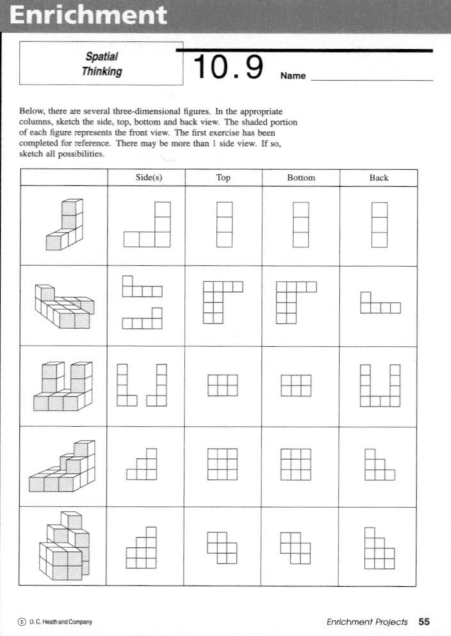

Answers
22. 5°; ∠R, none, $\overline{PQ}$, none
23. 57°, ∠U, ∠TSU, $\overline{ST}$, $\overline{TU}$
24. 24°, ∠C, ∠ABC, $\overline{AB}$, $\overline{AC}$
25. 8°, ∠D, ∠E, $\overline{EF}$, $\overline{DF}$

Chapter Summary

What did you learn?

Skills

1. Identify points, lines, and planes. **(10.1)**
   - Find the length of a line segment. **(10.1)**
   - Decide whether two lines are parallel. **(10.1)**
2. Classify angles as acute, right, obtuse, or straight. **(10.2)**
   - Use a protractor to measure an angle. **(10.2)**
3. Use a property of parallel lines. **(10.3)**
   - Identify vertical angles and corresponding angles. **(10.3)**
4. Identify line symmetry and rotational symmetry. **(10.4)**
5. Classify triangles by their sides and their angles. **(10.5)**
6. Classify quadrilaterals. **(10.6)**
7. Recognize congruent polygons and regular polygons. **(10.7)**
8. Measure the interior and exterior angles of a polygon. **(10.8)**
9. Compare side lengths and angle measures of a triangle. **(10.9)**
   - Use a property of isosceles triangles. **(10.9)**

em-Solving Strategies

10. Use geometric figures such as lines, segments, angles, and polygons to model and solve real-life problems. **(10.1–10.9)**

Exploring Data

11. Use tables and graphs to solve problems. **(10.1–10.9)**

Why did you learn it?

Geometry is used in almost all parts of real life to measure, compare, and explain the shapes of things. For instance, you learned that a kaleidoscope contains images that are pentagons, hexagons, octagons, or other polygons. Geometry is also used to measure angles in the construction industry, to manufacture sails for windsurfboards, and to analyze the motion of engine parts. No matter which profession you choose, geometry can help you be more successful.

How does it fit into the bigger picture of mathematics?

The word geo-metry means "earth-measuring," and that describes geometry very well. In this chapter, you learned how to use geometry to measure line segments and angles. In this chapter, you were introduced to dozens of geometric terms. Many of these are familiar (triangle, rectangle, line, plane, and so on), but many are probably new (scalene, isosceles trapezoid, and exterior angle). It is important to continue to build your mathematical vocabulary. Doing this will help you communicate mathematics to others. Remember, however, that memorizing the meaning of mathematical terms is not nearly as important a skill as being able to understand mathematical properties.

COOPERATIVE LEARNING
Encourage students to study together. Emphasize the importance of teaching a classmate how to perform a skill or how to recall a procedure. When students work together, everyone wins. The students receiving help get additional instruction, and the students giving help gain a deeper understanding of the skills and concepts involved.

Chapter SUMMARY

In this chapter, students were introduced informally to some of the important concepts in geometry through simple methods such as measurement with ruler and protractor, paper-cutting, and dot paper. Students learned the basic language of points, lines, planes, and angles in Lessons 10.1 and 10.2. Lesson 10.3 used the properties of parallel lines to give students a chance for simple reasoning about angles. Lesson 10.4 introduced students to symmetry as a means of classifying figures. The basics of classification were developed further in Lessons 10.5 and 10.6 with triangles and quadrilaterals. In Lessons 10.7 and 10.8, polygons were used as a context in which students could learn about congruence of figures and about angle relationships. Finally, these two concepts—congruence and angle relationships—were developed further in Lesson 10.9.

Chapter REVIEW

Have students begin this Review in class and complete it as a homework assignment.

ASSIGNMENT GUIDE

*Basic/Average: Ex. 13–22, 29–41 odd, 25–27,

Above Average: Ex. 13–22, 29–41 odd, 47–53 odd, 25–27, 43–45 odd, 54–62

Advanced: Ex. 13–22, 29–41 odd, 47–53 odd, 25–27, 43–45 odd, 54–62

*For these students, you will need to limit assignments to cover only those lessons you chose to teach from this chapter.

Resources

Answer Masters, pp. 210, 211

In Exercises 1–4, use the figure at the right. (10.1–10.2)

2. $\overline{DE}, \overline{DF}, \overline{DC}, \overline{DB}, \overline{DH}$

1. Write two other names for the line $\overset{\leftrightarrow}{EG}$. $\overset{\leftrightarrow}{AG}, \overset{\leftrightarrow}{AE},$
2. Name five line segments that have D as an endpoint.
3. Write another name for the ray $\overset{\rightarrow}{HD}$. $\overset{\rightarrow}{HB}$
4. Write three other names for $\angle AEC$. $\angle CEA, \angle AED, \angle DEA$

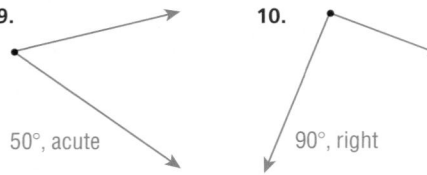

In Exercises 5–8, use the drawing of an anvil at the right. (10.1)

5. Name another point that lies in the same plane as C, D, and G. H
6. Name four line segments that lie in the same plane as A, B, and C. $\overline{AB}, \overline{BC}, \overline{CD}, \overline{AD}, \overline{AC}, \overline{BD}$
7. From the pattern, where do you think point F lies? See below.
8. Name 3 lines that are parallel to $\overset{\leftrightarrow}{BC}$. AD, EH, FG

7. Below B, so that $\overline{AB} \parallel \overline{EF}$ and $\overline{HE} \parallel \overline{GF}$

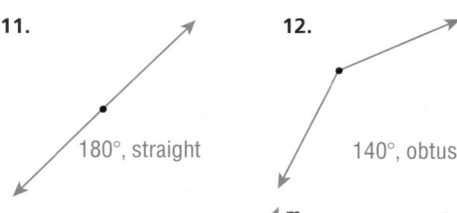

In Exercises 9–12, use a protractor to measure the angle. Is it acute, obtuse, right, or straight? (10.2)

9.

50°, acute

10.

90°, right

11.

180°, straight

12.

140°, obtuse

In Exercises 13–18, use the figure at the right. (10.3)

13. Which lines are parallel? m and n
14. Name 2 pairs of vertical angles. See margin.
15. List all angles whose measure is 110°. $\angle 1, \angle 4, \angle 5, \angle 8$
16. List all angles whose measure is 100°. $\angle 9, \angle 12, \angle 13, \angle 16$
⭐ 17. Which is greater: $m\angle 10$ or $m\angle 2$? Explain. See below.
18. List 2 pairs of corresponding angles that have different measures. See margin.

17. $m\angle 10$; $m\angle 10 = 80°$, $m\angle 2 = 70°$, and $80° > 70°$

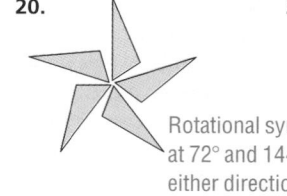

In Exercises 19–22, identify any symmetry of the figure. (10.4)

19.

1 line of symmetry

20.

Rotational symmetry at 72° and 144° in either direction

21.

4 lines of symmetry, rotational symmetry at 90° and 180° in either direction

22.

1 line of symmetry

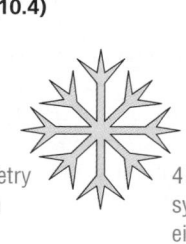

⭐ More difficult exercises

Answers

14. $\angle 1$ and $\angle 4$, $\angle 2$ and $\angle 3$, $\angle 5$ and $\angle 8$, $\angle 6$ and $\angle 7$, $\angle 9$ and $\angle 12$, $\angle 10$ and $\angle 11$, $\angle 13$ and $\angle 16$, $\angle 14$ and $\angle 15$

18. $\angle 1$ and $\angle 9$, $\angle 2$ and $\angle 10$, $\angle 3$ and $\angle 11$, $\angle 4$ and $\angle 12$, $\angle 5$ and $\angle 13$, $\angle 6$ and $\angle 14$, $\angle 7$ and $\angle 15$, $\angle 8$ and $\angle 16$

23. Research Project   Use magazines or newspapers to find examples of company logos that have symmetry. Trace the logos and describe the symmetry. **(10.4)**
Check students' work.

✪ **24. Try It Yourself**   Design a company logo that has at least one type of symmetry. Describe the company and explain how the logo relates to the company. **(10.4)**
Check students' work.

In Exercises 25–27, draw △ABC with the given side lengths. Then classify the triangle according to its sides and angles. (10.5)

25. $a = 2, b = 3, c = 4$
Scalene obtuse

26. $a = 5, b = 12, c = 13$
Scalene right

Isosceles acute
27. $a = 6, b = 6, c = 8$

In Exercises 28–41, match the polygon with a region at the right. Use each region exactly once. (10.5, 10.6)

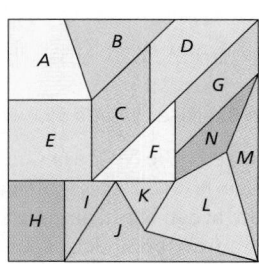

28. Rhombus   C

29. Isosceles trapezoid   D

30. Square   E

31. Isosceles triangle   F

32. Right triangle   I

33. Nonconvex quadrilateral   J

34. Rectangle   H

35. Parallelogram   G

36. Kite   L

37. Acute triangle   B

38. Obtuse triangle   M

39. Scalene quadrilateral   N

40. Trapezoid   A

41. Equilateral triangle   K

42.,–45. For drawings, see margin.

42. Draw a regular pentagon. Find the measure of each of its interior angles and exterior angles. **(10.8)**   108°, 72°

43. Draw a regular octagon. Find the measure of each of its interior angles and exterior angles. **(10.8)**   135°, 45°

44. Draw a regular hexagon. Then divide it into four congruent quadrilaterals. **(10.7)**

45. Draw a regular octagon. Then divide it into two congruent trapezoids and a rectangle. **(10.7)**

In Exercises 46 and 47, order the sides from the shortest to the longest. (10.9)

In Exercises 48 and 49, order the angles from the smallest to the largest. (10.9)

46.
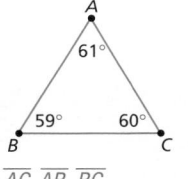
$\overline{AC}, \overline{AB}, \overline{BC}$

47.
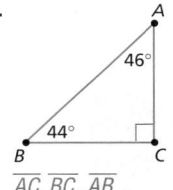
$\overline{AC}, \overline{BC}, \overline{AB}$

48.
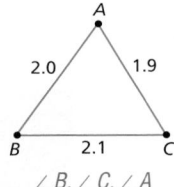
$\angle B, \angle C, \angle A$

49.
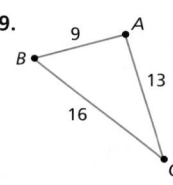
$\angle C, \angle B, \angle A$

In Exercises 50–53, find the measures of the angles of the triangle. (10.9)

50.
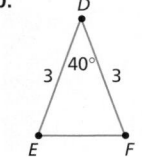
40°, 70°, 70°

51.
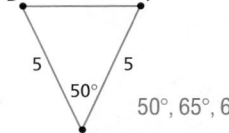
50°, 65°, 65°

52.
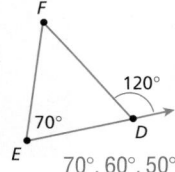
70°, 60°, 50°

53.
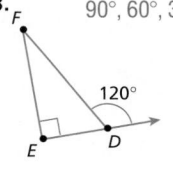
90°, 60°, 30°

Answers
42.
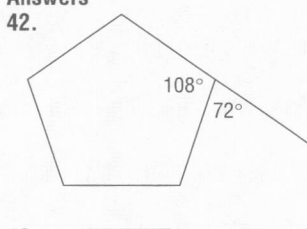

43.
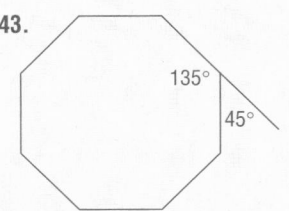

44.
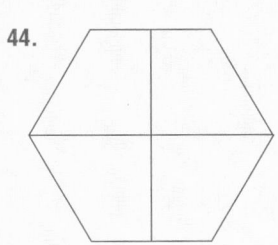

45.
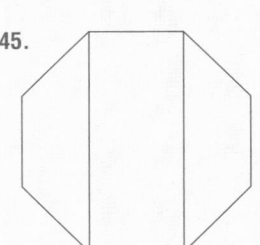

Chapter Review   **483**

In Exercises 54–57, use the diagram of the Remotely Operated Vehicle (ROV) traveling on the flat ocean floor.

54. The ROV moves from point *A* to point *B*. What type of triangle is △*ABE*?   Right

55. Triangle *AED* is isosceles. If $\overline{AE}$ and $\overline{DE}$ are the same length, which two angles of △*AED* will have the same measure?   ∠*A* and ∠*D*

56. In △*AEC*, *m*∠*C* is greater than *m*∠*A*. Which side is longer, $\overline{AE}$ or $\overline{EC}$? $\overline{AE}$

57. If *m*∠*BCE* = 75°, what is the measure of ∠*BEC*?   15°

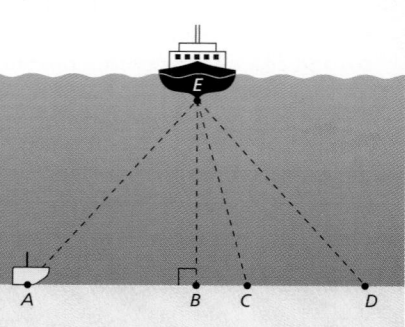

In Exercises 58 and 59, use the following information.

In 1994 the MIT Sea Grant College Program in Cambridge, Massachusetts, launched Odyssey II into the ocean. This unmanned sub relays data to a communication node suspended from a buoy. The communication node sends the data to the base station.

58. The unmanned sub leaves the communication node, travels a straight path for 1000 meters, and turns 90° to the left. The sub repeats this procedure until it returns to the communication node. If the sub remains at a constant depth and travels 4000 meters, what quadrilateral could describe the path of the sub?   Square

59. If the unmanned sub travels a 5-sided path before returning to the communication node, what is the sum of the interior angles of the pentagon?   540°

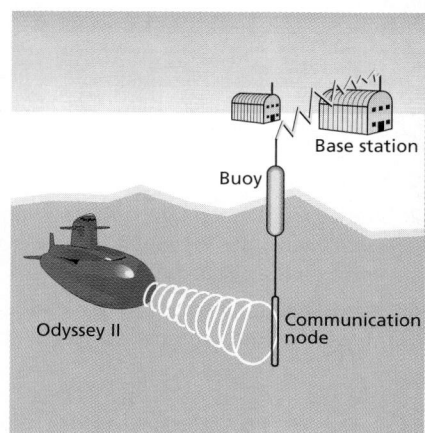

Base station

Buoy

Odyssey II

Communication node

In Exercises 60–62, identify the (approximate) type of symmetry.

1 line of symmetry

60.

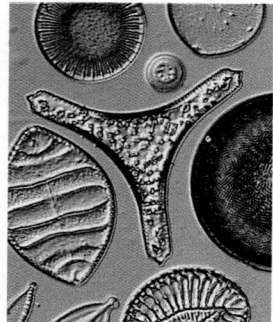

3 lines of symmetry, rotational symmetry at 120° in either direction

61.

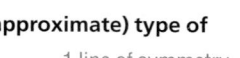

62.

5 lines of symmetry, rotational symmetry at 72° and 144° in either direction

In Exercises 1–3, classify the triangle by its sides and by its angles. (10.5)

1.

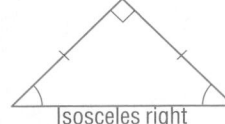

Isosceles right

2.

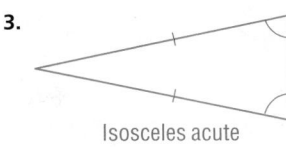

Scalene obtuse

3.

Isosceles acute

True or False? **In Exercises 4 and 5, decide whether the statement is true or false. Explain your reasoning. (10.6, 10.7)**

4. A regular quadrilateral is a square.   True, both figures have the same properties.

5. The opposite sides of a kite are parallel.   False, a kite is not a parallelogram.

In Exercises 6–8, match the angle with its measure. (10.2)

a. 155°

b. 135°

c. 42°

6.
b.

7.
c.

8.
a.

In Exercises 9–13, use the figure at the right. (10.1, 10.3)

9. Give another name for $\overleftrightarrow{MP}$. $\overleftrightarrow{MS}, \overleftrightarrow{MK}, \overleftrightarrow{PS}, \overleftrightarrow{PK}, \overleftrightarrow{KS}, i$

10. List the rays that have *P* as a beginning point.

11. List 2 pairs of vertical angles.

12. Is ∠*KML* ≅ ∠*PSR*? Explain.

13. Is ∠*PMN* ≅ ∠*PRS*? Explain.

14. Draw a five-pointed star that has a regular pentagon as its center. Discuss the symmetry of the star. **(10.4, 10.8)**   **10.–14.** See margin.

In Exercises15–17, use the figure at the right. (10.8)

15. What is the measure of ∠1?   40°

16. What is the measure of ∠2?   50°

17. Which is the longest side? $\overline{AB}$

In Exercises 18–20, use the diagram at the right, which shows a design for a laser television set. (10.2, 10.3)

18. Describe the relationship between the 3 beams as they leave the laser unit.   They are parallel.

19. How many right angles are formed by each color of laser beam?   3

20. How many of the 7 mirrors are parallel?   6

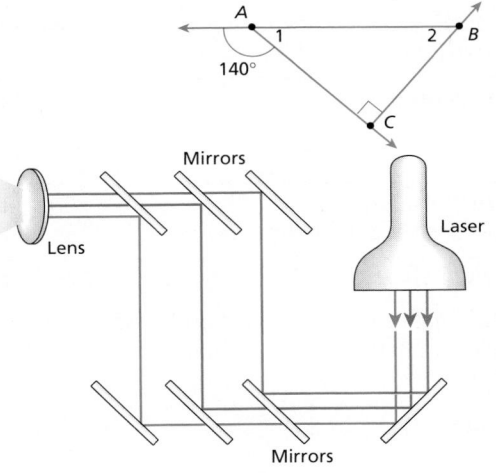

Mirrors

Lens

Laser

Mirrors

Chapter Test   **485**

Answers

10. $\overrightarrow{PS}, \overrightarrow{PM} (\overrightarrow{PK}), \overrightarrow{PN}, \overrightarrow{PR}$

11. ∠*KML* and ∠*NMP*, ∠*KMN* and ∠*LMP*, ∠*MPN* and ∠*RPS*, ∠*MPR* and ∠*NPS*

12. Yes; when two parallel lines are intersected by a third line, the corresponding angles are congruent.

13. Yes. ∠*PMN* ≅ ∠*KML* because vertical angles are congruent, ∠*KML* ≅ ∠*PSR* from Exercise 12, and ∠*PSR* ≅ ∠*PRS* is given; so ∠*PMN* ≅ ∠*PRS*.

14.

Has 5 lines of symmetry, has rotational symmetry at 72° and 144° in either direction.

◀ **Formal Assessment**

Three **Chapter Tests.** Form A is of average difficulty, Form B is of average difficulty in multiple choice format, and Form C is more challenging.

Available as copymasters, pages 166–174

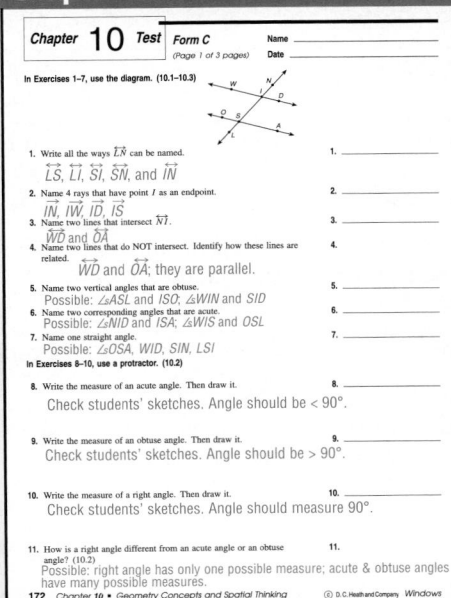

Chapter Test

Chapter **10** Test	Form C

(Page 1 of 3 pages)

Name _____

Date _____

In Exercises 1–7, use the diagram. (10.1–10.3)

1. Write all the ways $\overleftrightarrow{LN}$ can be named.   1. _____
   $\overleftrightarrow{LS}, \overleftrightarrow{LI}, \overleftrightarrow{SI}, \overleftrightarrow{SN},$ and $\overleftrightarrow{IN}$

2. Name 4 rays that have point *I* as an endpoint.   2. _____
   $\overrightarrow{IN}, \overrightarrow{IW}, \overrightarrow{ID}, \overrightarrow{IS}$

3. Name two lines that intersect $\overleftrightarrow{N1}$.   3. _____
   $\overleftrightarrow{WD}$ and $\overleftrightarrow{OA}$

4. Name two lines that do NOT intersect. Identify how these lines are related.   4. _____
   $\overleftrightarrow{WD}$ and $\overleftrightarrow{OA}$; they are parallel.

5. Name two vertical angles that are obtuse.   5. _____
   Possible: ∠*ASL* and *ISO*; ∠*WIN* and *SID*

6. Name two corresponding angles that are acute.   6. _____
   Possible: ∠*NID* and *ISA*; ∠*WIS* and *OSL*

7. Name one straight angle.   7. _____
   Possible: ∠*OSA*, *WID*, *SIN*, *LSI*

In Exercises 8–10, use a protractor. (10.2)

8. Write the measure of an acute angle. Then draw it.   8. _____
   Check students' sketches. Angle should be < 90°.

9. Write the measure of an obtuse angle. Then draw it.   9. _____
   Check students' sketches. Angle should be > 90°.

10. Write the measure of a right angle. Then draw it.   10. _____
    Check students' sketches. Angle should measure 90°.

11. How is a right angle different from an acute angle or an obtuse angle? (10.2)   11.
    Possible: right angle has only one possible measure; acute & obtuse angles have many possible measures.

172 *Chapter 10 • Geometry Concepts and Spatial Thinking*   © D.C. Heath and Company Windows

CHAPTER 11 ▪ OVERVIEW

Lesson	Pages	Goals	Meeting the NCTM Standards
11.1	488–491	1. Find the area and perimeter of polygons 2. Use area and perimeter to solve real-life problems	Communication, Reasoning, Connections, Patterns and Functions, Geometry
11.2	492–495	1. Determine whether two figures are congruent 2. Use congruence to solve real-life problems	Communication, Reasoning, Connections, Geometry
Lesson Investigation 11.3	496	Exploring Motion in a Plane	Algebra, Geometry
11.3	497–500	1. Reflect a figure about a line 2. Use properties of reflections to answer questions about real-life situations	Communication, Reasoning, Geometry, Measurement
Mixed Review	501	Review of arithmetic, algebra, and geometry	Number Relationships, Algebra, Geometry, Measurement
Career Interview	501	Research Scientist	Connections
11.4	502–505	1. Rotate a figure about a point 2. Use properties of rotations to answer questions about real-life situations	Communication, Connections, Geometry, Measurement
11.5	506–509	1. Translate a figure in a plane 2. Represent translations in a coordinate plane	Communication, Connections, Algebra, Geometry, Measurement
Mid-Chapter Self-Test	510	Diagnose student weaknesses and remediate with correlated Reteaching Copymasters	Assessment
Lesson Investigation 11.6	511	Exploring Similarity	Geometry, Measurement
11.6	512–516	1. Recognize similar figures 2. Use properties of similar figures	Communication, Reasoning, Connections, Number Relationships, Algebra, Probability, Geometry
Mixed Review	516	Review of arithmetic, algebra, and geometry	Problem Solving, Number Relationships, Probability
11.7	517–520	1. Use similar figures to solve real-life problems 2. Compare perimeters and areas of similar figures	Problem Solving, Communication, Connections, Number Relationships, Algebra, Geometry, Measurement
Lesson Investigation 11.8	521	Exploring Ratios with Right Triangles	Number Relationships, Algebra, Geometry, Measurement
11.8	522–525	1. Find trigonometric ratios 2. Use the Pythagorean Theorem to find trigonometric ratios	Communication, Connections, Number Relationships, Computation and Estimation, Patterns and Functions, Algebra, Geometry, Measurement
Using a Calculator	526	Solving Right Triangles	Number Relationships, Technology, Patterns and Functions, Algebra, Geometry
11.9	527–530	1. Use trigonometric ratios to solve right triangles 2. Use trigonometric ratios in real-life	Problem Solving, Communication, Connections, Number Relationships, Technology, Algebra, Geometry, Measurement
Chapter Summary	531	A restatement of what has been learned, why it has been learned, and how it fits into the structure of mathematics	Communication, Connections
Chapter Review	532–534	Review of concepts and skills learned in the chapter	Problem Solving, Connections
Chapter Test	535	Diagnose student weaknesses and remediate with correlated Reteaching Copymasters	Assessment

RESOURCES ORGANIZER

Lesson Pages	11.1 488–491	11.2 492–495	11.3 497–500	11.4 502–505	11.5 506–509	11.6 512–516	11.7 517–520	11.8 522–525	11.9 527–530
Lesson Plans	85	86	87	88	89	90	91	92	93
Problem of the Day	31	31	31	32	32	32	33	33	33
Warm-Up Exercises	31	31	31	32	32	32	33	33	33
Color Transparencies	—	45	—	45	46	46	48	—	48
Teaching Tools: Transparencies	T1, T2	T1, T2 T8, T12	T9	T2, T9	—	T8, T12	T3	—	—
Copymasters	C2, C3	C2, C3, C10, C18	C11	C3, C11	—	C10, C18	C4	—	—
Math Log	34	34	34	34	35	35, 36	36	36	36
Technology	63	—	—	—	64–66	—	—	67	—
Answer Masters	213, 214	215	216, 217	219	220, 221	222, 223	225	226, 227	228
Extra Practice	85	86	87	88	89	90	91	92	93
Reteaching Copymasters	85	86	87	88	89	90	91	92	93
Enrichment Projects	56–58	—	—	—	59, 60	61, 62	—	—	—
Alternative Assessment: Projects	35	—	—	—	—	—	35, 36	—	—
Partner Quizzes	—	—	—	—	54	—	—	—	—
Group Assessment	—	79, 80	—	—	—	—	—	—	—
Formal Assessment: Short Quizzes	—	175	—	176	—	179	—	180	—
Tests	—	—	—	—	177, 178	—	—	—	181–189
Overhead Manipulatives Kit	—	—	—	—	—	—	—	—	—
Complete Solutions Manual	Includes step-by-step solutions for all exercises in the student text								
Computerized Test Bank	Creates customized tests that include graphics								
Interactive CD-ROM Project	Provides an interactive and interdisciplinary chapter project								

CHAPTER 11 · RESOURCES

STARTERS

Problem of the Day

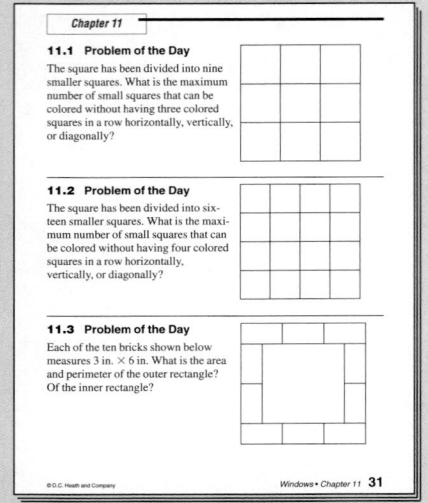

Warm-Up Exercises

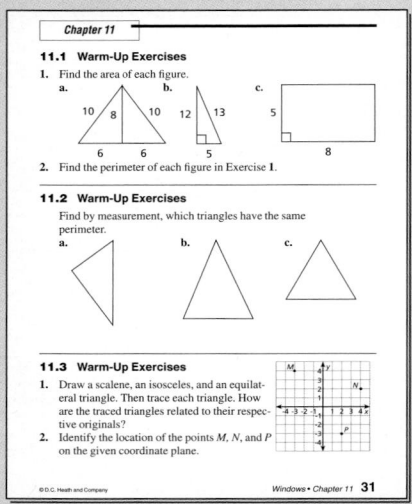

FOR TEACHERS

Answer Masters

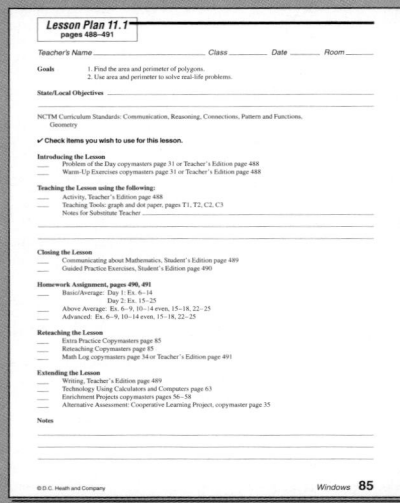

Lesson Plans

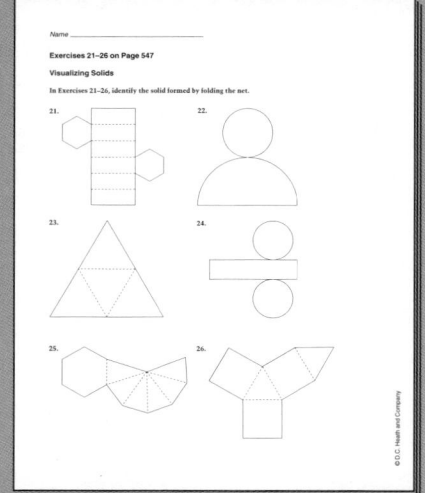

Teaching Tools

Teaching Tools includes:
Transparencies and Copymasters for classroom activities and study skills:

- Graph Paper
- Dot Paper (Geoboards)
- Algebra Tiles
- Number Counters
- Fraction Strips
- Models

REAL LIFE
Color Transparencies for Real-Life Applications

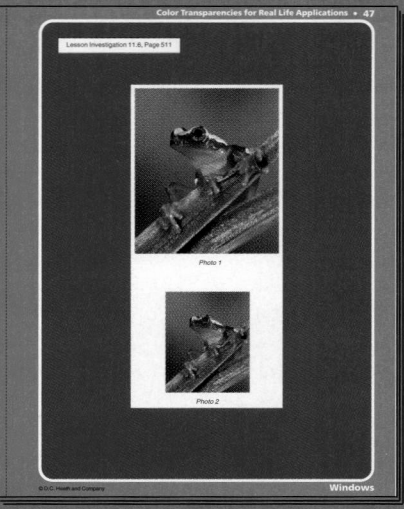

Technology: Using Calculators and Computers

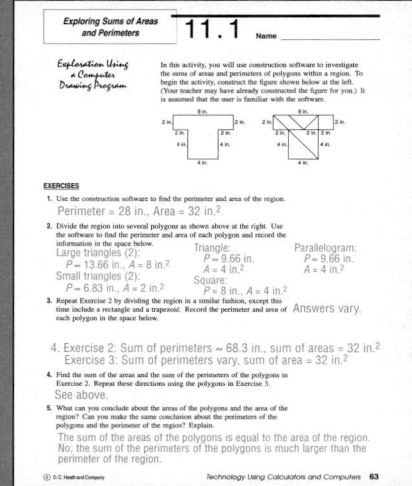

Also Available:

- Complete Solutions Manual
- Overhead Manipulatives Kit
- Computerized Testing Program

- **Interactive CD-ROM Projects**
  Interactive projects for solving real-world problems using multimedia
- **Interactions: Real Math–Real Careers**
  A videodisc–based resource that connects math to real careers and on-the-job problem solving
- **PACKETS® Performance Assessment for Middle School Mathematics**
  A program that links assessment and instruction

Alternative Assessment

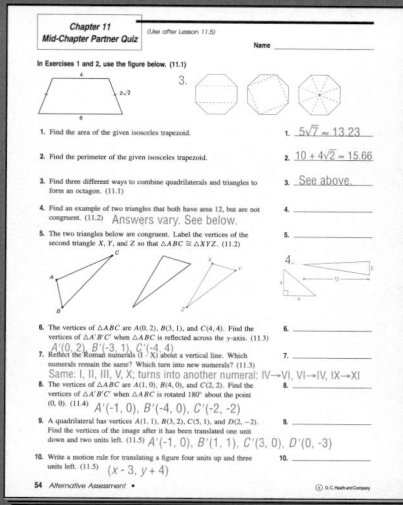

Alternative Assessment includes:
- Scoring Rubrics
- Portfolios
- Math Journals
- Projects
- Partner Quizzes
- Individual and Group Assessment

Formal Assessment

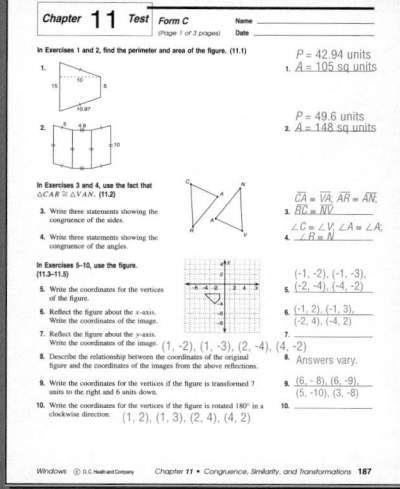

Formal Assessment includes:
- Short Quizzes (after every 2 lessons)
- Mid-Chapter Tests (2 forms)
- Chapter Tests (3 forms)
- Cumulative Tests (after every 3 Chapters)

Extra Practice Copymasters

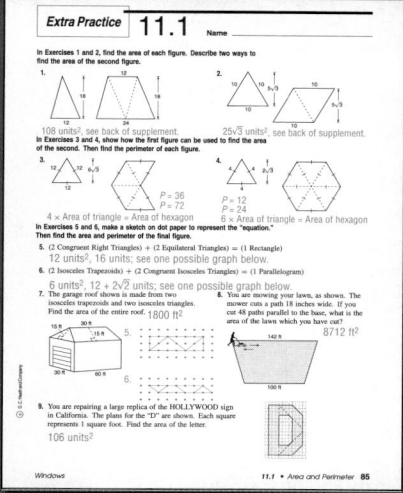

Reteaching Copymasters

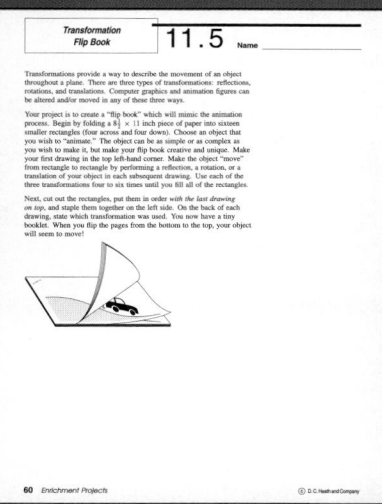

Enrichment Projects

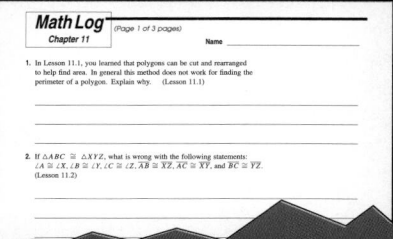

Math Log

Special Populations

Suggestions for providing equal access for:

Students Acquiring English Proficiency*

Have students begin by measuring and using formulas to find the area and perimeter of a variety of classroom objects. Then, have students use graph paper to determine area and perimeter by counting the number of lines and squares, respectively. This experience with using formulas and graph paper should help students feel more comfortable solving word problems by applying the concepts they have learned.

Students with Various Learning Styles*

In Lesson 11.1, some students will benefit from the hands-on approach to perimeter and area described above. You may need to spend more time with these students on the basic definitions of area and perimeter.

Underachieving Students*

Understanding will be enhanced if students are allowed to explore figures and come up with properties and relationships on their own using manipulatives.

Working in cooperative groups in Lessons 11.7 and 11.9 will help students with reading difficulties to apply the concepts they have learned to the word problems.

Gifted and Talented Students*

Ask students to make a polygon and turn it into a design, using rotations, reflections, and translations. Encourage students to enlarge their designs and paint them to create an abstract wall hanging.

* See page T19 for descriptions of these special populations.

CHAPTER 11 OVERVIEW

Congruence, Similarity, and Transformations

PACING CHART

Lesson	Basic/ Average Course	Above Average Course	Advanced Course
11.1	2 days	1 day	1 day
11.2	2 days	1 day	1 day
11.3	2 days	1 day	1 day
11.4	0 days	2 days	2 days
11.5	0 days	2 days	2 days
11.6	2 days	1 day	1 day
11.7	0 days	2 days	2 days
11.8	0 days	1 day	1 day
11.9	0 days	2 days	2 days

About the Chapter

In this chapter, students are introduced first to the basic technique of dissecting an irregular region into several smaller regular regions whose areas can be computed by formulas. In Lesson 11.2, the concept of congruence that was briefly introduced in the previous chapter is defined specifically for triangles, and students are given further opportunities for reasoning and critical thinking. Lessons 11.3–11.5 deal with the three isometric transformations—reflection, rotation, and translation. All three lessons strongly connect to algebra by their emphasis on coordinate geometry. Lesson 11.6 introduces another major topic of geometry, similarity; and in Lesson 11.7 students have an opportunity to maintain their skill in solving proportions as they apply similarity to indirect measurement problems. Lessons 11.8 and 11.9 take indirect measurement a step further into using trigonometry and the trigonometric ratios.

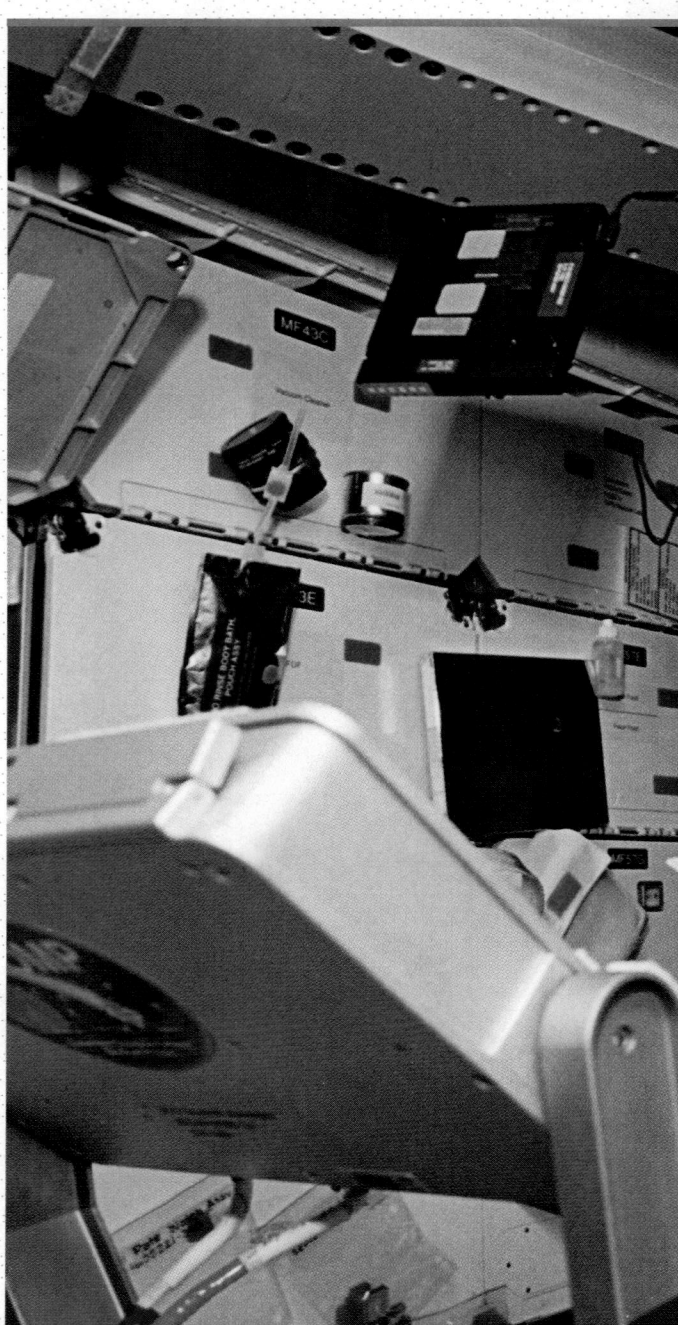

Daily exercise is an important factor in overcoming the adverse effects of weightlessness on the human body. So, NASA has installed exercise gear on the Space Shuttle Discovery's mid-deck. Mission specialist Jerry M. Linenger reported that running on the treadmill was a pleasure—just like being on Earth.

Real Life
Voyage to Mars

Anyone who has tried to pack a car trunk for a week-long camping trip will appreciate the enormous problems that engineers will have in packing a crowded space shuttle for a trip to Mars. In addition to food, water, clothing, fuel, and mission equipment, they need to pack tools and replacement parts for all the necessary pieces of on-board equipment.

In this chapter, you will learn how the shape of an object determines its geometric properties. For example, the amount of space an object takes up depends on both an object's size and its shape. For example, consider a round pencil with a 1-centimeter *diameter* cross section and a hexagonal pencil with a 1-centimeter *diagonal* cross section. The pencils are similar in dimensions, but the hexagonal pencil takes up about 15.5% less space.

1 cm
Cross section
17 cm
V ≈ 14.92 cm³

1 cm
Cross section
17 cm
V ≈ 12.61 cm³

Mars is like the earth in many ways. It has a solid surface, it rotates around the sun, and it has seasons. Martian seasons are identified because parts of the planet's surface change colors from blue to brown. These color changes occur when polar "ice" caps appear and disappear. The "ice" is solid carbon dioxide, not water.

Have each student find an interesting fact about Mars (for example, how far away it is, how long it would take a spacecraft to get there, and so on). Create a class poster incorporating all their information. Have students try to list all the supplies they think astronauts would need if they were travelling to Mars.

Multimedia Resources

Interactive CD-ROM Projects
A project for this chapter combines print, animation, sound and video presentations to capture students' interest in Animation. This interactive approach shows students how the math concepts and problem-solving strategies they are learning will be used in the future in dealing with important personal, national, and world issues.

The theme of Animation correlates to examples and exercises on pages 507 and 509.

Interactions: Real Math—Real Life
The theme of this chapter, Voyage to Mars, correlates with an episode of **Interactions** which is a videodisc-based multimedia resource that connects middle school math topics with real-life careers. In each of the twelve episodes, students go on-site with a variety of professionals to witness real-life applications of the math they are studying. Students see math concepts and problem-solving strategies in a context that helps them connect what they are studying to the world outside the classroom. **Interactions** was developed by the Foundation for Advancements in Science and Education (FASE) and is published by D.C. Heath and Company.

The theme of Voyage to Mars is continued throughout the chapter on pages 501 and 534.

Performance Assessment Resource

The PACKETS® Program: Performance Assessment for Middle School Mathematics was developed by Educational Testing Service and is published by D.C. Heath. **PACKETS** helps you assess your students' performances as they learn. You can use a wide variety of **PACKETS** Activity Units with this chapter because, in every activity, students will use ideas from all topic areas of mathematics. However, you can use the chart on page T16 to help you choose the **PACKETS** Activity Unit(s) that may fit best with this chapter.

PACING the Lesson

Suggested Number of Days
Basic/Average 2   Above Average 1
Advanced 1

PLANNING the Lesson

Lesson Plan 11.1, p. 85

ORGANIZER

Starters (reproduced below)
  Problem of the Day 11.1, p. 31
  Warm-Up Exercises 11.1, p. 31
Lesson Resources
  Teaching Tools
    Graph paper, pp. T1, C2
    Dot paper, pp. T2, C3
  Math Log, p. 34
  Technology, p. 63
  Answer Masters 11.1, pp. 213, 214
  Extra Practice Copymaster 11.1, p. 85
  Reteaching Copymaster 11.1, p. 85
  Enrichment Projects, pp. 56–58
Special Populations
  Suggestions, Teacher's Edition, p. 486D

LESSON Notes

Lesson Investigation
Discuss how the perimeter and area of the two triangles cut from the index card are affected by different arrangements of the cutouts.

ACTIVITY
Recall the formulas for the areas of a rectangle and a triangle. Ask students how these formulas are related to the formulas for the areas of a parallelogram and a trapezoid, respectively. Encourage students to use sketches of figures to explain the connections. (Hint: A parallelogram can be cut into a rectangle, and a trapezoid can be divided into two triangles.)

Example 1

Ask students if the perimeter of the parallelogram is twice the perimeter of the trapezoid from which it is constructed. No Have them explain their reasoning.

11.1 Area and Perimeter

What you should learn:

Goal 1 How to find the area and perimeter of polygons

Goal 2 How to use area and perimeter to solve real-life problems

Why you should learn it:

You can use area and perimeter to solve real-life problems, such as finding the area and perimeter of a miniature golf course.

Isosceles triangle: 24 in.², 26.4 in.; isosceles triangle: 24 in.², 22.4 in.; parallelogram: 24 in.², 26.4 in.; parallelogram: 24 in.², 22.4 in.; kite: 24 in.², 20 in.

Goal 1 Finding Area and Perimeter

LESSON INVESTIGATION

■ Investigating Area and Perimeter

Group Activity Use a 4-inch by 6-inch index card. Draw lines on each side to form 24 one-inch squares. Draw a diagonal and cut to form two triangles. Label the length of each side. Then place the triangles side by side to form different polygons. Name each polygon and find its area and perimeter. By rearranging the triangles, can you change the area? No Can you change the perimeter? Yes
See at left for polygons

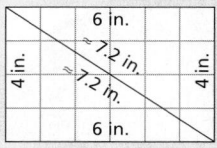

Area of Parallelograms and Trapezoids

Area of a Parallelogram: Area = (base) × (height)
Area of a Trapezoid: Area = $\frac{1}{2}$(base 1 + base 2) × (height)

Example 1   *Finding Areas of Polygons*

The trapezoid at the left has been duplicated. Then the trapezoid and its duplicate have been arranged to form a parallelogram. Find the area of each.

Solution For the trapezoid, the height is $h = 2$ and the lengths of the bases are $b_1 = 2$ and $b_2 = 4$.

$$\text{Area} = \frac{1}{2}(b_1 + b_2)h = \frac{1}{2}(2 + 4)(2) = 6$$

For the parallelogram, the height is $h = 2$ and the length of the base is $b = 6$.

$$\text{Area} = bh = (6)(2) = 12$$

The parallelogram has twice the area of the trapezoid. ■

488   Chapter **11** ▪ Congruence, Similarity, and Transformations

---

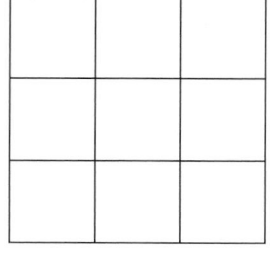
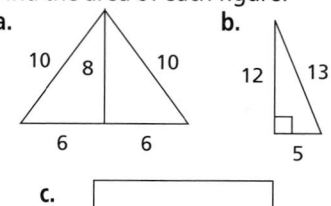
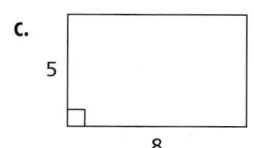

Goal 2 Solving Real-Life Problems

Real Life
Miniature Golf

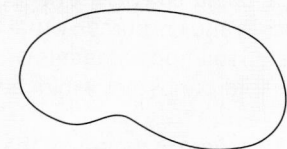

Example 2 *Finding Areas*

You are designing a miniature golf course. The plan for one hole is shown at the left. Each square represents 1 square foot. What is the total area of the green portion of the hole?

Solution One way to answer the question is to divide the green region into four smaller regions and find the area of each.

Region 1 (Rectangle):

Area = (Length)(Width) = $6 \times 4 = 24$ square feet

Region 2 (Parallelogram):

Area = (Base)(Height) = $7 \times 4 = 28$ square feet

Region 3 (Triangle):

Area = $\frac{1}{2}$(Base)(Height) = $\frac{1}{2}(7)(4) = 14$ square feet

Region 4 (Trapezoid):

Area = $\frac{1}{2}$(Base 1 + Base 2)(Height)

$= \frac{1}{2}(5 + 10)(4) = 30$ square feet

The total area of the green region is

Total Area = $24 + 28 + 14 + 30$

$= 96$ square feet. ∎

In Example 2, the perimeter of the green region (starting at *A*) is

Perimeter = $6 + \sqrt{32} + 7 + \sqrt{41} + 5 + 4 + 3 + 5 + 3 + 6 + 4$

$= 43 + \sqrt{32} + \sqrt{41}$

≈ 55.1 feet.

Each small square is 1 foot by 1 foot. The lengths of slanted sides can be found with the Pythagorean Theorem.

Communicating *about* MATHEMATICS

▶ **SHARING IDEAS about the Lesson**

Exploring Area Use a piece of graph paper to copy the outline of the green region shown in Example 2. Show other ways that the region can be divided into smaller regions. For each way, find the total area of the region. Check students' work.

Example 2

Have students describe how the green region can be divided into triangular regions.

Communicating *about* MATHEMATICS

EXTENSION
Challenge students to find the total area of the green region by subtracting the white areas from the complete grid.

Writing Prompt
Describe a way in which you might find the area and perimeter of an oddly shaped figure such as that shown below.

Technology

> *Exploring Sums of Areas and Perimeters* **11.1** Name _____

Exploration Using a Computer Drawing Program

In this activity, you will use construction software to investigate the sums of areas and perimeters of polygons within a region. To begin the activity, construct the figure shown below at the left. (Your teacher may have already constructed the figure for you.) It is assumed that the user is familiar with the software.

EXERCISES

1. Use the construction software to find the perimeter and area of the region.
   Perimeter = 28 in., Area = 32 in.²

2. Divide the region into several polygons as shown above at the right. Use the software to find the perimeter and area of each polygon and record the information in the space below.
   Large triangles (2): *P* ≈ 13.66 in., *A* = 8 in.²
   Small triangles (2): *P* ≈ 6.83 in., *A* = 2 in.²
   Triangle: *P* ≈ 9.66 in., *A* = 4 in.²
   Square: *P* = 8 in., *A* = 4 in.²
   Parallelogram: *P* ≈ 9.66 in., *A* = 4 in.²

3. Repeat Exercise 2 by dividing the region in a similar fashion, except this time include a rectangle and a trapezoid. Record the perimeter and area of each polygon in the space below. Answers vary.

4. Exercise 2: Sum of perimeters = 68.3 in., sum of areas = 32 in.²
   Exercise 3: Sum of perimeters vary, sum of area = 32 in.²

4. Find the sum of the areas and the sum of the perimeters of the polygons in Exercise 2. Repeat these directions using the polygons in Exercise 3.
   See above.

5. What can you conclude about the areas of the polygons and the area of the region? Can you make the same conclusion about the perimeters of the polygons and the perimeter of the region? Explain.
   The sum of the areas of the polygons is equal to the area of the region. No; the sum of the perimeters of the polygons is much larger than the perimeter of the region.

© D.C. Heath and Company   Technology Using Calculators and Computers **63**

EXERCISE Notes

ASSIGNMENT GUIDE

Basic/Average:
Day 1: Ex. 6–14
Day 2: Ex. 15–25

Above Average: Ex. 6–9, 10–14 even, 15–18, 22–25

Advanced: Ex. 6–9, 10–14 even, 15–18, 22–25

Selected Answers: Ex. 1–5, 6–23 odd

Guided Practice

▶ **Ex. 1–4** The grids require students to decide what measurements are needed. These exercises also encourage visual, non-formula-based solutions. Students with geoboard backgrounds may avoid the use of formulas.

▶ **Ex. 5** This exercise reinforces the relationship between the area of a rectangle and a parallelogram.

Independent Practice

▶ **Ex. 6, 7** These problems make connections between various formulas.

▶ **Ex. 10–14** Understanding how various polygons can be dissected gives students alternate strategies for finding an area and for understanding the attributes of the polygon.

Guided Practice

▶ **CHECK for Understanding**

1. 24 units², 22 units   2. 24 units², ≈ 22.8 units
3. 27.5 units², ≈ 21.1 units   4. 30 units², ≈ 22.6 units

In Exercises 1–4, find the area and perimeter of each figure.

1. 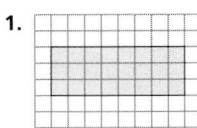   **2**   **3.** 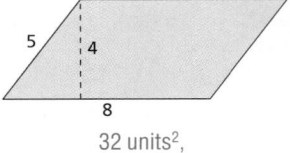   **4.**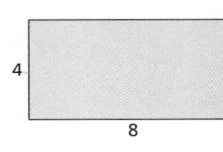

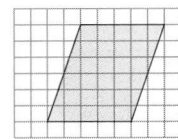

P **5.** The parallelogram at the right has been cut and rearranged to form a rectangle. Find the area and perimeter of each. Does rearranging change the area? Does it change the perimeter?
No, yes

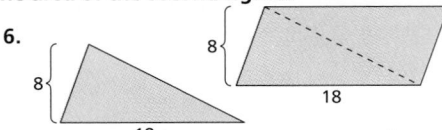   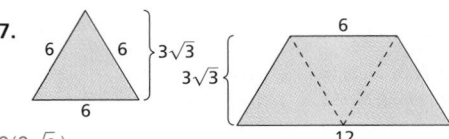

32 units²,   32 units²,
26 units   24 units

Independent Practice

6. 72 units², 144 units²; 8 × 18 or 2 × 72
In Exercises 6 and 7, find the area of each figure. Describe two ways to find the area of the second figure.

6. 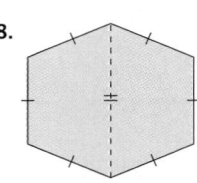   **7.**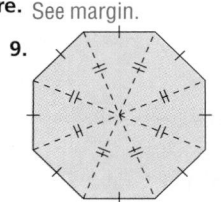

7. $9\sqrt{3} \approx 15.6$ units², $27\sqrt{3} \approx 46.8$ units²; $\frac{1}{2}(6+12)3\sqrt{3}$ or $3(9\sqrt{3})$

In Exercises 8 and 9, show how the second figure can be used to find the area of the first. Then find the perimeter of each figure. See margin.

8. 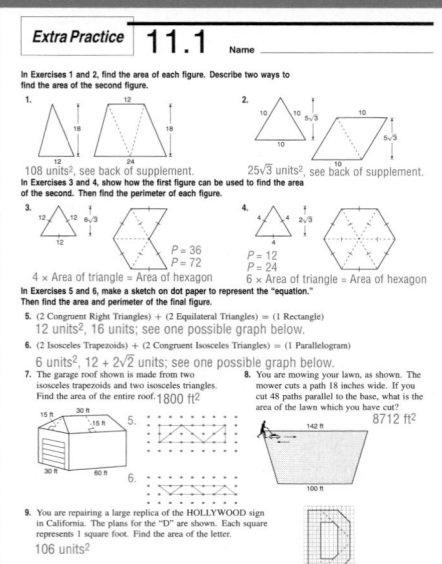   **9.**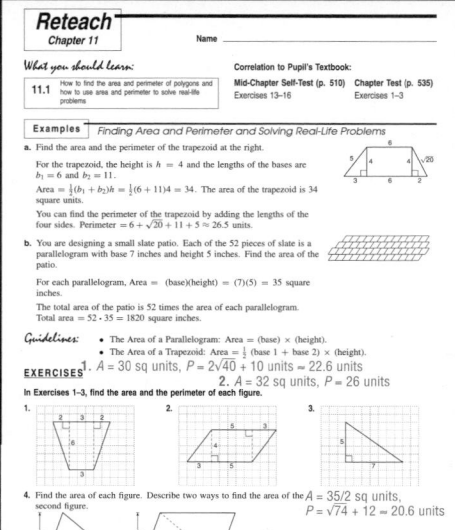

P *Drawing "Equations"* **In Exercises 10–14, make a sketch on dot paper to represent the "equation." Then find the area and perimeter of the final figure.** Check students' work. For sketches, see Additional Answers.

✪ **10.** (2 Congruent Right Triangles) + (1 Square) = (1 Parallelogram)

✪ **11.** (1 Trapezoid) + (1 Triangle) = (1 Parallelogram)

✪ **12.** (1 Isosceles Triangle) + (1 Isosceles Trapezoid) = (1 Pentagon)

✪ **13.** (2 Isosceles Trapezoids) + (1 Rectangle) = (1 Octagon)

✪ **14.** (2 Right Scalene Triangles) = (1 Kite)

✪ More difficult exercises
P Portfolio Opportunity

490 *Chapter 11* • *Congruence, Similarity, and Transformations*

Answers

8. $\frac{1}{2}(13 + 23)12 = 216$ units², $2 \times 216 = 432$ units²; 78 units, 62 units

9. $\frac{1}{2}(10)\,13.08 \approx 65.40$ units², $8 \times 65.40 \approx 523.20$ units²; 80 units, 38 units

Extra Practice

Extra Practice **11.1** Name _____

In Exercises 1 and 2, find the area of each figure. Describe two ways to find the area of the second figure.

1.   **2.**

108 units², see back of supplement.   25√3 units², see back of supplement.
In Exercises 3 and 4, show how the first figure can be used to find the area of the second. Then find the perimeter of each figure.

3.   **4.**

P = 36   P = 12
P = 72   P = 24
4 × Area of triangle = Area of hexagon   6 × Area of triangle = Area of hexagon
In Exercises 5 and 6, make a sketch on dot paper to represent the "equation." Then find the area and perimeter of the final figure.

5. (2 Congruent Right Triangles) + (2 Equilateral Triangles) = (1 Rectangle)
12 units², 16 units; see one possible graph below.

6. (2 Isosceles Trapezoids) + (2 Congruent Isosceles Triangles) = (1 Parallelogram)
6 units², 12 + 2√2 units; see one possible graph below.

7. The garage roof shown is made from two isosceles trapezoids and two isosceles triangles. Find the area of the entire roof. 1800 ft²

8. You are mowing your lawn, as shown. The mower cuts a path 18 inches wide. If you cut 48 paths parallel to the base, what is the area of the lawn which you have cut? 8712 ft²

5.
6.

9. You are repairing a large replica of the HOLLYWOOD sign in California. The plans for the "D" are shown. Each square represents 1 square foot. Find the area of the letter. 106 units²

Windows   11.1 • Area and Perimeter **85**

Reteaching

Reteach **Chapter 11** Name _____

What you should learn:
11.1 How to find the area and perimeter of polygons and how to use area and perimeter to solve real-life problems

Correlation to Pupil's Textbook:
Mid-Chapter Self-Test (p. 510) Chapter Test (p. 535)
Exercises 13–16   Exercises 1–3

Examples *Finding Area and Perimeter and Solving Real-Life Problems*

a. Find the area and the perimeter of the trapezoid at the right.
For the trapezoid, the height is $h = 4$ and the lengths of the bases are $b_1 = 6$ and $b_2 = 11$.
Area $= \frac{1}{2}(b_1 + b_2)h = \frac{1}{2}(6 + 11)4 = 34$. The area of the trapezoid is 34 square units.
You can find the perimeter of the trapezoid by adding the lengths of the four sides. Perimeter $= 6 + \sqrt{20} + 11 + 5 \approx 26.5$ units.

b. You are designing a small slate patio. Each of the 52 pieces of slate is a parallelogram with base 7 inches and height 5 inches. Find the area of the patio.
For each parallelogram, Area $=$ (base)(height) $= (7)(5) = 35$ square inches.
The total area of the patio is 52 times the area of each parallelogram.
Total area $= 52 \cdot 35 = 1820$ square inches.

Guidelines: • The Area of a Parallelogram: Area $=$ (base) × (height).
• The Area of a Trapezoid: Area $= \frac{1}{2}$ (base 1 + base 2) × (height).

EXERCISES 1. $A = 30$ sq units, $P = 2\sqrt{40} + 10$ units = 22.6 units
2. $A = 32$ sq units, $P = 26$ units
In Exercises 1–3, find the area and the perimeter of each figure.

1.   **2.**   **3.**

4. Find the area of each figure. Describe two ways to find the area of the second figure.
$A = 35/2$ sq units, $P = \sqrt{74} + 12 = 20.6$ units

$A_1 = 75$ sq units,
$A_2 = 2(75) = 150$ sq units or
$A_2 = 10(15) = 150$ sq units

Windows   Chapter 11 • Congruence, Similarity, and Transformations **85**

Polygon Puzzle **In Exercises 15–18, use the figure at the right. Each small square of the grid has an area of 1 square unit.** 15., 16. See Additional Answers.

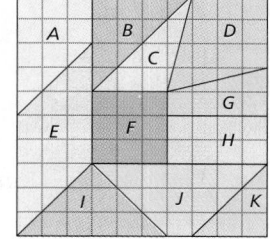

15. Name each type of polygon, A through K.

16. Find the area of each polygon.

17. Find the area of the entire figure. 100 units²

18. Which polygons have the same area? *B* and *H*, *C* and *G*, *D* and *J*, *F* and *I*

19. *Picture Frame* The polygons at the right can be put together to form a picture frame.

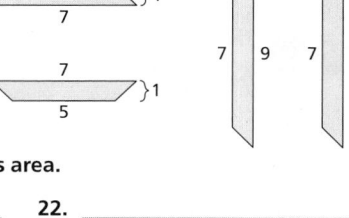

   a. Find the area of each polygon. See below.

   b. Sketch the picture frame. See Additional Answers.

   c. Find the area of the picture frame. 28 units²

   a. 6 units² , 6 units², 8 units², 8 units²

Geography **In Exercises 20–22, name the state. Then estimate its area.**

20.

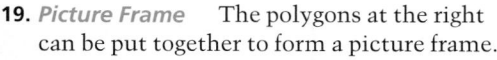

One unit ≈ 50 miles

Montana; 150,000 mi²

21.

One unit ≈ 33 miles

South Carolina; 30,000 mi²

22.

One unit ≈ 20 miles

Ohio; 40,000 mi²

Integrated Review

Making Connections within Mathematics

Describing Patterns **In Exercises 23 and 24, find the area of each figure.** See Additional Answers. **Use a table and a graph to organize your results. Then describe the pattern.**

23.

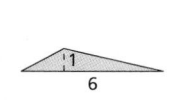 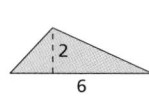 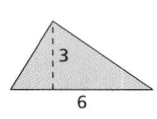 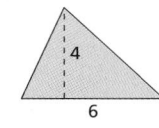 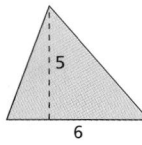

24.

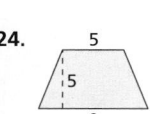 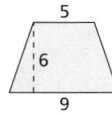 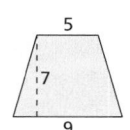 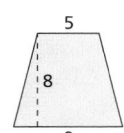 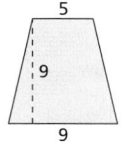

Exploration and Extension

25. *Nine Square Puzzle* Use 9 squares with sides of 1, 4, 7, 8, 9, 10, 14, 15, and 18 units to form a rectangle. Find the dimensions of the rectangle. 32 by 33
For rectangle, see margin.

11.1 • *Area and Perimeter* **491**

Enrichment

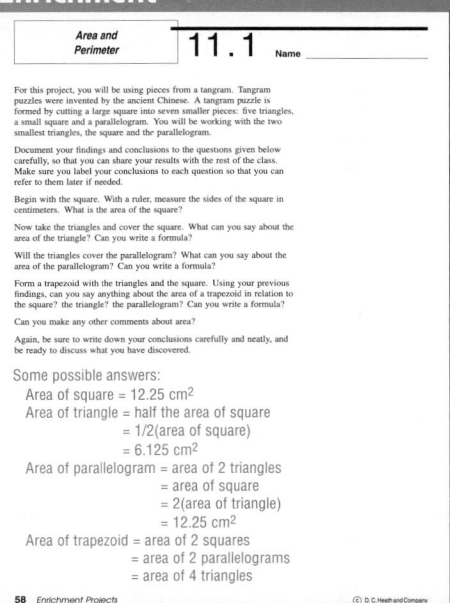

| Area and Perimeter | **11.1** Name _____ |

For this project, you will be using pieces from a tangram. Tangram puzzles were invented by the ancient Chinese. A tangram puzzle is formed by cutting a large square into seven smaller pieces: five triangles, a small square and a parallelogram. You will be working with the two smallest triangles, the square and the parallelogram.

Document your findings and conclusions to the questions given below carefully, so that you can share your results with the rest of the class. Make sure you label your conclusions to each question so that you can refer to them later if needed.

Begin with the square. With a ruler, measure the sides of the square in centimeters. What is the area of the square?

Now take the triangles and cover the square. What can you say about the area of the triangle? Can you write a formula?

Will the triangles cover the parallelogram? What can you say about the area of the parallelogram? Can you write a formula?

Form a trapezoid with the triangles and the square. Using your previous findings, can you say anything about the area of a trapezoid in relation to the square? the triangle? the parallelogram? Can you write a formula?

Can you make any other comments about area?

Again, be sure to write down your conclusions carefully and neatly, and be ready to discuss what you have discovered.

Some possible answers:
  Area of square = 12.25 cm²
  Area of triangle = half the area of square
     = 1/2(area of square)
     = 6.125 cm²
  Area of parallelogram = area of 2 triangles
     = area of square
     = 2(area of triangle)
     = 12.25 cm²
  Area of trapezoid = area of 2 squares
     = area of 2 parallelograms
     = area of 4 triangles

58 Enrichment Projects

© D.C. Heath and Company

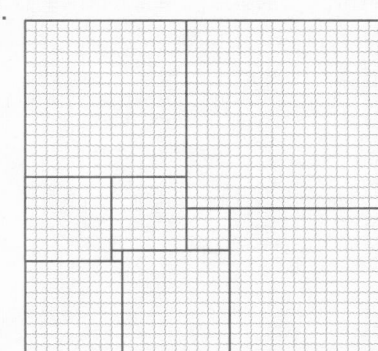

PACING the Lesson

Suggested Number of Days
Basic/Average 2 **Above Average** 1
Advanced 1

PLANNING the Lesson

Lesson Plan 11.2, p. 86

ORGANIZER

Starters (reproduced below)
Problem of the Day 11.2, p. 31
Warm-Up Exercises 11.2, p. 31
Lesson Resources
Color Transparencies
Picture for Ex. 23, p. 45
Teaching Tools,
Coordinate plane, pp. T8, C10
Protractor, pp. T12, C18
Graph paper, pp. T1, C2
Dot paper, pp. T2, C3
Math Log, p. 34
Answer Masters 11.2, p. 215
Extra Practice Copymaster 11.2, p. 86
Reteaching Copymaster 11.2, p. 86
Special Populations
Suggestions, Teacher's Edition, p. 486D

LESSON Notes

Be sure that students understand that, given a statement such as $\triangle ABC \cong \triangle DEF$, then the following correspondences are assumed: $A\leftrightarrow D$, $B\leftrightarrow E$, and $C\leftrightarrow F$.

Discuss how tracing paper can be used to demonstrate congruence of line segments, angles, and triangles.

Lesson Investigation
Challenge students to plot other points that form triangles that are congruent to $\triangle ABC$. Students should record the congruent triangle relationships in their journals.

11.2 Exploring Congruence

 What you should learn:

 *Why you should learn it:*

Goal 1 How to determine whether two figures are congruent

Goal 2 How to use congruence to solve real-life problems

You can use congruence to solve real-life problems, such as comparing the triangles used in an art piece.

Yes; $AB = DE = \sqrt{13}$, $AC = DF = \sqrt{34}$, $BC = EF = 7$, $m\angle A = m\angle D \approx 93°$, $m\angle B = m\angle E \approx 56°$, $m\angle C = m\angle F \approx 31°$; corresponding parts are congruent; corresponding sides are congruent and corresponding angles are congruent.

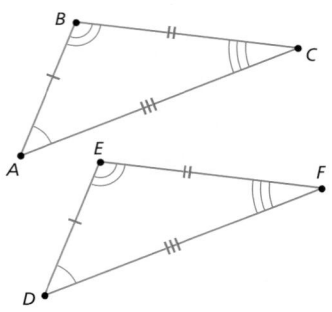

Goal 1 **Congruence and Measure**

In Chapter 10, you were introduced to the idea of *congruence*.

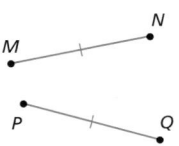

$\overline{MN} \cong \overline{PQ}$
Congruent line segments have the same length.

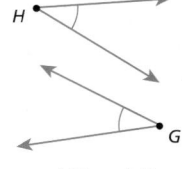

$\angle H \cong \angle G$
Congruent angles have the same measure.

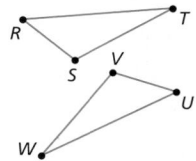

$\triangle RST \cong \triangle UVW$
Congruent triangles have the same size and shape.

LESSON INVESTIGATION

■ Investigating Congruence
Group Activity Plot the following points on graph paper: $A(-2, 7)$, $B(-4, 4)$, $C(3, 4)$, $D(-2, -3)$, $E(1, -5)$, $F(1, 2)$. Draw $\triangle ABC$ amd $\triangle DEF$. Do the triangles seem to be congruent? Find the length of each side. Then use a protractor to approximate the measure of each angle. What can you conclude? What can you say about the sides and angles of congruent triangles?

In the investigation, you may have discovered the following result about congruent triangles.

Congruent Triangles
$\triangle ABC \cong \triangle DEF$ if and only if the corresponding sides are congruent and the corresponding angles are congruent.

Corresponding Sides	Corresponding Angles
$\overline{AB} \cong \overline{DE}$	$\angle A \cong \angle D$
$\overline{BC} \cong \overline{EF}$	$\angle B \cong \angle E$
$\overline{AC} \cong \overline{DF}$	$\angle C \cong \angle F$

492 *Chapter 11 • Congruence, Similarity, and Transformations*

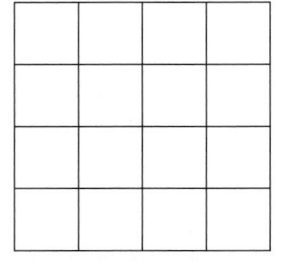

Goal 2 Using Congruence in Real Life

Example 1 Showing Two Triangles Are Congruent

You are using parts of photographs to create a collage. As part of the collage, you cut the photograph at the left along one of its diagonals. Are the resulting triangles congruent? Explain your reasoning.

Solution The resulting triangles are congruent. To show this, draw a rectangle and one of its diagonals, as shown at the right. You can conclude that $\triangle ABC$ is congruent to $\triangle CDA$ because the corresponding sides and angles are congruent.

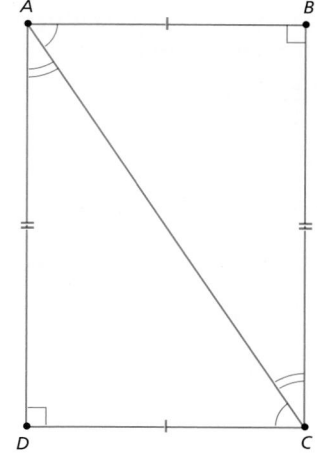

- $\overline{BC} \cong \overline{AD}$ • $\overline{AB} \cong \overline{CD}$
- $\overline{AC} \cong \overline{AC}$ • $\angle B \cong \angle D$
- $\angle CAB \cong \angle DCA$
- $\angle DAC \cong \angle ACB$

Explain why each of these statements is true. ∎

P Communicating about MATHEMATICS

> **SHARING IDEAS about the Lesson**

> ***Area, Perimeter, and Congruence*** Discuss the following questions with a partner. Use graph paper to help illustrate your answers. Check students' work.

> **A.** If two figures are congruent, must they have the same area and perimeter? Yes

> **B.** If two figures have exactly the same area, must they be congruent? No

> **C.** If two figures have the same perimeter, must they be congruent? No

> **D.** If two figures have the same area and perimeter, must they be congruent? No

Ask students: What are examples of congruence in real-life situations? Have students identify objects in their classroom that appear to be congruent.

Example 1
Explain to students that this sequence of statements with the corresponding reasons, is a *proof* that $\triangle ABC$ is congruent to $\triangle CDA$.
  Students will probably need to be reminded of the reasons for the last two congruence statements, namely, that these pairs of angles are *alternate interior angles*. For this you may wish to refer students to the Exploration and Extension section of Lesson 10.3, page 451.

Communicating about MATHEMATICS

Challenge students to justify their conclusions. You may wish to use this activity as a Lesson Investigation of your own.

Writing Prompt
Have students answer Ex. 1 of Guided Practice in their journals.

P Portfolio Opportunity

11.2 ▪ *Exploring Congruence* **493**

ASSIGNMENT GUIDE

Basic/Average:
Day 1: Ex. 10–16, 18–23
Day 2: Ex. 17, 24–32

Above Average: Ex. 11–17 odd, 18–22, 24–26, 28–32

Advanced: Ex. 11–17 odd, 18–22, 24–26, 28–32

Selected Answers: Ex. 1–9, 10–27 odd

Guided Practice

These exercises can be used as a five-minute in-class activity for partners.

Independent Practice

▶ **Ex. 10–15** Note that the diagram is unnecessary for these exercises. Without it, the exercises assess whether students understand the information conveyed by congruence statements.
▶ **Ex. 16, 17** These exercises could be done in class as a group activity.

EXERCISES

Guided Practice

▶ **CHECK for Understanding**

Corresponding sides are congruent and corresponding angles are congruent.

P 1. Writing In your own words, explain what it means for two figures to be congruent. Give examples of congruent figures in your classroom. Examples vary.

In Exercises 2–5, use the figure at the right. Write the congruence statement in words.

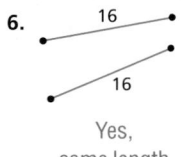 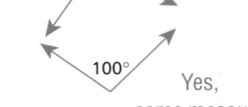 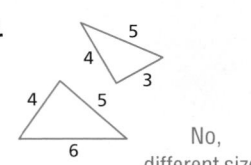 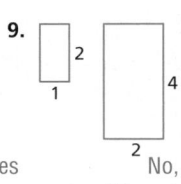

2. $\triangle RST \cong \triangle XYZ$ See margin.

3. $\overline{RS} \cong \overline{XY}$

4. $\angle T \cong \angle Z$

5. What other congruence statements are indicated in the figure?
$\overline{RT} \cong \overline{XZ}$, $\overline{ST} \cong \overline{YZ}$, $\angle R \cong \angle X$, $\angle S \cong \angle Y$

In Exercises 6–9, decide whether the figures are congruent. Explain.

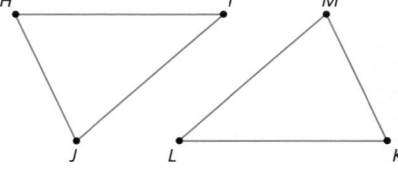

6.
16
16
Yes, same length

7.
100°
100°
Yes, same measure

8.
5
4
3
4   5
6
No, different sizes

9.
2
1
4
2
No, different sizes

Independent Practice

In Exercises 10–15, use the fact that $\triangle HIJ \cong \triangle KLM$ to complete the statement.

10. $\angle H \cong \boxed{?}\ \angle K$

11. $\overline{JH} \cong \boxed{?}\ \overline{MK}$

12. $\overline{ML} \cong \boxed{?}\ \overline{JI}$

13. $\angle J \cong \boxed{?}\ \angle M$

14. $\angle L \cong \boxed{?}\ \angle I$

15. $\overline{LK} \cong \boxed{?}\ \overline{IH}$

✪ 16. Drawing Draw an obtuse triangle on cardboard. Cut the triangle out and trace two copies. Label the copies as $\triangle FGH$ and $\triangle MNO$. Write all possible congruence statements about the two triangles. Check students' work. Answers vary.

✪ 17. Drawing Draw an acute triangle on cardboard. Cut the triangle out and trace two copies. Label the copies as $\triangle FGH$ and $\triangle MNO$. Write all possible congruence statements about the two triangles. Check students' work. Answers vary.

18. Congruent Polygons List each pair of congruent polygons.

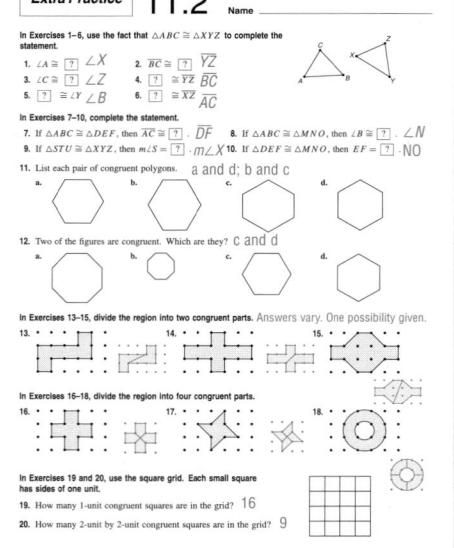

a.   b.   c.   d.   e.

b and d, c and e

✪ More difficult exercises
P Portfolio Opportunity

494 *Chapter 11* ▪ *Congruence, Similarity, and Transformations*

Answers
2. Triangle *RST* is congruent to triangle *XYZ*.
3. Segment *RS* is congruent to segment *XY*.
4. Angle *T* is congruent to angle *Z*.

Extra Practice

Extra Practice 11.2 Name _____

In Exercises 1–6, use the fact that $\triangle ABC \cong \triangle XYZ$ to complete the statement.

1. $\angle A \cong \boxed{?}\ \angle X$
2. $\overline{BC} \cong \boxed{?}\ \overline{YZ}$
3. $\angle C \cong \boxed{?}\ \angle Z$
4. $\boxed{?} \cong \overline{YZ}\ \overline{BC}$
5. $\boxed{?} \cong \angle Y\ \angle B$
6. $\boxed{?} \cong \overline{XZ}\ \overline{AC}$

In Exercises 7–10, complete the statement.
7. If $\triangle ABC \cong \triangle DEF$, then $\overline{AC} \cong \boxed{?}$. $\overline{DF}$
8. If $\triangle ABC \cong \triangle MNO$, then $\angle B \cong \boxed{?}$. $\angle N$
9. If $\triangle STU \cong \triangle XYZ$, then $m\angle S = \boxed{?}$. $m\angle X$
10. If $\triangle DEF \cong \triangle MNO$, then $EF = \boxed{?}$. NO

11. List each pair of congruent polygons.   a and d; b and c
a.   b.   c.   d.

12. Two of the figures are congruent. Which are they? c and d
a.   b.   c.   d.

In Exercises 13–15, divide the region into two congruent parts. Answers vary. One possibility given.
13.   14.   15.

In Exercises 16–18, divide the region into four congruent parts.
16.   17.   18.

In Exercises 19 and 20, use the square grid. Each small square has sides of one unit.
19. How many 1-unit congruent squares are in the grid? 16
20. How many 2-unit by 2-unit congruent squares are in the grid? 9

86 Exploring Congruence ▪ 11.2   Windows

Reteaching

Reteach Chapter 11 Name _____

What you should learn:
11.2 How to determine whether two figures are congruent and how to use congruence to solve real-life problems

Correlation to Pupil's Textbook:
Mid-Chapter Self-Test (p. 510) Chapter Test (p. 535)
Exercises 1–4   Exercise 20

Examples *Congruence and Measure and Using Congruence in Real Life*

a. Triangles PQR and XYZ at the right are congruent. Name three pairs of congruent sides and three pairs of congruent angles.

$\triangle PQR \cong \triangle XYZ$ if and only if the corresponding sides are congruent and the corresponding angles are congruent.

Corresponding Sides   Corresponding Angles
$\overline{PQ} \cong \overline{XY}$ $\angle P \cong \angle X$
$\overline{QR} \cong \overline{YZ}$ $\angle Q \cong \angle Y$
$\overline{RP} \cong \overline{ZX}$ $\angle R \cong \angle Z$

b. You are making two triangular banners from a piece of cloth which is a parallelogram in shape. Parallelogram $ABCD$ is shown at the right. Show that the two banners are congruent by naming two congruent triangles formed by drawing diagonal $\overline{AC}$.

You can conclude that $\triangle ABC \cong \triangle CDA$ because corresponding sides and angles are congruent.

Corresponding Sides   Corresponding Angles
$\overline{CB} \cong \overline{AD}$ $\angle B \cong \angle D$
$\overline{AB} \cong \overline{CD}$ $\angle BAC \cong \angle DCA$
$\overline{AC} \cong \overline{CA}$ $\angle BCA \cong \angle DAC$

Guidelines:
• Congruent line segments have the same length.
• Congruent angles have the same measure.
• Congruent triangles have the same size and shape.

EXERCISES

In Exercises 1–6, use the fact that $\triangle CDE \cong \triangle JKL$ to complete the statement.
1. $\angle E \cong \boxed{?}\ \angle L$
2. $\overline{CE} \cong \boxed{?}\ \overline{JL}$
3. $\boxed{?} \cong \angle J\ \angle C$
4. $\boxed{?} \cong \overline{JK}\ \overline{CD}$
5. $\overline{DE} \cong \boxed{?}\ \overline{KL}$
6. $\angle D \cong \boxed{?}\ \angle K$

86 Chapter 11 ▪ Congruence, Similarity, and Transformations   Windows

In Exercises 19–22, copy the figure on dot paper. Then divide it into 2 congruent parts. Give more than one answer, if possible.
Answers vary. Samples given.

——— one answer
- - - - another answer

19.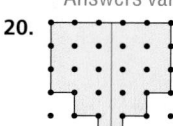

20.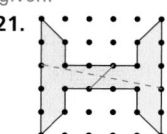

21.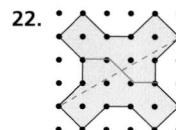

22.

23. *Photography*   Which of the photographs below are congruent? Explain how the photos could have been created. a and c, see margin.

a.    b.    c.

24. *Think about It*   Is there a type of triangle for which the following statements are both true? If so, sketch and describe such a triangle.

$\triangle ABC \cong \triangle ACB$ $\triangle ABC \cong \triangle BAC$ Yes, an equilateral triangle. Check students' work.

Integrated Review

Making Connections within Mathematics

Coordinate Geometry   **In Exercises 25–27, find the coordinates of the missing point so that the figures are congruent.**

25.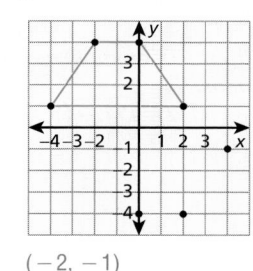

$(1, -3)$

26.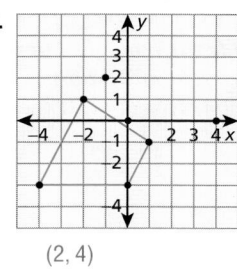

$(-2, -1)$

27.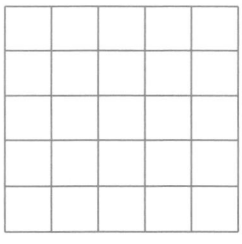

$(2, 4)$

Exploration and Extension

Counting Squares   **In Exercises 28–32, use the square grid at the right.**

28. How many 1-by-1 squares are in the grid? 25

29. How many 2-by-2 squares are in the grid? 16

30. How many 3-by-3 squares are in the grid? 9

31. How many 4-by-4 squares are in the grid? 4

32. How many squares are in the grid? 55

11.2 • *Exploring Congruence*   **495**

▶ **Ex. 19–22**   These exercises preview rotation and reflection symmetry.
▶ **Ex. 24**   Some students may not be aware of the fact that a triangle may be congruent to itself in more than one way, given certain conditions. Be sure to have students explain their reasoning in answering this question.

Integrated Review

These exercises, which should be assigned as a group, help to build visual skills.

Exploration and Extension

EXTENSION
Ask students whether they observe a pattern in the answers to these questions. Have students repeat the exercises for a 10 x 10 grid, and ask them what patterns they now observe.

Portfolio Opportunity: Math Log

If $\triangle ABC \cong \triangle XYZ$, what is wrong with the following statements:
$\angle A \cong \angle X$, $\angle B \cong \angle Y$, $\angle C \cong \angle Z$, $\overline{AB} \cong \overline{XZ}$, $\overline{AC} \cong \overline{XY}$, and $\overline{BC} \cong \overline{YZ}$.

Also available as a copymaster, page 34, Ex. 2

Short Quiz
Covers Lessons 11.1 and 11.2

Available as a copymaster, page 175

Alternative Assessment

Chapter 11 Group Assessment
An exploration for 3 or 4 students that develops deductive reasoning.

Chapter 11 Individual Assessment
A similar follow-up activity for individual students. Adds incentive for the group activity and measures individual competence in the activity.

Available as copymasters, pages 79, 80

Answer
23. Three prints were made from the same negative, then one of the prints was retouched in order to remove two of the windows.

Materials

Teaching Tools
Coordinate planes, pp. T9, C11

This investigation integrates previously learned skills with new content. The investigation is an introduction to slides, flips, and turns. Students should begin to predict what will happen when the coordinates are acted upon by addition, subtraction, or multiplication, or have been replaced by their opposites.

Materials Needed: graph paper and straightedge

Example — *Moving Objects in a Coordinate Plane*

Consider the triangle whose vertices are $A(0, 0)$, $B(3, 4)$ and $C(4, 1)$. Move each vertex according to the given motion rule. How is the new triangle related to the original triangle?

a. *Motion Rule:* Add 2 to x, add 3 to y.

b. *Motion Rule:* Keep x the same, replace y by $-y$.

c. *Motion Rule:* Subtract 4 from x, keep y the same.

Solution The results are shown below.

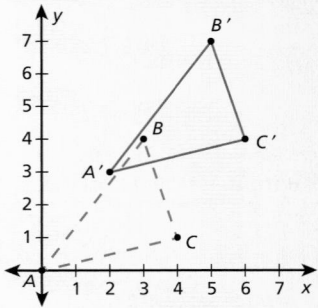 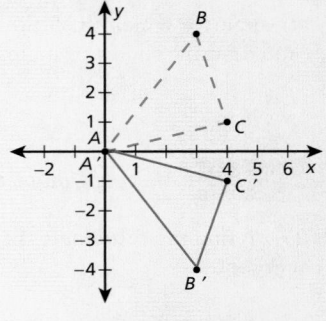 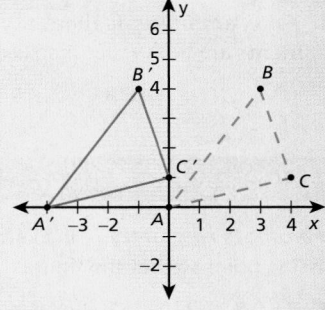

a. *Slide the triangle 2 units to the right and 3 units up.*
$(4, 1) \rightarrow (4+2, 1+3)$

b. *Flip the triangle about the x-axis.*
$(4, 1) \rightarrow (4, -1)$

c. *Slide the triangle 4 units to the left.*
$(4, 1) \rightarrow (4-4, 1)$

■

Exercises

In Exercises 1–8, sketch $\triangle ABC$ with $A(-4, -2)$, $B(-3, -4)$, and $C(-1, -1)$. Apply the motion rule and sketch the new triangle. Use tracing paper to decide whether the two triangles are congruent.

1. Add 5 to x, subtract 4 from y. Yes

2. Keep x the same, replace y by $-y$. Yes

3. Replace x by $-x$, add 2 to y. Yes

4. Add 3 to x, add 4 to y. Yes

5. Subtract 3 from x, add 2 to y. Yes

6. Subtract 5 from x, replace y by $-y$. Yes

7. Replace x by $-x$, keep y the same. Yes

8. Double x, keep y the same. No

9. In Exercises 1–8, is the new triangle congruent to the original triangle? See above. If so, explain how the original can be moved to form the new triangle. See margin.

Answer

9. 1. Slide the triangle 5 units to the right and 4 units down.

2. Flip the triangle about the x-axis.

3. Flip the triangle about the y-axis and slide it 2 units up.

4. Slide the triangle 3 units to the right and 4 units up.

5. Slide the triangle 3 units to the left and 2 units up.

6. Slide the triangle 5 units to the left and flip it about the x-axis.

7. Flip the triangle about the y-axis.

11.3

Line Reflections

 What you should learn:

Goal 1 How to reflect a figure about a line

Goal 2 How to use properties of reflections to answer questions about real-life situations

 Why you should learn it:

You can use properties of reflections to answer questions about real life, such as analyzing the symmetry of fabric pieces used to make clothing.

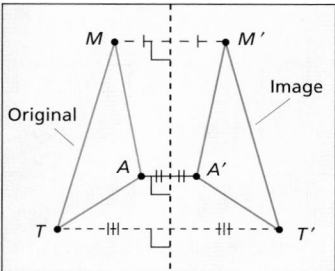

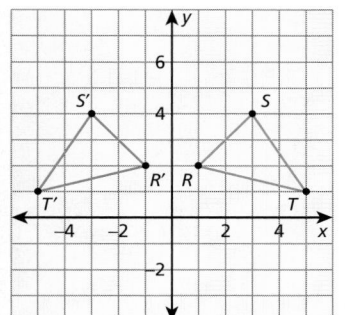

Goal 1 **Reflecting Figures about Lines**

LESSON INVESTIGATION

■ Investigating Line Reflections

Group Activity Draw $\triangle MAT$ on the left side of a piece of paper. Fold the paper in half. Hold the paper up to the light and mark the images of M, A, and T on the right side of the paper. Unfold the paper, label the images as M', A', and T'. Draw $\triangle M'\,A'\,T'$. What can you conclude? Draw the line segments $\overline{MM'}$, $\overline{AA'}$, and $\overline{TT'}$. How are these segments related to the fold in the paper?

$\triangle MAT \cong \triangle M'\,A'\,T'$, the segments are perpendicular to the fold and bisected by the fold.

In the investigation, you may have discovered the following properties of **reflections.**

Properties of Line Reflections

1. When a figure is reflected about a line, the image is congruent to the original figure.

2. In a reflection, the **reflection line** is perpendicular to and bisects each segment that joins an original point to its image.

Example 1 *Reflecting in a Coordinate Plane*

Consider the points $R(1, 2)$, $S(3, 4)$, and $T(5, 1)$ in a coordinate plane. Reflect each point about the y-axis. Then compare $\triangle RST$ with $\triangle R'S'T'$.

Solution From the figure at the left, you can see that the two triangles are congruent. Their orientation, however, is not the same. In $\triangle RST$, the vertices R, S, and T are in clockwise order; but in $\triangle R'S'T'$, the vertices are in counterclockwise order. This is comparable to the different orientations of your left and right hands. ■

▶ **PACING the Lesson**

Suggested Number of Days
Basic/Average 2 **Above Average** 1
Advanced 1

▶ **PLANNING the Lesson**

Lesson Plan 11.3, p. 87

ORGANIZER

Starters (reproduced below)
 Problem of the Day 11.3, p. 31
 Warm-Up Exercises 11.3, p. 31
Lesson Resources
 Teaching Tools,
  Coordinate planes, pp. T9, C11
 Math Log, p. 34
 Answer Masters 11.3, pp. 216, 217
 Extra Practice Copymaster 11.3, p. 87
 Reteaching Copymaster 11.3, p. 87
Special Populations
 Suggestions, Teacher's Edition, p. 486D

LESSON Notes

Many art and architectural designs are created from line reflections. Have students look for examples in the classroom, in magazines, and in buildings.

Lesson Investigation
Encourage students to repeat the investigation with a variety of polygonal shapes. Ask if they find similar results for these other shapes. They should.

Example 1

EXTENSION
Have students find the coordinates of R', S', and T'. $R'(-1, 2)$, $S'(-3, 4)$, $T'(-5, 1)$
Ask students how the coordinates of R, S, and T are related to the coordinates of R', S', and T'. *The x-coordinates of R', S', and T' are the opposites of the x-coordinates of R, S, and T, respectively.*
 Have students repeat the exercise (and Extension) for a reflection of $\triangle RST$ about the *x*-axis.

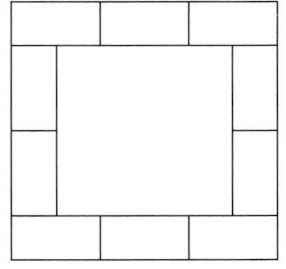
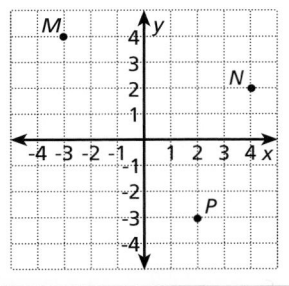

Have students refer back to Lesson 10.4. Then have them provide examples of figures having line symmetry.

Example 2

Discuss how lines of symmetry and reflection lines are related. Ask students: Does every object with a line of symmetry have a reflection line associated with it? Have students explain their answers.

Challenge students to find other examples of objects that have line symmetry.

Communicating
about **MATHEMATICS**

Have students repeat the activity with a variety of other shapes, such as squares, rectangles, and parallelograms. Ask students to write their conclusions.

Writing Prompt
Describe several objects that have
a. a vertical line of symmetry,
b. a horizontal line of symmetry, and
c. both types of symmetry.

Answer To Communicating

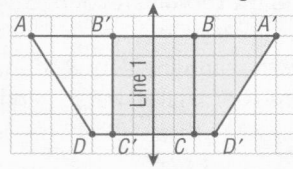

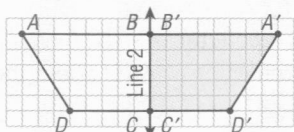

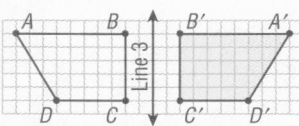

	Area	Perimeter
Original trapezoid	32.5 units²	$18 + \sqrt{34}$ ≈ 23.8 units
New trapezoid 1	45 units²	$18 + 2\sqrt{34}$ ≈ 29.7 units
New trapezoid 2	65 units²	$26 + 2\sqrt{34}$ ≈ 37.7 units
New trapezoid 3	65 units²	$36 + 2\sqrt{34}$ ≈ 47.7 units

Goal **2** **Reflections and Line Symmetry**

In Lesson 10.4, you studied line symmetry. The next example illustrates a connection between line symmetry and reflections.

Example 2 *Reflections and Line Symmetry*

You work for a company that creates patterns for clothing. The pattern shown at the left is marked on a folded piece of cloth. When the cloth is cut and unfolded, you obtain the pieces shown at the right. Which pairs are reflections? Which pieces have line symmetry?

Real Life
Clothing

The pattern pieces in Example 2 can be used to make the shirt above.

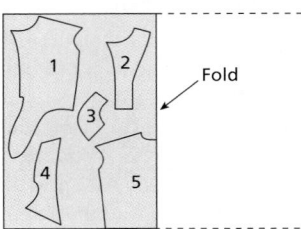

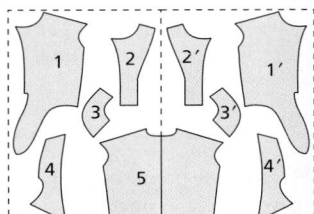

Solution Piece 1′ is a reflection of Piece 1. Piece 2′ is a reflection of Piece 2. Piece 3′ is a reflection of Piece 3. Piece 4′ is a reflection of Piece 4. Piece 5 has line symmetry, because it had one edge lying along the fold. ∎

Communicating *about* **MATHEMATICS**

▶ **SHARING IDEAS about the Lesson**

Area and Perimeter A trapezoid is reflected about the indicated lines. For each line, sketch the figure that consists of the original trapezoid and its image. Compare the area and perimeter of this new figure with the area and perimeter of the original trapezoid. See margin.

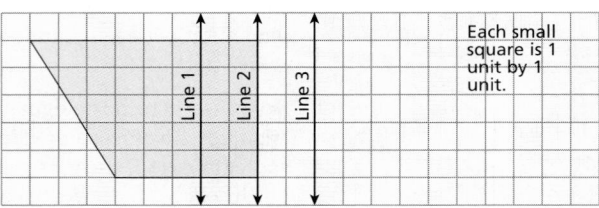

Each small square is 1 unit by 1 unit.

EXERCISES

Guided Practice

▶ CHECK for Understanding

In Exercises 1–4, draw the figure at the right in a coordinate plane. Then draw the indicated reflection. See margin.

1. Reflect the triangle about the *x*-axis.

2. Reflect the triangle about the *y*-axis.

3. Reflect the triangle about Line *p*.

4. Reflect the triangle about Line *q*.

Independent Practice

In Exercises 5–8, name the image of △*ABC* after the indicated reflection(s). (The image is a triangle.)

5. Reflect △*ABC* about the *x*-axis. △*ONM*

6. Reflect △*ABC* about the *y*-axis. △*DEF*

7. Reflect △*ABC* about the *x*-axis, then about the *y*-axis. △*RQP*

8. Reflect △*ABC* about the *y*-axis, then reflect it again about the *y*-axis. △*ABC*

9. *What Do You See?* When you look at yourself in a mirror, your right side appears to be on your left side. Is this also true when you look at a photo of yourself? Explain. See above.

10. *What Do You See?* You are walking by a truck delivery door at the back of a grocery store. A sign by the door reads as follows. Why would the sign be printed this way? See above.

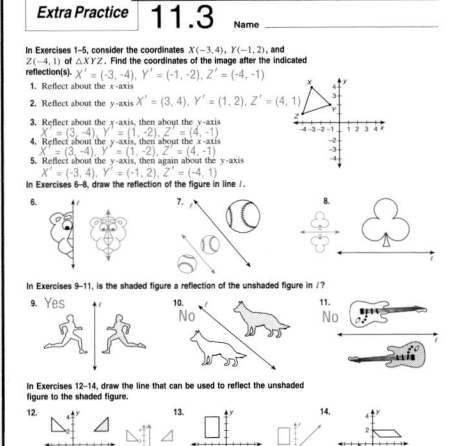

9. No, your right side is duplicated in a photo.
10. The sign is read in a rearview mirror.

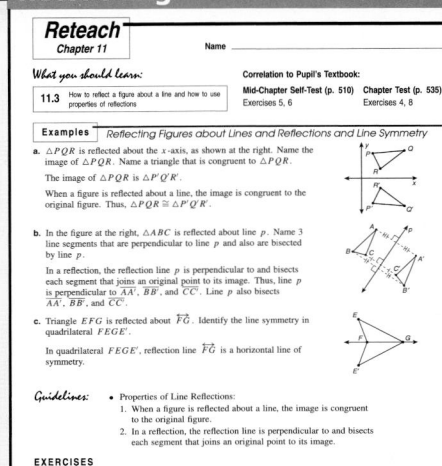

In Exercises 11–14, decide whether the red figure is a reflection of the blue figure in Line ℓ. If not, sketch the reflection of the blue figure. For sketches, see Additional Answers.

11.  No

12. 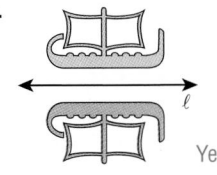 Yes

13. 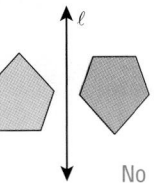 No

14.  Yes

11.3 ▪ Line Reflections **499**

ASSIGNMENT GUIDE

Basic/Average:
  Day 1: Ex. 5–16
  Day 2: Ex. 17–29
Above Average: Ex. 5–9, 11–23 odd, 24–29
Advanced: Ex. 5–9, 11–23 odd, 24–29
Selected Answers: Ex. 1–4, 5–27 odd

Guided Practice

Students should do these problems on graph paper in their groups, so that the paper can actually be folded.

Independent Practice

▶ **Ex. 9** Many extensions of this exercise are possible using standard mirrors.

▶ **Ex. 10** A common application of this type of reflected writing is the word **AMBULANCE** written on the front of an ambulance.

Answers

1.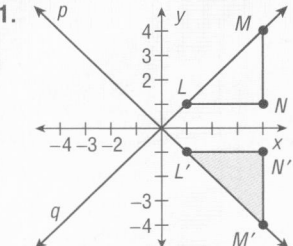

2.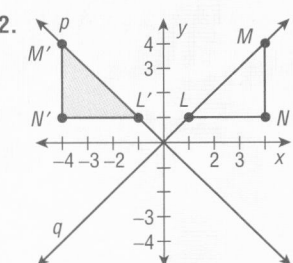

3.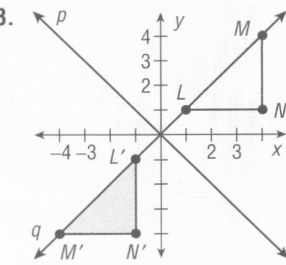

4.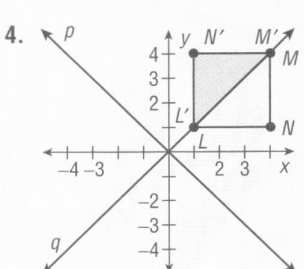

Extra Practice

Extra Practice **11.3** Name _____

In Exercises 1–5, consider the coordinates $X(-3, 4)$, $Y(-1, 2)$, and $Z(-4, 1)$ of △*XYZ*. Find the coordinates of the image after the indicated reflection(s). $X' = (-3, -4)$, $Y' = (-1, -2)$, $Z' = (-4, -1)$

1. Reflect about the *x*-axis

2. Reflect about the *y*-axis $X' = (3, 4)$, $Y' = (1, 2)$, $Z' = (4, 1)$

3. Reflect about the *x*-axis, then about the *y*-axis $X' = (3, -4)$, $Y' = (1, -2)$, $Z' = (4, -1)$

4. Reflect about the *y*-axis, then about the *x*-axis $X' = (3, -4)$, $Y' = (1, -2)$, $Z' = (4, -1)$

5. Reflect about the *y*-axis, then again about the *y*-axis $X' = (-3, 4)$, $Y' = (-1, 2)$, $Z' = (-4, 1)$

In Exercises 6–8, draw the reflection of the figure in line *l*.

In Exercises 9–11, is the shaded figure a reflection of the unshaded figure in *l*?

9. Yes 10. No 11. No

In Exercises 12–14, draw the line that can be used to reflect the unshaded figure to the shaded figure.

15. Which letters of the alphabet look like the same letter when reflected about a vertical line? List them. A, H, I, M, O, T, U, V, W, X, Y

16. Use a mirror to decode the secret message. "TOH OOT HTUOM YM MOM HO" "OH MOM MY MOUTH TOO HOT"

17. Use the letters from Exercise 15 to write your own coded message. Answers vary.

Windows 11.3 ▪ Line Reflections **87**

Reteaching

Reteach Chapter 11 Name _____

What you should learn:

11.3 How to reflect a figure about a line and how to use properties of reflections

Correlation to Pupil's Textbook:
Mid-Chapter Self-Test (p. 510) Chapter Test (p. 535)
Exercises 5, 6 Exercises 4, 8

Examples *Reflecting Figures about Lines and Reflections and Line Symmetry*

a. △*PQR* is reflected about the *x*-axis, as shown at the right. Name the image of △*PQR*. Name a triangle that is congruent to △*PQR*.

The image of △*PQR* is △*P'Q'R'*.

When a figure is reflected about a line, the image is congruent to the original figure. Thus, △*PQR* ≅ △*P'Q'R'*.

b. In the figure at the right, △*ABC* is reflected about line *p*. Name 3 line segments that are perpendicular to line *p* and also are bisected by line *p*.

In a reflection, the reflection line *p* is perpendicular to and bisects each segment that joins an original point to its image. Thus, line *p* is perpendicular to $\overline{AA'}$, $\overline{BB'}$, and $\overline{CC'}$. Line *p* also bisects $\overline{AA'}$, $\overline{BB'}$, and $\overline{CC'}$.

c. Triangle *EFG* is reflected about $\overleftrightarrow{FG}$. Identify the line symmetry in quadrilateral *FEGE'*.

In quadrilateral *FEGE'*, reflection line $\overleftrightarrow{FG}$ is a horizontal line of symmetry.

Guidelines: ▪ Properties of Line Reflections:
  1. When a figure is reflected about a line, the image is congruent to the original figure.
  2. In a reflection, the reflection line is perpendicular to and bisects each segment that joins an original point to its image.

EXERCISES

In Exercises 1–4, name the image of △*RST* after the indicated reflection(s).

1. Reflect △*RST* about the *y*-axis. *DEF*
2. Reflect △*RST* about the *x*-axis. *GHI*
3. Reflect △*RST* about the *y*-axis, then about the *x*-axis. *ABC*
4. Reflect △*RST* about the *x*-axis, then about the *y*-axis. *ABC*

Windows Chapter 11 ▪ Congruence, Similarity, and Transformations **87**

Lesson 11.3 **499**

► **Ex. 15, 16** Ask students to generalize what happens to the ordered pair (x, y) when it is reflected about the x-axis and y-axis.

► **Ex. 23, 24**

EXTENSION

Introduce the concept that the *angle of incidence* is equal in measure to the *angle of reflection*. Vary the size of the pool table and have students investigate where the ball starts, finishes, and so on.

Integrated Review

These exercises are a lighthearted review of the meaning of line symmetry.

Exploration and Extension

COOPERATIVE PROJECT

Work with the art department on similar cooperative projects. For example, students could cut one half of a face out of a magazine and use reflections to sketch what the missing half would look like.

Portfolio Opportunity: Math Log

Consider the points A(1, 2), B(3, 4), and C(5, 1) in a coordinate plane. Reflect each point about the given line ℓ. Find the coordinates of A′, B′, and C′ of the image.

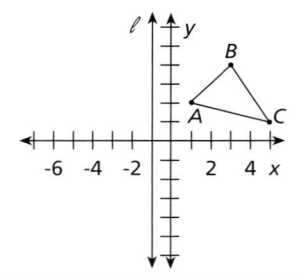

Also available as a copymaster, page 34, Ex. 3

Coordinate Geometry   In Exercises 15 and 16, sketch △*ABC* in a coordinate plane. Then sketch the images when the triangle is reflected about the x-axis and the y-axis. See Additional Answers.

15. A(1, 3), B(4, 1), C(2, −1)   **16.** A(0, 1), B(−2, −2), C(2, −2)

Coordinate Geometry   In Exercises 17–20, draw the figures in a coordinate plane. Then draw the line that can be used to reflect the blue figure to the red figure. See Additional Answers.

17. 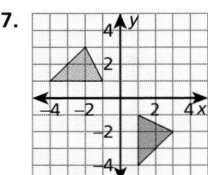   **18.** 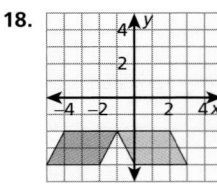   **19.** 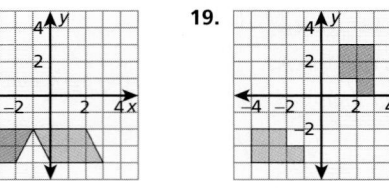   **20.**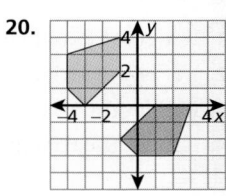

✪ **21.** *Repeated Reflections*   In a coordinate
Ⓟ plane, reflect a rectangle four times: first about the x-axis, then the y-axis, then the x-axis, and then the y-axis. Compare the final image with the original rectangle. See margin.

Ⓟ **22.** *Alphabet Reflection*   Which capital letters of the alphabet remain the same when reflected about a vertical line? Which letters remain the same when reflected about a horizontal line? See margin.

Playing Pool   **In Exercises 23 and 24, use the diagram at the right.**

23. The ball is shot from point (0, 3). Describe the line of reflection of its path. The line x = 4

✪ **24.** Suppose you shoot the ball in the same direction from point (0, 2). Sketch the path of the ball. Does the line of reflection change? No

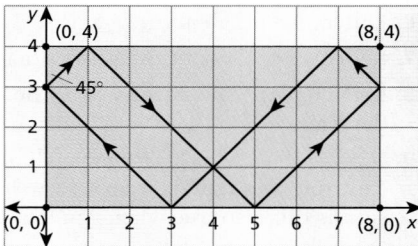

Integrated Review   *Making Connections within Mathematics*

Symmetrical Faces   **In Exercises 25–28, state whether the face has line symmetry. Which faces are reflections of each other?** Exercises 25 and 28

25.    **26.**    **27.**    **28.**

No   Yes   Yes   No

Exploration and Extension

✪ **29.** *Symmetrical Faces*   Find photographs in magazines or newspapers of faces that appear to have line symmetry and of faces that appear not to have line symmetry. Which type of photo is easier to find? Check students' work. Answers vary.

✪ More difficult exercises
Ⓟ Portfolio Opportunity

500   *Chapter 11* ▪ *Congruence, Similarity, and Transformations*

Answers
21. They are congruent and in the same place.
22. Vertical: A, H, I, M, O, T, U, V, W, X; horizontal: B, C, D, E, H, I, K, O, X

Mixed REVIEW

In Exercises 1–3, sketch two *noncongruent* trapezoids that have the given measures. Find the area of each. (11.1) For sample figures, see margin.

1. $b_1 = 6, b_2 = 12, h = 2$
18 units^2

2. $b_1 = 7, b_2 = 8, h = 4$
30 units^2

3. $b_1 = 1, b_2 = 9, h = 1$
5 units^2

In Exercises 4–7, rewrite the decimal as a simplified fraction. (6.6)

4. $0.\overline{1}$ $\frac{1}{9}$

5. $0.\overline{2}$ $\frac{2}{9}$

6. $0.\overline{3}$ $\frac{1}{3}$

7. $0.\overline{4}$ $\frac{4}{9}$

8. Use the result of Exercises 4–7 to describe a quick way to rewrite $\frac{n}{9}$ as a decimal. Write as $0.\overline{n}$

In Exercises 9–12, rewrite as a decimal. Round to two places. (6.7)

9. $\frac{8}{15}$ 0.53

10. $3\frac{2}{7}$ 3.29

11. $-\frac{8}{7}$ -1.14

12. $-4\frac{5}{6}$ -4.83

In Exercises 13–16, find the percent increase or decrease. (8.6)

13. Before: $42.12 **After:** $40.18 ≈ 4.6% decrease

14. Before: 3.6 lb **After:** 7.6 lb ≈ 111.1% increase

15. Before: 77.1° **After:** 66.1° ≈ 14.3% decrease

16. Before: 4.4 ft **After:** 6.3 ft ≈ 43.2% increase

Career Interview

Research Scientist

Carol Stoker is a research scientist at NASA Ames Research Center in Moffett Field, California. She has spent the past two years working in Antarctica because its environment most closely mirrors the conditions astronauts would face on the Moon and Mars.

Q: *What led you into this career?*
A: My primary interest has always been anything to do with the human exploration of Mars.

Q: *What math do you use in your work?*
A: I use lots of algebra, geometry, and calculus. Although I am always using computers, I must do the thinking. I need to understand the logic behind why things work.

Q: *What would you like to tell kids in school about math?*
A: Math is important for coping with everyday life decisions, not just for high-tech careers. Living in Antarctica where Radio Shack and K-Mart are not around the corner, I must estimate and order what supplies I will need for my entire trip. If a piece of equipment breaks, I can't just call out for repairs. I must use my problem-solving skills to figure out the solution on my own.

Answers to Mixed Review

1.

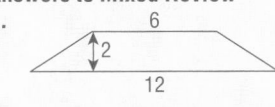

2.
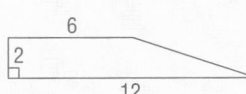
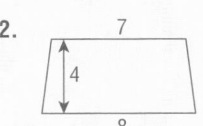

3.
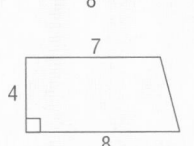
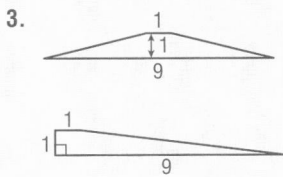

PACING the Lesson

Suggested Number of Days
Basic/Average 0 Above Average 2
Advanced 2

PLANNING the Lesson

Lesson Plan 11.4, p. 88

ORGANIZER

Starters (reproduced below)
Problem of the Day 11.4, p. 32
Warm-Up Exercises 11.4, p. 32
Lesson Resources
Color Transparencies
Picture for Lesson Investigation, p. 45
Teaching Tools,
Dot paper, pp. T2, C3
Coordinate planes, pp. T9, C11
Math Log, p. 34
Answer Masters 11.4, p. 219
Extra Practice Copymaster 11.4, p. 88
Reteaching Copymaster 11.4, p. 88
Special Populations
Suggestions, Teacher's Edition, p. 486D

LESSON Notes

Rotations are frequently used in the design of machinery, buildings, and commercial art. Ask students to identify rotations in everyday objects.

Example 1

Be sure students can identify each original point (*B*, for example) and its image (*B′*), before they attempt to construct the rotation angle (∠*BOB′*), where *O* is the origin in the coordinate plane. Have students determine the angle measure for each rotation of this example.

11.4 Rotations

What you should learn:

Goal 1 How to rotate a figure about a point

Goal 2 How to use properties of rotations to answer questions about real-life situations

Why you should learn it:

You can use properties of rotations to answer questions about real life, such as finding the angle of rotation of the minute hand of a clock.

Study Tip...
In Example 1, notice the patterns when an object is rotated 90° or 180° counterclockwise about the origin. For 90°, the point (*x, y*) is rotated to the point (−*y, x*). What is the pattern for 180°?

Goal 1 **Rotating Figures about Points**

In Lesson 11.3, you studied one type of **transformation**—a reflection about a line. In this lesson, you will study another type of transformation—a **rotation** about a point. Three examples are shown below.

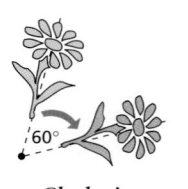 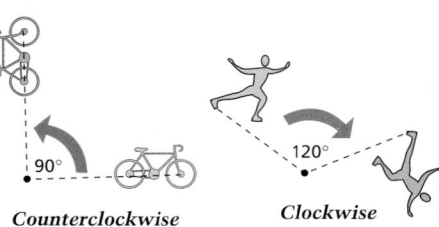

Clockwise rotation of 60°   *Counterclockwise rotation of 90°*   *Clockwise rotation of 120°*

Example 1 *Finding an Angle of Rotation*

The blue figure is rotated about the origin to become the red figure. Find the angle of rotation. Find the image's vertices.

a. 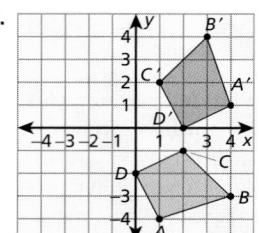 b.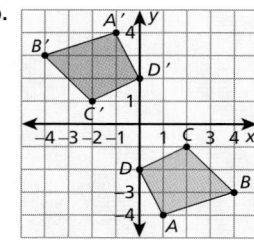

Solution

a. The blue figure is rotated counterclockwise 90°. The vertices of the original figure and the image are as follows.

$A(1, -4)$, $B(4, -3)$, $C(2, -1)$, $D(0, -2)$
$A'(4, 1)$, $B'(3, 4)$, $C'(1, 2)$, $D'(2, 0)$

b. The blue figure is rotated clockwise 180°. The vertices of the original figure and the image are as follows.

$A(1, -4)$, $B(4, -3)$, $C(2, -1)$, $D(0, -2)$
$A'(-1, 4)$, $B'(-4, 3)$, $C'(-2, 1)$, $D'(0, 2)$ ∎

502   *Chapter 11 • Congruence, Similarity, and Transformations*

LESSON INVESTIGATION

■ **Investigating Rotations about a Point**

Group Activity Copy each figure onto dot paper. Then copy the figure onto a piece of tracing paper. Rotate the figure the indicated number of degrees about Point *P*. Is the image congruent to the original figure? Yes

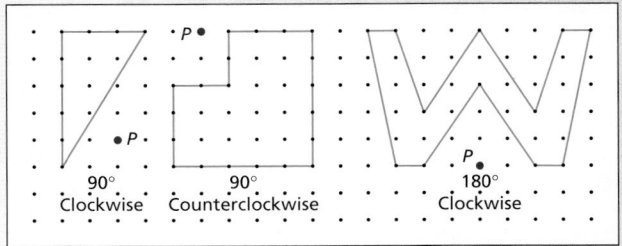

90°
Clockwise

90°
Counterclockwise

180°
Clockwise

Rotational symmetry is a special case of a rotation in which the figure fits back on itself.

In this investigation, you may have discovered that rotating a figure produces a congruent figure. Lengths, perimeters, and areas are not changed by rotations. Orientations of figures and locations of points *are* changed. For instance, when the number 6 is rotated 180°, it becomes the number 9.

Communicating about **MATHEMATICS**

▶ **SHARING IDEAS about the Lesson**

Rotating Clock Hands Each pair of clocks shows a beginning time and an ending time. Find the angle of rotation of the minute hand. Explain how you obtained the angle.

A.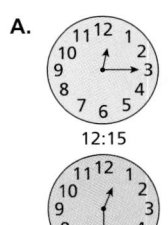
12:15

12:30

B.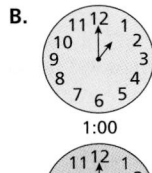
1:00

2:00

C.
2:22

2:45

$\frac{1}{4} \times 360° = 90°$

$\times 360° = 360°$

$\frac{23}{60} \times 360° = 138°$

11.4 ▪ *Rotations*   **503**

Communicating
about **MATHEMATICS**

If students have combination locks on their lockers, challenge them to describe the rotations involved in opening their lockers. (If students do not use such locks, you may want to bring a combination lock to class and demonstrate its use.)

Writing Prompt
Have students write in their journals an answer to Ex. 5 of Guided Practice.

ASSIGNMENT GUIDE

*Basic/Average:
Day 1: Ex. 7–13 odd, 15–18, 20–23, 27–30
Day 2: Ex. 8–14 even, 19, 24–26, 31–34

Above Average:
Day 1: Ex. 7–13, 15–18, 20–23, 27–30
Day 2: Ex. 8–14 even, 19, 24–26, 31–34

Advanced:
Day 1: Ex. 7–21 odd
Day 2: Ex. 23–29 odd, 31–34

Selected Answers: Ex. 1–6, 7–29 odd

*You may wish to omit this lesson for these students.

Guided Practice

Use these exercises as a think/share activity for students working with partners.

Independent Practice

▶ **Ex. 7–10** If students are having difficulty with these, you may wish to offer them tracing paper.

▶ **Ex. 15–18** Assign these exercises as a group. Students should begin by first determining the coordinates of △A′B′C′.

504 *Chapter 11*

EXERCISES

Guided Practice

▶ **CHECK for Understanding**

cl = clockwise, cc = counterclockwise

In Exercises 1–4, the blue figure has been rotated to produce the red figure. Estimate the angle and direction of the rotation.

1. 60° cl or 300° cc   2. 90° cc or 270° cl   3. 120° cc or 240° cl
4. 60° cc or 300° cl

1. 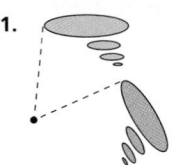   2. 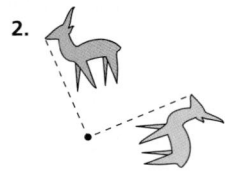   3. 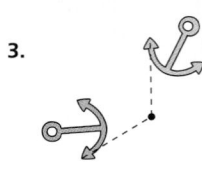   4.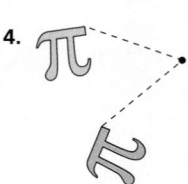

P **5.** Describe the relationship between rotations and rotational symmetry.
Rotational symmetry is a special case of a rotation in which the figure fits back on itself.

P **6.** *The Shape of Things* Describe two objects in your classroom that are rotations of each other. Answers vary.

Independent Practice

In Exercises 7–10, the blue figure is rotated clockwise about the origin to produce the red figure. Find the angle of rotation.

7.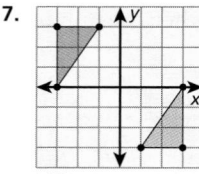
180°

8.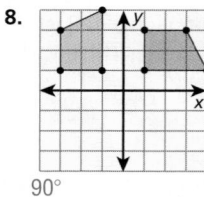
90°

9.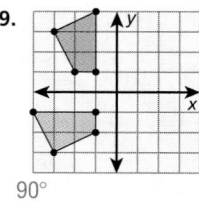
90°

10.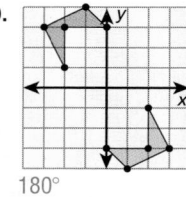
180°

In Exercises 11–14, estimate the angle and direction of rotation.

11.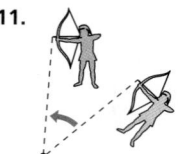
45° counterclockwise

12.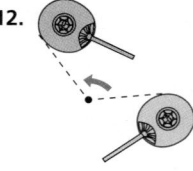
120° counterclockwise

13.
60° clockwise

14.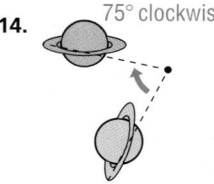
75° clockwise

In Exercises 15–18, △ABC is rotated 90° clockwise about the origin to produce △A′B′C′.

15. Find the measure of each.
   a. $\overline{A'C'}$ 4   **b.** $\overline{B'C'}$ 2   **c.** $\overline{A'B'}$ $\sqrt{20}$

16. What type of angle is ∠C′?   Right

17. Find the perimeter of △A′B′C′. Explain. $(6 + \sqrt{20})$ units

18. Find the area of △A′B′C′. Explain. 4 units²

17., 18. The perimeter and area are equal to those of △ABC.

504 *Chapter 11* • *Congruence, Similarity, and Transformations*   **P** Portfolio Opportunity

---

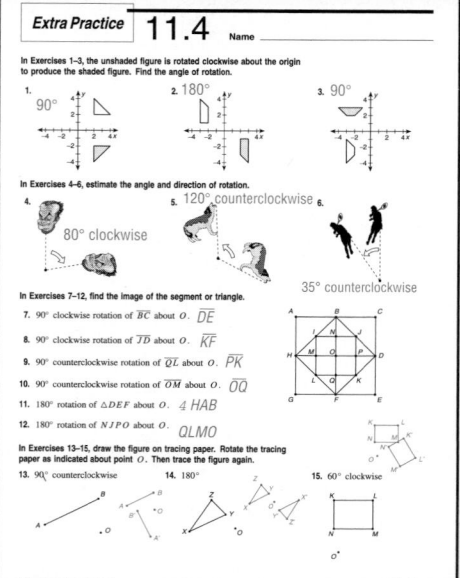
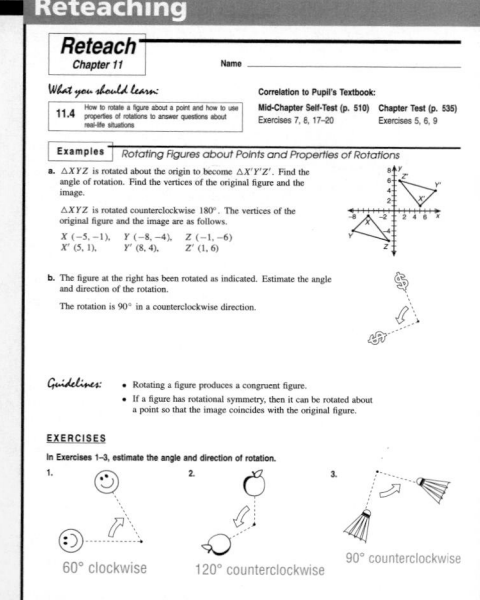

In Exercises 19–21, draw the figure on tracing paper. Rotate the tracing paper 90° clockwise about point *P*. Then trace the figure again. Check students' work.

19.

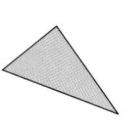

20.

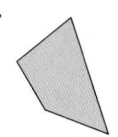

21.

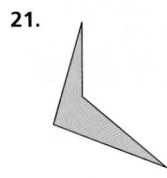

• *P*

P •

P •

In Exercises 22–26, find the image of the point, segment, or triangle.

22. 60° clockwise rotation of *D* about *E* B

23. 60° clockwise rotation of $\overline{BC}$ about *E* $\overline{CF}$

24. 60° counterclockwise rotation of △*ABC* about *C* △*BEC*

25. 180° rotation of $\overline{AC}$ about *C* $\overline{FC}$

26. 120° clockwise rotation of $\overline{CF}$ about *C* $\overline{CB}$

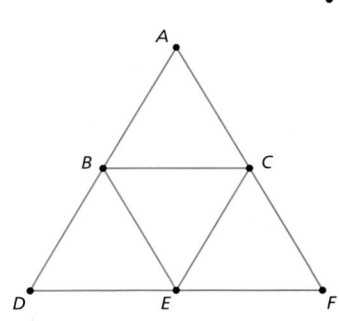

Integrated Review

Making Connections within Mathematics

Rotational Symmetry In Exercises 27–30, find the smallest angle that the figure can be rotated to coincide with itself.

27.

90°

28.

72°

29.

30°

30.

180°

Exploration and Extension

Reflections and Rotations In Exercises 31–34, use the figure at the right. **31.–33.** See figures at the right.

31. Copy the figure onto dot paper. Include the labels.

32. Reflect △*ABC* in Line *m* to produce △*DEF*.

33. Reflect △*DEF* in Line *n* to produce △*GHI*.

34. What single transformation relates △*ABC* to △*GHI*?
A 90° clockwise rotation about *P*

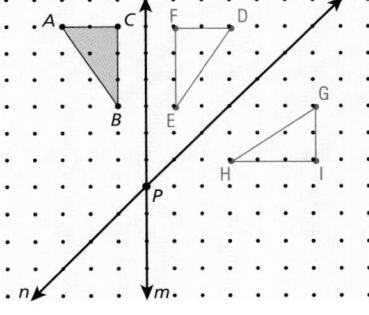

✪ More difficult exercises

▶ **Ex. 19–21** These problems could be used as a class activity to reinforce the idea of rotations.

▶ **Ex. 22–26** Students may need tracing paper. Problems could also be modeled at the overhead projector by individual students.

Integrated Review

▶ **Ex. 27–30**

EXTENSION
Have students do a poster of logos with rotational and/or reflectional symmetry.

Exploration and Extension

▶ **Ex. 31–34** Assign these exercises as a group. The goal of these problems is to generalize that when a figure is reflected about intersecting lines, it is equivalent to a rotation about the point of intersection, and the angle of rotation is twice the measure of the angle between the intersecting lines.

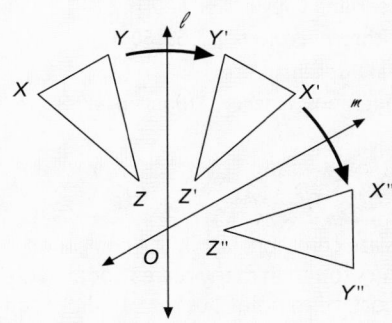

EXTENSION
Have students investigate what happens when the reflections occur about two *parallel* lines.

Portfolio Opportunity: Math Log

What can be determined about the symmetry of a figure when a 180° rotation produces the same image as a reflection.

Also available as a copymaster, page 34, Ex. 4

Short Quiz

Covers Lessons 11.3 and 11.4

Available as a copymaster, page 176

PACING the Lesson

Suggested Number of Days
Basic/Average 0   **Above Average** 2
Advanced 2

PLANNING the Lesson

Lesson Plan 11.5, p. 89

ORGANIZER

Starters (reproduced below)
Problem of the Day 11.5, p. 32
Warm-Up Exercises 11.5, p. 32
Lesson Resources
Color Transparencies
Picture for Communicating, p. 46
Math Log, p. 35
Technology, pp. 64–66
Answer Masters 11.5, pp. 220, 221
Extra Practice Copymaster 11.5, p. 89
Reteaching Copymaster 11.5, p. 89
Enrichment Projects, pp. 59, 60
Special Populations
Suggestions, Teacher's Edition, p. 486D

LESSON Notes

Slides are common within the computer graphics found in many recreational games. It is important to point out that all slides can be decomposed into a combination of horizontal and vertical movements.

Example 1

Ask students whether, in part **a,** slides of 6 units down and 5 units to the right would produce the same results as in the example.
Yes
   Ask: Does a slide of 7 units down and 4 units to the left produce the same image as found in part **b**?   Yes

11.5 Translations

What you should learn:

Goal 1 How to translate a figure in a plane

Goal 2 How to represent translations in a coordinate plane

Why you should learn it:

You can use translations to perform real-life actions, such as creating a computer graphic.

Goal 1   Translating Figures in a Plane

The third type of transformation you will study is a **translation** (or **slide**). When a figure is translated, each point of the figure is moved the same distance. The image of a translation is congruent to the original *and* has the same orientation as the original. The only difference between the original and the image is their locations in the plane.

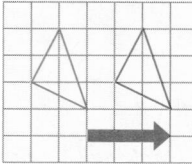 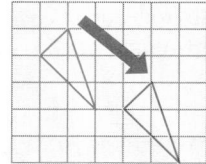

Slide 3 units right   *Slide 4 units down*   *Slide 3 units right and 2 units down*

Example 1   *Drawing Translations*

Draw each figure on dot paper. Then translate the figure the direction and distance indicated by the arrow. Write a verbal description of the translation.

a.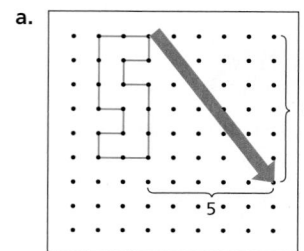

b.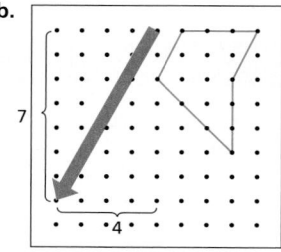

Solution   The translated figures are shown at the left.

a. This figure has been translated 5 units to the right and 6 units down.

b. This figure has been translated 4 units to the left and 7 units down. ■

506   *Chapter 11 • Congruence, Similarity, and Transformations*

STARTER: Problem of the Day

How many triangles are there?   13

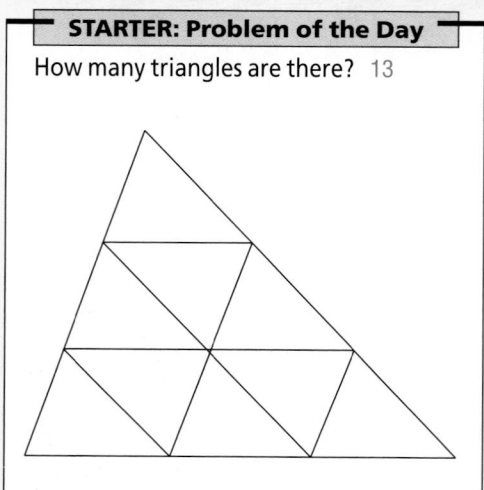

Also available as a copymaster, p. 32

STARTER: Warm-Up Exercises

1. Describe the horizontal and vertical routes needed to go from point A to point B in each diagram.

a.   **b.**

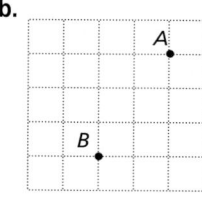

a. 4 units right, 3 units up; **b.** 2 units left, 3 units down

2. Evaluate each expression for the given values of x or y.
a. $x + 2$ for $x = 3, 5, -1$ 5, 7, 1
b. $y - 3$ for $y = 2, -3, 0$ $-1, -6, -3$

Also available as a copymaster, p. 32

Transformations (reflections, rotations, and translations) are used in computer graphics to produce animated motion.

Translating in a Coordinate Plane

Example **2**   *Translating in a Coordinate Plane*

Draw the parallelogram whose vertices are $A(-4, 3)$, $B(-1, 4)$, $C(3, 3)$, $D(0, 2)$. Then use the following motion rule to translate each vertex.

Original Figure		Image
(x, y)	$\Rightarrow$	$(x + 2, y - 5)$

Finally, write a verbal description of the transformation.

Solution The motion rule tells you to add 2 to each x-coordinate and subtract 5 from each y-coordinate.

Original		Image
$A(-4, 3)$	$\Rightarrow$	$A'(-2, -2)$
$B(-1, 4)$	$\Rightarrow$	$B'(1, -1)$
$C(3, 3)$	$\Rightarrow$	$C'(5, -2)$
$D(0, 2)$	$\Rightarrow$	$D'(2, -3)$

You can describe this translation verbally as *each point is slid 2 units to the right and 5 units down.* ∎

Communicating about **MATHEMATICS**

▶ **SHARING IDEAS about the Lesson**

Computer Graphics You are working as a computer artist for a company that produces animations. What type of transformation is used to move the penguin from each screen to the next?

Translation   Rotation

A. 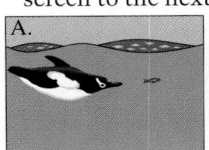   B.    C.

D.    E.    F.

Reflection   Translation   Translation

11.5 • *Translations*   **507**

A geoboard and dot paper are concrete models of a coordinate plane. Note that coordinate planes are used to locate positions on a computer screen or a calculator display.

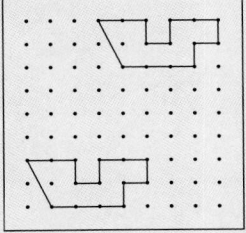

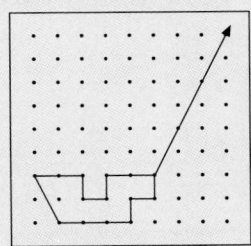

EXERCISE Notes

ASSIGNMENT GUIDE

*Basic/Average:
Day 1: Ex. 9–12, 17–23 odd
Day 2: Ex. 13, 14, 24–26, 30

Above Average:
Day 1: Ex. 9–12, 17–23 odd, 27–29
Day 2: Ex. 13, 14, 24–26, 30

Advanced:
Day 1: Ex. 9–14, 16–19
Day 2: Ex. 20–23, 27–30

Selected Answers: Ex. 1–8, 9–29 odd

*You may wish to omit this lesson for these students.

Guided Practice

▶ **Ex. 5–8** These exercises review the three transformations: reflections, rotations, and translations.

Independent Practice

▶ **Ex. 13–15** Assign these exercises as a group. Students may need help with Ex. 15. They should *not* try to apply the area formula for a trapezoid, since this results in a rather difficult expression involving radicals. A simpler approach is to dissect the trapezoid into a square whose area is $\sqrt{5} \cdot \sqrt{5} = 5$ and a triangle whose area is one half the area of the square.

EXERCISES

Guided Practice

▶ **CHECK for Understanding**

In Exercises 1–4, describe the translation verbally. See margin.

1. 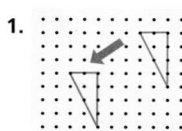   **2.** 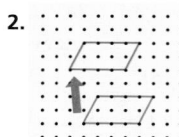   **3.** 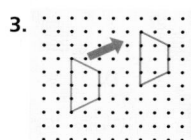   **4.**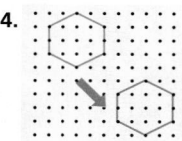

In Exercises 5–8, describe the transformation that maps the blue figure to the red figure. See margin.

5. 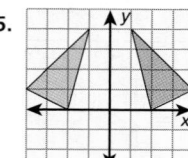   **6.** 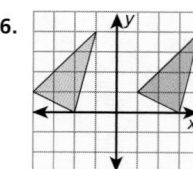   **7.** 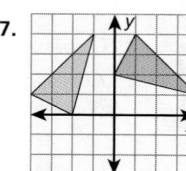   **8.**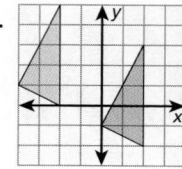

Independent Practice

For descriptions, see margin.

In Exercises 9–12, match the graph with the ordered pair that describes the translation. Then describe the translation verbally.

a. 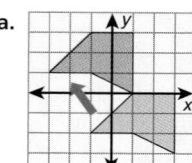   **b.** 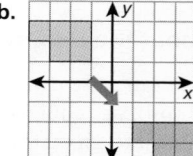   **c.** 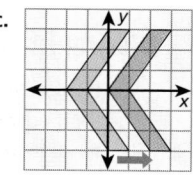   **d.**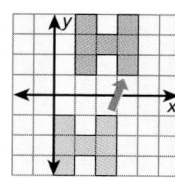

9. $(x + 2, y)$ c   **10.** $(x - 2, y + 3)$ a   **11.** $(x + 5, y - 5)$ b   **12.** $(x + 1, y + 5)$ d

13. Draw a trapezoid whose vertices are $A(-3, 3)$, $B(-1, 4)$, $C(2, 3)$, and $D(-2, 1)$. Then translate the trapezoid as indicated. See Additional Answers.

  a. 3 units to the left and 6 units down   **b.** 4 units to the right and 2 units down

  c. 5 units to the right and 3 units up   **d.** 1 unit to the left and 2 units up

14. The motion rule for the translation in Exercise 13a is $(x - 3, y - 6)$. Write the motion rule for the other three translations. **b.** $(x+4, y-2)$ **c.** $(x+5, y+3)$ **d.** $(x-1, y+$

15. Find the area of the trapezoid in Exercise 13. Then use the result to find the area of each of the translated trapezoids. Each area is $7\frac{1}{2}$ units².

Answers

1. Slide the figure 5 units to the left and 3 units down.
2. Slide the figure 1 unit to the left and 4 units up.
3. Slide the figure 5 units to the right and 2 units up.
4. Slide the figure 5 units to the right and 5 units down.
5. Reflect the figure in the *y*-axis.
6. Slide the figure 5 units to the right.
7. Rotate the figure 90° clockwise about the origin.
8. Slide the figure 4 units to the right and 2 units down.
9. Slide the figure 2 units to the right.
10. Slide the figure 2 units to the left and 3 units up.
11. Slide the figure 5 units to the right and 5 units down.
12. Slide the figure 1 unit to the right and 5 units up.

Extra Practice

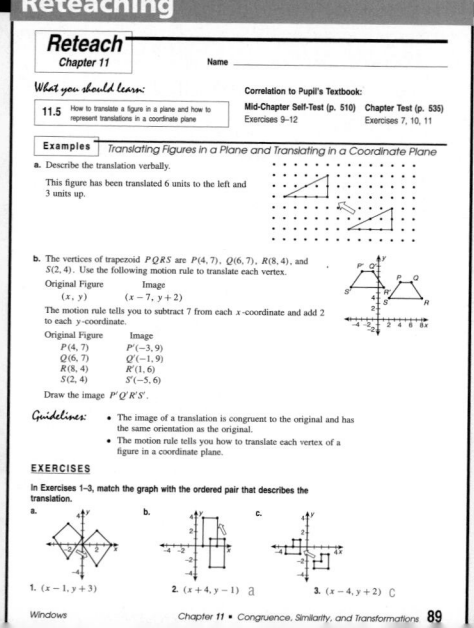

Extra Practice   **11.5**   Name _____

In Exercises 1–3, match the graph with the ordered pair that describes the translation. Then describe the translation verbally.

a.   b.   c.

     b.; 5 units left,   c.; 3 units left,
1. $(x - 5, y + 6)$ 6 units up   **2.** $(x - 3, y - 5)$ 5 units down   **3.** $(x - 5, y - 4)$

In Exercises 4–6, use the figure at the right to match the translation of $\square ABCD$ to $\square A'B'C'D'$ with the ordered pair that describes the translation.

  a.; 5 units left, 4 units down
a. $A'(1, 4)$, $B'(4, 5)$, $C'(5, 9)$, $D'(2, 8)$
b. $A'(2, 1)$, $B'(5, 2)$, $C'(6, 6)$, $D'(3, 5)$
c. $A'(3, 2)$, $B'(6, 3)$, $C'(7, 7)$, $D'(4, 6)$

4. $(x + 1, y)$ C   **5.** $(x - 1, y + 2)$ a   **6.** $(x, y - 1)$ b

In Exercises 7–9, use a straightedge and dot paper to translate the figure by the ordered pair.

7. $(x + 1, y + 1)$ **8.** $(x - 1, y - 2)$ **9.** $(x, y - 1)$

10. Find the name of Carl's dog. The dog's name has five letters. Given are the four ordered pairs that enable you to find the pup's name. Start at (1, 1) on the grid and write down each letter you land on according to the transformation.
1. Start at (1, 1)
2. $(x + 3, y + 7)$
3. $(x - 2, y - 4)$
4. $(x + 5, y - 2)$
5. $(x + 2, y + 7)$ ANGEL

11. Write your own message by giving the ordered pair transformations and a starting point.   Answers vary.

Windows   11.5 • Translations **89**

Reteaching

Reteach   Chapter 11   Name _____

What you should learn:
11.5 How to translate a figure in a plane and how to represent translations in a coordinate plane

Correlation to Pupil's Textbook:
Mid-Chapter Self-Test (p. 510)   Chapter Test (p. 535)
Exercises 9–12   Exercises 7, 10, 11

Examples   *Translating Figures in a Plane and Translating in a Coordinate Plane*

a. Describe the translation verbally.
This figure has been translated 6 units to the left and 3 units up.

b. The vertices of trapezoid $PQRS$ are $P(4, 7)$, $Q(6, 7)$, $R(8, 4)$, and $S(2, 4)$. Use the following motion rule to translate each vertex.

   Original Figure   Image
   (x, y) $(x - 7, y + 2)$
The motion rule tells you to subtract 7 from each *x*-coordinate and add 2 to each *y*-coordinate.

   Original Figure   Image
   $P(4, 7)$ $P'(-3, 9)$
   $Q(6, 7)$ $Q'(-1, 9)$
   $R(8, 4)$ $R'(1, 6)$
   $S(2, 4)$ $S'(-5, 6)$
Draw the image $P'Q'R'S'$.

Guidelines: • The image of a translation is congruent to the original and has the same orientation as the original.
• The motion rule tells you how to translate each vertex of a figure in a coordinate plane.

EXERCISES

In Exercises 1–3, match the graph with the ordered pair that describes the translation.

a.   b.   c.

1. $(x - 1, y + 3)$ **2.** $(x + 4, y - 1)$ a   **3.** $(x - 4, y + 2)$ C

Windows   Chapter 11 • Congruence, Similarity, and Transformations **89**

In Exercises 16–19, copy the figure and translate it twice, as indicated by the arrows. Is the final image a translation of the original figure? If so, describe the single translation that will produce the final image. For descriptions, see margin.

16.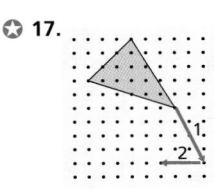

Yes

17.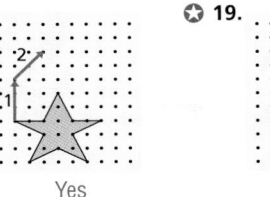

Yes

18.

Yes

19.

Yes

In Exercises 20–23, use the points *A*(0, 1), *B*(3, 4), and *C*(1, 5). Write the vertices of the image of △*ABC* after it has been translated by the given motion rule. See margin.

20. $(x, y + 7)$ **21.** $(x - 1, y + 1)$ **22.** $(x + 2, y - 3)$ **23.** $(x + 3, y + 4)$

24. Draw a triangle in a coordinate plane, and translate the triangle. What can you observe about the line segments that connect the vertices of the original triangle to the corresponding vertices of the image?
They are congruent and parallel.

Flying in Alabama **In Exercises 25 and 26, use the map at the right. The degree markings indicate the longitude (vertical lines) and latitude (horizontal lines).**

25. You leave Mobile and fly 2.9° north and 1.5° east. Are you flying to Birmingham or Montgomery? Explain. Montgomery is only 1.8° north.

26. You are flying from Huntsville to Mobile. Describe the translation that will take you there.
Fly 4° south and 1.7° west.

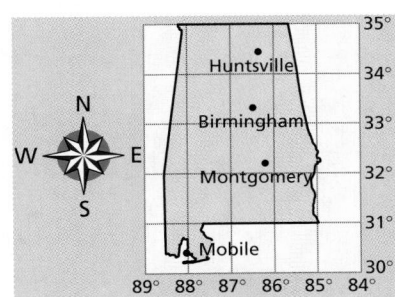

Integrated Review

Paper Folding **In Exercises 27–29, fold a piece of paper as shown at the right. Cut out a trapezoid and unfold the paper.** See margin.

27. How are the first and second trapezoids related?

28. How are the first and fourth trapezoids related?

29. How are the second and fourth trapezoids related?

Making Connections within Mathematics

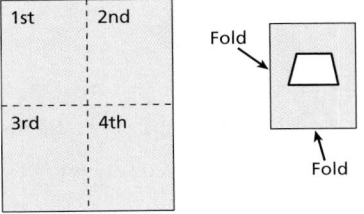

Exploration and Extension

30. *Animation* Create your own animation of at least 6 screens using the three types of transformations. Then explain the transformation that is used from each screen to the next. Check students' work.

✪ More difficult exercises
P Portfolio Opportunity

11.5 ▪ Translations **509**

Take this test as you would take a test in class. The answers to the exercises are given in the back of the book.

In Exercises 1–4, use the congruent triangles at the right to complete the statement. (11.2)

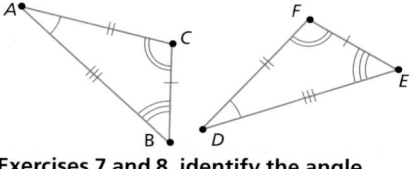

1. $\angle A \cong$ [?] $\angle D$
2. $\angle F \cong$ [?] $\angle C$
3. $\overline{AB} \cong$ [?] $\overline{DE}$
4. [?] $\cong \overline{DF}\,\overline{AC}$

In Exercises 5 and 6, identify the line of reflection. (11.3)

5.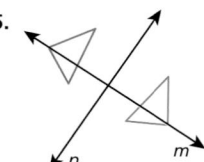

6.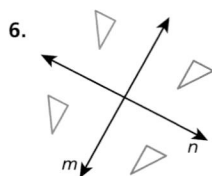

In Exercises 7 and 8, identify the angle and direction of the rotation. (11.4)

7.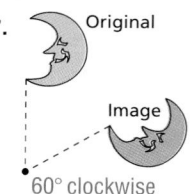
Original
Image
60° clockwise

8.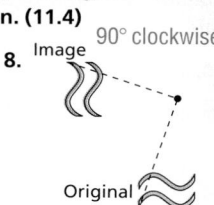
Image
90° clockwise
Original

In Exercises 9–12, write a verbal description of the translation. (11.5) See margin.

9.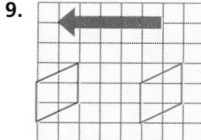
10.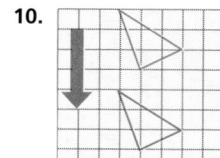
11.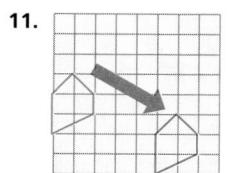
12.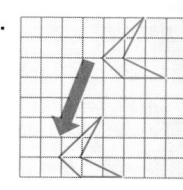

In Exercises 13–16, match the area expression with its polygon. (11.1)

a. $\frac{1}{2}$(Base)(Height)   b. (Base)(Height)   c. (Base)^2 d. $\frac{1}{2}$(Base 1 + Base 2)(Height)

13.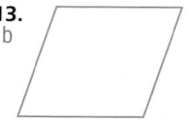
b

14.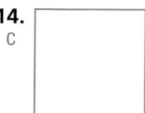
c

15.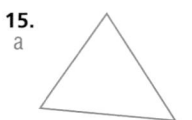
a

16.
d

In Exercises 17–20, use the carousel at the right.

17. Suppose all 8 horses are congruent. Describe the symmetry of the carousel. At 45°, 90°, 135°, 180°

18. Suppose every other horse is congruent. Describe the symmetry of the carousel. At 90°, 180°

19. Suppose every fourth horse is congruent. Describe the symmetry of the carousel. At 180°

20. The carousel rotates 15° per second. How long does it take to make one complete revolution? 24 seconds

17.–19. Rotational symmetry in either direction

Answers
9. Slide the figure 5 units to the left.
10. Slide the figure 4 units down.
11. Slide the figure 5 units to the right and 2 units down.
12. Slide the figure 2 units to the left and 5 units down.

Alternative Assessment ▶

A **Partner Quiz** assesses students' achievement and provides them with an opportunity to communicate about mathematics.
Available as copymaster, page 54

Formal Assessment ▶

Two **Mid-Chapter Tests** of average difficulty.
Available as copymasters, pages 177, 178

510   Chapter 11

Partner Quiz

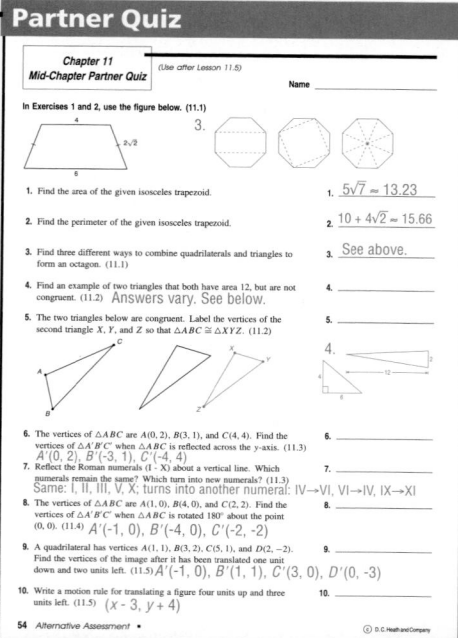

Chapter 11
Mid-Chapter Partner Quiz   (Use after Lesson 11.5)
Name _____

In Exercises 1 and 2, use the figure below. (11.1)

3.

1. Find the area of the given isosceles trapezoid.   1. $5\sqrt{7} \approx 13.23$
2. Find the perimeter of the given isosceles trapezoid.   2. $10 + 4\sqrt{2} \approx 15.66$
3. Find three different ways to combine quadrilaterals and triangles to form an octagon. (11.1)   3. See above.
4. Find an example of two triangles that both have area 12, but are not congruent. (11.2)   4. Answers vary. See below.
5. The two triangles below are congruent. Label the vertices of the second triangle X, Y, and Z so that $\triangle ABC \cong \triangle XYZ$. (11.2)   5.
6. The vertices of $\triangle ABC$ are $A(0, 2)$, $B(3, 1)$, and $C(4, 4)$. Find the vertices of $\triangle A'B'C'$ when $\triangle ABC$ is reflected across the y-axis. (11.3)   6. $A'(0, 2)$, $B'(-3, 1)$, $C'(-4, 4)$
7. Reflect the Roman numerals (I – X) about a vertical line. Which numerals remain the same? Which turn into new numerals? (11.3)   7. Same: I, II, III, V, X; turns into another numeral: IV→VI, VI→IV, IX→XI
8. The vertices of $\triangle ABC$ are $A(1, 0)$, $B(4, 0)$, and $C(2, 2)$. Find the vertices of $\triangle A'B'C'$ when $\triangle ABC$ is rotated 180° about the point $(0, 0)$. (11.4)   8. $A'(-1, 0)$, $B'(-4, 0)$, $C'(-2, -2)$
9. A quadrilateral has vertices $A(1, 1)$, $B(3, 2)$, $C(5, 1)$, and $D(2, -2)$. Find the vertices of the image after it has been translated one unit down and two units left. (11.5) $A'(-1, 0)$, $B'(1, 1)$, $C'(3, 0)$, $D'(0, -3)$ 9.
10. Write a motion rule for translating a figure four units up and three units left. (11.5) $(x - 3, y + 4)$ 10.

Mid-Chapter Test

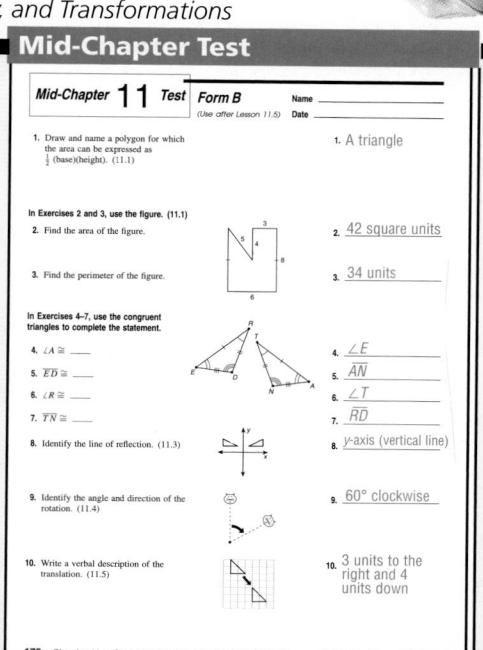

Mid-Chapter **11** Test   Form B
(Use after Lesson 11.5)   Name _____   Date _____

1. Draw and name a polygon for which the area can be expressed as $\frac{1}{2}$ (base)(height). (11.1)   1. A triangle
In Exercises 2 and 3, use the figure. (11.1)
2. Find the area of the figure.   2. 42 square units
3. Find the perimeter of the figure.   3. 34 units
In Exercises 4–7, use the congruent triangles to complete the statement.
4. $\angle A \cong$ ___   4. $\angle E$
5. $\overline{ED} \cong$ ___   5. $\overline{AN}$
6. $\angle R \cong$ ___   6. $\angle T$
7. $\overline{TN} \cong$ ___   7. $\overline{RD}$
8. Identify the line of reflection. (11.3)   8. y-axis (vertical line)
9. Identify the angle and direction of the rotation. (11.4)   9. 60° clockwise
10. Write a verbal description of the translation. (11.5)   10. 3 units to the right and 4 units down

Materials Needed: ruler, protractor, and calculator

Example   *Comparing Photo Sizes*

Photo 2 is a reduction of Photo 1. Use a ruler to measure the width and height of each photo. Then compare the ratios of widths and heights.

Solution   Photo 1 has a width of 7.6 centimeters and Photo 2 has a width of 4.5 centimeters. The ratio of these widths is

$$\frac{\text{Photo 1 width}}{\text{Photo 2 width}} = \frac{7.6 \text{ cm}}{4.5 \text{ cm}} \approx 1.7.$$

Photo 1 has a height of 9.1 centimeters and Photo 2 has a height of 5.4 centimeters. The ratio of these heights is

$$\frac{\text{Photo 1 height}}{\text{Photo 2 height}} = \frac{9.1 \text{ cm}}{5.4 \text{ cm}} \approx 1.7.$$

From these four measurements, it appears that the ratios are the same. ∎

Photo 1

Exercises

In Exercises 1–8, use a protractor and ruler to measure the indicated line segment or angle in both photos. Then find the ratio of the Photo 1 measurement to the Photo 2 measurement. See below.

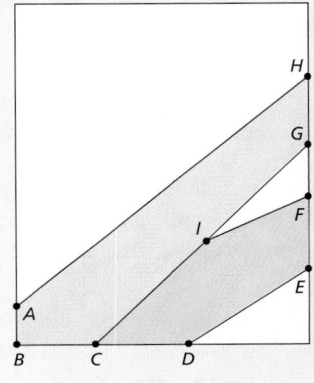

1. $\overline{AH}$ 2. $\overline{BD}$
3. $\overline{CG}$ 4. $\overline{EH}$
5. $\angle ABC$ 6. $\angle AHE$
7. $\angle BAH$ 8. $\angle GCD$

Photo 2

9. What do you conclude about the ratios of segments and angles in the photographs? Ratios of segments are equal, ratios of angles are equal.

1.–4. Each ratio is ≈1.7.   **5.–8.** Each ratio is 1.

Lesson Investigation 11.6   **511**

INVESTIGATION Notes

Materials
Color Transparencies
   Picture, p. 47
Teaching Tools
   Ruler and protractor, pp. T12, C18

The goal of the investigation is to have students recognize that the ratio of corresponding lengths is always the same, regardless of what segments are measured. The ratio of corresponding angles is always 1:1. If an overhead transparency is made of this page, the ratio of projected lengths to actual lengths (on the transparency) could also be computed. Be aware that students' measurements refer to the pupil text and not the reduced version in the teacher text.

PACING the Lesson

Suggested Number of Days
Basic/Average 2 **Above Average** 1
Advanced 1

PLANNING the Lesson

Lesson Plan 11.6, p. 90

ORGANIZER

Starters (reproduced below)
  Problem of the Day 11.6, p. 32
  Warm-Up Exercises 11.6, p. 32
Lesson Resources
  Color Transparencies
    Picture for Ex. 26–28, p. 46
  Teaching Tools,
    Coordinate plane, pp. T8, C10
    Protractor, pp. T12, C18
  Math Log, pp. 35, 36
  Answer Masters 11.6, pp. 222, 223
  Extra Practice Copymaster 11.6, p. 90
  Reteaching Copymaster 11.6, p. 90
  Enrichment Projects, pp. 61, 62
Special Populations
  Suggestions, Teacher's Edition, p. 486D

LESSON Notes

Similar figures occur frequently in nature, the arts, architecture, and textile designs. Caution students that many figures may look similar when, in fact, they are not. It is very important to look for the properties of similarity before deciding whether two shapes are similar.

Lesson Investigation
EXTENSION
Have students draw two triangles whose corresponding angles are congruent. Then have them measure the corresponding sides of the two triangles and write a ratio of lengths for each pair of corresponding sides. Ask students what they observe.   Ratios of corresponding sides are equal.

11.6 Exploring Similarity

What you should learn:

Goal 1 How to recognize similar figures

Goal 2 How to use properties of similar figures

Why you should learn it:
You can use properties of similar figures to solve real-life problems, such as finding the height of a sign.

Goal 1 Recognizing Similar Figures

In the *Investigation* on page 511, you discovered that the two photographs are **similar.** That is, they have the same rectangular shape, but are not necessarily the same size. Here are some other examples of similar and nonsimilar figures.

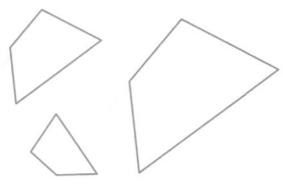   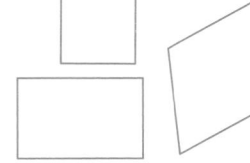

Similar   *Nonsimilar*

LESSON INVESTIGATION

■ Investigating Similar Triangles

Group Activity Plot the following points on a coordinate plane: $A(2, 4)$, $B(4, 0)$, $C(2, -1)$, $D(4, 8)$, $E(8, 0)$, and $F(4, -2)$. Draw $\triangle ABC$ and $\triangle DEF$. These triangles are similar. Use a protractor to measure each angle. How do the measures of the angles compare? They are equal.

Compute the length of each side. (You can use the Pythagorean Theorem.) Find the ratios of the lengths of corresponding sides. What can you conclude? They are equal.

In this investigation, you may have discovered the following properties of similar triangles.

$\triangle ABC \sim \triangle DEF$
~ *means "is similar to."*

Corresponding Angles
$m\angle A = m\angle D$
$m\angle B = m\angle E$
$m\angle C = m\angle F$

Corresponding Sides
$\dfrac{DE}{AB} = \dfrac{EF}{BC} = \dfrac{DF}{AC}$

Properties of Similar Triangles
1. Two triangles are similar if their corresponding angles have the same measures.
2. If two triangles are similar, the ratios of corresponding sides are equal. This common ratio is the **scale factor** of the one triangle to the other triangle.

STARTER: Problem of the Day
How many different squares can you find? What is the ratio of the area of the largest square to that of the smallest square?   15, 16:1

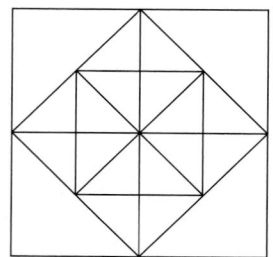

Also available as a copymaster, p. 32

STARTER: Warm-Up Exercises

1. In the following triangles, which angles have the same measure? Which side is opposite the right angle of each triangle?

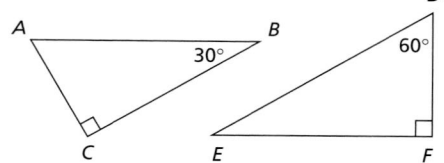

$\angle A$ and $\angle D$; $\angle B$ and $\angle E$; $\angle C$ and $\angle F$; $\overline{AB}$ and $\overline{DE}$

2. Solve for x or m.
a. $\frac{3}{4} \cdot 8 = x$ $x = 6$ b. $\frac{12}{8} \cdot 12 = m$ $m = 18$
c. $\frac{4}{15} = \frac{x}{12}$ $x = \frac{16}{5}$ d. $\frac{5}{4} = \frac{m}{12}$ $m = 15$

Also available as a copymaster, p. 32

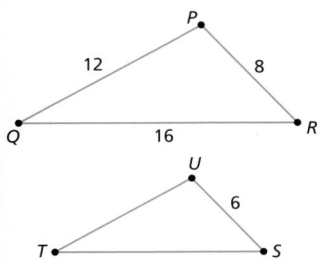

Example 1 — *Using Properties of Similar Triangles*

In the figure at the left, $\triangle PQR \sim \triangle UTS$. Find the lengths of $\overline{ST}$ and $\overline{TU}$.

Solution Because the triangles are similar, you know that the ratios of the lengths of corresponding sides are equal. You can use these ratios to write proportions that allow you to solve for the missing lengths.

$$\frac{US}{PR} = \frac{TU}{QP} \qquad\qquad \frac{US}{PR} = \frac{ST}{RQ}$$

$$\frac{6}{8} = \frac{TU}{12} \qquad\qquad \frac{6}{8} = \frac{ST}{16}$$

$$12 \cdot \frac{6}{8} = 12 \cdot \frac{TU}{12} \qquad 16 \cdot \frac{6}{8} = 16 \cdot \frac{ST}{16}$$

$$9 = TU \qquad\qquad 12 = ST$$

Example 2 — *Using Properties of Similar Figures*

Real Life
Sign Design

The symbol at the left represents the United States Medical Corps. You are given a copy of a symbol that is 4 inches tall and 5 inches wide, and are asked to create a sign that has a large Medical Corps symbol. If the large symbol is 6 feet wide, how tall should it be?

Solution Let H be the height of the large symbol.

$$\frac{\text{Large-symbol height}}{\text{Small-symbol height}} = \frac{\text{Large-symbol width}}{\text{Small-symbol width}}$$

$$\frac{H}{4 \text{ inches}} = \frac{6 \text{ feet}}{5 \text{ inches}}$$

$$\frac{H}{4 \text{ inches}} = \frac{72 \text{ inches}}{5 \text{ inches}}$$

$$H = 57.6 \text{ inches}$$

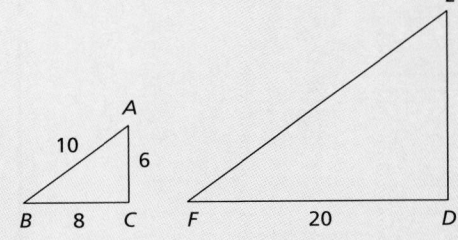

U.S. Medical Corps

The large symbol should be 57.6 inches or 4.8 feet tall. ∎

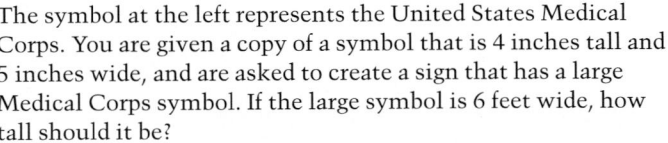

Communicating about **MATHEMATICS**

▶ **SHARING IDEAS about the Lesson**

Extending the Example In Example 2, if the large symbol is 9 feet tall, how wide should it be? $11\frac{1}{4}$ ft

11.6 • *Exploring Similarity* **513**

Properties of similar figures can be used to solve many problems in engineering and design.

Example 1 —————

Ask students to justify each step in the solution process.

Example 2 —————

Ask students: Suppose the large symbol is to be 4 feet wide. How tall should it be?
3.2 feet

Communicating about **MATHEMATICS**

Have students create other problems like Example 2 that use copies of shapes found in their classroom.

Writing Prompt
Explain by example the difference between congruent figures and similar figures.

OPTION: Extra Examples

Here is an additional example similar to Example 1.

Using Properties of Similar Triangles
In the figure shown, $\triangle ABC \sim \triangle EFD$. Find the lengths of $\overline{DE}$ and $\overline{EF}$.

Solution
Because the triangles are similar, you know that the ratios of the lengths of corresponding sides are equal. You can use these ratios to write proportions that allow you to solve for the missing lengths.

$$\frac{DE}{CA} = \frac{DF}{CB} \qquad\qquad \frac{EF}{AB} = \frac{DF}{CB}$$

$$\frac{DE}{6} = \frac{20}{8} \qquad\qquad \frac{EF}{10} = \frac{20}{8}$$

$$6 \cdot \frac{DE}{6} = 6 \cdot \frac{20}{8} \qquad 10 \cdot \frac{EF}{10} = 10 \cdot \frac{20}{8}$$

$$DE = 15 \qquad\qquad EF = 25$$

ASSIGNMENT GUIDE

Basic/Average:
Day 1: Ex. 9–14, 24, 26–28
Day 2: Ex. 17–23, 25, 30, 32–35
Above Average: Ex. 9, 11–15, 19, 20–24, 29–35
Advanced: Ex. 9, 11–15, 19, 20–24, 29–35
Selected Answers: Ex. 1–8, 9–31 odd

Guided Practice

▶ **Ex. 3, 4** Students need to observe the difference in angle measures in order to determine which figures are similar.
▶ **Ex. 5** Depending on which triangle measures are written in the numerator and denominator, six different proportions could be written.
▶ **Ex. 7** Make sure that all students can set up the correct proportions to solve these problems.

Independent Practice

▶ **Ex. 9, 10**

Common-Error Alert!

Students may erroneously assume that a similar orientation implies a similar shape.

▶ **Ex. 11–14** Assign these exercises as a group.
▶ **Ex. 15, 16** These problems could be done as a class activity with students demonstrating or explaining solutions to the group.

Guided Practice

▶ **CHECK for Understanding**

P **1.** *Writing* In your own words, state what it means for two figures to be similar. Answers vary.

P **2.** *The Shape of Things* Give some examples of similar figures in your classroom. Answers vary.

3. Which two figures are similar? a and c

a. 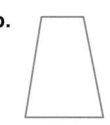 b. 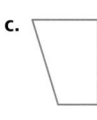 c.

4. Which two figures are similar? a and b

a. b. c.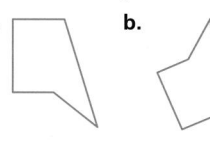

In Exercises 5–8, △*HIJ* ~ △*KLM*, as shown at the right.

5. Write three proportions for △*HIJ* and △*KLM*.

6. Find the scale factor of △*HIJ* to △*KLM*. $\frac{4}{3}$

7. Find *KM* and *IJ*. $13\frac{1}{2}$, 24

8. $m\angle H = m\angle$ [?]. K

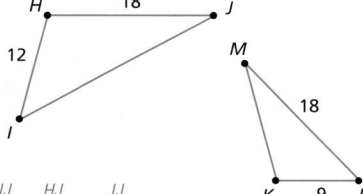

5. $\frac{HJ}{KM} = \frac{HI}{KL}$, $\frac{HI}{KL} = \frac{IJ}{LM}$, $\frac{HJ}{KM} = \frac{IJ}{LM}$

Independent Practice

9. Which two figures are similar? a and c

a.  b. 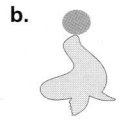 c.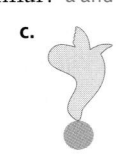

10. Which two figures are similar? a and c

a. b. c.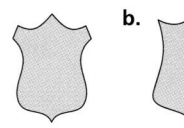

In Exercises 11–14, quadrilaterals *QRST* and *WXYZ* are similar, as shown at the right.

11. Write four equal ratios for *QRST* and *WXYZ*.

12. Find the scale factor of *QRST* to *WXYZ*. $\frac{5}{3}$

13. Find the following.
a. *QT* 15 b. *ST* 14 c. *XY* $3\frac{3}{5}$

14. $m\angle T = m\angle$ [?]. Z

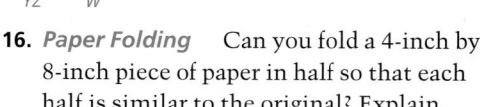

11. $\frac{QR}{WX} = \frac{RS}{XY} = \frac{ST}{YZ} = \frac{QT}{W}$

✪ **15.** *Paper Folding* Can you fold an $8\frac{1}{2}$-inch by 11-inch piece of paper in half so that each half is similar to the original? Explain.
No; $\frac{5.5}{8.5} \neq \frac{8.5}{11}$ and $\frac{4.25}{11} \neq \frac{8.5}{11}$

✪ **16.** *Paper Folding* Can you fold a 4-inch by 8-inch piece of paper in half so that each half is similar to the original? Explain.
No; $\frac{4}{4} \neq \frac{4}{8}$ and $\frac{2}{8} \neq \frac{4}{8}$

✪ More difficult exercises
P Portfolio Opportunities

514 *Chapter 11* ▪ *Congruence, Similarity, and Transformations*

Extra Practice

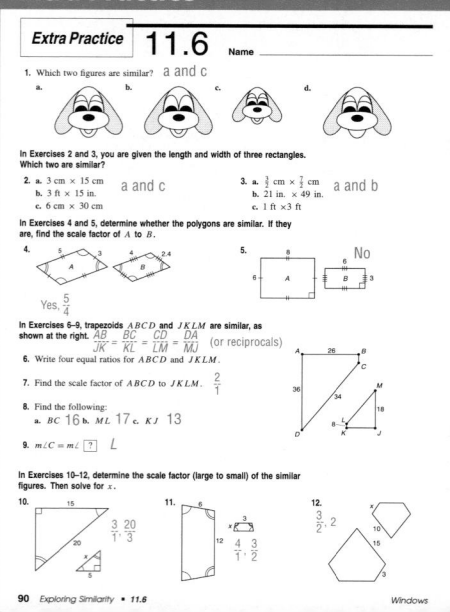

Reteaching

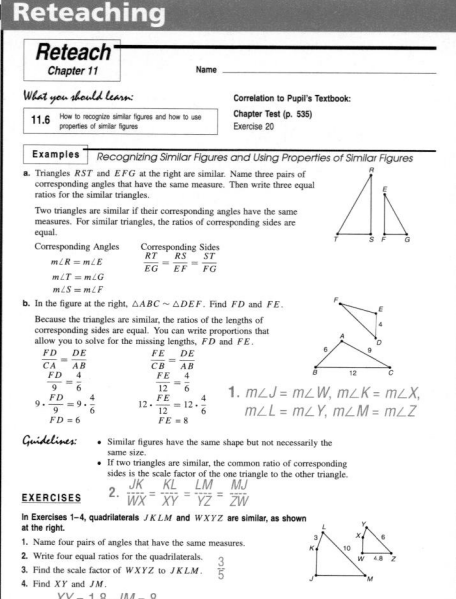

In Exercises 17–19, determine the scale factor (large to small) of the similar figures. Then solve for x.

17.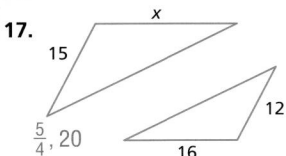
15
x
$\frac{5}{4}$, 20
12
16

18.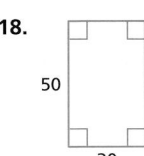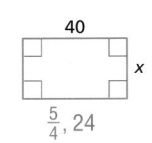
50
40
x
30
$\frac{5}{4}$, 24

19.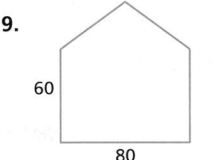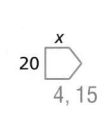
60
80
20
x
4, 15

True or False? In Exercises 20–23, is the statement true or false? Explain. See margin.

20. All congruent figures are similar. True
21. All similar figures are congruent. False
22. All squares are similar. True
23. All right triangles are similar. False

24. *What Do You Think?* One of your classmates says that the quadrilaterals ABCD and EFGH are similar. What do you think? Explain your reasoning.

25. *Drawing Triangles* Draw two isosceles right triangles that are not congruent. Are the triangles similar? Explain.

24., 25. See margin.

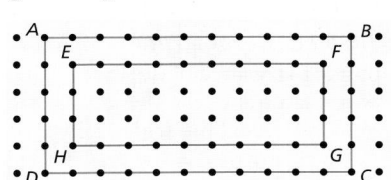

Giant Redwoods In Exercises 26–28, use the following information. 26., 27. See margin.

A 5-foot person is standing in the shadow of a giant redwood tree. The tips of the person's shadow and the tree's shadow coincide. The person's shadow is 4 feet long and the tree's shadow is 200 feet long.

26. Draw a diagram of the situation. Let a ray of sunlight be the third side of the triangle.

27. Explain why the two triangles are similar.

28. Find the height of the giant redwood tree. 250 ft

The world's largest tree in volume is a 275-foot Sierra redwood known as the General Sherman Tree. The tree is between 2200 and 2500 years old.

Integrated Review | *Making Connections within Mathematics*

Proportions In Exercises 29–31, match the proportion with the pair of similar figures. Then solve for x.

a.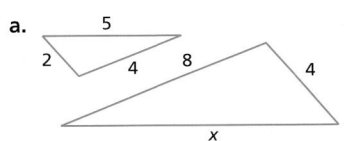
5
2
4
8
4
x

b.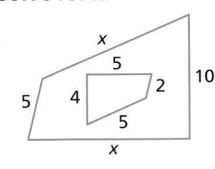
x
5
5
4
2
5
10
x

c.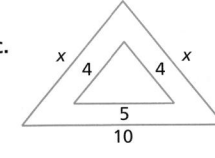
x
4
4
x
5
10

29. $\frac{2}{5} = \frac{5}{x}$ b, $12\frac{1}{2}$
30. $\frac{4}{x} = \frac{5}{10}$ c, 8
31. $\frac{8}{4} = \frac{x}{5}$ a, 10

⊕ More difficult exercises

11.6 • Exploring Similarity **515**

▶ **Ex. 20–23** Encourage students to draw a sketch to support their answers.
▶ **Ex. 25** Ask students: Are all isosceles triangles similar?
▶ **Ex. 26–28** Assign these exercises as a group.

EXTENSION
Have students plan an indirect measurement activity outdoors. Alternatively, wait until the end of the chapter, when additional approaches will be available to the students.

Integrated Review
These exercises offer good practice at recognizing corresponding parts of similar figures.

Answers
20. Congruent figures have the same size and shape, and similar figures have the same shape.
21. Similar figures may not be the same size.
22. All angles have the same measure and the ratios of corresponding sides are equal.
23. The two acute angles of a right triangle can vary.
24. They are not similar. $\frac{EF}{AB} = \frac{9}{11}$, $\frac{EH}{AD} = \frac{3}{5}$, $\frac{9}{11} \neq \frac{3}{5}$
25. Yes; corresponding angles have the same measure and the ratios of corresponding sides are equal.
26.

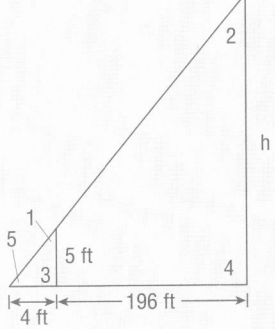

Figure not drawn to scale

27. The person and the tree are parts of parallel lines, while the tree's shadow and the ray of sunlight are parts of other lines. When two parallel lines are intersected by a third line, the corresponding angles are congruent; so ∠1 ≅ ∠2 and ∠3 ≅ ∠4. ∠5 is an angle of both triangles. Since the corresponding angles of the two triangles have the same measures, the two triangles are similar.

Assign these as a group. The activity should be done in class where different groups use a different-sized rectangle for the interior of the box. Have all groups report their results to the class.

Portfolio Opportunity: Math Log

1. In your own words, describe the difference between congruence and similarity.

2. If the scale factor of △ABC to △XYZ is less than one, is △XYZ larger, smaller, or equal in size to △ABC?

3. Is it possible to draw two regular pentagons that are not similar? Explain your answer.

Also available as a copymaster, pages 35, 36, Ex. 7–9

Short Quiz

Covers Lessons 11.5 and 11.6

Available as a copymaster, page 179

Exploration and Extension

Experimental Probability   **In Exercises 32–35, use a box, such as a shoe box, or a shoe-box lid. Draw a rectangle that is similar to (but smaller than) the base of the box. Cut the rectangle out and place it in the box.**   **32.–34.** Check students' work.

32. Toss a piece of unpopped popcorn (or a pebble) into the box 50 times. Record the number of times it lands on the paper rectangle. Let *n* be this number.

33. Divide *n* by 50. This is the experimental probability of landing on the paper rectangle.

✪ 34. Find the scale factor of the paper rectangle to the base of the box.

✪ 35. *Theoretical Probability*   Find the ratio of the area of the paper rectangle to the area of the base of the box. This is the theoretical probability. How does the theoretical probability relate to the experimental probability and the scale factor?   The theoretical probability should be approximately equal to the experimental probability and exactly equal to the square of the scale factor.

Mixed REVIEW

In Exercises 1–4, use the Pythagorean Theorem to solve for *x*. Round your result to 2 decimal places. (9.3)

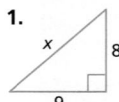

1.	2.	3.	4.
12.04	90.51	4.80	13.50

5. Which triangles in Exercises 1–4 are similar? **(11.6)** Those in Exercises 1 and 4

6. In △ABC, BC = 5, AC = 7, and AB = 10. Which angle is smallest? ∠A Which is largest? **(10.9)** ∠C

In Exercises 7–12, solve the percent problem. (7.8)

7. What is 15% of 55? 8.25

8. What is 115% of 77? 88.55

9. 66 is 150% of what number? 44

10. 80 is 40% of what number? 200

11. 53.76 is what percent of 112? 48%

12. 31.92 is what percent of 84? 38%

In Exercises 13–16, evaluate the expression when $x = -6$, $y = 2$, and $z = -3$.

13. $\left|\frac{x}{z}\right|$ 2

14. $|z| - |x|$ -3

15. $(|x| - |y|) \cdot z$ -12

16. $\frac{1}{x}(|y \cdot z|)$ -1

In Exercises 17–20, you have a bag that contains 22 yellow marbles, 20 red marbles, and 14 green marbles. You choose 1 marble from the bag. What is the probability that it is the indicated color? (8.8)

17. Yellow $\frac{11}{28}$

18. Red $\frac{5}{14}$

19. Green $\frac{1}{4}$

20. Red or Green $\frac{17}{28}$

---

516   *Chapter 11 · Congruence, Similarity, and Transformations*   ✪ More difficult exercises

---

Enrichment

| Golden Rectangles | **11.6** Name _____ |

The Golden Rectangle is the rectangle that has been shown to be the most pleasing to the human eye. The ratio of the width of a Golden Rectangle to its length is called the Golden Ratio, approximately 0.6 :1. The Golden Rectangle is used in many forms of advertising and manufacturing to appeal to consumers.

Your project is to find at least ten examples of Golden Rectangles in the classroom and/or at home. Fill in the chart below for the objects you have found.

	Object	Length	Width	Ratio (W:L)
1.				
2.				
3.				
4.				
5.				
6.				
7.				
8.				
9.				
10.				

Tables vary.

11.7

Problem Solving Using Similar Figures

What you should learn:

Goal 1 How to use similar figures to solve real-life problems

Goal 2 How to compare perimeters and areas of similar figures

Why you should learn it:

You can use properties of similar figures to solve real-life problems, such as finding the dimensions of a poster.

Real Life
Design

A

Thursday, April 2
3:30 PM
Room 2001

SPACE CLUB MEETING

7 inches

B

5 inches   C

Goal 1 ## Using Similar Figures

When two figures are similar, remember that corresponding angles are congruent and corresponding sides are proportional.

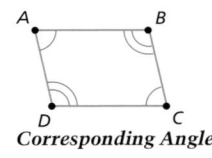
Corresponding Angles

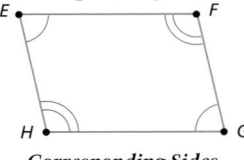
Corresponding Sides

$\angle A \cong \angle E, \angle B \cong \angle F$
$\angle C \cong \angle G, \angle D \cong \angle H$

$\dfrac{AB}{EF} = \dfrac{BC}{FG} = \dfrac{CD}{GH} = \dfrac{AD}{EH}$

Example 1   *Using Properties of Similar Figures*

You are designing a poster to advertise the next meeting of the Space Club. You begin by drawing the sketch shown at the left. You want the actual poster to have a base of 2 feet. Describe the measures of the actual poster.

Solution   The angle measures of the actual poster are the same as the angle measures of the sketch. The actual poster has a base (and top) of 2 feet or 24 inches. You can find the length of the slanted sides of the parallelogram by using a proportion.

Verbal Model

$$\frac{\text{Side of actual poster}}{\text{Side of sketch}} = \frac{\text{Base of actual poster}}{\text{Base of sketch}}$$

Labels
Side of actual poster = x (inches)
Base of actual poster = 24 (inches)
Side of sketch = 7 (inches)
Base of sketch = 5 (inches)

Algebraic Model

$$\frac{x}{7} = \frac{24}{5}$$

$$7 \cdot \frac{x}{7} = 7 \cdot \frac{24}{5}$$
$$x = 33.6$$

The length of each slanted side should be 33.6 inches. ■

▶ **PACING the Lesson**

Suggested Number of Days
Basic/Average 0   **Above Average** 2
Advanced 2

▶ **PLANNING the Lesson**

Lesson Plan 11.7, p. 91

ORGANIZER

Starters (reproduced below)
    Problem of the Day 11.7, p. 33
    Warm-Up Exercises 11.7, p. 33
Lesson Resources
    Color Transparencies
        Picture for Ex. 10–14, p. 48
    Teaching Tools,
        Triangular dot paper, pp. T3, C4
    Math Log, p. 36
    Answer Masters 11.7, p. 225
    Extra Practice Copymaster 11.7, p. 91
    Reteaching Copymaster 11.7, p. 91
Special Populations
    Suggestions, Teacher's Edition, p. 486D

LESSON Notes

Remind students that if two corresponding angles are congruent then their measures are the same. And if corresponding sides of a figure are proportional, then the ratios of corresponding sides are equal.

Example 1

Ask students: Suppose you wanted the slanted side to be 3.5 feet. What should the length of the base be?   2.5 feet

---

STARTER: Problem of the Day

How many lines of symmetry does each figure have?

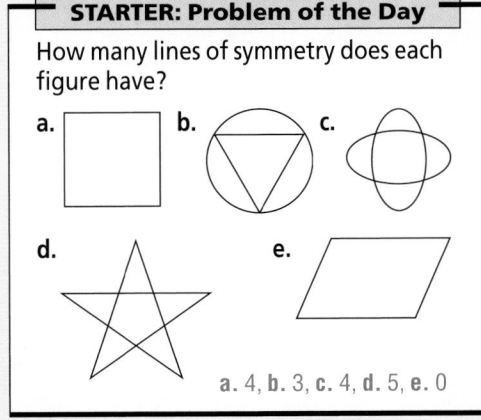

a.   b.   c.

d.   e.

a. 4, b. 3, c. 4, d. 5, e. 0

Also available as a copymaster, p. 33

STARTER: Warm-Up Exercises

Find the area of the figure *ABCD*.

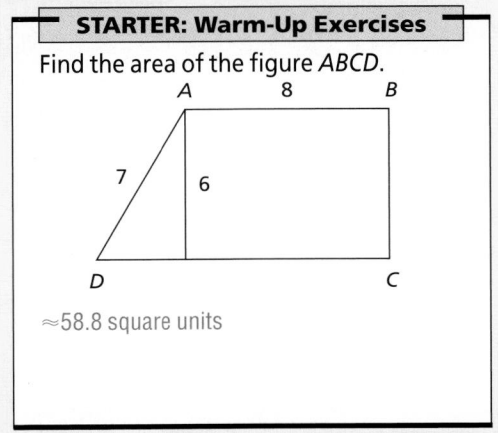

A   8   B

7   6

D   C

≈58.8 square units

Also available as a copymaster, p. 33

Review the definitions of perimeter and area for a triangle and for a quadrilateral.

Example 2

Compare the perimeter of the poster sketch in Example 1 to the perimeter of an actual poster whose slanted side is 3.5 feet in length.

$$\frac{\text{perimeter of poster sketch}}{\text{perimeter of actual poster}} = \frac{24}{144} = \frac{1}{6}$$

 Communicating
about **MATHEMATICS**

For the similar triangles shown below, have students find the ratio of the perimeter of figure **b** to the perimeter of figure **a**.

a.   **b.**

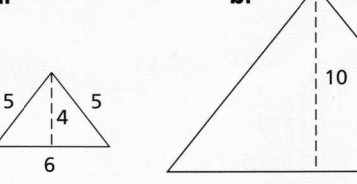

$$\frac{\text{perimeter of figure b}}{\text{perimeter of figure a}} = \frac{40}{16} = 2.5$$

Writing Prompt
Summarize the main ideas of today's lesson in your own words.

Example 2 *Comparing Perimeters and Areas*

Compare the perimeter and area of the poster sketch in Example 1 to the actual poster.

Solution The perimeters of the sketch and poster are

$$\text{Perimeter} = AB + BC + CD + AD$$
$$= 5 + 7 + 5 + 7$$
$$= 24 \text{ inches.} \qquad \textit{Perimeter of sketch}$$

$$\text{Perimeter} = 24 + 33.6 + 24 + 33.6$$
$$= 115.2 \text{ inches.} \qquad \textit{Perimeter of poster}$$

The ratio of the perimeter of the actual poster to the perimeter of the sketch is

$$\frac{\text{Perimeter of Actual Poster}}{\text{Perimeter of Sketch}} = \frac{115.2 \text{ inches}}{24 \text{ inches}} = 4.8.$$

To find the area of the sketch, you need to measure its height, as shown at the left. The area is

$$\text{Area of sketch} = (\text{Base})(\text{Height})$$
$$= (5)(6.8)$$
$$= 34 \text{ square inches.} \quad \textit{Area of sketch}$$

In the *Communicating* feature below, you are asked to find the area of the actual poster. ∎

C. 3; the ratio of any corresponding lengths = 4.8, while the ratio of the areas ≠ 4.8.

Communicating about MATHEMATICS

▶ **SHARING IDEAS about the Lesson**

Comparing Perimeter and Area   32.64 in., $\frac{24}{5} = \frac{x}{6.8}$

A. Find the height of the actual poster in inches. Explain.

B. Find the area of the actual poster in square inches. 783.36 in.²

C. Which of the following ratios is *not* equal to 4.8? What can you conclude? See above.

1. $\dfrac{\text{Base of Poster}}{\text{Base of Sketch}}$ 2. $\dfrac{\text{Height of Poster}}{\text{Height of Sketch}}$ 3. $\dfrac{\text{Area of Poster}}{\text{Area of Sketch}}$

4. $\dfrac{\text{Perimeter of Poster}}{\text{Perimeter of Sketch}}$ 5. $\dfrac{\text{Length of Slanted Side of Poster}}{\text{Length of Slanted Side of Sketch}}$

EXERCISES

Guided Practice

▶ **CHECK for Understanding** 3. 36 in., $1\frac{1}{2}$ in.; 72 in.^{2}, $\frac{1}{8}$ in.^{2}

Model Car **You are designing a model car that is a scale replica of a full-sized car. The license plate on the car is 6 inches by 12 inches. The model's license plate has a length of $\frac{1}{2}$ inch.**

1. Find the height of the model's license plate. $\frac{1}{4}$ in.
2. Find the scale factor of the car to the model. 24
3. Find the perimeter and area of each license plate.
4. Find the ratio of the car plate's perimeter to the model plate's perimeter. Compare the result to the scale factor. 24, it is the same.
5. Find the ratio of the car plate's area to the model plate's area. How does this ratio compare to the scale factor? 576, it is equal to the square of the scale factor.

The world's smallest running car is powered by a tiny electric motor. The white objects in the photo are grains of rice.

Independent Practice

6. *Estimation* The actual painting is 26 inches high. Use the reduction below to estimate the width of the actual painting.

50 in.

7. *Like Father, Like Son* The scale factor of a baby lizard to its parent is 1 to 16. The parent is 24 centimeters long. How long is the baby? 1.5 cm

8. *Estimation* The blueprint below is drawn with a scale factor of $\frac{1}{16}$ inch to 1 foot. Estimate the perimeter and area of the actual room. 98 ft, 468 ft^2

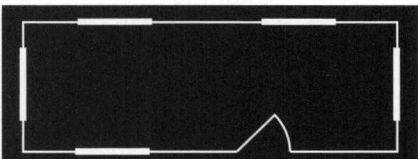

9. *USA Map* The continental United States is about 2500 miles wide. Use the map to estimate its height. 1563 miles

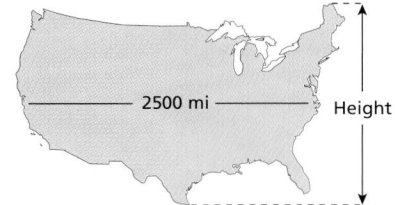

2500 mi — Height

11.7 • Problem Solving Using Similar Figures **519**

EXERCISE Notes

ASSIGNMENT GUIDE
*Basic/Average:
Day 1: Ex. 6–9, 15, 16
Day 2: Ex. 10–14, 17–20
Above Average:
Day 1: Ex. 6–9, 15, 16
Day 2: Ex. 10–14, 17–20
Advanced:
Day 1: Ex. 8–14
Day 2: Ex. 16–20
Selected Answers: Ex. 1–5, 6–15 odd
*You may wish to omit this lesson for these students.

Guided Practice
Have individual groups answer these questions before sharing with the whole class.

Independent Practice
▶ **Ex. 6–9** Students will need rulers in order to complete these exercises. Once again, be aware that students' answers are based on the full-sized pupil page.

Lesson 11.7 **519**

Keepers of the Secret   **In Exercises 10–14, use the photo at the right.**

Keepers of the Secret, at the right, was painted by Julie Kramer Cole. The actual painting is 16 inches wide. The painting contains four owls. Two are clearly visible. Can you find the other two? **12., 13.** See below.

10. Find the height of the actual painting. 20 in.

11. Find the scale factor of the actual painting to the photo. $\frac{64}{11}$

✪ 12. Find the perimeter and area of the actual painting. Then find the perimeter and area of the photo (use inches).

✪ 13. Find the ratio of the painting's perimeter to the photo's perimeter. How does this ratio compare to the scale factor?

✪ 14. Find the ratio of the painting's area to the photo's area. How does this ratio compare to the scale factor?
$\frac{4096}{121}$, it equals the square of the scale factor

| Integrated Review | *Making Connections within Mathematics*

Similar Figures   **In Exercises 15 and 16, use the fact that the figures are similar to solve for x. Then find the perimeter and area of each figure.**

15. 13

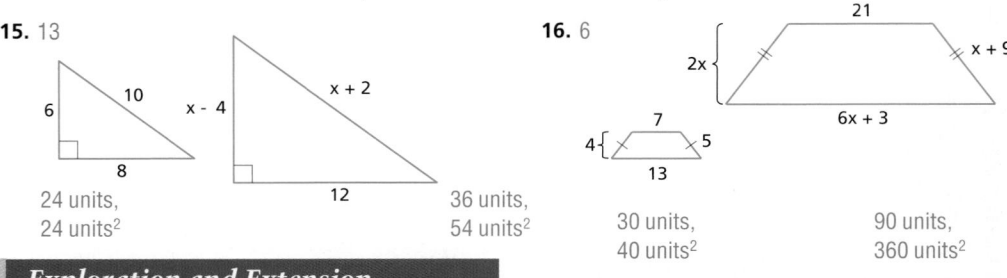

24 units,
24 units²

36 units,
54 units²

16. 6

30 units,
40 units²

90 units,
360 units²

| Exploration and Extension |

P *Triangle Grid*   **In Exercises 17–20, copy the triangular grid at the right on isometric dot paper. Then decide whether it is possible to outline four different sizes of similar figures with the indicated shape, none overlapping. Illustrate the similar figures with a sketch.** For sketches, see Additional Answers.

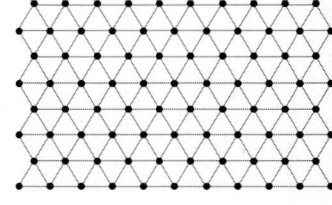

✪ **17.** Triangles Yes   ✪ **18.** Trapezoids Yes

✪ **19.** Hexagons Yes   ✪ **20.** Parallelograms Yes

12. 72 in., 320 in.²; $12\frac{3}{8}$ in., $9\frac{29}{64}$ in.²

13. $\frac{64}{11}$, it equals the scale factor

✪ More difficult exercises
P Portfolio Opportunity

Materials Needed: protractor, ruler, paper, calculator

Example   *Finding Ratios of Side Lengths*

Draw a right triangle whose acute angles measure 25° and 65°. Measure the side lengths, a, b, and c, to the nearest millimeter. Then use a calculator to compute the ratios $\frac{a}{b}$, $\frac{a}{c}$, and $\frac{b}{c}$.

Solution   Begin by drawing a right angle, as shown below. Then choose any point on the horizontal ray and label it point A. With your protractor, measure and draw an angle of 25°. Use the ruler to measure the side lengths. For the triangle below, the lengths are $a \approx 35$ millimeters, $b \approx 75$ millimeters, and $c \approx 83$ millimeters. The ratios of the side lengths are

$$\frac{a}{b} \approx \frac{35}{75} \approx 0.467, \quad \frac{a}{c} \approx \frac{35}{83} \approx 0.422, \quad \frac{b}{c} \approx \frac{75}{83} \approx 0.904.$$

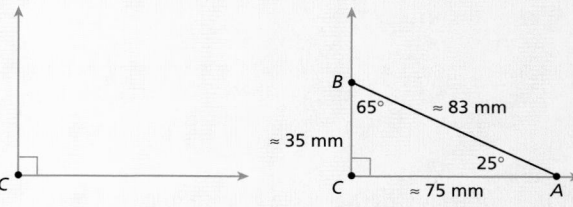

Exercises

1. varies, varies, varies, ≈ 0.839, ≈ 0.643, ≈ 0.766

2. varies, varies, varies, 1, ≈ 0.707, ≈ 0.707

Group Activity   **In Exercises 1–3, each person in your group should draw right triangles that have the given angle measures and complete the table.** **3.** varies, varies, varies, ≈ 0.577, 0.5, ≈ 0.866

	$m\angle C$	$m\angle A$	$m\angle B$	a	b	c	$\frac{a}{b}$	$\frac{a}{c}$	$\frac{b}{c}$
1.	90°	40°	50°	?	?	?	?	?	?
2.	90°	45°	45°	?	?	?	?	?	?
3.	90°	30°	60°	?	?	?	?	?	?

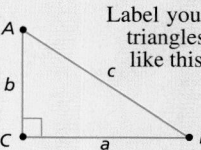

Label your triangles like this.

In Exercises 4 and 5, discuss the questions with others in your group.

4. Are all the triangles drawn for Exercise 1 similar to each other? What about Exercises 2 and 3? Yes, yes, yes

5. What can you observe about the ratios found by each person in your group? The ratios should be approximately equal.

Lesson Investigation 11.8   **521**

Materials
Teaching Tools
  Ruler and protractor, pp. T12, C18

In order to compare class results for the example shown, make sure that all students use the same labeling, where a = shorter leg, b = longer leg, and c = hypotenuse. In the exercises, students need to pay attention to how they label their triangles. In the sample shown, it appears that side b < side a. However, the purpose of this diagram is simply to remind students that side a is opposite $\angle A$, side b is opposite $\angle B$, and so on.

PACING the Lesson

Suggested Number of Days
Basic/Average 0   Above Average 1
Advanced 1

PLANNING the Lesson

Lesson Plan **11.8**, p. 92

LESSON Notes

Trigonometry is used in a variety of real-life applications from economics to architecture, from music to physics. Students should memorize the trigonometric ratios for future use. Encourage them to record the ratios in their journals.

Ask students to explain why all right triangles that have an acute angle of a given measure are similar to each other.

Example 1

Ask students why $\overline{PQ}$ is not referred to as the adjacent side of $\angle P$. *$\overline{PQ}$ is given the special name hypotenuse*

11.8

Trigonometric Ratios

 What you should learn:

 Goal 1 How to find trigonometric ratios

Goal 2 How to use the Pythagorean Theorem to find trigonometric ratios

Why you should learn it:

You can use trigonometric ratios to solve real-life problems, such as comparing heights of a hot-air balloon.

Goal 1 **Finding Trigonometric Ratios**

In the ancient Greek language, the word "trigonometry" means "measurement of triangles." A **trigonometric ratio** is a ratio of the lengths of two sides of a right triangle. The three basic trigonometric ratios are **sine, cosine,** and **tangent,** which are abbreviated as *sin, cos,* and *tan.*

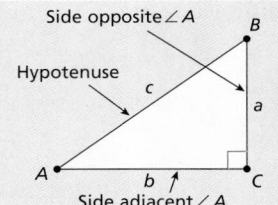

Trigonometric Ratios

$$\sin A = \frac{\text{Side opposite } \angle A}{\text{Hypotenuse}} = \frac{a}{c}$$

$$\cos A = \frac{\text{Side adjacent to } \angle A}{\text{Hypotenuse}} = \frac{b}{c}$$

$$\tan A = \frac{\text{Side opposite } \angle A}{\text{Side adjacent to } \angle A} = \frac{a}{b}$$

Because all *right* triangles that have a given measure for $\angle A$ are similar, the value of a trigonometric ratio depends only on the measure of $\angle A$. It does not depend on the triangle's size.

Example 1 *Finding Trigonometric Ratios*

For the triangle at the left, find the sine, cosine, and tangent of $\angle P$ and $\angle Q$.

Solution   The length of the hypotenuse is 5.

For $\angle P$, the length of the opposite side is 4, and the length of the adjacent side is 3.

For $\angle Q$, the length of the opposite side is 3, and the length of the adjacent side is 4.

$$\sin P = \frac{\text{opp.}}{\text{hyp.}} = \frac{4}{5}$$

$$\cos P = \frac{\text{adj.}}{\text{hyp.}} = \frac{3}{5}$$

$$\tan P = \frac{\text{opp.}}{\text{adj.}} = \frac{4}{3}$$

$$\sin Q = \frac{\text{opp.}}{\text{hyp.}} = \frac{3}{5}$$

$$\cos Q = \frac{\text{adj.}}{\text{hyp.}} = \frac{4}{5}$$

$$\tan Q = \frac{\text{opp.}}{\text{adj.}} = \frac{3}{4}$$ ∎

STARTER: Problem of the Day

The three triangles are similar. Solve for *x*.

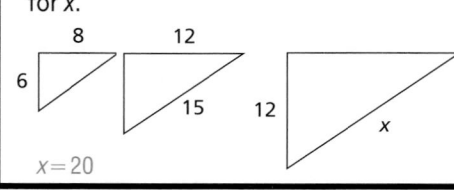

x = 20

Also available as a copymaster, p. 33

STARTER: Warm-Up Exercises

1. Find *p* for the given values of *m* and *n*, where $p^2 = m^2 + n^2$.
   a. $m = 2, n = 4$ *$p = \sqrt{20}$*
   b. $m = 8, n = 6$ *$p = 10$*
2. Identify the hypotenuse for each triangle.
   a. In $\triangle ABC$, $m\angle A = 60°$, and $m\angle B = 30°$.
   b. In $\triangle RST$, $m\angle R = 45°$, and $m\angle S = 45°$.
   c. In $\triangle JKL$, $m\angle J = 40°$, and $m\angle K = 50°$.
   a. side $\overline{AB}$, b. side $\overline{RS}$, c. side $\overline{JK}$

Also available as a copymaster, p. 33

Goal 2 — Using the Pythagorean Theorem

Example 2 — *Using the Pythagorean Theorem*

Draw an isosceles right triangle. Then use the triangle to find the sine, cosine, and tangent of 45°.

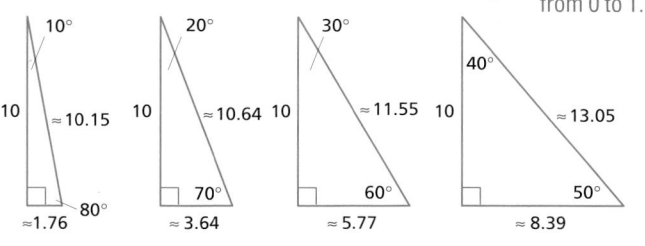

Solution Begin by drawing an isosceles right triangle. Each acute angle of such a triangle measures 45°. Because all isosceles right triangles are similar, it doesn't matter what size triangle you draw. To make the calculations simple, you can choose each leg to have a length of 1. Using the Pythagorean Theorem, you can write

$$c^2 = a^2 + b^2 \qquad \textit{Pythagorean Theorem}$$
$$c^2 = 1^2 + 1^2 \qquad \textit{Substitute for a and b.}$$
$$c = \sqrt{2}\ . \qquad \textit{Square Root Property}$$

Now, using $a = 1$, $b = 1$, $c = \sqrt{2}$, you can find the sine, cosine, and tangent as follows.

$$\sin 45° = \frac{\text{opp.}}{\text{hyp.}} = \frac{1}{\sqrt{2}} \approx 0.707$$

$$\cos 45° = \frac{\text{adj.}}{\text{hyp.}} = \frac{1}{\sqrt{2}} \approx 0.707$$

$$\tan 45° = \frac{\text{opp.}}{\text{adj.}} = \frac{1}{1} = 1$$

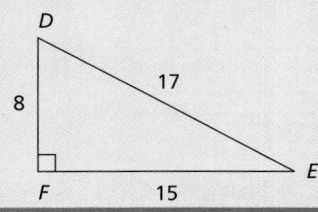
Communicating *about* MATHEMATICS

▶ **SHARING IDEAS about the Lesson**

Comparing Sines of Acute Angles Use the following triangles to find the sine of 10°, 20°, 30°, 40°, 50°, 60°, 70°, and 80°. Organize your results in a table. What conclusions can you make about the values of the sine of an angle? They range from 0 to 1.

A	sin A
10°	≈ 0.173
20°	≈ 0.342
30°	≈ 0.500
40°	≈ 0.643
50°	≈ 0.766
60°	≈ 0.866
70°	≈ 0.940
80°	≈ 0.985

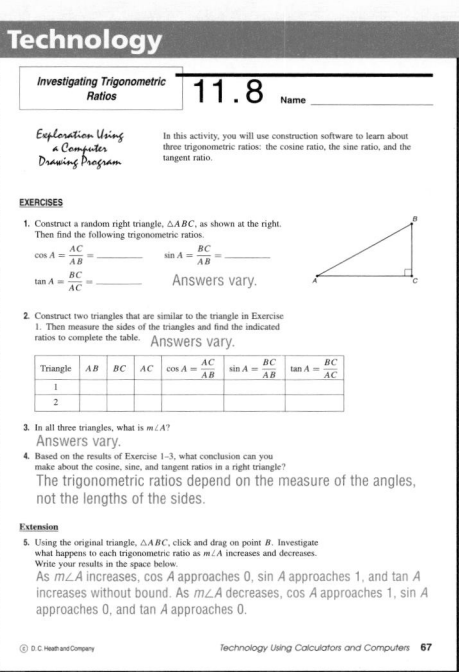

Ⓟ Portfolio Opportunity

11.8 • Trigonometric Ratios **523**

OPTION: Extra Examples

Here is an additional example similar to Example 1.

Finding Trigonometric Ratios
For the triangle at the right, find the sine, cosine, and tangent of ∠D and ∠E.

Solution
The length of the hypotenuse is 17.
For ∠D, the length of the opposite side is 15, and the length of the adjacent side is 8.

$$\sin D = \frac{\text{opp.}}{\text{hyp.}} = \frac{15}{17}$$

$$\cos D = \frac{\text{adj.}}{\text{hyp.}} = \frac{8}{17}$$

$$\tan D = \frac{\text{opp.}}{\text{adj.}} = \frac{15}{8}$$

For ∠E, the length of the opposite side is 8, and the length of the adjacent side is 15.

$$\sin E = \frac{\text{opp.}}{\text{hyp.}} = \frac{8}{17}$$

$$\cos E = \frac{\text{adj.}}{\text{hyp.}} = \frac{15}{17}$$

$$\tan E = \frac{\text{opp.}}{\text{adj.}} = \frac{8}{15}$$

Have students state the Pythagorean Theorem in words.

Example 2

Addressing Misconceptions

Have students verify the assertion of this example that, in finding the sine, cosine, and tangent of 45°, the *size* of the triangle drawn does not matter. Have students repeat the activity using an isosceles right triangle whose legs are each 5 units in length.

Communicating *about* MATHEMATICS

Have students compare the cosines of the given angles. Ask them what conclusions can be made. As angle measures increase from 0° to 90°, the cosine decreases.

Writing Prompt
Explain why all right triangles with a 10° angle are similar.

Technology

Investigating Trigonometric Ratios | **11.8** Name _____

Exploration Using a Computer Drawing Program — In this activity, you will use construction software to learn about three trigonometric ratios: the cosine ratio, the sine ratio, and the tangent ratio.

EXERCISES

1. Construct a random right triangle, △ABC, as shown at the right. Then find the following trigonometric ratios.

$$\cos A = \frac{AC}{AB} = \underline{\ \ \ } \qquad \sin A = \frac{BC}{AB} = \underline{\ \ \ }$$
$$\tan A = \frac{BC}{AC} = \underline{\ \ \ } \qquad \text{Answers vary.}$$

2. Construct two triangles that are similar to the triangle in Exercise 1. Then measure the sides of the triangles and find the indicated ratios to complete the table. Answers vary.

Triangle	AB	BC	AC	$\cos A = \frac{AC}{AB}$	$\sin A = \frac{BC}{AB}$	$\tan A = \frac{BC}{AC}$
1						
2						

3. In all three triangles, what is m∠A? Answers vary.
4. Based on the results of Exercise 1–3, what conclusion can you make about the cosine, sine, and tangent ratios in a right triangle? The trigonometric ratios depend on the measure of the angles, not the lengths of the sides.

Extension

5. Using the original triangle, △ABC, click and drag on point B. Investigate what happens to each trigonometric ratio as m∠A increases and decreases. Write your results in the space below. As m∠A increases, cos A approaches 0, sin A approaches 1, and tan A increases without bound. As m∠A decreases, cos A approaches 1, sin A approaches 0, and tan A approaches 0.

© D.C. Heath and Company — *Technology Using Calculators and Computers* **67**

Lesson 11.8 **523**

ASSIGNMENT GUIDE

*Basic/Average:
Day 1: Ex. 13–23 odd, 30, 31
Day 2: Ex. 24–29, 33, 35

Above Average: Ex. 13–23 odd, 27–29, 32–35

Advanced: Ex. 13–23 odd, 27–29, 32–35

Selected Answers: Ex. 1–11, 12–31 odd

*You may wish to omit this lesson for these students.

Guided Practice

▶ **Ex. 4, 5** These exercises reinforce the idea that all 40°-50°-90° triangles are similar.
▶ **Ex. 6–11** These exercises assess students' understanding of the trigonometric definitions.

Independent Practice

▶ **Ex. 12–17** You may wish to have students verify that the lengths of the three sides satisfy the Pythagorean Theorem. This will help to prepare for the next group of exercises (Ex. 18–21).

Answers

18. $\sin 60° = \dfrac{\sqrt{75}}{10} \approx 0.866$

$\cos 60° = \dfrac{5}{10} = 0.5$

$\tan 60° = \dfrac{\sqrt{75}}{5} \approx 1.732$

$\sin 30° = \dfrac{5}{10} = 0.5$

$\cos 30° = \dfrac{\sqrt{75}}{10} \approx 0.866$

$\tan 30° = \dfrac{5}{\sqrt{75}} \approx 0.577$

19. $\sin 60° = \dfrac{\sqrt{3}}{2} \approx 0.866$

$\cos 60° = \dfrac{1}{2} = 0.5$

$\tan 60° = \dfrac{\sqrt{3}}{1} = \sqrt{3} \approx 1.732$

$\sin 30° = \dfrac{1}{2} = 0.5$

$\cos 30° = \dfrac{\sqrt{3}}{2} \approx 0.866$

$\tan 30° = \dfrac{1}{\sqrt{3}} \approx 0.577$

20. $\sin 50.2° = \dfrac{6}{\sqrt{61}} \approx 0.768$

$\cos 50.2° = \dfrac{5}{\sqrt{61}} = 0.640$

$\tan 50.2° = \dfrac{6}{5} = 1.2$

$\sin 39.8° = \dfrac{5}{\sqrt{61}} = 0.640$

$\cos 39.8° = \dfrac{6}{\sqrt{61}} \approx 0.768$

$\tan 39.8° = \dfrac{5}{6} \approx 0.833$

524 *Chapter 11*

Guided Practice

▶ **CHECK for Understanding**

In Exercises 1–3, match the trigonometric ratio with its definition.

a. $\dfrac{\text{Side opposite } \angle Q}{\text{Hypotenuse}}$
b. $\dfrac{\text{Side opposite } \angle Q}{\text{Side adjacent } \angle Q}$
c. $\dfrac{\text{Side adjacent } \angle Q}{\text{Hypotenuse}}$

1. $\tan Q$ b
2. $\cos Q$ c
3. $\sin Q$ a

4. Sketch a 40°-50°-90° triangle. Use a ruler to approximate the sine, cosine, and tangent of 40°. Check students' work; 0.643, 0.766, 0.839

5. Sketch a 40°-50°-90° triangle that is larger than the one in Exercise 4. Approximate the sine, cosine, and tangent of 40°. Do you get the same results as in Exercise 4? Yes

In Exercises 6–11, use △XYZ at the right to find the trigonometric ratio.

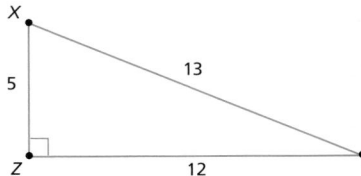

6. $\sin X$ $\dfrac{12}{13} \approx 0.923$
7. $\sin Y$ $\dfrac{5}{13} \approx 0.385$
8. $\cos X$ $\dfrac{5}{13} \approx 0.385$
9. $\cos Y$ $\dfrac{12}{13} \approx 0.923$
10. $\tan X$ $\dfrac{12}{5} = 2.4$
11. $\tan Y$ $\dfrac{5}{12} \approx 0.417$

Independent Practice

In Exercises 12–17, use △DEF at the right to find the trigonometric ratio.
14. $\dfrac{3}{\sqrt{45}} \approx 0.447$ **15.** $\dfrac{6}{\sqrt{45}} \approx 0.894$

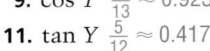

12. $\sin D$ $\dfrac{6}{\sqrt{45}} \approx 0.894$
13. $\sin E$ $\dfrac{3}{\sqrt{45}} \approx 0.447$
14. $\cos D$
15. $\cos E$
16. $\tan D$ $\dfrac{6}{3} = 2$
17. $\tan E$ $\dfrac{3}{6} = 0.5$

In Exercises 18–21, solve the triangle for its unlabeled angle and side. Then write six trigonometric ratios that can be formed with the triangle. For ratios, see margins, pages 524, 525

18.
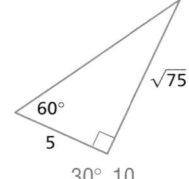
30°, 10

19.
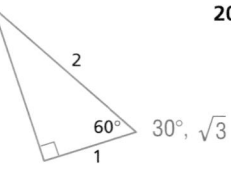
30°, $\sqrt{3}$

20.
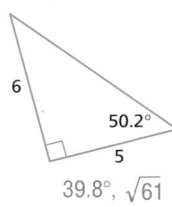
39.8°, $\sqrt{61}$

21.
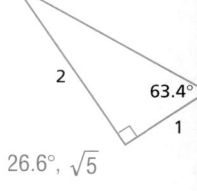
26.6°, $\sqrt{5}$

In Exercises 22 and 23, draw a right triangle, △ABC, that has the given trigonometric ratios. See margin, page 525.

22. $\tan A = \dfrac{15}{8}$, $\cos B = \dfrac{15}{17}$

23. $\sin A = \dfrac{2}{\sqrt{13}}$, $\cos A = \dfrac{3}{\sqrt{13}}$

524 *Chapter 11 • Congruence, Similarity, and Transformations*

Extra Practice

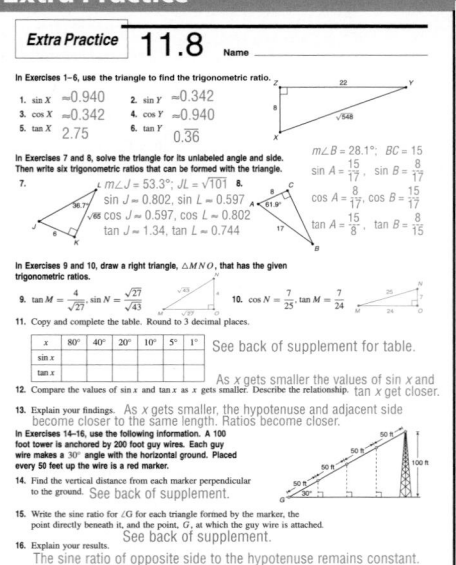

Reteaching

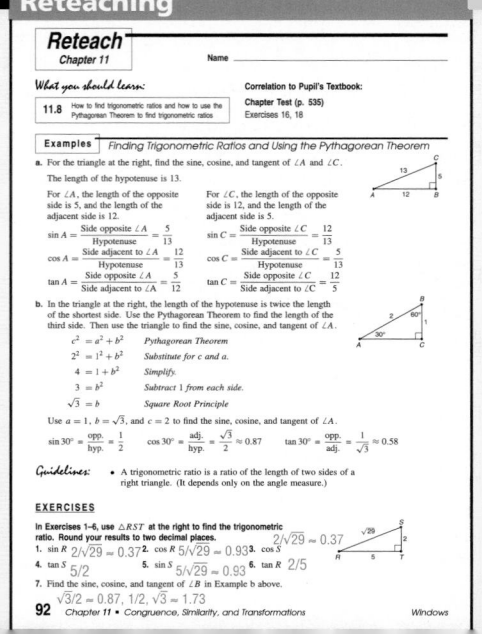

In Exercises 24–26, use the triangles and data that you recorded in
Communicating about Mathematics **on page 523.**

24. Copy and complete the table.   ≈ 0.173, ≈ 0.342, ≈ 0.500, ≈ 0.643, ≈ 0.766, ≈ 0.866, ≈ 0.940, ≈ 0.985;
≈ 0.985, ≈ 0.940, ≈ 0.866, ≈ 0.766, ≈ 0.643, ≈ 0.500, ≈ 0.342, ≈ 0.173

x	10°	20°	30°	40°	50°	60°	70°	80°
sin x	?	?	?	?	?	?	?	?
cos x	?	?	?	?	?	?	?	?

25. Describe the relationship between the sine and cosine values in the
table.   sin x = cos (90° − x)

26. From the table, which angle has the property that sin A = cos A? Draw
a triangle that illustrates your answer. Explain your reasoning.   45°, 45° = 90°−45°

Ballooning   **In Exercises 27–29, use the following
information.**

A balloon is released and travels straight upward. You
are standing 20 meters from the point of release of the
balloon.

27. Write the tangent ratio for each height of the
balloon shown in the diagram.   1, 2

28. Does tan A increase or decrease as $m\angle A$ increases?
Explain.   Increases, only the numerator increases

29. How high is the balloon when tan $A = \frac{1}{2}$?
10 meters

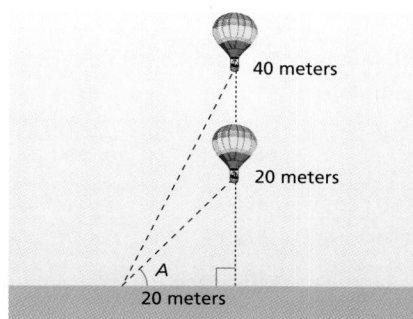

40 meters

20 meters

A

20 meters

Integrated Review

30. *Estimation*   Which of the following best
approximates the measure of the peak of
the triangular front of the pyramid on a
dollar bill?

    a. 24° **b.** 44° **c.** 64° **d.** 84°   b

Making Connections within Mathematics

31. *Estimation*   Which of the following best
approximates the measure of the base angles of the triangular front of the pyramid
on a dollar bill?

    a. 8° **b.** 28° **c.** 48° **d.** 68°   d

Exploration and Extension

**In Exercises 32–35, each of the triangles is similar to one of the triangles at
the bottom of page 523. Write a proportion that allows you to solve for x.
Then solve for x.**

32.
$\frac{25}{13.05} = \frac{x}{10}$,
≈ 19.16
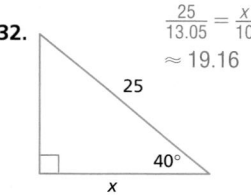
25
40°
x

33.
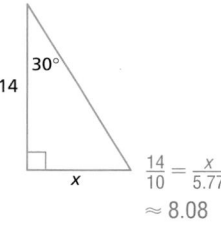
30°
14
x
$\frac{14}{10} = \frac{x}{5.77}$,
≈ 8.08

34.
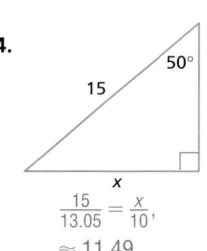
15
50°
x
$\frac{15}{13.05} = \frac{x}{10}$,
≈ 11.49

35. $\frac{22}{3.64} = \frac{x}{10}$,
≈ 60.44
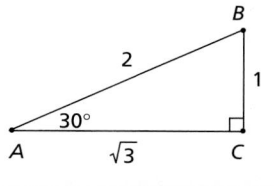
20°
x
22

✪ More difficult exercises
P Portfolio Opportunity

11.8 • *Trigonometric Ratios*   **525**

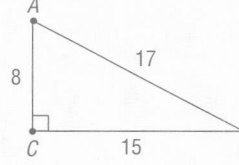
Answers
21. $\sin 63.4° = \frac{2}{\sqrt{5}} \approx 0.894$

$\cos 63.4° = \frac{1}{\sqrt{5}} \approx 0.447$

$\tan 63.4° = \frac{2}{1} = 2$

$\sin 26.6° = \frac{1}{\sqrt{5}} \approx 0.447$

$\cos 26.6° = \frac{2}{\sqrt{5}} \approx 0.894$

$\tan 26.6° = \frac{1}{2} \approx 0.5$

22.
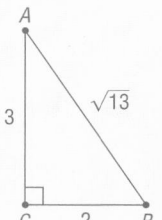
A
8
17
C 15 B

23.
A
3
$\sqrt{13}$
C 2 B

Sin 30° is obtained on a graphing calculator by entering `sin` 30 (not 30 `sin`).

In Exercise 2, you may want to have each student choose a different acute angle and complete the table. After collecting the results and discussing them as a class, students will have more confidence to make a general rule that applies to all acute angles.

Scientific calculators are able to evaluate the sine, cosine, and tangent of an angle.

Example — Using a Scientific Calculator

Use a scientific calculator to evaluate the sine, cosine, and tangent of 30° and 60°. Then use the triangle at the right to evaluate the same trigonometric ratios. Compare your results.

Solution Before beginning, make sure your calculator is set in *degree mode.* (Scientific calculators have another angle measure mode called *radian mode.* This mode will not produce the correct values for this example.)

30°		Display	60°		Display
30	sin	0.5	60	sin	0.866025
30	cos	0.866025	60	cos	0.5
30	tan	0.577350	60	tan	1.732051

Using the triangle at the left, you can find the trigonometric ratio as follows.

$$\sin 30° = \frac{1}{2} = 0.5 \qquad \sin 60° = \frac{\sqrt{3}}{2} \approx 0.866$$

$$\cos 30° = \frac{\sqrt{3}}{2} \approx 0.866 \qquad \cos 60° = \frac{1}{2} = 0.5$$

$$\tan 30° = \frac{1}{\sqrt{3}} \approx 0.577 \qquad \tan 60° = \frac{\sqrt{3}}{1} = 1.732$$

Exercises

1. Use a scientific calculator to evaluate the sine, cosine, and tangent of 15° and 75°. Then use the triangle at the right to evaluate the same trigonometric ratios. Compare your results. Results are the same.
   sin 15° ≈ 0.259, cos 15° ≈ 0.966, tan 15° ≈ 0.268; sin 75° ≈ 0.966, cos 75° ≈ 0.259, tan 75° ≈ 3.732

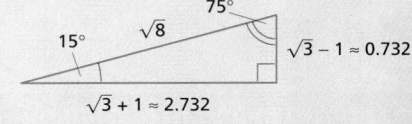

$\sqrt{3} - 1 \approx 0.732$

$\sqrt{3} + 1 \approx 2.732$

P 2. *Discovering a Trigonometric Property* Choose any acute angle, *A*. Then use a scientific calculator to complete the table. What can you conclude? Write your conclusion as a rule that applies to all acute angles. Check students' work.

A	sin A	(sin A)²	cos A	(cos A)²	(sin A)² + (cos A)²
?	?	?	?	?	?

$(\sin A)^2 + (\cos A)^2 = 1$

11.9

Problem Solving Using Trigonometric Ratios

▶**PACING** the Lesson

Suggested Number of Days
Basic/Average 0 **Above Average** 2
Advanced 2

▶**PLANNING** the Lesson

Lesson Plan 11.9, p. 93

What you should learn:

Goal 1 How to use trigonometric ratios to solve right triangles

Goal 2 How to use trigonometric ratios to solve real-life problems

Why you should learn it:

You can use trigonometric ratios to solve real-life measurement problems, such as finding the height of a building.

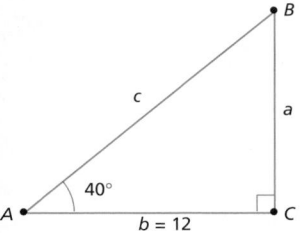

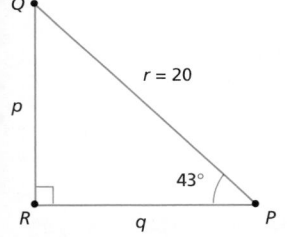

Goal 1 **Solving Right Triangles**

In Lesson 9.3, you learned how to use the Pythagorean Theorem to solve a right triangle. In that situation, you were given the lengths of two sides of the triangle and asked to find the length of the third side.

In this lesson, you will learn how to solve a right triangle when you are given the length of only one of the sides and the measure of one of the acute angles.

Example 1 *Solving a Right Triangle*

a. In $\triangle ABC$ at the left, find a.
b. In $\triangle PQR$ at the left, find q.

Solution

a. To find a, you can write the trigonometric ratio for the tangent of A.

$$\tan A = \frac{a}{b} \qquad \textit{Definition of tangent of A}$$
$$\tan 40° = \frac{a}{12} \qquad \textit{Substitute for A and b.}$$
$$0.8391 \approx \frac{a}{12} \qquad \textit{Use a calculator.}$$
$$12(0.8391) \approx 12\left(\frac{a}{12}\right) \qquad \textit{Multiply each side by 12.}$$
$$10.07 \approx a \qquad \textit{Simplify.}$$

The length of $\overline{BC}$ is about 10.07.

b. To find q, you can write the trigonometric ratio for the cosine of P.

$$\cos P = \frac{q}{r} \qquad \textit{Definition of cosine of P}$$
$$\cos 43° = \frac{q}{20} \qquad \textit{Substitute for P and r.}$$
$$0.7314 \approx \frac{q}{20} \qquad \textit{Use a calculator.}$$
$$20(0.7314) \approx 20\left(\frac{q}{20}\right) \qquad \textit{Multiply each side by 20.}$$
$$14.63 \approx q \qquad \textit{Simplify.}$$

The length of $\overline{RP}$ is about 14.63. ■

11.9 • *Problem Solving Using Trigonometric Ratios* **527**

ORGANIZER

Starters (reproduced below)
  Problem of the Day 11.9, p. 33
  Warm-Up Exercises 11.9, p. 33
Lesson Resources
  Color Transparencies
    Diagram for Example 2, p. 48
  Math Log, p. 36
  Answer Masters 11.9, p. 228
  Extra Practice Copymaster 11.9, p. 93
  Reteaching Copymaster 11.9, p. 93
Special Populations
  Suggestions, Teacher's Edition, p. 486D

LESSON Notes

Have students record in their journals the two methods for solving right triangles. Be sure the conditions for implementing each approach are included.

Example 1
Have students explain why neither the sine nor the cosine ratio should be used in part **a**. Ask students how the sine ratio might be used in part **b**.
Since $m\angle Q = 90° - 43° = 47°$, use $\sin 47° = \frac{q}{20}$ to solve for q.

Example 2

A *clinometer* is an instrument that can be used to measure angles of elevation. This tool could be used to gather information as required in the example.

Communicating
about MATHEMATICS

Many students may not have seen a carpenter's level or know how to use it. If possible, ask a student who has a level and can demonstrate its use to do so for the class prior to the assignment. Alternatively, invite a student from the carpentry shop to do a demonstration for the class.

Writing Prompt
What does it mean to *solve* for the parts of a triangle?

Gregory and Carolynn Schipa are the owners of The Weather Hill Restoration Company, which specializes in restoring historical buildings.

Answer to Communicating

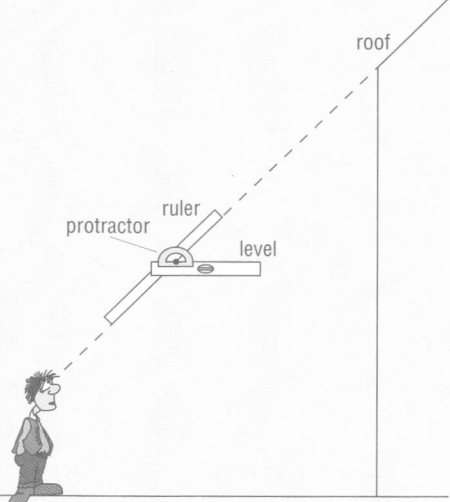

Goal 2 **Solving Real-Life Problems**

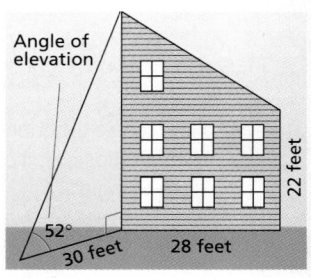
Real Life
Construction

Example 2 *Using Trigonometric Ratios*

You are restoring a historical building. To estimate the height of the roof's peak, you stand 30 feet back from the building and measure the angle to the peak to be 52=×". How high is the peak? Use your result to find the area of the side of the building.

Solution Let h represent the height of the building (in feet).

$$\tan 52° = \frac{h}{30} \qquad \textit{Definition of tangent}$$

$$1.280 \approx \frac{h}{30} \qquad \textit{Use a calculator.}$$

$$30(1.280) \approx 30 \cdot \frac{h}{30} \qquad \textit{Multiply each side by 30.}$$

$$38.4 \approx h \qquad \textit{Simplify.}$$

The height of the building is about 38.4 feet. To find the area of the side, use the formula for the area of a trapezoid. (The height of the building is one of the bases of the trapezoid.)

$$\text{Area} = \frac{1}{2}(\text{Base 1} + \text{Base 2})(\text{Height})$$
$$\approx \frac{1}{2}(38.4 + 22)(28)$$
$$\approx 845.6$$

The area of the side is about 845.6 square feet.

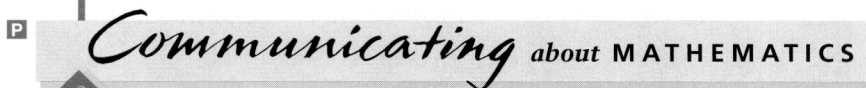

Communicating *about* MATHEMATICS

▶ **SHARING IDEAS about the Lesson**

Cooperative Learning

Measuring Angles A carpenter's level can be used to draw horizontal lines. Explain to your partner how you could use a carpenter's level and a protractor to estimate the angle of a roof. See margin.

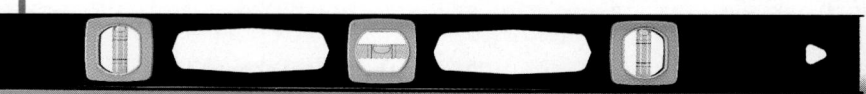

EXERCISES

Guided Practice

▶ CHECK for Understanding

In Exercises 1–4, use the triangle at the right.

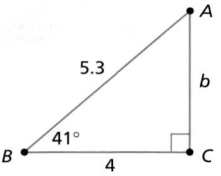

1. Use tan 41° to solve for b. ≈ 3.48
2. Use sin 41° to solve for b. ≈ 3.48
3. Use the Pythagorean Theorem to solve for b. ≈ 3.48
4. *It's Up to You* Which of the methods in Exercises 1–3 do you prefer? Explain your reasoning. Answers vary.

Flagpole **In Exercises 5 and 6, use the diagram at the right.**

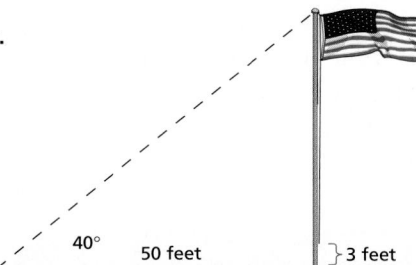

5. You stand 50 feet from the flagpole. The angle from the point where you stand to the top of the flagpole is 40°. How tall is the flagpole? ≈ 41.95 ft
6. The rope used to raise and lower the flag is secured three feet above the ground. What is the minimum length of the rope? (*Hint:* The rope must be tied in a loop.) ≈ 77.90 ft

Independent Practice

In Exercises 7–10, find the value of the trigonometric ratio.

7. cos 33° ≈ 0.839   8. tan 74° ≈ 3.487   9. sin 44° ≈ 0.695   10. cos 80° ≈ 0.174

In Exercises 11–14, find the length of the labeled side. Round your results to two decimal places.

11. 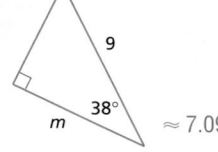 ≈ 7.09
12. 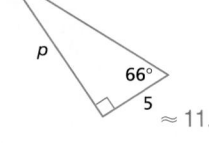 ≈ 11.23
13. 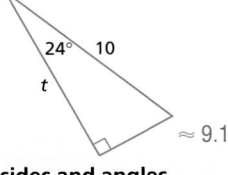 ≈ 9.14
14. 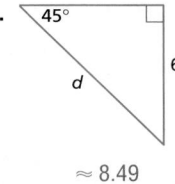 ≈ 8.49

In Exercises 15–18, solve the right triangle for all labeled sides and angles. Round your results to two decimal places. See margin.

15.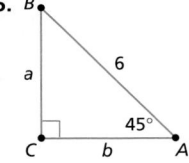
16.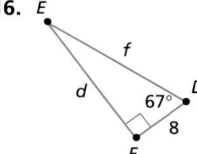
17.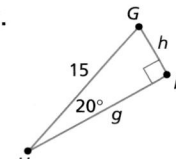
18.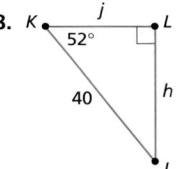

11.9 • *Problem Solving Using Trigonometric Ratios* **529**

EXERCISE Notes

ASSIGNMENT GUIDE
*Basic/Average:
  Day 1: Ex. 7–19 odd, 25, 27
  Day 2: Ex. 20–24, 29
Above Average:
  Day 1: Ex. 7–19 odd, 20
  Day 2: Ex. 21–29
Advanced:
  Day 1: Ex. 7–19 odd
  Day 2: Ex. 21–24, 25–29 odd
Selected Answers: Ex. 1–6, 7–27 odd

* You may wish to omit this lesson for these students.

Guided Practice
Have individual groups answer these questions before sharing with the entire class.
▶ **Ex. 4** It is important for students to recognize that there is more than one way to solve for b, and some methods might be better than others.

Independent Practice
▶ **Ex. 7–10** Make sure that students set their calculators to *degree* mode rather than *radian* mode.
▶ **Ex. 15–18** There are different methods of solution, so students should be encouraged to record their work in a neat and organized fashion.

Extra Practice

Extra Practice 11.9 Name _____

In Exercises 1–3, find the value of the trigonometric ratio. Round your answer to four decimal places.
1. tan 62° 1.8807   2. cos 57° 0.5446   3. sin 89° 0.9998

In Exercises 4–6, find the length of the labeled side. Round your results to two decimal places.
4. 15.49   5. 9.54   6. 5.71

In Exercises 7–9, solve the right triangle for all labeled sides and angles. Round your results to two decimal places.
7. $m\angle N = 48°$ $o = 20.07$ $n = 22.29$
8. $m\angle R = 61°$ $p = 6.65$ $q = 13.72$
9. $m\angle V = 28°$ $t = 15.05$ $s = 17.04$

10. From a 150 feet observation tower on the coast, a coast guard officer sights a boat in difficulty. The angle of depression of the boat is 4°, as shown. How far is the boat from the shoreline? ≈2145 ft

11. A train is traveling up a slight grade with an angle of inclination of only 2°. After traveling 1 mile, what is the vertical change in feet? (1 mile = 5280 feet) ≈184 ft

12. Use the diagram to find the distance across the bridge. ≈499 ft

Windows   11.9 • Problem Solving Using Trigonometric Ratios **93**

Reteaching

Reteach Chapter 11 Name _____

What you should learn:
11.9 How to use trigonometric ratios to solve right triangles and how to use trigonometric ratios to solve real-life problems

Correlation to Pupil's Textbook:
Chapter Test (p. 535)
Exercises 12, 13, 17, 19

Example Solving Right Triangles and Solving Real-Life Problems
a. You are designing a ramp for performing tricks on water skis. If the length of the ramp is 12 feet, what is the length of the vertical drop, d?

To find d, you can write the trigonometric ratio for the sine of $\angle D$.

$\sin D = \dfrac{d}{c}$ *Definition of sine of D*

$\sin 10° = \dfrac{d}{12}$ *Substitute for D and c.*

$0.1736 = \dfrac{d}{12}$ *Use a calculator.*

$12(0.1736) \approx \dfrac{12d}{12}$ *Multiply each side by 12.*

$2.08 \approx d$ *Simplify.*

The length of the vertical drop, d, is about 2.08 feet.

Guidelines: • You can use a trigonometric ratio to solve a right triangle when you are given the length of one of the sides and the measure of one of the acute angles.

EXERCISES

In Exercises 1–4, find x. Round your results to two decimal places.
1. 10.46   2. 9.77   3. 21.25   4. 12.72

5. If you change your ramp design in Example a so that the ramp is elevated 25° from the water, what is the length of the vertical drop, d? ≈ 5.07 feet

Windows   Chapter 11 • Congruence, Similarity, and Transformations **93**

Answers
15. $a \approx 4.24$, $b \approx 4.24$, $m\angle B = 45°$
16. $d \approx 18.85$, $f \approx 20.47$, $m\angle E = 23°$
17. $h \approx 5.13$, $g \approx 14.10$, $m\angle G = 70°$
18. $h \approx 31.52$, $i \approx 24.63$, $m\angle J = 38°$

Lesson 11.9 **529**

► **Ex. 21–24** Assign these exercises as a group.

Integrated Review

These exercises review simple percents.

Exploration and Extension

This is an excellent opportunity for students to generate their own overview of Chapters 10 and 11.

Portfolio Opportunity: Math Log

Use the figure below. Find two different ways to find *a*.

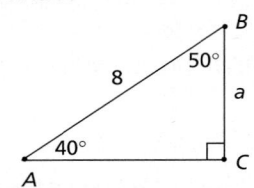

Also available as a copymaster, page 36, Ex. 12

---

19. *Loading Dock*   The angle of depression between the road and the loading ramp is 8°. Find the height, *h*, of the loading dock. ≈ 2.99 ft

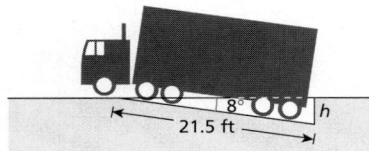

20. *Lighthouse*   You are standing on a path 10 meters from a lighthouse. The angle of elevation to the top is 50°. How tall is the lighthouse? ≈ 11.92 m

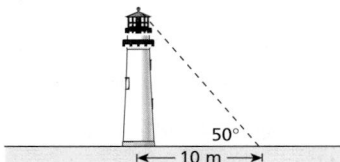

Giraffes   **In Exercises 21–24, use the following information.**

You are standing 22 meters from a mother giraffe and her baby. The angle of elevation to the mother's head is 11° and the angle to the baby's head is 5°.

✪ **21.** How tall is the mother? ≈ 4.276 m

✪ **22.** How tall is the baby? ≈ 1.925 m

✪ **23.** What is the difference in heights of the two giraffes? ≈ 2.35 m

✪ **24.** Is the difference in height equal to 22 sin(11°–5°)? Explain.
No, the 6° angle is in a triangle that is not a right triangle.

Integrated Review

Making Connections within Mathematics

Television Channels   **In Exercises 25–28, use the graph at the right.** *(Source: Nielsen Media Research)*

25. What percent of the possible channels are watched by people who receive 36 channels? ≈ 36%

26. What percent of the possible channels are watched by people who receive 58 channels? ≈ 24%

27. What percent of the possible channels are watched by people who receive 80 channels? ≈ 18%

28. If the people who receive 80 channels watched the same percent as those who receive 36 channels, how many channels would they watch? 29

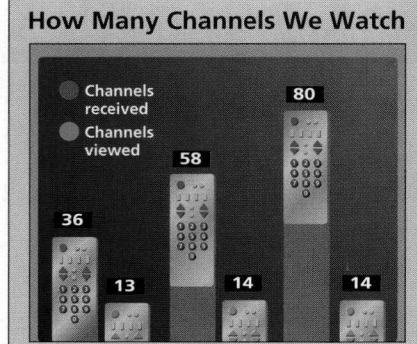

How Many Channels We Watch

Studies show that people don't watch more channels when more are available.

Exploration and Extension

✪ **29.** *You Be the Teacher*   Imagine that you are teaching this course and are writing a test that covers the geometry in Chapters 10 and 11. Write a test that has 20 questions and covers the important concepts in the two chapters. In your test, include at least one multiple-choice question, at least one question that requires a calculator, and at least one question that requires a paragraph answer. Check students' work.

✪ More difficult exercises
P Portfolio Opportunity

Chapter Summary

What did you learn?

Skills

1. Find the area and perimeter of a polygon. **(11.1)**
2. Determine whether two figures are congruent. **(11.2)**
3. Reflect a figure in a line. **(11.3)**
   - Connect reflections and line symmetry. **(11.3)**
4. Rotate a figure about a point. **(11.4)**
   - Connect rotations and rotational symmetry. **(11.4)**
5. Translate a figure in a plane. **(11.5)**
   - Translate a figure in a coordinate plane. **(11.5)**
6. Recognize similar figures. **(11.6)**
   - Use properties of similar figures. **(11.6)**
   - Compare perimeters and areas of similar figures. **(11.7)**
7. Find trigonometric ratios. **(11.8)**
   - Use trigonometric ratios to solve right triangles. **(11.9)**

em-Solving Strategies

8. Use geometric figures to model and solve real-life problems. **(11.1–11.9)**

Exploring Data

9. Use tables and graphs to solve problems. **(11.1–11.9)**

Why did you learn it?

Congruence, similarity, and transformations can be used to answer questions about many real-life situations. For instance, in this chapter you learned how to analyze the symmetry of clothing patterns, how to use transformations to create computer animations, how to use properties of similar figures to plan a sign or a poster, and how to use trigonometric ratios to indirectly measure the height of a building.

How does it fit into the bigger picture of mathematics?

Before studying this chapter, you already knew that part of geometry is measuring lengths, angles, perimeters, and areas. In this chapter, you learned that geometry is more than measuring. It is also about comparing figures to determine whether they are congruent or similar. For instance, if one figure can be slid, flipped, or rotated so that it fits exactly on top of another figure, then the two figures are congruent. Knowing that figures are congruent or similar is important because it can save you problem-solving time. For instance, if you have already measured the angles of one figure, you don't need to remeasure the angles of a figure that you know is similar (because you know the similar figure must have the same angle measures).

Chapter Summary **531**

COOPERATIVE LEARNING
Encourage students to study together. Emphasize the importance of teaching a classmate how to perform a skill or how to recall a procedure. When students work together, everyone wins. The students receiving help get additional instruction, and the students giving help gain a deeper understanding of the skills and concepts involved.

Chapter SUMMARY

In this chapter, students were introduced in Lesson 11.1 to the basic technique of dividing up an irregular region into several smaller regular regions whose area can be computed with formulas. In Lesson 11.2, the concept of congruence, briefly introduced in the previous chapter, was defined specifically for triangles. Students were given further opportunities for identifying congruent figures by reasoning and critical thinking. Lessons 11.3–11.5 dealt with the three isometric transformations, reflection, rotation, and translation. Lesson 11.6 introduced another major topic of geometry, similarity. In Lesson 11.7 students had an opportunity to maintain their skill in solving proportions as they applied the concept of similarity to indirect measurement. Lessons 11.8 and 11.9 took indirect measurement a step further into trigonometry and the use of trigonometric ratios.

Chapter REVIEW

Have students begin this Review in class and complete it as a homework assignment.

ASSIGNMENT GUIDE

*Basic/Average:
Ex. 1–9 odd, 18–21 even, 42–61

Above Average and Advanced:
Ex. 12–28 even, 30–38 even, 42–61

*For these students, you will need to limit assignments to cover only those lessons you chose to teach from this chapter.

Resources
Answer Masters, pp. 229, 230

In Exercises 1–4, find the perimeter and area of the polygon. (11.1)

1.
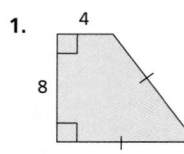

2.
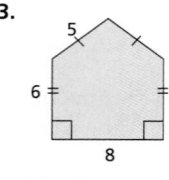

3.
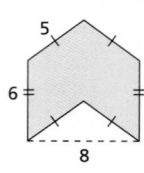

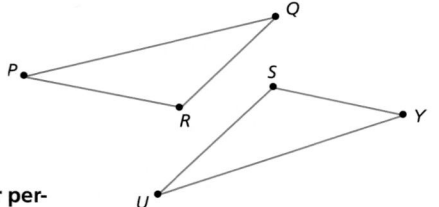

32 units, 56 units²   28 units, 32 units²   30 units, 60 units²   32 units, 48 units²

In Exercises 5–10, use the fact that △PQR ≅ △UYS to complete the statement. (11.2)

5. $\overline{PQ} \cong \boxed{?}\ \overline{UY}$

6. $\angle S \cong \boxed{?}\ \angle R$

7. $\angle Q \cong \boxed{?}\ \angle Y$

8. $\overline{SU} \cong \boxed{?}\ \overline{RP}$

9. $\angle U \cong \boxed{?}\ \angle P$

10. $\overline{QR} \cong \boxed{?}\ \overline{YS}$

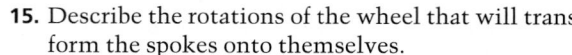
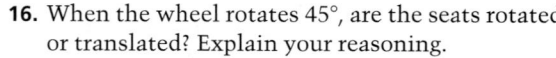

In Exercises 11–14, find the vertices of the figure after performing the indicated transformation. (11.3–11.5)

11. Reflect the figure in the *y*-axis.

12. Rotate the figure counterclockwise 90° about the origin.

13. Translate the figure 6 units to the right and 5 units down.

14. Reflect the figure in the *x*-axis, then translate it 2 units to the right. **11.–14.** See margin.

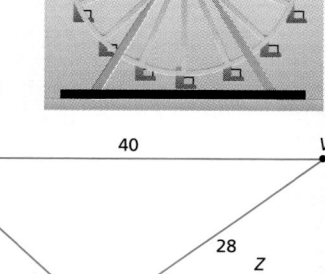

Ferris Wheel **In Exercises 15–17, use the Ferris wheel at the right. (11.3–11.5) 15.–17.** See margin.

15. Describe the rotations of the wheel that will transform the spokes onto themselves.

16. When the wheel rotates 45°, are the seats rotated or translated? Explain your reasoning.

✪ 17. With the seats, does the Ferris wheel have any lines of symmetry? Without the seats, does it have any lines of symmetry? Explain.

In Exercises 18–21, use the fact that △UVW ~ △XYZ. (11.6) 18. See below.

18. Write three proportions for △UVW and △XYZ.

19. Find the scale factor of △XYZ to △UVW. $\frac{1}{4}$

20. Find UW and YZ. 24 and 7

21. Find the ratio of the perimeter of △XYZ to the perimeter of △UVW. Is this ratio equal to the scale factor? $\frac{1}{4}$, yes

18. $\frac{UV}{XY} = \frac{UW}{XZ}$, $\frac{UV}{XY} = \frac{VW}{YZ}$, $\frac{UW}{XZ} = \frac{VW}{YZ}$

Answers
11. (1, 2), (3, 3), (5, 1), (3, 0)
12. (−2, −1), (−3, −3), (−1, −5), (0, −3)
13. (5, −3), (3, −2), (1, −4), (3, −5)
14. (1, −2), (−1, −3), (−3, −1), (−1, 0)
15. 22.5°, 45°, 67.5°, 90°, 112.5°, 135°, 157.5°, 180° in either direction
16. Translated, the bottoms of the seats remain parallel to the ground.
17. No, yes. The seats all face one way and make the wheel unsymmetrical.

In Exercises 22–24, complete the statement using *always, sometimes, or never*. (11.6)

22. Two congruent figures are ☐ similar. always

23. Two similar figures are ☐ congruent. sometimes

24. A square and a trapezoid are ☐ similar. never

Dollar Bills   **In Exercises 25–28, use the drawing of the dollar bill. (11.7)**

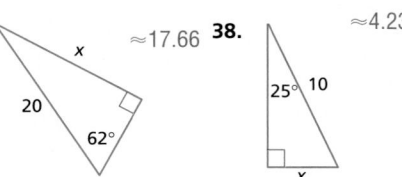

25. The actual width of a dollar bill is 6.6 centimeters. Use the scale drawing at the right to find the actual length. 15.4 cm

26. Find the scale factor of an actual dollar bill to the drawing. 2.2

27. Find the area of the bill and its drawing. 101.64 cm², 21 cm²

28. Find the ratio of the area of an actual bill to the area of the drawing. How does this relate to the scale factor?
4.84, it is the square of the scale factor.

In Exercises 29–34, use △*MNO* to find the trigonometric ratio. Round your result to two decimal places. (11.8)

29. sin *M* 0.89   **30.** sin *N* 0.45

31. cos *M* 0.45   **32.** cos *N* 0.89

33. tan *M* 2   **34.** tan *N* 0.5

In Exercises 35–38, find the value of *x*. (11.9)

35.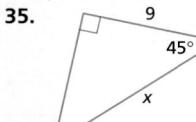
9
45°
x
≈12.73

36.
7
≈10.00
35°
x

37.
x
≈17.66
20
62°

38.
≈4.23
25° 10
x

Drawing a Diagram   **In Exercises 39–41, use the following information. (11.9)**

A helicopter is hovering over a lifeboat that is floating in the ocean. You are in another boat that is 300 feet from the lifeboat. From your location, the angle of elevation to the helicopter is 42°.

39. Draw a diagram of the situation.   See margin.

40. *Without* using a calculator, estimate the height of the helicopter.   Estimates vary.

41. Use trigonometry and a calculator to find the height of the helicopter.   ≈270.12 ft

Because of their ability to hover, land, and take off in small areas, helicopters are often used in rescue operations.

Answer 39.

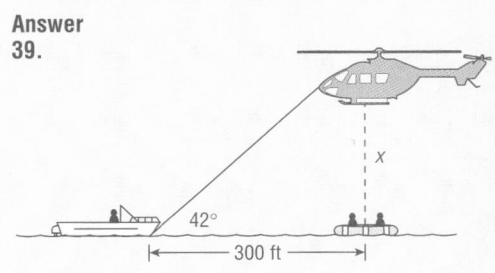

Figure not drawn to scale

Real Li

Connecti

Voyage to Mars In Exercises 42–60, use the figure to find the indicated measure. (11.1, 11.2, 11.6, 11.8)

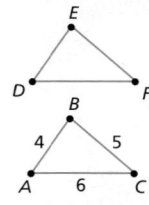

△*ABC* ≅ △ *DEF*

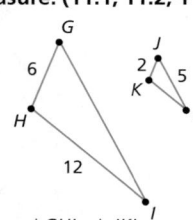

△*GHI* ~ △ *JKL*

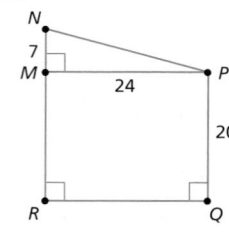

This painting is by artist Kelly Freas. It first appeared on the cover of a science fiction novel in 1954. The title of the painting is hidden in VI.

42. **a:** Length of $\overline{EF}$ 5
43. **c:** Length of $\overline{DF}$ 6
44. **d:** Perimeter of △*DEF* 15
45. **e:** Perimeter of *MPQR* 88
46. **f:** Length of $\overline{KL}$ 4
47. **g:** Perimeter of △*GHI* 33
48. **h:** Perimeter of △*JKL* 11
49. **i:** Length of $\overline{NP}$ 25
50. **j:** Perimeter of △*MNP* 56
51. **k:** Area of △*MNP* 84
52. **l:** Tangent of ∠*P* $\frac{7}{24}$
53. **m:** Tangent of ∠*N* $\frac{24}{7}$
54. **n:** Sine of ∠*P* $\frac{7}{25}$
55. **o:** Length of $\overline{QR}$ 24
56. **r:** Cosine of ∠*P* $\frac{24}{25}$
57. **s:** Area of *MPQR* 480
58. **t:** Perimeter of *NPQR* 96
59. **u:** Area of *NPQR* 564
60. **w:** Scale factor of △*GHI* to △*JKL* 3

⊘ 61. **Voyage to Mars** Use the letter codes found in Exercises 42-60 to decode the following messages. Each message is related to a CD that was developed by the Planetary Society, Time Warner Interactive Group, and Russia's Institute for Space Research. (Some of the messages are names of people who worked on the project and the other messages are items that are contained on the CD.) The CD will be part of a space capsule that will be sent to Mars in 1995.

III. War of the Worlds

I. $6\ 5\ \frac{24}{25}\ \frac{7}{24}$ $480\ 5\ 33\ 5\ \frac{7}{25}$ Carl Sagan

II. $56\ 564\ 15\ 25\ 96\ 11$ $\frac{24}{7}\ 88\ \frac{24}{25}\ \frac{24}{25}\ 25\ \frac{7}{24}$ Judith Merril

III. $3\ 5\ \frac{24}{25}$ $24\ 4$ $96\ 11\ 88$ $3\ 24\ \frac{24}{25}\ \frac{7}{24}\ 15\ 480$

IV. $480\ 96\ 5\ \frac{24}{25}$ $96\ \frac{24}{25}\ 88\ 84$ Star Trek

V. $96\ 11\ 88$ $\frac{24}{7}\ 5\ \frac{24}{25}\ 96\ 25\ 5\ \frac{7}{25}$ The Martian Chronicles
   $6\ 11\ \frac{24}{25}\ 24\ \frac{7}{25}\ 25\ 6\ \frac{7}{24}\ 88\ 480$

VI. $\frac{7}{24}\ 25\ 96\ 96\ \frac{7}{24}\ 88$ $33\ \frac{24}{25}\ 88\ 88\ \frac{7}{25}$ $\frac{24}{7}\ 5\ \frac{7}{25}$
   Little Green Man

This photo was taken on Mars during the Viking II mission.

In Exercises 1–3, find the area and perimeter of the figure. (11.1)

1.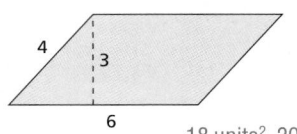

   18 units², 20 units

2.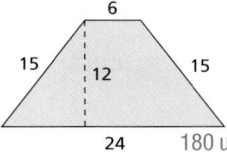

   180 units², 60 units

3. 60 units², 40 units

   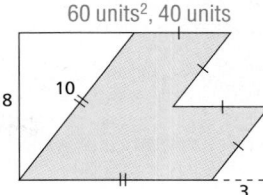

In Exercises 4–7, write the coordinates of the image of △**MNP. (11.3–11.5)**

4. Reflect △*MNP* in the *y*-axis. *M'*(4, 2), *N'*(2, 1), *P'*(1, 4)

5. Rotate △*MNP* clockwise 90° about the origin. **5., 6.** See above.

6. Rotate △*MNP* clockwise 180° about the origin.

5. *M'*(2, 4), *N'*(1, 2), *P'*(4, 1)   6. *M'*(4, −2), *N'*(2, −1), *P'*(1, −4)

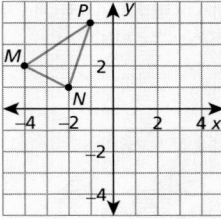

7. Translate △*MNP* 2 units to the right and 3 units down.
   M'(−2, −1), *N'*(0, −2), *P'*(1,1)

In Exercises 8–11, state whether the blue lion is congruent to the red lion. If it is, describe the transformation that will map the blue lion to the red lion. (11.2–11.5) 10. Translation 2 units to the right and 3 units down

8.

   Yes

   Reflection over the line

9.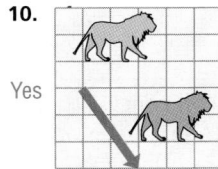

   Yes

   Rotation 45° clockwise

10.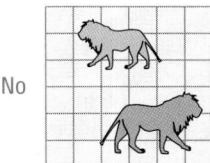

    Yes   No

In Exercises 12 and 13, use the diagram at the right. (11.9)

12. How high is the bird? ≈ 42.84 ft

13. Find the distance between the bird and point *P*. ≈ 52.30 ft

In Exercises 14 and 15, you are creating a small model of a sculpture that is 78 inches high and 24 inches wide. (11.7)

14. If the model is 6 inches wide, how tall should it be? 19.5 in.

15. If the model is 6 inches high, how wide should it be? ≈ 1.85 in.

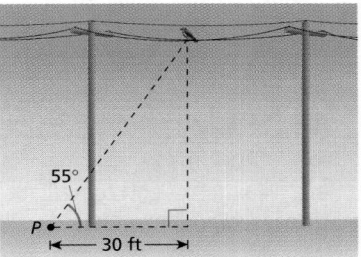

In Exercises 16–20, use the triangles at the right. (11.2, 11.6, 11.8)

16. Find tan 35°. ≈ 0.700

17. Use the result of Exercise 16 to find *AC*. ≈ 11.20 cm

18. Find cos 35°. ≈ 0.819

19. Use the result of Exercise 18 to find *EF*. ≈ 17.20 cm

20. Are △*ABC* and △*DEF* congruent or similar? Explain.
    Similar, the corresponding angles are congruent and *CB* ≠ *EF*.

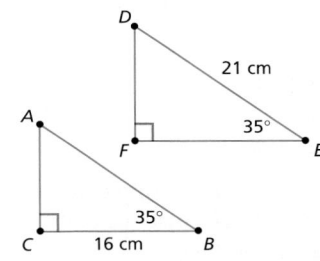

Chapter Test **535**

◄ Formal Assessment

Three **Chapter Tests.** Form A is of average difficulty, Form B is of average difficulty in multiple choice format, and Form C is more challenging.
Available as copymasters, pages 181–189

Chapter Test **535**

CHAPTER 12 GOALS

CHAPTER 12 ▪ OVERVIEW

RESOURCES ORGANIZER

Lesson Pages	12.1 539–542	12.2 544–547	12.3 549–552	12.4 554–557	12.5 559–562	12.6 564–568	12.7 569–572	12.8 573–576
Lesson Plans	94	95	96	97	98	99	100	101
Problem of the Day	34	34	34	35	35	35	36	36
Warm-Up Exercises	34	34	34	35	35	35	36	36
Color Transparencies	49	50, 51	52	—	—	52	53	53
Teaching Tools: Transparencies Copymasters	— C22	— C23–C30	— C23, C28	T1, T9 C2, C11	— —	— —	— —	— —
Math Log	37	37	37	38	38	38, 39	39	39
Technology	69	—	—	—	70, 71	—	—	72
Answer Masters	232, 233,	234	235, 236	238	239	240	242, 243	244, 245
Extra Practice Copymasters	94	95	96	97	98	99	100	101
Reteaching Copymasters	94	95	96	97	98	99	100	101
Enrichment Projects	63, 64	—	65, 66	—	—	—	—	—
Alternative Assessment: Projects Partner Quizzes Group Assessment	37 — —	— — 81, 82	— — —	— 55 —	— — —	— — —	37, 38 — —	— — —
Formal Assessment Short Quizzes Tests	— —	190 —	— —	191 192, 193	— —	194 —	— —	195 196–204
Overhead Manipulatives Kit	—	—	—	—	—	—	—	—
Complete Solutions Manual	Includes step-by-step solutions for all exercises in the student text							
Computerized Test Bank	Creates customized tests that include graphics							
Interactive CD-ROM Project	Provides an interactive and interdisciplinary chapter project							

STARTERS

Problem of the Day

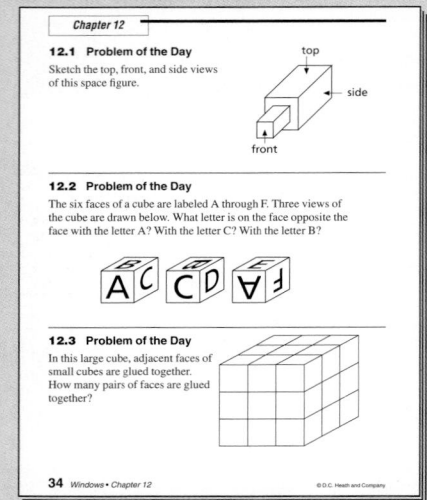

Chapter 12

12.1 Problem of the Day

Sketch the top, front, and side views of this space figure.

12.2 Problem of the Day

The six faces of a cube are labeled A through F. Three views of the cube are drawn below. What letter is on the face opposite the face with the letter A? With the letter C? With the letter B?

12.3 Problem of the Day

In this large cube, adjacent faces of small cubes are glued together. How many pairs of faces are glued together?

34 Windows • Chapter 12   © D.C. Heath and Company

Warm-Up Exercises

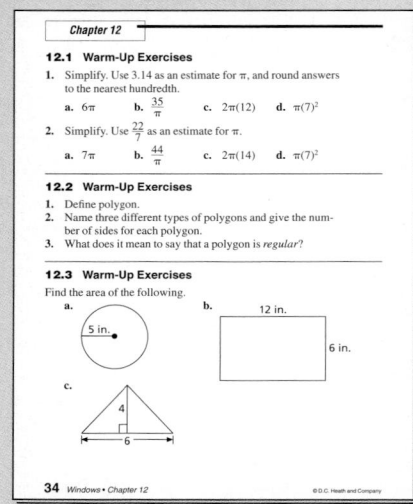

Chapter 12

12.1 Warm-Up Exercises

1. Simplify. Use 3.14 as an estimate for π, and round answers to the nearest hundredth.

   a. 6π b. $\frac{35}{\pi}$ c. $2\pi(12)$ d. $\pi(7)^2$

2. Simplify. Use $\frac{22}{7}$ as an estimate for π.

   a. 7π b. $\frac{44}{\pi}$ c. $2\pi(14)$ d. $\pi(7)^2$

12.2 Warm-Up Exercises

1. Define polygon.
2. Name three different types of polygons and give the number of sides for each polygon.
3. What does it mean to say that a polygon is *regular*?

12.3 Warm-Up Exercises

Find the area of the following.

a. (circle with 5 in. radius)   b. (rectangle 12 in. by 6 in.)

c. (triangle with height 4 and base 6)

34 Windows • Chapter 12   © D.C. Heath and Company

FOR TEACHERS

Answer Masters

Answers for Lesson 12.1, pages 541 and 542

1. Both relate the diameter to the circumference.
2. $\approx 25,000$ miles
3. $\overline{BC}$
4. $\overline{AB}, \overline{AC}$
5. ≈ 44.0 cm
6. ≈ 153.9 cm^2
7. 7.5 cm, 4.5 cm^2
8. 37.1 in., 109.3 in.^{2}
9. 25.1 in., 50.2 in.^{2}
10. 50.2 in., 201.0 in.^{2}
11. 0.7 ft, 1.4 ft
12. 11.5 in., 23.0 in.
13. 2.4 in., 4.7 in.
14. 9.5 mm, 19.0 mm
15. 5.7 in.^{2}
16. 31.7 in.^{2}
17. 13.8 mm^2
18. 9.4 ft^2

19.
Radius	1	2	3	4	5	6
Circumference	6.28	12.56	18.84	25.12	31.40	37.68

For every one-unit increase in the radius, the circumference increases 6.28 units.

20.
Radius	1	2	3	4	5	6
Circumference	3.14	12.56	28.26	50.24	78.50	113.04

For every one-unit increase in the radius after the first increase, the area increases by the square of the ratio of the radius to the previous radius.

21. The circumference doubles; $C_1 = \pi d$, $C_2 = \pi(2d) = 2(\pi d)$. The area quadruples; $A_1 = \pi r^2$, $A_2 = \pi(2r)^2 = \pi(4r^2) = 4(\pi r^2)$
22. Answers vary.
23. 113.04 in.^{2}
24. 8
25. 18.84 in.^{2}
26. 62.8 mi
27. 314 mi^2
28. 39 %

232 Windows Answer Masters   © D.C. Heath and Company

Lesson Plans

Lesson Plan 12.1
pages 539–542

Teacher's Name _____ Class _____ Date _____ Room _____

Goals   1. Find the circumference of a circle.
            2. Find the area of a circle.

State/Local Objectives

NCTM Curriculum Standards: Communication, Reasoning, Connections, Number Relationships, Computation and Estimation, Technology, Patterns and Functions, Algebra, Geometry, Measurement

✔ **Check items you wish to use for this lesson.**

Introducing the Lesson
___ Problem of the Day copymaster page 34 or Teacher's Edition page 539
___ Warm-Up Exercises copymaster page 34 or Teacher's Edition page 539

Teaching the Lesson using the following:
___ Alternate Approach for Example 2, Teacher's Edition page 540
___ Extra Examples, Teacher's Edition page 540
___ Color Transparencies: picture for Example 2 and diagram for Ex. 26–28, page 49
___ Teaching Tools: copy of pies for Ex. 31, 32, page C22
___ Notes for Substitute Teacher

Closing the Lesson
___ Communicating about Mathematics, Student's Edition page 540
___ Guided Practice Exercises, Student's Edition page 541

Homework Assignment, pages 541, 542
___ Basic/Average: Day 1: Ex. 7–17 odd, 19–22
                   Day 2: Ex. 26–29, 31
___ Above Average: Ex. 7–17 odd, 19–22, 26–29, 32
___ Advanced: Ex. 7–17 odd, 19–22, 26–29, 32

Reteaching the Lesson
___ Extra Practice Copymasters page 94
___ Reteaching Copymasters page 94
___ Math Log copymaster page 37 or Teacher's Edition page 542

Extending the Lesson
___ Writing, Teacher's Edition page 540
___ Enrichment, Teacher's Edition page 542
___ Technology Using Calculators and Computers copymaster page 69
___ Enrichment Projects copymasters pages 63, 64

Notes

94 Windows   © D.C. Heath and Company

Teaching Tools

Name _____

Exercises 21–26 on Page 547

Visualizing Solids

In Exercises 21–26, identify the solid formed by folding the net.

21.   22.
23.   24.
25.   26.

Teaching Tools includes:
Transparencies and Copymasters for classroom activities and study skills:

- Graph Paper
- Dot Paper (Geoboards)
- Algebra Tiles
- Number Counters
- Fraction Strips
- Models

REAL LIFE

Color Transparencies for Real-Life Applications

Lesson 12.2, Page 547, Exercises 31–33

Windows

Technology: Using Calculators and Computers

Investigating Relationships in a Circle   **12.1** Name _____

Exploration Using a Computer Drawing Program

In this activity, you will use dynamic construction software to investigate several relationships that exist in all circles. When completing the exercises, remember that $\pi \approx 3.1416$. It is assumed that the user is familiar with the software.

Directions

1. Construct a random circle.
2. Construct $\overline{AB}$ and $\overleftrightarrow{AB}$.
3. Construct $\overline{BC}$, or $\overleftrightarrow{AB}$, with point C on the circle.
4. Hide $\overleftrightarrow{AB}$.
5. To change the diameter of the circle, click and drag on point B.

EXERCISES

1. Name a radius and diameter of the circle.
   $\overline{AB}$ or $\overline{AC}$; $\overline{BC}$

2. Measure the radius, r, and the diameter, d, of the circle. Then find the ratio of the diameter to the radius. Repeat this for several different circles and record your results in the table. Answers vary.

Circle	r	d	$\frac{d}{r}$
1			
2			
3			

3. What relationship exists between the radius and diameter of a circle? Include a formula in your explanation.
   $\frac{d}{r} = 2$ or $2r = d$

4. Measure the diameter, d, and the circumference, C, of the circle. Then find the ratio of the circumference to the diameter. Repeat this for several different circles and record your results in the table. Answers vary.

Circle	d	C	$\frac{C}{d}$
1			
2			
3			

5. What relationship exists between the circumference and diameter of a circle? Include a formula in your explanation.
   $\frac{C}{d} = \pi$ or $C = \pi d$

6. Rewrite the formula in Exercise 5 using the radius of a circle instead of the diameter.
   $C = 2\pi r$

© D.C. Heath and Company   Technology Using Calculators and Computers **69**

Also Available:

- Complete Solutions Manual
- Overhead Manipulatives Kit
- Computerized Testing Program

- **Interactive CD-ROM Projects**
  Interactive projects for solving real-world problems using multimedia

- **Interactions: Real Math–Real Careers**
  A videodisc–based resource that connects math to real careers and on-the-job problem solving

- **PACKETS® Performance Assessment for Middle School Mathematics**
  A program that links assessment and instruction

ASSESSMENT

Alternative Assessment

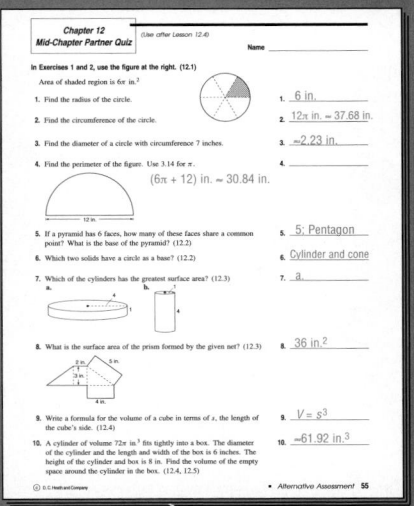

Alternative Assessment includes:
- Scoring Rubrics
- Portfolios
- Math Journals
- Projects
- Partner Quizzes
- Individual and Group Assessment

Formal Assessment

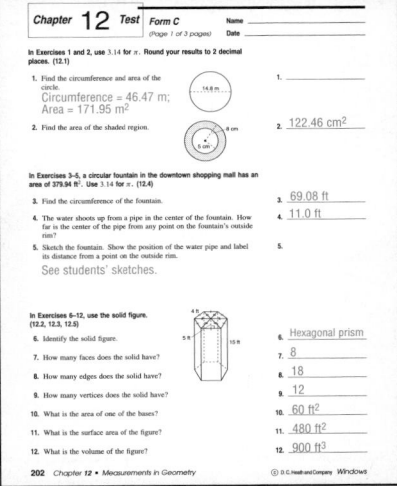

Formal Assessment includes:
- Short Quizzes (after every 2 lessons)
- Mid-Chapter Tests (2 forms)
- Chapter Tests (3 forms)
- Cumulative Tests (after every 3 Chapters)

MEETING INDIVIDUAL NEEDS

Extra Practice Copymasters

Reteaching Copymasters

Enrichment Projects

Math Log

Special Populations
Suggestions for providing equal access for:

Students Acquiring English Proficiency*
In Lesson 12.2, the use of three dimensional models will help students recognize the attributes of various solids. To practice the vocabulary, describe properties of different solids and have students provide the correct name and locate various examples in the classroom.

Students with Various Learning Styles*
Use three-dimensional models of solids on an everyday basis. Having students make their own models will help them internalize the concepts taught in this chapter. Nets for making models are available as copymasters in Teaching Tools.
In Lesson 12.4, use cubes to help your students grasp the concept of volume.

Underachieving Students*
The more hands-on activities that these students are involved in, the better their understanding. Have students make their own set of solids and have them measure heights, radii, and so on.
Students who have difficulty reading will need special help interpreting word problems. Cooperative group problem solving will assist in meeting this need.

Gifted and Talented Students*
Have students work in groups to draw a net for a prism that has a regular pentagon as its base. Have groups cut out and assemble their nets. Then have them find the surface area and volume of the prism. Suggest that they divide the pentagon into three triangles in order to find the area of the base. Have groups exchange their prisms and check one another's work.

* See page T19 for descriptions of these special populations.

Measurements in Geometry

CHAPTER 12 OVERVIEW

PACING CHART

Lesson	Basic/ Average Course	Above Average Course	Advanced Course
12.1	2 days	1 day	1 day
12.2	2 days	1 day	1 day
12.3	2 days	2 days	2 days
12.4	2 days	1 day	1 day
12.5	2 days	1 day	1 day
12.6	2 days	2 days	2 days
12.7	2 days	2 days	2 days
12.8	0 days	1 day	1 day

About the Chapter

The geometry introduced in the preceding chapter was limited to planar figures. This chapter extends students' measurement techniques to space figures—polyhedrons and regular solids. In the preceding chapter, students used formulas for measuring the areas of planar regions. In this chapter, students begin by learning an additional formula, the circle area formula, that they will need for the measurement of the surface area of spatial figures, in particular cylinders and cones.

Next, in Lesson 12.2, students are introduced to the terminology of polyhedrons and regular solids and to the characteristic net that is associated with, and helps the understanding of each space figure. In Lesson 12.3, the area addition techniques for planar figures that were taught in the preceding chapter are now applied to the nets associated with prisms and cylinders in order to compute their surface area.

The remaining lessons of this chapter are concerned with the concept of volume. Lessons 12.4 and 12.5 teach the volume formulas for prisms and cylinders. In several exercises at this stage, students are encouraged informally to reason about how changes in linear measurements affect the volume of space figures. Lessons 12.6 offers a hands-on demonstration of how the volumes of pyramids and cones are related to those of prisms and cylinders, respectively. Lesson 12.7 has a similar hands-on method of arriving at a volume formula for a sphere. The chapter closes by clarifying the issue of how linear changes affect both area and volume.

To draw plans for buildings or manufactured items, drafters use triangles with their T squares and drawing boards. Product designer Sava Cvek created the triangles shown here to make his drawing tasks easier. Two of the triangles have "wheels" so they can be moved into position easily and the other is an "adjustable triangle." The scale drawing is Sava Cvek's plan for the adjustable triangle.

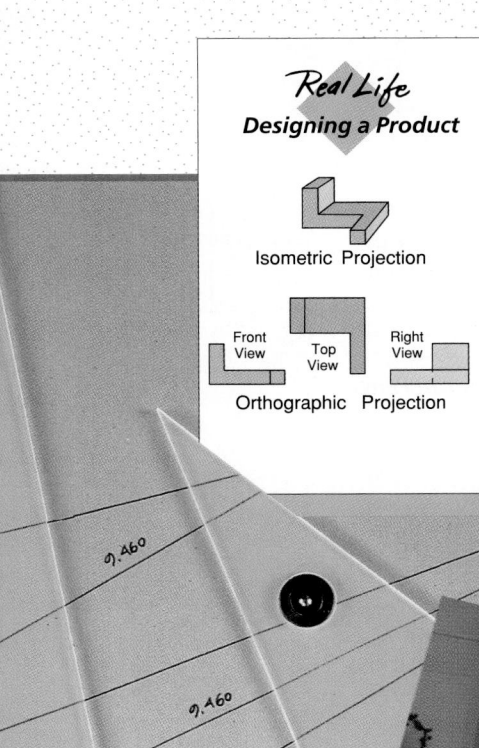

Real Life
Designing a Product

Isometric Projection

Front View | **Top View** | **Right View**

Orthographic Projection

This chapter introduces you to measurement formulas for three-dimensional objects, thus it contains many two-dimensional drawings of three-dimensional shapes. Most of these drawings are *isometric projections* which look realistic, but are not accurate drawings of the sides of the objects.

To provide information about the exact size and shape of a three-dimensional object, scale drawings are made of its top, side and front. These drawings are called *orthographic* (right angle) *projections*.

Materials
Teaching Tools
   Graph paper, pp. T1, C2
   Ruler, pp. T12, C18

Rolling the circular object is a fairly accurate way for students to determine the circumference. Using yarn or string doesn't always yield accurate measures.

EXTENSION
Have students make a graph of their data. They should put the diameter on the *x*-axis, the circumference on the *y*-axis. The data should be approximately linear and close to the line defined by the equation $C = \pi d$.

Materials Needed: can or paper-towel tube, ruler, graph paper

As shown at the right, the **diameter** of a circle is the distance across the circle through its **center.** The **circumference** of a circle is the distance around the circle. In this investigation, you will explore the relationship between the diameter and circumference of a circle.

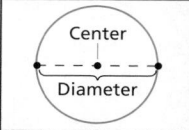

| **Example** | *Comparing Diameter and Circumference* |

Mark a point on the rim of a can. Place the marked point on a piece of paper and mark the paper. Then roll the can *without slipping* so it makes exactly one turn and make another mark on the paper. Measure the distance between the marks. Find the ratio of this distance to the diameter of the can.

Solution   The measurements you obtain depend on the size of the can. The can shown below has a diameter of 2.5 inches. When it is rolled around once, it rolls 7.9 inches, which means that the circumference of the can is 7.9 inches. For this can, the ratio of the circumference to the diameter is

$$\frac{\text{Circumference}}{\text{Diameter}} = \frac{7.9 \text{ inches}}{2.5 \text{ inches}} = 3.16.$$

In the exercises below, you are asked to repeat this experiment with other circular objects.

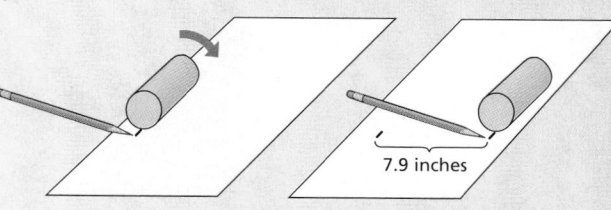

7.9 inches

Exercises

1. *Group Activity*   Each person in your group should use a different can, paper-towel tube, or other circular object. If possible, each person should use an object with a different diameter. Repeat the experiment described in the example. Compare the ratios obtained in your group.   Check students' work.

P 2. In your group, discuss the result obtained in Exercise 1. Did everyone obtain about the same ratio as was obtained in the example? If not, the people who obtained different ratios should repeat their experiments. Write a statement about the relationship between the circumference and diameter of a circle. $\frac{\text{Circumference}}{\text{Diameter}} \approx 3.14$

P Portfolio Opportunity

12.1

Circle Relationships

What you should learn:

Goal 1 How to find the circumference of a circle

Goal 2 How to find the area of a circle

Why you should learn it:

You can use the circumference and area of a circle to solve real-life problems, such as finding the circumference of a jar lid.

Goal 1 ### The Circumference of a Circle

As shown at the right, the **diameter** of a circle is the distance across the circle through its **center.** The **radius** of a circle is the distance from the center to any point on the circle. The **circumference** of a circle is the distance around the circle.

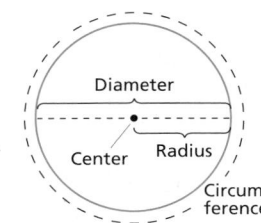

In the investigation on page 538, you may have discovered a special relationship that is true of *all circles.* The ratio of the circumference of any circle to its diameter is about 3.14. This special number is denoted by the Greek letter *pi,* which is written as π. Pi is an irrational number. To four decimal places, $\pi \approx 3.1416$.

> **The Circumference of a Circle**
>
> Let d be the diameter of a circle and let r be its radius. The circumference, C, of the circle is
>
> $$C = \pi d \qquad \text{or} \qquad C = 2\pi r.$$

Real Life
Packaging

10 cm

Example 1 *Finding the Circumference of a Circle*

Find the circumference of the jar lid at the left.

Solution Because the jar lid has a diameter of 10 centimeters, it follows that its circumference is

$C = \pi d$ *Formula for circumference*
$\approx 3.14(10)$ *Substitute for π and d.*
$= 31.4$ *Simplify.*

The circumference of the jar lid is about 31.4 centimeters. If you need a more accurate measurement for the circumference, you can use a scientific calculator, as shown on page 543. ∎

12.1 • Circle Relationships **539**

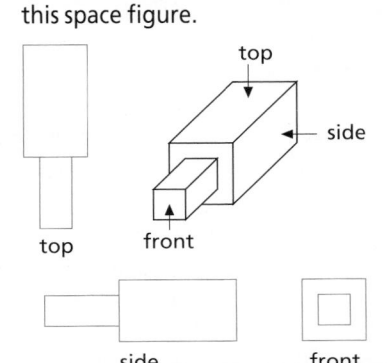

LESSON Notes

Ask students to give examples of circles in real life for which knowing the circumference is important. Have students record the examples in their math journals. Examples might include the distance a tire travels in one revolution.

▶ **Example 1**

Use the (round) lid of a coffee can or some such object to illustrate that $C = \pi d$. Using a measuring tape, measure the diameter of the lid. Compute πd, then compare the result with the circumference you measure for the lid.

ALTERNATE APPROACH
Using Cutouts On page 540, students are shown one method for estimating the area of a circle. You can use an overhead projector to demonstrate the area of a circle in a different way. Prepare beforehand on acetate a large circle that has been divided into 16 congruent sectors as shown below. In class, label one radius r, and establish the fact that half the circumference can therefore be labeled $(\frac{1}{2} \cdot 2\pi r)$ or πr.

(continued)
Lesson 12.1 **539**

In class, have one or two students cut out the circle and then cut along each diameter so that the 16 congruent sectors are separated.

Now show the students how to arrange the 16 sectors to form a figure that looks like a parallelogram.

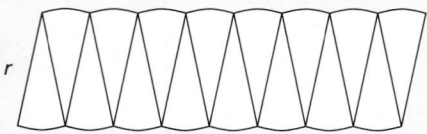

Ask students these questions.
What is the height of the parallelogram?   *r*
What is the length of its base? πr
What is its area? πr^2
What can be deduced about the area of the circle?   The area of the circle is πr^2

Example 2

Remind students of the order of operations. They must square the radius before multiplying by π when calculating area. Discuss the order in which the numbers and operations should be entered in a calculator.

Communicating
about MATHEMATICS

You may wish to make a connection between these problems and the making of circle graphs in data analysis.

Writing Prompt
In your own words, describe the difference between area and circumference.

Technology

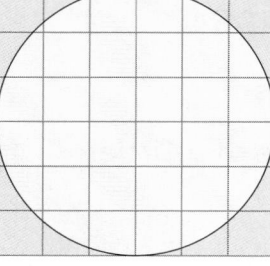

The circle at the left has a radius of 3 units. To estimate the area of the circle, you can reason that each blue corner region has an area of about 2 square units. Because the area of the square is 6^2 or 36 square units, you can reason that the area of the circle must be about $36 - 4(2)$ or 28 square units. The following formula tells you that the *exact* area of the circle is 9π or about 28.3 square units.

> **The Area of a Circle**
> Let *r* be the radius of a circle. The area, *A*, of the circle is
> $$A = \pi r^2.$$

Real Life
Government

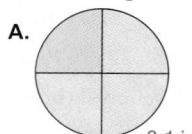

|← 4.75 in. →|

Example 2   *Finding the Area of a Circle*

Find the area of the presidential seal at the left.

Solution   The diameter of the seal is 4.75 inches. This implies that the radius is

$$r = \tfrac{1}{2}(4.75) = 2.375 \text{ inches.}$$

Using this measurement, you can find the area of the seal.

$A = \pi r^2$ *Formula for area of a circle*
$\approx 3.14(2.375)^2$ *Substitute for π and r.*
≈ 17.7 *Simplify.*

The area of the seal is about 17.7 square inches. ∎

Communicating about MATHEMATICS

▶ **SHARING IDEAS about the Lesson**

Parts of Circles   Each of the circles below has a diameter of 4 inches, and is divided into congruent parts. Find the area of the blue portion of each circle.

A.   **B.**   **C.**

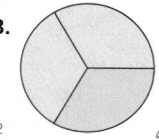

3.1 in.²   4.2 in.²   2.1 in.²

OPTION: Extra Examples
Here are additional examples similar to those of the lesson.

1. Finding the Circumference of a Circle
Find the circumference of a plate that has a 9-inch diameter.
Solution
Because the plate has a diameter of 9 inches, it follows that its circumference is
$C = \pi d$ Formula for circumference
$\approx 3.14(9)$ Substitute for π and *d*.
$= 28.3$ Simplify.
The circumference of the plate is about 28.3 inches.

2. Finding the Area of a Circle.
Find the area of a clock face that has a 5-inch diameter.
Solution
The diameter of the clock face is 5 inches. This implies that the radius is $r = \tfrac{1}{2}(5) = 2.5$ inches. Using this measurement, you can find the area of the clock face.
$A = \pi r^2$ Formula for area of a circle
$\approx 3.14(2.5)^2$ Substitute for π and *r*.
$= 19.6$ Simplify.
The area of the clock face is about 19.6 square inches.

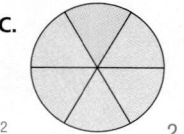

EXERCISES

Guided Practice

▶ **CHECK for Understanding**

1. How does the formula for the circumference of a circle relate to the Lesson Investigation on page 538? Both relate the diameter to the circumference.

2. *Estimation* Earth has a radius of about 4000 miles. Estimate its circumference at the equator. ≈ 25,000 mi

In Exercises 3–6, use the figure at the right.

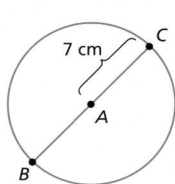

3. Name the diameter. $\overline{BC}$

4. Name a radius. $\overline{AB}, \overline{AC}$

5. Find the circumference. ≈ 44.0 cm

6. Find the area. ≈ 153.9 cm²

Independent Practice

In Exercises 7–10, find the circumference and area of the figure. Use 3.14 for π. Round your result to one decimal place.

7.

$d = 2.4$ cm   7.5 cm, 4.5 cm²

8.

$d = 11.8$ in.   37.1 in., 109.3 in.²

9.
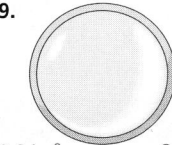
$r = 4$ in.   25.1 in., 50.2 in.²

10.

$r = 8$ in.
50.2 in., 201.0 in.²

In Exercises 11–14, find the radius and diameter of the figure. Use 3.14 for π. Round your result to one decimal place.

11.

$C = 4.4$ ft
0.7 ft, 1.4 ft

12.
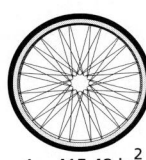
$A = 415.48$ in.²
6.9 in., 3.8 in.²

13.

$A = 17.7$ in.²
11.5 in., 23.0 in.   2.4 in., 4.7 in.

14.

$C = 59.69$ mm
9.5 mm, 19.0 mm

In Exercises 15–18, find the area of the blue portion of the figure. Use 3.14 for π. Round your result to one decimal place.

15.
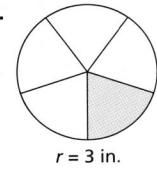
$r = 3$ in.
5.7 in.²

16.
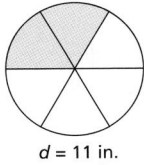
$d = 11$ in.
31.7 in.²

17.
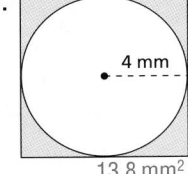
4 mm
13.8 mm²

18.
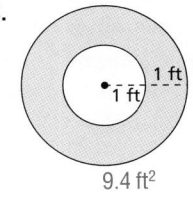
1 ft / 1 ft
9.4 ft²

12.1 ▪ *Circle Relationships*   **541**

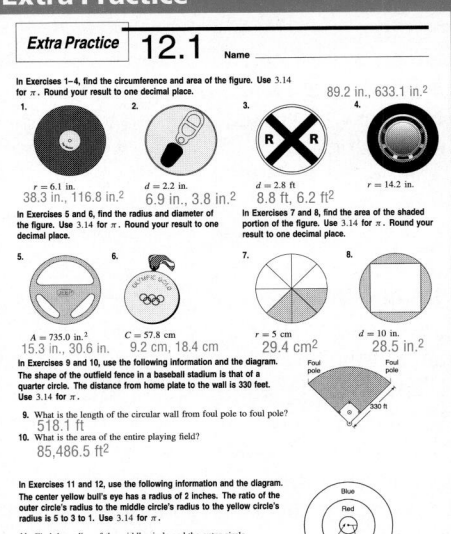   
EXERCISE Notes

ASSIGNMENT GUIDE

Basic/Average:
Day 1: Ex. 7–17 odd, 19–22
Day 2: Ex. 26–29, 31

Above Average:
Ex. 7–17 odd, 19–22, 26–29, 32

Advanced: Ex. 7–17 odd, 19–22, 26–29, 32

Selected Answers: Ex. 1–6, 7–29 odd

Guided Practice

Use these exercises as an in-class small-group summary activity.

Independent Practice

▶ **Ex. 11–14** Since these exercises involve solving equations rather than evaluating a formula, be sure to preview them in class.

Patterns   **In Exercises 19 and 20, create a table. Then describe the pattern.**   See Additional Answers.

✪ **19.** Find the circumferences of circles whose radii are 1, 2, 3, 4, 5, and 6.

✪ **20.** Find the areas of circles whose radii are 1, 2, 3, 4, 5, and 6.

✪ **21.** If the diameter of a circle is doubled, will the area and circumference of the circle double? Explain.   See Additional Answers.

P **22.** Instead of $C = \pi d$, some people prefer to use the formula $C = 2\pi r$ for the circumference of a circle. Which formula do you prefer? Why?   Answers vary.

Pizza   **In Exercises 23–25, a pizza with a 12-inch diameter is cut into pieces that each have an area of 14.14 square inches.**

✪ **23.** Find the area of the entire pizza.   113.04 in.²

✪ **24.** How many pieces make up the pizza?   8

✪ **25.** If the pizza had been cut into 6 pieces, what would have been the area of each?   18.84 in.²

Washington, D.C.   **In Exercises 26–28, use the map at the right.**

26. The road around Washington, D.C., is called the *Beltway*. Estimate the length of a trip on the Beltway around the entire city.   62.8 mi

27. Estimate the area inside the Beltway.   314 mi²

28. *Estimation*   About what percent of the region inside the Beltway is Washington, D.C.?   39%

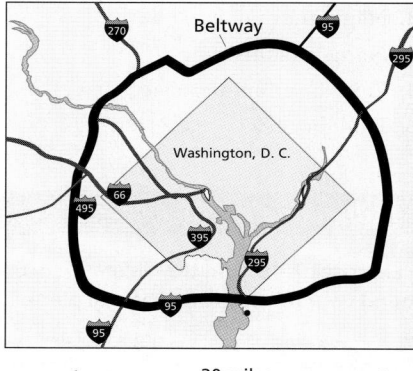
Beltway
Washington, D. C.
◄—— 20 miles ——►

Integrated Review   *Making Connections within Mathematics*

29. *Intersecting Circles*   Two circles of the same size can have no points in common, 1 point in common, 2 points in common, or they may coincide (have all points in common). Draw these four cases.

30. *Intersecting Circles*   Draw the different ways that 3 circles of the same size can intersect.
29., 30. See Additional Answers.

Exploration and Extension

✪ **31.** *Pie Puzzle*   Using four straight cuts, you can cut a pie into eight congruent pieces. Can you cut a pie into eight congruent pieces using only three straight cuts? (You can rearrange the pieces after each cut.) If you can, show how.   Yes, see Additional Answers.

✪ **32.** *Pie Puzzle*   Using only two straight cuts and one curved cut, can you cut a pie into eight pieces so that each piece has about the same area? (You can't rearrange the pieces after cutting.) Explain.
Yes, see Additional Answers.

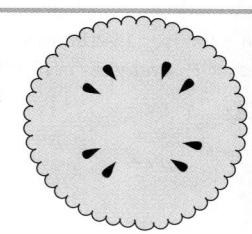

✪ More difficult exercises
P Portfolio Opportunity

▶ **Enrichment**

Suppose your group manages two radio stations, KJLM and WXYZ. Both stations are located in areas that have an average of 5 households per square mile. Station KJLM has a signal range of 100 miles. WXYZ's signal has a range of 50 miles. Have students work together in groups to answer the following questions:

1. How many square miles are in each station's listening area?   KJLM has 34,100 mi² and WXYZ has 7,850 mi².

2. If you decide to charge for advertising based on the average number of houses in the listening area, how will the advertising rates compare for the two stations?   The rates for KJLM should be 4 times those of WXYZ.

3. What other factors would you need to consider when determining how to set the advertising rates?   Answers will vary but might include whether major highways go through the areas, the average income and spending habits of the populations, and the types of radio shows aired on the stations.

4. Suppose you had a client who already advertised on WXYZ and wanted to begin advertising on KJLM. Also suppose that the client claimed that the rate for KJLM should only be twice that of WXYZ because the station's signal was only twice as strong. Put together a presentation to convince the client that your rates make sense.

USING A CALCULATOR
Circumference and Area of a Circle

Many calculators have a special key for π. The following example shows how to use this key to calculate the circumference and area of a circle.

In Lesson 12.1, students used the approximations 3.14 and 3.1416 for π. By using the $\boxed{\pi}$ key in this investigation, students are using a more precise approximation. Have students press $\boxed{\pi}$ $\boxed{=}$ to display this approximation. Then have students find the circumference and area of the circle in Example 1 using 3.1416 or 3.14. Have students compare their results with those obtained in the investigation. Which answer do they think is most accurate? When would this be important?

Note that from this point on, when computing the circumference or the area of a circle, the calculator key for π will be used.

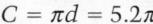

Example   *Calculating Circumference and Area*

Use a scientific calculator to find the circumference and area of the circle at the right. Round your result to two decimal places.

Solution   The radius of the circle is 2.6 inches. This implies that the diameter is 2(2.6) or 5.2 inches.

$C = \pi d = 5.2\pi$ *Circumference*
$A = \pi r^2 = \pi(2.6)^2$ *Area*

r = 2.6 in.

The keystrokes for evaluating the circumference and area are as follows.

Keystrokes	Display	Conclusion
5.2 $\boxed{\times}$ $\boxed{\pi}$ $\boxed{=}$	16.3362818	$C \approx 16.34$ in.
$\boxed{\pi}$ $\boxed{\times}$ 2.6 $\boxed{x^2}$ $\boxed{=}$	21.23716634	$A \approx 21.24$ in.^{2}

Exercises

1. 10.68 cm, 9.08 cm^2 2. 34.56 ft, 95.03 ft^2
3. 12.25 in., 11.95 in.^{2} 4. 32.67 m, 84.95 m^2

In Exercises 1–4, find the circumference and area of the indicated circle. Round your results to two decimal places.

1. $r = 1.7$ cm   2. $r = 5.5$ ft   3. $d = 3.9$ in.   4. $d = 10.4$ m

5. A circle has a circumference of 10 inches. Find the diameter and radius of the circle. Round your results to two decimal places. 3.18 in., 1.59 in.

6. A circle has an area of 6 square meters. Find the radius and diameter of the circle. Round your results to two decimal places. 1.38 m, 2.76 m

In Exercises 7–10, find the area of the blue portion of the circle. Round your result to two decimal places.

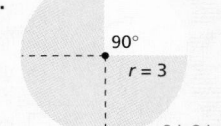
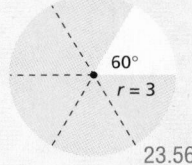
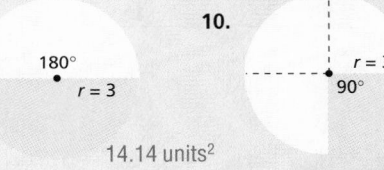

7. 90° $r = 3$ 8. 60° $r = 3$ 9. 180° $r = 3$ 10. $r = 3$ 90°

21.21 units^2 23.56 units^2 14.14 units^2 7.07 units^2

11. Which of the following is the best approximation of π? Explain.

   a. 3.14   b. 3.1416   c. $\frac{22}{7}$ d. $\frac{355}{113}$ d, it is closer to 3.14159265 than the others.

12.2 Polyhedrons and Other Solids

 What you should learn:

 Why you should learn it:

You can use polyhedrons and other solids as models for real-life objects, such as a stick of pepperoni or an apple.

Goal 1 — Identifying Parts of Polyhedrons

A **polyhedron** is a solid that is bounded by polygons, which are called **faces.** The segments where the faces meet are **edges,** and the points where the edges meet are **vertices.** Two common types of polyhedrons are **prisms** and **pyramids.**

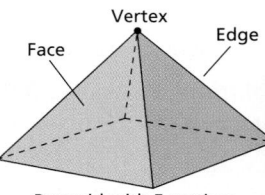

Pyramid with 5 vertices, 5 faces, and 8 edges

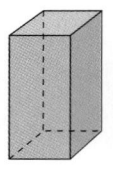 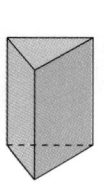 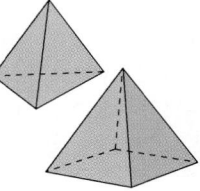 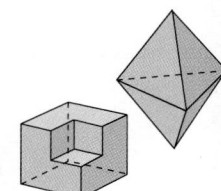

Prisms   *Pyramids*   *Other polyhedrons*

A **net** is a pattern that can be folded to form a solid. The next example shows nets for a prism and a pyramid.

Example 1 — *Identifying Parts of Polyhedrons*

Describe the polyhedron that results from folding each net.

a.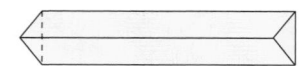

b.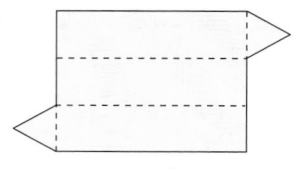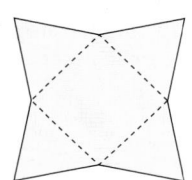

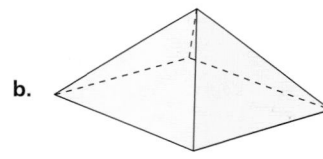

Solution

a. When the net is folded, it forms a prism. The prism has 5 faces, 9 edges, and 6 vertices, as shown at the left.

b. When the net is folded, it forms a pyramid. The pyramid has 5 faces, 8 edges, and 5 vertices, as shown at the left. ∎

Goal 2 — Identifying Parts of Other Solids

Three other types of common solids, a sphere, a cylinder, and a cone, are shown below.

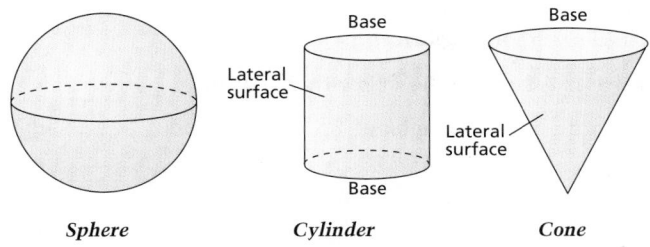

Sphere   *Cylinder*   *Cone*

Real Life
Food Shapes

Example 2 — *Identifying Solids*

Describe the approximate shape of each food before it is cut. Then describe the shape of the cut portions.

a.    **b.**

Solution

a. Before it is cut, the pepperoni is approximately a cylinder. The shape would be more like a cylinder if the ends were flat instead of rounded. After it is cut, most pieces are almost exact cylinders. The circular bases of each cut piece are large and the lateral surface is small.

b. Before it is cut, the apple is approximately a sphere. The cut piece is not a sphere—it is called a wedge. ∎

Communicating *about* MATHEMATICS

▶ **SHARING IDEAS about the Lesson**

Describing Solids In Example 2, you can see that a cylinder can be cut to form smaller cylinders. Is this true of other types of solids? For instance, can a prism be cut to form two prisms? True of prisms and pyramids; not true of spheres and cones.

Have students record in their math journals that some solid figures are not composed entirely of flat surfaces. In fact, some sides may be rounded or curved. Ask students to give examples of such solids found in real life.

Example 2

Have students bring in household objects that have shapes and properties similar to those studied here.

Problem Solving

Prisms and pyramids can be classified by the shape of their bases. For example, a rectangular prism is a prism whose base is rectangular. For prisms and pyramids, a relationship exists between the number of faces, the number of vertices, and the number of edges. The same relationship holds regardless of the shape of the polygonal base. Challenge students to complete the table below in order to systematically record the number of vertices, faces, and edges for each of the listed polyhedrons:

	Prism			Pyramid		
	Faces	Vertices	Edges	Faces	Vertices	Edges
Triangular	?	?	?	?	?	?
Rectangular	?	?	?	?	?	?
Pentagonal	?	?	?	?	?	?
Hexagonal	?	?	?	?	?	?

Then use the information from the table to write a formula that shows the relationship. If E= number of edges, V= number of vertices, and F= number of faces, then $E+2=V+F$.

Communicating *about* MATHEMATICS

Students could sketch or use modeling clay or styrofoam from packaging to explore these questions.

Writing Prompt

Name five common objects in the room, identifying each object as an example of one of the solids studied in class today.

ASSIGNMENT GUIDE

Basic/Average:
Day 1: Ex. 10–15, 21–25 odd
Day 2: Ex. 16–19, 27–31

Above Average:
Ex. 10–20, 21–33 odd

Advanced: Ex. 10–20, 21–33 odd

Selected Answers: Ex. 1–9, 11–29 odd

Guided Practice

▶ **Ex. 6** Students may have difficulty naming part *b* as a base, because in this diagram the cone is not "standing" on it.

Independent Practice

▶ **Ex. 10–13** If you assign the Writing Prompt, these diagrams may help students with their response.
▶ **Ex. 14, 15** You may wish also to ask students how these figures differ from one another.
▶ **Ex. 16–20** The exercises can be done as a group activity. Many students may need to cut, fold, and tape in order to answer these questions.

Answer 20.

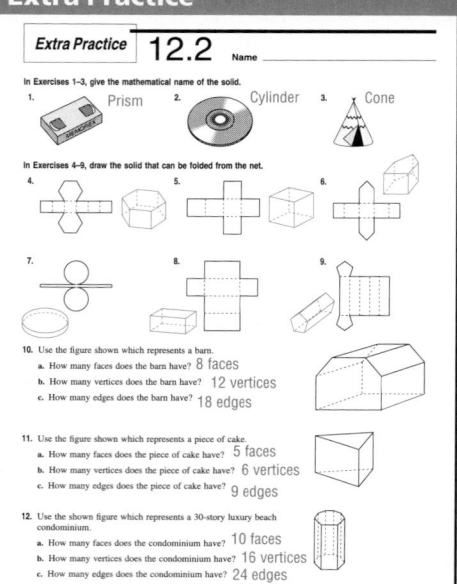

Guided Practice

▶ **CHECK for Understanding**

In Exercises 1–5, match the solid with its name.

a. Pyramid **b.** Sphere **c.** Cone **d.** Prism **e.** Cylinder

1. 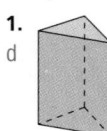 d

2. 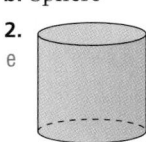 e

3. 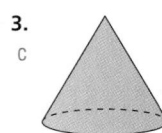 c

4. 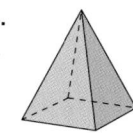 a

5. 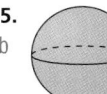 b

In Exercises 6–9, identify the parts of the solid.

6.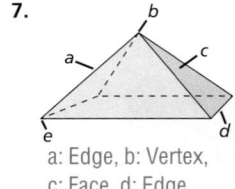
a: Lateral surface,
b: Base

7.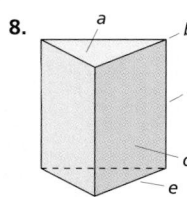
a: Edge, b: Vertex,
c: Face, d: Edge,
e: Vertex

8.
a: Face, b: Vertex,
c: Edge, d: Face, e: Edge

9.
a: Lateral surface,
b: Base

Independent Practice

In Exercises 10–13, identify the solid.

10.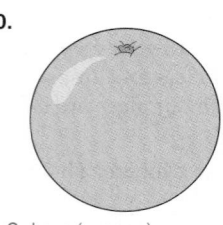
Sphere (orange)

11.
Prism (speaker)

12.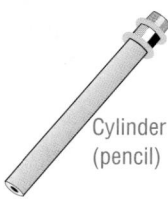
Cylinder (pencil)

13.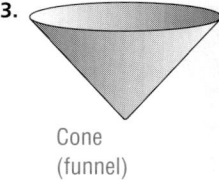
Cone (funnel)

P 14. How are prisms and cylinders alike?
Have 2 bases

P 15. How are pyramids and cones alike?
Have 1 base

Nets **In Exercises 16–19, which of the nets can be folded to form a cube?**

16.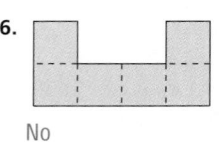
No

17.
No

18.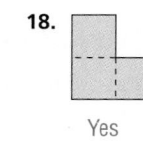
Yes

19.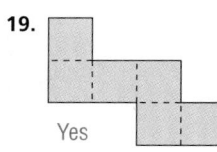
Yes

✪ **20.** *Think about It* Sketch other nets that can be folded to form a cube.
P How many different nets are possible? 11, for nets, see margin.

✪ More difficult exercises
P Portfolio Opportunity

Extra Practice

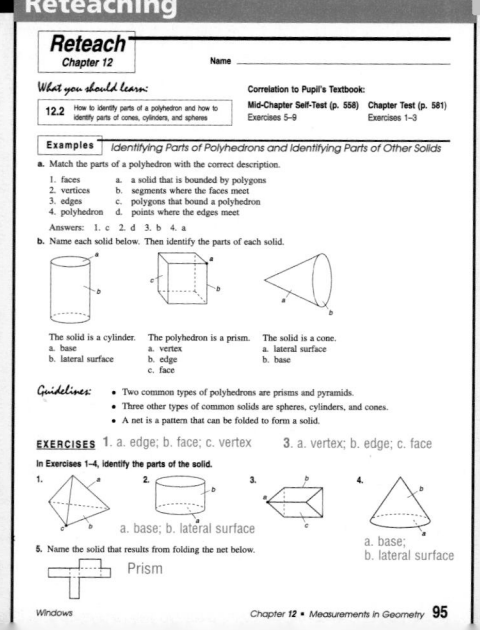

Extra Practice **12.2** Name _____

In Exercises 1–3, give the mathematical name of the solid.
1. Prism 2. Cylinder 3. Cone

In Exercises 4–9, draw the solid that can be folded from the net.
4. 5. 6.
7. 8. 9.

10. Use the figure shown which represents a barn.
   a. How many faces does the barn have? 8 faces
   b. How many vertices does the barn have? 12 vertices
   c. How many edges does the barn have? 18 edges

11. Use the figure shown which represents a piece of cake.
   a. How many faces does the piece of cake have? 5 faces
   b. How many vertices does the piece of cake have? 6 vertices
   c. How many edges does the piece of cake have? 9 edges

12. Use the shown figure which represents a 30-story luxury beach condominium.
   a. How many faces does the condominium have? 10 faces
   b. How many vertices does the condominium have? 16 vertices
   c. How many edges does the condominium have? 24 edges

Windows   12.2 • Polyhedrons and Other Solids **95**

Reteaching

Reteach Chapter 12   Name _____

What you should learn:
12.2 How to identify parts of a polyhedron and how to identify parts of cones, cylinders, and spheres

Correlation to Pupil's Textbook:
Mid-Chapter Self-Test (p. 558) Chapter Test (p. 581)
Exercises 5–9   Exercises 1–3

Examples *Identifying Parts of Polyhedrons and Identifying Parts of Other Solids*

a. Match the parts of a polyhedron with the correct description.
   1. faces   a. a solid that is bounded by polygons
   2. vertices   b. segments where the faces meet
   3. edges   c. polygons that bound a polyhedron
   4. polyhedron d. points where the edges meet
   Answers: 1. c 2. d 3. b 4. a

b. Name each solid below. Then identify the parts of each solid.

The solid is a cylinder.
a. base
b. lateral surface

The polyhedron is a prism.
a. vertex
b. edge
c. face

The solid is a cone.
a. lateral surface
b. base

Guidelines: • Two common types of polyhedrons are prisms and pyramids.
• Three other types of common solids are spheres, cylinders, and cones.
• A net is a pattern that can be folded to form a solid.

EXERCISES 1. a. edge; b. face; c. vertex   3. a. vertex; b. edge; c. face

In Exercises 1–4, identify the parts of the solid.
1. 2. 3. 4.
a. base; b. lateral surface

a. base;
b. lateral surface

5. Name the solid that results from folding the net below. Prism

Windows   Chapter 12 • Measurements in Geometry **95**

Visualizing Solids In Exercises 21–26, identify the solid formed by folding the net.

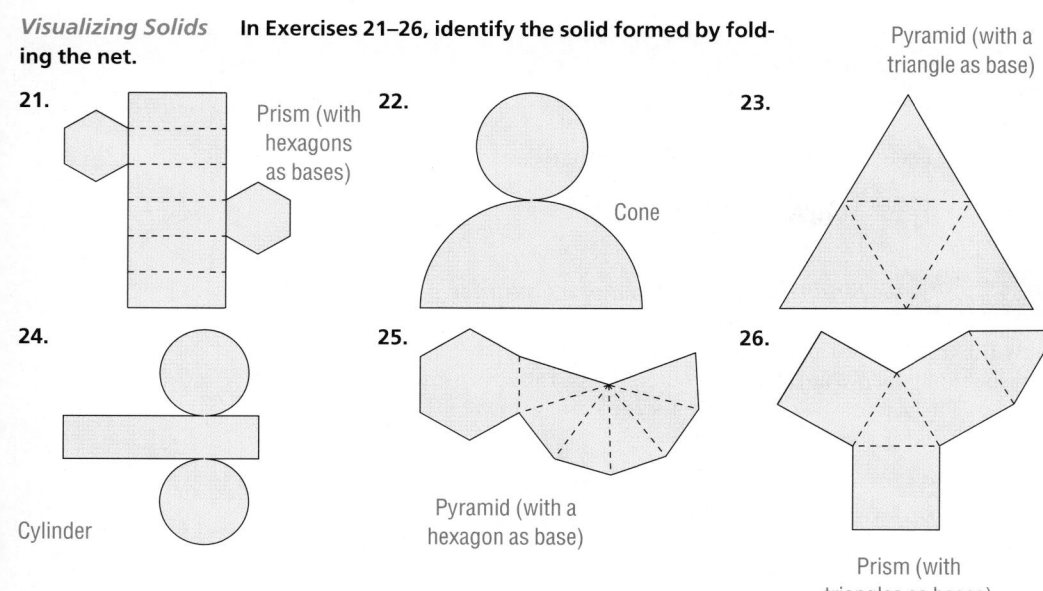

21. Prism (with hexagons as bases)

22. Cone

23. Pyramid (with a triangle as base)

24. Cylinder

25. Pyramid (with a hexagon as base)

26. Prism (with triangles as bases)

▶ **Ex. 21–26** Make sure that in their answers to these exercises, students identify the base of each solid.

Integrated Review

Making Connections within Mathematics

Perimeter In Exercises 27–30, find the perimeter (or circumference) and the area of the figure.

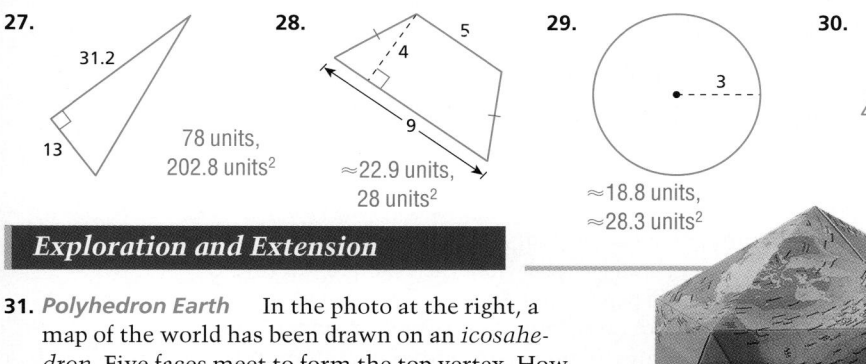

27.
31.2
13
78 units,
202.8 units²

28.
5
4
9
≈22.9 units,
28 units²

29.
3
≈18.8 units,
≈28.3 units²

30.
8   8
8
24 units,
≈27.7 units²

Exploration and Extension

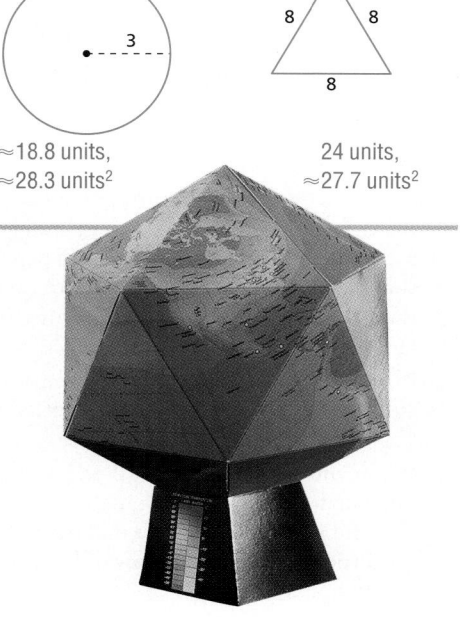

31. *Polyhedron Earth* In the photo at the right, a map of the world has been drawn on an *icosahedron*. Five faces meet to form the top vertex. How many faces does the solid have? **20**

32. Each face of an *octahedron* is an equilateral triangle. From its name, how many faces does an octahedron have? **8**

33. An icosahedron and an octahedron each have faces that are equilateral triangles. Sketch a pyramid whose faces are all equilateral triangles. This type of pyramid is called a *tetrahedron*. How many faces does it have? **4**

▶ **Ex. 27, 28** These exercises review the Pythagorean Theorem. Note that in Ex. 28, you may need to help students deduce the length (2) of the shorter leg of the triangle, and hence the hypotenuse, etc.

Exploration and Extension

Note that a color transparency of Polyhedron Earth is available in the supplement Color Transparencies, page 50.

Portfolio Opportunity: Math Log

Find an example of a prism, pyramid, sphere, cylinder, and cone in your classroom.

Also available as a copymaster, page 37, Ex. 2

Short Quiz

Covers Lessons 12.1 and 12.2

Available as a copymaster, page 190

Alternative Assessment

Chapter 12 Group Assessment
An activity for 3–4 students that explores the relationship between the number of vertices, faces, and edges of pyramids.

Chapter 12 Individual Assessment
A similar follow-up activity for individual students. Adds incentive for the group activity and measures individual competence in the activity.

Available as copymasters, pages 81, 82

12.2 ▪ *Polyhedrons and Other Solids* **547**

Materials
Teaching Tools
  Ruler, pp. T12, C18

Make sure that students realize that 9.4 in. is the circumference of the circles that form the bases of the cylinder.
  It may take a while for students to successfully get all three pieces to fit on the paper *and* to be a net for a cylinder. The difficulty of this problem is addressed in Ex. 3.

Materials Needed: paper, compass, scissors, ruler, calculator, transparent tape

In this investigation, you will explore the surface area of a cylinder.

| **Example** | *Find the Surface Area of a Cylinder* |

Draw the three pieces shown below on an $8\frac{1}{2}$-inch by 11-inch sheet of paper. Cut the pieces out and tape them to form a cylinder. The area of the three pieces is the *surface area* of the cylinder. What is the surface area?

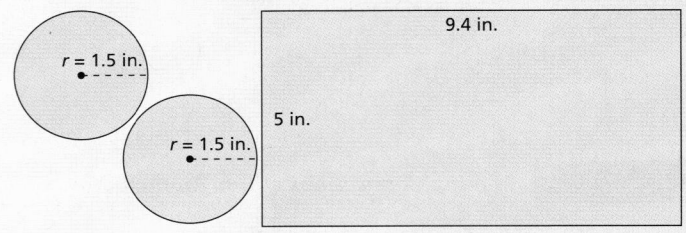

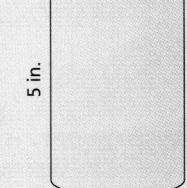

Solution The circles each have an area of $\pi \cdot 1.5^2$ or about 7.07 square inches. The area of the rectangle is $5 \cdot 9.4$ or 47 square inches. The total area of the three pieces is

$$2(\pi \cdot 1.5^2) + (5 \cdot 9.4) \approx 61.14 \text{ square inches.}$$

After the pieces are cut and taped together they form a cylinder, as shown at the right. ■

Exercises

1. *Group Activity* With other members of your group, use an $8\frac{1}{2}$-inch by 11-inch sheet of paper to create a cylinder, as shown in the example. All three pieces must fit on a single piece of paper. Your goal is to create a cylinder that has the largest possible surface area. After creating your cylinder, find its surface area. Then compare your group's results with the results of other groups. Check students' work.

2. In Exercise 1, suppose you had been asked to create the "biggest" possible cylinder. What different interpretations could be made of the word "biggest"? Surface area, volume, height, or radius

3. When you positioned the rectangle and circles on the piece of paper, which did you draw first: the rectangle or the circles? If you drew the circles first, how did you decide how to make a rectangle that fit the circles? If you drew the rectangle first, how did you decide how to make circles that fit the rectangle? See margin.

Answer
3. If you drew the circles first: you should solve $C = 2\pi r$ for C, after measuring r, and use the value of C as the length of the rectangle. If you drew the rectangle first: you should measure the length of the rectangle, substitute that length for C in $C = 2\pi r$ and solve for r.

12.3 Exploring Surface Area of Prisms and Cylinders

PACING the Lesson

Suggested Number of Days
Basic/Average 2   **Above Average** 2
Advanced 2

PLANNING the Lesson

Lesson Plan 12.3, p. 96

What you should learn:

Goal 1 How to find the surface area of a prism and a cylinder

Goal 2 How to use surface area to answer questions about real life

Why you should learn it:

You can use surface area to answer questions about real life, such as comparing the amount of material used to make cereal containers.

Goal 1   **Finding Surface Area**

The **surface area** of a polyhedron is the sum of the areas of its faces. The figures below show how to find the surface area of a prism and a cylinder. Notice that in each case you obtain the surface area by adding the area of the vertical "sides" to the areas of the top and bottom.

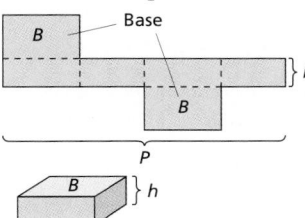

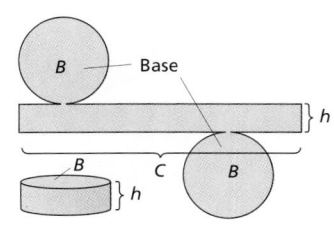

Surface Area of Prism and Cylinder

Prism: The surface area is $S = 2B + Ph$, where B is the area of a base, P is the perimeter of a base, and h is the height of the prism.

Cylinder: The surface area is $S = 2B + Ch$, where B is the area of a base, C is the circumference of a base, and h is the height of the cylinder.

Example 1   *Finding Surface Area*

Find the surface area of the cylinder at the left.

Solution   The radius of each base is 4 inches, which means that each base has a surface area of $B = \pi r^2$ or 16π square inches. The circumference of each base is $C = 2(4)\pi$ or 8π inches, and the height is $h = 6$ inches. The surface area is

$$S = 2B + Ch \qquad \textit{Formula for surface area}$$
$$= 2(16\pi) + (8\pi)(6) \qquad \textit{Substitute for B, C, and h.}$$
$$= 32\pi + 48\pi \qquad \textit{Simplify.}$$
$$= 80\pi \qquad \textit{Simplify.}$$
$$\approx 251.3 \qquad \textit{Use a calculator.}$$

The surface area is about 251.3 square inches. ∎

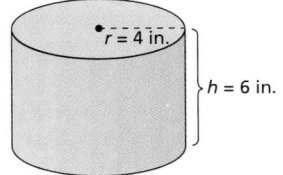
$r = 4$ in.
$h = 6$ in.

12.3 • *Exploring Surface Area of Prisms and Cylinders*   **549**

ORGANIZER

Starters (reproduced below)
  Problem of the Day 12.3, p. 34
  Warm-Up Exercises 12.3, p. 34
Lesson Resources
  Color Transparencies
    Picture for Ex. 19, 20, p. 52
  Teaching Tools
    Prism and cylinder models, pp. C23, C28
  Math Log, p. 37
  Answer Masters 12.3, pp. 235, 236
  Extra Practice Copymaster 12.3, p. 96
  Reteaching Copymaster 12.3, p. 96
  Enrichment Projects, pp. 65, 66
Special Populations
  Suggestions, Teacher's Edition, p. 536D

LESSON Notes

Paper nets are helpful in demonstrating how the surface areas of these figures are found. Refer to the list of Lesson Resources above.

Vocabulary Alert!

Students should record the definition of *surface area* in their math journals. Explain that to find the surface area of a solid figure, students will have to use skills they have already mastered, such as finding areas of flat (two-dimensional) geometric shapes.
   Note that all prisms in this chapter have lateral faces that are rectangles.

Common-Error Alert!

A confusing feature of finding the surface area of solids is keeping track of whether the area for each surface of the solid has already been computed. A systematic approach for keeping track of the surfaces may help. Suggest that students begin by naming all the surfaces of a given solid (A, B, C, etc.).

Example 1

Before using the formula that is given for computing the surface area, have students list the surfaces that comprise the solid (two bases and the rounded side). Explain that the surface area will be the sum of these areas. Emphasize and illustrate that the sum of the surface areas is what the formula is expressing. Students won't have to memorize the formulas if they can identify the surfaces that compose the solid.

STARTER: Problem of the Day

In this large cube, adjacent faces of small cubes are glued together. How many pairs of faces are glued together?

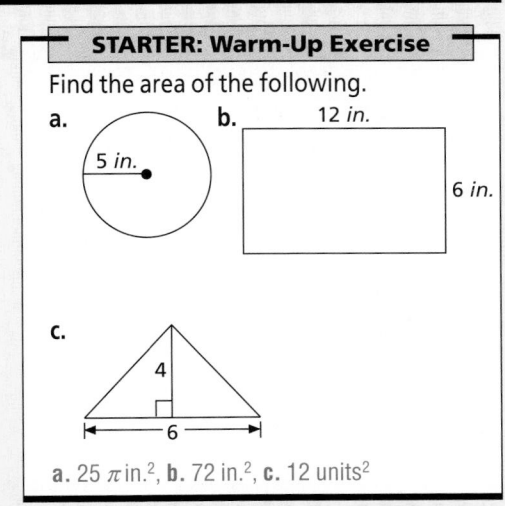

54

Also available as a copymaster, page 34

STARTER: Warm-Up Exercise

Find the area of the following.

a.
5 in.

b.   12 in.

6 in.

c.

4

6

a. 25 π in.², b. 72 in.², c. 12 units²

Also available as a copymaster, page 34

Lesson 12.3 **549**

Ask students to give real-life examples of situations in which surface area might be considered in making decisions. Examples might include: when deciding how much paint will be needed to paint a house, how much paper will be needed to wrap a gift, and what shape of container uses the least material in its construction. Let students discuss some possibilities, and then ask them to record some examples in their math journals.

Example 2

If possible, use models for this example.

Explain how the formulas are equivalent to finding the area of each face of the containers and adding them together. This is not immediately apparent for $S = 2B + Ph$, where P is the perimeter of the base and h is the height of the prism. The widths of the lateral faces make up the perimeter of the base, so the sum of their areas is the same as the perimeter of the base times the height:
$(2 \times 10) + (6 \times 10) + (2 \times 10) + (6 \times 10) =$
$(2 + 6 + 2 + 6) \times 10$.

Some students may feel more confident about their solutions if they compute the area of each face, then add them. Let students use the method that makes them feel more confident about their results.

Communicating about MATHEMATICS

Discuss real-life situations in which containers that hold the same amount of liquid might be compared to each other. Answers will vary but might include businesses making decisions about the cost of packaging, when the least surface area is best; or visibility of the package, when a greater surface area is best.

EXTENSION

Place six prisms (boxes) on your desk. Label them a, b, c, d, e, and f. Ask students to arrange them in order of increasing surface area (estimated). Then have each group calculate the surface area and check their predictions.

Writing Prompt

If one cylinder is shorter than a second cylinder, will its surface area be less? Explain your answer.

Example 2 *Comparing Surface Areas*

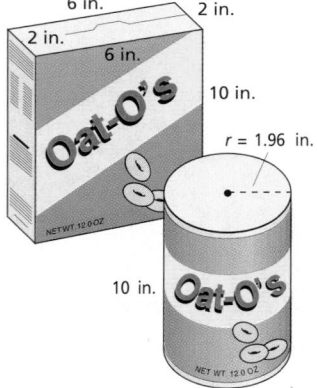

Real Life
Package Design

The two cereal containers at the left hold about the same amount of cereal. Which container uses less material?

Solution You can compare the amount of material needed to make each container by comparing their surface areas. The container with the smaller surface area uses less material. The area of each base of the prism is $2 \cdot 6$ or 12 square inches. Thus, the surface area of the prism is

$S = 2B + Ph$	*Surface area of prism*
$= 2(12) + (16)(10)$	*Substitute.*
$= 184$ square inches.	*Simplify.*

The area of each base of the cylinder is $\pi 1.96^2$ or about 12.07 square inches. Thus, the surface area of the cylinder is

$S = 2B + Ch$	*Surface area of cylinder*
$\approx 2(12.07) + (2 \cdot 1.96 \cdot \pi)(10)$	*Substitute.*
≈ 147.3 square inches.	*Simplify.*

Thus, the cylindrical package has less surface area, which implies that it uses less material. ∎

Communicating about MATHEMATICS

> **SHARING IDEAS about the Lesson**

Comparing Surface Areas Each of the following containers holds the same amount of liquid. Just from looking at the containers, which do you think has the least surface area? Find the surface area of each. Did you guess correctly? B

A.
12, 6, 3
252 units²

B.
6, 6, 6
216 units²

C.
4, 9, 6
228 units²

OPTION: Extra Examples

Here is an additional example similar to Example 1.

Finding Surface Area
Find the surface area of the prism.

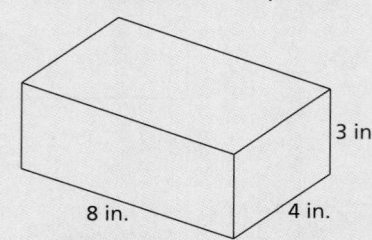

3 in.
8 in.
4 in.

Solution
The area of each base of the prism is $4 \cdot 8$ or 32 square inches. Thus, the surface area of the prism is

$S = 2B + Ph$	Surface area of prism
$= 2(32) + (24)(3)$	Substitute.
$= 136$ square inches	Simplify.

The surface area is 136 square inches.

EXERCISES

Guided Practice

▶ **CHECK for Understanding**

In Exercises 1–4, use the following figures.

1. A: Prism (with rectangles as bases),
B: Prism (with triangles as bases),
C: Cylinder

A.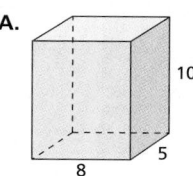

B.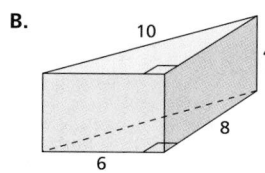

C.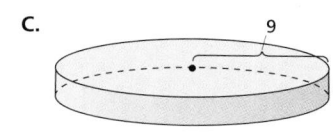

1. Identify each figure.   See above.

2. Find the surface area of Figure A. 340 units²

3. Find the surface area of Figure B.
144 units²

4. Find the surface area of Figure C.
≈622.0 units²

Independent Practice

In Exercises 5–12, find the surface area of the solid.

5.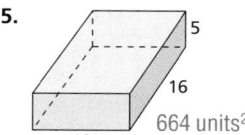
664 units²

6.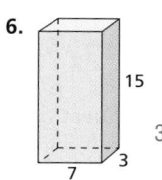
342 units²

7.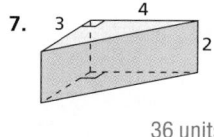
36 units²

8.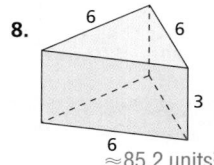
≈85.2 units²

9.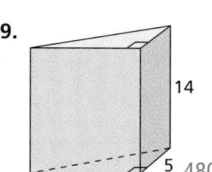
480 units²

10.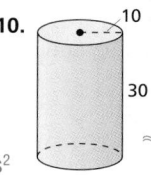
≈2513.3 units²

11.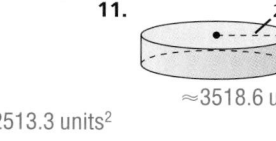
≈3518.6 units²

12.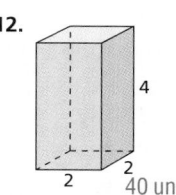
40 units²

13. Draw a cube. Use dashed lines and shading to make the cube appear three dimensional. If each edge of the cube is 4 inches long, what is its surface area?   96 in.²

14. *Guess, Check, and Revise*   Draw a prism that has a surface area of 52 square units. (There is more than one correct answer.)   Answers vary.

In Exercises 15 and 16, use the cube at the right.

15. Find the surface area of the cube.   24 in.²

16. Imagine that the cube is cut into eight congruent smaller cubes. Find the surface area of each.   6 in.²

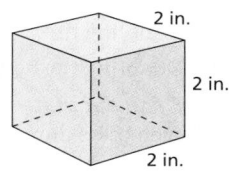

✪ More difficult exercises

12.3 ▪ *Exploring Surface Area of Prisms and Cylinders*   **551**

Lesson 12.3 **551**

Gift Wrapping   In Exercises 17 and 18, consider a gift box that measures
45 centimeters by 27 centimeters by 6 centimeters.

✪ 17. Which sheet of wrapping paper should you choose to wrap
the gift? Explain.   b, for explanation, see margin.

a. 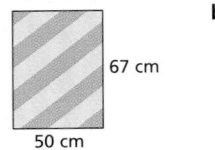 67 cm 50 cm

b. 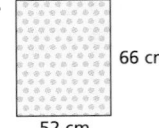 66 cm 52 cm

c. 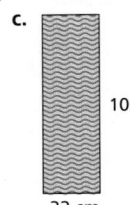 102 cm 32 cm

✪ 18. Describe the smallest rectangular piece of wrapping paper
that could be used to wrap the box. Compare its area with
the surface area of the box.   See margin.

Totem Poles   In Exercises 19 and 20, use the following.

A totem pole is to be carved out of a cylindrical log. The log is
22 feet long and has a diameter of 4 feet.

19. What is the surface area of the cylindrical pole?   ≈301.6 ft²

✪ 20. Will the surface area of the totem pole be greater than or
less than the surface area of the log? Explain.
Answer could be *less than* if a large amount is cut away and the surface is not highly
irregular. Otherwise the answer would be *greater than*.

*Native American tribes in the
Pacific Northwest carved their
family and clan emblems on
totem poles.*

| **Integrated Review** | *Making Connections within Mathematics* |

21. *Estimation*   Which best estimates the surface area of this book?   c
    a. 100 in.²   **b.** 170 in.²   **c.** 220 in.²   **d.** 300 in.²

22. *Estimation*   Which best estimates the surface area of a 12-ounce
soda pop can?   a
    a. 100 in.²   **b.** 170 in.²   **c.** 220 in.²   **d.** 300 in.²

Exploration and Extension

True or False?   In Exercises 23–26, is the statement true or false? Explain
your answer by drawing any necessary diagrams.   For diagrams, see Additional Answers.

✪ 23. Doubling the width of a shoe box doubles the base area of the box.   True
✪ 24. Doubling the height of a shoe box doubles the surface area of the box.   False
✪ 25. Doubling the radius of a cylinder doubles the surface area of the cylinder.   False
✪ 26. Doubling the height of a cylinder doubles the area of its curved surface.   True
✪ 27. *Think about It*   What happens to the surface area of a shoe box if
[P] each of its dimensions is doubled? Give an example.
It is quadrupled. Surface area of a 6 in. by 4 in. by 12 in. shoe box is 288 in.², surface
area of a 12 in. by 8 in. by 24 in. box is 1152 in.², 1152 ÷ 288 = 4.

✪ More difficult exercises
[P] Portfolio Opportunity

Answers
17. In **c**, the area of the paper is too small to cover
the box; also, the paper is not wide enough: it
needs to be (27 + 6) cm wide. In **a**, the paper is
not wide enough: it needs to be (45 + 6) cm wide.
18. 66 cm × 51 cm and 102 cm × 33 cm, the
paper's area is 72 cm² more than the box's surface
area.

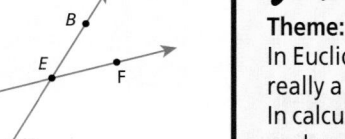
Milestones DESCRIBING MOTION

1500 — 1600 — 1700 — 1800 — 1900 — 2000

Camera Obscura 1500

First photo 1826

Motion picture camera, 1880's

Technicolor 1930

Video games 1972

When the two great mathematicians, Isaac Newton (1642–1727) and Gottfried von Leibniz (1646–1716), developed calculus, they were foreshadowing the development of animation and video games. Just as each frame of a cartoon shows a slight change of movement from the previous one, calculus describes the paths of moving objects by breaking the movements down into smaller and smaller increments.

Even though Walt Disney (1901–1966) did not invent animation, his name has become synonymous with it. At 16 he helped make cartoon ads for movies. In 1923, he moved to Los Angeles but could not find movie work. So, he set up a studio in his garage and in 1928 made the classic *Steamboat Willie* cartoon.

• Think of the minute hand of a clock. Describe the path its tip makes in one hour. A complete circle

• Think of the hour hand of a clock. Describe the path its tip makes in one hour. An arc of 30° on a circle

Mickey Mouse with his creator, Walt Disney

Milestones

Theme: Area and Motion

In Euclidean geometry, the formula $A = \ell w$ is really a definition for the area of a rectangle. In calculus, the problem of finding the area under any curve led to the development of *limits*. Archimedes (287–212 B.C.) is said to have introduced the *exhaustion* or limiting method for finding the area of any figure.

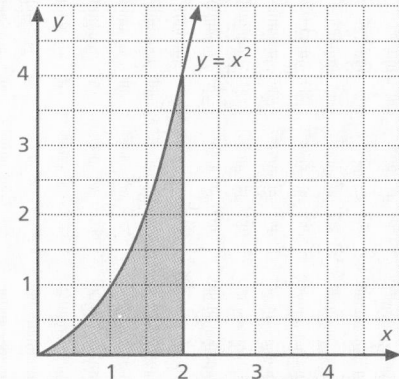

The graph above shows a portion of the line $y = x^2$ from $x = 0$ to $x = 2$. Describe how you would estimate the area under the curve. Compare your answer with your classmates to find a better estimate. Answers vary.

This problem is one of the classic problems in calculus. Using the limiting method of calculus, it can be shown that the area under this particular portion of the curve (from $x = 0$ to $x = 2$) is $A = \frac{2^3}{3}$, or $\frac{8}{3}$. How close was your class estimate? Answers vary.

Library Skills

Have students use library resources to research the history of methods of finding area from ancient to modern times. Students should also include the history of π in their report.

ORGANIZER

Starters (reproduced below)
    Problem of the Day 12.4, p. 35
    Warm-Up Exercises 12.4, p. 35
Lesson Resources
    Teaching Tools,
      Coordinate planes, pp. T9, C11
      Graph paper, pp. T1, C2
    Math Log, p. 38
    Answer Masters 12.4, p. 238
    Extra Practice Copymaster 12.4, p. 97
    Reteaching Copymaster 12.4, p. 97
Special Populations
    Suggestions, Teacher's Edition, p. 536D

LESSON Notes

Apart from their use in Example 1, wooden cubes are helpful in *introducing* the concept of volume.

Remind students that a prism has two congruent bases, and that the remaining faces are all rectangles. The base of a prism can be any polygon. The name of the polygonal base, such as "rectangle," can be used as an adjective to describe a prism, such as a "rectangular prism." Have students give examples of other prisms that can be described by the shape of the bases. Examples should include rectangular prism, triangular prism, pentagonal prism, and hexagonal prism.

    Have students record in their math journal that the formula for the volume for a prism is $V = Bh$, and that the formula for the base B depends on the shape of the base.

Example 1
This example could easily be done as a group problem-solving activity.

    Have students generalize the concept illustrated in this example: The number of different prisms that can be constructed from n cubes is the same as the number of ways n can be factored into three positive integers.

Historical Note
In ancient Greece, the scientist Archimedes was known as the local volume expert because of his book, *The Sand Reckoner,* which described the volume of the universe in terms of the number of grains of sand it could hold! The emperor called on Archimedes to compute the volume of a crown. Computing the volume of irregular-shaped figures was difficult, so some goldsmiths cheated customers by using a smaller volume of gold than they

(continued)

554 *Chapter 12*

12.4 Exploring Volumes of Prisms

What you should learn:

    How to find the volume of a prism

Goal 2
    How to use the volume of a prism to solve real-life problems

Why you should learn it:

You can use the volume of a prism to solve real-life problems, such as designing a television studio.

Study Tip...
The formula for the volume of a rectangular prism, $V = lwh$, is a special case of the formula for a general prism. For instance, in the rectangular prism below, notice that the area of each base is $B = lw$, which means that the volume is $V = Bh = lwh$.

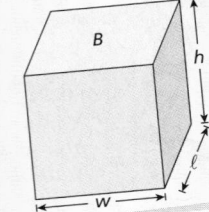

554   Chapter **12** ▪ *Measurements in Geometry*

Goal 1   **Finding the Volume of a Prism**

The **volume** of a solid is a measure of how much it will hold. The standard measures of volume are **cubic units** such as cubic inches, cubic centimeters, and cubic feet. Other measures of volume, such as liters, are discussed on page 560.

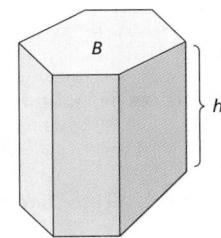

The Volume of a Prism

1. The volume of a prism is the product of its height and the area of its base. That is, $V = Bh$ where B is the area of a base and h is the height of the prism.

2. The volume of a rectangular prism (a prism whose sides are all rectangles) is the product of its length, width, and height. That is, $V = lwh$, where l is the length, w is the width, and h is the height of the prism

Example 1   *Prisms with the Same Volume*

How many different shapes of rectangular prisms can be formed with 64 cubes, each of which is 1 cubic inch?

Solution   You need to find all the ways that 64 can be factored into three positive integers. After trying different combinations, you can discover that there are 7 different ways, 6 of which are shown below. (The prism that is 1 by 1 by 64 is not shown.)

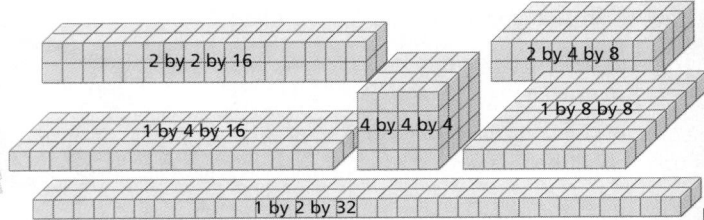

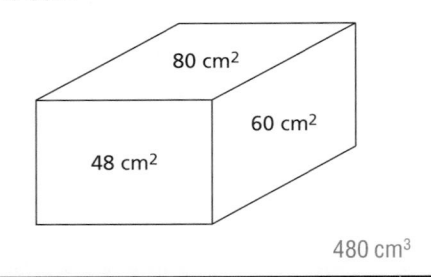

Goal 2 Solving Real-Life Problems

Example 2 *Finding the Volume of a Room*

You are designing a studio room for a television talk show. You want the room to have enough seats for an audience of 100. In addition to the audience, the room will have up to 20 staff members and guests. A building code suggests that the room have about 480 cubic feet of air per person. Describe some of the possible room dimensions.

Solution For each of the 120 people to have 480 cubic feet of air space, the room should have a volume of at least

$120(480) = 57{,}600$ cubic feet. *Volume of room*

Typical room heights range between 7 and 12 feet. If the studio is 12 feet high, then the area of its base should be $\frac{1}{12}(57{,}600)$ or 4800 square feet. One possible solution would be to have a base that is 60 feet by 80 feet, as shown below.

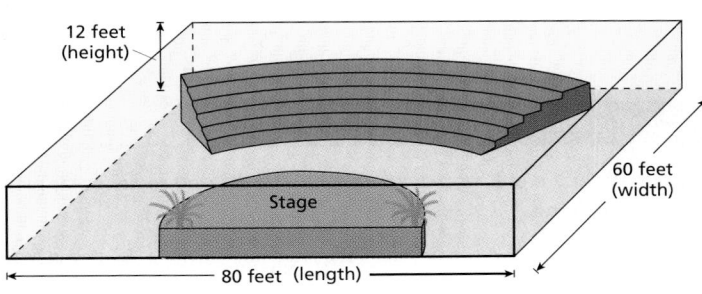

12 feet (height)

60 feet (width)

Stage

80 feet (length)

After Lisa Johnson-Smith graduated from Temple University in Philadelphia with a major in journalism, she accepted a job in Washington, D.C., as the host and associate producer of Black Entertainment Television's (BET) new talk show called Teen Summit.

Volume of Room = (length)(width)(height) = 57,600 cubic feet ∎

P **Communicating** *about* MATHEMATICS

▶ **SHARING IDEAS about the Lesson**

Cooperative Learning

Designing a Studio Example 2 describes only one of many possible designs for the studio. Work with a partner to sketch some other possible designs. Describe their dimensions, advantages, and disadvantages. Remember that you can change the room's height. Compare the floor space for different room heights. Check students' work.

(continued)

claimed. While taking a bath, Archimedes considered the fact that the height of water rose in the tub when he got in. This observation led him to experiment and discover that objects with the same volume displaced the same amount of water. This gave a method for measuring the volume of objects with irregular shapes.

Challenge students to think of other examples from real life in which volumes are important. Have them record the examples in their math journals.

Example 2

Remind students to consider issues such as having enough room for cameras and lighting equipment in places where they will not be seen when shots of the audience are shown. Ask students to think of other real-life considerations that might influence the shape of the room.

Communicating about MATHEMATICS

Have students discuss real-life considerations when designing their studios. For example, rent for the space might be charged based on the area of the floor.

In a cooperative learning setting, encourage students to make a scale model of a studio. This will offer an opportunity for students to review their understanding of ratios and proportions.

Writing Prompt
Explain why volume is measured in cubic units and not, for example, in terms of styrofoam peanuts.

EXERCISE Notes

ASSIGNMENT GUIDE

Basic/Average:
Day 1: Ex. 7–17 odd, 23–25 odd
Day 2: Ex. 18–22, 26, 27

Above Average:
Ex. 7–17 odd, 18, 22, 25–28

Advanced: Ex. 7–17 odd, 18, 22, 25–28

Selected Answers: Ex. 1–6, 7–23 odd

Guided Practice

▶ **Ex. 1** Students may count *or* use a formula for this exercise.

Independent Practice

▶ **Ex. 7, 8** Students need much practice sketching in three dimensions.
▶ **Ex. 9–12** If possible, have students find the volume of real objects in the classroom.
▶ **Ex. 13–16** This type of problem needs to be modeled during the lesson.

EXERCISES

Guided Practice

▶ **CHECK for Understanding**

1. Which of these prisms have the same volume? Explain.   b and c, each volume is 36 units^3

 **a.**   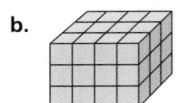 **b.**   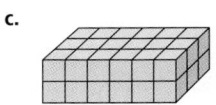 **c.**   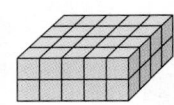 **d.**

Ⓟ **2.** In your own words, state the formula for the volume of a rectangular prism.
Volume = length × width × height

In Exercises 3–6, state whether the figure is a prism. If the figure is a prism, find its volume.

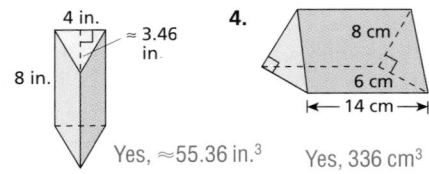

3. 4 in. ≈ 3.46 in. 8 in.   Yes, ≈55.36 in.^{3}

4. 8 cm, 6 cm, 14 cm   Yes, 336 cm^3

5. 3 ft, 4 ft, 4 ft   No

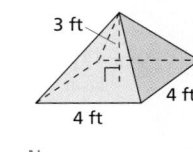
6. 3 cm, 4 cm, 2 cm   Yes, 12 cm^3

Independent Practice

In Exercises 7 and 8, sketch and label the indicated rectangular prism. Then find its volume.   For sketches, see margin.

7. Length: 2 in., Width: 3 in., Height: 5 in.   30 in.^{3} **8.** Length: 5 in., Width: 4 in., Height: 6 in.
120 in.^{3}

In Exercises 9–12, find the volume of the prism.

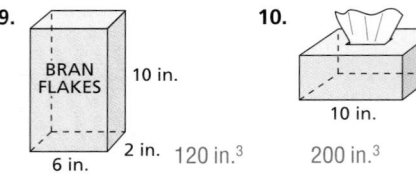

9. BRAN FLAKES, 10 in., 2 in., 6 in.   120 in.^{3}

10. 4 in., 5 in., 10 in.   200 in.^{3}

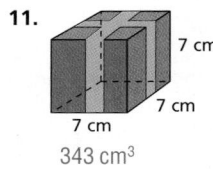
11. 7 cm, 7 cm, 7 cm   343 cm^3

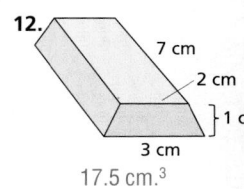
12. 7 cm, 2 cm, 3 cm, 1 cm   17.5 cm.^{3}

In Exercises 13–16, solve for *x*.

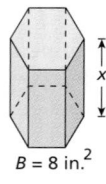
13. $V = 24$ in.^{3} x $B = 8$ in.^{2} 3 in.

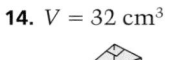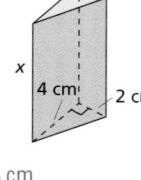
14. $V = 32$ cm^3 x 4 cm   2 cm   8 cm

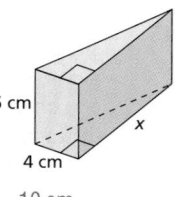
15. $V = 120$ cm^3 6 cm x 4 cm   10 cm

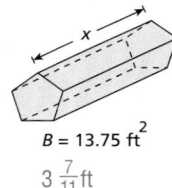
16. $V = 50$ ft^3 x x $B = 13.75$ ft^2 $3\frac{7}{11}$ ft

Ⓟ Portfolio Opportunity

Answers

7.
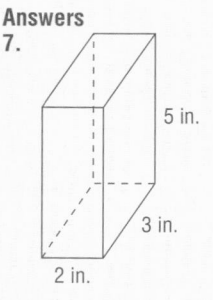
5 in., 3 in., 2 in.

8.
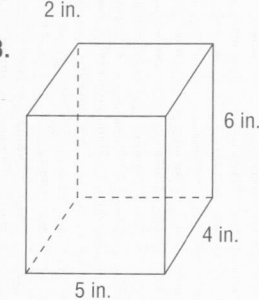
6 in., 4 in., 5 in.

Extra Practice

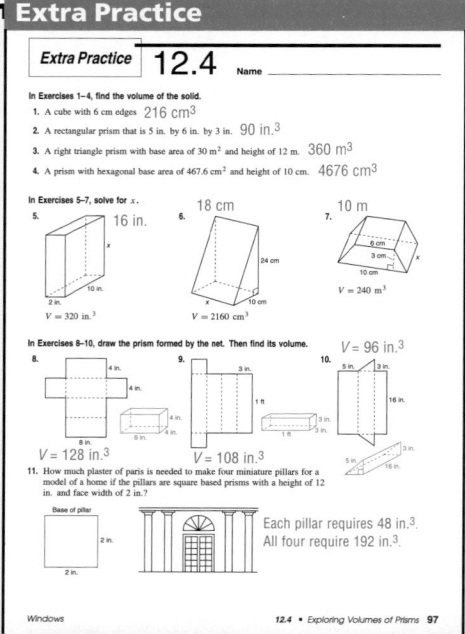

Extra Practice 12.4 Name _____

In Exercises 1–4, find the volume of the solid.
1. A cube with 6 cm edges   216 cm^3
2. A rectangular prism that is 5 in. by 6 in. by 3 in.   90 in.^{3}
3. A right triangle prism with base area of 30 m^2 and height of 12 m.   360 m^3
4. A prism with hexagonal base area of 467.6 cm^2 and height of 10 cm.   4676 cm^3

In Exercises 5–7, solve for *x*.
5. 16 in., 10 in., 2 in. $V = 320$ in.^{3}
6. 18 cm, 24 cm, 6 cm, 10 cm $V = 2160$ cm^3
7. 10 m, 6 m, 3 cm, x $V = 240$ m^3

In Exercises 8–10, draw the prism formed by the net. Then find its volume.
8. 4 in., 4 in., 8 in. $V = 128$ in.^{3}
9. 3 in., 4 in., 1 ft. $V = 108$ in.^{3} $V = 96$ in.^{3}
10. 5 in., 3 in., 16 in., 5 in., 3 in.

11. How much plaster of paris is needed to make four miniature pillars for a model of a home if the pillars are square based prisms with a height of 12 in. and face width of 2 in.?
Base of pillar   2 in.   2 in.
Each pillar requires 48 in.^{3}.
All four require 192 in.^{3}.

Windows   *12.4 ▪ Exploring Volumes of Prisms* **97**

Reteaching

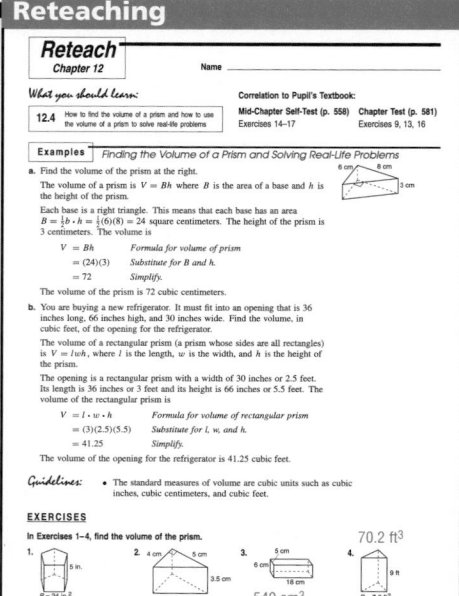

Reteach Chapter 12 Name _____

What you should learn:
| 12.4 | How to find the volume of a prism and how to use the volume of a prism to solve real-life problems |

Correlation to Pupil's Textbook:
Mid-Chapter Self-Test (p. 558)   Chapter Test (p. 581)
Exercises 14–17   Exercises 9, 13, 16

Examples *Finding the Volume of a Prism and Solving Real-Life Problems*

a. Find the volume of the prism at the right.
The volume of a prism is $V = Bh$ where B is the area of a base and h is the height of the prism.
Each base is a right triangle. This means that each base has an area $B = \frac{1}{2}b \cdot h = \frac{1}{2}(6)(8) = 24$ square centimeters. The height of the prism is 3 centimeters. The volume is
$V = Bh$ Formula for volume of prism
$= (24)(3)$ Substitute for B and h.
$= 72$ Simplify.
The volume of the prism is 72 cubic centimeters.

b. You are buying a new refrigerator. It must fit into an opening that is 36 inches long, 66 inches high, and 30 inches wide. Find the volume, in cubic feet, of the opening for the refrigerator.
The volume of a rectangular prism (a prism whose sides are all rectangles) is $V = lwh$, where l is the length, w is the width, and h is the height of the prism.
The opening is a rectangular prism with a width of 30 inches or 2.5 feet. Its length is 36 inches or 3 feet and its height is 66 inches or 5.5 feet. The volume of the rectangular prism is
$V = l \cdot w \cdot h$ Formula for volume of rectangular prism
$= (3)(2.5)(5.5)$ Substitute for l, w, and h.
$= 41.25$ Simplify.
The volume of the opening for the refrigerator is 41.25 cubic feet.

Guidelines: • The standard measures of volume are cubic units such as cubic inches, cubic centimeters, and cubic feet.

EXERCISES
In Exercises 1–4, find the volume of the prism.
1. 5 in., $B = 24$ in.^{2} 120 in.^{3}
2. 4 cm, 5 cm, 3.5 cm   35 cm^3
3. 5 cm, 6 cm, 18 cm   540 cm^3
4. 9 ft, $B = 7.8$ ft^2 70.2 ft^3

Windows   *Chapter 12 ▪ Measurements in Geometry* **97**

17. *Visualizing Solids*   You are given 36 1-inch cubes. Describe the different shapes of rectangular prisms you can build using all the cubes. Of these, which has the greatest surface area?   See margin.

18. Sketch a rectangular prism that is 2 by 3 by 4. Find its surface area, S, and volume, V.   52 units², 24 units³
   a. If you double one dimension, how do S and V change?   a.–c. See margin.
   b. If you double two dimensions, how do S and V change?
   c. If you double all three dimensions, how do S and V change?

Designing a Tent   In Exercises 19–22, use the diagram of a tent at the right.

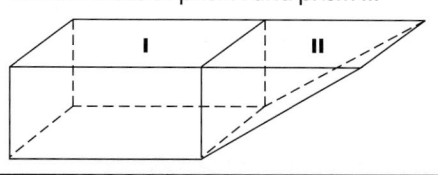
6 ft   15 ft   15 ft

19. How much canvas is used to create the tent? (All sides, including the bottom, are made of canvas.)   ≈603 ft²

20. How many cubic feet of air does the tent hold?   675 ft³

21. Design a different tent that has the same volume but uses less canvas. Which design do you prefer? Explain.   Answers vary.

22. *Swimming Pools*   Which two pools hold the same amount of water?   a and b

a.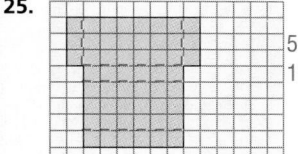
40   20   6   10

b.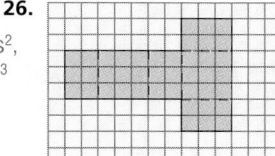
40   15   5

c.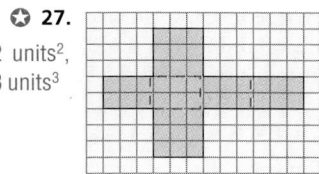
30   20   8   10

Integrated Review   *Making Connections within Mathematics*

Coordinate Geometry   In Exercises 23 and 24, plot the points in a coordinate plane. Connect the points and shade the figure so that it looks like a prism. Label the prism's dimensions and find its volume.   For plots, see margin.

23. $(2, 0)$, $(1, 1)$, $(-2, 0)$, $(-1, 1)$, $(1, -4)$, $(2, -5)$, $(-1, -4)$, $(-2, -5)$ 15 units³
24. $(1, 2)$, $(4, 5)$, $(7, 2)$, $(4, 0)$, $(1, -3)$, $(7, -3)$ 45 units³

Exploration and Extension

Nets   In Exercises 25–27, copy the net and use dashed lines to show how to fold the net to form a prism. Then find its surface area and volume.   42 units², 18 units³

25.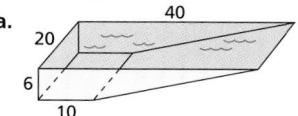

✪ 26. 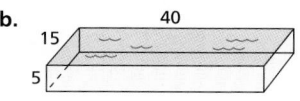   54 units², 18 units³

✪ 27. 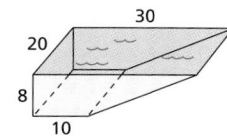   42 units², 18 units³

28. *It's Up to You*   In Exercises 25–27, is it easier to find the prism's surface area or its volume? Explain your reasoning.
   Answers may include: surface area, because you can just count the green squares.

✪ More difficult exercises

12.4 ▪ *Exploring Volumes of Prisms*   **557**

▶ **Ex. 17, 18**   Assign these exercises as a group activity.
▶ **Ex. 19–21**   Assign these exercises as a group.

Integrated Review
This section is a neat combination of coordinate geometry, visualization in 3-D, and volume measurement.

Exploration and Extension
These problems could be done in class. Students may need to cut, fold, and tape in order to be successful.

Portfolio Opportunity: Math Log
In your own words, explain why the volume of the figure shown below is the same as the sum of the volumes of prism I and prism II, but the surface area of the figure is not the same as the sum of the surface areas of prism I and prism II.

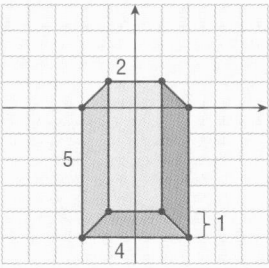

Also available as a copymaster, page 38, Ex. 4

Short Quiz
Covers Lessons 12.3 and 12.4
Available as a copymaster, page 191

Answers
17. 1 by 1 by 36, 1 by 2 by 18, 1 by 3 by 12, 1 by 4 by 9, 1 by 6 by 6, 2 by 2 by 9, 2 by 3 by 6, 3 by 3 by 4; 1 by 1 by 36
18. a. The surface area of 4 of the faces doubles while the surface area of 2 of the faces remains the same. The volume doubles.
b. The surface area of 4 of the faces doubles while the surface area of 2 of the faces quadruples. The volume quadruples.
c. The surface area quadruples. The volume is multiplied by 8.
23.
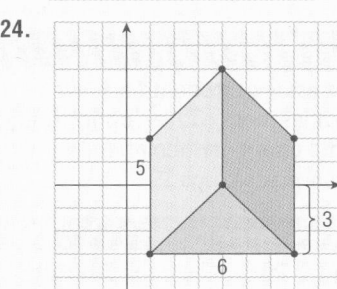

24.

Take this test as you would take a test in class. The answers to the exercises are given in the back of the book.
1. ≈18.8 cm, ≈28.3 cm² **2.** ≈15.7 in., ≈19.6 in.²

In Exercises 1 and 2, find the circumference and area of the circle. (12.1)

In Exercises 3 and 4, find the area of the blue region (12.1) 3. ≈13.7 ft² **4.** ≈58.9 yd²

1.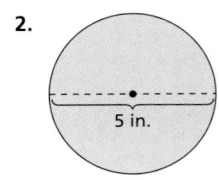
3 cm

2.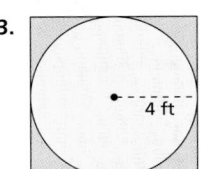
5 in.

3.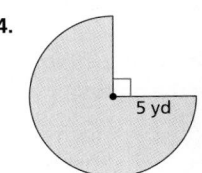
4 ft

4.
5 yd

In Exercises 5–9, match the name with a part of the solid at the right. (12.2–12.3)

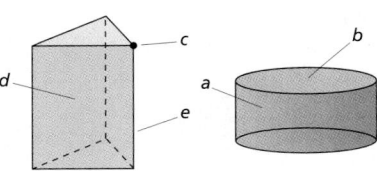

5. Face d   **6.** Vertex c

7. Edge e   **8.** Base b

9. Lateral surface a

In Exercises 10–13, find the surface area of the solid. (12.3)

10. Diameter: 24 mm
Height: 2 mm
≈1055.6 mm²

11. Diameter: 14 mm
Length: 49 mm
AA Battery
≈2463.0 mm²

12. 0.75 in.
0.75 in.
0.75 in.
3.375 in.²

13.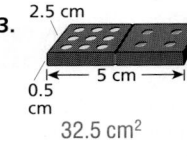
2.5 cm
5 cm
0.5 cm
32.5 cm²

In Exercises 14–17, find the volume of the prism. (12.4)

14.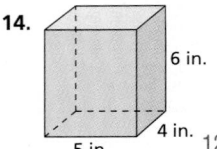
6 in.
4 in.
5 in.
120 in.³

15.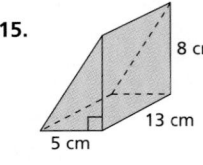
8 cm
13 cm
5 cm
260 cm³

16.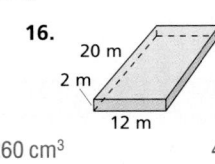
20 m
2 m
12 m
480 m³

17.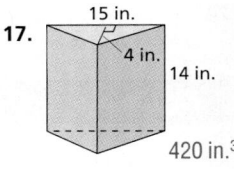
15 in.
4 in.
14 in.
420 in.³

In Exercises 18–20, use the following information.

The Large Electron-Positron Collider, on the border of France and Switzerland, is the largest scientific instrument in the world. It can accelerate particles to nearly the speed of light. The collider is circular, with a diameter of 5.41 miles.   **19.** ≈22.99 mi²

18. Find the circumference of the collider.   ≈17.00 mi

19. Find the area of the land inside the collider.

20. The collider's tunnel has a radius of 1.91 feet. What is the tunnel's circumference?   ≈12.00 ft

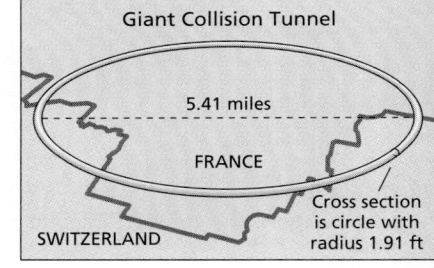
Giant Collision Tunnel
5.41 miles
FRANCE
Cross section is circle with radius 1.91 ft
SWITZERLAND

Partner Quiz

Chapter 12
Mid-Chapter Partner Quiz   (Use after Lesson 12.4)
Name _____

In Exercises 1 and 2, use the figure at the right. (12.1)

Area of shaded region is 6π in.²

1. Find the radius of the circle.   **1.** 6 in.

2. Find the circumference of the circle.   **2.** 12π in. ≈ 37.68 in.

3. Find the diameter of a circle with circumference 7 inches.   **3.** ≈2.23 in.

4. Find the perimeter of the figure. Use 3.14 for π.   **4.**
(6π + 12) in. ≈ 30.84 in.
12 in.

5. If a pyramid has 6 faces, how many of these faces share a common point? What is the base of the pyramid? (12.2)   **5.** 5; Pentagon

6. Which two solids have a circle as a base? (12.2)   **6.** Cylinder and cone

7. Which of the cylinders has the greatest surface area? (12.3)   **7.** a.
a.   b.

8. What is the surface area of the prism formed by the given net? (12.3)   **8.** 36 in.²

9. Write a formula for the volume of a cube in terms of s, the length of the cube's side. (12.4)   **9.** V = s³

10. A cylinder of volume 72π in.³ fits tightly into a box. The diameter of the cylinder and the length and width of the box is 6 inches. The height of the cylinder and box is 8 inches. Find the volume of the empty space around the cylinder in the box. (12.4, 12.5)   **10.** ≈61.92 in.³

© D. C. Heath and Company   ▪ Alternative Assessment **55**

Mid-Chapter Test

Mid-Chapter **12** Test Form B   Name _____
(Use after Lesson 12.4)   Date _____

In Exercises 1 and 2, use 3.14 for π. (12.1)

1. Find the area and the circumference of the circle.
A = 379.94 sq yds;
C = 69.08 yds
d = 22 yd
1. _____

2. Find the area of the shaded region.
d = 20 ft
2. 39.25 sq ft

In Exercises 3 and 4, find the surface area of the solid. Use 3.14 for π. (12.3)

3.
6.4 m
5.2 m
16 m
3. 437.76 m²

4.
14 in.
2 in.
4. 395.64 in²

5. Draw a rectangular prism. Label a face, an edge, a vertex, and a base. (12.2)
Check students' sketches.
5. _____

In Exercises 6 and 7, Mrs. Fleming bought a freezer. It is 4 feet long, 2 feet wide, and has a volume of 36 cubic feet. (12.4)

6. Find the freezer's height.   **6.** 4.5 feet

7. Sketch the completed freezer and label each dimension.
Check students' sketches.   **7.** _____

Windows ℗ © D. C. Heath and Company   Chapter **12** ▪ Measurements in Geometry **193**

12.5

Exploring Volumes of Cylinders

▶ **PACING** the Lesson

Suggested Number of Days
Basic/Average 2   Above Average 1
Advanced 1

▶ **PLANNING** the Lesson

Lesson Plan 12.5, p. 98

What you should learn:

Goal 1 How to find the volume of a cylinder

Goal 2 How to use the volume of a cylinder to solve real-life problems

Why you should learn it:

You can use the volume of a cylinder to solve real-life problems, such as comparing the amount of soda pop in different sizes of containers.

Goal 1 **Finding the Volume of a Cylinder**

Each stack of pennies at the right forms a cylinder. As the number of pennies increases, the height and volume of the stack increase.

You can find the volume of a cylinder in the same way you find the volume of a prism. That is, you multiply the height of the cylinder by the area of its base.

The Volume of a Cylinder

The volume of a cylinder is the product of its height and the area of its base. That is, $V = Bh$, where B is the area of a base and h is the height.

Example 1 *Finding Volumes of Cylinders*

Find the volume of each cylinder at the left.

Solution

a. The area of the base of this cylinder is $\pi(3^2)$ or about 28.27 square meters. The volume of the cylinder is

$V = Bh$	*Volume of a cylinder*
$\approx (28.27)(5)$	*Substitute for B and h.*
≈ 141.4	*Simplify.*

The volume is about 141.4 cubic meters.

b. The area of the base of this cylinder is $\pi(2^2)$ or about 12.57 square meters. The volume of the cylinder is

$V = Bh$	*Volume of a cylinder*
$\approx (12.57)(7)$	*Substitute for B and h.*
≈ 88.00	*Simplify.*

The volume is about 88.0 cubic meters. ∎

Which cylinder appears to have the greater volume? After finding the volumes, does it surprise you that the green cylinder has about 60% more volume than the blue one?

$r = 3$ m

$h = 5$ m

$r = 2$ m

b.

$h = 7$ m

12.5 • *Exploring Volumes of Cylinders* **559**

ORGANIZER

Starters (reproduced below)
  Problem of the Day 12.5, p. 35
  Warm-Up Exercises 12.5, p. 35
Lesson Resources
  Math Log, p. 38
  Technology, pp. 70, 71
  Answer Masters 12.5, p. 239
  Extra Practice Copymaster 12.5, p. 98
  Reteaching Copymaster 12.5, p. 98
Special Populations
  Suggestions, Teacher's Edition, p. 536D

LESSON Notes

Vocabulary Alert!

Have students define *cylinder* and record the formula for the volume of a cylinder ($V = Bh$) in their math journals. A cylinder has two congruent bases that are circles, and the lateral surface is curved. Ask students to compare the description of a cylinder to that of a prism. It is very important that students see the connection between the volume of a prism and the volume of a cylinder.

Example 1

Discuss how the visual appearance of two cylinders may sometimes make the comparison of their volumes difficult. Ask students how manufacturers might use similar relationships to make their products seem less expensive compared to other companies' products.

Challenge students to give examples of products that are packaged in cylindrical containers. Have them record selected examples in their math journals. Then ask students to identify objects whose volumes are measured in different units.

Example 2

Emphasize to students that understanding volumes is important for deciding which of several products is a better buy. Ask: Why might the six-pack of sodas appear to be the better buy if no computation of volume were made? Have students bring in various products for volume comparison.

Communicating about MATHEMATICS

The volume of soda pop cans is given both in ounces (oz) and in milliliters (ml). For example, a 12 oz. soda can is also labeled as 355 ml. Use a ruler that is marked with centimeters to estimate the volume in cubic centimeters. Use this result to determine the number of cubic centimeters (cc) in a milliliter.   1 cc = 1 ml

Writing Prompt
A prism with a regular triangular base just fits inside a cylinder. Another prism with a regular hexagonal base just fits inside the same cylinder. How do the volumes of these solids compare?

You have learned that cubic units are the standard units for volume. There are, however, many other commonly used units for volume. Some examples are liters, gallons, quarts, and fluid ounces. To compare volumes that are measured in different units, it helps to change one or more of the measures so that each volume is measured in the same units.

1 liter =
33.8 fluid ounces

Real Life
Unit Prices

$1.79

$1.99

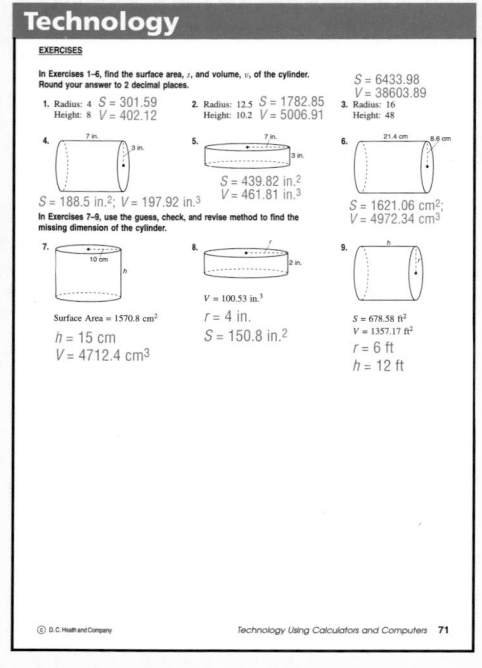

Example 2   *Comparing Volumes*

You are shopping for soda pop, the 2-liter bottle or the 6-pack. Which container has the greater volume? Which is the better buy?

Solution   One way to compare the two volumes is to find how many fluid ounces are in the 2-liter bottle. Using the fact that 1 liter is equal to 33.8 fluid ounces, it follows that the 2-liter bottle has a volume of 67.6 fluid ounces. Because the six-pack contains 6(12) or 72 fluid ounces, you can conclude that it has the greater volume.

To decide which is the better buy, you can find the unit price of each container.

$$\text{Unit price} = \frac{\$1.79}{67.6 \text{ fl oz}}$$
$$\approx \$0.026 \text{ per fl oz}   \textit{Bottle}$$

$$\text{Unit price} = \frac{\$1.99}{72 \text{ fl oz}}$$
$$\approx \$0.028 \text{ per fl oz}   \textit{Six-pack}$$

The bottle is a slightly better buy.

Communicating about MATHEMATICS

▶ **SHARING IDEAS about the Lesson**

Changing Units of Measure   Use a ruler to help you approximate the volume (in cubic inches) of a 12-ounce soda pop can. Then use your result to complete the following.

A. 1 fluid ounce = ? cubic inches.   ≈1.8408

B. 1 cubic inch = ? fluid ounce.   ≈0.5432

What do you notice about the two values?   They are reciprocals.

OPTION: Extra Examples

Here is an additional example similar to Example 1.

Finding the Volume of a Cylinder
Find the volume of each cylinder.

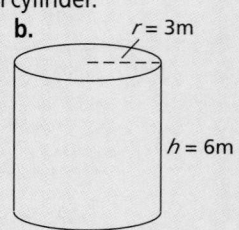

a. $r = 4$m $h = 3$m

b. $r = 3$m $h = 6$m

Solution

a. The area of the base of this cylinder is $\pi(4^2)$ or about 50.27 square meters. The volume of the cylinder is

$V = Bh$ Volume of a cylinder
$\approx (50.27)(3)$ Substitute for B and h.
≈ 150.8 Simplify.

The volume is about 150.8 cubic meters.

b. The area of the base of this cylinder is $\pi(3^2)$ or about 28.27 square meters. The volume of the cylinder is

$V = Bh$ Volume of a cylinder
$\approx (28.27)(6)$ Substitute for B and h.
≈ 169.6 Simplify.

The volume is about 169.6 cubic meters.

EXERCISES

Guided Practice

For the rest of this chapter, computations involving π have been done using the π key on a calculator. Answers will vary slightly when $\pi = 3.14$ is used.

▶ CHECK for Understanding

In Exercises 1–4, use the cylinder at the right.

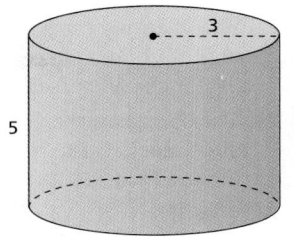

1. Find the area of the base, B. ≈ 28.274 units^2

2. What is the height, h, of the cylinder? 5 units

3. State the formula for the volume of the cylinder. $V = Bh$

4. Find the volume of the cylinder. ≈ 141.37 units^3

Hockey Puck In Exercises 5 and 6, a hockey puck has a 3-inch diameter and a height of 1 inch.

5. What is the area of its base? ≈ 7.1 in.^{2}

6. What is the volume of the hockey puck? ≈ 7.1 in.^{3}

Independent Practice

In Exercises 7–10, find the volume of the cylinder.

7.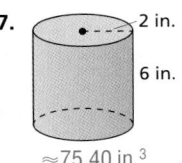
2 in.
6 in.
≈ 75.40 in.^{3}

8.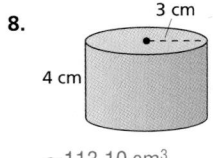
3 cm
4 cm
≈ 113.10 cm^3

9.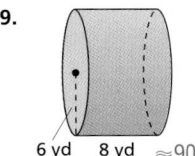
6 yd   8 yd ≈ 904.78 yd^3

10.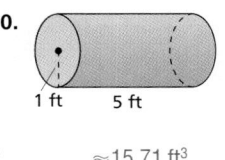
1 ft   5 ft ≈ 15.71 ft^3

In Exercises 11–14, find the height or the radius of the base.

11.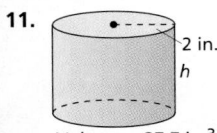
2 in.
h
Volume = 37.7 in.^{3}
≈ 3.00 in.

12.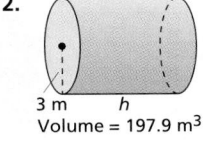
3 m h
Volume = 197.9 m^3
≈ 7.00 m

13.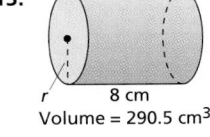
r 8 cm
Volume = 290.5 cm^3
≈ 3.40 cm

14.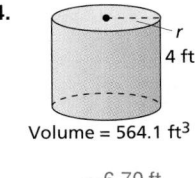
r
4 ft
Volume = 564.1 ft^3
≈ 6.70 ft

In Exercises 15–18, Cylinder A has a 6-inch diameter and a height of 4 inches. Cylinder B has a 4-inch diameter and a height of 6 inches. 16.–18. See margin.

15. Without doing any calculations, do you think the volume of cylinder A is greater than, less than, or equal to the volume of cylinder B? Greater than

16. Sketch cylinder A and find its volume.

17. Sketch cylinder B and find its volume.

18. Does the cylinder with the greater volume also have the greater surface area? Explain.

19. *Snare Drum* A snare drum has a 14-inch diameter and a height of 5 inches. What is the volume of the snare drum? ≈ 769.7 in.^{3}

20. *Bass Drum* A bass drum has a 20-inch diameter and a height of 14 inches. What is the volume of the bass drum? ≈ 4398.2 in.^{3}

✪ More difficult exercises

12.5 • *Exploring Volumes of Cylinders*   **561**

EXERCISE Notes

ASSIGNMENT GUIDE

Basic/Average:
Day 1: Ex. 7–13, 25, 26
Day 2: Ex. 15–19, 21–24, 27

Above Average:
Ex. 7–19 odd, 21–24, 26–30

Advanced: Ex. 7–19 odd, 21–24, 26–30

Selected Answers: Ex. 1–6, 7–27 odd

Guided Practice

▶ Ex. 5, 6

Common-Error Alert!

Students often make the error of using the diameter rather than the radius when substituting in the surface area and volume formulas.

Independent Practice

▶ **Ex. 11–14** Do a sample in class of solving for the radius or for the height.
▶ **Ex. 15–18** Assign these exercises as a group.
▶ **Ex. 19, 20** Once more, alert students to the error of using the diameter instead of the radius in the appropriate formulas.

Answers

16.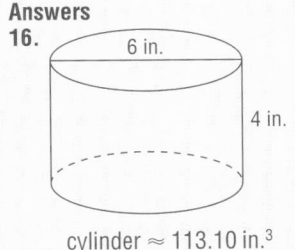
6 in.
4 in.
cylinder ≈ 113.10 in.^{3}

17.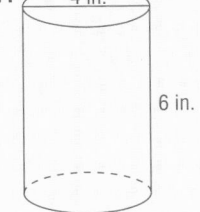
4 in.
6 in.
cylinder ≈ 75.40 in.^{3}

18. Yes, cylinder A has a surface area of 42π in.^{2} while cylinder B has a surface area of 32π in.^{2}.

Lesson 12.5 **561**

▶ **Ex. 21–24** Assign these exercises as a group. You may need to explain to students that the "cylinder" whose volume changes as the piston moves up and down is the cylindrical space within which gases are compressed and ignited.

Integrated Review

You may wish to observe that three different versions of a cylinder net are represented in this section.

Exploration and Extension

This section offers an opportunity to discuss the important technique of subtraction of volumes in order to compute the volume of hollow cylindrical objects—rings, pipes, storage tanks, and so on.

Engine Size   In Exercises 21–24, use the following information.

A cylinder in a V8 engine has a diameter of 4.00 inches. The height of the cylinder is 3.42 inches.

21. What is the volume of the cylinder?   ≈42.977 in.³

✪ 22. When the piston is fully extended, the height of the cylinder changes from 3.42 inches to 0.42 inch. What is the volume at this point?   ≈5.278 in.³

✪ 23. The change in the volume times the number of cylinders is the size of the engine in cubic inches. Find the size of the engine.   ≈301.59 in.³

24. What is the size of the engine in liters? (Hint: 1 liter = 61.02 cubic inches.)   ≈4.94 liters

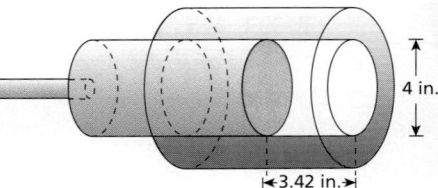
4 in.
3.42 in.

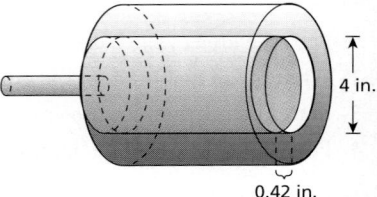
4 in.
0.42 in.

Integrated Review   *Making Connections within Mathematics*

Nets   In Exercises 25–27, find the volume and surface area of the solid formed by the net.

25.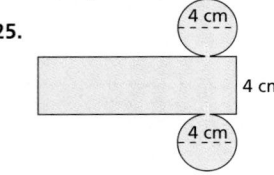
4 cm
4 cm
4 cm

≈50.27 cm³, ≈75.40 cm²

26.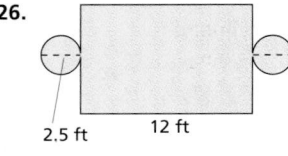
12 ft
2.5 ft

≈58.90 ft³, ≈104.07 ft²

27.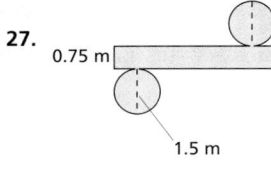
0.75 m
1.5 m

≈1.33 m³, ≈7.07 m²

Exploration and Extension

Ringette   In Exercises 28–30, use the following.

Ringette is a sport similar to ice hockey that is played in Canada, Europe, and the northern United States. The object of the game is to shoot a rubber ring into a net. The volume of the ring is the volume of the cylinder with the outer diameter minus the volume of the cylinder with the inner diameter.

✪ 28. Find the volume of the cylinder with the inner diameter.

✪ 29. Find the volume of the cylinder with the outer diameter.

✪ 30. Find the volume of the ring.   ≈296.9 cm³

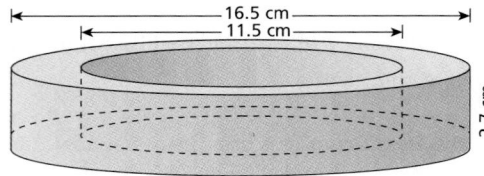
16.5 cm
11.5 cm
2.7 cm

28. ≈280.45 cm³
29. ≈577.33 cm³

Materials Needed: thin cardboard, compass, scissors, ruler, unpopped popcorn, paper clips

In this investigation, you will explore the concept of volume.

Example — *Exploring the Volume of a Cone*

Use a compass to draw a circle with a 4-inch radius on a piece of cardboard. Cut it out. Draw a line segment from the circle to its center and cut along the segment. Overlap the cardboard to form an open cone and fix the cardboard with paper clips. Fill the open cone level with unpopped popcorn. (Don't pile the corn above the rim of the open cone.) How many pieces of corn did you use?

Solution The steps used to create and fill the open cone are shown below. The number of pieces of corn depends on the shape of the open cone.

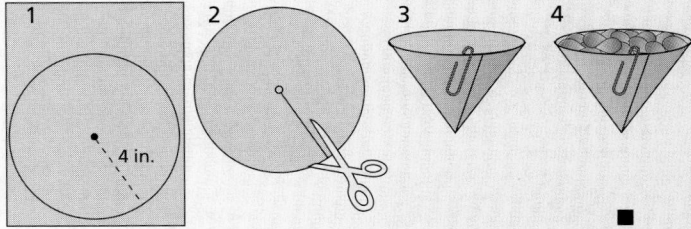

Exercises

1. **Group Activity** With other members of your group, create the open cone described in the example. Alter the size of the open cone as shown below. For each size, fill the open cone and count the number of pieces of corn. Record your results in a table. Check students' work.

  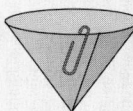 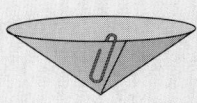

2. Describe the dimensions of the open cone that holds the most popcorn. Compare your group's results with the results of other groups.
   The cone that holds the most popcorn has $r \approx 3.3$ in. and $h \approx 2.3$ in.

PACING the Lesson

Suggested Number of Days
Basic/Average 2   **Above Average** 2
Advanced 2

PLANNING the Lesson

Lesson Plan 12.6, p. 99

ORGANIZER

Starters (reproduced below)
    Problem of the Day 12.6, p. 35
    Warm-Up Exercises 12.6, p. 35
Lesson Resources
    Color Transparencies
      Picture for Ex. 23–25, p. 52
    Math Log, pp. 38, 39
    Answer Masters 11.6, p. 240
    Extra Practice Copymaster 12.6, p. 99
    Reteaching Copymaster 12.6, p. 99
Special Populations
    Suggestions, Teacher's Edition, p. 536D

LESSON Notes

Vocabulary Alert!

Have students record the definition of a *pyramid* in their math journals—A pyramid has one polygonal base, and the remaining faces are all triangles. Note that if the base of a pyramid is a quadrilateral, the base is a rectangle.

Ask students how pyramids and prisms are related. Next, ask students to record the definition of a *cone* in their math journals—A cone has one base that is a circle; the remaining face is curved and comes to a point. Ask students how cones and cylinders are related. Emphasize the analogy: Pyramids are to prisms as cones are to cylinders.

Example 1

Point out that, unlike most of the math formulas that students usually encounter for which variables can be directly substituted, volume formulas have a variable *B* that requires a preliminary computation before we can apply the formula

Common-Error Alert!

Make sure that students understand that the height of a pyramid as used in the volume formula is the *vertical* height.

12.6 Exploring Volumes of Pyramids and Cones

What you should learn:

Goal 1 How to find the volume of a pyramid and a cone

Goal 2 How to use the volume of a pyramid and a cone to solve real-life problems

Why you should learn it:

You can use the volume of a pyramid or a cone to solve real-life problems, such as finding the volume of a rocket.

Goal 1 **Volumes of Pyramids and Cones**

To discover the volume of a pyramid, consider a prism that has the same height and base as the pyramid. Fill the pyramid with sand and pour the sand into the prism. The prism will be filled with exactly three pyramids of sand. This suggests that the pyramid has one-third the volume of the prism. The same relationship is true of a cone and a cylinder.

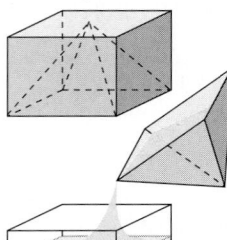
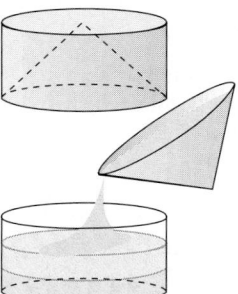

The Volume of a Pyramid or a Cone

The volume of a pyramid or a cone is one-third the product of its height and the area of its base. That is, $V = \frac{1}{3}Bh$, where B is the area of a base and h is the height of the pyramid or cone.

Example 1   *Finding Volumes of Pyramids*

Find the volume of the pyramid, which has a square base.

Solution   The base of the pyramid is square with an area of 6 • 6 or 36 square inches. Because the height of the pyramid is 8 inches, it follows that the volume of the pyramid is

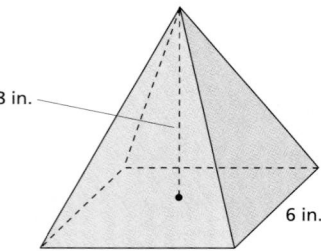

$$V = \tfrac{1}{3}Bh \qquad \textit{Volume of a pyramid}$$
$$= \tfrac{1}{3}(36)(8) \quad \textit{Substitute for B and h.}$$
$$= 96 \qquad\quad \textit{Simplify.}$$

The pyramid has a volume of 96 cubic inches. ∎

Roll a sheet of paper to make a cylinder. Use measurement to find its volume.
Answers will vary

Also available as a copymaster, page 35

┌─── **STARTER: Warm-Up Exercises** ───┐
1. Find the volume of a cylinder of radius 3 cm and height 14 cm.   395.84 cm³
2. Find the volume of a 3 x 3 square prism whose height is 12.   108 units³

Also available as a copymaster, page 35

Goal 2 Solving Real-Life Problems

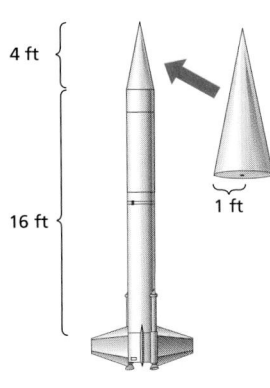

Real Life
Rocket Design

Example 2 *Finding a Volume*

You are designing a rocket, as shown at the left. The rocket is made by placing a cone on top of a cylinder. What is the total volume of the rocket?

Solution The volume of the rocket is the sum of the volumes of the cone and the cylinder.

$V = \frac{1}{3}Bh$ *Volume of a cone*

$= \frac{1}{3}(\pi r^2)(h)$ *Volume of base is πr^2.*

$= \frac{1}{3}(\pi \cdot 1^2)(4)$ *Substitute for r and h.*

$= \frac{4}{3}\pi$ *Simplify.*

≈ 4.19 *Use a calculator.*

$V = Bh$ *Volume of cylinder*

$= (\pi r^2)(h)$ *Volume of base is πr^2.*

$= (\pi \cdot 1^2)(16)$ *Substitute for r and h.*

$= 16\pi$ *Simplify.*

≈ 50.27 *Use a calculator.*

The volume of the rocket is about 4.19 + 50.27, or about 54.5 cubic feet. ∎

Communicating about MATHEMATICS

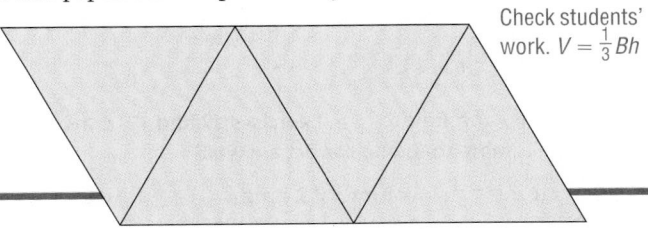

▶ **SHARING IDEAS about the Lesson**

Building a Tetrahedron The net below is made of 4 equilateral triangles. It can be folded to form a 4-sided figure called a **tetrahedron.** Make a tetrahedron out of cardboard or stiff paper. Then explain how you can find its volume.

Check students' work. $V = \frac{1}{3}Bh$

12.6 · *Exploring Volumes of Pyramids and Cones* **565**

Challenge students to give examples of cones and pyramids used in real life. Answers will vary. Examples: Some large cities in the northern United States store road salt in large cones; large coffee grinders have inverted pyramids into which the coffee beans are dumped. Ask students: Why might cones and pyramids sometimes be better suited for storage than cylinders and prisms?

Example 2

Discuss why an important part of a rocket design is the nose cone. Also ask students to describe how they would determine the volume of a sharpened pencil.

Communicating about MATHEMATICS

Ask students to explain how the tetrahedron fits the definition for pyramid. The base is a polygon and all the remaining faces are triangles.

Writing Prompt
Why do you think ice cream containers are in the shape of a cone rather than a pyramid?

◢ **OPTION: Extra Examples**

Here is an additional example similar to Example 1.

Finding the Volume of a Pyramid
Find the volume of the pyramid that has a rectangular base.

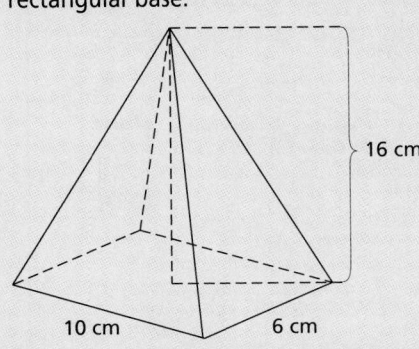

Solution
The base of the pyramid is a rectangle with an area of 10 • 6 or 60 square centimeters. Because the height of the pyramid is 16 centimeters, it follows that the volume of the pyramid is

$V = \frac{1}{3}Bh$ Volume of a pyramid

$= \frac{1}{3}(60)(16)$ Substitute for B and h.

$= 320$ Simplify.

The pyramid has a volume of 320 cubic centimeters.

ASSIGNMENT GUIDE

Basic/Average:
Day 1: Ex. 9–21 odd
Day 2: Ex. 20, 22, 27, 28, 33–36

Above Average:
Day 1: Ex. 9–21 odd
Day 2: Ex. 20, 22, 27, 28, 33–36

Advanced: Day 1: Ex. 9–21 odd
Day 2: Ex. 27, 33–36

Selected Answers: Ex. 1–8, 9–31 odd

Guided Practice

You could have this section completed by groups in order to assess understanding of the goals of the lesson.

Independent Practice

▶ **Ex. 9–16** Encourage students to show the setup of each problem, even though they may use a calculator to compute the final answer. This is essential for trouble-shooting potential errors in understanding.

▶ **Ex. 17, 18** Have students share their answers with the entire class.

Guided Practice

▶ **CHECK for Understanding**

The base of a pyramid is a polygon.
The base of a cone is a circle.

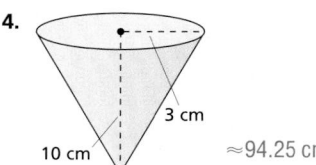

1. How do the bases of pyramids and cones differ?

2. The cylinder and the cone have the same height and radius. Explain how their volumes compare.
   The cylinder has 3 times the volume of the cone.

In Exercises 3 and 4, find the volume of the solid.

3. 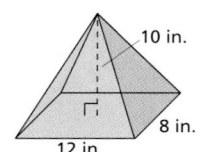 320 in.^{3}

4. ≈94.25 cm^3

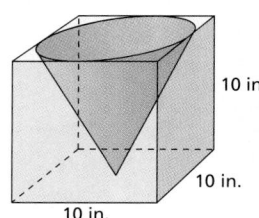

In Exercises 5–8, use the figure at the right.

5. What is the radius of the cone?   5 in.
6. What is the height of the cone?   10 in.
7. Find the volume of the cone.   ≈261.80 in.^{3}
8. Explain how to find the volume of the blue portion of the cube. Then find it.
   Subtract the volume of the cone from the volume of the cube. ≈738.20 in.^{3}

Independent Practice

In Exercises 9–16, find the volume of the solid.

9. 1200 cm^3 10. 10 in.^{3}

9.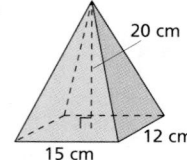

10.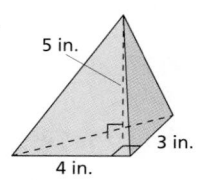

11. 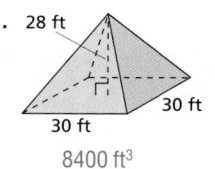 8400 ft^3

12. 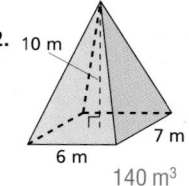 140 m^3

13. 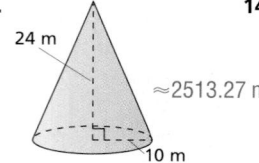 ≈2513.27 m^3

14. ≈1809.56 ft^3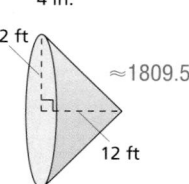

15. 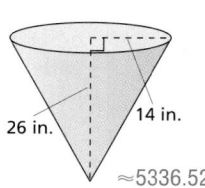 ≈5336.52 in.^{3}

16. 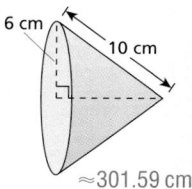 ≈301.59 cm^3

P *Guess, Check, and Revise* **In Exercises 17 and 18, draw the indicated figure. (There is more than one correct answer.)** Check students' work.

⊗ 17. A pyramid with a volume of 24 mm^3

⊗ 18. A cone with a volume of 24π ft^3

⊗ More difficult exercises
P Portfolio Opportunity

Extra Practice

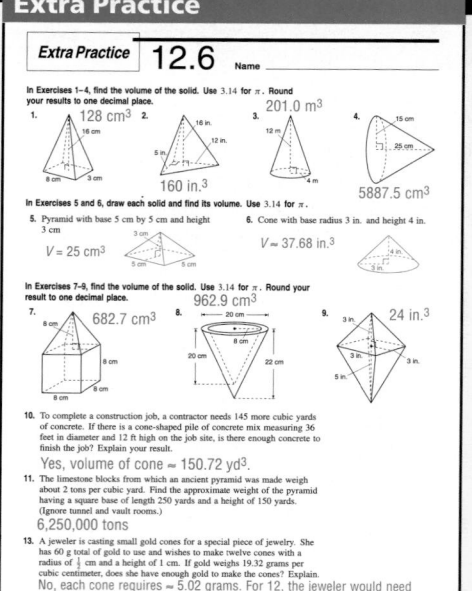

Reteaching

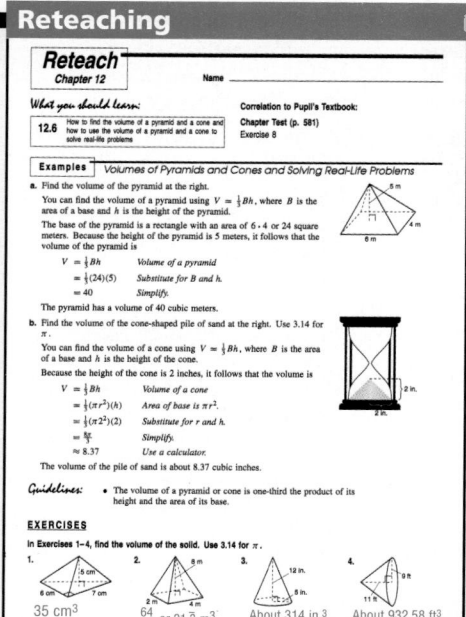

In Exercises 19–22, find the volume of the blue region.

19.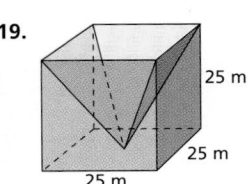
25 m
25 m
25 m

≈10,416.67 m³

20.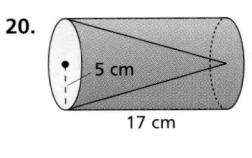
5 cm
17 cm

≈890.12 cm³

21.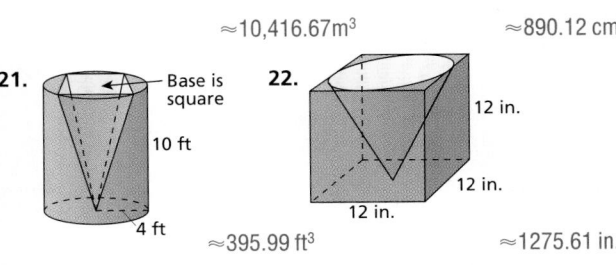
Base is square
10 ft
4 ft

≈395.99 ft³

22.
12 in.
12 in.
12 in.

≈1275.61 in.³

Tornadoes **In Exercises 23–25, use the photo and caption information.**

23. Describe the location of the *base* of the tornado.   It is 300 ft in the air.

24. What is the area of the base, B?   ≈31,415.927 ft²

25. What is the volume of the tornado?   ≈3,141,592.7 ft³

26. *Think about It*   Which has a greater effect on the volume of a cone, doubling the radius or doubling the height? Explain your reasoning.   See margin.

27. Copy and complete the table. Round your results to 2 decimal places.   302.5 ft³

Solid	Base Area	Height	Volume
Pyramid	121 ft²	7.5 ft	?
Pyramid	486 cm²	?	3199.5 cm³
Pyramid	?	5.6 in.	630 in.³

337.5 in.²   19.75 cm

28. Copy and complete the table. Round your results to 2 decimal places.

≈89.80 m³

Solid	Radius	Height	Volume
Cone	3.5 m	7 m	?
Cone	?	9.4 cm	629.99 cm³
Cone	10.2 mm	?	2179 mm³

≈8.00 cm   ≈20.00 mm

Integrated Review

Fresh Air   **In Exercises 29–32, use the graph at the right.** *(Source: National Academy of Sciences)*

29. What does one small block represent?   1 ft³ of fresh air

30. How much fresh air per minute circulates around a first-class passenger?   50 ft³

31. How much more fresh air per minute circulates around a pilot than around an economy class passenger?   143 ft³

32. How much fresh air per minute would circulate around 80 seats in economy class?   560 ft³

Making Connections within Mathematics

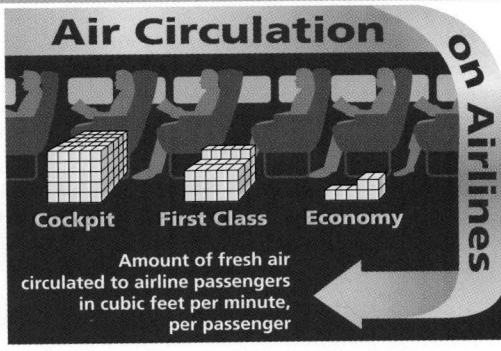
Air Circulation
on Airlines
Cockpit   First Class   Economy
Amount of fresh air circulated to airline passengers in cubic feet per minute, per passenger

A tornado is a funnel (cone-shaped) cloud. The winds in a tornado can whirl around at more than 200 miles per hour. This tornado has a base diameter of about 200 feet and a height of about 300 feet.

▶ **Ex. 19–22**   Having classroom models of these solids (preferably of plexiglass) would be very helpful.
▶ **Ex. 23–25**   Assign these exercises as a group.
▶ **Ex. 27, 28**
GROUP ACTIVITY
These exercises could be done in class as a group activity.

Integrated Review

EXTENSION
You may wish to discuss the current no-smoking regulation on airlines.

Answer
26. Doubling the radius; the radius is squared, while the height is not.

12.6 • *Exploring Volumes of Pyramids and Cones*   **567**

Make sure students understand that the four congruent angles that form the vertex of this pyramid are *not* right angles. Otherwise the vertex would lie in the plane of the base and there would be no pyramid! In Ex. 36, make sure that students compute the area of a triangle using the altitude to the side of the square.

Portfolio Opportunity: Math Log

1. Which has a greater impact on the volume of a cone, tripling the height or doubling the radius? Explain your answer.

2. Compare the volumes of a pyramid and a prism if the bases of the pyramid and the prism are congruent, but the height of the pyramid is three times the height of the prism.

Also available as a copymaster, pages 38, 39, Ex. 6, 7

Short Quiz

Covers Lessons 12.5 and 12.6

Available as a copymaster, page 194

Exploration and Extension

Making a Paper Pyramid **In Exercises 33–36, use the figure. (The figure is not drawn to scale.)** Check students' work.

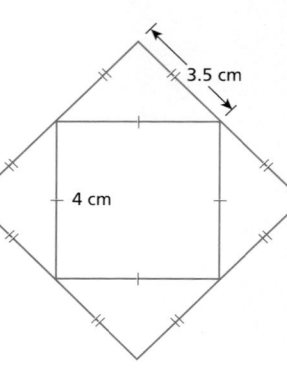

✪ **33.** Use a ruler to draw a full-scale copy of the figure on stiff paper. Cut the figure out. Then fold and tape the figure to form a pyramid.

✪ **34.** Use a ruler to measure the height of the pyramid. Then find the volume of the pyramid. ≈2.1 cm, ≈11.2 cm³

✪ **35.** Explain how to find the surface area of the pyramid. Add the areas of its 5 faces.

✪ **36.** Find the surface area of the pyramid. ≈39.0 cm²

Mixed REVIEW

In Exercises 1–4, find the volume of the figure. (12.4–12.6)

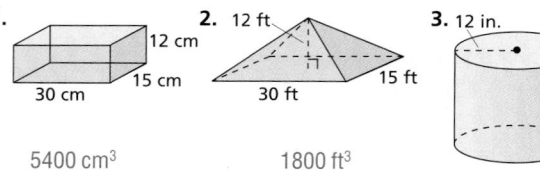

1.

5400 cm³

2. 12 ft

1800 ft³

3. 12 in.

≈8143.01 in.³

4. 12 m

≈2714.34 m³

In Exercises 5–8, use Pascal's Triangle on page 372 to answer the question. (8.7–8.8)

5. How many ways can you select 3 people from a group of 6? 20

6. How many ways can you select 4 birds from a flock of 5? 5

7. How many ways can you select 3 animals from a herd of 7? 35

8. How many ways can you select 2 goldfish from 5 goldfish? 10

In Exercises 9–14, solve the equation. (4.5)

9. $4x + 3 = 2$ $-\frac{1}{4}$

10. $2b + 5 = 7 - 5b$ $\frac{2}{7}$

11. $\frac{3}{8}r + 2 = \frac{7}{8}r$ 4

12. $0.6 + 0.2y = 0.5y$ 2

13. $\frac{4}{3} - \frac{5}{7}s = \frac{3}{2}s$ $\frac{56}{93}$

14. $42 + 3m = -4m$ -6

In Exercises 15–20, solve the inequality. (9.7)

15. $24 \le -2y$ $y \le -12$

16. $13z + 26 > 0$ $z > -2$

17. $7 - 6t > 4t$ $t < \frac{7}{10}$

18. $r - \frac{6}{5} < \frac{5}{6}$ $r < \frac{61}{30}$

19. $-\frac{33}{2}p \ge \frac{11}{4}$ $p \le -\frac{1}{6}$

20. $\frac{11}{8}p \le -\frac{33}{4}$ $p \le -6$

▶ **Enrichment**

Compare the volumes of a cone and a pyramid that have the same height *h*, if the length of the side of the square base of the pyramid is equal to the radius *r* of the base of the cone. The volume V of the cone is given by $V = \pi r^2 h$ and, since the side of the square base is also *r*, the volume *V* of the pyramid is given by $V = r^2 h$. The volume of the cone is π times (or more than 3 times) the volume of the pyramid.

12.7 Exploring Volumes of Spheres

What you should learn:

Goal 1 How to find the volume of a sphere

Goal 2 How to use the volume of a sphere to solve real-life problems

Why you should learn it:

You can use the volume of a sphere to solve real-life problems, such as finding the volume of a natural gas storage tank.

Goal 1 Finding Volumes of Spheres

To discover the volume of a sphere, consider a sphere that is cut into two halves, called **hemispheres.** An open cone is fitted inside one of the hemispheres. The open cone is then filled with sand, which is poured into the hemisphere. The hemisphere will be filled with exactly two cones of sand. Because the volume of the cone is $\frac{1}{3}Bh$, which is $\frac{1}{3}(\pi r^2)r$ or $\frac{1}{3}\pi r^3$, it follows that the volume of the sphere is $4(\frac{1}{3}\pi r^3)$ or $\frac{4}{3}\pi r^3$.

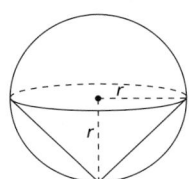

> **Volume of a Sphere**
>
> The volume of a sphere is four-thirds times π times the cube of its radius. That is, $V = \frac{4}{3}\pi r^3$, where r is the radius.

Example 1

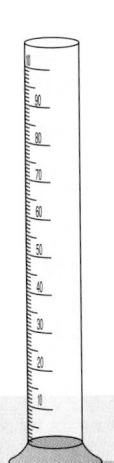

Finding the Volume of a Sphere

The cylinder at the left is used in chemistry to measure volumes in cubic centimeters (1 cubic centimeter is equal to 1 milliliter). Cut a small hole in a Ping-Pong ball, fill the ball with water, and pour the water into a cylinder. How high in the cylinder will the water come?

Solution The radius of the Ping-Pong ball is 1.9 centimeters, which implies that its volume is as follows.

$V = \frac{4}{3}\pi r^3$ *Volume of a sphere*

$= \frac{4}{3}\pi(1.9)^3$ *Substitute for r.*

≈ 28.73 *Use a calculator.*

The volume is about 28.73 cubic centimeters. This means that the water will be just below the 29 milliliter mark. ∎

▶ **PLANNING the Lesson**

Lesson Plan 12.7, p. 100

ORGANIZER

Starters (reproduced below)
   Problem of the Day 12.7, p. 36
   Warm-Up Exercises 12.7, p. 36
Lesson Resources
   Color Transparencies
     Picture for Ex. 29, 30, p. 53
   Math Log, p. 39
   Answer Masters 12.7, pp. 242, 243
   Extra Practice Copymaster 12.7, p. 100
   Reteaching Copymaster 12.7, p. 100
Special Populations
   Suggestions, Teacher's Edition, p. 536D

LESSON Notes

Have students record in their math journals the formula for computing the volume of a sphere. The derivation of this formula requires mathematics that is beyond the scope of this book, but the demonstration here can be very convincing for students, especially if one of the students (rather than you) is invited to do the measuring!

Review the order in which numbers would be entered in a calculator when using the formula for the volume of a sphere. Students may need to be reminded how to work with the fraction $\frac{4}{3}$ with or without a calculator.

Be sure that students can provide examples of spheres found in real-life situations. If possible, bring several models of spheres to class.

Example 1

Ask students to indicate how the volume of a solid ball that is the same size as a ping pong ball can be measured with the cylinder used in this example. By using Archimedes' water displacement principle.

STARTER: Problem of the Day	**STARTER: Warm-Up Exercises**
A wooden cylinder is 20 cm in height and has a radius of 5 cm. A hole 6 cm in diameter is drilled from the center of one circular base to the center of the other circular base. What is the volume of the wood that remains? 1004.8 cm³	**1.** Use a calculator to compute the following. **a.** $(3.2)^3$ **b.** $(12.1)^3$ **c.** $(7)^3$ **a.** 32.768, **b.** 1771.561, **c.** 343 **2.** Use a calculator to write the following as decimals. **a.** $\frac{5}{3}$ **b.** $\frac{7}{4}$ **c.** $\frac{9}{5}$ **a.** 1.6667, **b.** 1.75, **c.** 1.8
Also available as a copymaster, page 36	Also available as a copymaster, page 36

Challenge students to think of examples of spheres that occur naturally.   Answers will vary but might include the planets, bubbles, and so on.

Example 2

The results of this example may be surprising to many students. Remind them that the same thing occurs when the edge lengths of a cube are doubled; the volume increases by a factor of 8 (or 2^3).

Communicating
about MATHEMATICS

Working together, have students investigate a variety of possible storage tanks that have different shapes but contain the same volume. Discuss what advantages different shapes might have for storing different kinds of things, such as grain, salt, gas, and oil.

Writing Prompt
Suppose that a cube has an edge length of 4 units, and a sphere has a diameter of 4 units. How do their volumes compare? Explain the difference. (Refer to Ex. 15.)

Spherical storage tanks, such as those at the right, are sometimes used to store natural gas and other gases. The advantage of the spherical design is that the pressure of the gas is evenly distributed on all parts of the tank's surface.

Real Life
Industry

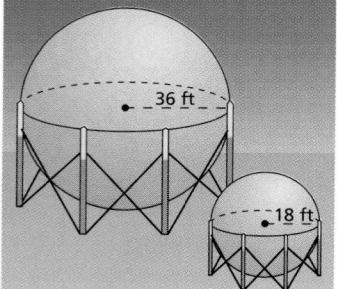

Example 2   *Finding the Volume of a Sphere*

You are designing a spherical storage tank for natural gas. The radius of the tank is 18 feet. How many cubic feet of natural gas will the tank hold? If you double the radius, will the tank hold twice as much?

Solution

$$V = \tfrac{4}{3}\pi r^3 \qquad \textit{Volume of a sphere}$$
$$= \tfrac{4}{3}\pi(18)^3 \qquad \textit{Substitute for r.}$$
$$= 7776\pi \qquad \textit{Simplify.}$$
$$\approx 24{,}429 \qquad \textit{Use a calculator.}$$

The tank holds about 24,429 cubic feet of gas. If you doubled the radius, the volume would be

$$V = \tfrac{4}{3}\pi(36)^3 = 62{,}208\pi \approx 195{,}432 \text{ cubic feet.}$$

This volume is 8 times as much (not twice as much) as the volume of the original tank. ∎

P   ## *Communicating* *about* MATHEMATICS

▶ **SHARING IDEAS about the Lesson**

Cooperative Learning

Guess, Check, and Revise   Work with a partner. You are designing a spherical storage tank that is to contain 30,000 cubic feet of natural gas. Use the guess, check, and revise problem-solving strategy to find the radius of the tank. ≈ 19.3 ft

EXERCISES

Guided Practice

▶ CHECK for Understanding

In Exercises 1–5, use the figure at the right.

1. Name a radius. $\overline{AB}, \overline{AC}, \overline{AD}$

2. Is $\overline{AD}$ a radius? Explain. Yes, see below.

3. Name a diameter. What is its measure? $\overline{BC}$, 4 ft

4. What is one half of a sphere called? A hemisphere

5. Find the volume of the sphere. ≈ 33.51 ft^3

2. It is a segment from the center to the surface.

Independent Practice

In Exercises 6–13, find the volume of the ball.

6. $r = 1.5$ in.

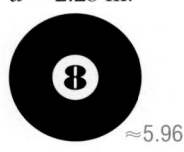

≈ 14.14 in.^{3}

7. $r = 12$ cm

≈ 7238.23 cm^3

8. $d = 8.6$ in.

≈ 333.04 in.^{3}

9. $d = 1.68$ in.

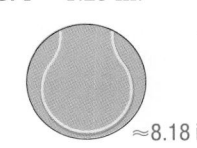

≈ 2.48 in.^{3}

10. $d = 2.25$ in.

≈ 5.96 in.^{3}

11. $r = 11$ cm

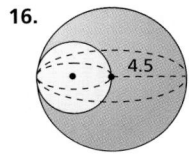

≈ 5575.28 cm^3

12. $d = 8.25$ in.

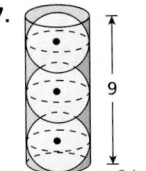

≈ 294.01 in.^{3}

13. $r = 1.25$ in.

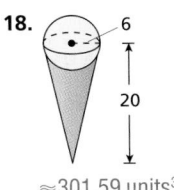

≈ 8.18 in.^{3}

⚙ 14. From your knowledge of the balls in Exercises 6–13, order them from smallest to largest. Given 1 inch = 2.54 centimeters, write each volume in cubic centimeters. Did you order the balls correctly? Explain. See margin.

In Exercises 15–18, find the volume of the blue portion of the figure.

15.

8
8
8
4

≈ 243.92 units^3

16.

4.5

≈ 333.99 units^3

17.

9

≈ 21.21 units^3

18.

6
20

≈ 301.59 units^3

⚙ 19. Which is larger, the circumference or height of the cylinder in Exercise 17? Explain. Circumference; $C = 3\pi$ units, $h = 9$, $3\pi > 9$

⚙ More difficult exercises

12.7 • Exploring Volumes of Spheres 571

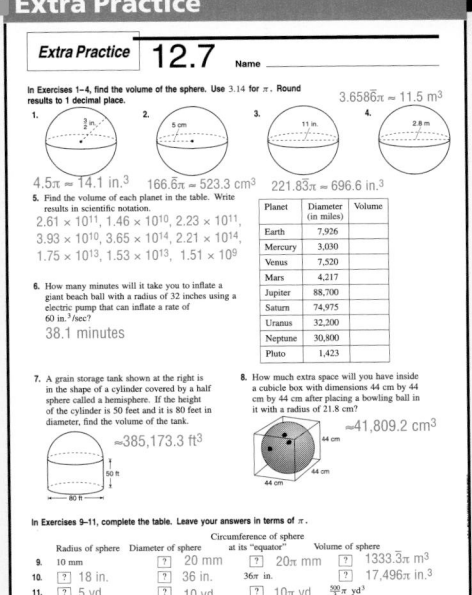
Lesson 12.7 **571**

Guess, Check, and Revise **In Exercises 20–23, find the radius of the sphere with the given volume.**

20. 1436.76 cm^3 ≈7.0 cm   21. 659.58 ft^3 ≈5.4 ft

22. $32.52 \, \pi \text{ cm}^3$ ≈2.9 cm   23. $2929.33 \, \pi \text{ in.}^3$ ≈13.0 in.

✪ 24. What happens to the volume of a sphere when the radius doubles? Triples? Quadruples? Describe the pattern.

✪ 25. *Visualization* Describe the intersection of a sphere and a plane that cuts through the center of the sphere.
24., 25. See margin.

Earth and Moon **In Exercises 26–28, use the following.**

Earth has a diameter of about 8000 miles. The volume of the moon is $\frac{1}{50}$ that of Earth.

26. Find the volume of Earth. ≈268.1 billion mi³

27. Find the volume of the moon. ≈5.4 billion mi³

28. What is the moon's diameter? ≈2176 mi

Sunsphere **In Exercises 29 and 30, use the photo caption.**

29. What is the volume of the sphere? ≈369,120.9 ft³

30. What is the distance from the bottom of the sphere to the ground? 177 ft

This 266-foot tower, called the Sunsphere, was built for the 1982 World's Fair in Knoxville, Tennessee. The diameter of the sphere is about 89 feet.

Integrated Review

Making Connections within Mathematics

Volume **In Exercises 31–34, find the volume of the solid. Explain your reasoning.**

31.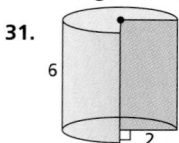
6
2

32.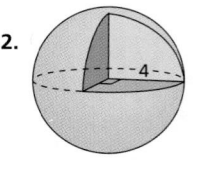
4

33.
9
4

34.
11
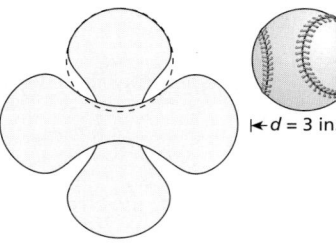

32. ≈234.57 units³
$V = \frac{7}{8}(\frac{4}{3}\pi \cdot 4^3)$

31. ≈56.55 units³, $V = \frac{3}{4}(\pi \cdot 2^2 \cdot 6)$

≈113.10 units³
$V = \frac{3}{4}(\frac{1}{3}\pi \cdot 4^2 \cdot 9)$

≈2787.64 units³
$V = \frac{1}{2}(\frac{4}{3}\pi \cdot 11^3)$

Exploration and Extension

Surface Area **In Exercises 35 and 36, use the figure at the right, which shows a flattened baseball covering.**

✪ 35. From the figure, which of the following is the correct formula for the surface area of a sphere? Explain. See below.

    a. $S = 2\pi r^2$ **b.** $S = 3\pi r^2$ **c.** $S = 4\pi r^2$ **d.** $S = 5\pi r^2$

✪ 36. Find the surface area of a baseball. ≈28.27 in.²

✪ 37. Use the information in Exercises 26–28 to find the surface area of Earth. ≈201.06 million mi²

35. c, for explanation, see margin.

|←d = 3 in.→|

572 Chapter **12** ▪ *Measurements in Geometry*

✪ More difficult exercises

572 *Chapter 12*

12.8

Exploring Similar Solids

What you should learn:

Goal 1 How to explore ratios of measurements of similar figures

Goal 2 How to use ratios of measurements of similar figures

Why you should learn it:

You can use ratios of measurements of similar figures to solve real-life problems, such as finding the surface area or volume of a building.

Baby mammals are not geometrically similar to their parents (their proportions are different), but baby reptiles are geometrically similar to their parents.

Goal 1 — Exploring Measures of Similar Solids

Two solids are similar if they have the same shape and their corresponding lengths are proportional. Here are two examples.

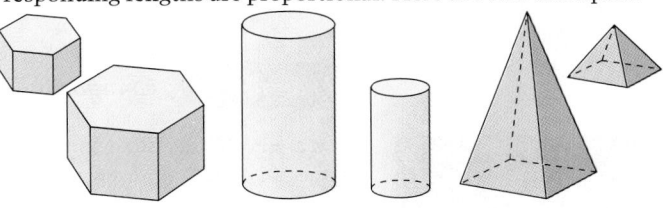

| *Similar* | *Similar* | *Not similar* |

LESSON INVESTIGATION

■ Investigating Ratios of Similar Solids

Group Activity Use wooden cubes to build cubes that have edge lengths of 1, 2, 3, 4, and 5 inches. Call the 1-inch cube the *original* cube, and the other cubes the *new* cubes. Find the surface area and volume of each cube. Record your results in a table, like that shown below. (In the table, *S* is the surface area and *V* is the volume.) Describe the pattern for the ratios in your table.

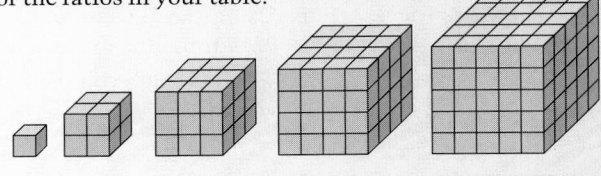

Edge	New edge / Orig. edge	S (in.²)	New S / Orig. S	V (in.³)	New V / Orig. V
1 in.	1	6	1	1	1
2 in.	2	24	4	8	8
3 in.	?	54?	9 ?	27?	27 ?
4 in.	?	96?	16 ?	64?	64 ?
5 in.	?	150?	25 ?	125?	125 ?

For descriptions of patterns, see margin.

▶ **PACING the Lesson**

Suggested Number of Days
Basic/Average 0 **Above Average** 1
Advanced 1

▶ **PLANNING the Lesson**

Lesson Plan 12.8, p. 101

ORGANIZER

Starters (reproduced below)
  Problem of the Day 12.8, p. 36
  Warm-Up Exercises 12.8, p. 36
Lesson Resources
  Color Transparencies
    Picture for Example 1, p. 53
  Math Log, p. 39
  Technology, p. 72
  Answer Masters 12.8, pp. 244, 245
  Extra Practice Copymaster 12.8, p. 101
  Reteaching Copymaster 12.8, p. 101
Special Populations
  Suggestions, Teacher's Edition, p. 536D

LESSON Notes

Vocabulary Alert!

Ask students to describe what they believe similar solids are before defining this precisely. Review what is meant by *proportional*—the ratios formed by all pairs of corresponding sides are the same. It may be necessary to have students identify corresponding edges, heights, and diameters of similar solids. Remind students about some of the properties of similar triangles. Then have them record the definition of similar solids in their math journals.

Have students work together in groups to complete the lesson investigation. If wooden cubes are not available, take care that students can use the visual models to identify the correct number of smaller unit cubes that compose the larger cubes.

EXTENSION

Have students build similar prisms that are not cubes. The dimensions might be $1 \times 2 \times 3$, $2 \times 4 \times 6$, and so on. Work through several examples to make sure that students see the k^2 and k^3 relationships for surface area and volume, respectively.

Answer
Lesson Investigation To get an edge ratio, use the number of the ratio's position. To get an *S* ratio, use the number of the ratio's position squared. To get a *V* ratio, use the number of the ratio's position cubed.

STARTER: Problem of the Day
How many triangles can you find in this figure? 28

Also available as a copymaster, page 36

STARTER: Warm-Up Exercises

1. Compute the volume of the following prisms.
a. Rectangular 3 in. by 4 in. base, with height 10 in.
b. Rectangular 6 in. by 8 in. base, with height 20 in.
a. 120 in.³, **b.** 960 in.³

2. Compute the volume of the following cylinders.
a. Base radius 3 in., with height 10 in.
b. Base radius 6 in., with height 20 in.
a. 90 in.³, **b.** 720 in.³

Also available as a copymaster, page 36

Have students give examples of models that are used to represent larger solids in real life. Have students record the examples in their journals.

Example 1
Challenge students to explain clearly why the scale factor is not the same for surface area as for volume.

Communicating about MATHEMATICS

CLASS PROJECT
Have students work in teams to estimate how many LEGO® bricks would be needed to build a 10-ft model of a skyscraper such as the Sears tower in Chicago. (Hint: Students must first identify resources to find the dimensions of the actual building, then determine the scale of the model. They will also need to determine how many LEGO® pieces are required for a surface area of 1 square foot; this will help them estimate an answer to the problem.)

Writing Prompt
In your own words, describe what similar solids are.

Answer to Communicating
You can multiply each dimension of the model by 8 to find the dimensions of the actual room in feet (16 ft by 16 ft by 8 ft), then use the dimensions of the actual room to find the surface area and volume of the room. Or you can find the surface area (16 in.²) of the model and multiply by 8² to find the surface area of the actual room in square feet, and you can find the volume (4 in.³) of the model and multiply by 8³ to find the volume of the actual room in cubic feet.

Real Life
Architecture

Architects often build scale models of buildings they are designing. A common scale factor is $\frac{1}{8}$ inch to 1 foot.

Goal 2   **Comparing Ratios of Similar Solids**

In the investigation on page 573, you may have discovered the following relationships between measures of similar solids.

Ratios of Measures of Similar Solids
1. If two solids are similar with a scale factor of k, then the ratio of their surface areas is k^2.
2. If two solids are similar with a scale factor of k, then the ratio of their volumes is k^3.

Example 1   *Comparing Surface Areas and Volumes*

You are building a scale model of a building. In your model a length of $\frac{1}{8}$ inch represents a length of 1 foot in the building.

a. What is the scale factor of the building to the model?

b. What is the ratio of the surface area of the building to the surface area of the model?

c. What is the ratio of the volume of the building to the volume of the model?

Solution

a. To find the scale factor, find the ratio of 1 foot to $\frac{1}{8}$ inch.

$$\frac{1 \text{ foot}}{\frac{1}{8} \text{ inch}} = \frac{12 \text{ inches}}{\frac{1}{8} \text{ inch}} = 12 \cdot \frac{8}{1} = 96$$

The scale factor is 96. That is, the building's lengths are 96 times as large as the model's lengths.

b. Using a scale factor of 96, the building's surface area is 96^2 or 9216 times the model's surface area.

c. The building's volume is 96^3 or 884,736 times the model's volume. ∎

P   *Communicating* about MATHEMATICS

▶ **SHARING IDEAS about the Lesson**

Scale Models   In Example 1, a rectangular room in the model is 2-inches by 2-inches by 1-inch. Describe two different ways to find the surface area and volume of the actual room in the building.   See margin.

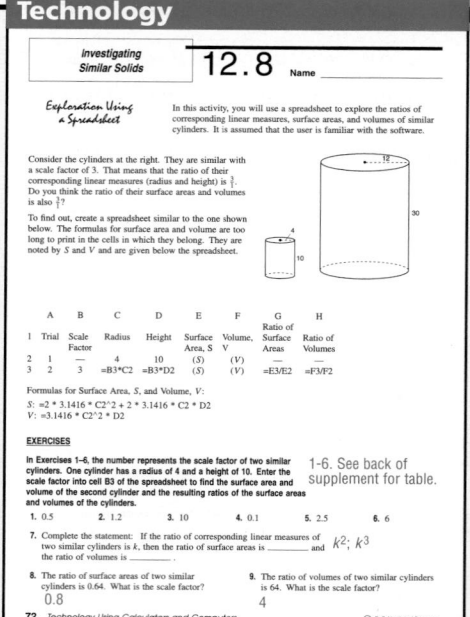

Technology

investigating
Similar Solids   **12.8**   Name _____

Exploration Using a Spreadsheet   In this activity, you will use a spreadsheet to explore the ratios of corresponding linear measures, surface areas, and volumes of similar cylinders. It is assumed that the user is familiar with the software.

Consider the cylinders at the right. They are similar with a scale factor of 3. That means that the ratio of their corresponding linear measures (radius and height) is $\frac{1}{3}$. Do you think the ratio of their surface areas and volumes is also $\frac{1}{3}$?

To find out, create a spreadsheet similar to the one shown below. The formulas for surface area and volume are too long to print in the cells in which they belong. They are noted by S and V and are given below the spreadsheet.

	A	B	C	D	E	F	G	H
							Ratio of	
1	Trial	Scale Factor	Radius	Height	Surface Area, S	Volume, V	Surface Areas	Ratio of Volumes
2	1	—	4	10	(S)	(V)	—	—
3	2	3	=B3*C2	=B3*D2	(S)	(V)	=E3/E2	=F3/F2

Formulas for Surface Area, S, and Volume, V:
S: $=2 * 3.1416 * C2^2 + 2 * 3.1416 * C2 * D2$
V: $=3.1416 * C2^2 * D2$

EXERCISES

In Exercises 1–6, the number represents the scale factor of two similar cylinders. One cylinder has a radius of 4 and a height of 10. Enter the scale factor into cell B3 of the spreadsheet to find the surface area and volume of the second cylinder and the resulting ratios of the surface areas and volumes of the cylinders.

1–6. See back of supplement for table.

1. 0.5   2. 1.2   3. 10   4. 0.1   5. 2.5   6. 6

7. Complete the statement: If the ratio of corresponding linear measures of two similar cylinders is k, then the ratio of surface areas is _____ and the ratio of volumes is _____. k^2; k^3

8. The ratio of surface areas of two similar cylinders is 0.64. What is the scale factor?   0.8

9. The ratio of volumes of two similar cylinders is 64. What is the scale factor?   4

EXERCISES

Guided Practice

▶ CHECK for Understanding   For explanations, see margin.

In Exercises 1–3, decide whether the figures are similar. Explain.

1.
Yes
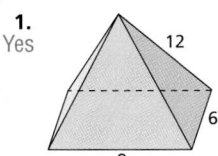

2.
No
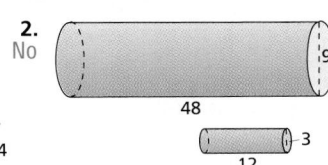

3.
Yes
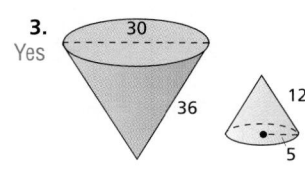

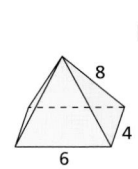

In Exercises 4–8, use the rectangular prisms at the right.

4. Explain why the prisms are similar.   See margin.

5. Find the scale factor of Prism A to Prism B.   6

6. Find the surface area of Prism B.   592 units²

7. Use a ratio of measures of similar solids to find the surface area of Prism A. Check your answer.   21,312 units²

8. How are the two volumes related? Explain.
Volume of Prism A = 6³ • Volume of Prism B

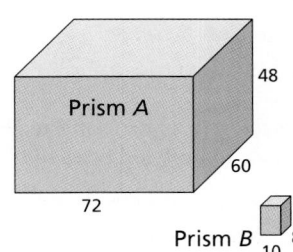

Prism A

Prism B

Independent Practice

In Exercises 9 and 10, match the solid with a similar solid.

9.   b
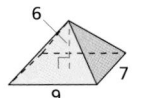

a.

b.
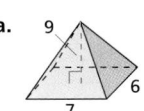

c.
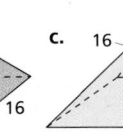

10.   C
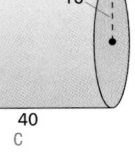

a.
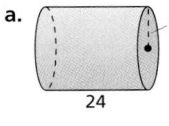

b.
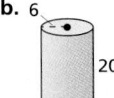

c.
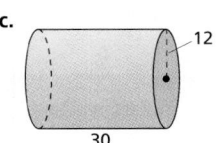

In Exercises 11 and 12, use a proportion to solve for x and y in the similar solids.

11.
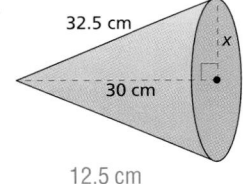

32.5 cm

30 cm

12.5 cm   5 cm

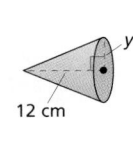

12 cm

12.
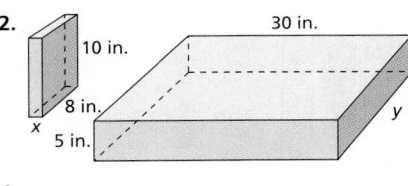

30 in.

10 in.

8 in.

5 in.

1 2/3 in.   24 in.

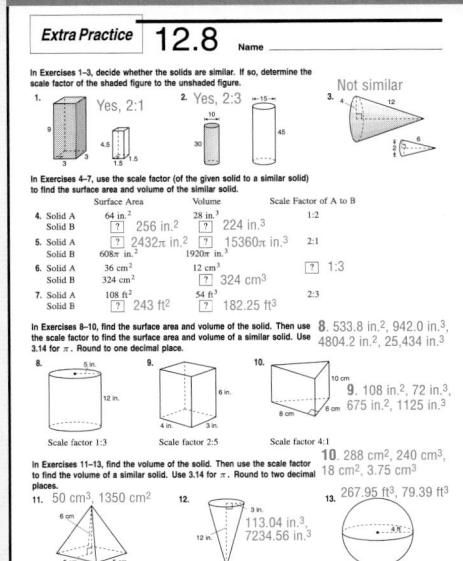
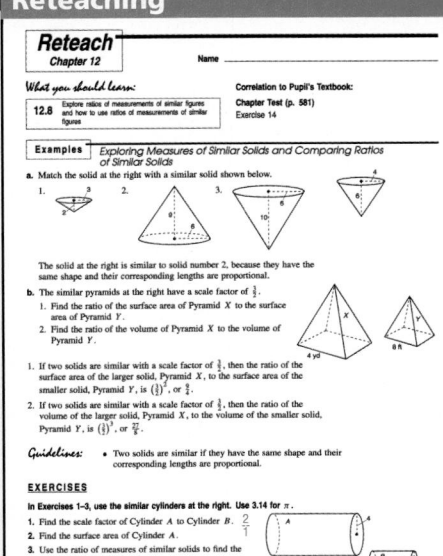

ASSIGNMENT GUIDE

*Basic/Average:
  Day 1: Ex. 9–11 odd, 13–16
  Day 2: Ex. 17–20, 23, 25

Above Average:
  Ex. 9–11 odd, 13–16, 17–25 odd

Advanced: Ex. 9–11 odd, 13–16, 17–25 odd

Selected Answers: Ex. 1–8, 9–21 odd

*You may wish to omit this lesson for these students.

Guided Practice

▶ **Ex. 1–3**   Students need to verify that corresponding parts are proportional.
▶ **Ex.4–8**   Some students may need visually to rotate the prisms in order to "see" the similarity.

Independent Practice

▶ **Ex. 9, 10**   Students should not rely on eyesight. Encourage them to set up appropriate proportions to check.
▶ **Ex. 11**   The Pythagorean Theorem is needed to solve for the radius x.

Answers

1. They have the same shape and their corresponding lengths are proportional $\left(\frac{9}{6} = \frac{6}{4} = \frac{12}{8}\right)$.

2. Their corresponding lengths are not proportional $\left(\frac{48}{12} \neq \frac{9}{3}\right)$.

3. They have the same shape and their corresponding lengths are proportional. $\left(\frac{36}{12} = \frac{15}{5}\right)$.

4. They have the same shape and their corresponding lengths are proportional $\left(\frac{72}{12} = \frac{60}{10} = \frac{48}{8}\right)$.

13. Copy and complete the table. The scale factor is the ratio of lengths of Solid A to Solid B.   Row 1: 5 ft; $44\frac{4}{9}$ ft²; $11\frac{1}{9}$ ft³   Row 2: 20 m; 4600 m²; 50,000 m³

Scale Factor	Solid A Length	Solid A Surface Area	Solid A Volume	Solid B Length	Solid B Surface Area	Solid B Volume
3	15 ft	400 ft²	300 ft³	?	?	?
$\frac{1}{10}$	2 m	46 m²	50 m³	?	?	?
7.5	?	11,137.5 cm²	?	3 cm	?	162 cm³
$\frac{1}{16}$	4 in.	?	64 in.³	?	24,576 in.²	?

Row 3: 22.5 cm; 68,343.75 cm³; 198 cm²   Row 4: 96 in.²; 64 in.; 262,144

Designing a Tunnel   **In Exercises 14–16, use the following.**

You are designing a tunnel through a mountain. In your model, a length of $\frac{1}{12}$ inch represents a length of 1 foot in the actual tunnel.

14. Find the scale factor of the actual tunnel to the model.   144

15. Find the ratio of the surface area of the actual tunnel to the surface area of the model.   20,736

16. Find the ratio of the volume of the actual tunnel to the volume of the model.   2,985,984

Logical Reasoning   **In Exercises 17–20, complete the statement using always, sometimes, or never.**

✪ **17.** Two spheres are [?] similar.   always

✪ **19.** Two cones are [?] similar.   sometimes

✪ **18.** A cube is [?] similar to a pyramid.   never

✪ **20.** A cylinder is [?] similar to itself.   always

Integrated Review   *Making Connections within Mathematics*

P **21.** *You Be the Teacher*   Your classmate says that because the two solids at the right have the same surface area and volume, they must be similar. Do they have the same surface area and volume? Are they similar? How would you explain your answer to your classmate?
Yes, no, they do not have the same shape.

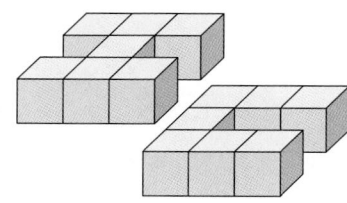

Exploration and Extension

Drawing Solids   **In Exercises 22–25, draw and label a solid that is similar to the given solid. (There are two possible answers.)**   See margin.

✪ **22.** Scale factor: $\frac{1}{2}$

✪ **23.** Scale factor: $\frac{1}{3}$

✪ **24.** Scale factor: 2

✪ **25.** Scale factor: $\frac{2}{3}$

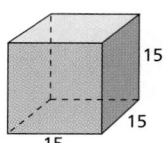

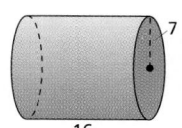

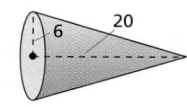

✪ More difficult exercises
P Portfolio Opportunity

12

Chapter Summary

What did you learn?

Skills

1. Find the circumference of a circle. **(12.1)**
2. Find the area of a circle. **(12.1)**
3. Identify different types of solids. **(12.2)**
   - Identify faces, edges, and vertices of polyhedrons. **(12.2)**
4. Find the surface area of a solid.
   - Find the surface area of a prism and a cylinder. **(12.3)**
5. Find the volume of a solid.
   - Find the volume of a prism. **(12.4)**
   - Find the volume of a cylinder. **(12.5)**
   - Find the volume of a pyramid and a cone. **(12.6)**
   - Find the volume of a sphere. **(12.7)**
6. Compare the surface areas and volumes of similar solids. **(12.8)**

Problem-Solving Strategies

7. Model and solve real-life problems. **(12.1–12.8)**

Exploring Data

8. Use tables and graphs to solve problems. **(12.1–12.8)**

Why did you learn it?

From the variety of the real-life examples in this chapter, you can see that measurements of circles and solids are used in almost all walks of life. For instance, in this chapter, you saw how to find the area of one side of the presidential seal. You also learned how surface area can be used to measure the amount of material needed to manufacture different types of containers, how volume can be used to help design a television studio, how volume can be used to decide which type of container is a better buy, how to find the volume of a rocket, and how volume can be used to find how much gas can be stored in a spherical storage tank.

How does it fit into the bigger picture of mathematics?

In this chapter, you studied many different formulas. Some of these formulas are used often enough that you should memorize them. For instance, it is helpful to remember that the circumference of a circle is $C = \pi d$ and the area of a circle is $A = \pi r^2$. In addition to memorizing formulas, we hope that this chapter has helped build your sense of what surface area and volume are actually measuring. For instance, you can think of the surface area as a measure of the material needed to cover the solid and you can think of volume as a measure of the material needed to fill the solid.

SUMMARY and REVIEW

COOPERATIVE LEARNING

Encourage students to study together. Emphasize the importance of teaching a classmate how to perform a skill or how to recall a procedure. When students work together, everyone wins. The students receiving help get additional instruction, and the students giving help gain a deeper understanding of the skills and concepts involved.

Chapter SUMMARY

This chapter extended students' measurement techniques to include space figures. Students began by learning the circle area formula needed for the measurement of the surface area of cylinders and cones. Students were then introduced to the terminology of space solids and to the nets or patterns associated with them. The area addition techniques for planar figures that were taught in the preceding chapter were applied in this chapter to the nets for prisms and cylinders in order to help visualize and compute their surface area. The second half of the chapter was concerned with the concept of volume. Lessons 12.4 and 12.5 taught the volume formulas for prisms and cylinders, and students were encouraged to reason informally about how changes in linear measurements would affect the volume of space figures. Lessons 12.6 and 12,7 offered hands-on demonstrations of how the volumes of prisms, cylinders, pyramids, cones, and spheres are related to one another. The chapter closed by clarifying the issue of how linear changes affect both area and volume.

Have students begin this Review in class and complete it as a homework assignment.

ASSIGNMENT GUIDE

*Basic/Average:
Ex. 1–35

Above Average:
Ex. 1–35 odd, 37–47, 49–52 odd

Advanced:
Ex. 1–35, 37–52

*For these students, you will need to limit assignments to cover only those lessons you chose to teach from this chapter.

Resources
Answer Masters, pp. 246, 247

In Exercises 1–8, match the expression with its formula. (12.1–12.7)

a. $V = \frac{1}{3}Bh$ **b.** $S = 2B + Ph$ **c.** $V = Bh$ **d.** $V = \pi r^2 h$

e. $A = \pi r^2$ **f.** $S = 2B + Ch$ **g.** $V = \frac{4}{3}\pi r^3$ **h.** $C = \pi d$

1. Circumference of a circle   h
2. Area of a circle   e
3. Surface area of a prism   b
4. Surface area of a cylinder   f
5. Volume of a prism   c
6. Volume of a cylinder   d
7. Volume of a pyramid or a cone   a
8. Volume of a sphere   g

In Exercises 9 and 10, find the circumference and area of the circle. (12.1)

✪ 11. Are the blue areas equal? Explain. **(12.1)**

9.
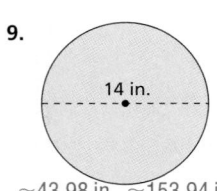
14 in.
≈43.98 in., ≈153.94 in.²

10.
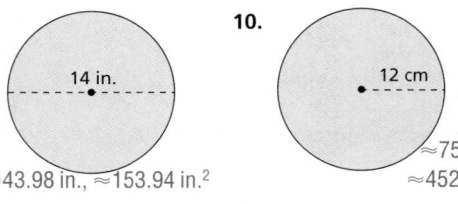
12 cm
≈75.40 cm,
≈452.39 cm²

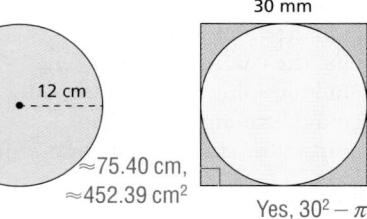
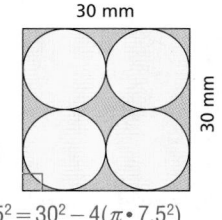
30 mm   30 mm
30 mm   30 mm
Yes, $30^2 - \pi \cdot 15^2 = 30^2 - 4(\pi \cdot 7.5^2)$

In Exercises 12–15, describe the solid that will result from folding the net. (12.2)

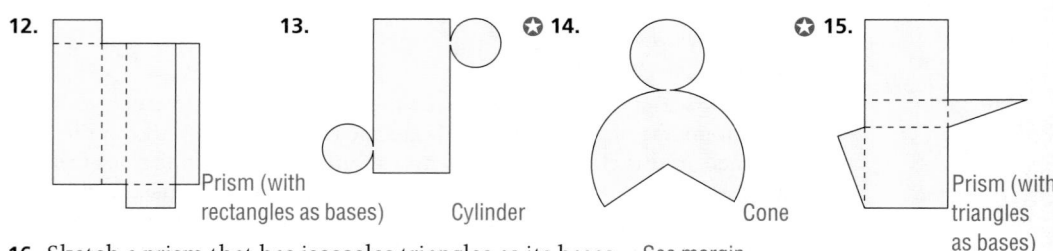

12.
Prism (with rectangles as bases)

13.
Cylinder

✪ 14.
Cone

✪ 15.
Prism (with triangles as bases)

16. Sketch a prism that has isosceles triangles as its bases.   See margin.

In Exercises 17–20, use the figure at the right. (12.2)

17. Identify the solid.   Pyramid (with a hexagon as base)
18. How many faces does the solid have?   7
19. How many vertices does the solid have?   7
20. How many edges does the solid have?   12

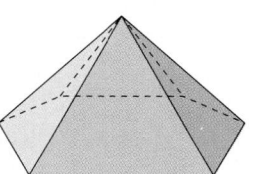

In Exercises 21–24, find the surface area of the solid. (12.3)

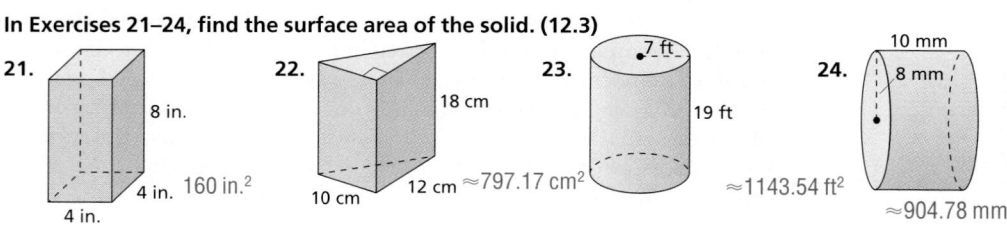

21.
8 in.
4 in.
4 in.
160 in.²

22.
18 cm
10 cm
12 cm
≈797.17 cm²

23.
7 ft
19 ft
≈1143.54 ft²

24.
10 mm
8 mm
≈904.78 mm²

Answer
16.

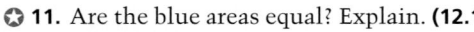

In Exercises 25–32, find the volume of the solid. (12.4–12.7)

25. 672 yd³   **28.** ≈1570.80 cm³
27. ≈3015.93 ft³

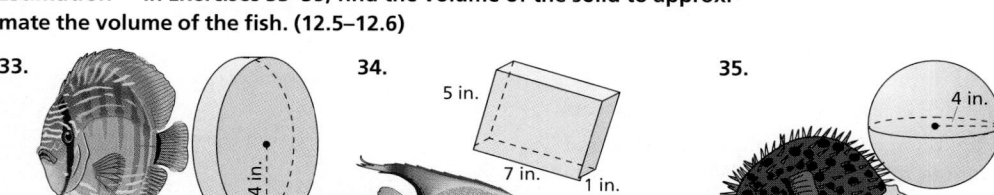

25.
12 yd
4 yd
14 yd

26.
10 in.
8 in.   16 in.
384 in.³

27.
8 ft
15 ft

28.
10 cm
5 cm

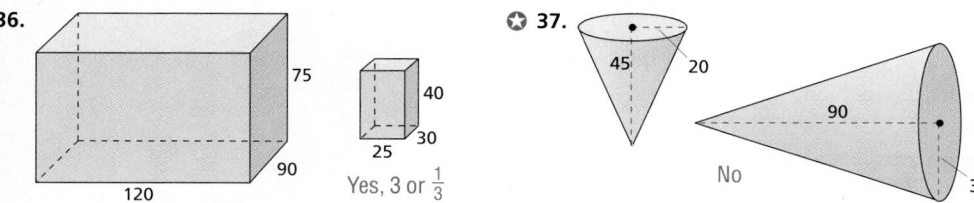

29.
7 m
6 m   56 m³
4 m

30. 8 mm
24 mm   8 mm
512 mm³

31.
14 in.
17 in.
≈872.32 in.³

32.
40 cm
≈268,082.57 cm³

Estimation   **In Exercises 33–35, find the volume of the solid to approximate the volume of the fish. (12.5–12.6)**

33.
4 in.
1 in.
≈50.3 in.³

34.
5 in.
7 in.   1 in.
35 in.³

35.
4 in.
≈268.1 in.³

In Exercises 36 and 37, decide whether the solids are similar. If so, find the scale factor. (12.8)

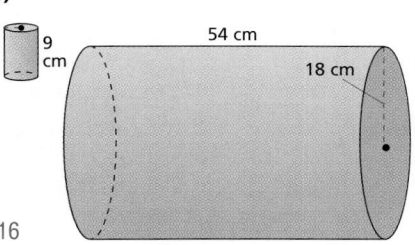

36.
75
90
120
40
25   30
Yes, 3 or $\frac{1}{3}$

⭐ **37.**
45   20
90
30
No

In Exercises 38–41, use the similar cylinders at the right. (12.8)

38. Find the scale factor of the large cylinder to the smaller cylinder.   6

39. What is the radius of the small cylinder?   3 cm

40. Find the ratio of the surface area of the large cylinder to the surface area of the small cylinder.   36

41. How many of the small cylinders will hold as much water as the large cylinder? Explain.   216, $6^3 = 216$

9 cm
54 cm
18 cm

FOCUS ON   *Designing a Product*

Designing a Model Train   **In Exercises 42–48, you are designing model-train cars with shapes like those shown at the right.**

42. Find the surface area and volume of the refrigerator car.   105.75 in.², 61.875 in.³

43. Find the surface area and volume of the gondola car.   65.5 in.², 27.1875 in.³

⭐ **44.** Find the surface area and volume of the tank car. (Hint: The surface area of a sphere of radius r is $S = 4\pi r^2$.)   ≈107.21 in.², ≈82.58 in.³

⭐ **45.** Find the surface area and volume of the passenger car.   ≈120.25 in.², ≈78.34 in.³

46. An actual refrigerator car is 60 feet long. Find the scale factor of an actual train to the model train. $\frac{960}{11}$

47. Find the ratio of the surface area of the actual train to the model train. What is the   See
surface area of the actual refrigerator car?   below.

48. Find the ratio of the volume of the actual train to the model train. What is the volume of the actual refrigerator car? $\frac{884{,}736{,}000}{1331}$, ≈23,801.65 ft³   **47.** $\frac{921{,}600}{121}$, ≈5593.39 ft²

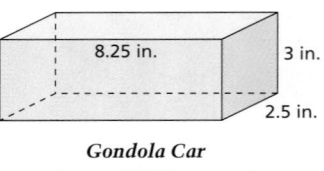

Refrigerator Car

8.25 in.   3 in.

2.5 in.

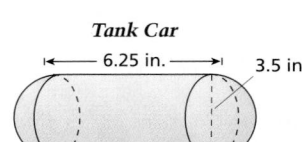

Gondola Car

|←—— 7.25 in. ——→|

1.5 in.

2.5 in.

Tank Car

|←—— 6.25 in. ——→| 3.5 in.

Passenger Car

2.5 in.

9 in.   2.5 in.

Designing a Tunnel   **In Exercises 49–52, use the following information.**

You work for a construction company. You are assigned to design and supervise the construction of a straight railroad tunnel through a mountain. The tunnel needs to be 30 feet high for train clearance and 20 feet wide. The tunnel will be 13,200 feet long.   **49., 52.** See margin.

⭐ **49.** The tunnel can be modeled as half of a cylinder on top of a rectangular prism, so that cross sections of the tunnel are arches. Sketch the tunnel and label your sketch.

⭐ **50.** How much dirt and rock will be removed from the tunnel?   ≈7,353,451 ft³

⭐ **51.** Find the surface area of the inside of the tunnel. (Do not include the area of each end.) ≈1,206,690 ft²

⭐ **52.** Suppose that each cross section was a half circle with 30-foot radius. Would this design require more or less removal of dirt and rock? Explain.

The longest railroad tunnel in the United States is the Moffat Tunnel. This 6.2-mile tunnel cuts through the Rocky Mountains in Colorado.

Answers
49.

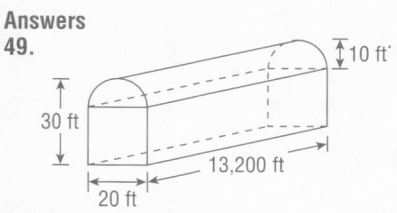

10 ft

30 ft

13,200 ft

20 ft

Figure not drawn to scale

52. More. The cross section of the tunnel has an area of ≈ 557.08 ft², while the cross section of the half circle has an area of ≈ 1413.72 ft².

In Exercises 1–3, use the prism at the right. (12.2)

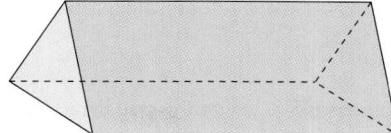

1. How many faces does the prism have?   5
2. How many vertices does the prism have?   6
3. How many edges does the prism have?   9

In Exercises 4–7, use the cylinder at the right. (12.1, 12.3, 12.5)

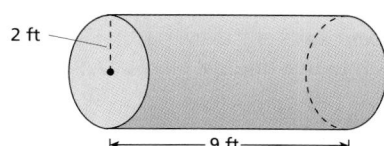

4. Find the circumference of one of the bases.   ≈12.57 ft
5. Find the area of one of the bases.   ≈12.57 ft²
6. Find the surface area of the cylinder.   ≈138.23 ft²
7. Find the volume of the cylinder.   ≈113.10 ft³

In Exercises 8–11, find the indicated measure of the solid. (12.3, 12.4, 12.6)

8. Volume

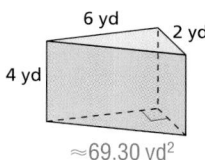

4 cm   16 cm³

9. Volume

6 ft
3 ft
4 ft
5 ft
96 ft³

10. Surface area

3 in.
2 in.
4 in.
52 in.²

11. Surface area

6 yd   2 yd
4 yd
≈69.30 yd²

In Exercises 12–16, use the similar solids at the right. (12.3, 12.4, 12.8)

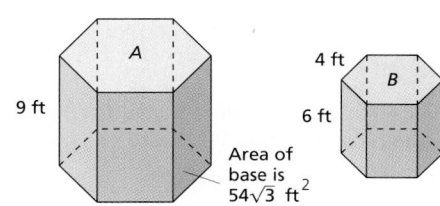

12. Find the surface area of Figure A.   ≈511.06 ft²
13. Find the volume of Figure A.   ≈841.78 ft³
14. Find the scale factor of Figure A to Figure B. $\frac{3}{2}$
15. Find the surface area of Figure B.   ≈227.14 ft²
16. Find the volume of Figure B.   ≈249.42 ft³

A

4 ft
B
6 ft

9 ft

Area of base is
$54\sqrt{3}$ ft²

In Exercises 17–19, use the diagram below. (12.3, 12.5)

17., 18. See below.

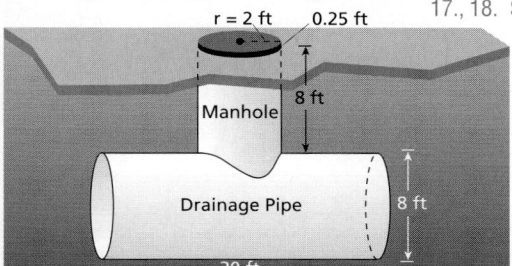

r = 2 ft   0.25 ft

8 ft
Manhole

Drainage Pipe   8 ft

20 ft

17. What is the surface area of the manhole cover?
18. Approximate the volume of the manhole.
19. What is the volume of the 20-foot cylinder?   ≈1005.31 ft³

17. ≈28.27 ft²   18. 100.53 ft³

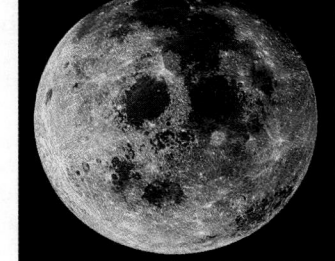

The moon's diameter is about 2160 miles.

20. What is the volume of the moon? (12.7)
≈5,276,700,000 mi³

Chapter Test

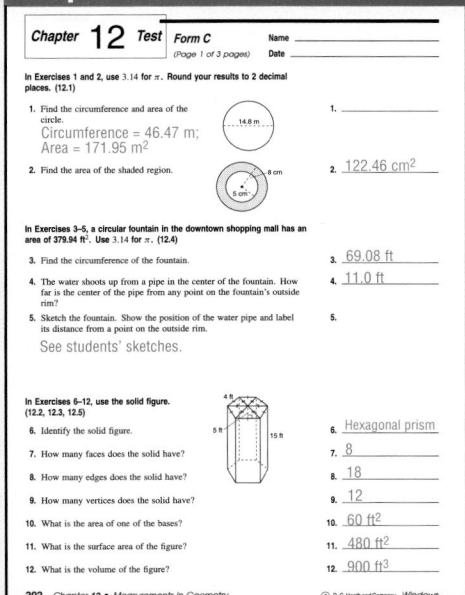

Chapter **12** Test   Form C   Name _____
(Page 1 of 3 pages)   Date _____

In Exercises 1 and 2, use 3.14 for π. Round your results to 2 decimal places. (12.1)

1. Find the circumference and area of the circle.   14.8 m   1. _____
Circumference = 46.47 m;
Area = 171.95 m²

2. Find the area of the shaded region.   8 cm / 5 cm   2. 122.46 cm²

In Exercises 3–5, a circular fountain in the downtown shopping mall has an area of 379.94 ft². Use 3.14 for π. (12.4)

3. Find the circumference of the fountain.   3. 69.08 ft
4. The water shoots up from a pipe in the center of the fountain. How far is the center of the pipe from any point on the fountain's outside rim?   4. 11.0 ft
5. Sketch the fountain. Show the position of the water pipe and label its distance from a point on the outside rim.   5. See students' sketches.

In Exercises 6–12, use the solid figure. (12.2, 12.3, 12.5)

6. Identify the solid figure.   6. Hexagonal prism
7. How many faces does the solid have?   7. 8
8. How many edges does the solid have?   8. 18
9. How many vertices does the solid have?   9. 12
10. What is the area of one of the bases?   10. 60 ft²
11. What is the surface area of the figure?   11. 480 ft²
12. What is the volume of the figure?   12. 900 ft³

202   Chapter 12 • Measurements in Geometry   © D.C. Heath and Company   Windows

Cumulative **REVIEW** ▪ *Chapters* **7–12**

In Exercises 1–4, evaluate the expression. Then simplify, if possible. (7.1, 7.2, 7.4, 7.5)

1. $\frac{1}{2} + \frac{1}{3}$ $\frac{5}{6}$　　**2.** $\frac{3}{4} \cdot \frac{8}{9}$ $\frac{2}{3}$　　**3.** $\frac{7}{12} - \frac{5}{12}$ $\frac{2}{12}, \frac{1}{6}$　　**4.** $\frac{12}{5} \div \frac{3}{5}$ 4

In Exercises 5–8, solve the equation. (7.1, 7.2, 7.4, 7.5)

5. $y + \frac{3}{4} = \frac{1}{2}$ $-\frac{1}{4}$　　**6.** $\frac{1}{3}m = \frac{1}{6}$ $\frac{1}{2}$　　**7.** $\frac{4}{5} = 8a$ $\frac{1}{10}$　　**8.** $\frac{2}{7} = b - \frac{3}{2}$ $\frac{25}{14}$

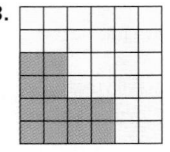 **In Exercises 9–12, use a calculator to evaluate the expression. Round your result to two decimal places. (7.1–7.5)**

9. $\frac{31}{40} \cdot \frac{26}{51}$ 0.40　　**10.** $\frac{76}{55} + \frac{7}{35}$ 1.58　　**11.** $\frac{93}{95} - \frac{54}{73}$ 0.24　　**12.** $\frac{9}{92} \div \frac{26}{70}$ 0.26

In Exercises 13–16, write the fraction that represents the portion of the figure's area that is blue. Then write the fraction as a percent. (7.6)

13.　　　　　**14.**　　　　　**15.**　　　　　**16.**

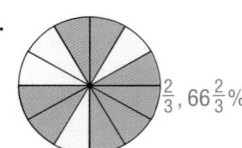 $\frac{1}{3}, 33\frac{1}{3}\%$　　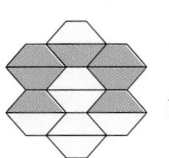 $\frac{2}{3}, 66\frac{2}{3}\%$　　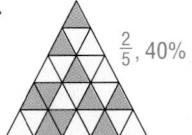 $\frac{1}{2}, 50\%$　　$\frac{2}{5}, 40\%$

Job Security　　**In Exercises 17 and 18, use the circle graph. (7.7, 7.8)** *(Source: Delotte and Touche Trade Survey)*

17. Write each percent as a simplified fraction.

18. Five hundred people participated in the survey. How many people answered in each category?
　　17.–18. See margin.

In Exercises 19–22, write the verbal phrase as a rate or ratio. State whether it is a rate or a ratio. (8.1)

19. 5 gallons used to drive 100 miles.　20 mi/gal, rate

20. Drove 25 kilometers in 40 minutes.

21. 18 people out of 24 people attended.　$\frac{3}{4}$, ratio

22. 99 chicks out of 100 chicks survived.　$\frac{99}{100}$, ratio
　　20. 0.625 km/min, rate

How Secure Do You Feel in Your Job ?
- 3% Don't know
- Secure 55%
- 14% Not secure
- 28% Somewhat secure

In Exercises 23–26, solve the proportion. (8.2)

23. $\frac{3}{4} = \frac{x}{32}$ 24　　**24.** $\frac{18}{5} = \frac{3}{y}$ $\frac{5}{6}$　　**25.** $\frac{z}{6} = \frac{5}{9}$ $\frac{10}{3}$　　**26.** $\frac{24}{w} = \frac{3}{5}$ 40

In Exercises 27 and 28, use the table at the right that shows the number of points Tyrone "Muggsy" Bogues scored in each season in the National Basketball Association. (8.6)

27. Find the percent decrease in points from the 1989–90 season to the 1990–91 season.　≈25.6%

28. Find the percent increase in points from the 1990–91 season to the 1991–92 season.　≈28.5%

Season	Points
1989–90	763
1990–91	568
1991–92	730
1992–93	808

Cumulative Test

Cumulative Test	Chapters 7–12	Name ___
	(Page 1 of 8 pages)	Date ___

In Exercises 1–4, evaluate the expression. Then simplify, if possible. (7.1, 7.2, 7.4, 7.5)

1. $\frac{3}{8} + \frac{5}{6}$　　1. $1\frac{5}{24}$

2. $\frac{6}{7} - \frac{3}{14}$　　2. $\frac{9}{14}$

3. $\frac{3}{5} \cdot \frac{9}{10}$　　3. $\frac{27}{50}$

4. $\frac{2}{3} \div \frac{4}{5}$　　4. $\frac{5}{6}$

In Exercises 5–8, solve the equation. (7.1, 7.2, 7.4, 7.5)

5. $x - \frac{1}{2} = \frac{5}{6}$　　5. $x = 1\frac{1}{3}$

6. $b + \frac{2}{3} = 1\frac{1}{5}$　　6. $b = \frac{14}{15}$

7. $4e = \frac{3}{7}$　　7. $e = \frac{3}{28}$

8. $\frac{2}{5}h = \frac{1}{10}$　　8. $h = \frac{1}{2}$

In Exercises 9–12, use a calculator to evaluate the expression. Round your result to two decimal places. (7.1–7.5)

9. $\frac{34}{45} + \frac{13}{14}$　　9. 1.68

10. $\frac{25}{31} \cdot \frac{12}{21}$　　10. 0.46

11. $\frac{16}{17} - \frac{6}{7}$　　11. 0.08

12. $\frac{21}{25} \div \frac{5}{9}$　　12. 1.51

Windows ⓒ D.C. Heath and Company　　Chapters 7–12 ▪ Cumulative Test **205**

Answers
17. Secure: $\frac{11}{20}$, somewhat secure: $\frac{7}{25}$, not

secure: $\frac{7}{50}$, don't know: $\frac{3}{100}$
18. Secure: 275, somewhat secure: 140, not secure: 70, don't know: 15

Formal Assessment ▶

A **Cumulative Test** of average difficulty for Chapters 7–12
Available as copymasters, pages 205–212

582　*Chapter 12*

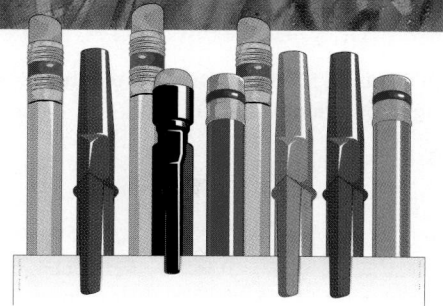

Probability In Exercises 29–30, you have 3 regular pencils, 2 colored pencils, 1 mechanical pencil, and 3 ballpoint pens. (8.7, 8.8)

29. How many different ways could you choose one pencil and one pen?   18

30. If you randomly pick one writing instrument, what is the probability that it is a pencil? $\frac{2}{3}$

In Exercises 31–34, solve the equation and decide whether the solution is rational or irrational. (9.1–9.2)

31. $x^2 = 121$ 11, −11 rational   **32.** $84 = y^2$ $\sqrt{84}, -\sqrt{84}$ **33.** $504 = 4n^2$ $\sqrt{126}, -\sqrt{126}$ irrational   **34.** $-8 = m^2 - 17$ 3, −3 rational

In Exercises 35–37, a and b are the lengths of the legs of a right triangle, and c is the length of the hypotenuse. Find the missing length. (9.3)

35. $a = 7, b = 24$ $c = 25$ **36.** $a = 5, c = 14.87$ $b \approx 14.00$ **37.** $b = 13, c = 15.26$ $a \approx 7.99$

In Exercises 38–43, solve the inequality. Then graph the solution on a number line. (9.5–9.7)   For graphs, see margin.

38. $x + 14 \leq 9$ $x \leq -5$ **39.** $\frac{2}{3} < -4y$ $y < -\frac{1}{6}$ **40.** $-17 \leq -12n + 19$ $n \leq 3$

41. $5(1 + 2p) < 13$ $p < \frac{4}{5}$ **42.** $2(7 - x) > 4x$ $x < \frac{7}{3}$ **43.** $3(5 + x) \leq \frac{1}{4}(20 + 8x)$ $x \leq -10$

In Exercises 44–47, decide whether the triangle can have the given side lengths. Explain. (9.3, 9.8)   **47.** Yes; $8 + 10 > 17$, $8 + 17 > 10$, $10 + 17 > 8$

44.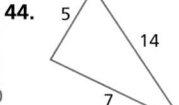
$+ 7 \not> 14$

45.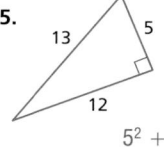
Yes
$5^2 + 12^2 = 13^2$

46.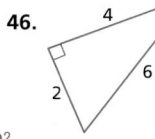
No
$2 + 4 \not> 6$

47.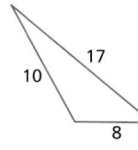

48. ***Television*** If you have a 25-inch diagonal television screen and its width is 16.7 inches, what is its length? (9.4) ≈ 18.60 in.

In Exercises 49–56, use the figure at the right. (10.1–10.3)

49. Write two other names for the line $\overleftrightarrow{EH}$.   See margin.

50. List five line segments that have C as an endpoint.   See margin.

51. Write another name for $\overrightarrow{KH}$. $\overrightarrow{KG}$

52. Write three other names for $\angle JKG$. $\angle JKH, \angle HKJ, \angle GKJ$

53. List 2 pairs of vertical angles.   See margin.

54. List 4 angles whose measure is 70°. $\angle ACB, \angle KCF \angle CED, \angle HEF$

55. List 2 pairs of congruent corresponding angles.   See margin.

56. List 2 pairs of noncongruent corresponding angles.   See margin.

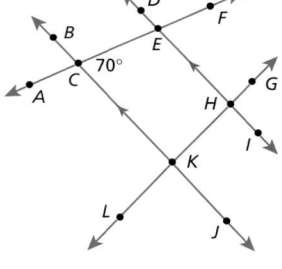

Answers

38.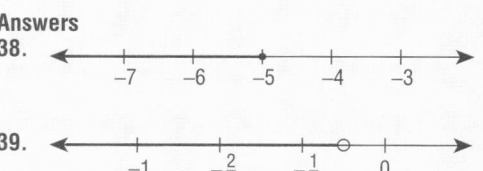

39.

40.

41.

42.

43.

49. $\overleftrightarrow{EI}, \overleftrightarrow{ED}, \overleftrightarrow{DH}, \overleftrightarrow{DI}, \overleftrightarrow{HI}$
50. $\overline{CA}, \overline{CE}, \overline{CF}, \overline{CB}, \overline{CK}, \overline{CJ}$
53. $\angle ACB$ and $\angle KCE$, $\angle BCE$ and $\angle ACK$, and 6 other pairs
55. $\angle ACB$ and $\angle CED$, $\angle BCE$ and $\angle DEF$, and 6 other pairs
56. $\angle ACB$ and $\angle LKC$, $\angle ACK$ and $\angle LKJ$, and 6 other pairs

In Exercises 57–60, use a protractor to measure the angle. Is it acute, obtuse, right, or straight? (10.2)

57.

Straight

58.

Acute

59.

Obtuse

60.

Acute

In Exercises 61–64, identify the polygon. (Be specific.) Then find *x*. (10.6, 10.8)

Pentagon, 119°

61.

43° *x*

Scalene
right triangle, 47°

62.

x 142° *x*

94°

Kite, 62°

63.

x *x*

103°

Isosceles trapezoid, 77°

64.

x

73° 118°

140°

In Exercises 65 and 66, identify any symmetry of the figure. (10.4)   1-line symmetry

In Exercises 67 and 68, order the angles from the smallest to the largest. (10.9)

65.

66.

67. *B*

7 15

A

12

C

C, B, A,

68.

E

5.4 5.5

D

5.6

F, D, E

F

65. 2-line symmetry, 180° rotational symmetry

In Exercises 69–72, find the area and perimeter of the polygon. (11.1)

69.

6

8 10

72 units², 36 units

70.

16

17 14

224 units², 66 units

71.

8

4.5

4

≈24.19 units², 21 units

72.

5 6

30 units², 24 units

In Exercises 73–75, use the figure at the right, where △*ABC* is reflected in line ℓ. (11.3)

73. Is △*ABC* congruent to △*A'B'C'*?   Yes

74. Is the length of $\overline{BB'}$ half the length of $\overline{CC'}$? Explain.

75. Is *CM* = *C'M*? Explain.   **74., 75.** See margin.

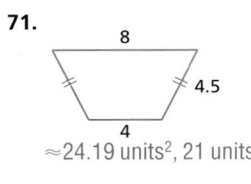

A *C* *M* *C'*

B *N* *B'* *A'*

ℓ

In Exercises 76–78, use the figure at the right, where △*DEF* is rotated about point *O*. (11.4)

Clockwise

76. Is the rotation clockwise or counterclockwise?

77. Is △*DEF* congruent to △*D'E'F'*?   Yes

78. Is *DD'* = *FF'*? Explain.   See margin.

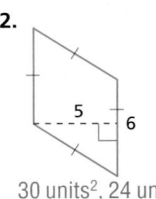

E *D'*

D *E'*

F'

F

O

Indirect Measurement **In Exercises 79 and 80, you are measuring the width of the river shown in the diagram. To begin, you place stakes at points *A* and *B*. Then you measure $\overline{AB}$ and $\angle B$. (11.8)**

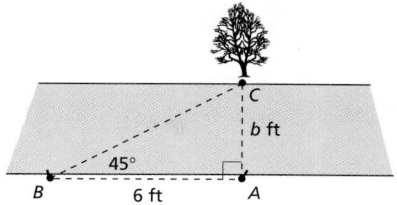

79. Write the trigonometric ratio for the tangent of $\angle B$. $\frac{b}{6}$

80. Find the width of the river. 6 ft

In Exercises 81–84, find the circumference and area of the circle. Round your results to two decimal places. (12.1)

81.

$r = 9$ mm 56.55 mm
254.47 mm²

82.

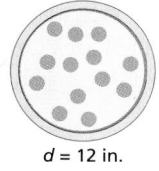

$d = 1.5$ cm 4.71 cm
1.77 cm²

83.

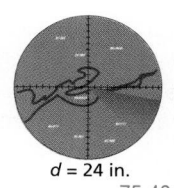

$d = 12$ in. 37.70 in.
113.10 in.²

84.

$d = 24$ in. 75.40 in.
452.39 in.²

In Exercises 85–88, find the surface area and volume of the solid. Round your results to two decimal places. (12.3–12.5)

85.

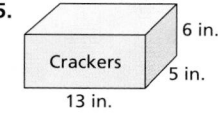

6 in.
5 in.
13 in.
346 in.², 390 in.³

86.

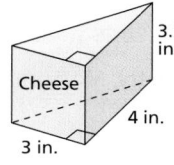

3.5 in.
4 in.
3 in.
54 in.², 21 in.³

87.

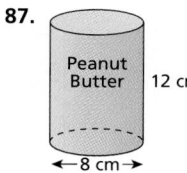

Peanut Butter 12 cm
8 cm
402.12 cm², 603.19 cm³

88.

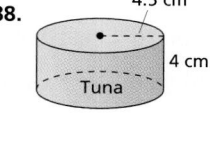

4.5 cm
4 cm
Tuna
240.33 cm², 254.47 cm³

In Exercises 89–92, find the volume of the solid. Round your result to two decimal places. (12.6, 12.7)

89.

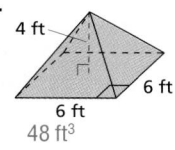

4 ft
6 ft
6 ft
48 ft³

90.

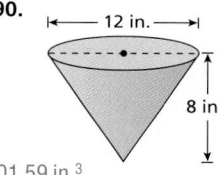

12 in.
8 in.
301.59 in.³

91.

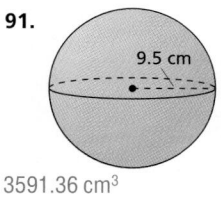

9.5 cm
3591.36 cm³

92.

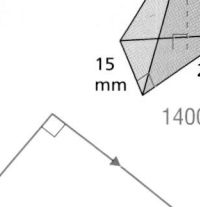

4.5 cm
28 mm
15 mm
20 mm
1400 mm³

93. *Writing* Trace the polygon at the right on a piece of paper. Then draw a larger, similar polygon. Find the side lengths in centimeters, angle measures, and areas of each polygon. Write a statement that compares these measures. **(11.6)** See margin.

Cumulative Review **585**

CHAPTER 13 GOALS

CHAPTER 13 ▪ OVERVIEW

RESOURCES ORGANIZER

Lesson Pages	13.1 588–591	13.2 593–596	13.3 598–601	13.4 604–607	13.5 610–613	13.6 614–618	13.7 619–622	13.8 623–626
Lesson Plans	102	103	104	105	106	107	108	109
Problem of the Day	37	37	37	38	38	38	39	39
Warm-Up Exercises	37	37	37	38	38	38	39	39
Color Transparencies	54	54	—	55	55	56	56	57
Teaching Tools: Transparencies Copymasters	T1 C2	T8, T9 C10, C11	T9 C11	T9 C11	T9 C11	T1 C2	T8, T9 C10, C11	T9 C11
Math Log	40	40	41	41	41	42	42	42
Technology	—	74	—	75	—	76, 77	—	78
Answer Masters	252, 253	254–256	257–259	261	262, 263	264, 265	267, 268	269
Extra Practice Copymasters	102	103	104	105	106	107	108	109
Reteaching Copymasters	102	103	104	105	106	107	108	109
Enrichment Projects	—	67, 68	69–71	—	—	—	—	—
Alternative Assessment: Projects Partner Quizzes Group Assessment	— — —	— — —	— — —	— 56 —	39, 40 — —	— — —	— — 83, 84	40 — —
Formal Assessment: Short Quizzes Tests	— —	213 —	— —	214 215, 216	— —	217 —	— —	218 219–227
Overhead Manipulatives Kit	—	—	—	—	—	—	—	—
Complete Solutions Manual	Includes step-by-step solutions for all exercises in the student text							
Computerized Test Bank	Creates customized tests that include graphics							
Interactive CD-ROM Project	Provides an interactive and interdisciplinary chapter project							

STARTERS

Problem of the Day

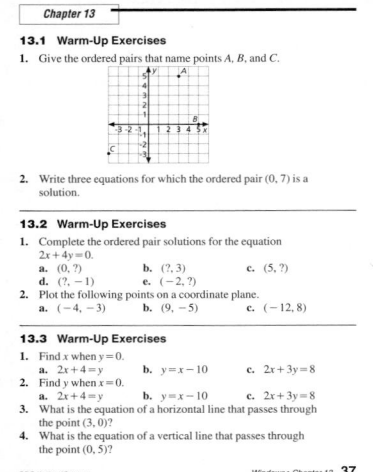

Chapter 13

13.1 Problem of the Day
The last seven sightings of Halley's comet are listed in the table. The data follow a linear pattern. Examine the pattern and predict the date of the next (eighth) sighting. How old will you then be?

(S) Sighting	(Y) Year	(S) Sighting	(Y) Year
1	1531	5	1835
2	1607	6	1910
3	1682	7	1986
4	1758	8	?

13.2 Problem of the Day
Adam is thinking of a number. If he multiplies the number by 3 and adds 11, he gets the same answer as he would if he had multiplied the number by 4 and subtracted 4. What is his number?

13.3 Problem of the Day
Find four natural numbers whose sum is equal to their product. (Hint: A number can be used more than once.)

© D.C. Heath and Company · Windows • Chapter 13 **37**

Warm-Up Exercises

Chapter 13

13.1 Warm-Up Exercises
1. Give the ordered pairs that name points A, B, and C.

2. Write three equations for which the ordered pair (0, 7) is a solution.

13.2 Warm-Up Exercises
1. Complete the ordered pair solutions for the equation $2x + 4y = 0$.
   a. $(0, ?)$ b. $(?, 3)$ c. $(5, ?)$
   d. $(?, -1)$ e. $(-2, ?)$
2. Plot the following points on a coordinate plane.
   a. $(-4, -3)$ b. $(9, -5)$ c. $(-12, 8)$

13.3 Warm-Up Exercises
1. Find x when $y = 0$.
   a. $2x + 4 = y$ b. $y = x - 10$ c. $2x + 3y = 8$
2. Find y when $x = 0$.
   a. $2x + 4 = y$ b. $y = x - 10$ c. $2x + 3y = 8$
3. What is the equation of a horizontal line that passes through the point (3, 0)?
4. What is the equation of a vertical line that passes through the point (0, 5)?

© D.C. Heath and Company · Windows • Chapter 13 **37**

FOR TEACHERS

Answer Masters

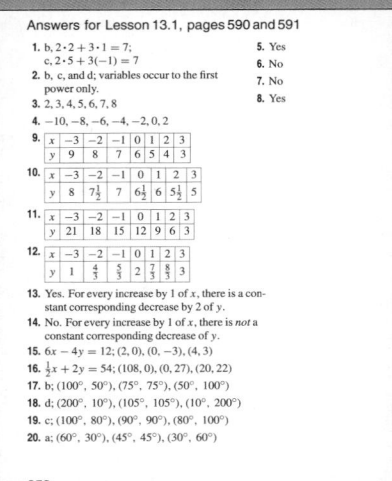

Answers for Lesson 13.1, pages 590 and 591

1. b, $2 \cdot 2 + 3 \cdot 1 = 7$;
   c, $2 \cdot 5 + 3(-1) = 7$
2. b, c, and d; variables occur to the first power only.
3. 2, 3, 4, 5, 6, 7, 8
4. $-10, -8, -6, -4, -2, 0, 2$
5. Yes
6. No
7. No
8. Yes

9.
x	-3	-2	-1	0	1	2	3
y	9	8	7	6	5	4	3

10.
x	-3	-2	-1	0	1	2	3
y	8	$7\frac{1}{2}$	7	$6\frac{1}{2}$	6	$5\frac{1}{2}$	5

11.
x	-3	-2	-1	0	1	2	3
y	21	18	15	12	9	6	3

12.
x	-3	-2	-1	0	1	2	3
y	1	$\frac{4}{3}$	$\frac{5}{3}$	2	$\frac{7}{3}$	$\frac{8}{3}$	3

13. Yes. For every increase by 1 of x, there is a constant corresponding decrease by 2 of y.
14. No. For every increase by 1 of x, there is *not* a constant corresponding decrease of y.
15. $6x - 4y = 12$; (2, 0), (0, -3), (4, 3)
16. $\frac{1}{2}x + 2y = 54$; (108, 0), (0, 27), (20, 22)
17. b; (100°, 50°), (75°, 75°), (50°, 100°)
18. d; (200°, 10°), (105°, 105°), (10°, 200°)
19. c; (100°, 80°), (90°, 90°), (80°, 100°)
20. a; (60°, 30°), (45°, 45°), (30°, 60°)

252 Windows · Answer Masters   © D. C. Heath and Company

Lesson Plans

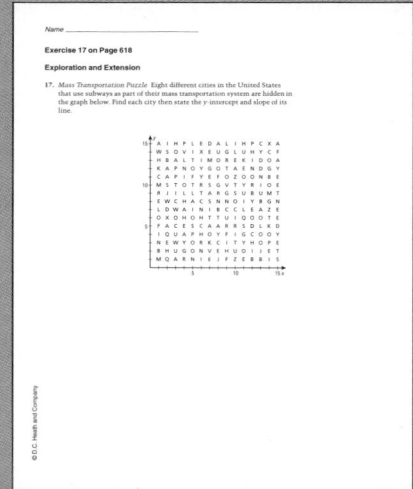

Lesson Plan 13.1 pages 588–591

Teacher's Name _____ Class _____ Date _____ Room _____

Goals 1. Find solutions of linear equations in two variables.
2. Organize solutions of real-life problems using linear equations.

State/Local Objectives

NCTM Curriculum Standards: Communication, Connections, Patterns and Functions, Algebra, Statistics, Geometry, Measurement

✔ **Check items you wish to use for this lesson.**

Introducing the Lesson
___ Problem of the Day copymaster page 37 or Teacher's Edition page 588
___ Warm-Up Exercises copymaster page 37 or Teacher's Edition page 588

Teaching the Lesson using the following:
___ Extra Examples, Teacher's Edition page 589
___ Color Transparencies: diagram for Example 2, page 54
___ Teaching Tools: graph paper, pages T1, C2
___ Notes for Substitute Teacher

Closing the Lesson
___ Communicating about Mathematics, Student's Edition page 589
___ Guided Practice Exercises, Student's Edition page 590

Homework Assignment, pages 590, 591
___ Basic/Average: Day 1: Ex. 5–13 odd, 21–23
                Day 2: Ex. 24–27, 29–33 odd
___ Above Average: Ex. 5–19 odd, 24–30, 32, 33
___ Advanced: Ex. 5–19 odd, 24–30, 32, 33

Reteaching the Lesson
___ Extra Practice Copymasters page 102
___ Reteaching Copymasters page 102
___ Math Log copymaster page 40 or Teacher's Edition page 591

Extending the Lesson
___ Writing, Teacher's Edition page 589
___ Enrichment, Teacher's Edition page 591

Notes

102 Windows   © D.C. Heath and Company

Teaching Tools

Name _____

Exercise 17 on Page 618

Exploration and Extension

17. *Mass Transportation Puzzle* Eight different cities in the United States that use subways as part of their mass transportation system are hidden in the graph below. Find each city then state the y-intercept and slope of its line.

© D.C. Heath and Company

Teaching Tools includes:
Transparencies and Copymasters for classroom activities and study skills:
- Graph Paper
- Dot Paper (Geoboards)
- Algebra Tiles
- Number Counters
- Fraction Strips
- Models

REAL LIFE

Color Transparencies for Real-Life Applications

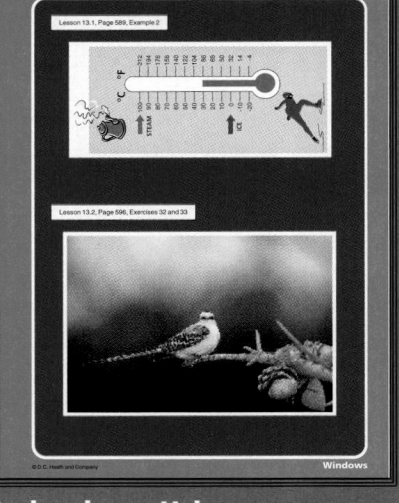

Color Transparencies for Real Life Applications • 54

Lesson 13.1, Page 589, Example 2

Lesson 13.2, Page 596, Exercises 32 and 33

© D.C. Heath and Company   Windows

Technology: Using Calculators and Computers

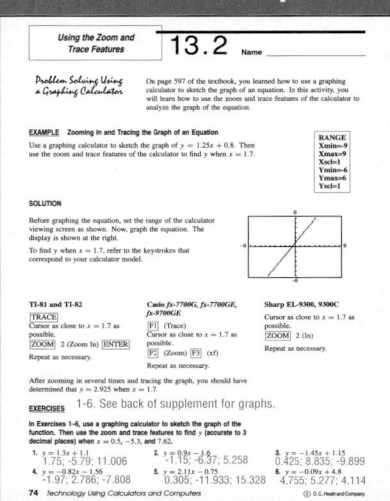

Using the Zoom and Trace Features   **13.2** Name _____

Problem Solving Using a Graphing Calculator

On page 597 of the textbook, you learned how to use a graphing calculator to sketch the graph of an equation. In this activity, you will learn how to use the zoom and trace features of the calculator to analyze the graph of the equation.

EXAMPLE Zooming in and Tracing the Graph of an Equation

Use a graphing calculator to sketch the graph of $y = 1.25x + 0.8$. Then use the zoom and trace features of the calculator to find y when $x = 1.7$.

RANGE
Xmin=-9
Xmax=9
Xscl=1
Ymin=-6
Ymax=6
Yscl=1

SOLUTION

Before graphing the equation, set the range of the calculator viewing screen as shown. Now, graph the equation. The display is shown at the right.

To find y when $x = 1.7$, refer to the keystrokes that correspond to your calculator model.

TI-81 and TI-82
TRACE
Cursor as close to $x = 1.7$ as possible.
ZOOM 2 (Zoom In) ENTER
Repeat as necessary.

Casio fx-7700G, fx-7700GE, fx-9700GE
F1 (Trace)
Cursor as close to $x = 1.7$ as possible.
F2 (Zoom) F3 (xf)
Repeat as necessary.

Sharp EL-9300, 9300C
Cursor as close to $x = 1.7$ as possible.
ZOOM 2 (In)
Repeat as necessary.

After zooming in several times and tracing the graph, you should have determined that $y = 2.925$ when $x = 1.7$.

EXERCISES 1–6. See back of supplement for graphs.

In Exercises 1–6, use a graphing calculator to sketch the graph of the function. Then use the zoom and trace features to find y (accurate to 3 decimal places) when $x = 0.5, -5.3$, and 7.62.

1. $y = 1.3x + 1.1$ 2. $y = 0.9x - 1.8$ 3. $y = -1.45x + 1.15$
   1.75; -5.79; 11.006   -1.15; -6.37; 5.258   0.425; 8.835; -9.899
4. $y = -0.82x - 1.56$ 5. $y = 2.11x - 0.75$ 6. $y = -0.09x + 4.8$
   -1.97; 2.786; -7.808   0.305; -11.933; 15.328   4.755; 5.277; 4.114

74 Technology Using Calculators and Computers   © D.C. Heath and Company

Also Available:

- Complete Solutions Manual
- Overhead Manipulatives Kit
- Computerized Testing Program

- **Interactive CD-ROM Projects**
  Interactive projects for solving real-world problems using multimedia
- **Interactions: Real Math–Real Careers**
  A videodisc–based resource that connects math to real careers and on-the-job problem solving
- **PACKETS® Performance Assessment for Middle School Mathematics**
  A program that links assessment and instruction

ASSESSMENT

Alternative Assessment

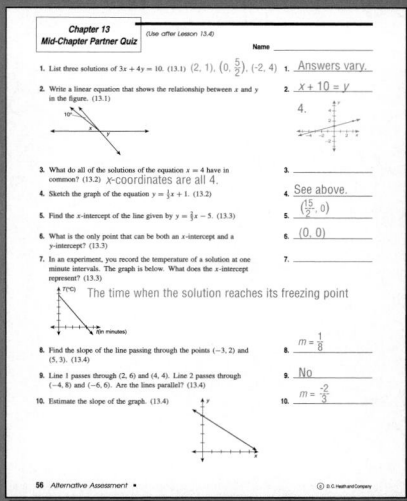

Alternative Assessment includes:
- Scoring Rubrics
- Portfolios
- Math Journals
- Projects
- Partner Quizzes
- Individual and Group Assessment

Formal Assessment

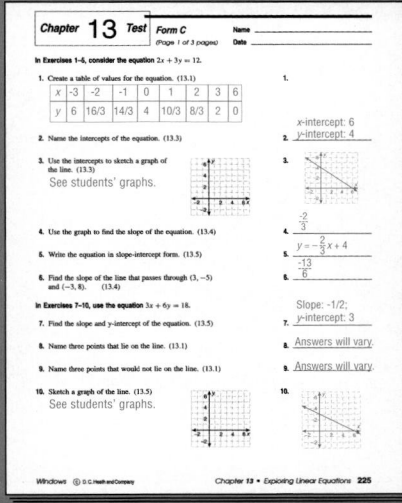

Formal Assessment includes:
- Short Quizzes (after every 2 lessons)
- Mid-Chapter Tests (2 forms)
- Chapter Tests (3 forms)
- Cumulative Tests (after every 3 Chapters)

MEETING INDIVIDUAL NEEDS

Extra Practice Copymasters

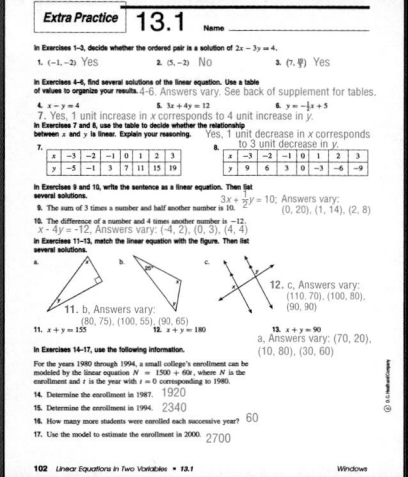

Reteaching Copymasters

Enrichment Projects

Math Log

Special Populations
Suggestions for providing equal access for:

Students Acquiring English Proficiency*
Students will find the lessons in this chapter easier to understand if they have opportunities to apply the concepts in real-life situations. Lesson 13.6 gives many real-life applications; however, students may need assistance with the vocabulary. Students can use maps to practice graphing ordered pairs and finding distance and midpoints.

Students with Various Learning Styles*
Provide students with plenty of graph paper. Strongly encourage students to use the graph paper to make their tables of values and to use rulers to draw all lines.

In finding the slope in the exercises of Lesson 13.4, students who benefit from a **tactile** approach may find it easier to plot the points rather than use the formula.

Underachieving Students*
Students who enjoy the graphing calculator activity on page 597 may want to check their work in Lesson 13.3 by using the zoom and trace functions to find the intercepts. Allow these students to experiment with graphing scatter plots on graphing calculators in Lesson 13.6.

Gifted and Talented Students*
Have groups of students use coordinate planes to graph data from newspapers, magazines, and books. Have students explain which sets of data have a linear relationship. Students should pick one set of data that has a linear relationship and draw a line that best fits the points. Then they should create real-life questions relating to the graph and give the answers. Students could then present this information to the class.

*See page T19 for descriptions of these special populations.

PACING CHART

About the Chapter

As has been emphasized throughout these teacher notes, the underlying purpose of building students' algebraic skills is the ability to model and solve real-life problems by writing, graphing, and solving an equation or inequality. Linear equations and inequalities in *one* variable have already been a topic of several chapters in this text, notably Chapters 4, 8, 9. This chapter, which strongly emphasizes coordinate geometry, takes a closer look at linear equations and inequalities in *two* variables.

Lessons 13.1 and 13.2 show students how to use a table of values to organize solutions of a given linear equation and how to graph the equation. The reverse process is also presented (in Example 2 of 13.2)—how to graph data from a given table and *find* an equation that fits or models the data. Lessons 13.3 and 13.4 explore two important features of a linear equation—intercepts (and how they can be used to sketch a quick graph of the equation) and slope. Lesson 13.5 teaches students how to identify the slope and *y*-intercept of a line from its equation and, based on these features, how to sketch a quick graph of the line. In Lesson 13.6, students revisit two distinct problem-solving techniques—the algebraic modeling plan and the scatter plot. Lesson 13.7 introduces students to solving and graphing linear inequalities in two variables and, finally, Lesson 13.8 offers students two further coordinate geometry formulas—the distance- and midpoint-formulas.

Exploring Linear Equations

LESSONS

Increased air pollution from motor-vehicle emissions has led to the passage of federal and state clean air laws which mandate alternatives to gasoline driven vehicles in the near future. The Aztec, a solar electric car developed by students at Massachusetts Institute of Technology, can travel 135 miles between charges at a top speed of 50 miles per hour.

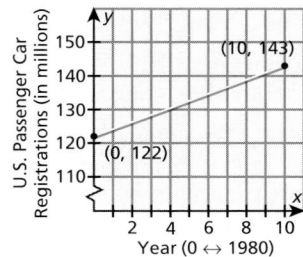

Real Life
Advanced Transportation

The *slope* of the graph of a nonvertical line describes how the line slants from left to right. In this chapter, you will learn how in real-life situations, slope is used to describe a constant, or average, rate of change; for example, the change in motor vehicle registrations over time.

The linear graph at the left shows the number of United States passenger car registrations from 1980 through 1990. Since the line slants upward, its slope is positive. The slope tells us that the average increase in car registrations from 1980 through 1990 was about 2.1 million cars per year.

$$\text{Slope} = \frac{\text{Change in } y\text{-values}}{\text{Change in } x\text{-values}}$$
$$= \frac{143 - 122}{10} = 2.1$$

Using the Page

Check whether students understand the graph by asking them to describe the change in the number of car registrations between 1984 and 1985, 1989 and 1990, 1980 and 1981. Car registrations increased by approximately 2 million.

Investigate further the relationship between the slope of the line and the change in car registrations over time by asking students what they could say about car registrations if the line was steeper, if the line was flatter but still slanted upward, if the line was flat, or if the line was slanted downward. Registrations increased more than 2 million per year, increased less than 2 million per year, stayed the same each year, decreased per year.

Multimedia Resources

Interactive CD-ROM Projects
A project for this chapter combines print, animation, sound and video presentations to capture students' interest in Mass Transportation. This interactive approach shows students how the math concepts and problem-solving strategies they are learning will be used in the future in dealing with important personal, national, and world issues.

The theme of Mass Transportation correlates to examples and exercises on pages 616, 618, 630.

Interactions: Real Math—Real Life
The theme of this chapter, Advanced Transportation, correlates with an episode of **Interactions** which is a videodisc-based multimedia resource that connects middle school math topics with real-life careers. In each of the twelve episodes, students go on-site with a variety of professionals to witness real-life applications of the math they are studying. Students see math concepts and problem-solving strategies in a context that helps them connect what they are studying to the world outside the classroom. **Interactions** was developed by the Foundation for Advancements in Science and Education (FASE) and is published by D.C. Heath and Company.

The theme of Advanced Transportation is continued throughout the chapter on pages 602, 616, 618, and 630.

Performance Assessment Resource
The PACKETS® Program: Performance Assessment for Middle School Mathematics was developed by Educational Testing Service and is published by D.C. Heath. **PACKETS** helps you assess your students' performances as they learn. You can use a wide variety of **PACKETS** Activity Units with this chapter because, in every activity, students will use ideas from all topic areas of mathematics. However, you can use the chart on page T16 to help you choose the **PACKETS** Activity Unit(s) that may fit best with this chapter.

PACING the Lesson

Suggested Number of Days
Basic/Average 0   Above Average 1
Advanced 1

PLANNING the Lesson

Lesson Plan 13.1, p. 102

ORGANIZER

Starters (reproduced below)
   Problem of the Day 13.1, p. 37
   Warm-Up Exercises 13.1, p. 37
Lesson Resources
   Color Transparencies
      Diagram for Example 2, p. 54
   Teaching Tools
      Graph paper, pp. T1, C2
   Math Log, p. 40
   Answer Masters 13.1, pp. 252, 253
   Extra Practice Copymaster 13.1, p. 102
   Reteaching Copymaster 13.1, p. 102
Special Populations
   Suggestions, Teacher's Edition, p. 586D

LESSON Notes

Have students define linear equations in their math journals and write both examples and nonexamples. Ask them to indicate why their nonexamples are not linear. For example, $y = x + 2$ is a linear equation; $y^2 = x + 4$ is not a linear equation because the y has an exponent greater than one; $x + 2y$ is not a linear equation because it is not an equation.

   Ask students to explain why $y = \frac{1}{x}$ is not a linear equation.   This is the same as $y = x^{-1}$, so the exponent on x is not 1.   Remind students that π is not a variable but is a number.

Example 1

Have students choose other values for x to illustrate that many different numbers can be substituted for x.

13.1 Linear Equations in Two Variables

What you should learn:

Goal 1 How to find solutions of a linear equation in two variables

Goal 2 How to organize solutions of real-life problems using linear equations

Why you should learn it:

You can use linear equations in two variables to solve real-life problems, such as comparing Fahrenheit and Celsius temperature scales.

Goal 1 ## Solutions of Linear Equations

In this chapter, you will study **linear equations** in two variables. Here are some examples.

$$y = 2x + 1 \qquad C = \pi d \qquad A = 1.06P$$

In a linear equation, variables occur only to the first power. Equations such as $A = \pi r^2$ and $V = s^3$ are not linear.

On page 136, you learned that an ordered pair (x, y) is a **solution** of an equation involving x and y if the equation is true when the values of x and y are substituted into the equation. Most equations involving two variables have many solutions. For instance, three solutions of $y = x + 3$ are shown below.

Equation	Solution (x, y)	Check by Substituting
$y = x + 3$	$(1, 4)$	$4 = 1 + 3$
$y = x + 3$	$(2, 5)$	$5 = 2 + 3$
$y = x + 3$	$(3, 6)$	$6 = 3 + 3$

To find solutions of linear equations in two variables, choose a value for one of the variables, substitute that value into the equation, and then solve for the other variable.

Example 1 *Finding Solutions of Linear Equations*

List several solutions of $2x + y = 10$.

x-Value	y-Value	Solution
0	10	$(0, 10)$
1	8	$(1, 8)$
2	6	$(2, 6)$
3	4	$(3, 4)$

Solution   Begin by choosing values of x. Substitute each value into the equation and solve the resulting equation for y.

Choose an x-Value	Substitute for x	Solve for y	Solution
$x = 0$	$2(0) + y = 10$	$y = 10$	$(0, 10)$
$x = 1$	$2(1) + y = 10$	$y = 8$	$(1, 8)$
$x = 2$	$2(2) + y = 10$	$y = 6$	$(2, 6)$
$x = 3$	$2(3) + y = 10$	$y = 4$	$(3, 4)$

A **table of values** like that shown at the left can help you organize solutions that you have found.

STARTER: Problem of the Day

The last seven sightings of Halley's comet are listed in the table. The data follow a linear pattern. Examine the pattern and predict the date of the next (eighth) sighting. How old will you then be?

(S) Sighting	(Y) Year	(S) Sighting	(Y) Year
1	1531	5	1835
2	1607	6	1910
3	1682	7	1986
4	1758	8	?

2061; most students will be about 80.

Also available as a copymaster, p. 37

STARTER: Warm-Up Exercises

1. Give the ordered pairs that name points *A*, *B*, and *C*.

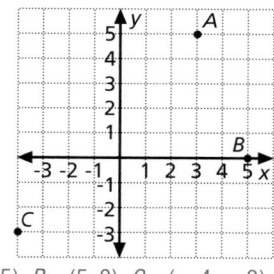

$A = (3, 5)$, $B = (5, 0)$, $C = (-4, -3)$

2. Write three equations for which the ordered pair (0, 7) is a solution.

Answers will vary.

Also available as a copymaster, p. 37

Solving Real-Life Problems

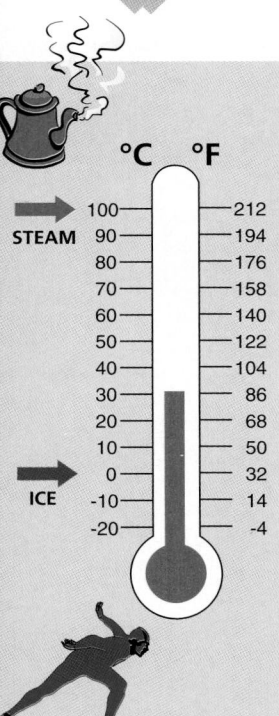

Real Life
Temperature

°C   °F

100 ——— 212
STEAM 90 ——— 194
80 ——— 176
70 ——— 158
60 ——— 140
50 ——— 122
40 ——— 104
30 ——— 86
20 ——— 68
10 ——— 50
0 ——— 32
ICE -10 ——— 14
-20 ——— -4

Example 2   *Problem Solving: Organizing Solutions*

The relationship between Fahrenheit temperature F and Celsius temperature C is given by the linear equation

$$F = \tfrac{9}{5}C + 32.$$

You are designing a poster to help people convert between the two temperature scales. Which temperatures would you use as samples on the poster?

Solution   There are several possible temperatures that would be good to use. For instance, on the Celsius scale, water freezes at 0° and boils at 100°. On the Fahrenheit scale, 68° is a comfortable temperature and -4° is very cold.

To find values of F that correspond to values of C, use the following steps.

C-Value	Substitute	Solve for *F*	Solution
$C = 0$	$F = \tfrac{9}{5}(0) + 32$	$F = 32$	$(0, 32)$
$C = 100$	$F = \tfrac{9}{5}(100) + 32$	$F = 212$	$(100, 212)$

To find values of C that correspond to values of F, use the following steps.

F-Value	Substitute	Solve for *C*	Solution
$F = 68$	$68 = \tfrac{9}{5}C + 32$	$C = 20$	$(20, 68)$
$F = -4$	$-4 = \tfrac{9}{5}C + 32$	$C = -20$	$(-20, -4)$

After finding several other temperatures, you could represent them with a poster like that shown at the left. ■

Communicating about **MATHEMATICS**

Cooperative Learning

▶ **SHARING IDEAS about the Lesson**

Mental Math Work with a partner. Here are two rules that people use to mentally change between Fahrenheit and Celsius temperatures. Apply the rules to the temperatures in Example 2. How are the two rules related to each other?

A. To change from Celsius to Fahrenheit, divide by 5, multiply by 9, and add 32.

B. To change from Fahrenheit to Celsius, subtract 32, divide by 9, and multiply by 5.

The rules consist of opposite operations done in reverse order.

13.1 • *Linear Equations in Two Variables*   **589**

Explain that linear equations with two variables can be used to show relationships between two quantities. For example, if a job pays $5 per hour, then $p = 5h$ is a linear equation that shows the relationship between pay (p) and number of hours worked (h). Challenge students to give other examples from real life of linear relationships between quantities.

Example 2

Note that in the solutions for the example, C corresponds to the x-coordinate and F corresponds to the y-coordinate. For example:

(0, 32)
↑ ↑
C F

Have students name other temperatures with which most people are familiar. Include these examples on a poster constructed by students.
Answers will vary but might include body temperature.

Communicating about **MATHEMATICS**

MENTAL MATH
To quickly estimate the conversion from Celsius to Fahrenheit, use the fact that $\tfrac{9}{5}$ is approximately $\tfrac{10}{5}$, or 2. If you double a temperature given in Celsius then add 32, your estimate will be a little high.

To quickly estimate a conversion from Fahrenheit to Celsius, use the fact that $\tfrac{5}{9}$ is slightly more than $\tfrac{5}{10}$, or $\tfrac{1}{2}$. If you subtract 32 from a temperature given in Fahrenheit then halve the result, your estimate will be a little low. Apply these estimation rules to the temperatures in Example 2.

Writing Prompt
Write one sentence that describes a linear equation.

OPTION: Extra Examples

Here is an additional example similar to Example 1.
Finding Solutions of Linear Equations
List several solutions of $x + 3y = 14$.
Solution
Begin by choosing values of x. Substitute each value into the equation and solve the resulting equation for y.

Choose an *x* value	Substitute for *x*	Solve for *y*	Solution
$x = 8$	$8 + 3y = 14$	$y = 2$	$(8, 2)$
$x = 5$	$5 + 3y = 14$	$y = 3$	$(5, 3)$
$x = 2$	$2 + 3y = 14$	$y = 4$	$(2, 4)$
$x = -1$	$-1 + 3y = 14$	$y = 5$	$(-1, 5)$

ASSIGNMENT GUIDE

*Basic/Average:
Day 1: Ex. 5–19 odd, 21–23
Day 2: Ex. 24–27, 29–33 odd
Above Average:
Ex. 5–13 odd, 24–30, 32, 33
Advanced: Ex. 5–19 odd, 24–30, 32, 33
Selected Answers: Ex. 1–4, 5–31 odd

*You may wish to omit this lesson for these students.

Guided Practice

Use these exercises as an in-class check for solution format. Have students discuss which exercises can be done using mental math and which exercises require pencil and paper.

Independent Practice

▶ **Ex. 9–12** Help students develop a systematic plan for locating solutions (for example: choose $x = 0, 1, 2$ and find the corresponding y values).
▶ **Ex. 15, 16** You may wish to refer students to Lessons 2.6 and 2.7.
▶ **Ex. 17–20** Use these exercises as an in-class small-group activity that reviews some of the geometry of Chapter 10.

Guided Practice

▶ **CHECK for Understanding**

1. Which of the following are solutions of $2x + 3y = 7$? Explain.   b, $2 \cdot 2 + 3 \cdot 1 = 7$;
   a. $(1, 2)$ **b.** $(2, 1)$ c, $2 \cdot 5 + 3(-1) = 7$
   c. $(5, -1)$ **d.** $(4, -1)$

2. Which of the following equations are linear? Explain.
b, c, and d; variables occur to the first power only.
   a. $A = \pi r^2$ **b.** $C = 2\pi r$
   c. $r + \frac{1}{2}t = 30$ **d.** $100 - 6p = S$

In Exercises 3 and 4, complete the table of values showing solutions of the equation.

3. $y = x + 5$ **4.** $2x - y = 4$

x	-3	-2	-1	0	1	2	3
y	?	?	?	?	?	?	?

3.   2   3   4   5   6   7   8
4. -10 -8 -6 -4 -2 0   2

Independent Practice

In Exercises 5–8, decide whether the ordered pair is a solution of $7x - y = 5$.

5. $(0, -5)$ Yes   **6.** $(2, 1)$ No   **7.** $(-1, 12)$ No   **8.** $\left(\frac{1}{2}, -\frac{3}{2}\right)$ Yes

In Exercises 9–12, find several solutions of the linear equation. Use a table of values to organize your results.   See margin.

9. $x + y = 6$ **10.** $x + 2y = 13$ **11.** $6x + 2y = 24$ **12.** $y = \frac{1}{3}x + 2$

Describing Patterns   **In Exercises 13 and 14, use the table to decide**   For explanations, see margin.
whether the relationship between x and y is linear. Explain your reasoning.

13.

x	-3	-2	-1	0	1	2	3
y	15	13	11	9	7	5	3

Yes

14.

No

x	-3	-2	-1	0	1	2	3
y	1	2	4	7	11	16	22

In Exercises 15 and 16, write the sentence as a linear equation. Then list several solutions.   For solutions, see margin.

15. The difference of 6 times a number and 4 times another number is 12. $6x - 4y = 12$

16. The sum of half a number and twice another number is 54. $\frac{1}{2}x + 2y = 54$

Geometry   **In Exercises 17–20, match the linear equation with the figure. Then list several solutions.**   For solutions, see margin.

a. 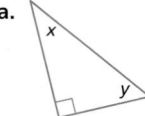   **b.** 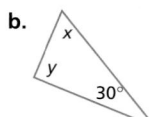   **c.** 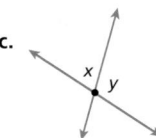   **d.**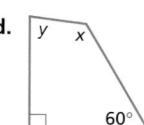

⭐ **17.** $x + y = 150°$ b   ⭐ **18.** $x + y = 210°$ d   ⭐ **19.** $x + y = 180°$ c   ⭐ **20.** $x + y = 90°$ a

⭐ More difficult exercises

Answers

9.

x	-3	-2	-1	0	1	2	3
y	9	8	7	6	5	4	3

10.

x	-3	-2	-1	0	1	2	3
y	8	$7\frac{1}{2}$	7	$6\frac{1}{2}$	6	$5\frac{1}{2}$	5

11.

x	-3	-2	-1	0	1	2	3
y	21	18	15	12	9	6	3

12.

x	-3	-2	-1	0	1	2	3
y	1	$\frac{4}{3}$	$\frac{5}{3}$	2	$\frac{7}{3}$	$\frac{8}{3}$	3

13. For every increase by 1 of x, there is a constant corresponding decrease by 2 of y.
14. For every increase by 1 of x, there is *not* a constant corresponding decrease of y.
15. $(2, 0), (0, -3), (4, 3)$
16. $(108, 0), (0, 27), (20, 22)$
17. $(100°, 50°), (50°, 100°), (75°, 75°)$
18. $(200°, 10°), (10°, 200°), (105°, 105°)$
19. $(100°, 80°), (80°, 100°), (90°, 90°)$
20. $(60°, 30°), (30°, 60°), (45°, 45°)$

Extra Practice

Reteaching

Unit Conversions In Exercises 21–23, use the equation $y = 2.54x$ which relates a centimeter measurement, y, to an inch measurement, x.

21. How long, in centimeters, is a 12-inch ruler?   30.48 cm

22. How long, in inches, is a 100-centimeter ruler?   ≈39.37 in.

23. Create a table to help convert between inches and centimeters.   See margin.

Children's Books   **In Exercises 24–27, use the following information.**

For 1987 through 1992, the amount A (in billions of dollars) spent each year on children's books in the United States can be modeled by the linear equation $A = 0.87 + 0.2t$ where $t = 1$ corresponds to 1987. *(Source: Book Industry Group, Inc.)*

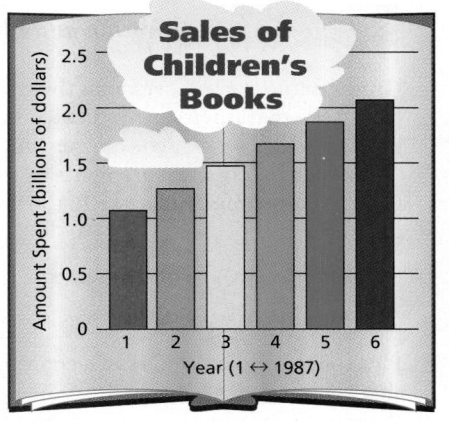

24. How much was spent in 1987? $1.07 billion

25. How much was spent in 1992? $2.07 billion

26. How much more was spent each year? $200 million

27. Use the graph to estimate the amount spent in 1996. Use the algebraic model to confirm your answer.
$2.87 billion

In Exercises 28 and 29, determine whether the equations have the same solutions. Explain your reasoning.   For explanations, see margin.

28. $3x + 5y = 16$ Yes
$12x + 20y = 64$

29. $9x - 2y = 18$ No
$18x - 4y = 30$

30. *Think about It*   Does a linear equation in two variables have a *finite* or an *infinite* number of solutions? Write a paragraph explaining your answer.   Infinite. Explanations vary.

Integrated Review   *Making Connections within Mathematics*

31. *Tables and Solutions*   Complete the table of values for the equation $x + y = 4$.

x	−3	−2	−1	0	1	2	3
y	?	?	?	?	?	?	?

7, 6, 5, 4, 3, 2, 1

32. *Scatter Plots and Patterns*   Construct a scatter plot for the data in Exercise 31. Describe the pattern.   For scatter plot, see margin.
For every increase of 1 by x, there is a corresponding decrease of 1 by y.

Exploration and Extension

33. *Finding a Pattern*   Consider the ordered pairs $\{(1, 3), (2, 5), (3, 7), (4, 9), (5, 11)\}$.
  a. In each ordered pair, how are x and y related? y is 1 more than twice x.
  b. How can you express this relationship as a linear equation? $y = 2x + 1$

Enrichment

The first four terms of a dot pattern are listed below.
How many dots are in the 5th term, the 10th term, and the nth term?
33, 73, $8n - 7$

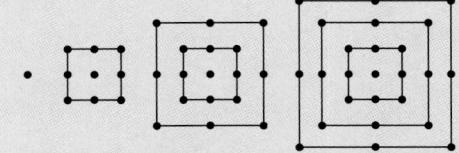

▶ **Ex. 24–27**   Use the bar graph data for these exercises to draw a scatter plot using an overhead graphing calculator. Use the line of best fit to model solutions for the students.
▶ **Ex. 30**
MATH JOURNAL
Use this exercise as a journal activity.

Integrated Review
This section provides students with an opportunity to revisit the material of Lessons 5.6 and 5.7.

Exploration and Extension
Have students find a *visual* pattern by graphing the ordered pairs.

Portfolio Opportunity: Math Log

Which of the following relationships are linear? Explain your answers.
a. The Pythagorean Theorem for a right triangle with a 10-inch hypotenuse.
b. The formula for the sum of the interior angles of a polygon with n sides.
c. The volume of a cylinder with a radius of 2.

Also available as a copymaster, page 40, Ex. 1

Answers

23.

in.	0.39	0.79	1	1.18	1.57
cm	1	2	2.54	3	4
in.	1.97	2	2.36	2.76	3
cm	5	5.08	6	7	7.62

28. When you divide both sides of the second equation by 4, you get the first equation.
29. When you divide both sides of the second equation by 2, you get $9x - 2y = 15$. Since the first equation is $9x - 2y = 18$, the expression $9x - 2y$ is equal to two different numbers.
32.

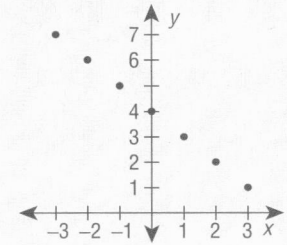

Materials
Teaching Tools
   Graph paper, pp. T1, C2

This investigation is a fun in-class paired lab activity.

The ordered pairs (foot, forearm) and (span, height) should all occur near the $y = x$ line. The ordered pairs (thumb, wrist) and (wrist, neck) should all occur near the $y = 2x$ line.

EXTENSION
Have students also plot the ordered pair (neck, waist).

Materials Needed: graph paper, measuring tape

Example   *Gathering and Plotting Data*

Group Activity Each person in the group should record the measurements indicated in the figure below. (You can use inches or centimeters, but make each pair of measurements in the same units.) Use the measurements to write the following four ordered pairs.

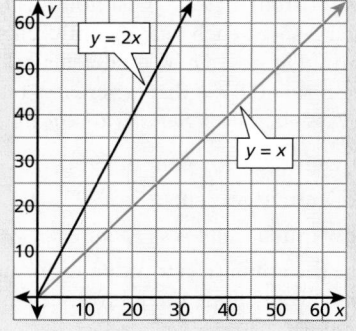

   (Span, Height)   (Foot, Forearm)

   (Thumb, Wrist),   (Wrist, Neck)

Plot the four ordered pairs in a coordinate plane like that shown at the right. Include the two lines. Everyone in the group should plot his or her measurements on the same coordinate plane.

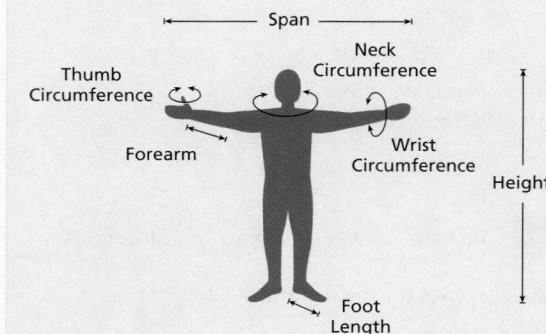

Exercises

1. *Group Activity*   Discuss any patterns you find in the points that your group plotted.   Answers vary.

2. Which of the points tended to fall on or near the line that is labeled $y = x$? How do the x- and the y-coordinates of points on this line compare?   (Span, Height), (Foot, Forearm); they are nearly equal.

3. Which of the points tended to fall on or near the line that is labeled $y = 2x$? How do the x- and the y-coordinates of points on this line compare?   (Thumb, Wrist), (Wrist, Neck); the y-coordinate is about twice the x-coordinate.

13.2

Exploring Graphs of Linear Equations

 What you should learn:

Goal 1 How to use a table of values to sketch the graph of a linear equation

Goal 2 How to recognize graphs of horizontal and vertical lines

 Why you should learn it:

You can use graphs of linear equations to help you recognize relationships between two variables, such as the relationship between the year and the enrollment in a class.

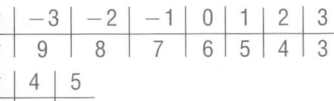

The points lie on a line.

Goal 1 **Graphing Linear Equations**

LESSON INVESTIGATION

■ **Investigating Graphs of Linear Equations**

Group Activity Use the techniques you studied in Lesson 13.1 to find several solutions of the equation $y = 6 - x$. Use x-values of $-3, -2, -1, 0, 1, 2, 3, 4$, and 5. Organize the nine solutions in a table of values. Then plot all nine solutions in a coordinate plane. What do you notice about the points? See answer at the left.

In this investigation, you may have discovered that all the solution points lie on a line.

> **Graph of a Linear Equation**
>
> The **graph** of an equation is the graph of all its solutions. The graph of every linear equation is a line.

Example 1 *Graphing a Linear Equation*

Sketch the graph of $y = 2x - 2$.

Solution Begin by making a table of values.

x-Value	Substitute	Solve for y	Solution
$x = -2$	$y = 2(-2) - 2$	$y = -6$	$(-2, -6)$
$x = -1$	$y = 2(-1) - 2$	$y = -4$	$(-1, -4)$
$x = 0$	$y = 2(0) - 2$	$y = -2$	$(0, -2)$
$x = 1$	$y = 2(1) - 2$	$y = 0$	$(1, 0)$
$x = 2$	$y = 2(2) - 2$	$y = 2$	$(2, 2)$
$x = 3$	$y = 2(3) - 2$	$y = 4$	$(3, 4)$

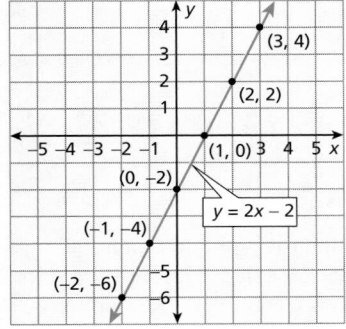

Plot the solutions in a coordinate plane. Finally, draw a line through the points. The line is the graph of the equation. ■

13.2 • *Exploring Graphs of Linear Equations* **593**

PACING the Lesson

Suggested Number of Days
Basic/Average 0   **Above Average** 1
Advanced 1

PLANNING the Lesson

Lesson Plan 13.2, p. 103

ORGANIZER

Starters (reproduced below)
  Problem of the Day 13.2, p. 37
  Warm-Up Exercises 13.2, p. 37
Lesson Resources
  Color Transparencies
    Picture for Ex. 32, 33, p. 54
  Teaching Tools
    Coordinate plane, pp. T8, C10
    Coordinate planes, pp. T9, C11
  Math Log, p. 40
  Technology, p. 74
  Answer Masters 13.2, pp. 254–256
  Extra Practice Copymaster 13.2, p. 103
  Reteaching Copymaster 13.2, p. 103
  Enrichment Projects, pp. 67, 68
Special Populations
  Suggestions, Teacher's Edition, p. 586D

LESSON Notes

Linear equations with two variables represent relationships between two quantities. A table can be used to display pairs of numbers that satisfy linear equations. Call attention to the term linear equation and the observation that the graph of a linear equation is a straight line.

Historical Note
As the French mathematician Rene Descartes one day lay ill in bed, he noticed a fly on the ceiling. He wondered whether the fly moved when he wasn't watching it. Since the ceiling was made of square tiles, he decided he could "fix" the fly's position by counting tiles over and up from a reference point. When he recovered from his illness, he formalized this system. It is now called the Cartesian Coordinate system.

Lesson Investigation
Repeat the investigation with other linear equations. This will provide more evidence that the graph of any linear equation is a straight line.

Example 1

Help students see that if they arrive at a solution to a linear equation that does not lie in the same line as the graph of the other solutions, then they have made an error. Ask students how many solutions would be needed in order to use the above method as a check.   At least three solutions

---

STARTER: Problem of the Day

Adam is thinking of a number. If he multiplies the number by 3 and adds 11, he gets the same answer as he would if he had multiplied the number by 4 and subtracted 4. What is his number?   15

Also available as a copymaster, p. 37

STARTER: Warm-Up Exercises

1. Complete the ordered pair solutions for the equation $2x + 4y = 0$.
a. $(0, ?)$ **b.** $(?, 3)$ **c.** $(5, ?)$
d. $(?, -1)$ **e.** $(-2, ?)$
a. 0, **b.** -6, **c.** $-\frac{5}{2}$, **d.** 2, **e.** 1

2. Plot the following points on a coordinate plane.
a. $(-4, -3)$ **b.** $(9, -5)$ **c.** $(-12, 8)$
Check students' work.

Also available as a copymaster, p. 37

When a line is horizontal, the relationship between x and y is such that x can be any number, while y remains the same in every ordered pair solution. Thus, the linear equation of a horizontal line only needs to specify the fixed value of y. For example, the horizontal line $y = 3$ contains ordered pairs of the form $(x, 3)$.

Similarly, when a line is vertical, x is the same in every ordered pair solution, so the equation of a vertical line needs only to specify the fixed value of x. For example, the vertical line $x = 5$ contains ordered pairs of the form $(5, y)$.

Example 2

Point out to students that the process shown here is the reverse of that presented in Example 1, where the equation was *given* and, based on the equation, a table of values was constructed. Here, a given table of values (real-life data) is used to construct a graph and, based on the graph, an equation is written. This process is typically applied in data analysis.

Communicating about MATHEMATICS

The point of intersection has coordinates that satisfy both equations. Have students explain why this point satisfies both equations. Ask: Could more than one point satisfy two different equations?

Writing Prompt

In your own words, explain how to sketch the graph of an equation.

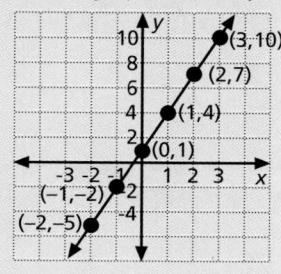

Goal 2   Horizontal and Vertical Lines

Some linear equations, such as $x = 3$, have just one variable. All solutions of this equation are of the form $(3, y)$. For instance, the points $(3, -2)$, $(3, -1.5)$, $(3, -1)$, $(3, 0)$, $(3, 0.5)$, and $(3, 2)$ are solutions of the equation. If you plot these points, you will notice that they lie on a vertical line.

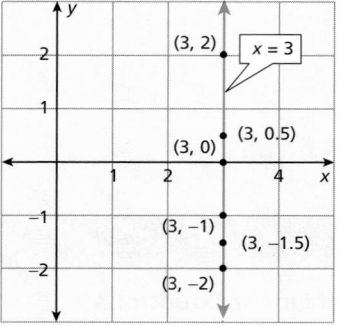

Graphs of Linear Equations in One Variable

1. The graph of the equation $x = a$ is a vertical line that passes through the point $(a, 0)$.
2. The graph of the equation $y = b$ is a horizontal line that passes through the point $(0, b)$.

Real Life
Education

Example 2   *Plotting Data*

The enrollments of two classes, Class A and Class B, for 1985 through 1995 are shown in the table. Let $t = 0$ represent 1985. Plot the data and describe the pattern.

t	0	1	2	3	4	5	6	7	8	9	10
A	36	36	36	36	36	36	36	36	36	36	36
B	31	32	33	34	35	36	37	38	39	40	41

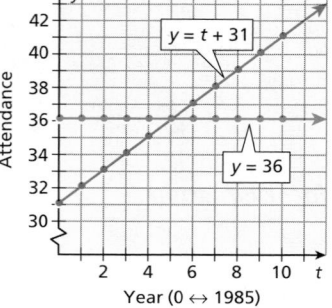

Solution   Begin by writing the data as ordered pairs. Then plot the points in a coordinate plane, as shown at the left. From the graphs, you can see that each class's enrollment is represented by a line. For Class A, the line is horizontal because the enrollment did not change. For Class B, the line is not horizontal—it slopes upward because the enrollment is increasing. The enrollment for each class can be modeled by a linear equation.

$y = 36$ *Class A*
$y = t + 31$ *Class B*   ∎

Communicating about MATHEMATICS

▶ **SHARING IDEAS about the Lesson**

Finding Points of Intersection   Find the point at which the two graphs in Example 2 intersect. Then interpret this point of intersection verbally in the context of the example.

(5, 36) The classes had the same enrollment in 1990.

OPTION: Extra Examples

Here is an additional example similar to Example 1.
Graphing a Linear Equation
Sketch the graph of $y = 3x + 1$.
Solution
Begin by making a table of values.

Plot the solutions in a coordinate plane. Finally, draw a line through the points. The line is the graph of the equation.

Choose an x value	Substitute for x	Solve for y	Solution
$x = -2$	$y = 3(-2) + 1$	$y = -5$	$(-2, -5)$
$x = -1$	$y = 3(-1) + 1$	$y = -2$	$(-1, -2)$
$x = 0$	$y = 3(0) + 1$	$y = 1$	$(0, 1)$
$x = 1$	$y = 3(1) + 1$	$y = 4$	$(1, 4)$
$x = 2$	$y = 3(2) + 1$	$y = 7$	$(2, 7)$
$x = 3$	$y = 3(3) + 1$	$y = 10$	$(3, 10)$

EXERCISES

Guided Practice

▶ **CHECK for Understanding**

See Example 1 on page 593.

1. *Writing*   In your own words, explain how to sketch the graph of an equation.

In Exercises 2–4, match the equation with the description of its graph.

a. Horizontal line   **b.** Vertical line   **c.** Slanted line

2. $2x + 3y = 8$ c   **3.** $y = 4$ a   **4.** $x = -2$ b

In Exercises 5–8, sketch the graph of the equation.   See margin.

5. $y = 5$ **6.** $x = -4$ **7.** $y = 3x - 1$ **8.** $x + y = 8$

Independent Practice

In Exercises 9–12, match each equation with its graph.

a. 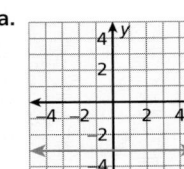   **b.** 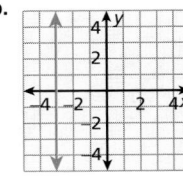   **c.** 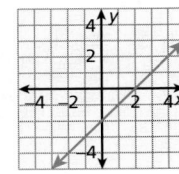   **d.**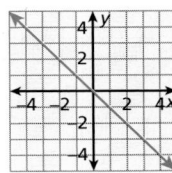

9. $y = x - 2$ c   **10.** $y = -x$ d   **11.** $y = -3$ a   **12.** $x = -3$ b

In Exercises 13–18, decide whether the ordered pair is a solution to the equation. If not, find a solution.   Solutions vary.

No, (2, 4)

13. $(0, 4)$; $x - y = 4$ No, $(0, -4)$ **14.** $(2, 5)$; $y = 7 - x$ Yes   **15.** $(-2, 4)$; $y = 8 - 2x$

16. $(1, -1)$; $y - 3x = 4$ **17.** $(-2, 9)$; $y = -5x - 1$ Yes   **18.** $(1, -3)$; $y = -3$ Yes

No, $(-1, 1)$

In Exercises 19–24, sketch the graph of the equation.   See Additional Answers.

19. $y = x + 4$ **20.** $y = 2x - 6$ **21.** $y = -1$

22. $x = \frac{3}{2}$ **23.** $y = \frac{x}{3}$ **24.** $y = \frac{1}{2}x - 5$

Points of Intersection   **In Exercises 25–27, graph both equations on the same coordinate plane. Then find the point of intersection of the two lines.**   For graphs, see Additional Answers.

25. $x + y = -2$ $(1, -3)$ **26.** $y = 6x + 14$ $(-2, 2)$ **27.** $x = -5$ $(-5, -4)$
$\quad y = x - 4$ $\quad y = 8 + 3x$ $\quad y = -4$

28. The point $(2, 5)$ lies on the graph of $y = cx + 1$. What is the value of c?   2

⭐ **29.** The point $(3, 4)$ lies on the graph of $y = cx - 8$. What is the value of c?   4

⭐ More difficult exercises

Extra Practice

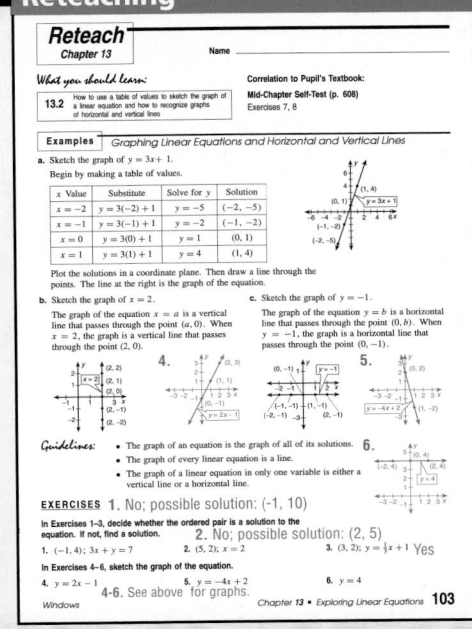

ASSIGNMENT GUIDE

*Basic/Average:
Day 1: Ex. 9–27 odd
Day 2: Ex. 28–30, 35–41 odd

Above Average:
Ex. 9–27 odd, 28–31, 33, 36–41

Advanced: Ex. 9–27 odd, 28–31, 33, 36–41

Selected Answers: Ex. 1–8, 9–37 odd

*You may wish to omit this lesson for these students.

Guided Practice

Use these exercises as an in-class summary activity to check for students' readiness for the Independent Practice exercises.

Independent Practice

▶ **Ex. 19–24, 28** and **29**   Use these exercises as an in-class small-group activity

Answers

5.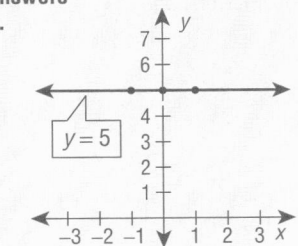

6.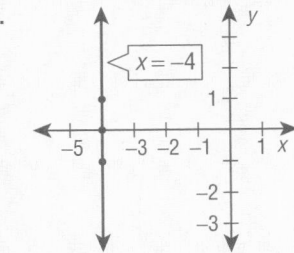

7.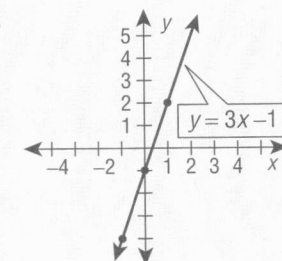

8.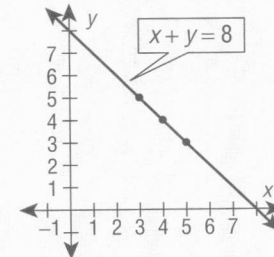

Integrated Review

Assign these exercises as a paired lab activity.

Exploration and Extension

By examining the pattern of change in the data, students can observe the linear relationships without knowing the concepts of slope or y-intercept. Before assigning these exercises, it would be helpful to do a similar one in class.

Portfolio Opportunity: Math Log

When graphing a linear equation in two variables, it is standard practice to choose values for *x* and solve for *y*. Will you get the same line if you choose values for *y* and solve for *x*? Demonstrate your answer with an example.

Also available as a copymaster, page 40, Ex. 2

Short Quiz

Covers Lessons 13.1 and 13.2

Available as a copymaster, page 213

---

30. *Geometry*   Sketch the graphs of the equations on the same coordinate plane. Which two lines are parallel?   For graphs, see Additional Answers.
  a. $y = 2x + 3$ **b.** $y = x + 3$ **c.** $y = 2x - 1$ a and c

31. In the coordinate plane, the graphs of $x = 0$ and $y = 0$ have special names. What are these names?   y-axis, x-axis

32. *Population*   For 1985 through 1989, the population P (in millions) of Oklahoma is given in the table. Let $t = 0$ represent 1985. Plot the data and describe the pattern. Is the pattern linear? Explain. *(Source: U.S. Bureau of the Census)*   See Additional Answers.

t	0	1	2	3	4
P	3.27	3.24	3.21	3.18	3.15

33. *Temperature*   The average daily temperature of Oklahoma City (in degrees Fahrenheit) from January through August is given in the table. Create a table so that the data can be graphed on a coordinate plane. Then plot the data and describe the pattern. Is the pattern linear? Explain. *(Source: U.S. National Oceanic and Atmospheric Administration)*   See Additional Answers.

Jan.	Feb.	Mar.	Apr.	May	June	July	Aug.
35.9	40.9	50.3	60.4	68.4	76.7	82.0	81.1

The Oklahoma state bird is the scissor-tailed flycatcher. It can catch insects in midair.

Integrated Review   **Making Connections within Mathematics**

For graphs, see Additional Answers.

Graphing Polygons   In Exercises 34–37, sketch the graphs of the equations on the same coordinate plane. What figure is formed by the graphs?

Parallelogram

34. $x = 3, x = -6, y = 1, y = -8$ Square   **35.** $y = 5, y = -5, y = 3x + 4, y = 3x - 4$

36. $y = -6, y = x, y = -x$ **37.** $y = -1, y = 4, y = 2x + 7, y = 7 - 2x$
Isosceles right triangle   Isosceles trapezoid

Exploration and Extension

Finding an Equation   In Exercises 38–41, create a table of values that   See margin.
represents the given graph. Describe the relationship between *x* and *y*.
Then write an equation that represents the relationship.

✪ **38.**   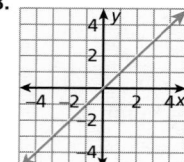   ✪ **39.**   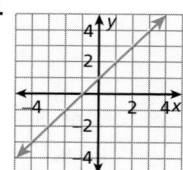   ✪ **40.**   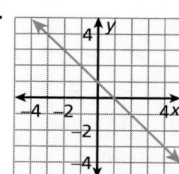   ✪ **41.**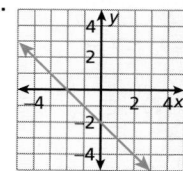

596   *Chapter 13 • Exploring Linear Equations*   ✪ More difficult exercises

---

Answers
38.–41. Answers vary.
38.

x	−2	−1	0	1	2
y	−2	−1	0	1	2

y equals x.
y = x

39.

x	−2	−1	0	1	2
y	−1	0	1	2	3

y is 1 more than x.
y = x + 1

40.

x	−2	−1	0	1	2
y	3	2	1	0	−1

x plus y equals 1.
x + y = 1

41.

x	−2	−1	0	1	2
y	0	−1	−2	−3	−4

x plus y equals −2.
x + y = −2

► **Enrichment**

Use a graphing calculator to graph $y = 2x$ and $y = 2^x$. Use the Trace or Zoom feature to find the points of intersection. The *x*-values are solutions of the equation $2x = 2^x$.   (1, 2) and (2, 4)

A graphing calculator can be used to sketch the graph of an equation. The following steps show how to use a Texas Instruments TI-82, a Casio *fx-7700G*, and a Sharp EL-9300C to sketch the graph of $y = 1.5x - 2$, as shown at the right. With each calculator, you must be sure the equation is in the form

$y = ($ expression involving $x)$.

You must also set the range by entering the least and greatest x and y values that you want to be used and the scale (units per tick mark). *

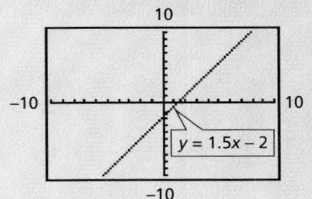

TI-82

WINDOW (Set range.)
  Xmin = −10
  Xmax = 10.
  Xscl = 1
  Ymin = −10
  Ymax = 10
  Yscl = 1
Y= 1.5 X, T, θ − 2
  :Y₁ = 1.5X − 2
  :Y₂ =
  :Y₃ =
  :Y₄ =
GRAPH
CLEAR (Clear Screen)

Casio *fx-7700G*

RANGE (Set range.)
  Xmin = −10
  max = 10
  scl = 1
  Ymin = −10
  max = 10
  scl = 1
EXE RANGE
SHIFT F5 (Cls) EXE
GRAPH 1.5 X, θ, T − 2
  Graph Y = 1.5X − 2
EXE
SHIFT F5 (Cls) EXE

Sharp EL-9300C

⊞
Y₁= 1.5 X/θ/T − 2
  Y₁ = 1.5X − 2 ENTER
RANGE (Set range.)
  Xmin = −10
  Xmax = 10
  Xscl = 1
  Ymin = −10
  Ymax = 10
  Yscl = 1
⊞
MENU A 1 CL

Exercises

In Exercises 1–4, sketch the graph. (Use the range shown above.) See margin.

1. $y = 2x - 3$ **2.** $y = 0.5x + 4$ **3.** $y = x - 5$ **4.** $y = 0.75x - 2$

In Exercises 5–8, sketch the graph. (Use the indicated range.) See margin.

5. $y = x + 20$
  Xmin = −10
  Xmax = 10
  Xscl = 1
  Ymin = −5
  Ymax = 35
  Yscl = 5

6. $y = 2x - 30$
  Xmin = −10
  Xmax = 10
  Xscl = 1
  Ymin = −60
  Ymax = 10
  Yscl = 5

7. $y = 10x + 200$
  Xmin = 0
  Xmax = 100
  Xscl = 10
  Ymin = 0
  Ymax = 1300
  Yscl = 100

8. $y = -75x + 2000$
  Xmin = 0
  Xmax = 20
  Xscl = 2
  Ymin = 0
  Ymax = 2100
  Yscl = 100

* Keystrokes for other calculators are listed in *Technology—Keystrokes for Other Graphing Calculators* found at the end of this text.

The ZOOM and TRACE features on the TI-82 and the SHARP EL-9300C and the TRACE feature on the Casio fx-7700GE and fx-9700GE allow you to enlarge the screen and find the coordinates of points on the line. As an introduction to Lesson 13.3, have students find the coordinates of the x- and y-intercepts for each graph using these features before they clear the screen.

Refer to pages 74 and 75 of the Technology supplement for further direction on how to use the ZOOM and TRACE features.

Answers
1.
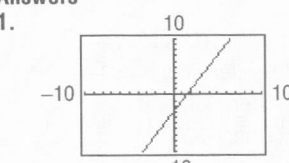

2.
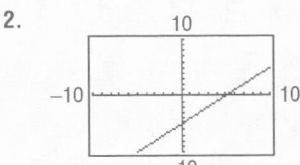

3.
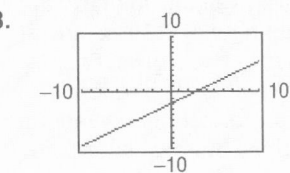

4.
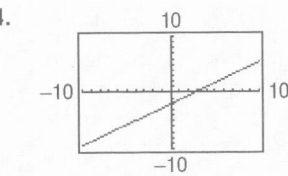

5.
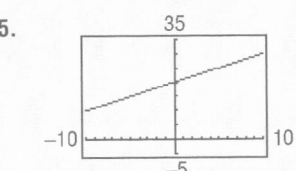

6.
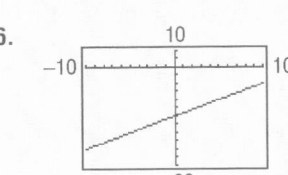

7.
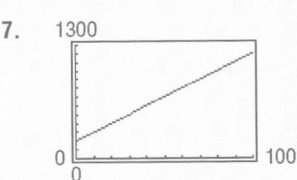

8.
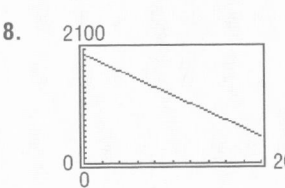

PACING the Lesson

Suggested Number of Days
Basic/Average 0   **Above Average** 1
Advanced 1

PLANNING the Lesson

Lesson Plan 13.3, p. 104

ORGANIZER

Starters (reproduced below)
  Problem of the Day 13.3, p. 37
  Warm-Up Exercises 13.3, p. 37
Lesson Resources
  Teaching Tools
    Coordinate planes, pp. T9, C11
  Math Log, p. 41
  Answer Masters 13.3, pp. 257–259
  Extra Practice Copymaster 13.3, p. 104
  Reteaching Copymaster 13.3, p. 104
  Enrichment Projects, pp. 69–71
Special Populations
  Suggestions, Teacher's Edition, p. 586D

LESSON Notes

Point out that all the points on the *x*-axis have a *y*-coordinate of 0 and all the points on the *y*-axis have an *x*-coordinate of 0. The *x*- and *y*-intercepts, together, define a given line. Furthermore, these points are frequently needed to gather useful information about relationships described by linear equations.

Vocabulary ALERT!

Ask students if they have heard the word "intercept" outside of mathematics. Challenge students to explain an interception in football in terms of lines.
The flight line of the ball crosses the running line of an opposing player, at which point he grabs the ball.

Example 1

Emphasize that the *x*-intercept is the point (2, 0) and that the *y*-intercept is the point (0, −3).

13.3 Exploring Intercepts of Graphs

What you should learn:

Goal 1 How to find intercepts of lines

Goal 2 How to use intercepts to sketch quick graphs

Why you should learn it:

You can use intercepts of lines to help solve real-life problems, such as finding the time and distance of a subway trip.

Goal 1

An **x-intercept** of a graph is the *x*-coordinate of a point where the graph crosses the *x*-axis. A **y-intercept** is the *y*-coordinate of a point where the graph crosses the *y*-axis. In the graph of $y = x + 2$ at the right, the x-intercept is -2 and the y-intercept is 2.

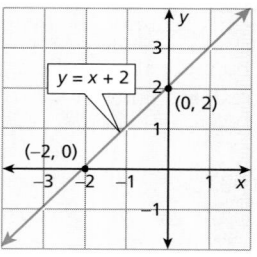

Finding Intercepts of Lines

1. To find an *x*-intercept of a line, substitute $y = 0$ into the equation and solve for *x*.

2. To find a *y*-intercept of a line, substitute $x = 0$ into the equation and solve for *y*.

Example 1   *Finding Intercepts of a Line*

Find the intercepts of the line given by $y = \frac{3}{2}x - 3$.

Solution

a. To find the x-intercept, let $y = 0$ and solve for *x*.

$$y = \frac{3}{2}x - 3 \qquad \textit{Rewrite original equation.}$$
$$0 = \frac{3}{2}x - 3 \qquad \textit{Substitute 0 for y.}$$
$$3 = \frac{3}{2}x \qquad \textit{Add 3 to each side.}$$
$$2 = x \qquad \textit{Multiply each side by } \frac{2}{3}.$$

The x-intercept is 2. The graph contains the point (2, 0).

b. To find the y-intercept, let $x = 0$ and solve for *y*.

$$y = \frac{3}{2}x - 3 \qquad \textit{Rewrite original equation.}$$
$$y = \frac{3}{2}(0) - 3 \qquad \textit{Substitute 0 for x.}$$
$$y = -3 \qquad \textit{Simplify.}$$

The y-intercept is -3. The graph contains the point (0, -3). ∎

598   Chapter *13* ▪ *Exploring Linear Equations*

STARTER: Problem of the Day

Find four natural numbers whose sum is equal to their product. (Hint: A number can be used more than once.)   1, 1, 2, 4

Also available as a copymaster, p. 37

STARTER: Warm-Up Exercises

1. Find *x* when $y = 0$.
a. $2x + 4 = y$ **b.** $y = x - 10$ **c.** $2x + 3y = 8$
a. $x = -2$, b. $x = 10$, c. $x = 4$

2. Find *y* when $x = 0$.
a. $2x + 4 = y$ **b.** $y = x - 10$ **c.** $2x + 3y = 8$
a. $y = 4$, b. $y = -10$, c. $y = \frac{8}{3}$

3. What is the equation of a horizontal line that passes through the point (3, 0)?
$y = 0$

4. What is the equation of a vertical line that passes through the point (0, 5)?
$x = 0$

Also available as a copymaster, p. 37

Goal 2 — Sketching Quick Graphs

To sketch the graph of a linear equation, you only need to find two solution points. The intercepts are good points to use.

Study Tip...

After sketching a quick graph of a line, you can check your graph by finding and plotting a third solution. If the third solution does not lie on the line, then you know that at least one of the three points was plotted incorrectly.

Sketching a Quick Graph of a Line

To sketch a quick graph of a linear equation, find two solutions of the equation. Any two solutions can be used, but the intercepts are often convenient. Plot the two solutions and draw a line through the two plotted points.

Example 2 — Sketching a Quick Graph

Sketch the graph of $x + y = 4$.

Solution Begin by finding the intercepts. To find the x-intercept, let $y = 0$ and solve for x.

$x + y = 4$	*Rewrite original equation.*
$x + 0 = 4$	*Substitute 0 for y.*
$x = 4$	*Simplify.*

The x-intercept is 4. The graph contains the point (4, 0). To find the y-intercept, let $x = 0$ and solve for y.

$x + y = 4$	*Rewrite original equation.*
$(0) + y = 4$	*Substitute 0 for x.*
$y = 4$	*Simplify.*

The y-intercept is 4. The graph contains the point (0, 4). Plot the points (4, 0) and (0, 4), as shown at the left. Then draw a line through the points. ∎

Communicating about MATHEMATICS

▶ SHARING IDEAS about the Lesson

Real Life
Transportation

Interpreting Intercepts Your distance (in miles) from home is represented by y, and the time (in minutes) you traveled is represented by x. The relationship between y and x is modeled by the equation $y = 5 - \frac{1}{2}x$. Find the two intercepts of the graph of this equation.

The y-intercept (5) **A.** Which intercept tells how many miles you are from home?

The x-intercept (10) **B.** Which intercept tells how many minutes you traveled?

P Portfolio Opportunity

13.3 • *Exploring Intercepts of Graphs* **599**

Have students plot any two points on a coordinate plane and draw a line through them. Ask: Can a different line containing these two points be drawn in the coordinate plane? This should demonstrate that exactly one line can be drawn through two given points. Thus, to graph a solution set of a linear equation, only two points are needed. Stress that substituting 0 for each variable of a linear equation and solving for the other variable is usually an easy way to find two solution points.

Example 2

Common-Error ALERT!

Sometimes, students will write the x- and y- intercepts as a single point. To avoid this error, recommend that students write (?, 0) beside the equation when they are finding the x-intercept and (0, ?) beside the equation when they are finding the y-intercept. The x- and y-intercepts can then be readily located.

Communicating about MATHEMATICS

For most real-life linear relationships, restrictions are placed on the possible values of x and y. Some values of x and y wouldn't make sense. Ask students to identify restrictions that they would place on x and y in the subway problem. Have them explain their restrictions.

Writing Prompt
So far in this chapter, I could really use help with . . .

OPTION: Extra Examples

Here is an additional example similar to Example 2.

Sketching a Quick Graph
Sketch the graph of $x - 3y = 3$.

Solution
Begin by finding the intercepts. To find the x-intercept, let $y = 0$ and solve for x.

$x - 3y = 3$.	Rewrite original equation.
$x - 3(0) = 3$	Substitute 0 for y.
$x = 3$	Simplify.

The x-intercept is 3. The graph contains the point (3, 0). To find the y-intercept, let $x = 0$ and solve for y.

$x - 3y = 3$.	Rewrite original equation.
$0 - 3y = 3$.	Substitute 0 for x.
$-3y = 3$	Simplify.
$y = -1$	Divide each side by -3.

The y-intercept is -1. The graph contains the point (0, -1). Plot the points (3, 0) and (0, -1), as shown. Then draw a line through the points.

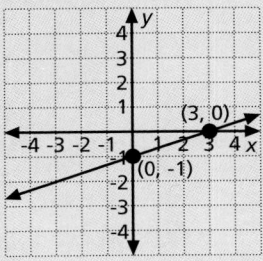

Lesson 13.3 **599**

EXERCISE Notes

ASSIGNMENT GUIDE

*Basic/Average:
Day 1: Ex. 7–25 odd
Day 2: Ex. 27–29, 33–37 odd

Above Average:
Ex. 7–29 odd, 30–32, 38–40

Advanced: Ex. 7–29 odd, 30–32, 38–40

Selected Answers: Ex. 1–6, 7–37 odd

*You may wish to omit this lesson for these students.

Guided Practice

Use these exercises as a small-group in-class 15-minute practice set.

Independent Practice

▶ **Ex. 7–10** For an alternative look at the meaning of intercept, you may wish to have students give their answers as ordered pairs.
▶ **Ex. 19–26** Reinforce students' solutions using a graphing calculator.

EXERCISES

Guided Practice

▶ **CHECK for Understanding** For explanations, see margin.

1. Find the x-intercept of $y = 2x - 1$. Explain each step. $\frac{1}{2}$
2. Find the y-intercept of $5x + 3y = 9$. Explain each step. 3

In Exercises 3–6, find the intercepts of the line. Then sketch a quick graph. See Additional Answers.

3. $x + y = 5$
   x-intercept: 5
   y-intercept: 5

4. $x - y = 5$
   x-intercept: 5
   y-intercept: -5

5. $y = \frac{5}{4}x + 3$
   x-intercept: $-\frac{12}{5}$
   y-intercept: 3

6. $-7x + 3y = -21$
   x-intercept: 3
   y-intercept: -7

Independent Practice

In Exercises 7–10, identify the intercepts of the graph. See margin.

7.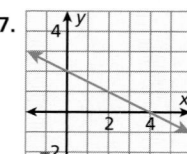
8.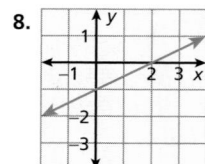
9.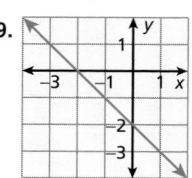
10.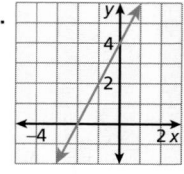

In Exercises 11–14, sketch a line having the given intercepts. See Additional Answers.

11. x-intercept: -1
    y-intercept: 5

12. x-intercept: -5
    y-intercept: -2

13. x-intercept: 2
    y-intercept: 6

14. x-intercept: 4
    y-intercept: -5

In Exercises 15–18, match the equation with its graph.

a.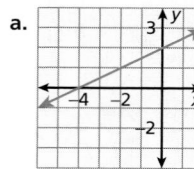
b.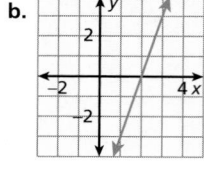
c.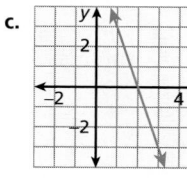
d.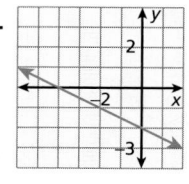

15. $y = \frac{1}{2}x + 2$ a
16. $y = -\frac{1}{2}x - 2$ d
17. $3x - y = 6$ b
18. $3x + y = 6$ c

In Exercises 19–26, sketch a quick graph of the line. Then create a table of values and compare the values with the points on the line. See Additional Answers.

19. $y = -3x + 6$
20. $y = 4x - 8$
21. $x - y = 1$
22. $x + y = -3$
23. $3x - 4y = 24$
24. $x + 5y = 5$
25. $y = -\frac{3}{2}x + 4$
26. $y = \frac{4}{3}x + 6$

In Exercises 27 and 28, use a calculator to find the intercepts of the line. Round your results to two decimal places.

27. $y = -3.64x + 2.18$
    x-intercept: 0.60
    y-intercept: 2.18

28. $y = 1.85x - 14.302$
    x-intercept: 7.73
    y-intercept: -14.30

600 *Chapter 13 ▪ Exploring Linear Equations*

Answers

1. $y = 2x - 1$ Rewrite original equation.
   $0 = 2x - 1$ Substitute 0 for y.
   $1 = 2x$ Add 1 to each side.
   $\frac{1}{2} = x$ Divide each side by 2.

2. $5x + 3y = 9$ Rewrite original equation.
   $5(0) + 3y = 9$ Substitute 0 for x.
   $3y = 9$ Simplify.
   $y = 3$ Divide each side by 3.

7. x-intercept: 4
   y-intercept: 2

8. x-intercept: 2
   y-intercept: -1

9. x-intercept: -2
   y-intercept: -2

10. x-intercept: -2
    y-intercept: 4

600 *Chapter 13*

Extra Practice

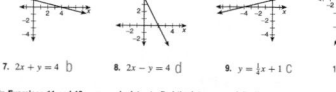

Extra Practice **13.3** Name _____

In Exercises 1–3, identify the intercepts of the graph.
1.
  x-intercept: -3,
  y-intercept: 3
2.
  x-intercept: 2
  y-intercept: -4
3.
  x-intercept: 2
  y-intercept: 4

In Exercises 4–6, sketch a line having the given intercepts.
4. x-intercept: -2
   y-intercept: 4
5. x-intercept: 1
   y-intercept: -3
6. x-intercept: none
   y-intercept: 2

In Exercises 7–10, match the equation with its graph.
a. b. c. d.

7. $2x + y = 4$ b
8. $2x - y = 4$ d
9. $y = \frac{1}{2}x + 1$ c
10. $y = -\frac{1}{2}x + 1$ a

In Exercises 11 and 12, use a calculator to find the intercepts of the line. Round your results to two decimal places.
11. $y = -2.15x + 4.25$ x-intercept: 1.98
    y-intercept: 4.25
12. $y = 3.65x - 10.25$ x-intercept: 2.81
    y-intercept: -10.25

13. The relationship between Fahrenheit temperature, F, and Celsius temperature, C, is given by the linear equation, $F = \frac{9}{5}C + 32$. Find the coordinates (C, F) of the intercepts of the graph and explain what they mean.
(0, 32), 0°C is equivalent to 32°F; (-17.7, 0), 0°F is equivalent to -17.7° C.

14. Your parents purchase a new automobile for $16,500. The value of the car depreciates linearly (at a constant rate). The value, V, of the car in terms of the number of years they own the car, t, is given by the equation, $V = 16500 - 1500t$. Find the coordinates (t, V) of the intercepts of the graph of the equation and explain what they mean.
(0, 16,500), After 0 years of ownership the car has a $16,500 value. (11, 0), the car has $0 value after 11 years.

104 *Exploring Intercepts of Graphs ▪ 13.3* Windows

Reteaching

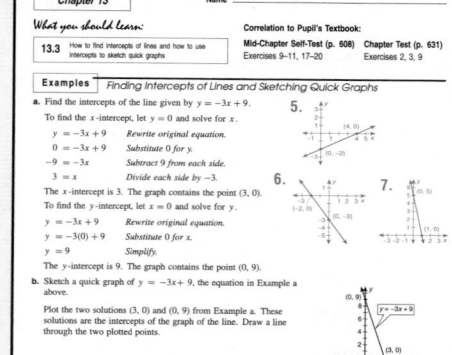

Reteach Chapter 13 Name _____

What you should learn:
13.3 How to find intercepts of lines and how to use intercepts to sketch quick graphs

Correlation to Pupil's Textbook:
Mid-Chapter Self-Test (p. 608) Chapter Test (p. 631)
Exercises 9–11, 17–20 Exercises 2, 3, 9

Examples Finding Intercepts of Lines and Sketching Quick Graphs

a. Find the intercepts of the line given by $y = -3x + 9$.
To find the x-intercept, let $y = 0$ and solve for x.
$y = -3x + 9$ Rewrite original equation.
$0 = -3x + 9$ Substitute 0 for y.
$-9 = -3x$ Subtract 9 from each side.
$3 = x$ Divide each side by -3.
The x-intercept is 3. The graph contains the point (3, 0).
To find the y-intercept, let $x = 0$ and solve for y.
$y = -3x + 9$ Rewrite original equation.
$y = -3(0) + 9$ Substitute 0 for x.
$y = 9$ Simplify.
The y-intercept is 9. The graph contains the point (0, 9).

b. Sketch a quick graph of $y = -3x + 9$, the equation in Example a above.
Plot the two solutions (3, 0) and (0, 9) from Example a. These solutions are the intercepts of the graph of the line. Draw a line through the two plotted points.

Guidelines: • An x-intercept of a graph is the x-coordinate of a point where the graph crosses the x-axis; a y-intercept of a graph is the y-coordinate of a point where the graph crosses the y-axis.

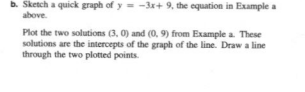
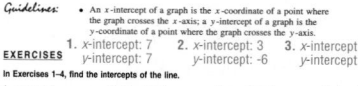

EXERCISES
In Exercises 1–4, identify the intercepts of the line.
1. $x + y = 7$ x-intercept: 7 y-intercept: 7
2. $2x - y = 6$ x-intercept: 3 y-intercept: -6
3. $y = \frac{1}{2}x + 3$ x-intercept: -6 y-intercept: 3
4. $4x - 3y = 24$ x-intercept: 6 y-intercept: -8

In Exercises 5–7, sketch a line having the given intercepts.
5. x-intercept: 4 y-intercept: -2
6. x-intercept: -2 y-intercept: -3
7. x-intercept: 1 y-intercept: 5
5-7. See above for graphs.

104 *Chapter 13 ▪ Exploring Linear Equations* Windows

29. *Error Analysis* A friend in your math class has sketched a quick graph of the line $4y = -6x + 8$ as shown at the right. Is the graph correct? If not, what did your friend do wrong?

No, the x-intercept should be $\frac{4}{3}$.

Business **In Exercises 30 and 31, use the following information.** 30.–31. See margin.

You own a car wash business and have discovered that the less you charge for a car wash, the more car washes you sell. Over an eight-week period, you try several prices for 1 week each, as shown in the table. p is the price of a car wash and x is the number of car washes you sold that week.

p	$12	$11	$10	$9	$8	$7	$6	$5
x	400	450	500	550	600	650	700	800

30. Draw a graph of the data.

31. Your total car wash income is

Income = (Price)(Number sold).

Make a table showing your total income for the different prices. Which price would you charge? Explain.

At age 13, Stephen Lovett started a car cleaning service, cleaning and waxing cars after school and on weekends. By age 18, he had five employees.

32. *Think about It* Not every graph of a line has two distinct intercepts. Give two examples where the graph of a line has only one intercept.
See margin.

Integrated Review

Making Connections within Mathematics

Coordinates **In Exercises 33–36, the point is on the line $9x + 6y = 36$. Find the missing coordinate.**

33. $(2, ?)$ 3 **34.** $(6, ?)$ -3 **35.** $(?, 9)$ -2 **36.** $(?, -6)$ 8

37. *Sketching a Graph* Use the points in Exercises 33–36 to sketch the graph of $9x + 6y = 36$. Then name 4 other points on the graph. For graph, see margin.
$(0, 6), (4, 0), (-4, 12), (-6, 15)$

Exploration and Extension

Technology **In Exercises 38–40, consider the equation $24x + 54y = 216$.**

38. Rewrite the equation in the form that can be used by a graphing calculator. $y = 4 - 4x \div 9$

39. Use a graphing calculator to sketch the graph. Use a range that makes both intercepts visible. See margin.

40. What are the intercepts of the graph? x-intercept: 9, y-intercept: 4

✪ More difficult exercises
Ⓟ Portfolio Opportunity

13.3 • *Exploring Intercepts of Graphs* **601**

Integrated Review

This section provides a useful review of Lesson 13.1.

Exploration and Extension

These exercises can be done in class using an overhead graphing calculator.

Portfolio Opportunity: Math Log

1. What do the x-intercepts of all graphs have in common? What does this fact have to do with the method for finding x-intercepts?

2. What do the y-intercepts of all graphs have in common? What does this fact have to do with the method for finding y-intercepts?

Also available as a copymaster, page 41, Ex. 3, 4

Answers

30.

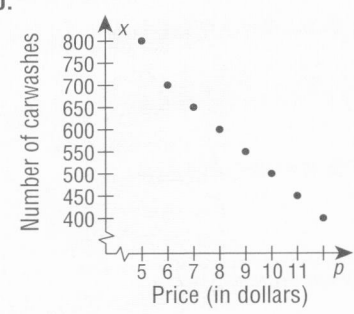

31.

P	$12	$11	$10	$9
I	$4800	$4950	$5000	$4950

P	$8	$7	$6	$5
I	$4800	$4550	$4200	$4000

$10, $10 is the price that results in the most income.

32. The graph of an equation such as $x = 3$ (a vertical line), the graph of an equation such as $y = 3$ (a horizontal line), the graph of an equation such as $y = 2x$ (a line through the origin)

37.

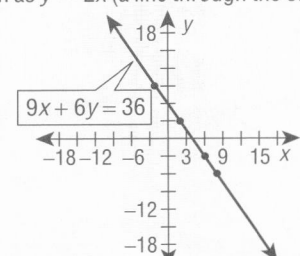

39.

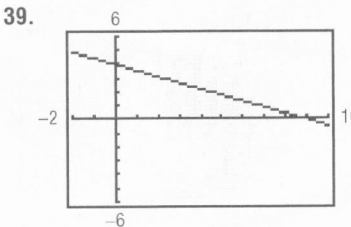

▶ **Enrichment**

Construct a table of values for $y = x^2$, using $x = -3, -2, -1, 0, 1, 2, 3$. Based on the graph, determine if $y = x^2$ is a linear equation. Explain your reasoning.

Mixed REVIEW

In Exercises 1–4, find the circumference and area of the indicated circle. (12.1)

1. $d = 7$ ft 　　　 **2.** $d = 32$ in. 　　　 **3.** $r = 8$ cm 　　　 **4.** $r = 24$ yd
3. ≈50.27 cm, ≈201.06 cm² 　　　　　　　　　　　　 4. ≈150.80 yd, ≈1809.56 yd²

In Exercises 5–8, find the surface area and volume of the solid. (12.3–12.5) 　See margin.

5. 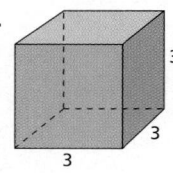 　 **6.** 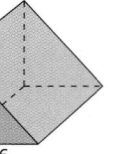 40　18　16 　 **7.** 5　7 　 **8.** 20　10　16

3　3　3

In Exercises 9–12, find the x- and y-intercepts. (13.3)

9. $y = x - 12$ 　 **10.** $2x = y + 4$ 　 **11.** $3x + 3y = 9$ 　 **12.** $\frac{2}{3}y = \frac{2}{5}x + 6$
12, −12 　　　 2, −4 　　　　 3, 3 　　　　　 − 15, 9

In Exercises 13 and 14, is △ABC a right triangle? Explain. (9.4)

13. $A(1, 2)$, $B(5, 2)$, $C(0, 2)$
No; A, B, and C lie on a line.

14. $A(1, -1)$, $B(1, 0)$, $C(5, -1)$
See margin.

Career Interview

Design and Construction Manager

Howard Haywood works for the Massachusetts Bay Transit Authority (MBTA), the oldest transit system in the United States. He is responsible for administering all MBTA construction—tunnels, subway systems, rail systems, bridges, etc.

Q: *What led you to this career?*
A: I began my career in general construction.
Q: *What math do you use on your job?*
A: Basic math, algebra, geometry, and calculus. However, I feel that the most important math concepts I use are the problem solving skills such as the ability to decide what steps to take, what math operations to use, how to evaluate the results, and how to determine if the solution is reasonable.
Q: *What would you like to tell kids about school?*
A: When I was in fifth grade through junior high, I thought that I was a better reader than math student. Then one of my teachers explained to me that math is just like reading. It is a language that has logical steps and a logical progression. Once I tried to "read" math and comprehend it, I found it wasn't so hard.

LESSON INVESTIGATION 13.4
Exploring the Slope of a Line

Materials Needed: geoboards or dot paper

Example	*Exploring Slope*

This dot paper activity helps students visualize the concept of slope as rate of vertical change to horizontal change. Use Ex. 1–8 as a 20-minute lead-in to the formula for the slope of a line.
    Definition of slope is explored in Lesson 13.4.

Use a geoboard or dot paper to model the indicated lines.

a. The line slopes up 2 units for each 3 units to the right.

b. The line slopes down 4 units for each 3 units to the right.

c. The line slopes up 3 units for each 3 units to the right.

Solution   You can use the hypotenuse of a right triangle to model each line. The vertical side of the triangle models the number of units moved up or down. The horizontal side models the number of units moved to the right.

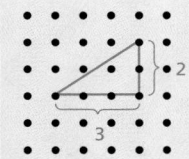 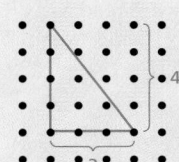 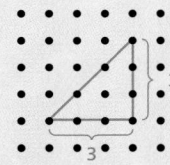

Slopes up 2 units for each 3 units to the right.

Slopes down 4 units for each 3 units to the right.

Slopes up 3 units for each 3 units to the right. ■

Exercises

In Exercises 1–4, describe the slope of the hypotenuse. See margin.

1.    **2.** 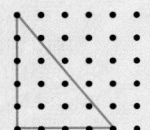   **3.** 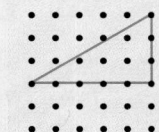   **4.**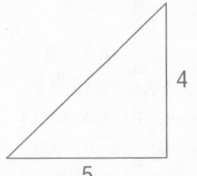

In Exercises 5–8, use a geoboard or dot paper to model the line. See margin.

5. The line slopes up 4 units for each 5 units to the right.

6. The line slopes down 4 units for each 5 units to the right.

7. The line slopes down 1 unit for each 4 units to the right.

8. The line slopes up 2 units for each 4 units to the right.

Answers
1. The line slopes up 3 units for each 4 units to the right.
2. The line slopes down 4 units for each 2 units to the right.
3. The line slopes down 5 units for each 4 units to the right.
4. The line slopes up 3 units for each 5 units to the right.
5.

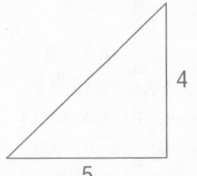

6.

7.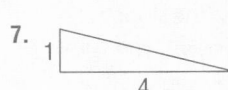

8.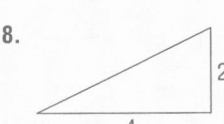

PACING the Lesson

Suggested Number of Days
Basic/Average 0   Above Average 1
Advanced 1

PLANNING the Lesson

Lesson Plan 13.4, p. 105

ORGANIZER

Starters (reproduced below)
Problem of the Day 13.4, p. 38
Warm-Up Exercises 13.4, p. 38

Lesson Resources
Color Transparencies
Diagrams for Ex. 17–20, p. 55
Teaching Tools
Coordinate planes, pp. T9, C11
Math Log, p. 41
Technology, p. 75
Answer Masters 13.4, p. 261
Extra Practice Copymaster 13.4, p. 105
Reteaching Copymaster 13.4, p. 105

Special Populations
Suggestions, Teacher's Edition, p. 586D

LESSON Notes

Students should record the formula for slope in their math journals and explain it in their own words. Then discuss why vertical lines were excluded from the definition of slope.

Addressing Misconceptions

Be sure that students understand the function of the subscripted notation in the slope formula. The variables x and y are placeholders for all possible values, while x_1 and y_1 indicate that a particular point has been identified whose coordinates must be substituted for x_1 and y_1 in order to apply the formula.

Example 1

It is important to illustrate that it does not matter which point is chosen as (x_1, y_1). Ask students to switch points in the slope formula, compute the slopes again, and compare results.

13.4 Exploring Slope

What you should learn:

Goal 1 How to find the slope of a line

Goal 2 How to interpret the slope of a line

Why you should learn it:

You can use the slope of a line to solve real-life problems, such as describing the steepness of a hill.

Goal 1 Finding the Slope of a Line

To find the slope of a line, choose two points on the line. Call the points (x_1, y_1) and (x_2, y_2). The **slope** is the ratio of the change in y to the change in x.

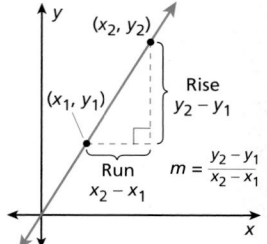

Change in $y = y_2 - y_1 = $ "Rise"

Change in $x = x_2 - x_1 = $ "Run"

These expressions are read as "y sub 2 minus y sub 1" and "x sub 2 minus x sub 1."

> **Finding the Slope of a Line**
> The slope m of the nonvertical line passing through the points (x_1, y_1) and (x_2, y_2) is $m = \dfrac{y_2 - y_1}{x_2 - x_1} = \dfrac{\text{Rise}}{\text{Run}}$.

Example 1 *Finding the Slope of a Line*

Study Tip...
When you are using the formula for slope, it doesn't matter which point you represent with (x_1, y_1). For instance, in Example 1a, the point (1, 2) is represented with (x_1, y_1) and (3, 5) is represented with (x_2, y_2). Try switching the points and applying the formula. You will obtain the same slope.

a. To find the slope of the line through (1, 2) and (3, 5), let (1, 2) be (x_1, y_1), and let (3, 5) be (x_2, y_2). Then the slope is
$$m = \frac{5-2}{3-1} = \frac{3}{2}.$$

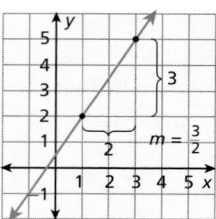

b. To find the slope of the line through (2, 5) and (5, 1), let (2, 5) be (x_1, y_1), and let (5, 1) be (x_2, y_2). Then the slope is
$$m = \frac{1-5}{5-2} = \frac{-4}{3} = -\frac{4}{3}.$$

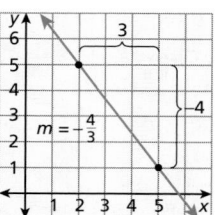

> **STARTER: Problem of the Day**
>
> Given the line $y = 3x + 1$, complete the table below.
>
> | x | 0 | 1 | 2 | 3 |
> |---|---|---|---|---|
> | y | 1 | 4 | 7 | 10 |
>
> Find the difference between each value of y in the table. Compare that difference with the coefficient of x in the equation. The difference is always 3, the same value as the coefficient of x in the equation. This is the slope of the graph of the equation.

Also available as a copymaster, p. 38

> **STARTER: Warm-Up Exercises**
>
> **1.** Simplify.
> **a.** $\dfrac{7-(-3)}{(-2-5)}$ **b.** $\dfrac{(-3-5)}{(2-7)}$ **c.** $\dfrac{(0-8)}{(-7-1)}$
> **a.** $-\dfrac{10}{7}$, **b.** $\dfrac{8}{5}$, **c.** 1
>
> **2.** Substitute, as indicated, into each expression and evaluate.
> **a.** $m = 8, n = -3$; $4m + 3n$
> **b.** $w = 7, v = 3$; $9v - 4w$
> **a.** 23, **b.** -1

Also available as a copymaster, p. 38

Goal 2 Interpreting Slope

The slope of a line tells you whether the line rises to the right, falls to the right, or is horizontal. (Slope is not defined for vertical lines.) If you imagine that you are walking *to the right* on the line, a positive slope means you are walking uphill, a negative slope means you are walking downhill, and a zero slope means you are walking on level ground.

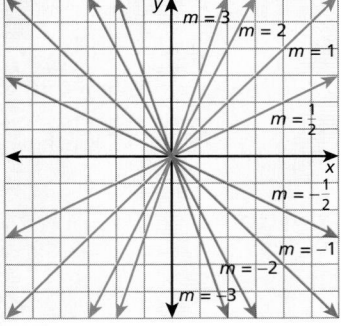

Positive Slope

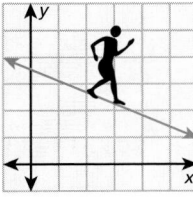
Negative Slope

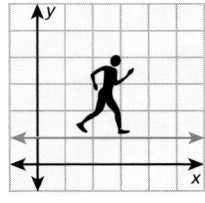
Zero Slope

The slope of a line also tells you how steep the line is. For instance, a line with a slope of 3 is steeper than a line with a slope of 2. Similarly, a line with a slope of -3 is steeper than a line with a slope of -2.

Example 2 Comparing the Slopes of Two Lines

Compare the slopes of the lines through the indicated points.

Line 1: $(2, 5)$, $(5, 2)$ **Line 2:** $(3, 6)$, $(6, 3)$

Solution

Line 1: $m = \dfrac{2-5}{5-2} = \dfrac{-3}{3} = -1$

Line 2: $m = \dfrac{3-6}{6-3} = \dfrac{-3}{3} = -1$

Each line has a slope of -1. From the graphs of the lines at the left, you can see that they are parallel. This is another use of slope—lines with the same slope are parallel. ■

You can use any two points to find the slope. Since the points all lie on the same line, using any two points will produce the same slope.

🅿 *Communicating* about MATHEMATICS

▶ **SHARING IDEAS about the Lesson**

Finding the Slope of a Line The points $(-1, 1)$, $(0, 3)$, $(1, 5)$, $(2, 7)$, and $(3, 9)$ all lie on a line. Which two points would you use to find the slope? Can you use any two? Explain.

See above.

Students often confuse "no slope" with "zero slope." Emphasize that a horizontal line has zero slope. Because slope is not defined for vertical lines, we say that vertical lines have no slope. Students should record these relationships in their math journals.

Example 2
Have students draw a third line that is parallel to the two lines in the example. Then ask them how they can verify that the three lines are parallel to each other. Students should compute the slope of the third line.

Communicating about MATHEMATICS

Have students find two points that satisfy $3x + 2y = 6$ and use them to compute the slope of the graph of the given equation. Ask: Without graphing the equation, can you say if the slope is uphill or downhill? Explain.

Writing Prompt
Create a funny mathematical bumper sticker using the concept of slope.

Technology

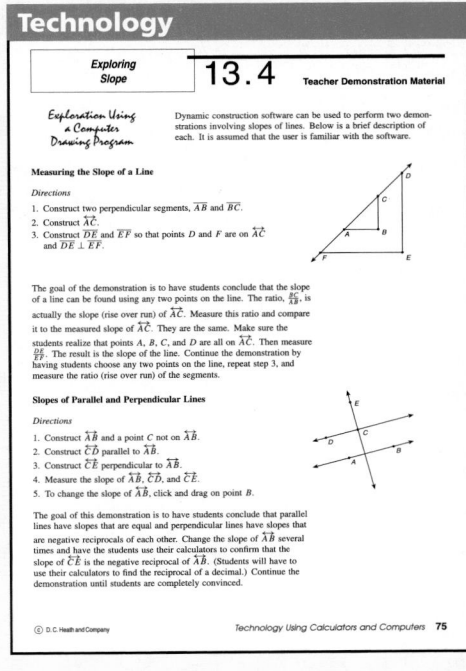

OPTION: Extra Examples

Here is an additional example similar to Example 1.

Finding the Slope of a Line.

a. To find the slope of the line through $(3, -4)$ and $(-2, 1)$, let $(3, -4)$ be (x_1, y_1) and let $(-2, 1)$ be (x_2, y_2). Then the slope is:
$$m = \frac{1-(-4)}{-2-3} = \frac{5}{-5} = -1.$$

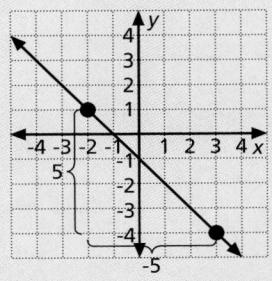

b. To find the slope of the line through $(2,5)$ and $(0, -1)$, let $(2,5)$ be (x_1, y_1) and let $(0, -1)$ be (x_2, y_2). Then the slope is:
$$m = \frac{-1-5}{0-2} = \frac{-6}{-2} = 3.$$

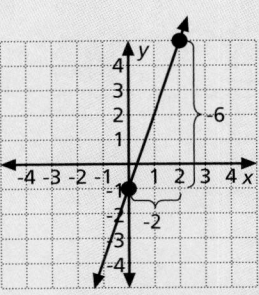

ASSIGNMENT GUIDE

*Basic/Average:
Day 1: Ex. 7–19 odd, 35, 36
Day 2: Ex. 21–33 odd

Above Average:
Ex. 7–33 odd, 35, 36

Advanced: Ex. 7–33 odd, 35, 36

Selected Answers: Ex. 1–6, 7–33 odd

*You may wish to omit this lesson for these students.

Guided Practice

Use these exercises as an in-class summary and provide students with plenty of extra practice similar to these.

Independent Practice

▶ **Ex. 9–16** Require students to format a solution similar to the models provided in Example 1 of the lesson.

Answers

13.
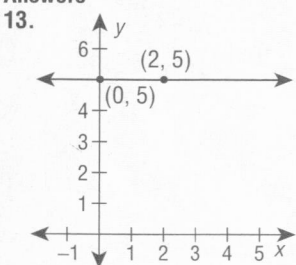

14.
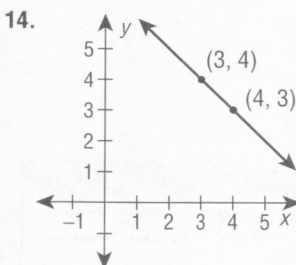

15.
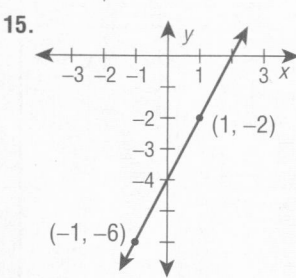

16.
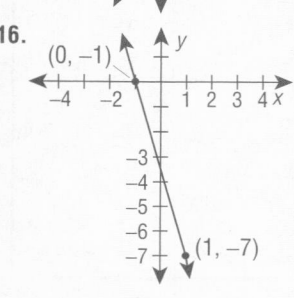

EXERCISES

Guided Practice

▶ **CHECK for Understanding**

In Exercises 1–4, find the slope of the line.

1.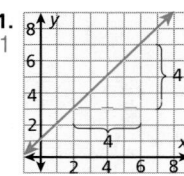

2.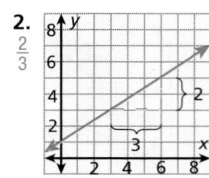

3.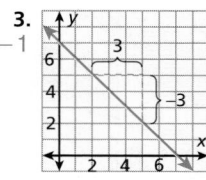

4.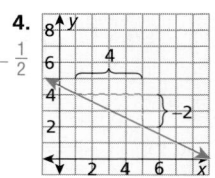

5. Find the slope of the line through $(-1, 3)$ and $(4, 2)$. $-\frac{1}{5}$

6. Sketch a line with a slope of 3 and another with a slope of 4. Which is steeper?
The line with a slope of 4

Independent Practice

In Exercises 7 and 8, which slope is steepest?

7. $m = \frac{5}{2}$, $m = 3$, $m = 0$, $m = 5$ $\quad m = 5$

8. $m = -1$, $m = -6$, $m = -4$, $m = -\frac{17}{4}$
$\quad m = -6$

In Exercises 9–12, find the slope of the line.

9. 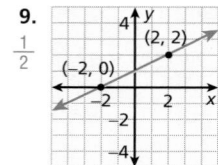 $\frac{1}{2}$

10. 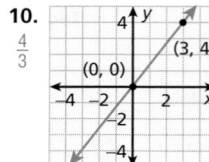 $\frac{4}{3}$

11. 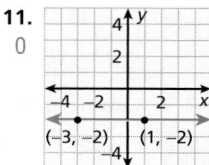 0

12. 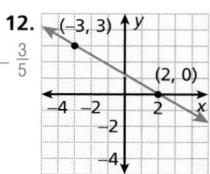 $-\frac{3}{5}$

In Exercises 13–16, plot the points. Then find the slope of the line through the points. For plots, see margin.

13. $(2, 5)$, $(0, 5)$ $\quad 0$

14. $(3, 4)$, $(4, 3)$ $\quad -1$

15. $(1, -2)$, $(-1, -6)$ $\quad 2$

16. $(0, -1)$, $(1, -7)$ $\quad -6$

In Exercises 17–20, find the slope. (Assume a left-to-right orientation.)

17. 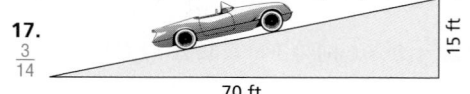 $\frac{3}{14}$
70 ft / 15 ft

18.  $-\frac{1}{7}$
14 ft / 2 ft

19. 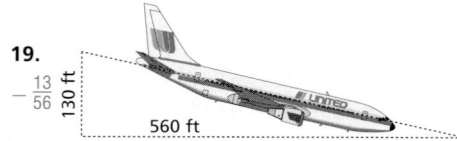 $-\frac{13}{56}$
560 ft / 130 ft

20.  $\frac{5}{13}$
65 meters / 25 meters

Extra Practice

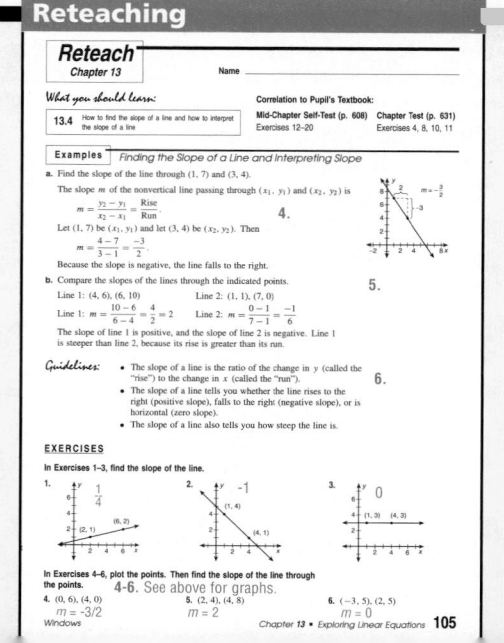

Extra Practice **13.4** Name _____

In Exercises 1–3, determine whether a line with given slope rises to the right, falls to the right, is horizontal or is vertical.
1. $m = -\frac{1}{4}$ Falls to the right 2. $m = 10$ Rises to the right 3. $m = 0$ Horizontal

In Exercises 4 and 5, determine which slope is steeper.
4. $m = 3$, $m = \frac{1}{2}$, $m = 4$, $m = \frac{4}{5}$ 5. $m = -6$, $m = -\frac{1}{2}$, $m = -4$, $m = 0$
$m = 4$ is steeper. $\qquad m = -6$ is steeper.

In Exercises 6–8, find the slope of the line.
6. $\frac{2}{5}$ 7. $-\frac{5}{6}$ 8. $-\frac{3}{5}$

In Exercises 9–12, plot the points. Then find the slope of the line through the points. 9–12. See back of supplement for graphs.
9. $(2, 6)$, $(-3, 4)$ $m = 2/5$ 10. $(0, 4)$, $(-3, 0)$ $m = 4/3$
11. $(-1, -2)$, $(-3, -2)$ $m = 0$ 12. $(0, -6)$, $(2, -1)$ $m = -5/2$

In Exercises 13–15, find the slope. Assume a left-to-right orientation.
13. 830 ft / 210 ft $\frac{1}{3}$ 14. $\frac{14}{17}$ 940 ft / 1020 ft 15. 30 ft / 16 ft $\frac{8}{15}$

In Exercises 16–18, find the slope of the hypotenuse.
16. $\frac{13}{12}$ $-\frac{5}{12}$ 17. $\frac{15}{8}$ 18. $\frac{4}{3}$

In Exercises 19–22, find the slope of $\overleftrightarrow{MN}$ and $\overleftrightarrow{XY}$. Are the line parallel? Explain. $\overleftrightarrow{MN} \parallel \overleftrightarrow{XY}$, $m\overleftrightarrow{MN} = 3 = m\overleftrightarrow{XY}$
19. $M(0, 1)$, $N(-1, -2)$, $X(0, -6)$, $Y(2, 0)$ $\overleftrightarrow{MN} \not\parallel \overleftrightarrow{XY}$, $m\overleftrightarrow{MN} = 1/2$, $m\overleftrightarrow{XY} = -1/2$
20. $M(4, 8)$, $N(-2, 5)$, $X(2, -1)$, $Y(-4, 2)$
21. $M(0, 1)$, $N(-1, -4)$, $X(5, 3)$, $Y(-5, 1)$ 22. $M(0, 6)$, $N(3, 8)$, $X(6, 2)$, $Y(-3, -4)$
$\overleftrightarrow{MN} \not\parallel \overleftrightarrow{XY}$, $m\overleftrightarrow{MN} = 5$, $m\overleftrightarrow{XY} = 1/5$ $\overleftrightarrow{MN} \parallel \overleftrightarrow{XY}$, $m\overleftrightarrow{MN} = 2/3 = m\overleftrightarrow{XY}$

Windows $\qquad$ **13.4** ▪ Exploring Slope **105**

Reteaching

Reteach Chapter 13 Name _____

What you should learn:
| **13.4** | How to find the slope of a line and how to interpret the slope of a line |

Correlation to Pupil's Textbook:
Mid-Chapter Self-Test (p. 608) Chapter Test (p. 631)
Exercises 12–20 Exercises 4, 8, 10, 11

Examples Finding the Slope of a Line and Interpreting Slope

a. Find the slope of the line through $(1, 7)$ and $(3, 4)$.

The slope m of the nonvertical line passing through (x_1, y_1) and (x_2, y_2) is
$$m = \frac{y_2 - y_1}{x_2 - x_1} = \frac{\text{Rise}}{\text{Run}}$$
Let $(1, 7)$ be (x_1, y_1) and let $(3, 4)$ be (x_2, y_2). Then
$$m = \frac{4 - 7}{3 - 1} = \frac{-3}{2}$$
Because the slope is negative, the line falls to the right.

b. Compare the slopes of the lines through the indicated points.
Line 1: $(4, 6)$, $(6, 10)$ $\qquad$ Line 2: $(1, 1)$, $(7, 0)$
Line 1: $m = \frac{10 - 6}{6 - 4} = \frac{4}{2} = 2$ $\qquad$ Line 2: $m = \frac{0 - 1}{7 - 1} = \frac{-1}{6}$
The slope of line 1 is positive, and the slope of line 2 is negative. Line 1 is steeper than line 2, because its rise is greater than its run.

Guidelines: • The slope of a line is the ratio of the change in y (called the "rise") to the change in x (called the "run").
• The slope of a line tells you whether the line rises to the right (positive slope), falls to the right (negative slope), or is horizontal (zero slope).
• The slope of a line also tells you how steep the line is.

EXERCISES

In Exercises 1–3, find the slope of the line.
1. $\frac{1}{4}$ 2. -1 3. 0

In Exercises 4–6, plot the points. Then find the slope of the line through the points. 4–6. See above for graphs.
4. $(0, 6)$, $(4, 0)$ 5. $(2, 4)$, $(4, 8)$ 6. $(-3, 5)$, $(2, 5)$
$m = -3/2$ $\qquad m = 2$ $\qquad m = 0$

Windows $\qquad$ Chapter **13** ▪ Exploring Linear Equations **105**

Geometry In Exercises 21–24, find the slope of the hypotenuse.

21. $-\frac{3}{4}$
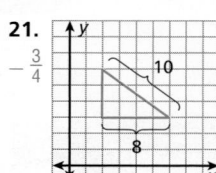

22. $\frac{5}{12}$
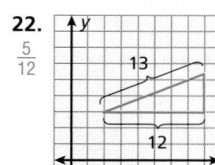

23. 1
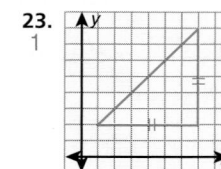

24. $-\frac{8}{15}$
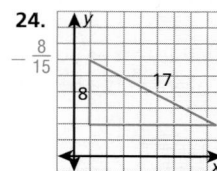

Geometry In Exercises 25–28, find the slopes of $\overleftrightarrow{AB}$ and $\overleftrightarrow{CD}$. Are the lines parallel? Explain. For explanations, see margin.

25. $A(3, 3), B(1, -2), C(-4, 4), D(-3, -1)$ No **26.** $A(1, 1), B(0, -2), C(-5, 1), D(-3, -2)$ No

27. $A(2, 3), B(0, -2), C(4, 3), D(6, 8)$ Yes **28.** $A(-2, -2), B(2, 6), C(-1, -4), D(-5, 4)$ No

Stairs In Exercises 29–31, find the slope of each set of stairs.

29. 1
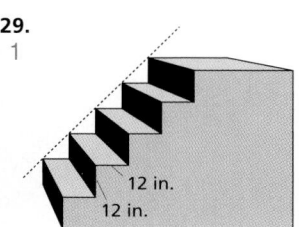
12 in.
12 in.

30. $\frac{5}{6}$
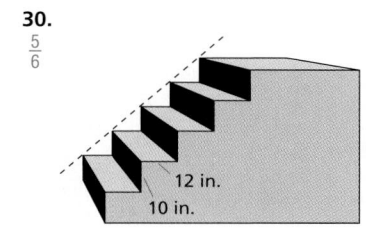
12 in.
10 in.

31. $\frac{4}{3}$
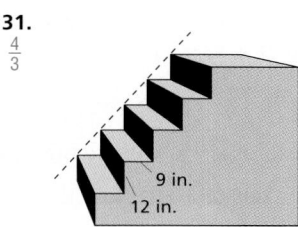
9 in.
12 in.

32. *Designing Stairs* You are helping to write a building code that is concerned with public safety. What is the steepest slope for a set of stairs that you think would be safe? Illustrate your answer with a scale drawing.
Answers vary.

Integrated Review
Making Connections within Mathematics

Patterns In Exercises 33 and 34, find the slope of the line through each pair of points. Then describe the pattern. See descriptions below.

33. a. $(-6, 3), (7, 16)$ 1 **b.** $(1, 0), (-2, -9)$ 3 **c.** $(-1, 1), (-4, -14)$ 5 **d.** $(0, -5), (1, 2)$ 7
34. a. $(0, -4), (2, -2)$ 1 **b.** $(1, 5), (-1, -3)$ 4 **c.** $(1, -2), (2, 7)$ 9 **d.** $(0, 8), (-1, -8)$ 16
33. Slopes are consecutive odd numbers.
34. Slopes are consecutive perfect-square numbers.

Exploration and Extension

Misleading Graphs In Exercises 35 and 36, use the graphs at the right.
Each is about 3000.
35. Estimate the slope of each graph.

36. Which of the graphs is more misleading? Explain your reasoning.
b, looks like the graph goes closer to the origin than it actually does.

a.
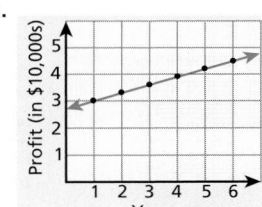

b.
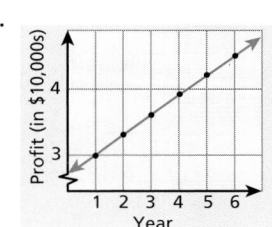

✪ More difficult exercises
P Portfolio Opportunity

13.4 • *Exploring Slope* **607**

▶ **Ex. 25–29** Before assigning these, you may need to review the concept of *parallelogram*.
▶ **Ex. 32**
EXTENSION
Have students measure the height and width of stairway steps in their home or school and determine the slope.

Integrated Review

Assign these exercises as an in-class small-group practice.

Exploration and Extension

Connect the slope concept in these exercises with Lesson 5.5 on misleading graphs, page 214. Demonstrate the change in appearance of a graph caused by using different scales on the x- and y-axes. This can be demonstrated on an overhead graphing calculator by adjusting the range or window.

Portfolio Opportunity: Math Log

As a line rising to the right gets steeper, what happens to its slope? As a line falling to the right gets steeper, what happens to its slope?

Also available as a copymaster, page 41, Ex. 5

Short Quiz

Covers Lessons 13.3 and 13.4

Available as a copymaster, page 214

Enrichment

Have students use the concept of slope to determine which of the following sets of points are on the same straight line.
a. (2, 1), (6, 7), (10, 13) Yes
b. (-6, 8), (3, 2), (14, 10) No

Answers
25. Slopes are different ($\frac{5}{2}$ and -5).
26. Slopes are different (3 and $-\frac{3}{2}$).
27. Slopes are the same ($\frac{5}{2}$ and $\frac{5}{2}$).
28. Slopes are different (2 and -2).

Take this test as you would take a test in class. The answers to the exercises are given in the back of the book.

In Exercises 1–3, use the equation $y = 28x$, which relates ounces, x, to grams, y. (13.1)

1. A magazine weighs 10 ounces. What is its measure in grams?   280 grams

2. A textbook has a measure of 700 grams. What is its weight in ounces?   25 ounces

3. Which measure is greater, 1 pound (16 ounces) or 1 kilogram (1000 grams)? Explain.   1 kilogram, 1 pound = 448 grams

In Exercises 4–6, decide whether the ordered pair is a solution of the equation $3x + 4y = 28$. (13.1)

4. $(0, 7)$ Yes

5. $\left(9, -\frac{1}{4}\right)$ No

6. $(8, 1)$ Yes

In Exercises 7 and 8, use the equation $2x + 5y = 42$. (13.2)

7. Copy and complete the table.

x	1	6	?	?
y	?	?	0	4

21, 11
8, 6

8. Use the table of values in Exercise 7 to sketch the graph of $2x + 5y = 42$.   See margin.

In Exercises 9–11, find the x- and y-intercepts. (13.3)

9. $8x + 2y = 32$ 4, 16

10. $4x + 5y = 20$ 5, 4

11. $12x + 8y = 24$ 2, 3

In Exercises 12–15, find the slope of the line that passes through the points. (13.4)

12. $(2, 9), (4, 12)$ $\frac{3}{2}$

13. $(5, 2), (3, 6)$ -2

14. $(7, 5), (3, 2)$ $\frac{3}{4}$

15. $(0, 7), (2, 10)$ $\frac{3}{2}$

16. Which of the lines in Exercises 12–15 are parallel? (13.4)   Those in Exercises 12 and 15

In Exercises 17–20, decide whether the graph is correct or incorrect. If it is incorrect, sketch the correct graph. (13.3, 13.4)

17. $y = 2x + 1$

18. $y = 2x - 1$

19. $y = -x - 1$

20. $y = \frac{3}{2}x$

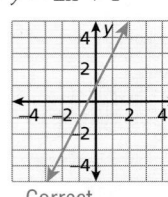
Correct

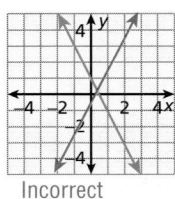
Incorrect

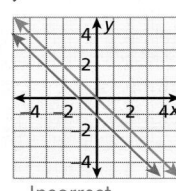
Incorrect

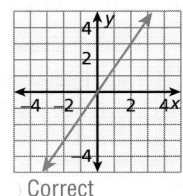
Correct

Answer

8.

Graph with points (1, 8) and (6, 6).

Alternative Assessment ▶

A **Partner Quiz** assesses students' achievement and provides them with an opportunity to communicate about mathematics.
Available as a copymaster, page 56

Formal Assessment ▶

Two **Mid-Chapter Tests** of average difficulty.
Available as copymasters, pages 215, 216

608   Chapter 13

Partner Quiz

Chapter 13
Mid-Chapter Partner Quiz   (Use after Lesson 13.4)

Name _____

1. List three solutions of $3x + 4y = 10$. (13.1)   (2, 1), $\left(0, \frac{5}{2}\right)$, (-2, 4)   1. Answers vary.

2. Write a linear equation that shows the relationship between x and y in the figure. (13.1)   2. $x + 10 = y$

4.

3. What do all of the solutions of the equation $x = 4$ have in common? (13.2) x-coordinates are all 4.   3. _____

4. Sketch the graph of the equation $y = \frac{1}{2}x + 1$. (13.2)   4. See above.

5. Find the x-intercept of the line given by $y = \frac{2}{3}x - 5$. (13.3)   5. $\left(\frac{15}{2}, 0\right)$

6. What is the only point that can be both an x-intercept and a y-intercept? (13.3)   6. (0, 0)

7. In an experiment, you record the temperature of a solution at one minute intervals. The graph is below. What does the x-intercept represent? (13.3)   7. The time when the solution reaches its freezing point

8. Find the slope of the line passing through the points $(-3, 2)$ and $(5, 3)$. (13.4)   8. $m = \frac{1}{8}$

9. Line 1 passes through (2, 6) and (4, 4). Line 2 passes through $(-4, 8)$ and $(-6, 6)$. Are the lines parallel? (13.4)   9. No

10. Estimate the slope of the graph. (13.4)   10. $m = \frac{-2}{3}$

56   Alternative Assessment •

Mid-Chapter Test

Mid-Chapter 13 Test   **Form B**   Name _____
(Use after Lesson 13.4)   Date _____

In Exercises 1–3, use the equation $F = 3.28M$, which relates feet F to meters M. (13.1)

1. A door is 2.5 meters high. What is its height in feet? Round your answer to the nearest whole number.   1. 8 feet

2. A room is 16 feet long. What is its length in meters? Round your answer to the nearest whole number.   2. 5 meters

3. Which is a greater distance, a kilometer (1000 meters) or a mile (5280 feet)? Explain.   3. _____
   A mile; 5280 ft ≈ 1610 m > 1000 m

In Exercises 4–7, use the equation $3x + y = 12$. (13.2, 13.3)

4. Decide whether (2, 6) is a solution.   4. Yes

5. Complete a table of values for the equation.   5. _____
   See back of supplement for table.

6. Sketch the graph of the equation.   6.

7. Identify the x and y-intercepts for the equation.   7. x-intercept: 4 y-intercept: 12

In Exercises 8 and 9, find the slope of the line that passes through the points. (13.4)

8. (4, 2), (6, 5)   8. $\frac{3}{2}$

9. $(-2, -3), (-4, -1)$ 9. -1

10. Sketch the graphs of $y = x + 4$ and $y = 2x + 4$ on the same coordinate plane. (13.3)   10.

11. Are the lines parallel? Explain. (13.4)   11. No, their slopes are different so there will be a point of intersection.

216   Chapter 13 • Exploring Linear Equations

Materials Needed: graphing calculator

Example 1 *Comparing Graphs of Linear Equations*

Use a graphing calculator to compare the graphs of the following equations.

a. $y = 2x + 3$ **b.** $y = -x + 3$ **c.** $y = \frac{1}{2}x + 3$

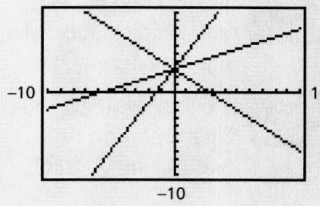

Solution Enter each equation into a graphing calculator. Then graph all three equations on the same calculator screen, as shown at the right. From the screen, you can see that all three lines have the same *y*-intercept. That is, each crosses the *y*-axis at the same point (0, 3).

Example 2 *Comparing Graphs of Linear Equations*

Use a graphing calculator to compare the graphs of the following equations.

a. $y = 2x - 3$ **b.** $y = 2x - 1$ **c.** $y = -2x + 3$

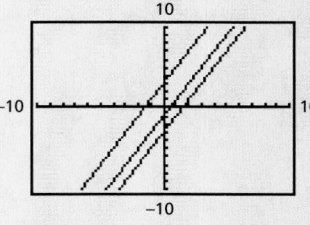

Solution Enter each equation into a graphing calculator. Then graph all three equations on the same calculator screen, as shown at the right. From the screen, you can see that all three lines are parallel. Each has a slope of 2.

■

Exercises

1. Use a graphing calculator to compare the graphs of the following. What can you conclude?   Each has a *y*-intercept of − 4.
    a. $y = -x - 4$ **b.** $y = x - 4$ **c.** $y = -\frac{1}{2}x - 4$

2. Use a graphing calculator to compare the graphs of the following. What can you conclude?   All the lines are parallel with a slope of − 1.
    a. $y = -x + 5$ **b.** $y = -x - 2$ **c.** $y = -x + 1$

3. Without sketching the graph of $y = -x - 4$, find its slope and *y*-intercept. (Use the patterns you found in Exercises 1 and 2.) Use a graphing calculator to confirm your answers.   Slope: − 1, *y*-intercept: − 4

INVESTIGATION Notes

This investigation requires students to graph linear equations using the slope and *y*-intercept. Students are encouraged to explore visual patterns that connect the graph to the equation. Use the investigation as a lab to introduce Lesson 13.5.

    If graphing calculators are not available, the investigation can be demonstrated by the teacher using an overhead graphing calculator.

▶ **PLANNING the Lesson**

Lesson Plan **13.5**, p. 106

ORGANIZER

Starters (reproduced below)
  Problem of the Day 13.5, p. 38
  Warm-Up Exercises 13.5, p. 38
Lesson Resources
  Color Transparencies
    Picture for Ex. 24–26, p. 55
  Teaching Tools
    Coordinate planes, pp. T9, C11
  Math Log, p. 41
  Answer Masters 13.5, pp. 262, 263
  Extra Practice Copymaster 13.5, p. 106
  Reteaching Copymaster 13.5, p. 106
Special Populations
  Suggestions, Teacher's Edition, p. 586D

LESSON Notes

Explain to students that for an equation of the form $y = mx + b$, substituting $x = 0$ will always result in $y = b$. Therefore b is the y-intercept. Have students substitute $x = 0$ and confirm that $y = b$. Have them record the computation in their math journals.

ALTERNATE APPROACH

Verifying the Slope Formula It can also be shown that $\frac{y_2 - y_1}{x_2 - x_1}$ will always result in m.

Challenge students to work in groups to convince themselves of this. As a group activity, have each student make up an equation in the form $y = mx + b$, choose two points that satisfy the equation, and then ask another group member to compute the slope and verify the connection between the slope formula and the value of m in the slope-intercept form of an equation.

Example 1

Note that the "invisible 1" was written in to make identifying the slope easier.

13.5

The Slope-Intercept Form

What you should learn:

Goal 1 How to find the slope and y-intercept of a line from its equation

Goal 2 How to use the slope-intercept form to sketch a quick graph

Why you should learn it:

You can use the slope-intercept form of a line to solve real-life problems, such as finding the annual increase in a population.

Study Tip...
To use the slope-intercept form, you must first be sure that the linear equation is written in the form
$$y = mx + b.$$
For instance, you can write $x + y = 2$ in slope-intercept form by subtracting x from each side to obtain
$$y = -x + 2.$$

Goal 1  **Using the Slope-Intercept Form**

In the *Lesson Investigation* on page 609, you may have discovered that there is a quick way to find the slope and y-intercept of a line. For instance, the line given by $y = 2x + 3$ has a slope of 2 and a y-intercept of 3.

$$y = 2x + 3$$

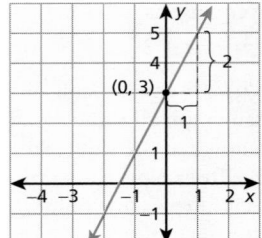

Slope is 2   **y-intercept is 3.**

> **The Slope-Intercept Form of the Equation of a Line**
> The linear equation
> $$y = mx + b$$
> is in **slope-intercept form.** The slope is m. The y-intercept is b.

Example 1   *Using the Slope-Intercept Form*

a. The line given by
$$y = x - 4$$
$$y = 1x + (-4)$$
    Slope   **y-intercept**
has a slope of 1 and a y-intercept of -4.

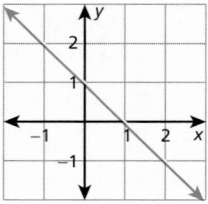

b. The line given by
$$y = -x + 1$$
$$y = (-1)x + 1$$
    Slope   **y-intercept**
has a slope of -1 and a y-intercept of 1.

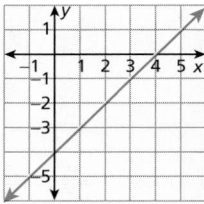

■

Examine the pattern of numbers in each row.

Row 1				1					
Row 2			2	3	4				
Row 3		5	6	7	8	9			
Row 4	10	11	12	13	14	15	16		
Row 5	17	18	19	20	21	22	23	24	25

What is the middle term in the 50th row?

2451; the pattern for the middle term of the nth row is $n^2 - n + 1$

Also available as a copymaster, p. 38

Rewrite the following equations so that they are of the form $y = \_\_\_\_$. For example: $2x + y = 1 \rightarrow y = -2x + 1$.

a. $y - 6x = 8$
b. $5x - y = 3$
c. $6y = 18 - 12x$
d. $3x + 6y = 12$
e. $-5x - y = 7$
f. $2x - 2y = 2$

a. $y = 6x + 8$, **b.** $y = 5x - 3$, **c.** $y = -2x + 3$
d. $y = -\frac{1}{2}x + 2$, **e.** $y = -5x - 7$, **f.** $y = x - 1$

Also available as a copymaster, page 38

In Lesson 13.3, you learned to sketch a line quickly using the *x*-intercept and *y*-intercept. The slope and *y*-intercept can also be used to sketch a quick graph.

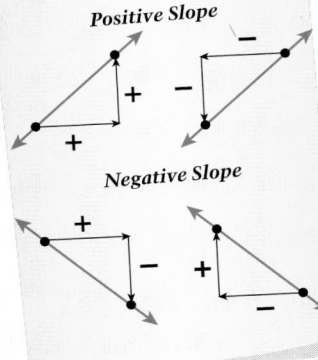

Positive Slope

Negative Slope

Example 2 *Sketching a Quick Graph*

Sketch a quick graph of $y = \frac{1}{2}x + 2$.

Solution Because this equation is in slope-intercept form, you can conclude that the slope is $\frac{1}{2}$ and the *y*-intercept is 2. To sketch the graph, first plot the *y*-intercept, (0, 2). Locate a second point on the line by moving 2 units to the right and 1 unit up. Then draw the line through the two points.

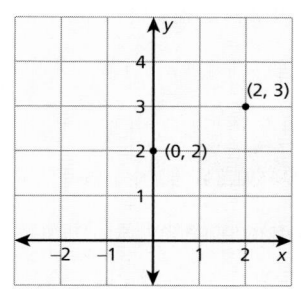

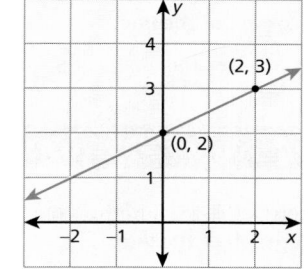

Plot the y-intercept. Then use the slope to find a second point.

Draw the line that passes through the two points. ∎

Communicating *about* MATHEMATICS

▶ **SHARING IDEAS about the Lesson**

Interpreting Slope From 1980 to 1992, the population *P* (in thousands) of Virginia can be modeled by

$$P = 85t + 5350 \qquad \textit{Population Model}$$

where $t = 0$ represents 1980. Copy and complete the table, which shows the population for each year. How is the slope related to the numbers in the table? *(Source: U.S. Bureau of the Census)* For table, see margin.

t	0	1	2	3	4	5	6	7	8	9	10	11	12
P	?	?	?	?	?	?	?	?	?	?	?	?	?

Constructing quick graphs is a convenient way to get useful information about relationships described by linear equations in two variables. The ability to construct quick graphs is a very important skill.

Common-Error Alert!

A common mistake made by students is to think that equations of the form $y = mx$ have no *y*-intercept. Have them record in their math journals that $y = mx$ is the same as $y = mx + 0$ and that the *y*-intercept is 0. (Note that the equation $x = 5$ cannot be put in the form $y = mx + b$ and it does not have a *y*-intercept.)

Example 2

When the slope is an integer, such as in $y = 3x + 5$, this quick graphing method can still be used. The slope can be thought of as $\frac{3}{1}$. Ask students to explain why this is an appropriate substitution.

Communicating *about* MATHEMATICS

Graphing a line is easy if the slope and *y*-intercept are known. Some lines do not have *y*-intercepts or slopes. Ask students whether this makes the lines harder to graph quickly. Discuss this in a small group.

Writing Prompt
In your own words, explain why $y = mx + b$ is called the slope-intercept form of the equation of a line.

Here is an additional example similar to Example 2.
Sketching a Quick Graph
Sketch a quick graph of $x + 2y = 6$.
Solution
The slope-intercept form of $x + 2y = 6$ is $y = -\frac{1}{2}x + 3$. So the slope is $-\frac{1}{2}$ and the *y*-intercept is 3. To sketch the graph, first plot the *y*-intercept, (0,3). Locate a second point on the line by moving 2 units to the left and 1 unit up, or 2 units to the right and 1 unit down. Then draw the line through the two points.

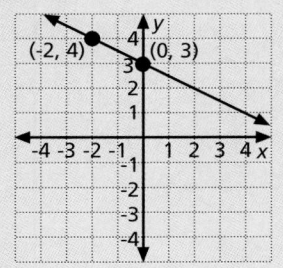

Answer to Communicating

t	p	t	p
0	5350	7	5945
1	5435	8	6030
2	5520	9	6115
3	5605	10	6200
4	5690	11	6285
5	5775	12	6370
6	5860		

EXERCISE Notes

ASSIGNMENT GUIDE

*Basic/Average:
Day 1: Ex. 9–19 odd, 27–30
Day 2: Ex. 20–23, 31–34

Above Average:
Ex. 9–23 odd, 27–37 odd

Advanced: Ex. 9–23 odd, 27–37 odd

Selected Answers: Ex. 1–7, 9–33 odd

*You may wish to omit this lesson for these students.

Guided Practice

▶ **Ex. 3** Have students discuss strategies for discovering the correct equation.
▶ **Ex. 4–7** Use these exercises to check for student understanding of the strategy for graphing shown in Example 2 of the lesson.

Independent Practice

▶ **Ex. 8–15** Ask students which "quick graph" method—using intercepts (Lesson 3.3) or slope-intercepts (Lesson 13.4)—seems more efficient.
The intercepts method is convenient for lines in the format $Ax + By = C$, the slope-intercept method for lines in the format $y = mx + b$.
▶ **Ex. 16–19** Assign these as a group for homework, and have students explain their choices.

Answers
4.

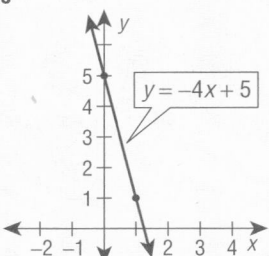

5.

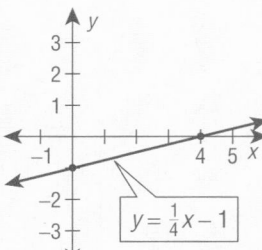

6.

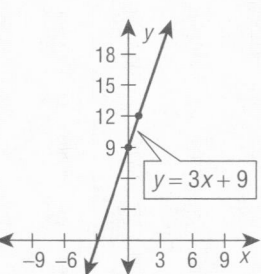

EXERCISES

Guided Practice

▶ **CHECK for Understanding**   2. Subtract $2x$ from each side to get $y = -2x + 5$.

P **1.** *Writing*   In your own words, explain why $y = mx + b$ is called the *slope-intercept form* of the equation of a line.   See page 610.

2. Explain how to write $2x + y = 5$ in slope-intercept form.

3. Which of the following is the equation of the line at the right? (There may be more than one correct equation.)   c and e

a. $y = 2x + 3$ b. $y = 2x - 3$ c. $y = -2x + 3$
d. $y = -2x - 3$ e. $2x + y = 3$ f. $2x - y = 3$

In Exercises 4–7, find the slope and y-intercept of the line. Then sketch a quick graph of the line.   For graphs, see margin.

4. $y = -4x + 5$
$-4, 5$

5. $y = \frac{1}{4}x - 1$
$\frac{1}{4}, -1$

6. $-3x + y = 9$
$3, 9$

7. $x + 2y = 16$
$-\frac{1}{2}, 8$

Independent Practice

For graphs, see Additional Answers.

In Exercises 8–15, find the slope and y-intercept of the line. Then sketch a quick graph of the line.

8. $y = x - 3$ $1, -3$

9. $y = -x + 3$ $-1, 3$

10. $y = -\frac{2}{3}x + 2$ $-\frac{2}{3}, 2$

11. $y = 3x$ $3, 0$

12. $6y = 24x + 30$ $4, 5$

13. $5x + 2y = 0$ $-\frac{5}{2}, 0$

14. $x + \frac{1}{2}y = 1$ $-2, 2$

15. $5x - 10y = 35$
$\frac{1}{2}, -\frac{7}{2}$

In Exercises 16–19, match the equation with its graph.

a.
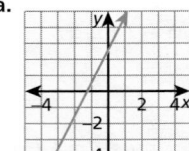

b.
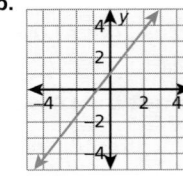

c.
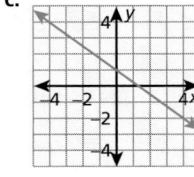

d.
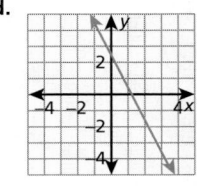

16. $y = -2x + \frac{5}{2}$ d

17. $y = 2x + \frac{5}{2}$ a

18. $y = \frac{4}{3}x + 1$ b

19. $y = -\frac{3}{4}x + 1$ c

Reasoning   **In Exercises 20–23, decide whether the statement is true or false. Explain.**

✪ **20.** The line $2x + 8y = 40$ has a slope of $\frac{1}{4}$ and a y-intercept of 5.   False, slope is $-\frac{1}{4}$.

✪ **21.** The line $3y = 6x + 5$ has a slope of 6 and a y-intercept of 5.   See below.

✪ **22.** The line $-20x + 15y = 15$ has a positive slope.   True, slope is $\frac{4}{3}$.

✪ **23.** If the slope of a line is 0, then the line is horizontal.   True, see margin.

21. False, slope is 2 and y-intercept is $\frac{5}{3}$.

✪ More difficult exercises
P Portfolio Opportunity

Extra Practice

Extra Practice **13.5**   Name ____

1-6. See back of supplement for graphs.

In Exercises 1–6, find the slope and y-intercept of the line. Then sketch a quick graph of the line.
$m = -1/2$; y-intercept: 2 $m = 3$; y-intercept: -2
1. $y = 2x + 4$ 2. $y = -\frac{1}{2}x + 2$ 3. $y = 3x - 2$
$m = 2$; y-intercept: 4
4. $8y = -32x + 56$ 5. $3x + 30y = 0$ 6. $6x + 3y = 27$
$m = -4$; y-intercept: 7 $m = -1/10$; y-intercept: 0 $m = -2$; y-intercept: 9

In Exercises 7–10, match the equation with its graph.

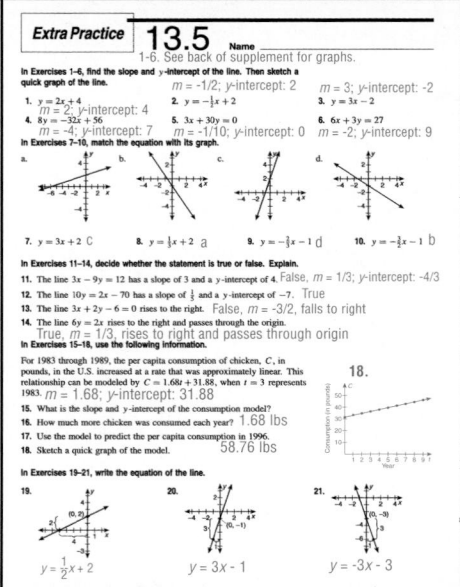

7. $y = 3x + 2$ C   8. $y = \frac{1}{2}x + 2$ a   9. $y = -\frac{3}{4}x - 1$ d   10. $y = -\frac{3}{4}x - 1$ b

In Exercises 11–14, decide whether the statement is true or false. Explain.
11. The line $3x - 9y = 12$ has a slope of 3 and a y-intercept of 4.   False, $m = 1/3$; y-intercept: -4/3
12. The line $10y = 2x - 70$ has a slope of $\frac{1}{5}$ and a y-intercept of -7.   True
13. The line $3x + 2y - 6 = 0$ rises to the right.   False, $m = -3/2$, falls to right
14. The line $6y = 2x$ rises to the right and passes through the origin.   True, $m = 1/3$, rises to right and passes through origin

In Exercises 15–18, use the following information.
For 1983 through 1989, the per capita consumption of chicken, C, in pounds, in the U.S. increased at a rate that was approximately linear. This relationship can be modeled by $C = 1.68t + 31.88$, when $t = 3$ represents 1983. $m = 1.68$; y-intercept: 31.88
15. What is the slope and y-intercept of the consumption model?
16. How much more chicken was consumed each year?   1.68 lbs
17. Use the model to predict the per capita consumption in 1996.   58.76 lbs
18. Sketch a quick graph of the model.

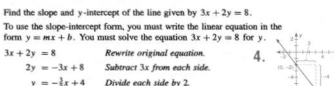

In Exercises 19–21, write the equation of the line.

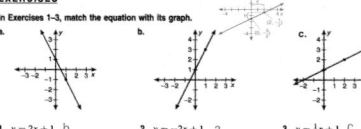

19. $y = \frac{1}{2}x + 2$ 20. $y = 3x - 1$ 21. $y = -3x - 3$

106   *The Slope-Intercept Form* ▪ *13.5*   Windows

Reteaching

Reteach   Chapter 13   Name ____

What you should learn:
13.5   How to find the slope and y-intercept of a line from its equation and how to use the slope-intercept form to sketch a quick graph

Correlation to Pupil's Textbook:
Chapter Test (p. 631)
Exercises 9, 12, 13

Examples   *Using the Slope-Intercept Form and Sketching Quick Graphs*

a. Find the slope and y-intercept of the line given by $y = -2x + 3$. Then sketch a quick graph of the line.

The line given by $y = -2x + 3$ is in the form $y = mx + b$. It has a slope of -2 and a y-intercept of 3. First plot the y-intercept, (0, 3). Locate a second point on the line by moving 1 unit to the right and 2 units down. Draw the line through the two points.

b. Find the slope and y-intercept of the line given by $3x + 2y = 8$.

To use the slope-intercept form, you must write the linear equation in the form $y = mx + b$. You must solve the equation $3x + 2y = 8$ for y.

$3x + 2y = 8$ *Rewrite original equation.*
$2y = -3x + 8$ *Subtract 3x from each side.*
$y = -\frac{3}{2}x + 4$ *Divide each side by 2.*

The line given by $y = -\frac{3}{2}x + 4$ has a slope of $-\frac{3}{2}$ and a y-intercept of 4.

Guidelines: • The linear equation $y = mx + b$ is in slope-intercept form. In this form, m is the slope and b is the y-intercept.

EXERCISES

In Exercises 1–3, match the equation with its graph.

1. $y = 2x + 1$ b   2. $y = -2x + 1$ a   3. $y = \frac{1}{2}x + 1$ C

In Exercises 4–6, find the slope and y-intercept of the line. Then sketch a quick graph for graphs.   4-6. See above for graphs.
4. $y = -\frac{4}{3}x - 2$ 5. $4x - 8y = 0$ 6. $7x - 14y = 21$
$m = -4/3$; $b = -2$ $m = 1/2$; $b = 0$ $m = 1/2$; $b = -3/2$

106   Chapter 13 ▪ *Exploring Linear Equations*   Windows

Population Model   In Exercises 24–26, use the following information.

From 1984 to 1992, the population P (in thousands) of North Carolina can be modeled by

$P = 82.3t + 5830.4$

where $t = 4$ represents 1984.

24. What is the slope and y-intercept of the population model?   82.3, 5830.4

25. How much did North Carolina's population increase each year? Does this rate of change correspond to the slope of the model or to the y-intercept of the model?   82,300; the slope

26. Sketch a quick graph of the model.   See margin.

Charlotte is the most populated city in North Carolina. It is the state's capital and was first settled in the mid-1700s.

In Exercises 27–30, write the equation of the line in slope-intercept form.

27.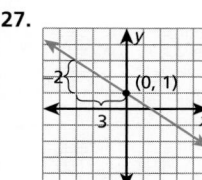

$y = -\frac{2}{3}x + 1$

28.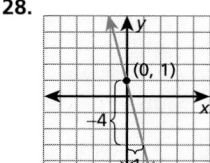

$y = -4x + 1$

29.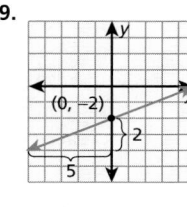

$y = \frac{2}{5}x - 2$

30.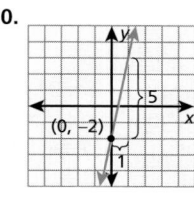

$y = 5x - 2$

Integrated Review

Making Connections within Mathematics

Coordinate Pairs   In Exercises 31–34, match the equation of the line with the pair of points that lie on the line. Explain your reasoning.   For explanation, see margin.

a. $(4, 2), (-2, -1)$ b. $(-2, 0), (4, -3)$ c. $(3, 7), (-1, -1)$ d. $(-1, 4), (3, -4)$

31. $y = 2x + 1$ c   **32.** $y = -2x + 2$ d   **33.** $y = \frac{1}{2}x$ a   **34.** $y = -\frac{1}{2}x - 1$ b

Exploration and Extension

Parallel or Perpendicular?   In Exercises 35–38, use the following information to decide whether the lines are parallel, perpendicular, or neither.

You know that two lines are *parallel* if they have the same slope. For two lines to be *perpendicular*, their slopes must be negative reciprocals of each other. For instance, the lines $y = 2x + 1$ and $y = -\frac{1}{2}x + 1$ are perpendicular because $-\frac{1}{2}$ is the negative reciprocal of 2.

35. $y = 3x - 2$
$y = 3x - 6$
Parallel

✪ **36.** $y = -\frac{1}{3}x + 2$
$y = 3x - 1$
Perpendicular

✪ **37.** $4x + 16y = 24$
$3x + 12y = 24$
Parallel

✪ **38.** $y = x + 1$
$x + y = 1$
Perpendicular

13.5 • *The Slope-Intercept Form*   **613**

> **Enrichment**
>
> Ask students to write a paragraph story that describes the graph below.

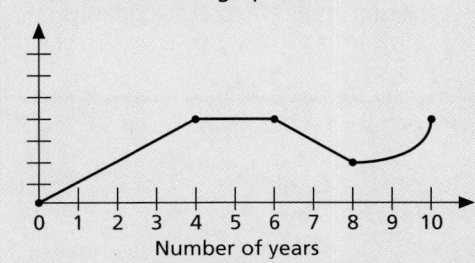

Number of years

▶ **Ex. 24–26**   In these exercises, $t = 4$ is used to represent the year 1984 to help clarify the model correspondence to the year.
▶ **Ex. 27–30**   Assign these after providing several models for the students.

Integrated Review

This section provides a quick review of Lessons 13.1 and 13.2.

Exploration and Extension

Connect these exercises to Lesson 10.3, page 448.

Portfolio Opportunity: Math Log

When making a sketch of a line that is given in slope-intercept form, in what order do you use the given information? Explain your answer.

Also available as a copymaster, page 41, Ex. 6

Alternative Assessment

Two graphing calculator projects that develop students' graphing calculator skills.

Available as a copymaster, pages 39, 40

Answers
7.

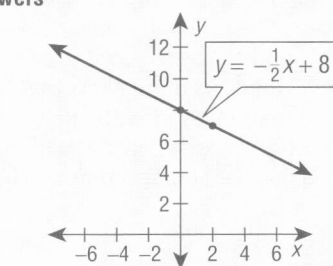

23. If the slope is 0, $\frac{y_2 - y_1}{x_2 - x_1} = 0$. Therefore, the numerator $y_2 - y_1 = 0$, and $y_2 = y_1$. Two points with the same y-coordinates are the same distance from the x-axis, so the line is horizontal.

26.

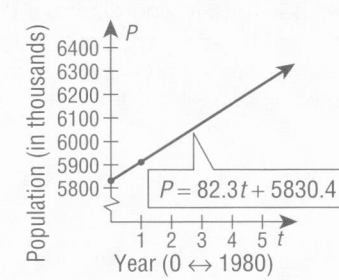

Year (0 ⟷ 1980)

31.–34. Compute the slope of the line that contains each pair of points in Parts a, b, c, and d. Then match the computed slopes with the coefficients of x in the equations.

PACING the Lesson

Suggested Number of Days
Basic/Average 0   Above Average 1
Advanced 1

PLANNING the Lesson

Lesson Plan 13.6, p. 107

ORGANIZER

Starters (reproduced below)
    Problem of the Day 13.6, p. 38
    Warm-Up Exercises 13.6, p. 38
Lesson Resources
    Color Transparencies
        Graph for Ex. 11, p. 56
    Teaching Tools
        Graph paper, pp. T1, C2
        Puzzle for Ex. 17, p. C31
    Math Log, p. 42
    Technology, pp. 76, 77
    Answer Masters 13.6, pp. 264, 265
    Extra Practice Copymaster 13.6, p. 107
    Reteaching Copymaster 13.6, p. 107
Special Populations
    Suggestions, Teacher's Edition, p. 586D

LESSON Notes

Vocabulary ALERT!

Remind students that a pair of numbers "satisfies" a linear equation if, upon substituting the number values into the equation, the resulting equation is a true statement. Point out that any pair of numbers that satisfies a linear equation can be expressed as an ordered pair of numbers that lie on the graph of the linear equation. The graph of a linear equation is a line and can be thought of as a picture of all the pairs of numbers that satisfy the equation. By identifying points on the graph of a linear equation, we can find pairs of numbers that satisfy the equation.

Example 1

Note that both x and y must be integers for the solution to make sense. Ask students how they can quickly recognize places on the graph that have integer coordinates. Ask whether any of the number pairs might include negative integers and have students explain their answers.

13.6 Problem Solving with Linear Equations

What you should learn:

Goal 1 How to use graphs of linear equations to solve real-life problems

Goal 2 How to use scatter plots to create graphical models

Why you should learn it:

You can use graphs of linear equations to solve real-life problems, such as analyzing the ticket sales necessary to raise a given amount of money.

Real Life
Ticket Prices

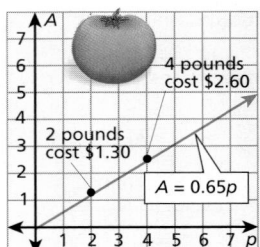

Goal 1   Using Graphs of Linear Equations

Throughout this chapter, you have studied several real-life situations that can be modeled with linear equations. Two quantities that can be modeled with a linear equation are said to have a **linear relationship.**

For instance, suppose tomatoes cost $0.65 a pound. The cost A (in dollars) of p pounds of tomatoes can be modeled by $A = 0.65p$. From the graph at the right, you can see that the relationship between A and p is linear. Each time you buy 1 more pound, the cost increases by $0.65.

4 pounds cost $2.60

2 pounds cost $1.30

$A = 0.65p$

Example 1   *Interpreting Linear Models*

You are planning a dinner to raise money for a volunteer fire department. You plan to charge $8 per adult and $4 per child, and want to raise $1200. Use a graph to analyze the following model.

Verbal Model $8 \cdot$ Number of Adults $+ \$4 \cdot$ Number of Children $= \$1200$

Labels   Number of adults $= x$
              Number of children $= y$

Algebraic Model $8 \cdot x + 4 \cdot y = 1200$

Solution One way to begin is to create a table of values. You can use the table of values to sketch a graph, as shown at the left. Notice that there are many ways to raise $1200. For instance, you could sell 150 adult tickets, or you could sell 100 adult tickets and 100 tickets for children.

x	0	25	50	75	100	125	150
y	300	250	200	150	100	50	0

Graph:
300 (0, 300)
250
200
Children
150
100 (100, 100)
50
(150, 0)
50 100 150 200 250 x
Adults

Using Scatter Plots

Real Life
Travel

Example 2 — *Using a Scatter Plot*

The amount of money A (in billions of dollars) spent by U.S. citizens in Latin America from 1985 through 1992 is given in the table. The year is represented by t with $t = 1$ corresponding to 1985. Draw a scatter plot of the data and use the result to estimate the amount spent in 1994.

Year	1985	1986	1987	1988	1989	1990	1991	1992
t	1	2	3	4	5	6	7	8
A	4.0	4.3	4.8	5.2	5.1	5.4	5.8	6.9

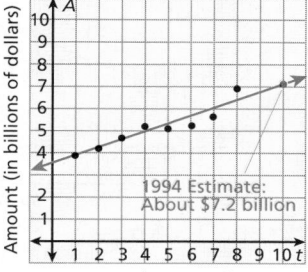

Solution Begin by writing the data as ordered pairs: (1, 4.0), (2, 4.3), (3, 4.8), (4, 5.2), (5, 5.1), (6, 5.4), (7, 5.8), and (8, 6.9). Then sketch a scatter plot, as shown at the left. From the scatter plot, it appears that variables almost have a linear relationship. Sketch the line that you think best fits the points. Then, use the line to estimate the amount spent in 1994. Using the point (10, 7.2), you can estimate that U.S. citizens spent about $7.2 billion in Latin America in 1994. ■

Communicating about MATHEMATICS

Cooperative Learning

▶ **SHARING IDEAS about the Lesson**

Using a Scatter Plot The scatter plot shown below shows the population (in thousands) of three different states from 1980 through 1992 with $t = 0$ corresponding to 1980. Use the scatter plot to estimate the population of each state in 1995 and 1998. *(Source: U.S. Bureau of the Census)*

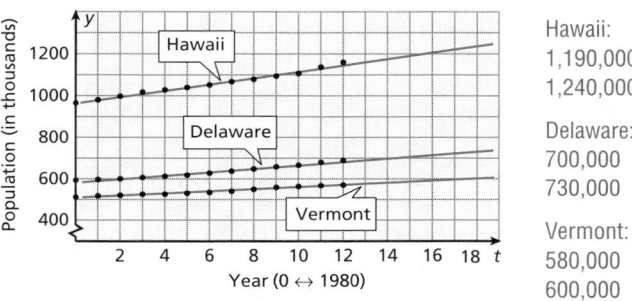

Hawaii:
1,190,000
1,240,000

Delaware:
700,000
730,000

Vermont:
580,000
600,000

Challenge students to give other examples of relationships between quantities in real life that are approximately linear. (Recall Lesson Investigation 13.2.)

Example 2

Be sure that students recognize how values from 1 to 8 can be used to represent years 1985 through 1992.

Communicating about MATHEMATICS

GROUP PROJECT
Have students suggest common quantities that they think might have a relationship that is approximately linear. Examples might include height and weight; time studied for a test and grade obtained. Have each group collect real data for one of their suggestions and make a scatter plot. Decide whether the relationship appears to be nearly linear. Use the scatter plot to make estimates about other data points.

Writing Prompt
Write a paragraph describing your feelings about being in math class this year.

Technology

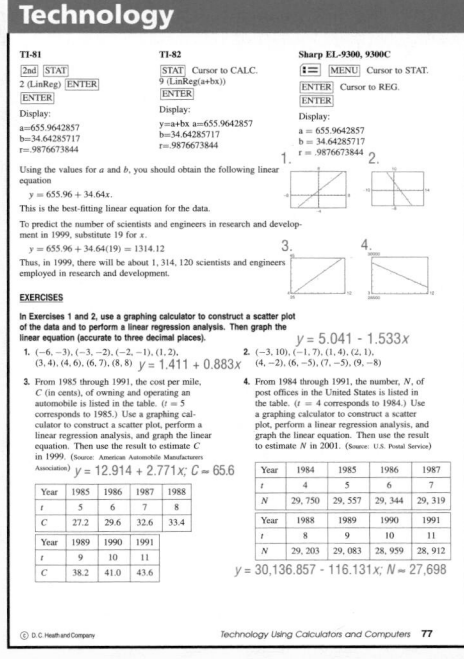

ASSIGNMENT GUIDE

*Basic/Average:
Day 1: Ex. 7–11 odd
Day 2: Ex. 13–17

Above Average:
Ex. 7–17

Advanced: Ex. 7–17

Selected Answers: Ex. 1–6, 7–15 odd

*You may wish to omit this lesson for these students.

Guided Practice

▶ **Ex. 1–2**
EXTENSION
Discuss with students the fact that exponential growth is constant *percent* rate of change.
▶ **Ex. 3–6** Use these as an in-class summary activity.

Independent Practice

▶ **Ex. 7, 8,** and **10** Refer students to Example 2 of the lesson.

Answers

4.

x	10	20	30	40
y	30	24	18	12

5.
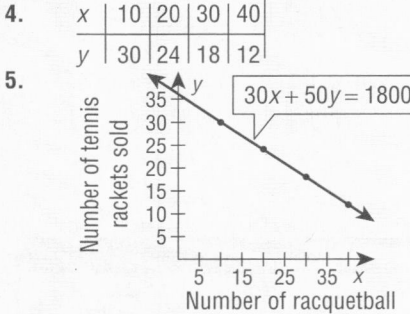

7.
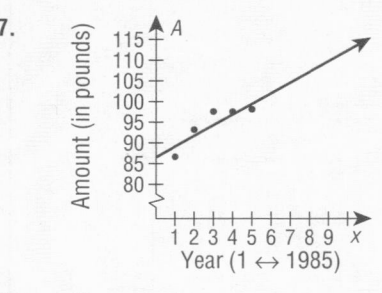

8.
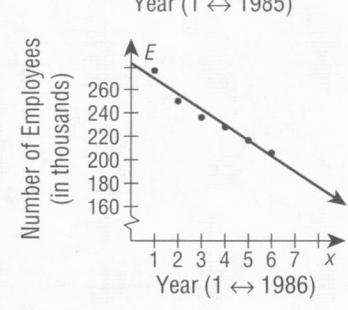

Guided Practice

▶ **CHECK for Understanding**

Which Is Linear? In Exercises 1 and 2, you have two companies. In Company A, the number of employees is increasing by 10% each year. In Company B, the number of employees is increasing by 10 each year. Let *n* be the number of employees and let *t* be the year, as indicated in the graph at the right.

1. For which company do *n* and *t* have a linear relationship? B

2. Each company began with 100 employees. How many employees will each company have in 10 years? A: 261, B: ≈200

P **Tennis and Racquetball** In Exercises 3–6, your company makes tennis rackets that sell for $50, and racquetball rackets that sell for $30. Your daily goal is to sell $1800 worth of rackets.

$$\$30 \cdot \begin{array}{c}\text{Number of}\\\text{racquetball}\\\text{rackets sold}\end{array} + \$50 \cdot \begin{array}{c}\text{Number of}\\\text{tennis rackets}\\\text{sold}\end{array} = \$1800$$

3. Write an algebraic model to represent the verbal model. $30x + 50y = 1800$

4. Find several solutions of the model. Organize the solutions with a table.

5. Sketch a graph for the data in Exercise 4. **4., 5.** See margin.

6. Interpret the intercepts of the graph in a real-life context. If only one kind of racket is sold, selling 60 racquetball rackets or 36 tennis rackets is necessary to reach your goal.

Independent Practice

7., 8. For scatter plots, see margin.

✪ 7. **Fruit Consumption** For 1985 through 1989, the average amount of fresh fruit *A* (in pounds) consumed by an American in a year is given in the table. Use a scatter plot to estimate the amount for 1994. **(Source: U.S. Department of Agriculture)** 115

✪ 8. **Railroad Employees** From 1986 through 1991, the number of railroad employees, *E* (in 1000s), is given in the table. Use a scatter plot to estimate the number (in 1000s) for 1993. **(Source: Association of American Railroads)** 176

Year	1985	1986	1987	1988	1989
A	86.8	93.1	97.5	97.4	98.8

Year	1986	1987	1988	1989	1990	1991
E	276	249	236	228	216	206

P 9. **Flowers** Your class is selling carnations and roses. Carnations cost $1.50 each and roses cost $3.00 each. Your class wants to earn $600. See margin.

a. Write a verbal and an algebraic model to represent the sales.

b. Create a table of values and graph the model.

c. Interpret the intercepts of the graph in a real-life context.

✪ More difficult exercises
P Portfolio Opportunity

Extra Practice

Reteaching

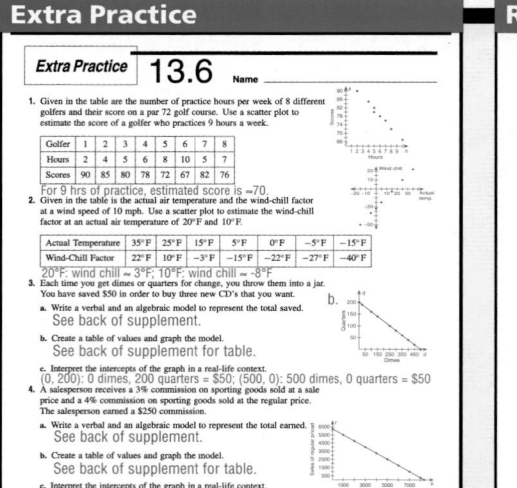

10. *Baseball Attendance* For 1984 through 1991, the attendance *A* (in thousands) at major league games is given in the table. Draw a scatter plot of the data and use the result to estimate the attendance in 1994. *(Source: The National League of Professional Baseball Clubs)* For scatter plot, see margin.

Year	1984	1985	1986	1987	1988	1989	1990	1991	
A	45,262	47,742	48,452	53,182	53,800	55,910	55,512	57,820	63,800

11. *Aluminum Cans* From 1972 through 1992, the number of cans produced from one pound of aluminum is shown in the graph at the right. *(Source: The Aluminum Association)*

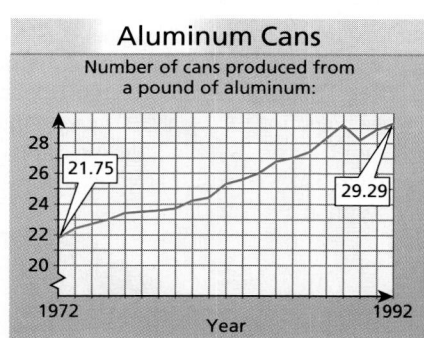

Aluminum Cans
Number of cans produced from a pound of aluminum:

   a. Estimate the number produced in 1980 and in 1987. 24.2, 27.4

   b. What does this graph tell you about aluminum cans produced during this 20-year period?

   c. Describe the pattern. Do you think the pattern could continue for another 20 years? Explain your reasoning. **b., c.** See margin.

12. *Chemistry* A pan of water that is 68°F is heated until it boils at 212°F. The graph at the right shows the time required to heat the water.

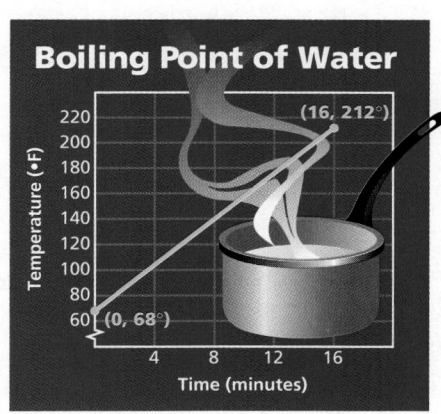

Boiling Point of Water

   a. How many minutes did it take the water to boil? 16

   b. Write a real-life interpretation of the slope by completing the following. "The water temperature increased at a rate of ? degrees per minute." 9

   c. Write a real-life interpretation of the *y*-intercept. "When the pan was put on the stove the water temperature was ? degrees" 68

Integrated Review   *Making Connections within Mathematics*

Visualizing Equations   **In Exercises 13–16, match the equation with its graph.**

a.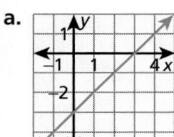
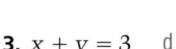

b.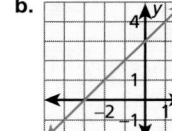
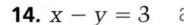

c.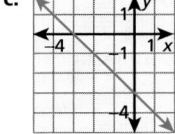

d.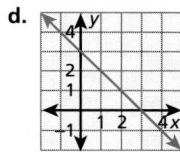

13. $x + y = 3$ d   **14.** $x - y = 3$ a   **15.** $x + y = -3$ c   **16.** $x - y = -3$ b

13.6 ▪ *Problem Solving with Linear Equations*   **617**

Answers
9. a.
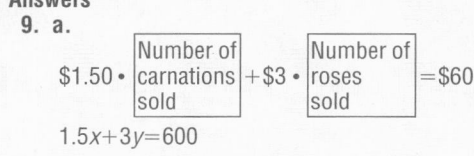

$$1.5x + 3y = 600$$

   b.
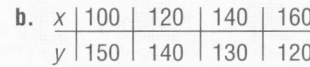

x	100	120	140	160
y	150	140	130	120

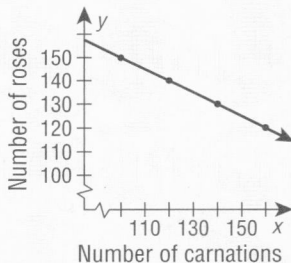

   c. If only one kind of flower is sold, selling 400 carnations or 200 roses is necessary to reach your goal.

10.
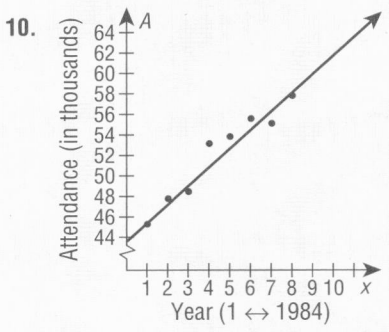

11. **b.** The amount of aluminum per can decreased.

   c. The pattern is close to being linear. Answers vary, but the limit would probably be reached before another 20 years.

ALTERNATIVE ASSESSMENT

Assign these exercises as out-of-class alternative assessment projects. After researching Ex. 18, students can prepare class presentations.

Portfolio Opportunity: Math Log

If three people were given the same data and asked to create a scatter plot and sketch a line that best fits the points, must all three people reach the same conclusion? Explain your answer. What guidelines would you use to sketch the line?

Also available as a copymaster, page 42, Ex. 7

Short Quiz

Covers Lessons 13.5 and 13.6

Available as a copymaster, page 217

Answers
17.

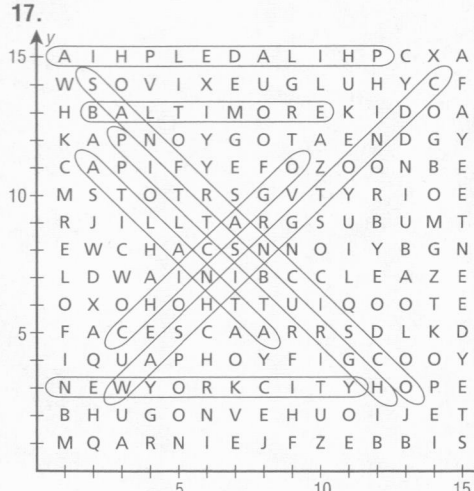

Answers to Mixed Review
5. It is the quotient of two integers.
6. Its decimal form terminates.
7. Its decimal form neither terminates nor repeats.
8. It is the quotient of two integers.

Exploration and Extension

17. For art, see margin.

✪ **17.** *Mass Transportation Puzzle* Eight different cities in the United States that use subways as part of their mass transportation system are hidden in the graph at the right. Find each city, then state the y-intercept and slope of its line. See below.

✪ **18.** *Research Project* Use your school's library or some other reference source to find data about the population of a state or country over a period of at least 10 years. Organize your findings with a table and a graph. Then use your results to predict the population at a future date.
Check students' work.

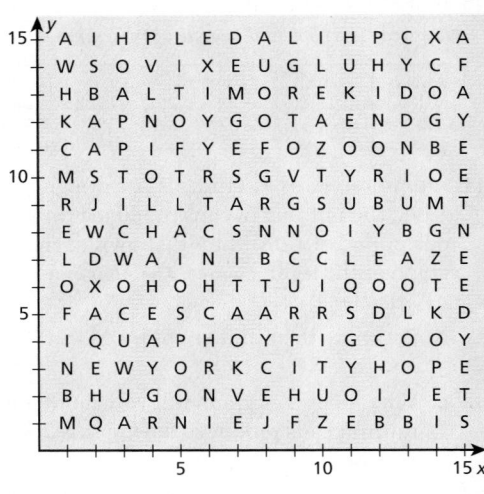

17. Atlanta: 13, −1   Pittsburgh: 15, −1
      Baltimore: 13, 0   New York City: 3, 0
      Chicago: 2, 1   San Francisco: 16, −1
      Philadelphia: 15, 0   Washington, D.C.: 0, 1

Mixed **REVIEW**

In Exercises 1–4, find the slope and y-intercept of the line. (13.5)

1. $y = 13x + 2$ **2.** $y = 4x + 21$ **3.** $3y = 12 + 3x$ **4.** $x = 2y + 4$
      13, 2   4, 21   1, 4 $\frac{1}{2}, -2$

In Exercises 5–8, decide whether the numbers are rational or irrational. Explain. (9.2)   For explanations, see margin.

5. $\frac{2}{3}$ Rational   **6.** $\sqrt{529}$ Rational   **7.** $\sqrt{599}$ Irrational   **8.** $\sqrt{\dfrac{81}{256}}$ Rational

In Exercises 9–12, find the least common multiple of the numbers. (6.4)

9. 24 and 36   72   **10.** 312 and 210   **11.** 111 and 55   6105   **12.** 176 and 264   528
                           10,920

In Exercises 13–16, solve the percent equation. (8.4)

13. What is 18% of 32?   5.76   **14.** 15 is 45% of what number? $33\frac{1}{3}$
15. 72 is what percent of 36?   200%   **16.** 17 is what percent of 40? $42\frac{1}{2}$%

In Exercises 17–20, decide whether the numbers can be side lengths of a triangle. (9.8)

17. 12, 24, 30   Yes   **18.** 21, 26, 46   Yes   **19.** 13, 14, 29   No   **20.** 18, 18, 38   No

✪ More difficult exercises
P Portfolio Opportunity

Enrichment

Refer students to Ex. 7, 8, and 10. By examining the amount of change between successive y-values, approximate predictions for future values could be made.

13.7

Graphs of Linear Inequalities

What you should learn:

Goal 1 How to check whether an ordered pair is a solution of linear inequality

Goal 2 How to sketch the graph of a linear inequality

Why you should learn it:

You can use graphs of linear inequalities to solve real-life problems, such as analyzing the ticket sales of a fund-raising dinner.

Goal 1 · Solutions of Linear Inequalities

In this lesson, you will study **linear inequalities** in x and y. Here are some examples.

$$y < mx + b, \quad y \le mx + b, \quad y > mx + b, \quad y \ge mx + b$$

An ordered pair (x, y) is a **solution** of a linear inequality if the inequality is true when the values of x and y are substituted into the inequality. For instance, $(1, 7)$ is a solution of $y > x + 5$ because $7 > 1 + 5$ is a true statement.

Example 1 *Checking Solutions of Inequalities*

Check whether the ordered pairs are solutions of $y \le -2x + 4$.

a. $(1, 1)$ **b.** $(2, 0)$ **c.** $(3, 0)$

Solution

(x, y)	Substitute	Conclusion
a. $(1, 1)$	$1 \overset{?}{\le} -2(1) + 4$	$(1, 1)$ is a solution.
b. $(2, 0)$	$0 \overset{?}{\le} -2(2) + 4$	$(2, 0)$ is a solution.
c. $(3, 0)$	$0 \overset{?}{\le} -2(3) + 4$	$(3, 0)$ is not a solution.

The graph of all solutions of $y \le -2x + 4$ is shown at the left. The blue region represents the solutions. For instance the points $(1, 1)$ and $(2, 0)$ lie in the blue region but the point $(3, 0)$ lies in the yellow region. From the graph, can you identify other solutions of the inequality? ∎

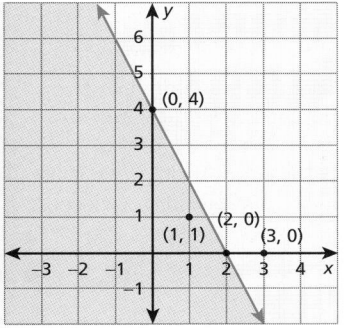

P LESSON INVESTIGATION

■ **Investigating Graphs of Linear Inequalities**

Group Activity Sketch the graph of $y = x + 2$. Then test several points above the line and below the line. Which group of points contains solutions of the inequality $y \ge x + 2$? What can you conclude about the graph of a linear inequality?   See answers at the left.

The group above the line; the graph contains all the points that are on one side of a line.

13.7 · *Graphs of Linear Inequalities*   **619**

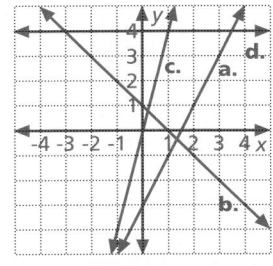

Lesson 13.7 **619**

Explain to students that the graph of a linear inequality is a half-plane, but in practice we can show only a small portion of this half-plane.

Example 2

Ask students:
What would the inequality $8x + 4y \geq 1200$ represent?

Communicating about MATHEMATICS

Challenge students to give real-life examples of quantities that are related by a linear inequality.   Answers will vary; one example is money invested at two different rates in order to make at least a specified return on the investment.

Writing Prompt
Explain the major differences between linear equations and linear inequalities.

The graph of $y < \frac{1}{2}x + 2$

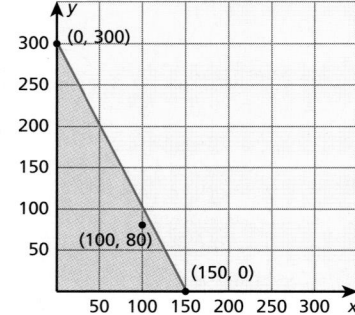

Real Life
Ticket Sales

Goal 2   **Graphing Linear Inequalities**

In the investigation on page 619, you may have discovered that the graph of the linear inequality $y \geq x + 2$ is a half-plane. This observation can be generalized to describe the graph of *any* linear inequality.

Sketching the Graph of a Linear Inequality
The graph of a linear inequality is a **half-plane** that consists of all points on one side of the line that is the graph of the corresponding linear equation.

For the inequality symbols $\geq$ and $\leq$, the points on the line are part of the graph. For the inequality symbols $>$ and $<$, the points on the line are not part of the graph (this is indicated by a dashed line).

Example 2   *Graphing a Linear Inequality*

In Example 1 on page 614, the linear model $8x + 4y = 1200$ represented the different ways that you could sell $8 adult tickets and $4 tickets for children to earn $1200 at a fund-raising dinner. Sketch the graph of

$$8x + 4y \leq 1200.$$

What do the solutions of this inequality represent?

Solution   The graph of this linear inequality is shown at the left. The solutions represent the different ways that you could sell tickets to earn an amount that is *less than or equal to* $1200. For instance, the point (100, 80) is a solution. With this solution you would have sold 100 adult tickets and 80 tickets for children for a total of

$$8(100) + 4(80) = \$1120. \quad \blacksquare$$

P

Communicating about MATHEMATICS

▶ **SHARING IDEAS about the Lesson**

Extending the Example Describe some other solutions of the inequality in Example 2. Which of the solutions represents the greatest number of ticket sales? Is this solution reasonable in the context of the example?

Answers vary; (0, 300); yes, when no adult tickets are sold you have to sell 300 tickets for children

---

OPTION: Extra Examples

Here is an additional example similar to Example 1.
Checking Solutions of Inequalities
Check whether the ordered pairs are solutions of $2x - 5y > 10$.
  a. (5, 0)   **b.** (1, −2)   **c.** (−1, −3)
Solution

(x, y)	Substitute	Conclusion
a. (5, 0)	$2(5) - 5(0) > 10$	(5, 0) is not a solution.
b. (1, −2)	$2(1) - 5(−2) > 10$	(1, −2) is a solution.
c. (−1, −3)	$2(−1) - 5(−3) > 10$	(−1, −3) is a solution.

The graph of all solutions of $2x - 5y > 10$ is shown. The shaded region represents the solutions. For instance, (1, −2) and (−1, −3) lie in the shaded region, but (5, 0) does not since the dotted line $2x - 5y = 10$ is not part of the graph.

EXERCISES

Guided Practice

▶ **CHECK for Understanding**

A solid line consists of points that are on the graph. A dashed line consists of points that are not on the graph.

In Exercises 1–4, does the inequality's graph use a solid or dashed line? Explain.

1. $x + y \geq 10$ Solid

2. $3x + 7y > 42$ Dashed

3. $12x - 17y < 200$ Dashed

4. $-9x + 20y \leq 150$ Solid

In Exercises 5–8, use the graph of $y > 2x - 4$ at the right.

5. Is $(2, 3)$ a solution?   Yes

6. Is $(3, 2)$ a solution?   No

7. Name five other solutions of the inequality.   Answers vary.

8. Find the slope and y-intercept of the dashed line. $2, -4$

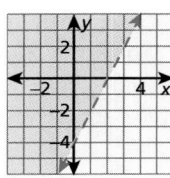

In Exercises 9–12, sketch the graph of the inequality.   See margin.

9. $y \leq x + 3$

10. $y \geq \frac{1}{2}x - 1$

11. $x - y > 2$

12. $x > -2$

Independent Practice

In Exercises 13–16, is the ordered pair a solution of $4x + 6y \leq 48$? Explain.

13. $(5, 5)$ No
$4 \cdot 5 + 6 \cdot 5 > 48$

14. $(10, -2)$ Yes
$4 \cdot 10 + 6(-2) \leq 48$

15. $(-2, 10)$ No
$4(-2) + 6 \cdot 10 > 48$

16. $(6, 4)$ Yes
$4 \cdot 6 + 6 \cdot 4 \leq 48$

In Exercises 17–20, match the inequality with its graph.

a. 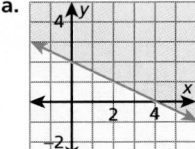   b. 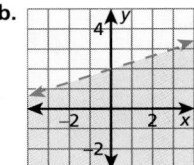   c. 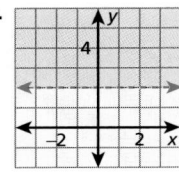   d.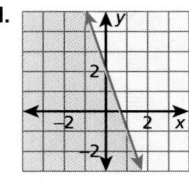

17. $y < \frac{1}{3}x + 2$ b

18. $y > 2$ c

19. $-3x - y \geq -2$ d

20. $x + 2y \geq 4$ a

In Exercises 21–24, graph the inequality. Then list several solutions.   Lists vary.

21. $y \leq \frac{1}{4}x + 1$

22. $y > -2x - 2$

23. $x + y < 25$

24. $4x + 3y \geq 9$

21.–24. For graphs, see Additional Answers.

In Exercises 25 and 26, use the following statement.

The sum of twice a number and five times another number is less than 30.

25. Which of the following inequalities represents the sentence?   b
   a. $7y < 30$ **b.** $2x + 5y < 30$ **c.** $2x + 5y > 30$ **d.** $2x + 5x < 30$

26. Graph the inequality in Exercise 25. Then list several solutions.
   Lists vary. For graph, see Additional Answers.

13.7 ▪ *Graphs of Linear Inequalities*   **621**

Extra Practice

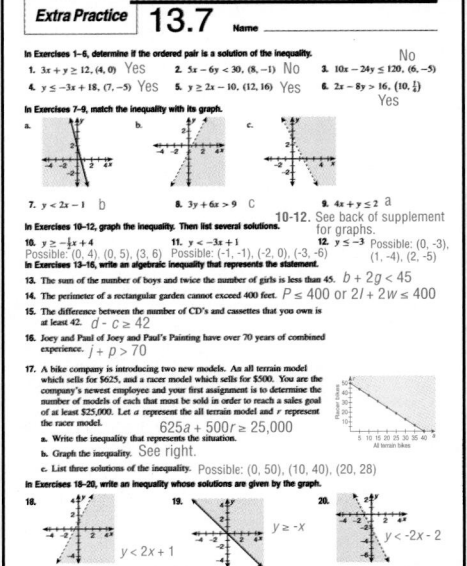

Reteaching

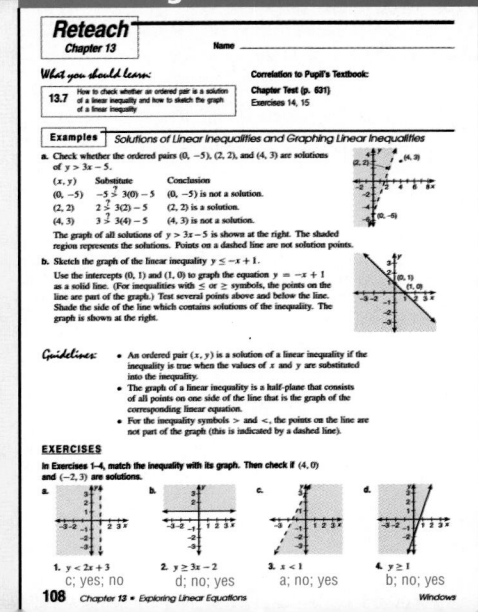

EXERCISE Notes

ASSIGNMENT GUIDE

*Basic/Average:
   Day 1: Ex. 13–19, 21–26
   Day 2: Ex. 27–35, 37, 39

Above Average:
   Day 1: Ex. 13–19, 21–26
   Day 2: Ex. 31–40

Advanced: Ex. 13–25, 31–40

Selected Answers: Ex. 1–12, 13–35 odd

*You may wish to omit this lesson for these students.

Guided Practice

Use this section as an in-class small-group summary.

Independent Practice

▶ **Ex. 17–20**   Students should explain their reasoning for each choice.
▶ **Ex. 25, 26**   Refer students to Example 3 of the lesson.

Answers
9.

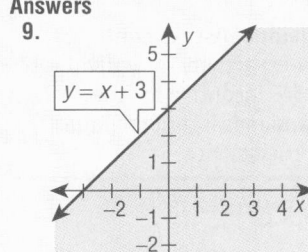

10.

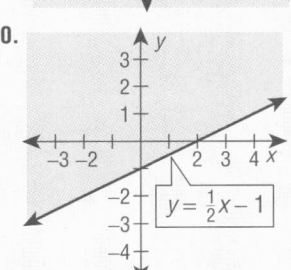

11.

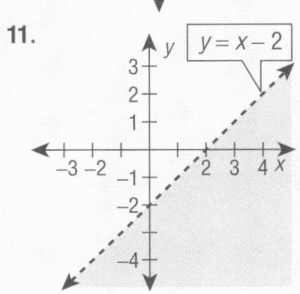

12.

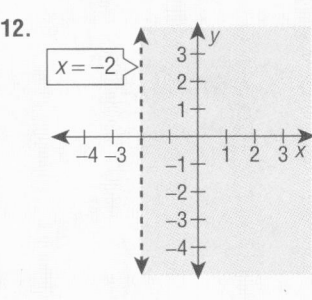

Lesson 13.7   **621**

Completing a Marathon **In Exercises 27–30, use the information in the photo caption and the following.**

You are in a marathon race (26.2 miles). To finish the marathon, you realize that you must walk part of the way. Let x represent the number of miles you walk and y represent the number of miles you run.

✪ **27.** You're not sure you can finish the marathon. Which of the following inequalities best describes your situation? Explain. c
   a. $x + y = 26.2$ b. $x + y \geq 26.2$ For explanation, see
   c. $x + y \leq 26.2$ d. $x + y < 26.2$ margin.

✪ **28.** Sketch a graph of the correct inequality in Exercise 27.

✪ **29.** Which of the inequalities in Exercise 27 can be interpreted as saying that "you are sure that you cannot finish the marathon." d

✪ **30.** *Problem Solving* Write a real-life interpretation of the other
Ⓟ two inequalities in Exercise 27. See margin.
   28. See Additional Answers.

A marathon is a long-distance race that covers 26.2 miles.

In Exercises 31–34, write an equation of the inequality.

31.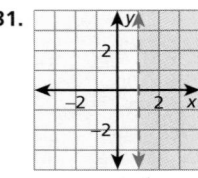
$x > 1$

32.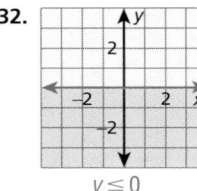
$y \leq 0$

33.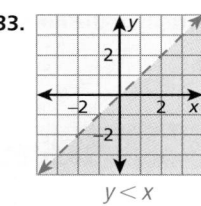
$y < x$

34.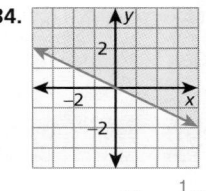
$y \geq -\frac{1}{2}x$

Integrated Review   *Making Connections within Mathematics*

Ⓟ *Error Analysis* **In Exercises 35 and 36, find the error in the graph, then correct it.**

35. $-2x + y > 2$
Line should be dashed.

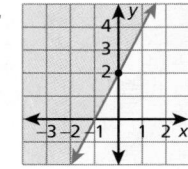

36. $9x - 3y \geq 12$
Shading should be below the line.

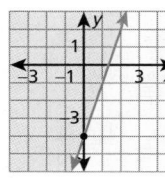

Exploration and Extension

Geometry **In Exercises 37–40, graph each inequality on the same coordinate plane. Identify the geometric figure formed by the set of points that are solutions of all the inequalities.** For graphs, see Additional Answers.

Isosceles trapezoid

✪ **37.** $\begin{cases} x \geq -3 \\ x \leq 3 \\ y \geq -2 \\ y \leq 2 \end{cases}$
Rectangle

✪ **38.** $\begin{cases} y < -x + 4 \\ x \geq 0 \\ y \geq 0 \end{cases}$
Right isosceles triangle

✪ **39.** $\begin{cases} y < x + 3 \\ y > x \\ y \geq -1 \\ y < 3 \end{cases}$
Parallelogram

✪ **40.** $\begin{cases} y < -\frac{1}{2}x + 4 \\ y > \frac{1}{2}x - 4 \\ x > -2 \\ x < 4 \end{cases}$

✪ More difficult exercises
Ⓟ Portfolio Opportunity

622 *Chapter 13 • Exploring Linear Equations*

Answers
27. The sum of the number of miles you walk and the number of miles you run could be equal to 26.2 if you finish the race, or could be less than 26.2 if you do not finish the race.
30. a. You are sure you can finish the marathon and not go any farther.
    b. You are sure you can finish the marathon and perhaps go farther.

13.8 The Distance and Midpoint Formulas

PACING the Lesson

Suggested Number of Days
Basic/Average 0   Above Average 2
Advanced 1

PLANNING the Lesson

Lesson Plan 13.8, p. 109

What you should learn:

Goal 1 How to find the distance between two points

Goal 2 How to find the midpoint between two points

Why you should learn it:

You can use the distance and midpoint formulas to solve real-life problems, such as finding a location for a telephone pole.

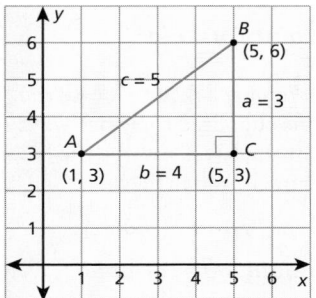

Goal 1 Using the Distance Formula

Suppose you were asked to find the distance between the points $A(1, 3)$ and $B(5, 6)$. How would you do it? One way is to draw a right triangle that has the line segment $\overline{AB}$ as its hypotenuse. The right angle occurs at the point C $(5, 3)$. As shown at the left, the lengths of the legs of the right triangle are

$$a = 6 - 3 = 3 \quad \text{and} \quad b = 5 - 1 = 4.$$

Using the Pythagorean Theorem, you can find the length of the hypotenuse.

$c^2 = a^2 + b^2$	*Pythagorean Theorem*
$c^2 = (3)^2 + (4)^2$	*Substitute for a and b.*
$c^2 = 25$	*Simplify.*
$c = 5$	*Square root principle*

By performing this process with two general points (x_1, y_1) and (x_2, y_2), you can obtain the **Distance Formula.**

> **The Distance Formula**
> The distance, d, between the points (x_1, y_1) and (x_2, y_2) is
> $$d = \sqrt{(x_2 - x_1)^2 + (y_2 - y_1)^2}.$$

Example 1 *The Distance between Two Points*

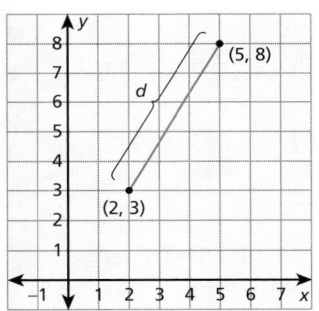

Find the distance between $(2, 3)$ and $(5, 8)$.

Solution Let $(x_1, y_1) = (2, 3)$ and $(x_2, y_2) = (5, 8)$.

$$\begin{aligned}
d &= \sqrt{(x_2 - x_1)^2 + (y_2 - y_1)^2} \\
&= \sqrt{(5 - 2)^2 + (8 - 3)^2} \\
&= \sqrt{3^2 + 5^2} \\
&= \sqrt{34} \\
&\approx 5.83
\end{aligned}$$

The distance between the points is about 5.83 units. ∎

13.8 • The Distance and Midpoint Formulas **623**

ORGANIZER

Starters (reproduced below)
    Problem of the Day 13.8, p. 39
    Warm-Up Exercises 13.8, p. 39
Lesson Resources
    Color Transparencies
        Diagram for Ex. 25, 26, p. 57
    Teaching Tools
        Coordinate planes, pp. T9, C11
    Math Log, p. 42
    Technology, p. 78
    Answer Masters 13.8, p. 269
    Extra Practice Copymaster 13.8, p. 109
    Reteaching Copymaster 13.8, p. 109
Special Populations
    Suggestions, Teacher's Edition, p. 586D

LESSON Notes

Common-Error Alert!

Review the Pythagorean Theorem and remind students of the order of operations. A common error is to compute $(a + b)^2$ instead of $a^2 + b^2$. Demonstrate the difference between the expressions by using appropriate examples.

Example 1

Have students draw the corresponding right triangle and label the coordinates of the vertex of the right angle. Then, in preparation for the next example, ask students to identify the midpoint of each leg of the right triangle.   Vertex of the right angle: (5, 3); midpoint of the horizontal leg: (3.5, 3); midpoint of the vertical leg: (5, 5.5)

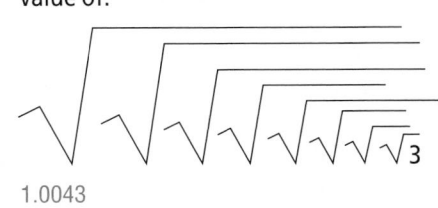

Have students write the Midpoint Formula in their math journals. Compare this formula with the formula for finding the midpoint between two numbers on the number line.

Lesson Investigation
PROBLEM-SOLVING STRATEGY
A problem-solving strategy for finding a formula is:
1. Make observations about the relationship.
2. Look for a pattern.
3. Make a guess at a formula based upon your observations and possible patterns.
4. Test (or verify) your guess.

Communicating
about **MATHEMATICS**

PROJECT
Ask students to determine real-life uses of the Distance Formula and the Midpoint Formula. Combine the class findings and create a bulletin board to share the results.

Writing Prompt
List any questions about the work you have done in this chapter that you don't understand.

a. $(3, 4)$
b. $(3, 4)$
c. $(-1, 2)$
d. $(5, 5)$

See formula below.

LESSON INVESTIGATION

■ **Investigating Midpoints**
Group Activity The **midpoint** of A and B is the point that lies on the line segment AB, halfway between the two points. Plot the following pairs of points. Then find the coordinates of each pair's midpoint. Describe a general procedure for finding the coordinates of the midpoint.

a. $A(1, 2), B(5, 6)$ **b.** $A(0, 3), B(6, 5)$
c. $A(2, 1), B(-4, 3)$ **d.** $A(3, 7), B(7, 3)$

In this investigation, you may have discovered the following formula for the midpoint between two points.

The Midpoint Formula
The **midpoint** between (x_1, y_1) and (x_2, y_2) is $\left(\frac{x_1 + x_2}{2}, \frac{y_1 + y_2}{2}\right)$.

Real Life
Surveying

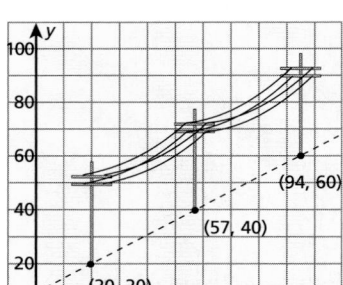

Example 2 *Using the Midpoint Formula*

You work for a telephone company. You are asked to locate the coordinates of a telephone pole that is supposed to lie halfway between two other poles, as shown at the left. Describe the location of the third pole. (The units are measured in feet.)

Solution Let $(x_1, y_1) = (20, 20)$ and $(x_2, y_2) = (94, 60)$.

$$\text{Midpoint} = \left(\frac{y_1 + y_2}{2}, \frac{y_1 + y_2}{2}\right) \quad \textit{Midpoint Formula}$$
$$= \left(\frac{20 + 94}{2}, \frac{20 + 60}{2}\right) \quad \textit{Substitute for coordinates.}$$
$$= (57, 40) \quad \textit{Simplify.}$$

The coordinates of the third pole are (57, 40). ■

Communicating about **MATHEMATICS**

▷ **SHARING IDEAS about the Lesson**

Extending the Example In Example 2, find the distances between the poles. What can you conclude?

≈ 42.06 ft, ≈ 42.06 ft; the distances are the same.

624 Chapter **13** • Exploring Linear Equations

OPTION: Extra Examples
Here are additional examples similar to those of the lesson.

1. The Distance Between Two Points
Find the distance between (3, −5) and (−4, 1).
Solution
Let $(x_1, y_1) = (3, -5)$ and $(x_2, y_2) = (-4, 1)$.
$$d = \sqrt{(x_2 - x_1)^2 + (y_2 - y_1)^2}$$
$$= \sqrt{(-4 - 3)^2 + (1 - (-5))^2}$$
$$= \sqrt{(-7)^2 + 6^2)}$$
$$= \sqrt{85} \approx 9.22$$
The distance between the points is about 9.22 units.

2. Using the Midpoint Formula
Find the midpoint between (3, −5) and (−4, 1).
Solution
Let $(x_1, y_1) = (3, -5)$ and $(x_2, y_2) = (-4, 1)$.
$$\text{Midpoint} = \left(\frac{x_1 + x_2}{2}, \frac{y_1 + y_2}{2}\right) \quad \text{Midpoint Formula}$$
$$= \left(\frac{3 + (-4)}{2}, \frac{-5 + 1}{2}\right) \quad \text{Substitute for coordinates.}$$
$$= \left(-\frac{1}{2}, -2\right) \quad \text{Simplify.}$$
The midpoint is $\left(-\frac{1}{2}, -2\right)$.

EXERCISES

Guided Practice

▶ CHECK for Understanding

In Exercises 1 and 2, find the distance between the points. Then find their midpoint. Check your results with a graph.

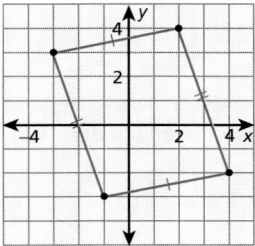

1. $(5, 4), (2, 0)$ $5, \left(\frac{7}{2}, 2\right)$ **2.** $(-1, -3), (-1, -7)$ $4, (-1, -5)$

Geometry   In Exercises 3 and 4, use the figure at the right.

3. Find the perimeter of the figure. ≈22.85

4. Show that the diagonals have the same midpoint.
See margin.

Independent Practice

In Exercises 5–8, use the graph to estimate the distance between the points. Then use the Distance Formula to check your estimate.

5. 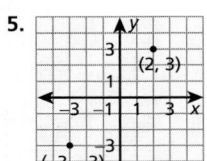 ≈7.8   **6.** 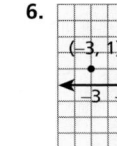 ≈6.4   **7.** 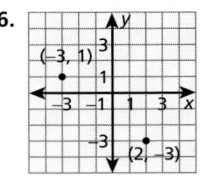 ≈7.6   **8.** 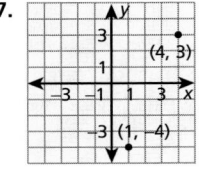 ≈9.9

In Exercises 9–12, use the graph to estimate the midpoint of the two points. Then use the Midpoint Formula to check your estimate.

9. 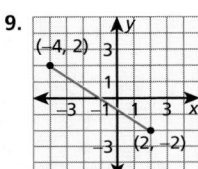 $(-1, 0)$ **10.** 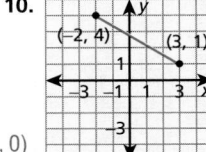 $\left(\frac{1}{2}, \frac{5}{2}\right)$ **11.** 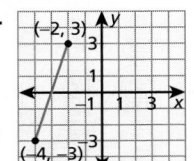 $(-3, 0)$ **12.** 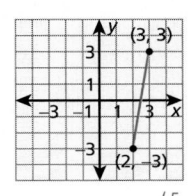 $\left(\frac{5}{2}, 0\right)$

In Exercises 13–16, find the perimeter of the polygon to two decimal places.

13. 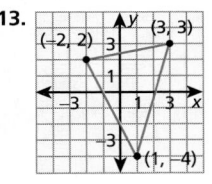 ≈19.09 units   **14.** 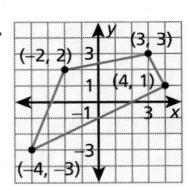 ≈21.66 units   **15.** 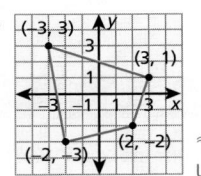 ≈19.69 units   **16.** 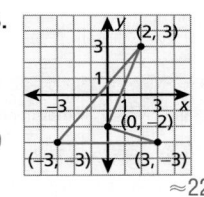 ≈22.36 units

In Exercises 17 and 18, decide whether △ABC is a right triangle. Explain.

✪ **17.** $A(0, 3), B(2, 5), C(2, 1)$
Yes, $(\sqrt{8})^2 + (\sqrt{8})^2 = 4^2$

✪ **18.** $A(1, 4), B(2, 1), C(5, 7)$
No, $5^2 + (\sqrt{10})^2 \neq (\sqrt{45})^2$

✪ More difficult exercises

13.8 • The Distance and Midpoint Formulas   **625**

EXERCISE Notes

ASSIGNMENT GUIDE
*Basic/Average:
  Day 1: Ex. 5–17 odd
  Day 2: Ex. 19–23 odd, 27–31 odd
Above Average:
  Day 1: Ex. 5–17 odd
  Day 2: Ex. 19–25 odd, 29–33 odd
Advanced: Ex. 5–23 odd, 27–33 odd
Selected Answers: Ex. 1–4, 5–29 odd

*You may wish to omit this lesson for these students.

Guided Practice
Assign these exercises as an in-class summary activity.

Independent Practice
▶ **Ex. 13–16** These exercises require several computations. Provide adequate time for students to work them.
▶ **Ex. 17, 18** These exercises connect the Distance Formula to the Pythagorean Theorem from Lesson 9.3. Note that students could answer these questions using slope.

Answer

4. $\left(\dfrac{2 + (-1)}{2}, \dfrac{4 + (-3)}{2}\right)$
$= \left(\dfrac{1}{2}, \dfrac{1}{2}\right),$
$\left(\dfrac{-3 + 4}{2}, \dfrac{3 + (-2)}{2}\right)$
$= \left(\dfrac{1}{2}, \dfrac{1}{2}\right)$

Lesson 13.8 **625**

Circles In Exercises 19 and 20, the labeled points are endpoints of a diameter of the circle. Find the center and radius of the circle.

19. $(-1, 1)$, $\sqrt{8}$

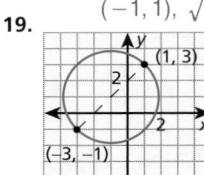

20. $(-1, -1)$, $\sqrt{13}$

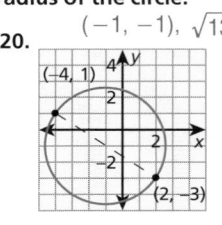

Parallelograms In Exercises 21 and 22, show that the diagonals of parallelogram *ABCD* have the same midpoints. See margin.

21.

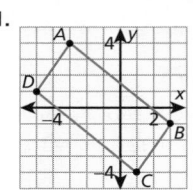

22.

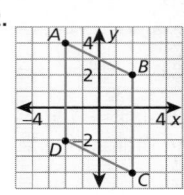

In Exercises 23 and 24, the expression represents the distance between two points. What are the points?

23. $\sqrt{(5-3)^2 + (6-1)^2}$ $(5, 6), (3, 1)$

24. $\sqrt{(0-4)^2 + (-8+2)^2}$ $(0, -8), (4, -2)$

Planning a Trip In Exercises 25 and 26, you live in Louisville, Kentucky, which has the latitude-longitude coordinates (46.2N, 72.6W), and are planning a trip to Wichita, Kansas, which has the latitude-longitude coordinates (37.4N, 97.2W).

✪ **25.** Use the map to estimate the distance between the two cities.   470 mi

✪ **26.** You are planning a stop halfway between the two cities. What are the latitude-longitude coordinates of the halfway point? If you average 50 miles per hour, how long will it take you to reach the halfway point?
(41.8N, 84.9W), 4.7 hours

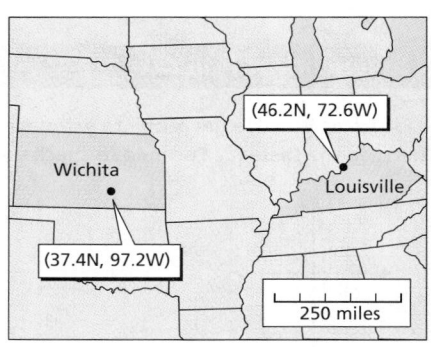

Integrated Review

Making Connections within Mathematics

Geometry In Exercises 27–30, find the area of the figure.

27.

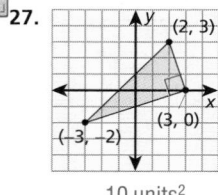

10 units²

28.

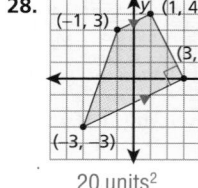

20 units²

29.

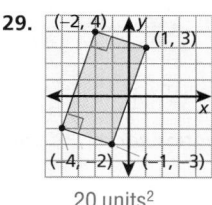

20 units²

30.

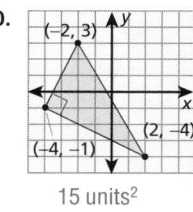

15 units²

Exploration and Extension

In Exercises 31–34, *C* is a midpoint of $\overline{AB}$. Find the coordinates of *B*. Explain your reasoning and illustrate your answer with a graph.

✪ **31.** $A(-4, 2)$, $C(-4, -1)$ $B(-4, -4)$

✪ **32.** $A(5, 3)$, $C(1, 3)$ $B(-3, 3)$

✪ **33.** $A(3, -2)$, $C(1, 0)$ $B(-1, 2)$

✪ **34.** $A(2, 5)$, $C(0, -1)$ $B(-2, -7)$

626   Chapter **13** · *Exploring Linear Equations*

✪ More difficult exercises

13 Chapter Summary

What did you learn?

Why did you learn it?

Linear equations can be used to model the relationships between many real-life quantities. For instance, in this chapter you saw how linear equations can be used to model the attendance at college football games, model a trip on a subway, model the populations of states, and model the amount of money earned at a fund-raising dinner. If you take Algebra 1 next year, you will study many other ways that linear equations are used to model real life. In fact, you will learn that a linear equation is the most widely used type of model in all of mathematics.

How does it fit into the bigger picture of mathematics?

The combination of algebra (equations) and geometry (graphs) that you studied in this chapter is called *analytic geometry*. Analytic geometry was developed about 350 years ago, and it has proved to be a very useful way to study both algebra and geometry. In this chapter you saw that you learn a lot about a linear equation by sketching its graph. For instance, from the graph you can find the intercepts and the slope—both of which have important real-life interpretations. As you continue your study of mathematics, remember that the old saying "a picture is worth a thousand words" applies to algebra as well as to other parts of life.

Chapter Summary **627**

COOPERATIVE LEARNING

Encourage students to study together. Emphasize the importance of teaching a classmate how to perform a skill or how to recall a procedure. When students work together, everyone wins. The students receiving help get additional instruction, and the students giving help gain a deeper understanding of the skills and concepts involved.

Chapter SUMMARY

Lessons 13.1 and 13.2 showed students how to use a table of values to organize solutions of a given linear equation and how to graph the equation. The reverse process was also presented (in Example 2 of 13.2)—how to graph data from a given table and *find* an equation that fits or models the data. Lessons 13.3 and 13.4 explored two important features of a linear equation—intercepts (and how they can be used to sketch a quick graph of the equation) and slope. Lesson 13.5 taught students how to identify the slope and y-intercept of a line from its equation and, based on these features, how to sketch a quick graph of the line. In Lesson 13.6, students revisited two distinct problem-solving techniques—the algebraic modeling plan and the scatter plot. Lesson 13.7 introduced students to solving and graphing linear inequalities in two variables and, finally, Lesson 13.8 offered students two further coordinate geometry formulas—the distance- and midpoint-formulas.

Chapter REVIEW

Have students begin this Review in class and complete it as a homework assignment.

ASSIGNMENT GUIDE

*Basic/Average
Ex. 1–33 odd, 35, 37, 43–56 odd, 62–66

Above Average:
Ex. 1–37 odd, 39–42, 43–55 odd, 57–60, 62–66

Advanced:
Ex. 1–37 odd, 39–42, 43–55 odd, 57–61, 67–71

*For these students, you will need to limit assignments to cover only those lessons you chose to teach from this chapter.

Resources

Color Transparencies
  Picture for Ex. 67–71, p. 57
Answer Masters, pp. 270–272

Answers

5.

x	−2	−1	0	1	2
y	−5	$-\frac{9}{2}$	−4	$-\frac{7}{2}$	−3

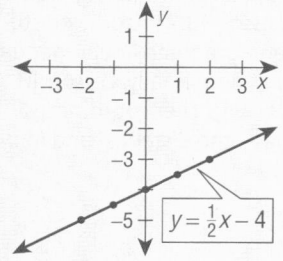

$y = \frac{1}{2}x - 4$

6.

x	−2	−1	0	1	2
y	$\frac{9}{2}$	$\frac{13}{4}$	2	$\frac{3}{4}$	$-\frac{1}{2}$

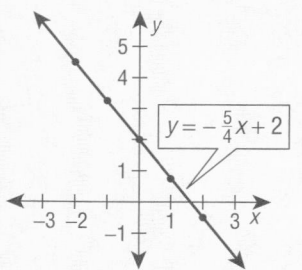

$y = -\frac{5}{4}x + 2$

7.

x	−2	−1	0	1	2
y	14	10	6	2	−2

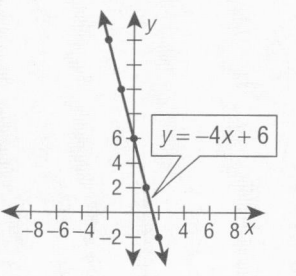

$y = -4x + 6$

In Exercises 1–4, is the ordered pair a solution of $5x + 2y = 40$? **(13.1)**

1. $(4, 10)$ Yes
2. $(7, 2)$ No
3. $(9, -2)$ No
4. $(-2, 25)$ Yes

In Exercises 5–8, create a table of values for the equation. Then use the table to sketch a graph of the equation. **(13.1, 13.2)** See margin.

5. $y = \frac{1}{2}x - 4$
6. $y = -\frac{5}{4}x + 2$
7. $y = -4x + 6$
8. $6x + 4y = 16$

In Exercises 9–12, decide whether the line is *horizontal, vertical,* or *slanted.* **(13.2)**

9. $y = -10x$ Slanted
10. $x = -4$ Vertical
11. $y = 10$ Horizontal
12. $12x - 6y = 54$ Slanted

In Exercises 13–16, sketch the line that has the given intercepts. **(13.3)** See Additional Answers.

13. x-intercept: −4
  y-intercept: 7
14. x-intercept: 1
  y-intercept: 4
15. x-intercept: 5
  y-intercept: −2
16. x-intercept: −6
  y-intercept: −1

In Exercises 17–20, use intercepts to sketch a quick graph of the line. **(13.3)** See Additional Answers.

17. $y = 2x + 6$
18. $y = -\frac{1}{3}x - 1$
19. $6x + y = 9$
20. $3x - 2y = 10$

In Exercises 21–24, estimate the slope of the line. **(10.4)**

21. $\frac{1}{2}$
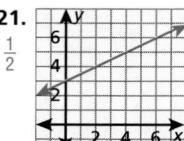
22. $-\frac{2}{3}$
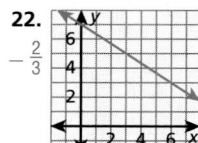
23. 0
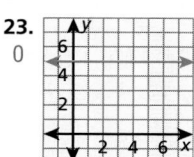
24. 3
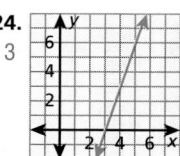

In Exercises 25–28, find the slope of the line through the points. **(13.4)**

25. $(5, 0), (-1, 6)$ -1
26. $(-2, -3), (1, 9)$ 4
27. $(-4, 2), (3, 4)$ $\frac{2}{7}$
28. $(0, 9), (8, -1)$ $-\frac{5}{4}$

29. Which equation is in slope-intercept form? **(13.5)** c

  a. $6y = 5x - 18$
  b. $x = \frac{6}{5}y + \frac{18}{5}$
  c. $y = \frac{5}{6}x - 3$
  d. $5x - 6y = 18$

30. Explain how to use the slope-intercept form to sketch a quick graph of a line. **(13.5)**
  See margin.

In Exercises 31–34, find the slope and *y*-intercept of the line. Then sketch a quick graph of the line. **(13.5)** For graphs, see margin.

31. $y = -\frac{3}{5}x$ $-\frac{3}{5}, 0$
32. $y = 4x + 5$ $4, 5$
33. $7x - 6y = 24$ $\frac{7}{6}, -4$
34. $x + 5y = 10$ $-\frac{1}{5}, 2$

In Exercises 35–38, find the equation of the line. **(13.1–13.5)**

35.
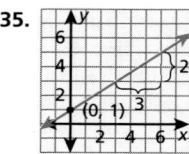
36.
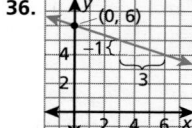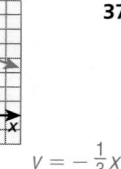
$y = \frac{2}{3}x + 1$
37.
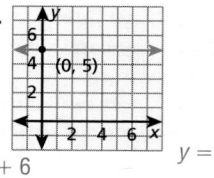
$y = -\frac{1}{3}x + 6$
$y = 5$
38.
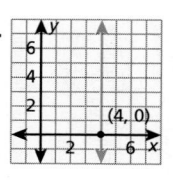
$x =$

Nursery   **In Exercises 39–42, consider the following.   (13.6)**

You own a nursery that sells shrubs and trees to landscapers. You sell rhododendrons for $40 and dogwood trees for $60 each. One day during planting season, you sell $2500 worth of rhododendrons and dogwood trees.

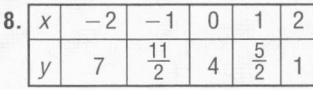

39. Write a verbal model that describes the sale of rhododendrons and dogwood trees.   See margin.

40. Use the verbal model to write an algebraic model. Let x represent the number of rhododendrons and y represent the number of dogwoods. $40x + 60y = 2500$

41. You sold 31 rhododendrons. How many dogwood trees did you sell?   21

42. Graph the linear model. Then list several other solutions.
       Lists vary. For graph, see margin on page 630.

In Exercises 43–48, decide whether the ordered pair is a solution of the inequality. Then decide whether a solid line or dashed line is used to graph the inequality. (13.7)

Yes, solid   No, solid

43. $y < 8x - 12$; $(4, 10)$ Yes,   **44.** $y \geq -4x + 9$; $(2, 2)$ **45.** $y \leq \frac{11}{2}x + 6$; $(-4, -12)$
                                   dashed
46. $-x + \frac{3}{4}y \leq 0$; $(6, 8)$ **47.** $-2y < 3x + 1$; $(1, -3)$ **48.** $3x - 7y < -21$; $(-1, 3)$
       Yes, solid   No, dashed   Yes, dashed

In Exercises 49–52, sketch the graph of the inequality. (13.7)   See margin on page 630.

49. $y > -2\frac{1}{2}$ **50.** $y < -x - 1$ **51.** $y \geq 7x + 6$ **52.** $2x - 3y \geq -15$

In Exercises 53–56, find the midpoint and length of the line segment. (13.8)

53.   **54.**   **55.**   **56.**

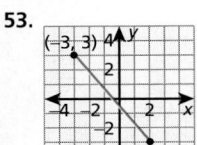   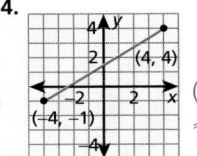   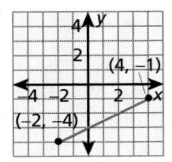   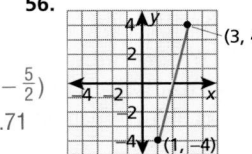

$(-\frac{1}{2}, 0)$ $(0, \frac{3}{2})$ $(1, -\frac{5}{2})$ $(3, 4)$
≈ 7.81 ≈ 9.43 ≈ 6.71
                                                                             $(2, 0)$
Geometry   **In Exercises 57–60, use the figure at the** ≈ 8.25
right. (13.8)

57. Find the length of each side of $\triangle ABC$. $\sqrt{50}$, $\sqrt{50}$, 10

58. Use the converse of the Pythagorean Theorem to show that $\triangle ABC$ is a right triangle.   See below.

59. Find the perimeter of $\triangle ABC$. ≈ 24.14 units

60. Find the area of $\triangle ABC$.   25 units^2

61. Consider a circle whose center is $(1, 2)$. Exactly two of the points, $(4, 5)$, $(-2, 6)$, and $(4, -1)$ are on the circle. Which two are they? Explain your reasoning.
       $(4, 5)$ and $(4, -1)$, their distances from $(1, 2)$ are the same ($\sqrt{18}$).

58. $(\sqrt{50})^2 + (\sqrt{50})^2 = 10^2$

★ More difficult exercises

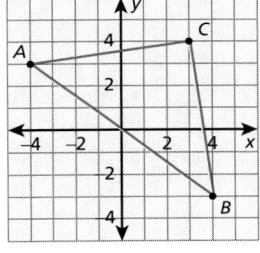

Chapter Review   **629**

8.

x	-2	-1	0	1	2
y	7	$\frac{11}{2}$	4	$\frac{5}{2}$	1

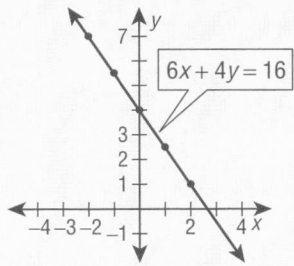

$6x + 4y = 16$

30. Plot the y-intercept, use the slope to plot a second point, draw the line that passes through the two points.

31.

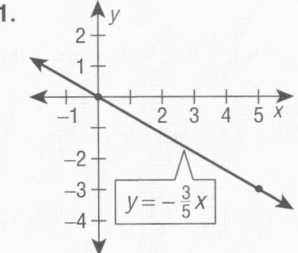

$y = -\frac{3}{5}x$

32.

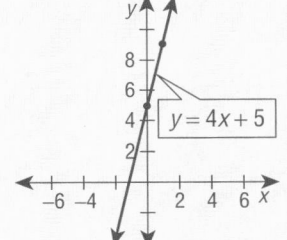

$y = 4x + 5$

33.

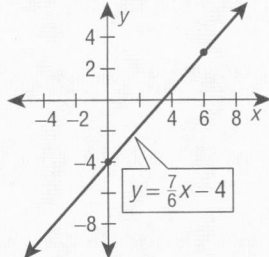

$y = \frac{7}{6}x - 4$

34.

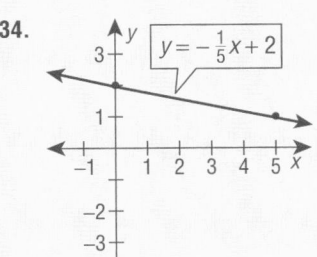

$y = -\frac{1}{5}x + 2$

39.

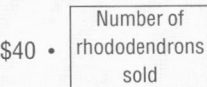   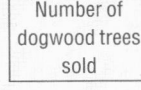

$\$40 \cdot$ | Number of rhododendrons sold | $+$ $\$60 \cdot$ | Number of dogwood trees sold |

$= \$2500$

Chapter 13 Review   **629**

FOCUS ON Advanced Transportation

Riding the Commuter Rail In Exercises 62–66, use the coordinate map and the following information.

You live in the suburb of a city that has a commuter rail system. There are two stations in the suburb. The stations, your house, and the homes of two friends, Felicia and Heather, are shown on the coordinate map. **63**. Felicia: Station 1, Heather: Station 2

62. Which station is nearer to your house? Station 2

63. Which station is nearer to each of your friends?

64. A new station is being built exactly halfway between Station 1 and Heather's house. What are the coordinates of the new station? (1, 9)

⭐ 65. During the next school year, each of you plans to use the nearest station. Will any of you go to the new one? Explain. See below.

⭐ 66. Could the new station have been located so that it would be closer to each of your houses than the two existing stations are? Explain.

65. Yes, Felicia and Heather; it is nearest.

66. Yes, one such location is (8, 10).

Bay Area Mass Transportation In Exercises 67–71, use the following information.

The cable car system in San Francisco, California, is part of the city's mass transit system. The other part of the system consists of buses and an electric rail system called *BART* for *Bay Area Rapid Transit*. **67.**, **69**. See margin.

67. You are riding a cable car whose speed is 9 miles per hour. The distance, d (in miles), you will travel in t hours is modeled by $d = 9t$. Sketch a graph of this model.

68. Use the model in Exercise 67 to find how far you will travel on a 10-minute cable car ride. $1\frac{1}{2}$ miles

69. You are riding a BART car whose speed is 50 miles per hour. The distance, d (in miles), you will travel in t hours is modeled by $d = 50t$. Sketch a graph of this model.

70. Use the model in Exercise 69 to find how far you will travel on a 10-minute BART car ride. $8\frac{1}{3}$ miles

⭐ 71. **Guess, Check, and Revise** Riding the bus to your work costs $0.75 per ride. Taking a taxi to work costs $3.25 per ride. Let x represent the number of times you rode the bus and let y represent the number of times you took a taxi. During the week, you took 10 rides and spent $12.50. How many times did you ride the bus? How many times did you take a taxi? 8, 2

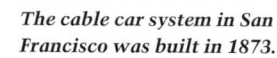

The cable car system in San Francisco was built in 1873.

Answers

42.
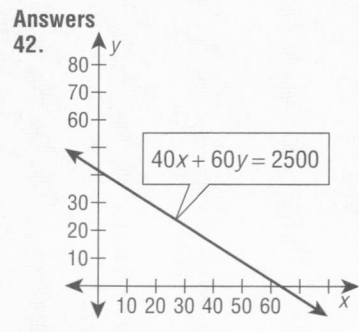
$40x + 60y = 2500$

49.
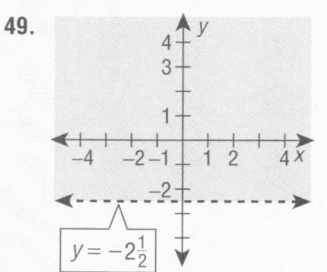
$y = -2\frac{1}{2}$

50.
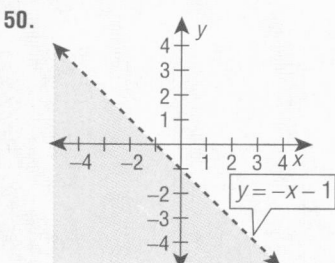
$y = -x - 1$

51.
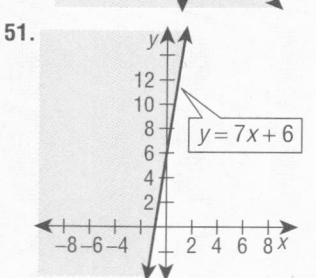
$y = 7x + 6$

52.
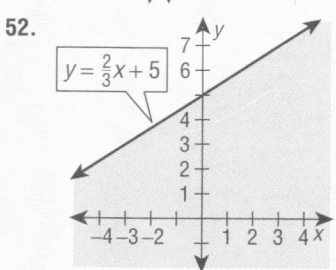
$y = \frac{2}{3}x + 5$

67.
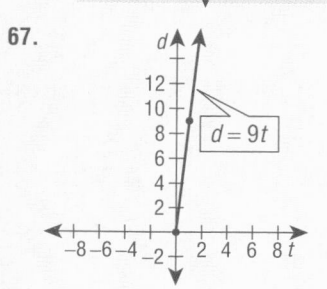
$d = 9t$

In Exercises 1–4, consider the equation $2x + 3y = 6$. (13.1, 13.3, 13.4)

1. Complete the following table of values for the equation.

x	−3	−2	−1	0	1	2	3
y	?	?	?	?	?	?	?

$4, \frac{10}{3}, \frac{8}{3}, 2, \frac{4}{3}, \frac{2}{3}, 0$

2. From your table of values, name the intercepts of the graph.   x-intercept: 3, y-intercept: 2

3. Sketch a quick graph of the line.   See margin.   **4.** Use the graph to find the slope of the line. $-\frac{2}{3}$

In Exercises 5–7, decide whether the ordered pair is a solution of $x + 3y = 13$. (13.2)

5. $(8, 3)$ No   **6.** $(1, 5)$ No   **7.** $(-2, 6)$ No

8. Find the slope of the line that passes through $(3, 5)$ and $(-3, 4)$. (13.4) $\frac{1}{6}$

9. Find the slope and y-intercept of the line $y = -2x + 4$. Then sketch the line. (13.5) $-2, 4$; For graph, see margin.

In Exercises 10 and 11, find the slope of the line. (13.4)

In Exercises 12 and 13, write an equation of the line. (13.5)

10.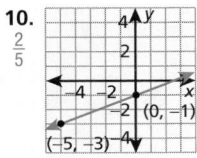
$\frac{2}{5}$

11.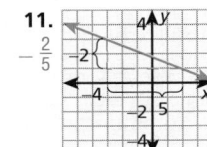
$-\frac{2}{5}$

12.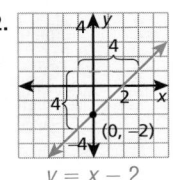
$y = x - 2$

13.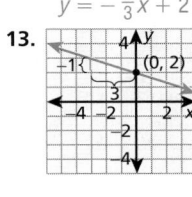
$y = -\frac{1}{3}x + 2$

14. Sketch the graph of $y < 3x$. (13.7)   See margin.   **15.** Sketch the graph of $y \geq 2x + 2$. (13.7)   See margin.

16. Find the distance between $(3, 0)$ and $(-1, 2)$. (13.8) $\sqrt{20}$

17. Find the midpoint between the points $(-3, -2)$ and $(5, 6)$. (13.8) $(1, 2)$

18. A circle in a coordinate plane has $(0, 0)$ and $(6, 8)$ as endpoints of a diameter. Find the area of the circle. Sketch your answer. (13.8) 25π; for sketch, see margin.

In Exercises 19 and 20, use the following.

The speed of an automobile, starting from rest, is shown in the graph at the right. At the end of 12 seconds, the automobile has reached a speed of 48 miles per hour. (13.6)

19. Let s represent the speed (in miles per hour) and let t represent the time (in seconds). Which of the following models is correct?   c

   a. $s = 48t$ **b.** $s = 12t$ **c.** $s = 4t$

20. Use the graph to estimate the speed of the automobile at the end of 8 seconds. Then use the correct model found in Exercise 19 to check your result.   32 mph

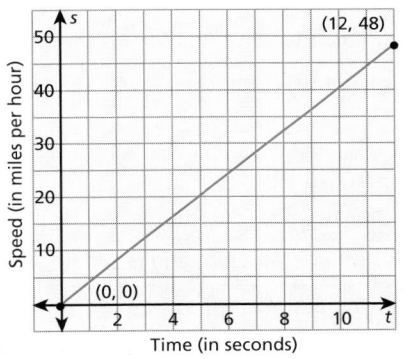

Chapter Test **631**

Answer to Chapter Review

69.

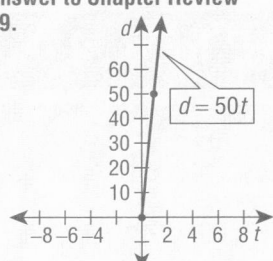
$d = 50t$

Answers to Chapter Test

3.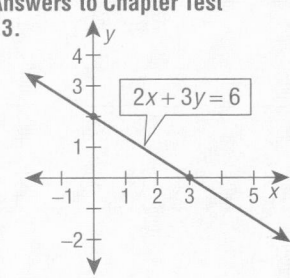
$2x + 3y = 6$

9.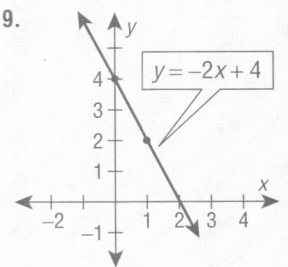
$y = -2x + 4$

14.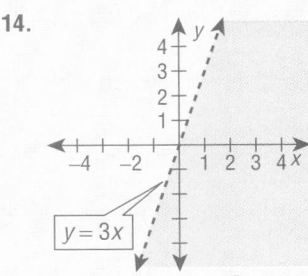
$y = 3x$

15.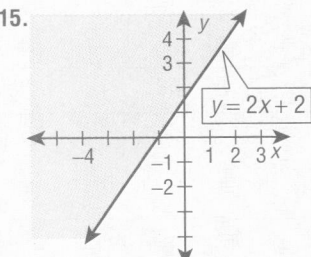
$y = 2x + 2$

18.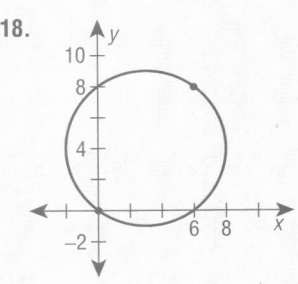

◀ Formal Assessment

Three **Chapter Tests.** Form A is of average difficulty, Form B is of average difficulty in multiple choice format, and Form C is more challenging.
Available as copymasters, pages 219–227

Chapter Test **631**

CHAPTER 14 GOALS

Lesson	Pages	Goals	Meeting the NCTM Standards
14.1	634–637	1. Find measures of central tendency 2. Use measures of central tendency to solve real-life problems	Problem Solving, Communication, Connections, Statistics, Probability
14.2	638–641	1. Organize data with a stem-and-leaf plot 2. Use two stem-and-leaf plots to compare two sets of data	Communication, Connections, Technology, Statistics, Probability
14.3	642–645	1. Organize data with a box-and-whisker plot 2. Use box-and-whisker plots to interpret real-life data	Communication, Reasoning, Connections, Number Relationships, Statistics
Using a Graphing Calculator	646	Box-and-Whisker Plots	Reasoning, Technology, Statistics
Mixed Review	647	Review of arithmetic, algebra, and geometry	Number Relationships, Algebra, Statistics, Geometry
Milestones	647	Apothecary Measurement	Communication, Connections
14.4	648–651	1. Organize data with a matrix 2. Add two matrices	Problem Solving, Communication, Reasoning, Connections, Computation and Estimation, Statistics
Mid-Chapter Self-Test	652	Diagnose student weaknesses and remediate with correlated reteaching Copymasters	Assessment
Lesson Investigation 14.5	653	Exploring Polynomials	Algebra, Geometry
14.5	654–657	1. Identify polynomials and write them in standard form 2. Use polynomials to solve real-life problems	Problem Solving, Communication, Reasoning, Connections, Algebra, Geometry
Lesson Investigation 14.6	658	Exploring Polynomial Addition	Algebra, Geometry
14.6	659–663	1. Add polynomials 2. Subtract polynomials	Problem Solving, Communication, Connections, Patterns and Functions, Algebra, Statistics, Geometry
Mixed Review	663	Review of arithmetic, algebra, and geometry	Computation and Estimation, Algebra, Statistics
Lesson Investigation 14.7	664	Exploring Polynomial Multiplication	Algebra, Geometry
14.7	665–668	1. Multiply a polynomial by a monomial 2. Use polynomial multiplication to solve geometry problems.	Communication, Reasoning, Connections, Algebra, Geometry, Measurement
Lesson Investigation 14.8	669	Exploring Binomial Multiplication	Algebra, Geometry
14.8	670–673	1. Multiply a binomial by a binomial 2. Use polynomial multiplication to solve real-life problems	Communication, Connections, Computation and Estimation, Patterns and Functions, Algebra, Geometry, Measurement
Chapter Summary	674	A restatement of what has been learned, why it has been learned, and how it fits into the structure of mathematics	Communication, Connections
Chapter Review	675–677	Review of concepts and skills learned in the chapter	Problem Solving, Connections
Chapter Test	678	Diagnose student weaknesses and remediate with correlated Reteaching Copymasters	Assessment

RESOURCES ORGANIZER

Lesson Pages	14.1 634–637	14.2 638–641	14.3 642–645	14.4 648–651	14.5 654–657	14.6 659–663	14.7 665–668	14.8 670–673
Lesson Plans	110	111	112	113	114	115	116	117
Problem of the Day	40	40	40	41	41	41	42	42
Warm-Up Exercises	40	40	40	41	41	41	42	42
Color Transparencies	58	—	—	—	58, 59	—	59	60
Teaching Tools:								
Transparencies	T1	T1	—	—	—	—	—	—
Copymasters	C2	C2	—	—	C32	—	—	—
Math Log	43	43	43	43	44	44	44	44
Technology	80	—	—	81, 82	—	—	—	—
Answer Masters	274	275, 276	277	279, 280	281, 282	283	285	286, 287
Extra Practice Copymasters	110	111	112	113	114	115	116	117
Reteaching Copymasters	110	111	112	113	114	115	116	117
Enrichment Projects	72–74	—	—	—	—	—	—	75, 76
Alternative Assessment:								
Projects	41	—	—	41	42	—	—	42
Partner Quizzes	—	—	—	57	—	—	—	—
Group Assessment	—	—	—	—	85, 86	—	—	—
Formal Assessment								
Short Quizzes	—	228	—	229	—	232	—	233
Tests	—	—	—	230, 231	—	—	—	234–242
Overhead Manipulatives Kit	—	—	—	—	Algebra Tiles	Algebra Tiles	Algebra Tiles	Algebra Tiles
Complete Solutions Manual	Includes step-by-step solutions for all exercises in the student text							
Computerized Test Bank	Creates customized tests that include graphics							
Interactive CD-ROM Project	Provides an interactive and interdisciplinary chapter project							

STARTERS

Problem of the Day

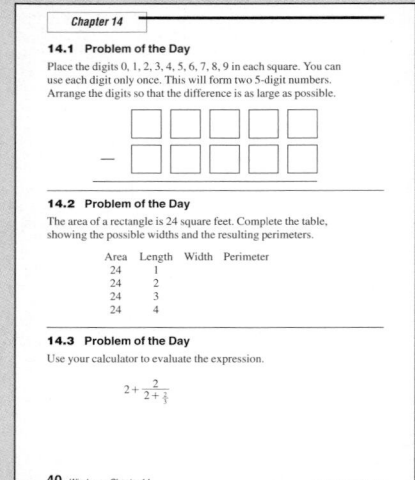

Chapter 14

14.1 Problem of the Day
Place the digits 0, 1, 2, 3, 4, 5, 6, 7, 8, 9 in each square. You can use each digit only once. This will form two 5-digit numbers. Arrange the digits so that the difference is as large as possible.

14.2 Problem of the Day
The area of a rectangle is 24 square feet. Complete the table, showing the possible widths and the resulting perimeters.

Area	Length	Width	Perimeter
24	1		
24	2		
24	3		
24	4		

14.3 Problem of the Day
Use your calculator to evaluate the expression.

$$2 + \frac{2}{2 + \frac{2}{3}}$$

40 Windows • Chapter 14

Warm-Up Exercises

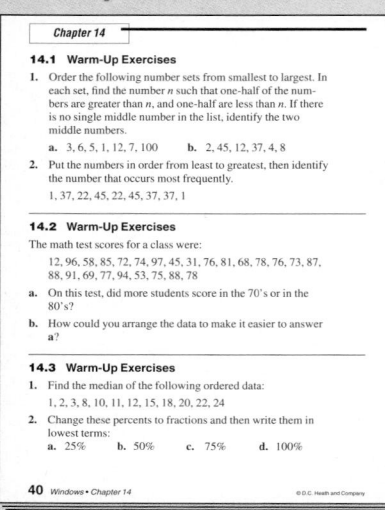

Chapter 14

14.1 Warm-Up Exercises
1. Order the following number sets from smallest to largest. In each set, find the number n such that one-half of the numbers are greater than n, and one-half are less than n. If there is no single middle number in the list, identify the two middle numbers.
   a. 3, 6, 5, 1, 12, 7, 100   b. 2, 45, 12, 37, 4, 8
2. Put the numbers in order from least to greatest, then identify the number that occurs most frequently.
   1, 37, 22, 45, 22, 45, 37, 37, 1

14.2 Warm-Up Exercises
The math test scores for a class were:
12, 96, 58, 85, 72, 74, 97, 45, 31, 76, 81, 68, 78, 76, 73, 87, 88, 91, 69, 77, 94, 53, 75, 88, 78
a. On this test, did more students score in the 70's or in the 80's?
b. How could you arrange the data to make it easier to answer a?

14.3 Warm-Up Exercises
1. Find the median of the following ordered data:
   1, 2, 3, 8, 10, 11, 12, 15, 18, 20, 22, 24
2. Change these percents to fractions and then write them in lowest terms:
   a. 25%   b. 50%   c. 75%   d. 100%

40 Windows • Chapter 14

FOR TEACHERS

Answer Masters

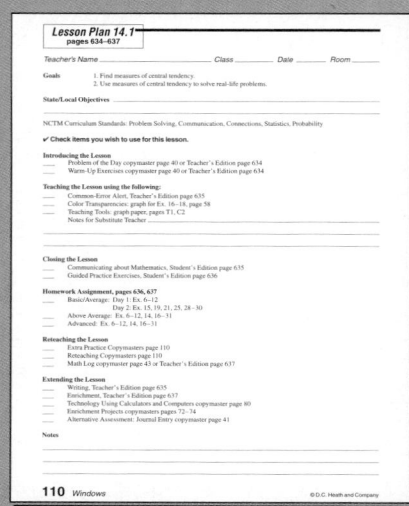

Answers for Lesson 14.1, pages 636 and 637

1. a. median, b. mode, c. mean
2. The numbers 3, 4, 5, 6, and 7 occur from 1 to 5 times each. 3, 3, 4, 4, 4, 4, 5, 5, 5, 5, 6, 6, 6, 6, 7
3. $4\frac{7}{8}$
4. 5
5. 5
6. 89, 90, 90
7. 54.1, 54, none
8. 37, 37, none
9. $58\frac{5}{9}$, 59, 60
10. 20; 0, 0, 1, 2, 2, 2, 3, 3, 3, 3, 4, 4, 4, 4, 4, 4, 5, 5, 5, 6
11. 3.2, 3.5, 4
12. Answers vary. One situation might be that the numbers are responses to the question "How many hours do you usually watch TV on a Sunday?"
13.–15. Measures and explanations vary.
16. 5
17. $2\frac{7}{11}$, 2, 1
18. The mean or median, the mode is not good because it is the smallest number.

19. 6.61, 6.6, none
20. More acidic, the 5th or 6th day
21.–22. Answers vary.
21. 13, 14, 15, 15, 16, 17
22. 8, 8, 8, 10, 10, 16
23. Answers vary. One wording might be as follows. In 1992 in Seattle, Washington, half the houses cost as much as or more than $141,300 and half the houses cost as much or less than $141,300.
24. 97
25.

26.

27. a. $\frac{5}{20}$ b. $\frac{1}{5}$ c. $\frac{5}{10}$ d. $\frac{1}{4}$
   e. $\frac{5}{20}$ f. $\frac{7}{10}$ g. $\frac{5}{20}$ h. 0
28.–30. See students' work.
31. Experimental results should roughly reflect theoretical results:

Windows Answer Masters

Lesson Plans

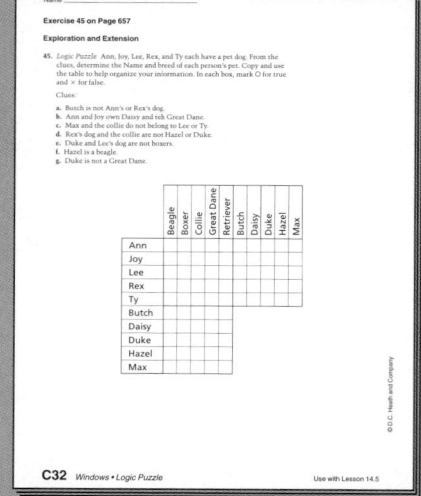

Lesson Plan 14.1
pages 634–637

Teacher's Name _____ Class _____ Date _____ Room _____

Goals
1. Find measures of central tendency.
2. Use measures of central tendency to solve real-life problems.

State/Local Objectives

NCTM Curriculum Standards: Problem Solving, Communication, Connections, Statistics, Probability

✔ Check items you wish to use for this lesson.

Introducing the Lesson
___ Problem of the Day copymaster page 40 on Teacher's Edition page 634
___ Warm-Up Exercises copymaster page 40 on Teacher's Edition page 634

Teaching the Lesson using the following:
___ Common-Error Alert, Teacher's Edition page 635
___ Color Transparencies: graph for Ex. 16–18, page 58
___ Teaching Tools: graph paper, pages T1, C2
___ Notes for Substitute Teacher

Closing the Lesson
___ Communicating about Mathematics, Student's Edition page 635
___ Guided Practice Exercises, Student's Edition page 636

Homework Assignment, pages 636, 637
___ Basic/Average: Day 1: Ex. 6–12
___   Day 2: Ex. 15, 19, 21, 25, 28 - 30
___ Above Average: Ex. 6–12, 14, 16–31
___ Advanced: Ex. 6–12, 14, 16–31

Reteaching the Lesson
___ Extra Practice Copymasters page 110
___ Reteaching Copymasters page 110
___ Math Log copymaster page 43 at Teacher's Edition page 637

Extending the Lesson
___ Writing, Teacher's Edition page 635
___ Enrichment, Teacher's Edition page 637
___ Technology Using Calculators and Computers copymaster page 80
___ Enrichment Projects copymasters page 72–74
___ Alternative Assessment: Journal Entry copymaster page 41

Notes

110 Windows

Teaching Tools

Name _____

Exercise 45 on Page 657

Exploration and Extension

45. *Logic Puzzle* Ann, Joy, Lee, Rex, and Ty each have a pet dog. From the clues, determine the Name and breed of each person's pet. Copy and use the table to help organize your information. In each box, mark O for true and × for false.

Clues:
a. Butch is not Ann's or Rex's dog.
b. Ann and Joy own Daisy and rtb Great Dane.
c. Max and the collie do not belong to Lee or Ty.
d. Rex's dog and the collie are not Hazel or Duke.
e. Duke and Lee's dog are not boxers.
f. Hazel is a beagle.
g. Duke is not a Great Dane.

	Beagle	Boxer	Collie	Great Dane	Retriever	Butch	Daisy	Duke	Hazel	Max
Ann										
Joy										
Lee										
Rex										
Ty										
Butch										
Daisy										
Duke										
Hazel										
Max										

C32 Windows • Logic Puzzle   Use with Lesson 14.5

Teaching Tools includes:
Transparencies and Copymasters for classroom activities and study skills:
▪ Graph Paper
▪ Dot Paper (Geoboards)
▪ Algebra Tiles
▪ Number Counters
▪ Fraction Strips
▪ Models

REAL LIFE

Color Transparencies for Real-Life Applications

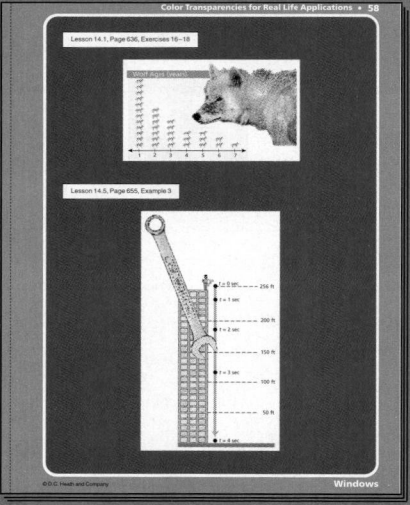

Color Transparencies for Real Life Applications • 58

Lesson 14.1, Page 636, Exercises 16–18

Lesson 14.5, Page 655, Example 3

Windows

Technology: Using Calculators and Computers

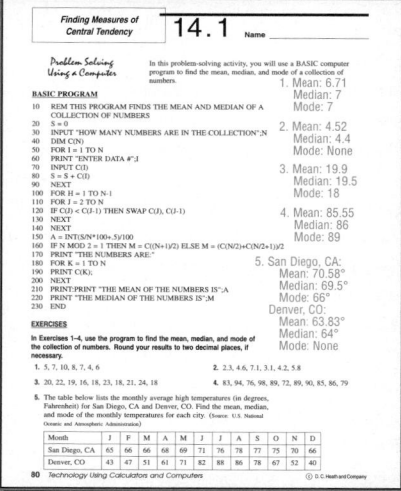

Finding Measures of Central Tendency   **14.1**   Name _____

Problem Solving Using a Computer
In this problem-solving activity, you will use a BASIC computer program to find the mean, median, and mode of a collection of numbers.

BASIC PROGRAM
```
10  REM THIS PROGRAM FINDS THE MEAN AND MEDIAN OF A
    COLLECTION OF NUMBERS
20  S = 0
30  INPUT "HOW MANY NUMBERS ARE IN THE COLLECTION";N
40  DIM C(N)
50  FOR I = 1 TO N
60  PRINT "ENTER DATA #";I
70  INPUT C(I)
80  S = S + C(I)
90  NEXT
100 FOR H = 1 TO N-1
110 FOR J = 2 TO N
120 IF C(J) < C(J-1) THEN SWAP C(J), C(J-1)
130 NEXT
140 NEXT
150 A = INT(S/N*100+.5)/100
160 IF N MOD 2 = 1 THEN M = C((N+1)/2) ELSE M = (C(N/2)+C(N/2+1))/2
170 PRINT "THE NUMBERS ARE:"
180 FOR K = 1 TO N
190 PRINT C(K);
200 NEXT
210 PRINT:PRINT "THE MEAN OF THE NUMBERS IS";A
220 PRINT "THE MEDIAN OF THE NUMBERS IS";M
230 END
```

EXERCISES
In Exercises 1–4, use the program to find the mean, median, and mode of the collection of numbers. Round your results to two decimal places, if necessary.
1. 5, 7, 10, 8, 7, 4, 6
2. 2, 3, 4, 6, 7, 1, 3, 1, 4, 2, 5, 8
3. 20, 22, 19, 16, 18, 15, 18, 21, 24, 18
4. 83, 94, 76, 98, 89, 72, 89, 90, 85, 85, 79
5. The table below lists the monthly average high temperatures (in degrees, Fahrenheit) for San Diego, CA and Denver, CO. Find the mean, median, and mode of the monthly temperatures for each city. (Source: U.S. National Oceanic and Atmospheric Administration)

Month	J	F	M	A	M	J	J	A	S	O	N	D
San Diego, CA	65	66	66	68	69	71	76	78	77	75	70	66
Denver, CO	43	47	51	61	71	82	88	86	78	67	52	40

1. Mean: 6.71
   Median: 7
2. Mean: 4.52
   Median: 4.4
   Mode: None
3. Mean: 19.9
   Median: 19.5
   Mode: 18
4. Mean: 85.55
   Median: 89
   Mode: 89
5. San Diego, CA:
   Mean: 70.58°
   Median: 69.5°
   Mode: 66°
   Denver, CO:
   Mean: 63.83°
   Median: 64°
   Mode: None

80 Technology Using Calculators and Computers

Also Available:

▪ Complete Solutions Manual
▪ Overhead Manipulatives Kit
▪ Computerized Testing Program

▪ **Interactive CD-ROM Projects**
Interactive projects for solving real-world problems using multimedia

▪ **Interactions: Real Math–Real Careers**
A videodisc–based resource that connects math to real careers and on-the-job problem solving

▪ **PACKETS® Performance Assessment for Middle School Mathematics**
A program that links assessment and instruction

ASSESSMENT

Alternative Assessment

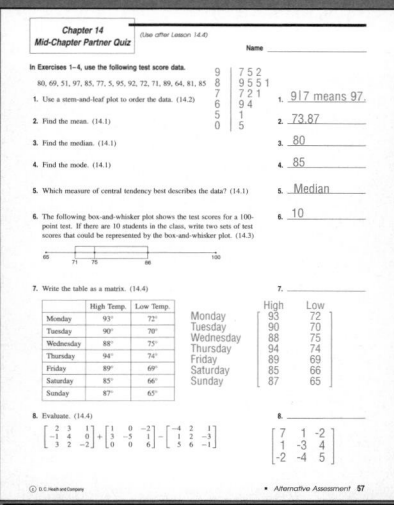

Alternative Assessment includes:
- Scoring Rubrics
- Portfolios
- Math Journals
- Projects
- Partner Quizzes
- Individual and Group Assessment

Formal Assessment

Formal Assessment includes:
- Short Quizzes (after every 2 lessons)
- Mid-Chapter Tests (2 forms)
- Chapter Tests (3 forms)
- Cumulative Tests (after every 3 Chapters)

MEETING INDIVIDUAL NEEDS

Extra Practice Copymasters

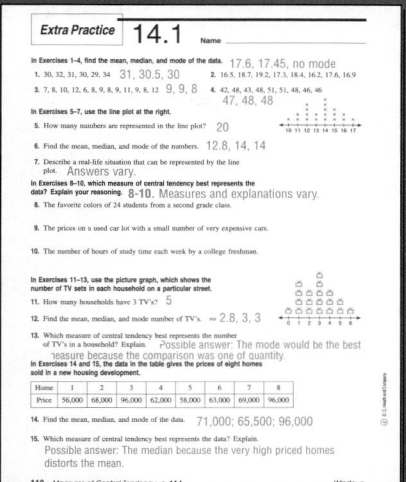

Reteaching Copymasters

Enrichment Projects

Math Log

Special Populations

Suggestions for providing equal access for:

*Students Acquiring English Proficiency

Reading tables and graphs will provide excellent opportunities for your students to develop and practice new vocabulary. Have students read tables and describe the data in complete sentences. Have students collect their own data and develop their own graphs.

Students with Various Learning Styles*

For these students, it is less important that they be able to do the calculations in Lessons 14.1–14.3 manually and more important that they be able to explain conclusions drawn about the results. Therefore, allow these students to use calculators and/or computers. In Lessons 14.5–14.8, encourage visual learners to use algebra tiles when completing the exercises.

Underachieving Students*

Divide students into groups and have them create and implement a one-question survey. Students can then use the data they collect to calculate various statistical measures and to make graphs to display their findings. Have them present these findings in the school newspaper or in another public forum.

Gifted and Talented Students*

Have students work in groups to create their own logic puzzle. Have them use the puzzle given in the Exploration and Extension of Lesson 14.5 as a model. Have them write clues and draw an appropriate grid. Groups can then exchange papers and solve one another's puzzles.

* See page T19 for descriptions of these special populations.

CHAPTER 14 OVERVIEW

PACING CHART

Lesson	Basic/ Average Course	Above Average Course	Advanced Course
14.1	2 days	1 day	1 day
14.2	2 days	1 day	1 day
14.3	2 days	2 days	2 days
14.4	0 days	1 day	1 day
14.5	0 days	1 day	1 day
14.6	0 days	1 day	1 day
14.7	0 days	0 days	2 days
14.8	0 days	0 days	1 day

About the Chapter

Since this is the final chapter of the program, encourage students to read the section on page 674 of the pupil text entitled "How does it fit into the bigger picture of mathematics?" The first half of this chapter is devoted to taking students further with the basic techniques of data analysis, while the second half introduces students to operations with polynomials.

Lessons 14.1–14.3 deal with the techniques for displaying data in an ordered manner such as a stem-and-leaf plot or a box-and-whisker plot, so that data can be more readily interpreted and analyzed for measures of central tendency, frequency distributions, and so on. Lesson 14.4 presents matrices as a further technique for arranging data so that arithmetic operations can be applied to the data according to well-defined rules.

Lessons 14.5 and 14.6 develop the concept of polynomials and suggest their use as models of certain kinds of real-life quantities. Students learn the technique of adding and subtracting polynomials. Lessons 14.7 and 14.8 show students how to apply the Distributive Property, first to the multiplication of a polynomial by a monomial, and finally to the multiplication of two binomials.

Zoos give animal specialists a chance to interact with endangered animals like the cheetah. By observing the animal's growth patterns and muscle tone, it is possible to study the role diet and exercise play in maintaining the animal's health and well being.

Real Life
Animal Care

Mouse
Lion
Elephant
Rhinoceros
Tortoise

2   10 22   50   70   100
    12

Advances in veterinary medicine have greatly improved animal care, led to the preservation of endangered species, and increased the health and life expectancy of livestock and pets.

The box plot shows the average life expectancy of certain animals.

Drawing and interpreting box-and-whisker plots is just one of the topics you will explore in this chapter.

Using the Page

Students may not be familiar with box-and-whisker plots. Therefore, you may want to give a general explanation of the graph and let students know they will learn how to make this type of graph in Lesson 14.3.

Have students work in groups to research an endangered species. Ask students to find how the population of the species has changed over time. Students should display the data using a graph. Also, have students find the life expectancy of the species. Collect the data from each group and create a box-and-whisker plot. Have students compare this graph with the one in the book. Ask students to explain any similarities and/or differences.

Multimedia Resources

Interactive CD-ROM Projects   A project for this chapter combines print, animation, sound and video presentations to capture students' interest in Age Distribution. This interactive approach shows students how the math concepts and problem-solving strategies they are learning will be used in the future in dealing with important personal, national, and world issues.
The theme of Age Distribution correlates to examples and exercises on pages 643 and 644.

Interactions: Real Math—Real Life
The theme of this chapter, Animal Care, correlates with an episode of **Interactions** which is a videodisc-based multimedia resource that connects middle school math topics with real-life careers. In each of the twelve episodes, students go on-site with a variety of professionals to witness real-life applications of the math they are studying. Students see math concepts and problem-solving strategies in a context that helps them connect what they are studying to the world outside the classroom. **Interactions** was developed by the Foundation for Advancements in Science and Education (FASE) and is published by D.C. Heath and Company.
The theme of Advanced Transportation is continued throughout the chapter on pages 636, 647, and 677.

Performance Assessment Resource
The PACKETS® Program: Performance Assessment for Middle School Mathematics was developed by Educational Testing Service and is published by D.C. Heath. **PACKETS** helps you assess your students' performances as they learn. You can use a wide variety of **PACKETS** Activity Units with this chapter because, in every activity, students will use ideas from all topic areas of mathematics. However, you can use the chart on page T16 to help you choose the **PACKETS** Activity Unit(s) that may fit best with this chapter.

PLANNING the Lesson

Lesson Plan 14.1, p. 110

ORGANIZER

Starters (reproduced below)
  Problem of the Day 14.1, p. 40
  Warm-Up Exercises 14.1, p. 40

Lesson Resources
  Color Transparencies
    Graph for Ex. 16–18, p. 58
  Teaching Tools
    Graph paper, pp. T1, C2
  Math Log, p. 43
  Technology, p. 80
  Answer Masters 14.1, p. 274
  Extra Practice Copymaster 14.1, p. 110
  Reteaching Copymaster 14.1, p. 110
  Enrichment Projects, pp. 72–74

Special Populations
  Suggestions, Teacher's Edition, p. 632D

LESSON Notes

Ask students to give examples of real-life situations (sports, academic records, sociological surveys, medical records, and so on) where a single number is used to represent a whole group of numbers. Have students record in their math journals that measures of central tendency are used to represent a typical number for a group of numbers.

Example 1

ACTIVITY
Have students think of each number as a pile of like objects. Then ask them what the mean represents. The mean represents the height of each pile if all the objects were redistributed to form equal piles. Use objects to demonstrate this concept, and/or illustrate the concept using a histogram.

14.1 Measures of Central Tendency

What you should learn:

Goal 1 How to find measures of central tendency

Goal 2 How to use measures of central tendency to solve real-life problems

Why you should learn it:

You can use measures of central tendency to solve real-life problems, such as describing the typical age of the people who attend a party.

Goal 1 Measures of Central Tendency

A **measure of central tendency** is a number that can be used to represent a group of numbers. Bar graphs (or histograms) can help you see numbers that are representative.

LESSON INVESTIGATION

■ **Investigating Central Tendencies**

Group Activity The three sets of data below show the ages of people at three different parties. For each party, state a single number that is most representative of the ages of the people. Explain how you chose your number and why you think it is representative.

Party 1: 13, 13, 13, 13, 13, 14, 14, 14, 14, 14 $13\frac{1}{2}$
Party 2: 11, 12, 13, 13, 13, 13, 13, 13, 13, 13   13
Party 3: 10, 11, 12, 13, 14, 15, 16, 17, 18, 19 $14\frac{1}{2}$

Numbers and explanations vary.

In this investigation, you may have chosen one or more of the most common measures of central tendency. They are called the **mean** (or average), **median**, and **mode**.

Example 1 *Finding Measures of Central Tendency*

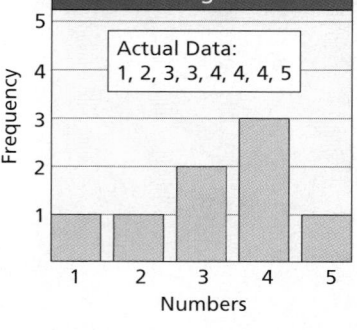

Find the mean, median, and mode of the data.

a. The *mean* of a group of numbers is the average of the numbers. For the numbers shown in the histogram at the left, the mean is

Mean $= \dfrac{1+2+3+3+4+4+4+5}{8} = \dfrac{26}{8} = 3.25.$

b. The *median* of a group of numbers is the middle number (or average of the two middle numbers) when the numbers are listed in order. Because the two middle numbers of the actual data are 3 and 4, the median is 3.5.

c. The *mode* of a group of numbers is the number that occurs most often. For the data at the left, the mode is 4. ■

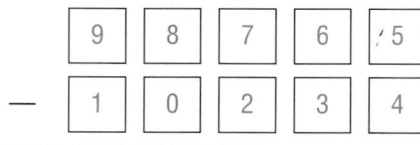

STARTER: Problem of the Day

Place the digits 0, 1, 2, 3, 4, 5, 6, 7, 8, 9 in each square. You can use each digit only once. This will form two 5-digit numbers. Arrange the digits so that the difference is as large as possible.

9	8	7	6	⁵5

−

1	0	2	3	4

Also available as a copymaster, page 40

STARTER: Warm-Up Exercises

1. Order the following number sets from smallest to largest. In each set, find the number *n* such that one-half of the numbers are greater than *n*, and one-half are less than *n*. If there is no single middle number in the list, identify the two middle numbers.
a. 3, 6, 5, 1, 12, 7, 100 **b.** 2, 45, 12, 37, 4, 8
a. 6, b. 8 and 12

2. Put the numbers in order from least to greatest, then identify the number that occurs most frequently.
1, 37, 22, 45, 22, 45, 37, 37, 1
1, 1, 22, 22, 37, 37, 37, 45, 45; 37

Also available as a copymaster, page 40

Goal 2 Using Measures of Central Tendency

The three measures of central tendency for a group of numbers can be exactly the same, almost the same, or very different. Here are some examples.

Group 1: 10, 11, 11, 12, 12, 12, 13, 13, 14
Group 2: 10, 11, 11, 12, 12, 12, 13, 13, 15
Group 3: 10, 10, 10, 12, 13, 13, 14, 14, 84

In Group 1, the mean, median, and mode are each 12. In Group 2, the mean is 12.1 and the median and mode are 12. In Group 3, the mean is 20, the median is 13, and the mode is 10.

Study Tip...
To find the median or the mode of a collection of numbers, you should first order the numbers from smallest to largest.

Real Life
Weather

Example 2 *Interpreting Central Tendencies*

The number of days of rain or snow per month in Boise, Idaho, and Lewiston, Idaho, is given in the table. Which measure of central tendency would you use to describe the typical number of days of rain or snow per month in each city?

Month	J	F	M	A	M	J	J	A	S	O	N	D
Boise	12	11	10	8	9	7	2	2	3	7	10	12
Lewiston	13	9	10	8	10	10	4	4	4	9	10	11

Solution The means, medians, and modes are as follows.

Boise: Mean = 7.75   Median = 8.5   Mode (none)
Lewiston: Mean = 8.5   Median = 9.5   Mode = 10

Boise does not have a mode because there is no number that occurs most often (2, 7, 10, and 12 each occur twice). Thus, the mode is not a good measure of the typical number of rain or snow days. Either of the other two measures could be used as a representative of the number of rain or snow days. You could say that Boise typically has 8 days of rain or snow per month and Lewiston typically has 9 days. ∎

Boise, once called the City of Trees, *is both the capital and the largest city in Idaho.*

[P] *Communicating* about MATHEMATICS

▶ **SHARING IDEAS about the Lesson**

The median or mode, which are both $4.75 per hour; 13 of the 16 salaries are $4.75 per hour.

Comparing Salaries A fast-food restaurant employs 16 people. Thirteen of the people make $4.75 per hour. The two assistant managers each make $10 per hour. The manager makes $16 per hour. What number best describes the typical hourly salary? Explain.

Common-Error Alert!

Groups of numbers with identical means can be quite different. The group 8, 8, 8, 8, 8, obviously has a mean value of 8. But the group 1, 4, 5, 11, 19 also has a mean value of 8, though the actual numbers in this group vary significantly. If the numbers in a group are about the same size, the median and mode will be about the same as the mean. If the median and mode are very different from the mean, the mean should not, without further inspection, be considered typical of the numbers in the group. Ask students to record this Alert in their math journals.

Example 2

Encourage students to identify measures of central tendency used to represent typical situations in other classes and report their findings.

Communicating
about MATHEMATICS

PROJECT
Have students find newspaper reports that use measures of central tendency to communicate the main ideas of the report. Then have them identify news reports that might be misleading if only *means* are given because, for example, sufficient information is not available to determine whether or not the means are typical of the numbers they represent.

PROJECT
Have students find histograms in newspapers in order to identify the mean, median, and mode of the numbers represented in the histograms.

Writing Prompt
My favorite use of a graphing calculator is . . .

OPTION: Extra Examples

Here is an additional example similar to Example 1.
Finding Measures of Central Tendency
Find the mean, median, and mode of the data.
Solution
88, 79, 93, 73, 84, 79, 91, 68, 83.

Mean = $\dfrac{88+79+93+73+84+79+91+68+83}{9}$

= $\dfrac{738}{9}$ = 82.

Arrange the numbers in order:
68, 73, 79, 79, 83, 84, 88, 91, 93
The median is the middle number, 83.
The mode is the number that occurs most often, 79.

Technology

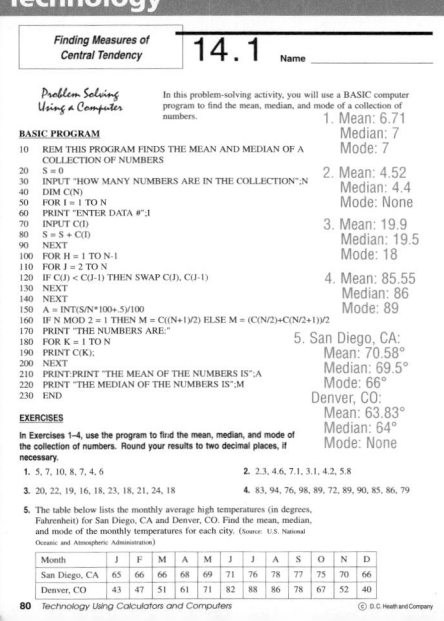

Finding Measures of Central Tendency **14.1** Name _____

Problem Solving Using a Computer

In this problem-solving activity, you will use a BASIC computer program to find the mean, median, and mode of a collection of numbers.

BASIC PROGRAM
```
10  REM THIS PROGRAM FINDS THE MEAN AND MEDIAN OF A
     COLLECTION OF NUMBERS
20  S = 0
30  INPUT "HOW MANY NUMBERS ARE IN THE COLLECTION";N
40  DIM C(N)
50  FOR I = 1 TO N
60  PRINT "ENTER DATA #";I
70  INPUT C(I)
80  S = S + C(I)
90  NEXT
100 FOR H = 1 TO N-1
110 FOR J = 2 TO N
120 IF C(J) < C(J-1) THEN SWAP C(J), C(J-1)
130 NEXT
140 NEXT
150 A = INT(S/N*100+.5)/100
160 IF N MOD 2 = 1 THEN M = C((N+1)/2) ELSE M = (C(N/2)+C(N/2+1))/2
170 PRINT "THE NUMBERS ARE:"
180 FOR K = 1 TO N
190 PRINT C(K);
200 NEXT
210 PRINT:PRINT "THE MEAN OF THE NUMBERS IS";A
220 PRINT "THE MEDIAN OF THE NUMBERS IS";M
230 END
```

EXERCISES
In Exercises 1–4, use the program to find the mean, median, and mode of the collection of numbers. Round your results to two decimal places, if necessary.

1. 5, 7, 10, 8, 7, 4, 6
2. 2.3, 4.6, 7.1, 3.1, 4.2, 5.8
3. 20, 22, 19, 16, 18, 23, 18, 21, 24, 18
4. 83, 94, 76, 98, 89, 72, 89, 90, 85, 86, 79

5. The table below lists the monthly average high temperatures (in degrees, Fahrenheit) for San Diego, CA and Denver, CO. Find the mean, median, and mode of the monthly temperatures for each city. (Source: U.S. National Oceanic and Atmospheric Administration)

Month	J	F	M	A	M	J	J	A	S	O	N	D
San Diego, CA	65	66	66	68	69	71	76	78	77	75	70	66
Denver, CO	43	47	51	61	71	82	88	86	78	67	52	40

1. Mean: 6.71
   Median: 7
   Mode: 7
2. Mean: 4.52
   Median: 4.4
   Mode: None
3. Mean: 19.9
   Median: 19.5
   Mode: 18
4. Mean: 85.55
   Median: 86
   Mode: 89
5. San Diego, CA:
   Mean: 70.58°
   Median: 69.5°
   Mode: 66°
   Denver, CO:
   Mean: 63.83°
   Median: 64°
   Mode: None

EXERCISE Notes

ASSIGNMENT GUIDE

Basic/Average:
   Day 1: Ex. 6–12
   Day 2: Ex. 15, 19, 21, 25, 28–30

Above Average:
   Ex. 6–12, 14, 16–31

Advanced: Ex. 6–12, 14, 16–31

Selected Answers: Ex. 1–5, 6–27 odd

Guided Practice

The terminology of this lesson may already be familiar to students. Use these exercises to open the lesson and check for students' prior knowledge of the concepts.

Independent Practice

▶ **Ex. 10–12** Refer students to Lesson 5.6 on line plots. This provides a connection to previously learned material.

▶ **Ex. 16–18** These exercises connect to Lesson 5.1.

Guided Practice

▶ **CHECK for Understanding**   a. Median   b. Mode   c. Mean

P 1. Name the measure of central tendency associated with each phrase.
   a. middle   **b.** most often   **c.** average

In Exercises 2–5, use the histogram at the right.   See margin.

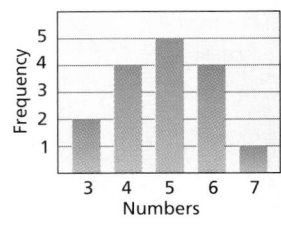

2. Describe and order the data that is represented.

3. Find the mean of the numbers. $4\frac{7}{8}$

4. Find the median of the numbers.   5

5. Find the mode of the numbers.   5

Independent Practice

In Exercises 6–9, find the mean, median, and mode of the data.

8. 37, 37, none

6. 85, 86, 90, 90, 91, 92   89, 90, 90

7. 52.8, 53.6, 53.9, 54, 54.5, 54.8, 55.1   54.1, 54, none

8. 34, 35, 36, 36, 37, 37, 38, 38, 39, 40

9. 55, 56, 57, 58, 59, 60, 60, 60, 62 $58\frac{5}{9}$, 59, 60

In Exercises 10–12, use the line plot at the right.   See margin.

10. How many numbers are represented in the line plot? List them in increasing order.

11. Find the mean, median, and mode of the numbers.

✪ 12. *Problem Solving*   Describe a real-life situation
P   that can be represented by the line plot.

P *Mean, Median, or Mode?*   **In Exercises 13–15, which measure of central tendency best represents the data? Explain your reasoning.**   Measures and explanations vary.

✪ 13. The salaries of 240 people in your neighborhood

✪ 14. The number of daily calories you consume for 30 days

✪ 15. The number of pairs of shoes owned by each person in your neighborhood

Wildlife Preservation   **In Exercises 16–18, use the picture graph, which shows the ages of the wolf population in a state park.**   17. $2\frac{7}{1}$, 2, 1

16. How many 3-year-old wolves are in the park?   5

17. Find the mean, median, and mode of the ages.

✪ 18. Which measure of central tendency best represents the age of the wolf population? Explain.
   The mean or median; the mode is not good because it is the smallest number.

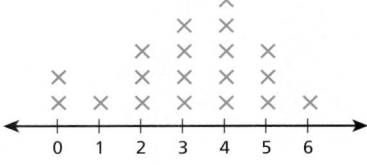

Wolf Ages (years)

636   Chapter **14** ▪ Exploring Data and Polynomials

✪ More difficult exercises
P Portfolio Opportunity

Answers

2. The numbers 3, 4, 5, 6, and 7 occur from 1 to 5 times each. 3, 3, 4, 4, 4, 4, 5, 5, 5, 5, 5, 6, 6, 6, 6, 7

10. 20; 0, 0, 1, 2, 2, 2, 3, 3, 3, 3, 4, 4, 4, 4, 4, 4, 5, 5, 5, 6

11. 3.2, 3.5, 4

12. Answers vary. One situation might be that the numbers are responses to the question "How many hours do you usually watch TV on a Sunday?"

23. Answers vary. One wording might be as follows. In 1992 in Seattle, Washington, half the houses cost as much as or more than $141,300 and half the houses cost as much as or less than $141,300.

636   Chapter 14

Extra Practice

Reteaching

Chemistry In Exercises 19 and 20, use the following information and data.

At a neighborhood swimming pool, you measure the pH level of the water each day for ten days. (The pH level of pure water is 7. Lower pH levels indicate that the water is acidic.) **19.** 6.61, 6.6, none

Data: 7.1, 6.9, 6.7, 6.5, 6.3, 6.9, 6.8, 6.5, 6.3, 6.1

19. Find the mean, median, and mode of the data.

20. The data is listed in order of the days the measurements were taken. Did the water tend to become more acidic or less acidic? On which day was a chemical added to change the pH level?
More acidic, the 5th or 6th day

In Exercises 21 and 22, list six numbers that have the indicated measures of central tendency. (There are many correct answers.) Answers vary.

21. The mean is 15, the median is 15, and the mode is 15.   13, 14, 15, 15, 16, 17

22. The mean is 10, the median is 9, and the mode is 8.   8, 8, 8, 10, 10, 16

23. *House Prices*   Explain the following statement in your own words. "In 1992, the median sales price of houses in Seattle, Washington, was \$141,300." *(Source: National Association of Realtors)*   See margin, page 636.

24. *Test Scores*   On your first four tests of the grading period, you had scores of 95, 89, 91, and 93. What score must you get on your final test to raise your average (mean) to 93?   97

Integrated Review   *Making Connections within Mathematics*

Histograms and Line Plots   In Exercises 25–27, use the following data.

Data: 1, 3, 5, 4, 2, 2, 3, 4, 6, 1, 4, 7, 2, 5, 4, 1, 2, 4, 6, 5   **25., 26.** See margin.

25. Construct a histogram.   **26.** Construct a line plot.

27. *Probability*   You are randomly selecting a number from the given data. Find the probability of choosing the indicated number.

a. 1 $\frac{3}{20}$ **b.** 2 $\frac{1}{5}$ **c.** 3 $\frac{1}{10}$ **d.** 4 $\frac{1}{4}$ **e.** 5 $\frac{3}{20}$ **f.** 6 $\frac{1}{10}$ **g.** 7 $\frac{1}{20}$ **h.** 8   0

Exploration and Extension

Experimental Probability   In Exercises 28–31, use a pair of six-sided dice.

28. Toss the dice 50 times and record the totals.   **28–30.** Check students' work.

29. Create a histogram of the data.

30. Find the mean, median, and mode of the data.

31. From your results, estimate the probability of tossing totals of 2, 3, 4, 5, 6, 7, 8, 9, 10, 11, and 12 with a pair of dice.   See margin.

14.1 ▪ Measures of Central Tendency   **637**

▶ **Ex. 19, 20**   Ask a science teacher at your school to show students a pH test.

Integrated Review

For these exercises, students should refer to Lessons 5.1, 5.2, and 5.8.

Exploration and Extension

Use these exercises as an in-class activity for teams of two to four students. Summarize class results with the data from each team.
Compare the experimental probability results to the known theoretical probability.

Theoretical Probabilities:

$P(2) = \frac{1}{36}$ $P(6) = \frac{5}{36}$ $P(10) = \frac{1}{12}$

$P(3) = \frac{1}{18}$ $P(7) = \frac{1}{6}$ $P(11) = \frac{1}{18}$

$P(4) = \frac{1}{12}$ $P(8) = \frac{5}{36}$ $P(12) = \frac{1}{36}$

$P(5) = \frac{1}{9}$ $P(9) = \frac{1}{9}$

Portfolio Opportunity: Math Log

Name a real-world application of a measure of central tendency. In your own words, describe the meaning of your example.

Also available as a copymaster, page 43, Ex. 1

Alternative Assessment

A journal entry activity that develops students' writing skills and their ability to interpret data.

Available as a copymaster, page 41

Answers
25.

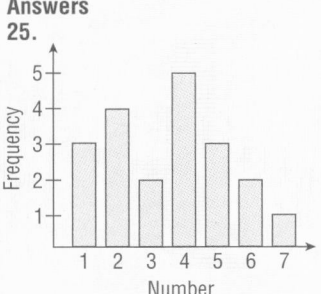

26.

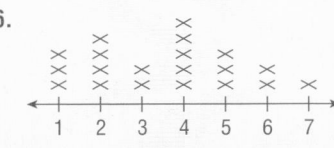

31. Students' experimental results should roughly reflect the theoretical results, which are

$\frac{1}{36}, \frac{2}{36} = \frac{1}{18}, \frac{3}{36} = \frac{1}{12}, \frac{4}{36} = \frac{1}{9}, \frac{5}{36}, \frac{6}{36}$

$= \frac{1}{6}, \frac{4}{36} = \frac{1}{9}, \frac{3}{36} = \frac{1}{12}, \frac{2}{36} = \frac{1}{18}, \frac{1}{36}.$

▶ **Enrichment**

Have students extend Ex. 28–31 using 12-sided dice (dodecahedrons) as well. Ask: What additional sums are now available? How does this affect the probability of each number occurring? Help students to compare the experimental results to the theoretical results.

PACING the Lesson

Suggested Number of Days
Basic/Average 2 **Above Average** 1
Advanced 1

PLANNING the Lesson

Lesson Plan 14.2, p. 111

ORGANIZER

Starters (reproduced below)
Problem of the Day 14.2, p. 40
Warm-Up Exercises 14.2, p. 40
Lesson Resources
Teaching Tools
Graph paper, pp. T1, C2
Math Log, p. 43
Answer Masters 14.2, pp. 275, 276
Extra Practice Copymaster 14.2, p. 111
Reteaching Copymaster 14.2, p. 111
Special Populations
Suggestions, Teacher's Edition, p. 632D

LESSON Notes

A stem-and-leaf plot is a systematic model for ordering data and for better understanding the data. After stem-and-leaf plots have been discussed, ask students to identify the types of data for which a stem-and-leaf plot would be useful.

Example 1

Show students how they can construct an unordered stem-and-leaf plot from the unordered data; then construct the ordered stem-and-leaf plot from the unordered one.

14.2

Stem-and-Leaf Plots

What you should learn:

 Goal 1 How to organize data with a stem-and-leaf plot

Goal 2 How to use two stem-and-leaf plots to compare two sets of data

Why you should learn it:

You can use stem-and-leaf plots to help interpret real-life data, such as deciding which part of the United States has a more urban population.

World Cup *Being able to organize data is important for businesses like the Miami clothing company started by Richard Gonzales. His company won the rights to use the official World Cup soccer logo and mascot for T-shirt designs.*

Goal 1 **Using Stem-and-Leaf Plots**

A **stem-and-leaf plot** is a technique for ordering data in increasing or decreasing order.

Example 1 *Making a Stem-and-Leaf Plot*

Use a stem-and-leaf plot to order the following data.

Unordered Data: 5, 10, 14, 44, 32, 35, 14, 28, 8, 13, 11, 25, 30, 15, 20, 9, 29, 20, 23, 40, 19, 31, 32, 32, 43, 42, 25, 37, 11, 8, 4, 43, 7, 24

Solution The numbers vary between 5 and 44, so you can let the *stem* represent the tens digits and let the *leaves* represent the units digits. Begin by creating an unordered stem-and-leaf plot as shown on the left. Then order the leaves to form an ordered stem-and-leaf plot as shown on the right.

	Unordered Plot			Ordered Plot
Stem	Leaves		Stem	Leaves
4	4 0 3 2 3		4	0 2 3 3 4
3	2 5 0 1 2 2 7		3	0 1 2 2 2 5 7
2	8 5 0 9 0 3 5 4		2	0 0 3 4 5 5 8 9
1	0 4 4 3 1 5 9 1		1	0 1 1 3 4 4 5 9
0	5 8 9 8 4 7		0	4 5 7 8 8 9

4 | 3 represents 43

You can use the ordered stem-and-leaf plot to order the data.

Ordered Data: 4, 5, 7, 8, 8, 9, 10, 11, 11, 13, 14, 14, 15, 19, 20, 20, 23, 24, 25, 25, 28, 29, 30, 31, 32, 32, 32, 35, 37, 40, 42, 43, 43, 44 ∎

When you make a stem-and-leaf plot, you should include a key that allows people to tell what the stem and leaves represent. For instance, in Example 1, by knowing that 4 | 3 represents 43, you know that the stem represents the tens digit and the leaves represent the units digits.

STARTER: Problem of the Day

The area of a rectangle is 24 square feet. Complete the table, showing the possible widths and the resulting perimeters.

Area	Length	Width	Perimeter
24	1	24	50
24	2	12	28
24	3	8	22
24	4	6	20

Also available as a copymaster, page 40

STARTER: Warm-Up Exercises

The math test scores for a class were:
12, 96, 58, 85, 72, 74, 97, 45, 31, 76, 81, 68, 78, 76, 73, 87, 88, 91, 69, 77, 94, 53, 75, 88, 78
a. On this test, did more students score in the 70's or in the 80's?
b. How could you arrange the data to make it easier to answer a?
a. More students scored in the 70's, b. Order the data .

Also available as a copymaster, page 40

Real Life
Social Studies

Example 2 — *Organizing Data*

The data below shows the percent of each state's population that is urban (lives in a city). Which group of states is more urban? *(Source: U.S. Bureau of Census)*

East of Mississippi: AL (60%), CT (79%), DE (73%), FL (85%), GA (63%), IL (85%), IN (65%), KY (52%), MA (84%), MD (81%), ME (45%), MI (71%), MS (47%), NC (50%), NH (51%), NJ (89%), NY (84%), OH (74%), PA (69%), RI (86%), SC (55%), TN (61%), VA (69%), VT (32%), WV (36%)

West of Mississippi: AK (68%), AR (54%), AZ (88%), CA (93%), CO (82%), HI (89%), IA (61%), ID (57%), KS (69%), LA (68%), MN (70%), MO (69%), MT (53%), ND (53%), NE (66%), NM (73%), NV (88%), OK (68%), OR (71%), SD (50%), TX (80%), UT (87%), WA (76%), WI (66%), WY (65%)

Solution A *double* stem-and-leaf plot can help you answer the question. The leaves representing the western states point to the left of the stem and the leaves representing the eastern states point to the right of the stem. From the double plot below, you can see that the western states tend to have more urban populations.

During much of the history of the United States, its population was mostly rural (lived in the country or in towns of less than 2500). Now, however, the population is mostly urban (lives in cities or towns of 2500 or more).

West		East
3	9	
9 8 8 7 2 0	8	1 4 4 5 5 6 9
6 3 1 0	7	1 3 4 9
9 9 8 8 8 6 6 5 1	6	0 1 3 5 9 9
7 4 3 3 0	5	0 1 2 5
	4	5 7
	3	2 6

0 | 7 | 1 represents 70% and 71% urban population

Communicating *about* MATHEMATICS

Cooperative Learning

▶ **SHARING IDEAS about the Lesson**

Group Project Use the data in Example 2 to draw a double stem-and-leaf plot that represents the rural (country) populations of the states. Compare your plot to that in Example 2. See margin.

Have students write in their journals that data should be organized in a structured way so that conclusions can be drawn easily.

Example 2

Have students rate, from 1 (= very easy) to 10 (= very hard), how difficult it is to answer the following question without reorganizing the data: Which group of states is more urban? Then have them rate the difficulty of answering the same question using the double stem-and-leaf plot.

Common-Error Alert!

Be sure students understand that "leaves" west and east of the "stem" are ones digits, and that the stem represents the tens digits.

Communicating *about* MATHEMATICS

Using a world atlas, have students find population data for different countries and make double stem-and-leaf plots that describe for those countries the percentage of populations living in rural and urban areas. Encourage students to select countries in different regions of the earth. Discuss students' findings. Ask them what the results suggest about the cultures of the various countries.

Writing Prompt
Describe any discoveries you've made about patterns in data during our discussions on stem-and-leaf plots.

Here is an additional example similar to Example 1.

Making a Stem-and-Leaf Plot
Use a stem-and-leaf plot to order the following data.

Unordered Data: 26, 26, 36, 12, 14, 25, 59, 62, 50, 62, 64, 74, 53, 75, 91, 75, 85, 75, 87, 86

Solution
The numbers vary between 12 and 91, so you can let the stem represent the tens digits. Begin by creating an unordered stem-and-leaf plot as shown. Then order the leaves to form an ordered stem-and-leaf plot.

Unordered Plot		Ordered Plot	
Stem	Leaves	Stem	Leaves
9	1	9	1
8	5 7 6	8	5 6 7
7	4 5 5 5	7	4 5 5 5
6	2 2 4	6	2 2 4
5	9 0 3	5	0 3 9
4		4	
3	6	3	6
2	6 6 5	2	5 6 6
1	2 4	1	2 4

You can use the ordered stem-and-leaf plot to order the data.

Ordered Data: 12, 14, 25, 26, 26, 36, 50, 53, 59, 62, 62, 64, 74, 75, 75, 75, 85, 86, 87, 91

Answer to Communicating

	6	4 8
0	5	0 3 5
7 7 6 3	4	0 5 8 9
9 5 4 4 2 2 2 1 1 0	3	1 1 5 7 9
9 7 4 0	2	1 6 7 9
8 3 2 2 1	1	1 4 5 5 6 6 9
7	0	

3|4|0 represents 43% western and 40% eastern rural population.

This plot represents the opposite to that of Example 2: the eastern states tend to have more rural populations.

ASSIGNMENT GUIDE

Basic/Average:
Day 1: Ex. 4–9, 12, 13
Day 2: Ex. 14–17

Above Average:
Ex. 4–11, 14–18

Advanced: Ex. 4–11, 14–18

Selected Answers: Ex. 1–3, 5–17 odd

Guided Practice

Use these exercises as a small-group 5-minute in-class check for understanding. Ask students to discuss the visual connection between a stem-and-leaf plot and a histogram or bar graph.

Independent Practice

▶ **Ex. 9** Use this exercise as a small-group in-class assignment. Remind students to do two stem-and-leaf plots. The first plot lists the data in the stem-and-leaf format. The second plot orders the leaves.

Answers

3.
```
6 | 5
5 | 0 2 4 5
4 | 1 3
3 | 0 2 2 3 4 8
2 | 1 4 8 9 9
1 | 0 7 8
0 | 1 2 2 5 6 8 8
```
6|5 represents 65.

7. Left side: 31, 34, 36, 42. 43, 45, 54, 56, 57, 62, 65, 71, 74, 77, 80, 83, 84, 88, 92, 92, 93, 97.
Right side: 31, 33, 34, 35, 37, 39, 40, 42, 43, 47, 56, 58, 58, 62, 63, 65, 66, 73, 74, 77, 83, 84, 91, 92.

9.
```
18 | 6
17 | 1 6
16 | 1 1 1 2 2 2 3 4 8
15 | 1 1 3 3 6 7 7 8 9 9 9
14 | 0 3 3 4 5 7 9 9
13 | 4 9 9 9
```
18|6 represents 186 mph.

Guided Practice

▶ **CHECK for Understanding**

In Exercises 1 and 2, list the data represented by the stem-and-leaf plot.

1.
```
3 | 1 2 4 4 6
2 | 0 3 5 7
1 | 0 1 5 5 6 9
0 | 2 2 8
```
3 | 1 represents 31

2, 2, 8, 10, 11, 15, 15, 16, 19, 20, 23, 25, 27, 31, 32, 34, 34, 36

2.
```
8 4 3 1 | 7 | 0 3 4 6
5 5 0 | 6 | 1 4 7
9 7 3 2 | 5 | 2 3 5 8 9
4 2 0 | 4 | 3
```
8 | 7 | 0 represents 7.8 and 7.0

Left side: 4.0, 4.2 5.2, 5.3, 5.7, 5.9, 6.5, 6.5, 7.1, 7.3, 7.8.
Right side: 4.3, 5. 5.3, 5.5, 5.8, 5.9, 6.4, 6.7, 7.0, 7.3, 7.6

3. Use a stem-and-leaf plot to order the following set of data.

18, 6, 52, 41, 43, 8, 29, 24, 33, 30, 2, 55, 28, 32 8, 21, 5, 2, 38, 10, 54, 65, 17, 29, 34, 50, 32, 1
See margin.

Independent Practice

For histograms, see Additional Answers.

In Exercises 4–6, list the data represented by the stem-and-leaf plot. Then draw a histogram for the data.

4.
```
6 | 4 6 6 8
5 | 0 2 3
4 | 1 8
3 | 5 7 9
2 | 0 1 1 3
```
6 | 4 represents 64

20, 21, 21, 23, 35, 37, 39, 41, 48, 50, 52, 53, 64, 66, 66, 68

5.
```
12 | 4 5 6 7
11 | 0 3 8 8 9
10 | 1 2 7
9 | 0 1
8 | 4 4 5 8
```
12 | 4 represents 124

13.5, 13.6, 14.3, 14.5, 14.9, 15.1, 15.9, 15.9, 16.1, 16.2, 16.3, 16.7, 17.2, 17.3, 17.4, 17.6, 17.8

84, 84, 85, 88, 90, 91, 101, 102, 107, 110, 113, 118, 118, 119, 124, 125, 126, 127

6.
```
17 | 2 3 4 6 8
16 | 1 2 3 7
15 | 1 9 9
14 | 3 5 9
13 | 5 6
```
17 | 2 represents 17.2

7. *Double Stem-and-Leaf Plot* List the two sets of data represented by the double stem-and-leaf plot at the right. See margin.

8. *Double Bar Graph* Draw a double bar graph to represent the data given in the double stem-and-leaf plot at the right. (*Hint:* Double bar graphs are described on page 199.) See Additional Answers.

```
7 3 2 2 | 9 | 1 2
8 4 3 0 | 8 | 3 4
7 4 1 | 7 | 3 4 7
5 2 | 6 | 2 3 5 6
7 6 4 | 5 | 6 8 8
5 3 2 | 4 | 0 2 3 7
6 4 1 | 3 | 1 3 4 5 7 9
```
7 | 9 | 1 represents 97 and 91

9. *Indianapolis 500* The winning speeds (in miles per hour) in the Indianapolis 500 from 1960 through 1994 are given below. Organize the data with an ordered stem-and-leaf plot. See margin.

1960 (139), 1961 (139), 1962 (140), 1963 (143), 1964 (147), 1965 (151), 1966 (144), 1967 (151), 1968 (153), 1969 (157), 1970 (156), 1971 (158), 1972 (163), 1973 (159), 1974 (159), 1975 (149), 1976 (149), 1977 (161), 1978 (161), 1979 (159), 1980 (143), 1981 (139), 1982 (162), 1983 (162), 1984 (164), 1985 (153), 1986 (171), 1987 (162), 1988 (145), 1989 (168), 1990 (186), 1991 (176), 1992 (134), 1993 (157), 1994 (161)

Extra Practice

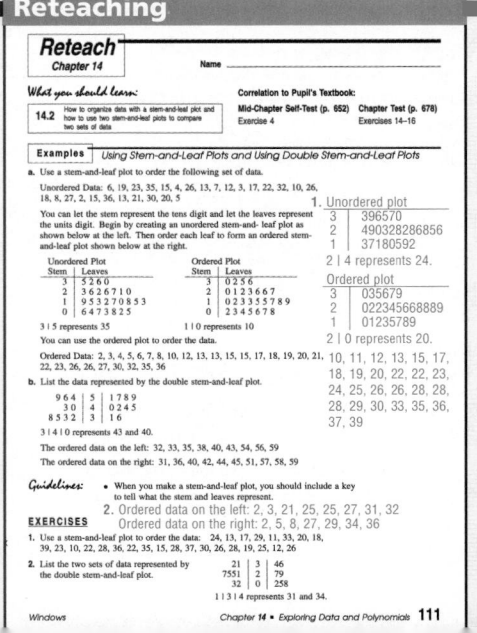

Extra Practice 14.2 Name ____

1. List the data represented by the stem-and-leaf plot. Then draw a histogram for the data.
```
7 | 0 1 2 2 3
6 | 1 7 7 8
5 | 2 3 3 4
4 | 2 3
3 | 0
```
7|0 represents 70.
30, 42, 43, 52, 53, 53, 54, 61, 67, 67, 68, 70, 71, 72, 72, 73

2. List the two sets of data represented by the double stem-and-leaf plot at the right.
```
5 5 3 | 3 | 8 8 9
9 8 7 6 | 2 | 0 1
       | 1 | 9
```
6|2|0 represents 2.6 and 2.0.
Group #1: 2.6, 2.7, 2.8, 2.9, 3.3, 3.5, 3.5
Group #2: 1.9, 2.0, 2.1, 3.8, 3.8, 3.9

3. Draw a double bar graph to represent the data in the double stem-and-leaf plot.
See right.

4. The following data represents the ages of customers in a fast food restaurant on a particular Saturday between 11:00 A.M. and 1:00 P.M. Organize the data with an ordered stem-and-leaf plot.
24 33 39 51 16 18 24 28 33 53
12 13 16 25 35 60 37 27 51 20
32 36 47 41 26 28 17 19 23 39
25 29 34 39 43 51 53 62 60 19
17 23 20 30 33 36 42 47 50
6|0 represents 60.

In Exercises 5 and 6, use the set of data below which shows the batting averages of the American League Batting Champions for the years 1970 through 1993.

1970(.329) 1971(.337) 1972(.318) 1973(.350) 1974(.364) 1975(.359) 1976(.333) 1977(.388) 1978(.333) 1979(.333) 1980(.390) 1981(.336) 1982(.332) 1983(.361) 1984(.343) 1985(.368) 1986(.357) 1987(.363) 1988(.366) 1989(.339) 1990(.329) 1991(.341) 1992(.343) 1993(.363)

5. Organize the data in a stem-and-plot.
```
0.39 | 0
0.38 | 8
0.37 |
0.36 | 1 3 3 4 6 8
0.35 | 0 7 9
0.34 | 1 3
0.33 | 2 3 3 6 7 9
0.32 | 9 9
0.31 | 8
```

6. Draw a histogram to represent the data.

14.2 ▪ Stem-and-Leaf Plots **111**
Windows

Reteaching

Reteach Chapter 14 Name ____

What you should learn:
14.2 How to organize data with a stem-and-leaf plot and how to use two stem-and-leaf plots to compare two sets of data.

Correlation to Pupil's Textbook:
Mid-Chapter Self-Test (p. 652) Chapter Test (p. 678)
Exercise 4   Exercises 14–16

Examples *Using Stem-and-Leaf Plots and Using Double Stem-and-Leaf Plots*

a. Use a stem-and-leaf plot to order the following set of data.

Unordered Data: 6, 19, 23, 35, 15, 4, 20, 12, 3, 17, 22, 32, 10, 26, 18, 8, 27, 2, 15, 36, 13, 21, 30, 20, 5

You can let the stem represent the tens digit and let the leaves represent the units digit. Begin by creating an unordered stem-and-leaf plot as shown below at the left. Then order each leaf to form an ordered stem-and-leaf plot shown below at the right.

1. Unordered plot
```
3 | 3 9 6 5 7 0
2 | 4 9 0 3 2 8 2 8 6 8 5 6
1 | 3 7 1 8 0 5 9 2
```
2|4 represents 24.

Unordered Plot
```
Stem | Leaves
3    | 5 2 6 0
2    | 3 6 2 6 7 1 0
1    | 9 5 3 2 7 0
0    | 6 4 7 3 8 2 5
```
3|5 represents 35.

Ordered Plot
```
Stem | Leaves
3    | 0 2 5 6
2    | 0 1 2 3 6 6 7
1    | 0 2 3 5 7 9
0    | 2 3 4 5 6 7 8
```
1|0 represents 10.

Ordered plot
```
3 | 0 3 5 6 7 9
2 | 0 2 2 3 4 5 6 6 8 8 8 9
1 | 0 1 2 3 5 7 8 9
```
2|0 represents 20.

You can use the ordered plot to order the data.

Ordered Data: 2, 3, 4, 5, 6, 7, 8, 10, 12, 13, 15, 15, 17, 18, 19, 20, 20, 21, 22, 23, 26, 26, 27, 30, 32, 35, 36

b. List the data represented by the double stem-and-leaf plot.
```
9 6 4 | 5 | 1 7 8 9
  3 0 | 4 | 0 2 4 5
8 5 3 2 | 3 | 1 6
```
3|4|0 represents 43 and 40.

10, 11, 12, 13, 15, 17, 18, 19, 20, 22, 22, 23, 24, 25, 26, 26, 28, 28, 28, 29, 30, 33, 35, 36, 37, 39

The ordered data on the left: 32, 33, 35, 38, 40, 43, 54, 56, 59
The ordered data on the right: 31, 36, 40, 42, 44, 45, 51, 57, 58, 59

Guidelines: • When you make a stem-and-leaf plot, you should include a key to tell what the stem and leaves represent.

EXERCISES
1. Use a stem-and-leaf plot to order the data: 24, 13, 17, 29, 11, 33, 20, 18, 39, 23, 10, 22, 28, 16, 37, 30, 26, 28, 19, 25, 12, 26

2. Ordered data on the left: 2, 3, 21, 25, 25, 27, 31, 32
   Ordered data on the right: 2, 5, 8, 27, 29, 34, 36

2. List the two sets of data represented by the double stem-and-leaf plot.
```
21 | 3 | 1 46
7551 | 2 | 79
  32 | 1 | 0 258
```
1|1|3|4 represents 31 and 34.

Chapter **14** ▪ *Exploring Data and Polynomials* **111**
Windows

Final Grades **In Exercises 10 and 11, use the set of data below, which lists the scores on a test for students.**

93, 84, 100, 92, 66, 89, 78, 52, 71, 85, 83, 95, 98, 99, 93, 81, 80, 79, 67, 59, 90, 85, 77, 62, 90, 78, 66, 63, 93, 87, 74, 96, 72, 100, 70, 73

10. Order the data in a stem-and-leaf plot.
See margin.

11. Draw a histogram to represent the data.
See Additional Answers.

Temperature **In Exercises 12 and 13, use the data, which lists the record high temperatures of Bismark, North Dakota, as of 1991.** *(Source: U.S. National Oceanic and Atmospheric Administration)*

Jan., 62°; Feb., 68°; Mar., 81°; Apr., 93°; May, 98°; June, 107°; July, 109°; Aug., 109°; Sep., 105°; Oct., 95°; Nov., 75°; Dec., 65°

12. Order the data in a stem-and-leaf plot.
See margin.

13. Draw a histogram to represent the data.
See Additional Answers.

Population **In Exercises 14 and 15, use the data below showing the per-cent of each state's population that is between 5 and 17 years old.** *(Source: U.S. Bureau of Census)*

East of the Mississippi: AL(19%), CT(16%), DE(17%), FL(16%), GA(19%), IL(18%), IN(19%), KY(19%), MA(16%), MD(17%), ME(18%), MI(19%), MS(21%), NC(17%), NH(18%), NJ(17%), NY(17%), OH(18%), PA(17%), RI(16%), SC(19%), TN(18%), VA(17%), VT(18%), WV(18%)

West of the Mississippi: AK(22%), AR(19%), AZ(19%), CA(18%), CO(19%), HI(17%), IA(19%), ID(23%), KS(19%), LA(21%), MN(19%), MO(19%), MT(20%), ND(20%), NE(20%), NM(21%), NV(17%), OK(19%), OR(19%), SD(21%), TX(20%), UT(26%), WA(19%), WI(19%), WY(22%)

14. Order the data with a double stem-and-leaf plot. See margin.

15. Find the mean, median, and mode for each group of states and for the total collection of states. East: 17.76%, 18%, none; West: 19.88%, 19%, 19%; Total: 18.82%, 19%, 19%

Integrated Review — Making Connections within Mathematics

16. *Probability* If you selected one score from the data in Exercise 10, what is the probability that it is greater than 80? $\frac{19}{36}$

17. *Probability* If you selected one temperature from the data in Exercise 12, what is the probability that it is less than 80°? $\frac{1}{3}$

Exploration and Extension

18. *Technology* If you have access to a random number generator (on a computer or a graphing calculator), use the number generator to list 40 numbers between 0 and 1. Multiply each number by 100 and round the result to the nearest whole number. Then organize the results with a stem-and-leaf plot. Do your results appear random? Explain your reasoning. Check students' work. Their results should appear random.

| MATH | (Cursor to PRB) |
| ENTER | ENTER |

Rand
　　　　　.1803911973

TI-81 or TI-82 Keystrokes

✪ More difficult exercises
Ⓟ Portfolio Opportunity

14.2 • *Stem-and-Leaf Plots* **641**

▶ **Ex. 10, 11** These exercises can be enriched by using the actual data from a previous class.
▶ **Ex. 14, 15** Use the results of these exercises for an in-class discussion of *why* the data shows a pattern and *why* the populations from the northwest states are higher.

Integrated Review

For help with these exercises, refer students to Lesson 5.8.

Exploration and Extension

This exercise could be used as a teacher lab demonstration using an overhead projector.

Portfolio Opportunity: Math Log

What is accomplished by organizing data in a stem-and-leaf plot?

Also available as a copymaster, page 43, Ex. 2

Short Quiz

Covers Lessons 14.1 and 14.2

Available as a copymaster, page 228

Enrichment

ALTERNATIVE ASSESSMENT
For a 20-point class report lab project, bring students to the reference section of the school library. Allow students to locate a data set of general interest. Have them construct a stem-and-leaf plot of the data (10 points) with a written interpretation of the patterns in the data (10 points).

Answer

```
10.  10 | 0 0
      9 | 0 0 2 3 3 3 5 6 8 9
      8 | 0 1 3 4 5 5 7 9
      7 | 0 1 2 3 4 7 8 8 9
      6 | 2 3 6 6 7
      5 | 2 9
5|2 represents 52.
```

```
12.  10 | 5 7 9 9
      9 | 3 5 8
      8 | 1
      7 | 5
      6 | 2 5 8
6|2 represents 62°.
```

```
14.              6 3 2 2 | 2 |
           1 1 1 0 0 0 0 | 2 | 1
  9 9 9 9 9 9 9 9 9 9 9 | 1 | 9 9 9 9 9
                      8 | 1 | 8 8 8 8 8 8
                    7 7 | 1 | 7 7 7 7 7 7 7
                        | 1 | 6 6 6 6
```

0|2|1 represents 20% population west of the Mississippi and 21% population east of the Mississippi between 5 and 17 years old.

PACING the Lesson

Suggested Number of Days
Basic/Average 2   **Above Average** 2
Advanced 2

PLANNING the Lesson

Lesson Plan 14.3, p. 112

ORGANIZER

Starters (reproduced below)
   Problem of the Day 14.3, p. 40
   Warm-Up Exercises 14.3, p. 40
Lesson Resources
   Math Log, p. 43
   Answer Masters 14.3, p. 277
   Extra Practice Copymaster 14.3, p. 112
   Reteaching Copymaster 14.3, p. 112
Special Populations
   Suggestions, Teacher's Edition, p. 632D

LESSON Notes

To draw a box-and-whisker plot, the data must first be ordered. Emphasize that the box-and-whisker plot provides a quick way to see how the numbers are distributed.

Example 1

Point out to students that in a box-and-whisker plot, the smallest and largest numbers are the ends of the "whiskers," the first and third quartiles are the ends of the "box," and the second quartile is in the interior of the box.

   Ask students to explain why the second quartile is not half the distance between the ends of the whiskers.   The second quartile is not the mean of the two extreme values.

   Ask also: Under what conditions would the second quartile be midway between the ends of the whiskers?   The second quartile would have to be the mean of the extreme values.

14.3   Box-and-Whisker Plots

What you should learn:

Goal 1   How to organize data with a box-and-whisker plot

Goal 2   How to use box-and-whisker plots to interpret real-life data

Why you should learn it:

You can use box-and-whisker plots to help interpret real-life data, such as describing the age distribution in a state.

Need to Know

When you draw a box-and-whisker plot, you should label five numbers: the smallest number, the quartiles, and the largest number. These five numbers should be spaced as they would be on a number line.

Goal 1   **Drawing Box-and-Whisker Plots**

The median (or **second quartile**) of an ordered collection of numbers roughly divides the collection into two halves: those below the median and those above the median. The **first quartile** is the median of the lower half, and the **third quartile** is the median of the upper half.

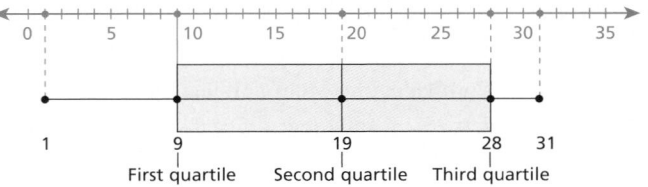

1,   5,   6,   12,   14,   18,   20,   26,   27,   29,   30,   31

First quartile   Second quartile   Third quartile

$\frac{6+12}{2} = 9$ $\frac{18+20}{2} = 19$ $\frac{27+29}{2} = 28$

A **box-and-whisker** plot of this data is shown below.

First quartile   Second quartile   Third quartile

Example 1   *Drawing a Box-and-Whisker Plot*

Draw a box-and-whisker plot for the following data.

   22, 65, 23, 19, 42, 62, 38, 29, 50, 46, 28, 36, 25, 40

Solution   Begin by writing the numbers in increasing order.

   19, 22, 23, 25, 28, 29, 36, 38, 40, 42, 46, 50, 62, 65

   Lower half   *Upper half*

From this ordering, you can see that the first quartile is 25, the second quartile is 37, and the third quartile is 46. A box-and-whisker plot for the data is shown below.

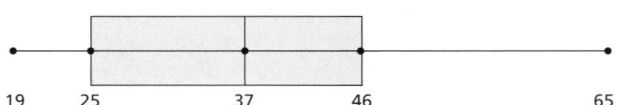

19   25   37   46   65   ∎

┌─────── **STARTER: Problem of the Day** ───────┐

Use your calculator to evaluate the expression.

$2 + \dfrac{2}{2 + \frac{2}{3}}$ 2.75

Also available as a copymaster, page 40

┌─────── **STARTER: Warm-Up Exercises** ───────┐

1. Find the median of the following ordered data:
1, 2, 3, 8, 10, 11, 12, 15, 18, 20, 22, 24
11.5

2. Change these percents to fractions and then write them in lowest terms:
a. 25%   **b.** 50%   **c.** 75%   **d.** 100%
a. $\frac{1}{4}$, b. $\frac{1}{2}$, c. $\frac{3}{4}$, d. 1

Also available as a copymaster, page 40

Using Box-and-Whisker Plots

Real Life
Social Studies

Francesco Schiappa and his great-grandson Joseph represent the four generations of one Rhode Island family.

Example 2   *Interpreting Box-and-Whisker Plots*

The box-and-whisker plots below show the age distributions of Alaska's and Rhode Island's populations. What do the plots tell you about the two states? *(Source: U.S. Bureau of Census)*

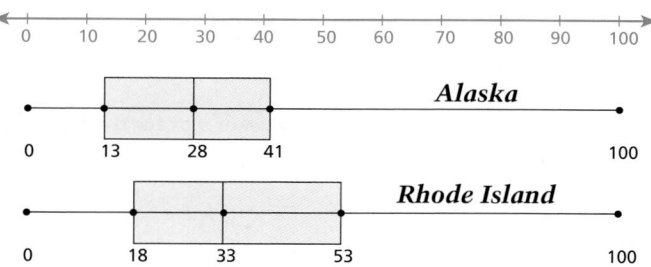

Solution   In Alaska, the median age is 28, which means that about 50% of the population is under 28. The box-and-whisker plot also tells you that 25% of the population is under 13 and 25% is over 41.

Rhode Island's population is quite a bit older. In that state, the median age is 33, which means that about 50% of the population is under 33. The box-and-whisker plot also tells you that 25% of the population is under 18 and 25% is over 53. ∎

P   *Communicating* about **MATHEMATICS**

▶ **SHARING IDEAS about the Lesson**

Extending the Example   The box-and-whisker plots below represent the age distributions for Florida and Utah. Which is which? Explain your reasoning.

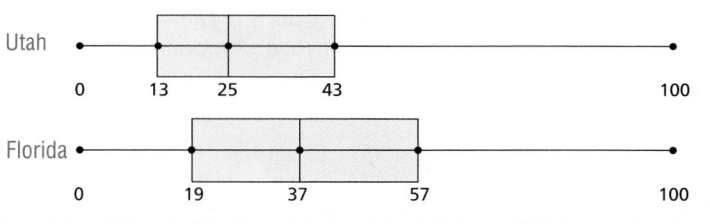

Many people move to Florida after retiring; so, Florida has a larger percent of older people.

P Portfolio Opportunity

Ask students to give real-life examples of data that might be best represented using box-and-whisker plots. Have students write the examples in their math journals.

Example 2

MAKING CONNECTIONS
Businesses often use similar information to determine where they would be most successful selling their products. Using the box-and-whisker plots of this example, have students decide whether a diaper-service business would be more likely to succeed in Alaska than in Rhode Island. Have them explain their answer.   In Alaska, because the population is younger and more likely to have young families in the near future.

Communicating
about **MATHEMATICS**

Have students identify and discuss the methods for communicating about data that they have learned thus far in Chapter 14. Then have them provide criteria for determining which methods are appropriate to use in different real-life situations. Students should record their criteria in their math journals.

Writing Prompt
Box-and-whisker plots are hard to construct because . . .

OPTION: Extra Examples

Here is an additional example similar to Example 1.

Drawing a Box-and-Whisker Plot
Draw a box-and-whisker plot for the following data. 54, 59, 39, 41, 46, 37, 36, 34, 22, 40, 61, 48, 45, 50, 28

Solution
Begin by writing the numbers in increasing order.
22, 28, 34, 36, 37, 39, 40, 41, 45, 46, 48, 50, 54, 59, 61

⏝ Lower half   ⏝ Upper half

From this ordering, you can see that the first quartile is 36, the second quartile is 41, and the third quartile is 50. A box-and-whisker plot for the data is shown below.

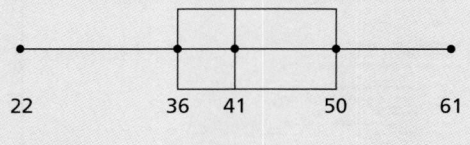

Answers

3.
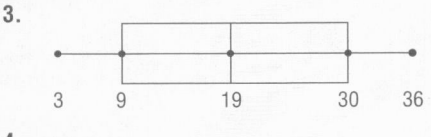

4.

9.
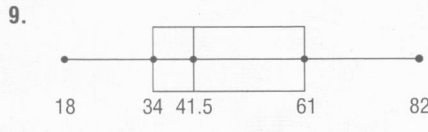

10.
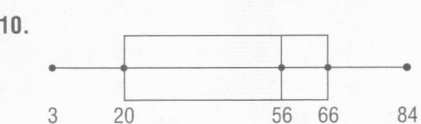

11. 39 is the largest number, not 37. The first quartile is 8.5, not 8. The second quartile is 18.5, not 18. The second quartile should be located $\frac{10}{19.5}$ of the way from 8.5 to 28, not where it is located now.

12. The median age is 30; 25% is under 16, 50% is under 30, and 25% is over 49.

13. Mississippi's population is younger than Florida's and Rhode Island's, and is older than Alaska's and Utah's.

EXERCISES

Guided Practice

▶ **CHECK for Understanding**

In Exercises 1 and 2, use the box-and-whisker plot at the right.

1. Name the smallest and largest numbers.   6, 56

2. Name the quartiles.   21, 34, 44

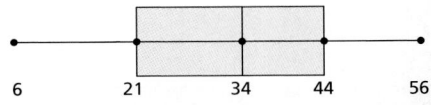

In Exercises 3 and 4, draw a box-and-whisker plot for the data.   See margin.

3. 3, 4, 8, 10, 13, 17, 21, 26, 29, 31, 32, 36

4. 12, 52, 25, 61, 66, 15, 6, 46, 39, 54, 34, 50, 21, 56, 70, 40

Independent Practice

In Exercises 5–8, use the box-and-whisker plot. There are 20 numbers in the collection, and each number is different.

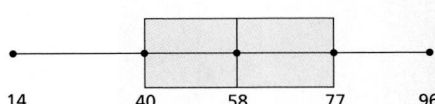

5. Name the smallest and largest numbers.   14, 96

6. Name the first, second, and third quartiles.   40, 58, 77

7. What percent of the numbers are less than 40?   25%

8. What percent of the numbers are between 40 and 77?   50%

In Exercises 9 and 10, draw a box-and-whisker plot of the data.   See margin.

9. 26, 60, 36, 44, 62, 24, 29, 50, 67, 72, 40, 41, 18, 39, 64, 82, 41, 49, 32, 42

10. 78, 22, 29, 67, 10, 62, 50, 72, 8, 63, 35, 80, 52, 3, 60, 18, 65, 61, 15, 84

✪ 11. *Error Analysis* The box-and-whisker plot at
Ⓟ the right is supposed to represent the following data. There are four errors. What are they?

   Data: 26, 10, 19, 34, 2, 5, 21, 12, 1, 39, 14, 30, 18, 37, 7, 24   See margin.

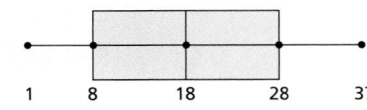

Social Studies **In Exercises 12 and 13, use the box-and-whisker plot, which shows the age distribution for Mississippi.** *(Source: U.S. Bureau of Census)*

See margin.

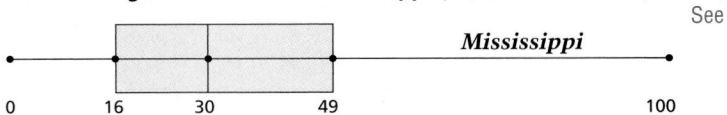

12. Write a description of Mississippi's population.

13. Compare Mississippi's population to the populations discussed on page 643.

✪ More difficult exercises
Ⓟ Portfolio Opportunity

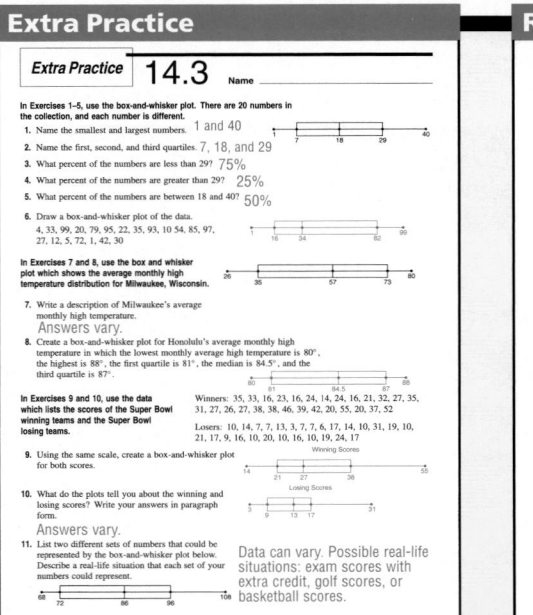

Extra Practice

Reteaching

In Exercises 14 and 15, use the following data, which lists the price in dollars of several receivers, CD players, and cassette decks in 1994. *(Source: Consumer Reports)* See margin.

Receivers:	CD Players:	Cassette Decks:
165, 200, 380, 260, 180,	170, 250, 270, 180, 140,	200, 225, 150, 285, 260,
300, 460, 390, 445, 225,	240, 195, 255, 160, 245,	230, 295, 255, 290, 195,
325, 400, 280, 360	200, 290, 230, 280	265, 280

Scientists band birds in order to study migration patterns.

14. Using the same scale, create a box-and-whisker plot for each stereo component.

15. *Writing*   What do the plots tell you about the prices of stereo components? Write your answer in paragraph form.

16. *Think about It*   List two different sets of 12 numbers that could be represented by the box-and-whisker plot below.

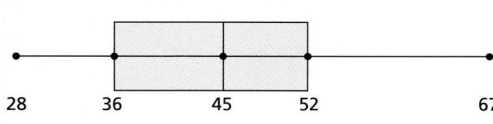

28   36   45   52   67

See margin.

Integrated Review

Making Connections within Mathematics

Percent   In Exercises 17–22, solve the percent equation. Round your result to 2 decimal places.

17. What is 25% of 78?   19.5

18. What is 75% of 130?   97.5

19. 16 is what percent of 36?   44.44%

20. 71 is what percent of 95?   74.74%

21. 48 is 20% of what number?   240

22. 84 is 60% of what number?   140

Exploration and Extension

For explanations, see margin.

Finding the Context   In Exercises 23–26, match the description with the most reasonable box-and-whisker plot. Explain your reasoning.

a. Season scores of a baseball team

b. Weights in pounds of students in 4th-grade class

c. Scores on a 100-point test

d. Ages in years in an algebra class

23.
d

13 14 15 16   37

24.
c

62   73   82   89   100

25.
b

56   62 65   72   107

26.
a

0   2   4 5   13

14.3 • Box-and-Whisker Plots   **645**

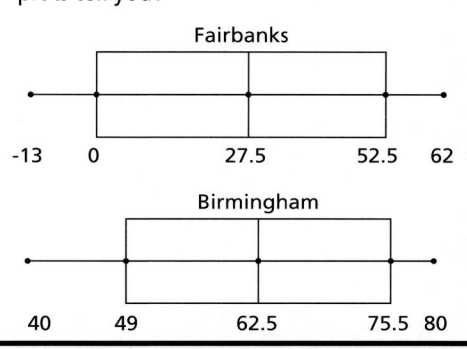
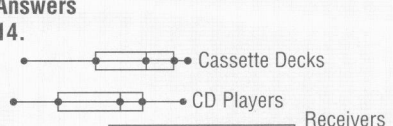

TECHNOLOGY Notes

By choosing Freq: 1, data does not have to be entered in pairs as was done on page 223. It is assumed that each number that is entered occurs once only.

[ZOOM] [9] (ZoomStat) redefines the viewing WINDOW so that all statistical data points are displayed. For one-variable plots (histograms and box plots), only Xmin and Xmax are adjusted. For this reason, set the value given for Ymax in the WINDOW shown.

Some graphing calculators can be used to sketch box-and-whisker plots. The following steps show how to use a Texas Instruments TI-82 to sketch the box-and-whisker plot shown at the right. The data for the plot is the same as that used in Example 1 on page 642.

22, 65, 23, 19, 42, 62, 38, 29, 50, 46, 28, 36, 25, 40

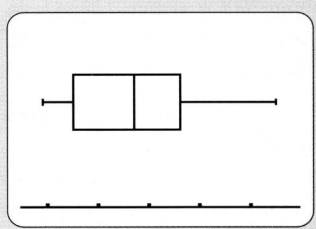

TI-82*

To enter data in a list: [STAT] [ENTER] (Edit)

L1(1) = 22 [ENTER]	L1(6) = 62 [ENTER]	L1(11) = 28 [ENTER]
L1(2) = 65 [ENTER]	L1(7) = 38 [ENTER]	L1(12) = 36 [ENTER]
L1(3) = 23 [ENTER]	L1(8) = 29 [ENTER]	L1(13) = 25 [ENTER]
L1(4) = 19 [ENTER]	L1(9) = 50 [ENTER]	L1(14) = 40 [ENTER]
L1(5) = 42 [ENTER]	L1(10) = 46 [ENTER]	

RANGE
Xmin = 50
Xmax = 70
Xscl = 1
Ymin = 700
Ymax = 1000
Yscl = 50

To set boxplot: [2nd] [STAT PLOT] [ENTER] (Plot 1)

Choose the following: On, Type: ⊢□⊢ , Xlist: L1, Freq: 1
[ZOOM] [9]

To find the minimum, maximum, first quartile, median, and third quartile:
[TRACE] and [◁] or [▷]

Exercises

In Exercises 1–4, use a graphing calculator to sketch a box-and-whisker plot for the data. See margin.

1. 15, 19, 37, 15, 25, 33, 30, 27, 31, 37, 37, 14, 28, 34, 24, 25, 35, 18

2. 52, 79, 82, 56, 67, 69, 70, 73, 59, 64, 69, 72, 79, 58, 54, 60, 53, 67

3. 21, 24, 23, 26, 29, 23, 24, 25, 28, 28, 29, 24, 25, 27, 56, 42, 28, 24

4. 39, 52, 36, 45, 42, 43, 37, 43, 46, 42, 38, 34, 36, 45, 49, 34, 45, 48

P In Exercises 5–7, create a collection of 16 numbers that corresponds to the box-and-whisker plot. Use a graphing calculator to confirm your answer. (There are many correct collections.) Answers vary.

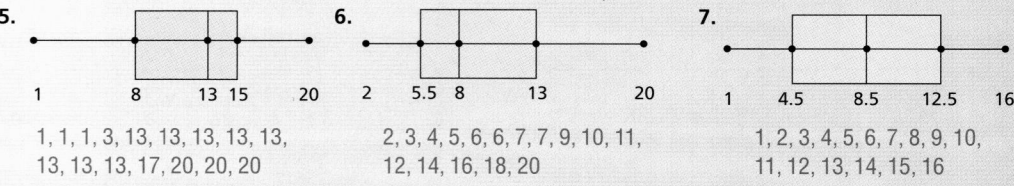

5.
1, 1, 1, 3, 13, 13, 13, 13, 13,
13, 13, 13, 17, 20, 20, 20

6.
2, 3, 4, 5, 6, 6, 7, 7, 9, 10, 11,
12, 14, 16, 18, 20

7.
1, 2, 3, 4, 5, 6, 7, 8, 9, 10,
11, 12, 13, 14, 15, 16

* Keystrokes for other graphing calculators are listed in *Technology—Keystrokes for Other Graphing Calculators* found at the end of this text.

Answers

1.
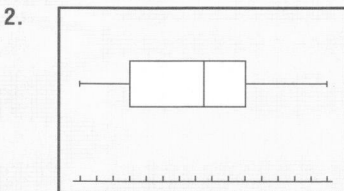

2.
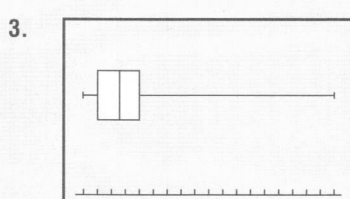

3.

4.
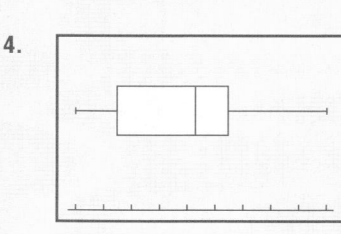

Mixed REVIEW

In Exercises 1–8, use △*ABC* at the right. (11.8)

1. Find the length of the hypotenuse. $\sqrt{97}$
2. Find the area of the triangle. 18 units^2
3. Find sin *A*.   4. Find cos *A*.   5. Find tan *A*.
6. Find sin *B*.   7. Find cos *B*.   8. Find tan *B*.

3. ≈0.406   4. ≈0.914
5. ≈0.444   6. ≈0.914
7. ≈0.406   8. 2.25

In Exercises 9–12, use the following data. (14.1, 14.2)

1.5, 1.6, 1.8, 1.8, 1.9, 2.3, 2.4, 2.4, 2.7, 2.7, 2.7, 3.0, 3.0, 3.1

9. What is the mean of the data?   2.35
10. What is the median of the data?   2.4
11. What is the mode of the data?   2.7
12. Create a stem-and-leaf plot for the data.
See margin.

In Exercises 13–16, solve the proportion. (8.2)

13. $\frac{x}{13} = \frac{4}{12}$ $\frac{13}{3}$
14. $\frac{b}{6} = \frac{6}{16}$ $\frac{9}{4}$
15. $\frac{3}{2} = \frac{15}{r}$ 10
16. $\frac{4}{s} = \frac{21}{18}$ $\frac{24}{7}$

Milestones   APOTHOCARY MEASUREMENT

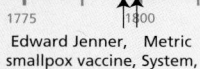 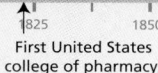 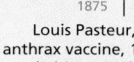 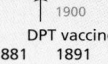 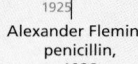 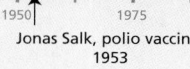

1775	1800	1825	1850	1875	1900	1925	1950	1975

Edward Jenner, smallpox vaccine, 1796   Metric System, 1799   First United States college of pharmacy, 1821   Louis Pasteur, anthrax vaccine, 1881 (rabies, 1885)   DPT vaccine, 1891   Alexander Fleming, penicillin, 1928   Jonas Salk, polio vaccine, 1953

APOTHOCARY DRY MEASURES

20 GRAINS = 1 SCRUPLE
3 SCRUPLES = 1 DRAM
8 DRAMS = 1 OUNCE APOTHOCARY

APOTHOCARY LIQUID MEASURES

60 MINIMS (OR DROPS) = 1 FLUID DRAM
8 FLUID DRAMS = 1 FLUID OUNCE APOTHOCARY
16 FLUID OUNCES = 1 PINT

Advances in veterinary medicine have paralleled those in human medicine. The healing effects of certain botanical compounds have been known since pre-history. By the Middle Ages, medicines were dispensed by *apothocaries*, persons who prepared and sold drugs.

For centuries, apothocaries had their own formulas for drugs. In 1542, the first standard table of drugs, or *Pharmacopoeia* (from which we get the terms *pharmacy* and *pharmacist*) was published in Germany. The first United States *Pharmacopoeia* was commissioned by the Continental Congress for the army of the American Revolution in 1778. In 1906, under the Pure Food and Drugs Act, *The United States Pharmacopoeia—The National Formulary* was finally made a legal standard.   ≈ 1.5432 grains

• *Today, all medical formulas use metric units. If 1 dry grain = 0.0648 grams, then how many grains are in a 100 mg tablet?*

• *If 1 drop = 0.0616 milliliters, then how many drops are in a 100 mL medicine bottle?* ≈ 1623.38 drops

Mixed Review   **647**

Milestones

Theme: Measures

The metric system is an international standard system of measurement developed in France at the time of the French Revolution. The United States is the only industrialized country to maintain its own system of measurement, the customary system. (See the Measurement Tables found on pages 680 and 681.) At the time of the adoption of the Constitution of the United States, both Thomas Jefferson and John Adams encouraged adopting the metric system. However, there was resistance in the 1790's and there is still resistance in the 1990's.

1. One pound is the mass of 27.692 cubic inches of water. One fluid ounce of water occupies 1.80469 cubic inches of space. One kilogram is the mass of 1000 cubic centimeters of water. One milliliter of water occupies 1 cubic centimeter of space.

  a. How many fluid ounces are in 1 pound of water? ≈15.344

  b. How many milliliters are in 1 kilogram of water. 1000

  c. How many cubic inches does 1 ounce of water occupy? ≈1.731

  d. How many cubic centimeters does 1 gram of water occupy? 1

2. Some people say that converting in the metric system is easier than in the customary system. Explain why you agree or disagree? Answers vary.

Library Skills

Have students use library resources to research the history of the metric system in the United States. After completing their research, students should write a convincing argument as to why the United States should, or should not, adopt the metric system.

Answer to Mixed Review

12.
```
3 | 0 0 1
2 | 3 4 4 7 7 7
1 | 5 6 8 8 9
```
1|5 represents 1.5.

LESSON Notes

Matrices are used to represent data sets for more than one category. In the Warm-Up Exercise, Boise and Lewiston both have rainfall data sets. A matrix for this data would look like the interior of the table. Each column is a data set. A matrix can be thought of as a table of data without the labels.

Ask students to write a matrix for the table in the Warm-Up Exercise. Notice that two matrices are equal only if each entry in one matrix is equal to the corresponding entry in the other matrix. For example:

$$\begin{bmatrix} 12 & 23 \\ 11 & 9 \\ 10 & 10 \end{bmatrix} \neq \begin{bmatrix} 19 & 23 \\ 11 & 12 \\ 10 & 10 \end{bmatrix}$$

Example 1

Emphasize the similarity between the matrix and the table that was used to first organize the data.

14.4 Exploring Data and Matrices

What you should learn:

Goal 1 How to organize data with a matrix

Goal 2 How to add and subtract two matrices

Why you should learn it:
You can use matrices to help organize real-life data, such as the data that represents income, expenses, and profit for a business.

Real Life Business

Goal 1 — Using Matrices

A **matrix** is a rectangular arrangement of numbers into rows and columns. For instance, the matrix

$$\begin{bmatrix} 2 & -4 & 5 \\ -3 & 1 & 0 \end{bmatrix}$$

has two rows and three columns. The numbers in the matrix are called **entries.** In the above matrix, the entry in the second row and third column is 0. The entry in the first row and second column is −4.

The plural of *matrix* is *matrices.* Two matrices are **equal** if all of the entries in corresponding positions are equal.

$$\begin{bmatrix} -1 & \frac{3}{2} \\ \frac{1}{4} & 0 \end{bmatrix} = \begin{bmatrix} -1 & 1.5 \\ 0.25 & 0 \end{bmatrix} \qquad \begin{bmatrix} -3 & 2 \\ 4 & 1 \end{bmatrix} \neq \begin{bmatrix} 2 & -3 \\ 1 & 4 \end{bmatrix}$$

You can think of a matrix as a type of table that can be used to organize data.

Example 1   *Writing a Table as a Matrix*

You are opening two fast-food restaurants. The gross income for each of the first four months is shown in the table at the left. Write this table as a matrix. For Restaurant 1, which month had the greatest income? For Restaurant 2, which month had the greatest income?

Solution   The matrix associated with the table has four rows and two columns.

	Restaurant 1	Restaurant 2
April	\$142,560	\$209,905
May	\$158,430	\$213,413
June	\$162,578	\$206,784
July	\$178,865	\$198,450

Income	Restaurant 1	Restaurant 2
April	142,560	209,905 — Greatest
May	158,430	213,413
June	162,578	206,784
July	178,865	198,450

Greatest

For Restaurant 1, the greatest income occurred in July. For Restaurant 2, the greatest income occurred in May. ∎

Goal 2 Adding and Subtracting Matrices

To **add** or **subtract** matrices, you simply add or subtract corresponding entries, as shown in Example 2.

Need to Know
You cannot add or subtract matrices that are different sizes. For instance, you cannot add a matrix that has three rows and two columns to a matrix that has two rows and two columns.

Example 2 Adding and Subtracting Matrices

a. $\begin{bmatrix} 3 & -2 \\ 0 & 4 \end{bmatrix} + \begin{bmatrix} 1 & 5 \\ -2 & 3 \end{bmatrix} = \begin{bmatrix} 3+1 & -2+5 \\ 0+-2 & 4+3 \end{bmatrix}$

$= \begin{bmatrix} 4 & 3 \\ -2 & 7 \end{bmatrix}$

b. $\begin{bmatrix} 3 & -2 \\ 0 & 4 \end{bmatrix} - \begin{bmatrix} 1 & 5 \\ -2 & 3 \end{bmatrix} = \begin{bmatrix} 3-1 & -2-5 \\ 0--2 & 4-3 \end{bmatrix}$

$= \begin{bmatrix} 2 & -7 \\ 2 & 1 \end{bmatrix}$ ∎

Example 3 Subtracting Matrices

Real Life Business

Your expenses for the two restaurants described in Example 1 are shown in the table at the left. Use subtraction of matrices to find your monthly profit for each restaurant.

Solution To find the monthly profit, subtract the expense matrix from the income matrix.

	Restaurant 1	Restaurant 2
April	$124,792	$205,316
May	$138,716	$197,438
June	$158,914	$192,765
July	$163,047	$186,652

Income $\begin{bmatrix} 142,560 & 209,905 \\ 158,430 & 213,413 \\ 162,578 & 206,784 \\ 178,865 & 198,450 \end{bmatrix}$ − Expenses $\begin{bmatrix} 124,792 & 205,316 \\ 138,716 & 197,438 \\ 158,914 & 192,765 \\ 163,047 & 186,652 \end{bmatrix}$ = Profit $\begin{bmatrix} 17,768 & 4,589 \\ 19,714 & 15,975 \\ 3,664 & 14,019 \\ 15,818 & 11,798 \end{bmatrix}$ ∎

Ⓟ

Communicating about MATHEMATICS

▶ **SHARING IDEAS about the Lesson**

Extending the Example Create a table that shows the monthly profit for each restaurant in Example 3. Which restaurant had the greater income for the four months? Which had the greater profit? Which restaurant had the better record? Explain your reasoning.

For table, see margin. . Restaurant 2; Restaurant 1; Restaurant 1, profit was greater.

Matrices can be added or subtracted only if they are the same size, that is, if they have the same number of rows and columns.

Example 2
Common-Error Alert!

Some students find that they make fewer careless errors when subtracting integers if they transform problems from subtraction to addition by changing the sign of the subtrahend (i.e., the number being subtracted). To make this transformation with matrices, the sign of each entry in the subtrahend matrix must be changed. Corresponding entries in each matrix are then added.

Example 3

Refer to the table and stress the meaning of each number in both the income and expenses tables, referenced by restaurant and month.

Communicating about MATHEMATICS

Spreadsheets are software packages designed to operate like matrices. They contain rows and columns into which numbers are entered. Appropriate computation formulas for operating on the numbers are also entered into the program.

Writing Prompt
Matrices remind me most of the following topics in mathematics . . .

Answer to Communicating

Profit	Restaurant 1	Restaurant 2
April	$17,768	$4,589
May	$19,714	$15,975
June	$3,664	$14,019
July	$15,818	$11,798

Technology

(Calculator key-sequence reference for Casio fx-7700G, fx-7700GE, 9700GE, with worked examples and Exercises 1–8.)

OPTION: Extra Examples

Here is an additional example similar to Example 2.

Adding and Subtracting Matrices

a. $\begin{bmatrix} 2 & -3 \\ -1 & 4 \\ 0 & 3 \end{bmatrix} + \begin{bmatrix} 1 & 5 \\ -2 & -4 \\ 2 & -6 \end{bmatrix} = \begin{bmatrix} 2+1 & -3+5 \\ -1+(-2) & 4+(-4) \\ 0+2 & 3+(-6) \end{bmatrix} = \begin{bmatrix} 3 & 2 \\ -3 & 0 \\ 2 & -3 \end{bmatrix}$

b. $\begin{bmatrix} -2 & 4 \\ 3 & -5 \end{bmatrix} - \begin{bmatrix} -3 & 6 \\ 0 & -3 \end{bmatrix} = \begin{bmatrix} -2-(-3) & 4-6 \\ 3-0 & -5-(-3) \end{bmatrix} = \begin{bmatrix} 1 & -2 \\ 3 & -2 \end{bmatrix}$

ASSIGNMENT GUIDE

*Basic/Average:
Day 1: Ex. 7–19 odd
Day 2: Ex. 21–24, 30, 31
Above Average:
Ex. 7–19 odd, 21–27, 29, 30–33
Advanced: Ex. 7–19 odd, 21–27, 29, 30–33
Selected Answers: Ex. 1–6, 7–29 odd

* You may wish to omit this lesson for these students.

Guided Practice

Use these exercises as a small-group end-of-the-period summary.

Independent Practice

▶ **Ex. 17–20** Use these exercises to foster discussion about operations. Have student pairs generate possible solutions.

Guided Practice

▶ **CHECK for Understanding**

In Exercises 1–3, use the matrix at the right.

$$\begin{bmatrix} 2 & -5 \\ 0 & 3 \\ -4 & 1 \end{bmatrix}$$

1. How many rows and columns does the matrix have? 3, 2
2. What is the entry in the first row and second column? -5
3. Describe the position of -4. In the third row and first column
4. *True or False?* Are the following matrices equal? Explain.

$$\begin{bmatrix} 0 & \frac{5}{4} & -1 \\ -\frac{8}{5} & 2 & 3 \end{bmatrix} \stackrel{?}{=} \begin{bmatrix} 0 & 1.25 & -1 \\ -1.6 & 2 & 3 \end{bmatrix}$$ Yes, the entries in corresponding positions are equal ($\frac{5}{4} = 1.25$ and $-\frac{8}{5} = -1.6$).

In Exercises 5 and 6, find the matrix sum or difference.

5. $\begin{bmatrix} 2 & 3 & 0 \\ -3 & 0 & -1 \end{bmatrix} + \begin{bmatrix} -4 & 1 & -5 \\ -6 & 7 & 2 \end{bmatrix}$

6. $\begin{bmatrix} 2.1 & -1.5 \\ -3.5 & 6.4 \end{bmatrix} - \begin{bmatrix} 1.8 & 4.8 \\ -1.1 & -0.8 \end{bmatrix}$

5. $\begin{bmatrix} -2 & 4 & -5 \\ -9 & 7 & 1 \end{bmatrix}$ 6. $\begin{bmatrix} 0.3 & -6.3 \\ -2.4 & 7.2 \end{bmatrix}$

Independent Practice

In Exercises 7–14, find the sum and difference of the matrices. See margin.

7. $\begin{bmatrix} -2 & 3 \\ 1 & -5 \end{bmatrix}, \begin{bmatrix} -1 & 4 \\ -6 & 0 \end{bmatrix}$

8. $\begin{bmatrix} 5 & 2 \\ -2 & 7 \end{bmatrix}, \begin{bmatrix} -8 & 0 \\ -9 & 3 \end{bmatrix}$

9. $\begin{bmatrix} -4 & -5 & 2 \\ 0 & -9 & -3 \end{bmatrix}, \begin{bmatrix} -6 & 3 & 2 \\ 1 & -1 & 4 \end{bmatrix}$

10. $\begin{bmatrix} -4 & 4 \\ 5 & 3 \\ -6 & -2 \end{bmatrix}, \begin{bmatrix} 4 & 7 \\ 2 & -1 \\ -3 & -8 \end{bmatrix}$

11. $\begin{bmatrix} 3 & 5 & -6 \\ -4 & 0 & -6 \\ 4 & 8 & 1 \end{bmatrix}, \begin{bmatrix} -7 & 0 & 3 \\ -1 & -4 & 5 \\ 4 & -2 & 9 \end{bmatrix}$

12. $\begin{bmatrix} 4 & 2 & 8 \\ -2 & 6 & -1 \\ 7 & 9 & -1 \end{bmatrix}, \begin{bmatrix} 12 & -10 & -6 \\ -5 & 0 & 11 \\ -1 & 2 & 3 \end{bmatrix}$

13. $\begin{bmatrix} \frac{1}{3} & \frac{2}{3} & \frac{1}{3} \\ \frac{1}{4} & \frac{1}{4} & \frac{3}{4} \\ \frac{1}{5} & \frac{2}{5} & \frac{3}{5} \end{bmatrix}, \begin{bmatrix} \frac{2}{3} & \frac{2}{3} & \frac{1}{3} \\ \frac{3}{4} & \frac{1}{4} & \frac{1}{2} \\ \frac{1}{5} & \frac{3}{5} & \frac{1}{5} \end{bmatrix}$

14. $\begin{bmatrix} 4.1 & 2.5 & -2.3 \\ 6.8 & 0.4 & -7.3 \\ -4.8 & 4.7 & -5.0 \end{bmatrix}, \begin{bmatrix} -6.3 & 1.5 & 3.6 \\ 2.1 & 4.7 & -1.7 \\ 5.3 & 2.1 & 4.7 \end{bmatrix}$

Mental Math **In Exercises 15 and 16, use mental math to find *a*, *b*, *c*, and *d*.**

15. $\begin{bmatrix} 2a & b \\ c-3 & 2d \end{bmatrix} = \begin{bmatrix} -8 & 3 \\ 1 & -5 \end{bmatrix}$ $-4, 3, 4, -\frac{5}{2}$

16. $\begin{bmatrix} -4 & 6 \\ c-1 & -3d \end{bmatrix} = \begin{bmatrix} a+2 & 3b \\ 7 & 6 \end{bmatrix}$
$-6, 2, 8, -2$

In Exercises 17–20, find two matrices whose sum is the given matrix. Don't use 0 as an element of either matrix. (There are many correct answers.) Answers vary.

✪ 17. $\begin{bmatrix} 2 & 5 \\ 6 & 3 \end{bmatrix}$ ✪ 18. $\begin{bmatrix} 0 & 0 \\ 0 & 0 \end{bmatrix}$ ✪ 19. $\begin{bmatrix} 1 & 0 \\ 0 & 1 \end{bmatrix}$ ✪ 20. $\begin{bmatrix} 0 & 1 \\ 1 & 0 \end{bmatrix}$

$\begin{bmatrix} 1 & 3 \\ 2 & -4 \end{bmatrix}, \begin{bmatrix} 1 & 2 \\ 4 & 7 \end{bmatrix}$ $\begin{bmatrix} 1 & 1 \\ 1 & 3 \end{bmatrix}, \begin{bmatrix} -1 & -1 \\ -1 & -3 \end{bmatrix}$ $\begin{bmatrix} 3 & 2 \\ -7 & -4 \end{bmatrix}, \begin{bmatrix} -2 & -2 \\ 7 & 5 \end{bmatrix}$ $\begin{bmatrix} 6 & -1 \\ 8 & 3 \end{bmatrix}, \begin{bmatrix} -6 & 2 \\ -7 & -3 \end{bmatrix}$

650   Chapter **14** ▪ *Exploring Data and Polynomials*   ✪ More difficult exercises

---

Answers

7. $\begin{bmatrix} -3 & 7 \\ -5 & -5 \end{bmatrix}, \begin{bmatrix} -1 & -1 \\ 7 & -5 \end{bmatrix}$

8. $\begin{bmatrix} -3 & 2 \\ -11 & 10 \end{bmatrix}, \begin{bmatrix} 13 & 2 \\ 7 & 4 \end{bmatrix}$

9. $\begin{bmatrix} -10 & -2 & 4 \\ 1 & -10 & 1 \end{bmatrix}, \begin{bmatrix} 2 & -8 & 0 \\ -1 & -8 & -7 \end{bmatrix}$

10. $\begin{bmatrix} 0 & 11 \\ 7 & 2 \\ -9 & -10 \end{bmatrix}, \begin{bmatrix} -8 & -3 \\ 3 & 4 \\ -3 & 6 \end{bmatrix}$

11. $\begin{bmatrix} -4 & 5 & -3 \\ -5 & -4 & -1 \\ 8 & 6 & 10 \end{bmatrix}, \begin{bmatrix} 10 & 5 & -9 \\ -3 & 4 & -11 \\ 0 & 10 & -8 \end{bmatrix}$

12. $\begin{bmatrix} 16 & -8 & 2 \\ -7 & 6 & 10 \\ 6 & 11 & 2 \end{bmatrix}, \begin{bmatrix} -8 & 12 & 14 \\ 3 & 6 & -12 \\ 8 & 7 & -4 \end{bmatrix}$

13. $\begin{bmatrix} 1 & \frac{4}{3} & \frac{2}{3} \\ 1 & \frac{1}{2} & \frac{5}{4} \\ \frac{2}{5} & 1 & \frac{4}{5} \end{bmatrix}, \begin{bmatrix} -\frac{1}{3} & 0 & 0 \\ -\frac{1}{2} & 0 & \frac{1}{4} \\ 0 & -\frac{1}{5} & \frac{2}{5} \end{bmatrix}$

14. $\begin{bmatrix} -2.2 & 4 & 1.3 \\ 8.9 & 5.1 & -9 \\ 0.5 & 6.8 & -0.3 \end{bmatrix}, \begin{bmatrix} 10.4 & 1 & -5.9 \\ 4.7 & -4.3 & -5.6 \\ -10.1 & 2.6 & -9.7 \end{bmatrix}$

650   *Chapter 14*

Pet Store In Exercises 21–24, use the following information.

You are opening 2 pet stores. The gross income for each store for the first four months is shown in the left table and the expenses are shown in the right table. **21., 23.** See Additional Answers.

Gross Income	Pet Store 1	Pet Store 2
May	$231,450	$206,210
June	$265,985	$319,754
July	$303,442	$321,615
August	$324,570	$256,419

Expenses	Pet Store 1	Pet Store 2
May	$208,345	$200,926
June	$247,913	$296,575
July	$287,500	$306,480
August	$317,940	$238,212

21. Write each table as a matrix. Store 1: August
22. For each pet store, which month had the greatest income?
23. Find the monthly profit for each store. Store 2: July
24. Which store had a greater profit during the first four months?
    Store 1

Geometry   In Exercises 25–27, use the table at the right, which lists the sides of 4 different triangles.

25. Write the table as a matrix.   See Additional Answers.
26. Which, if any, of the triangles are right?   Triangles 2 and 3
27. Find the perimeter of each triangle.
    22, 36, 9, 20.2

	Side 1	Side 2	Side 3
Triangle 1	5	7	10
Triangle 2	9	12	15
Triangle 3	0.9	4	4.1
Triangle 4	5	6	9.2

Integrated Review
Making Connections within Mathematics

Geometry   In Exercises 28 and 29, the matrix contains information about a rectangle or a circle. Copy and complete the matrix.

28.
Length	Width	Perimeter	Area

$$\begin{bmatrix} 8 & 2 & ?\ 20 & ?\ ] \ 16 \\ ? & 10 & 4 & ?\ 28 & 40 \\ ? & 12 & 8 & 40 & ?\ ] \ 96 \\ ? & 14 & 16 & ?\ 60 & 224 \end{bmatrix}$$

29.
Radius	Diameter	Circumference	Area

$$\begin{bmatrix} 1 & ?\ 2 & ?\ 2\pi & ?\ ] \ \pi \\ ?\ 3 & 6 & ?\ 6\pi & ?\ ] \ 9\pi \\ ?\ 5 & 10 & ?\ 10\pi & ?\ ] \ 25\pi \\ 7 & ?\ 14 & ?\ 14\pi & ?\ ] \ 49\pi \end{bmatrix}$$

Exploration and Extension

Magic Squares   In Exercises 30–33, complete the matrix so that every row and column has the same sum. Use the numbers 1–9 only once per matrix.   See Additional Answers.

⊛ 30. $\begin{bmatrix} 3 & 8 & 4 \\ ? & ? & ? \\ ? & ? & ? \end{bmatrix}$ ⊛ 31. $\begin{bmatrix} ? & ? & ? \\ 2 & 6 & 7 \\ ? & ? & ? \end{bmatrix}$ ⊛ 32. $\begin{bmatrix} ? & ? & 1 \\ ? & ? & 5 \\ ? & ? & 9 \end{bmatrix}$ ⊛ 33. $\begin{bmatrix} 3 & ? & ? \\ 5 & ? & ? \\ 7 & ? & ? \end{bmatrix}$

14.4 • *Exploring Data and Matrices*   **651**

▶ **Ex. 21–24**   Assign these exercises as a group.
▶ **Ex. 25–27**   Use these exercises as a connection to Lesson 9.3 on the Pythagorean Theorem.

Integrated Review
Have students compare and contrast matrices and tables as a format for data organization.

Exploration and Extension
For extra credit, have students research information on magic squares and write a paragraph describing them.

EXTENSION
Multiplication of a scaler with a matrix
A scalar is a real number. To multiply a scalar with a matrix, each entry of the matrix must be multiplied by the scalar. Have students multiply the matrix below by the scalar −5.

$$-5 \begin{bmatrix} -4 & 2 & 8 \\ -3 & -6 & 0 \\ 12 & 8 & -3 \end{bmatrix} \begin{bmatrix} 20 & -10 & -40 \\ 15 & 30 & 0 \\ -60 & -40 & 15 \end{bmatrix}$$

Portfolio Opportunity: Math Log
Explain why matrices that are different sizes cannot be added or subtracted.

Also available as a copymaster, page 43, Ex. 4

Short Quiz
Covers Lessons 14.3 and 14.4

Available as a copymaster, page 229

Alternative Assessment
A cooperative learning activity that exposes students to an application of matrices.

Available as a copymaster, page 41

▶ **Enrichment**

Linear Algebra and Modern Algebra are branches of mathematics that deal with using matrices and the relationships between matrix operations. Amalie "Emmy" Noether was a distinguished mathematician in these so-called higher algebras. Emmy's father was a mathematician. So, unlike most women of her time, she was given the opportunity to study mathematics. In 1922 she became a mathematics professor at a university in Germany, although many professors at the school objected to a woman holding a position at the university. One of her mathematical discoveries bears her name, and college students who study higher mathematics learn about mathematical objects called Noetherian Rings.

Have students research Emmy Noether's life and draw conclusions about why male mathematicians greatly outnumber female mathematicians.

Take this test as you would take a test in class. The answers to the exercises are given in the back of the book.

In Exercises 1–3, use the temperatures at the right. (14.1)

80°, 81°, 82°,
83°, 85°, 87°,
87°, 89°, 89°,
87°, 84°, 81°

1. What is the mean of the data? $84\frac{7}{12}°$

2. What is the median of the data? $84\frac{1}{2}°$

3. What is the mode of the data? 87°

In Exercises 4–6, use the table, which lists the normal monthly rainfall (in inches) in Miami and Jacksonville, Florida. (14.2)

Month	J	F	M	A	M	J	J	A	S	O	N	D
Miami	2.0	2.1	2.4	2.9	6.2	9.3	5.7	7.6	7.6	5.6	2.7	1.8
Jacksonville	3.3	3.9	3.7	2.8	3.6	5.7	5.6	7.9	7.1	2.9	2.2	2.7

4. Create a double stem-and-leaf plot for the data above. Use the whole numbers for the stem and tenths for the leaves. See margin.

5. Find the median rainfall for Miami. 4.25 in.   6. Find the mean rainfall for Jacksonville. ≈4.2

In Exercises 7–12, use the following temperatures (in degrees Fahrenheit), which are the record highs for May for the indicated cities. (14.3) 7., 11. See margin.

Juneau, 82°; Phoenix, 113°; Denver, 96°; Washington, 99°; Wichita, 100°; Boston, 95°; Detroit, 93°; Minneapolis, 96°; Cleveland, 92°; Oklahoma City, 104°; El Paso, 104°; Spokane, 96°

7. Order the data from least to greatest.   8. Find the first quartile. 94°

9. Find the second quartile. 96°   10. Find the third quartile. 102°

11. Draw a box-and-whisker plot of the data.   12. What percent of the data is above the first quartile? 75%

In Exercises 13–15, use the box-and-whisker plot at the right. (14.3)

13. What is the 3rd quartile? 35

14. What is the greatest number in the data? 64

15. What is the median of the data? 24

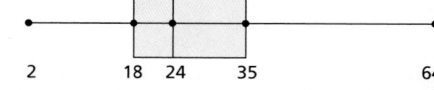

2   18 24   35   64

In Exercises 16–18, find the sum or difference. (14.4)

16. $\begin{bmatrix} 2 & 3 \\ 9 & 8 \end{bmatrix} + \begin{bmatrix} 6 & 2 \\ 11 & 0 \end{bmatrix}$ $\begin{bmatrix} 8 & 5 \\ 20 & 8 \end{bmatrix}$

17. $\begin{bmatrix} 4 & 5 \\ 6 & 8 \end{bmatrix} - \begin{bmatrix} 1 & 3 \\ 8 & 21 \end{bmatrix}$ $\begin{bmatrix} 3 & 2 \\ -2 & -13 \end{bmatrix}$

18. $\begin{bmatrix} 21 & 18 \\ 19 & 40 \end{bmatrix} - \begin{bmatrix} 20 & 6 \\ -4 & 16 \end{bmatrix}$ $\begin{bmatrix} 1 & 12 \\ 23 & 24 \end{bmatrix}$

19. The table at the right gives the scores of three students for three tests. Rewrite the table as a matrix. See margin.

20. Which student had the highest average for the three tests? Student 1

Test	1	2	3
Student 1	74	88	95
Student 2	86	83	81
Student 3	82	71	86

Answers

4.

```
        9 | 3
        8 |
  9   1 | 7 | 6 6
        6 | 2
    7 6 | 5 | 6 7
        4 |
9 7 6 3 | 3 |
9 8 7 2 | 2 | 0 1 4 7 9
        1 | 8
```

1|7|6 represents 7.1 in. in Jacksonville and 7.6 in. in Miami

7. 82°, 92°, 93°, 95°, 96°, 96°, 96°, 99°, 100°, 104°, 104°, 113°

11.

```
•————————[  |  ]————————•
82      94 96  102      113
```

19.

	Test 1	Test 2	Test 3
Student 1	⎡ 74	88	95 ⎤
Student 2	⎢ 86	83	81 ⎥
Student 3	⎣ 82	71	86 ⎦

Alternative Assessment ▶

A **Partner Quiz** assesses students' achievement and provides them with an opportunity to communicate about mathematics.
Available as a copymaster, page 57

Formal Assessment ▶

Two **Mid-Chapter Tests** of average difficulty.
Available as copymasters, pages 230, 231

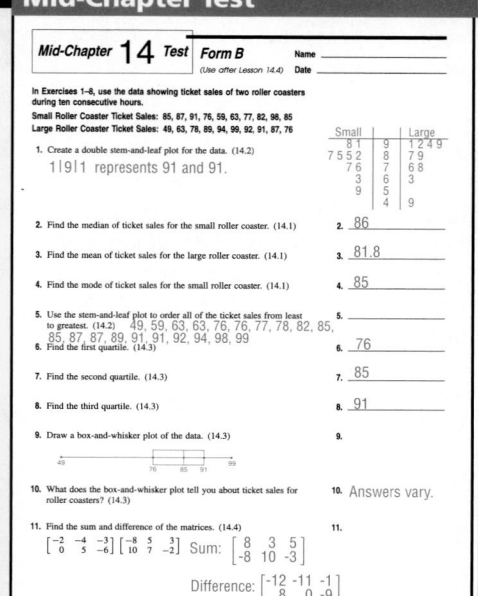

INVESTIGATION Notes

Materials
Teaching Tools
  Algebra tiles, pp. T4, C5

Operations of polynomials is the emphasis of the second half of this chapter. Algebra tiles provide an excellent format for understanding polynomials. Use this investigation to help students with quadratic polynomials.

EXTENSION
Use this investigation to recall the concept of like and unlike terms. For example, ask students to explain, based on the tile model, why $2x^2$ cannot be added to $3x$.

Ex. 19–21 on page 656 provide additional practice with the algebra tiles.

Materials Needed: algebra tiles

In this investigation, you will use algebra tiles like those below to represent expressions called *polynomials*.

This x by x tile represents x^2.

This x by 1 tile represents x.

This 1 by 1 tile represents 1.

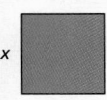

Example | *Exploring Polynomials with Algebra Tiles*

Use algebra tiles to represent the expression $2x^2 + 3x + 5$.

Solution You can represent this expression using two of the large square tiles, three of the rectangular tiles, and 5 small square tiles.

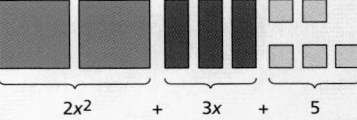

$$2x^2 \quad + \quad 3x \quad + \quad 5$$

Exercises

In Exercises 1–4, write the expression that is represented by the algebra tiles.

$3x^2 + 2x + 4$

1.

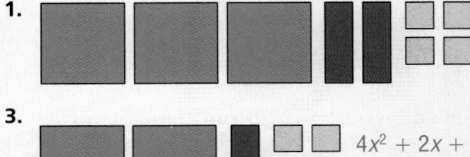

2.

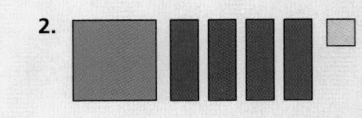 $x^2 + 4x + 1$

3.

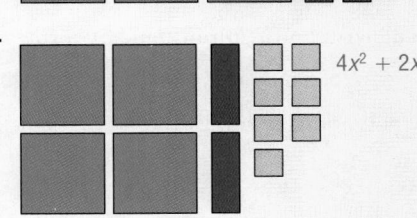 $4x^2 + 2x + 7$

4.

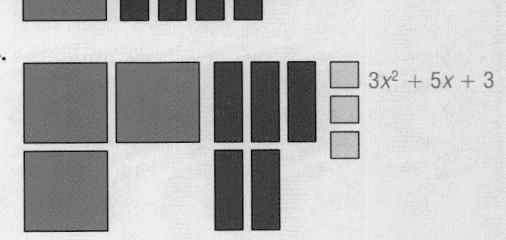 $3x^2 + 5x + 3$

In Exercises 5–8, use algebra tiles to represent the expression. Sketch your result. See margin.

5. $3x^2 + 2x + 7$

6. $4x^2 + 5x + 3$

7. $x^2 + 6x + 4$

8. $5x^2 + 7x + 1$

P Portfolio Opportunity

Answers
5.

6.

7.

8.

PACING the Lesson
Suggested Number of Days
Basic/Average 0   **Above Average** 1
Advanced 1

PLANNING the Lesson
Lesson Plan 14.5, p. 114

ORGANIZER

Starters (reproduced below)
  Problem of the Day 14.5, p. 41
  Warm-Up Exercises 14.5, p. 41
Lesson Resources
  Color Transparencies
    Diagram for Example 3, p. 58
    Picture for Ex. 34–36, p. 59
  Teaching Tools
    Puzzle for Ex. 45, p. C32
  Math Log, p. 44
  Answer Masters 14.5, pp. 281, 282
  Extra Practice Copymaster 14.5, p. 114
  Reteaching Copymaster 14.5, p. 114
Special Populations
  Suggestions, Teacher's Edition, p. 632D

LESSON Notes

Explain to students that in the general term ax^n of a polynomial, when $n = 0$, $ax^n = a$, which is the nonvariable (or constant) term of the polynomial.

Example 1

Addressing Misconceptions

Remind students that the power of the term $3m$ is 1, and that the power of the term 5 is 0. That is, $3m = 3m^1$ and $5 = 5m^0$.
  Some formulas for solving equations, such as the quadratic formula, are given in terms of the coefficients of a polynomial. To correctly use these formulas, the polynomial must be written in standard form.

Example 2

The coefficients of variables in a polynomial are considered to be the *resulting coefficients* after all the subtractions have been changed to additions. For example, $3x^2 - 5x - 2$ may be transformed into $3x^2 + (-5)x + (-2)$ so that the coefficient of x^2 is 3, the coefficient of x is -5, and the constant term of the expression is -2.

14.5   Exploring Polynomials

What you should learn:

Goal 1 How to identify polynomials and write them in standard form

Goal 2 How to use polynomials to solve real-life problems

Why you should learn it:

You can use polynomials to solve real-life problems, such as finding the time it takes for a wrench to fall from the top of a building.

> **Need to Know**
> The terms of a polynomial are considered to include any minus signs in the polynomial. For instance, the terms of $2x^2 - x + 4$ are $2x^2$, $-x$, and 4. The coefficient of x^2 is 2 and the coefficient of x is -1.

Goal 1  **Identifying Polynomials**

A **polynomial** is an expression that has one or more terms of the form ax^n where the coefficient a is any real number and the exponent n is a whole number. Polynomials are identified by the number of terms.

Type of Polynomial	Number of Terms	Example
Monomial	One	$3x^2$
Binomial	Two	$n + 4$
Trinomial	Three	$2y^2 + 4y - 5$

A polynomial is written in **standard form** if the powers of the variable decrease from left to right.

Example 1   *Rewriting in Standard Form*

Original Polynomial	Rewrite in Standard Form
$3m + 4m^3 - 2m^2 + 5$	$4m^3 - 2m^2 + 3m + 5$ ∎

If two terms have the same variable, raised to the same power, they are called *like terms*. When you combine like terms of a polynomial (by adding their coefficients), you are *simplifying* the polynomial.

Example 2   *Simplifying Polynomials*

Simplify the polynomial and write the result in standard form.

a. $3x^2 - 4x + x^2 + 5x$ **b.** $5n^2 + 6 + 4n - 7$ ∎

Solution   To simplify the polynomials, collect like terms, and add their coefficients.

$$\textbf{a.} \quad 3x^2 - 4x + x^2 + 5x = 3x^2 + x^2 - 4x + 5x$$
$$= (3 + 1)x^2 + (-4 + 5)x$$
$$= 4x^2 + x$$

$$\textbf{b.} \quad 5n^2 + 6 + 4n - 7 = 5n^2 + 4n + 6 - 7$$
$$= 5n^2 + 4n - 1 \quad ∎$$

> ┌ **STARTER: Problem of the Day** ┐
>
> Write an expression for the length of $\overline{AB}$. Find its length for $x = 0.01$. Should you simplify the expression first? Why or why not?
>
> A •———•———•———————• B
> $2x + 5$ $x + 3$ $20x + 1$
>
> $AB = 2x + 5 + x + 3 + 20x + 1 = 23x + 9$
> For $x = 0.01$, $AB = 9.23$; yes, simplifying first means just one substitution.

Also available as a copymaster, page 41

> ┌ **STARTER: Warm-Up Exercises** ┐
>
> **1.** How are the terms $3y$ and $3y^2$ alike? How are they different?
> They both have 3 as a coefficient; they both involve the variable y. The y in the second term is squared, unlike the first.
>
> **2.** What do the prefixes mono-, bi-, and tri- mean?
> One, two, three

Also available as a copymaster, page 41

Goal 2 · Using Polynomials in Real Life

When you drop a heavy object, does it fall at a constant speed or does it fall faster and faster the longer it is in the air? The answer is that it falls faster and faster.

Example 3 · *Using a Polynomial*

A construction worker 256 feet above the ground accidentally drops a wrench from the top of a skyscraper. The height h (in feet) of the wrench after t seconds is given by

$$h = -16t^2 + 256.$$

Find the height when t is 0 seconds, 1 second, 2 seconds, 3 seconds, and 4 seconds. How long does the wrench take to hit the ground?

Solution To find the height, substitute the values of t into the polynomial $-16t^2 + 256$.

Time	Substitute	Height
$t = 0$ (seconds)	$h = -16(0)^2 + 256 = 0 + 256$	256 feet
$t = 1$ (second)	$h = -16(1)^2 + 256 = -16 + 256$	240 feet
$t = 2$ (seconds)	$h = -16(2)^2 + 256 = -64 + 256$	192 feet
$t = 3$ (seconds)	$h = -16(3)^2 + 256 = -144 + 256$	112 feet
$t = 4$ (seconds)	$h = -16(4)^2 + 256 = -256 + 256$	0 feet

Because the height is 0 feet after 4 seconds, you can conclude that the wrench took 4 seconds to fall to the ground. ∎

Diagram labels (left margin): $t = 0$ sec — 256 ft; $t = 1$ sec; 200 ft; $t = 2$ sec; 150 ft; $t = 3$ sec; 100 ft; 50 ft; $t = 4$ sec

Communicating about MATHEMATICS

▶ **SHARING IDEAS about the Lesson**

Extending the Example During the first second of fall, the wrench in Example 3 fell 16 feet (from a height of 256 feet to a height of 240 feet). How far did it fall during its second, third, and fourth seconds of fall? Organize your results in a table like that below.

Time	0 to 1	1 to 2	2 to 3	3 to 4
Falling Distance	16 feet	? feet	? feet	? feet

48   80   112

Do your results confirm that the wrench is falling faster and faster? Explain your reasoning.

Yes. During each second after the first, the wrench falls 32 feet per second faster than it fell during the previous second.

Many real-life situations can be modeled by formulas and expressions that are polynomials. Situations describing the motion of objects or the surface area of a can are just two examples of ways that polynomials help us understand our environment.

Example 3

Vocabulary Alert!

The process of substituting values of t into a polynomial is called *evaluating* the polynomial. Ask students to evaluate the polynomial at $t = 5$. Can the outcome represent a real-life situation?
—144 feet; no

Communicating about MATHEMATICS

The wrench in Example 3 is falling faster and faster every second. The rate at which the wrench is falling is called its speed or *velocity*. The rate at which the speed of the wrench is increasing is called its *acceleration*.

Writing Prompt
During this past week, I used math outside the classroom to . . .

OPTION: Extra Examples

Here are extra examples similar to some of those of the lesson.

1. Rewriting in Standard Form

Original Polynomial	Standard Form
$4y^2 - y^3 - 6 + y$	$-y^3 + 4y^2 + y - 6$

2. Simplifying Polynomials
Simplify the polynomial and write the result in standard form.

a. $4x + 5x^2 - 6x - x^2$ **b.** $2 + 5n - 3n^2 - 2$

Solution

a. $4x + 5x^2 - 6x - x^2 = 5x^2 - x^2 + 4x - 6x$
$= (5 - 1)x^2 + (4 - 6)x$
$= 4x^2 - 2x$

b. $2 + 5n - 3n^2 - 2 = -3n^2 + 5n + 2 - 2$
$= -3n^2 + 5n$

ASSIGNMENT GUIDE

*Basic/Average:
Day 1: Ex. 15–21
Day 2: Ex. 23–33 odd, 37–40, 41, 45

Above Average:
Ex. 15–33 odd, 34–44, 45

Advanced: Ex. 15–33 odd, 34–44, 45

Selected Answers: Ex. 1–14, 15–43 odd

*You may wish to omit this lesson for these students.

Guided Practice

▶ **Ex. 2, 3, 5** Help students understand why these are not examples of a polynomial: the power must be a whole number.
▶ **Ex. 12–14** Refer students to the lesson opening on page 654.

Independent Practice

▶ **Ex. 18** Students will need help understanding why the expression is not a polynomial.
▶ **Ex. 22–27** Before assigning these, check for students' understanding of the term "standard form."

Guided Practice

P ▶ CHECK for Understanding

In Exercises 1–8, is the expression a polynomial? Explain.

1., 4., 6.–8. Each coefficient is a real number and each exponent is a whole number.
2., 3., 5. The negative exponent is not a whole number.

1. $y + 1$ Yes
2. $3t^{-3}$ No
3. $4n^{-2} - 7$ No
4. 5   Yes
5. $3x^2 + x^{-1}$ No
6. $4s^3 - 8s^2 + 12$ Yes
7. $\sqrt{5}r^2 - \frac{1}{2}$ Yes
8. $2m^4 + m - 4$ Yes

In Exercises 9–11, write the polynomial in standard form. Then state its terms.

9. $4x - 2 + 3x^2$ $3x^2 + 4x - 2;$ $3x^2, 4x, -2$
10. $10 - 5r^3 + 4r$ $-5r^3 + 4r + 10;$ $-5r^3, 4r, 10$
11. $3p - 16p^2 - 12 + p^3$ $p^3 - 16p^2 + 3p - 12;$ $p^3, -16p^2, 3p, -12$

In Exercises 12–14, simplify the polynomial. Then identify its type.

12. $t^2 + t - 5t + 2t^2$ $3t^2 - 4t$, binomial
13. $12 - 6x^3 + 5x^3 - 7$ $-x^3 + 5$, binomial
14. $2n + 1 + 12n - 8$ $14n - 7$, binomial

Independent Practice

In Exercises 15–18, is the expression a polynomial? If it is, state whether it is a monomial, a binomial, or a trinomial.

15. $\frac{1}{2}t^2 - 5t + 3$ Yes, trinomial
16. $9n - \sqrt{2}n^3$ Yes, binomial
17. $6.2y^4$ Yes, monomial
18. $\frac{6}{x^2} - 3x^3$ No

P In Exercises 19–21, match the algebra tiles with a polynomial. Then simplify the polynomial and sketch a rearranged version of the tiles that represent the simplified expression.   For sketches, see margin.

a.
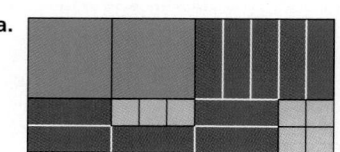
$2x^2 + 9x + 10$

b.
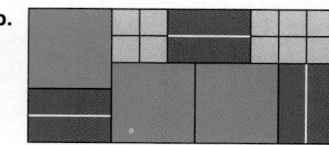
$2x^2 + 10x + 7$

c.
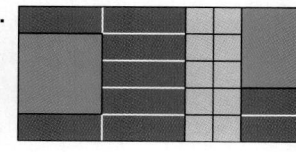
$3x^2 + 6x + 10$

19. $x^2 + 7x + 10 + x^2 + 2x$ c
20. $2x^2 + 5x + 3 + 5x + 4$ a
21. $x^2 + 2x + 4 + 2x^2 + 4x + 6$ b

In Exercises 22–27, write the polynomial in standard form and list its terms.   See margin.

22. $14m - 10m^2 + 5m^3$
23. $6x^3 - x - 2x^2$
24. $5 - 11y - 8y^3$
25. $9z^2 - 7z + 3 - z^3$
26. $2 - t^4 + t^2 + t$
27. $w + 4w^2 - 3 + 15w^3$

In Exercises 28–33, simplify and write in standard form.

28. $y + 2y^2 - 3y$ $2y^2 - 2y$
29. $x^3 - 3x + 5x - x^3$ $2x$
30. $8 - 4x^2 + 10x^2 - 11$ $6x^2 - 3$
31. $15 + 7s^3 - 21 - 3s^2 + s^3$ $8s^3 - 3s^2 - 6$
32. $\frac{4}{3}m - 7 - \frac{2}{3}m + 8$ $\frac{2}{3}m + 1$
33. $1.1r^2 - 2.9r + 1.8r^2 + 3.3r$ $2.9r^2 + 0.4r$

P Portfolio Opportunity

Answers

19.

20.
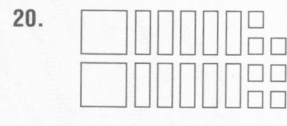

21.
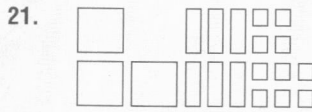

22. $5m^3 - 10m^2 + 14m;\ 5m^3, -10m^2, 14m$
23. $6x^3 - 2x^2 - x;\ 6x^3, -2x^2, -x$
24. $-8y^3 - 11y + 5;\ -8y^3, -11y, 5$
25. $-z^3 + 9z^2 - 7z + 3;\ -z^3, 9z^2, -7z, 3$
26. $t^4 + t^2 + t + 2; -t^4, t^2, t, 2$
27. $15w^3 + 4w^2 + w - 3;\ 15w^3, 4w^2, w, -3$

656   Chapter 14

Extra Practice

Extra Practice   14.5   Name _____

In Exercises 1–3, is the expression a polynomial? If it is, state whether it is a monomial, a binomial, or a trinomial.

1. $\sqrt{3}x^3 - 2x + 4$ Yes, a trinomial
2. $\frac{1}{2}x^2 - 4.2x$ Yes, a binomial
3. $6x - \frac{2}{x^3} + 11$ Not a polynomial

In Exercises 4–6, match the algebra tiles with a polynomial. Then simplify the polynomial and sketch a rearranged version of the tiles that represent the simplified expression.

a.   b.   c.

4. $x^2 + 5x + 2 + 4 + x^2 + 4x$ a, $4x^2 + 6x + 8$
b, $2x^2 + 9x + 6$
5. $5x + 2 + x^2 + 4 + 7x + x^3 + 2$ c, $2x^2 + 12x + 8$
6. $3x^2 + 4 + 4x + 4 + 2x + x^2$

In Exercises 7–9, write the polynomial in standard form and list its terms.

7. $3z - 2z^3 + 14z^2$ $-2z^3 + 14z^2 + 3z, -2z^3, 14z^2, 3z$
8. $6x^4 - 2x + \frac{1}{2}x^2$ $6x^4 + (1/2)x^2 - 2x, 6x^4, (1/2)x^2, -2x$
9. $10 - 2y - 3y^3$ $-3y^3 - 2y + 10, -3y^3, -2y, 10$

In Exercises 10–13, simplify and write in standard form.

10. $3x - 2x^2 + 7x$ $-2x^2 + 10x$
11. $z^4 - 3x^2 + z - 4z^2$ $z^4 - 7z^2 + z$
12. $5 - 4x^2 + 6 - 11x^2$ $-15x^2 + 11$
13. $\frac{8}{5}m^2 - 6 + 3m^2 - 11$ $\frac{19}{5}m^2 - 17$

In Exercises 14–17, use the following information.
The Sears Tower in Chicago as of 1993 is the world tallest building. It's construction was completed in 1974. It is 110 stories high and measures 1454 feet in height. A penny is dropped from the top and its height, h, after t seconds is given by the equation $h = -16t^2 + 1454$.

14. Complete the table.   See back of supplement.

t	1	2	3	4	5	6	7	8	9	10
h										

15. What is the penny's height after 6 seconds?   878 ft
16. When will the penny hit the ground?   Between 9 and 10 seconds
17. If the penny was thrown upward with a velocity of 20 ft/sec the equation would be its height would be $h = -16t^2 + 20t + 1454$. Find its height after 10 seconds and 11 seconds. Explain your results.
54 ft, -262 ft; It takes between 10 and 11 seconds for the penny to strike the ground.

114   Exploring Polynomials • 14.5   Windows

Reteaching

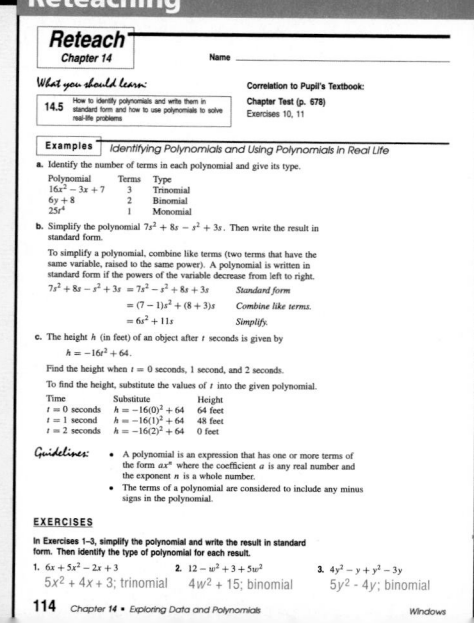

Reteach   Chapter 14   Name _____

What you should learn:
14.5 How to identify polynomials, standard form and how to use polynomials to solve real-life problems

Correlation to Pupil's Textbook:
Chapter Test (p. 678)
Exercises 10, 11

Examples   *Identifying Polynomials and Using Polynomials in Real Life*

a. Identify the number of terms in each polynomial and give its type.

Polynomial	Terms	Type
$16x^2 - 3x + 7$	3	Trinomial
$6y + 8$	2	Binomial
$25x^4$	1	Monomial

b. Simplify the polynomial $7x^2 + 8x - x^2 + 3x$. Then write the result in standard form.

To simplify a polynomial, combine like terms (two terms that have the same variable, raised to the same power). A polynomial is written in standard form if the powers of the variable decrease from left to right.

$7x^2 + 8x - x^2 + 3x = 7x^2 - x^2 + 8x + 3x$ *Standard form*
$= (7 - 1)x^2 + (8 + 3)x$ *Combine like terms.*
$= 6x^2 + 11x$ *Simplify.*

c. The height h (in feet) of an object after t seconds is given by
$h = -16t^2 + 64$.

Find the height when $t = 0$ seconds, 1 second, and 2 seconds.

To find the height, substitute the values of t into the given polynomial.

Time	Substitute	Height
$t = 0$ seconds	$h = -16(0)^2 + 64$	64 feet
$t = 1$ second	$h = -16(1)^2 + 64$	48 feet
$t = 2$ seconds	$h = -16(2)^2 + 64$	0 feet

Guidelines:
• A polynomial is an expression that has one or more terms of the form ax^n where the coefficient a is any real number and the exponent n is a whole number.
• The terms of a polynomial are considered to include any minus signs in the polynomial.

EXERCISES

In Exercises 1–3, simplify the polynomial and write the result in standard form. Then identify the type of polynomial for each result.

1. $6x + 5x^2 - 2x + 3$ $5x^2 + 4x + 3$; trinomial
2. $12 - w^2 + 3 + 5w^2$ $4w^2 + 15$; binomial
3. $4y^2 - y + y^2 - 3y$ $5y^2 - 4y$; binomial

114   Chapter 14 • Exploring Data and Polynomials   Windows

Look Out Below! In Exercises 34–36, use the following information.

You are standing on the Royal Gorge Bridge and accidentally drop your camera. The height h in feet of the camera after t seconds is modeled by

$$h = -16t^2 + 1053.$$

34. Copy and complete the table.

See margin.

t	0	1	2	3	4	5	6	7	8	9
h	?	?	?	?	?	?	?	?	?	?

35. What is the camera's height after 4 seconds? 797 ft

36. When will the camera hit the water?
In ≈ 8.11 seconds

The Royal Gorge Bridge in Colorado is the highest bridge in the world. It is 1,053 feet above the water level.

Integrated Review

Making Connections within Mathematics

Language Skills In Exercises 37–40, match the term with a phrase.

a. Three years **b.** Having two modes **c.** Single color photo **d.** Speak many languages

37. Polyglot d **38.** Monochrome c **39.** Bimodal b **40.** Triennium a

Mental Math In Exercises 41–44, evaluate the polynomial for the given values.

41. $t^2 + 7t - 11$; $t = -1, 0, 2$ $-17, -11, 7$ **42.** $-x^2 + 3x + 9$; $x = -2, 0, 5$ $-1, 9, -1$

43. $2n^3 - 6n + 12$; $n = -3, 0, 3$ $-24, 12, 48$ **44.** $-s^3 + 6s^2 - 8$; $s = -1, 0, 4$ $-1, -8, 24$

Exploration and Extension

45. *Logic Puzzle* Ann, Joy, Lee, Rex, and Ty each have a pet dog. From the clues, determine the name and breed of each person's pet. Copy and use the table to help organize your information. In each box, mark ○ for true and × for false.

Clues:

a. Butch is not Ann's or Rex's dog.

b. Ann and Joy own Daisy and the Great Dane.

c. Max and the collie do not belong to Lee or Ty.

d. Rex's dog and the collie are not Hazel or Duke.

e. Duke and Lee's dog are not boxers.

f. Hazel is a beagle.

g. Duke is not a Great Dane.

h. Two of the dogs are a boxer and a retriever.

	Beagle	Boxer	Collie	Great Dane	Retriever	Butch	Daisy	Duke	Hazel	Max
Ann										
Joy										
Lee										
Rex										
Ty										
Butch										
Daisy										
Duke										
Hazel										
Max										

Ann - collie - Daisy, Joy - Great Dane - Butch, Lee - beagle - Hazel, Rex - boxer - Max, Ty - retriever - Duke

★ More difficult exercises
P Portfolio Opportunity

14.5 • Exploring Polynomials **657**

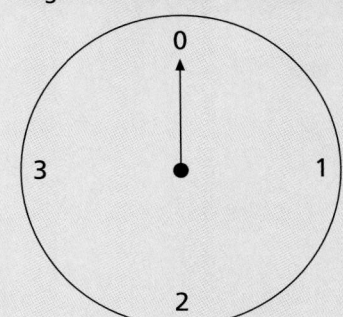
Answer

34.

t	0	1	2	3	4
h	1053	1037	989	909	797

t	5	6	7	8	9
h	653	477	269	29	0

Materials
Teaching Tools
 Algebra tiles, pp. T4, C5

The algebra tile investigations help students to visually explore the nature of polynomial operations. Use the tiles as a lab time in class with students working in pairs on Ex. 1–7.

The tiles should especially help students who believe they can add unlike terms such as $5x^2$ and $3x$.

Materials Needed: algebra tiles

In this investigation, you will use algebra tiles to explore polynomial addition.

Example *Exploring Polynomial Addition*

Use algebra tiles to represent the polynomials $2x^2 + 3x + 3$ and $x^2 + x + 2$. Then combine the tiles to form one group. What polynomial is represented by the group?

Solution You can represent the two polynomials as follows.

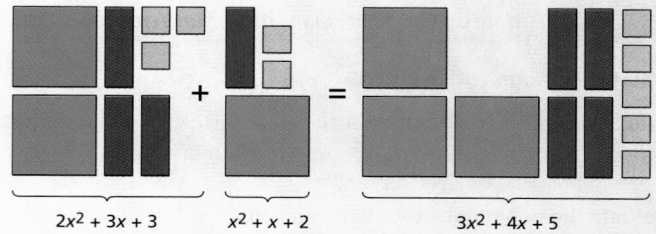

$$2x^2 + 3x + 3 \qquad x^2 + x + 2 \qquad 3x^2 + 4x + 5$$

The combined group represents the polynomial $3x^2 + 4x + 5$. This polynomial is called the **sum** of the two original polynomials. It can be written as the *polynomial equation*

$$(2x^2 + 3x + 3) + (x^2 + x + 2) = 3x^2 + 4x + 5.\qquad\blacksquare$$

Exercises

1. $(3x^2 + x + 5) + (2x^2 + 3x + 2) = 5x^2 + 4x + 7$
2. $(x^2 + 3x + 10) + (3x^2 + 2x + 2) = 4x^2 + 5x + 12$

In Exercises 1 and 2, write the polynomial equation suggested by the algebra tiles.

1. 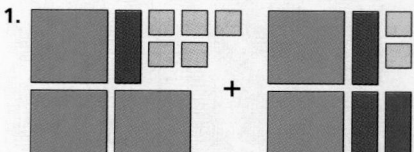   **2.**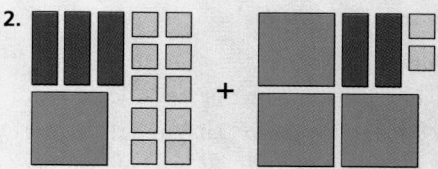

In Exercises 3–6, use algebra tiles to find the sum.   Check students' work.

3. $(3x^2 + 2x + 7) + (x^2 + x + 1)$ $4x^2 + 3x + 8$ **4.** $(4x^2 + 5x + 3) + (2x^2 + 1)$ $6x^2 + 5x + 4$
5. $(x^2 + 6x + 4) + (3x^2 + 2x)$ $4x^2 + 8x + 4$ **6.** $(5x^2 + 7x + 1) + (4x + 3)$ $5x^2 + 11x + 4$
P **7.** *Writing*   In your own words, explain how to add two polynomials.

7. Add the coefficients of like terms.

14.6

Adding and Subtracting Polynomials

What you should learn:

 Goal 1 How to add two or more polynomials

 Goal 2 How to subtract two polynomials

Why you should learn it:

You can use polynomial subtraction to solve geometry problems, such as finding the area of a region.

Goal 1 Adding Polynomials

In the *Lesson Investigation* on page 658, you may have discovered that you can **add** two polynomials by *combining like terms*. For instance, to add $2x^2 + 3x + 3$ and $x^2 + x + 2$, you can write the following.

$$(2x^2 + 3x + 3) + (x^2 + x + 2) = 2x^2 + 3x + 3 + x^2 + x + 2$$
$$= 2x^2 + x^2 + 3x + x + 3 + 2$$
$$= 3x^2 + 4x + 5$$

This technique is called the *horizontal format* for adding polynomials. You can also use a *vertical format*.

$$
\begin{array}{ll}
2x^2 + 3x + 3 & \textit{Write each polynomial in standard form.} \\
\underline{x^2 + x + 2} & \textit{Line up like terms.} \\
3x^2 + 4x + 5 & \textit{Add coefficients of like terms.}
\end{array}
$$

The **degree** of a polynomial is its largest exponent. *Any* two polynomials can be added. They do not have to have the same degree.

2nd-Degree Polynomial

$$2n^2 - 5n + 3$$

3rd-Degree Polynomial

$$-n^3 - 4n^2 + 7$$

> **Study Tip...**
>
> When you use a vertical format to add two polynomials, be sure that you line up the like terms. Sometimes this means leaving a space. For instance, in Example 1a the polynomial $2n^3 + 3n + 6$ is written with a blank space because there is no n^2-term.

Example 1 Adding Polynomials

Add the polynomials.

a. $(-n^3 + 2n^2 - n + 4) + (2n^3 + 3n + 6)$

b. $(x^3 + 5x^2 - 2x + 3) + (2x^2 + 4x - 5)$

Solution You can use either a horizontal or vertical format. The vertical format is shown below.

Line up like terms.	Line up like terms.

a.
$$
\begin{array}{r}
-n^3 + 2n^2 - n + 4 \\
\underline{2n^3 + 3n + 6} \\
n^3 + 2n^2 + 2n + 10
\end{array}
$$

b.
$$
\begin{array}{r}
x^3 + 5x^2 - 2x + 3 \\
\underline{2x^2 + 4x - 5} \\
x^3 + 7x^2 + 2x - 2
\end{array}
$$
■

14.6 • *Adding and Subtracting Polynomials* **659**

▶ **PACING the Lesson**

Suggested Number of Days
Basic/Average 0   **Above Average** 1
Advanced 1

▶ **PLANNING the Lesson**

Lesson Plan 14.6, p. 115

ORGANIZER

Starters (reproduced below)
 Problem of the Day 14.6, p. 41
 Warm-Up Exercises 14.6, p. 41
Lesson Resources
 Math Log, p. 44
 Answer Masters 14.6, p. 283
 Extra Practice Copymaster 14.6, p. 115
 Reteaching Copymaster 14.6, p. 115
Special Populations
 Suggestions, Teacher's Edition, p. 632D

LESSON Notes

Students may need to be reminded of the definition of *like* terms—terms that have the same variables raised to the same powers. Have students record in their math journals that the degree of a term is its exponent and the degree of a polynomial is the greatest exponent among all its terms. Remind students also that they may want to write down the "invisible 1" coefficients to help them avoid addition errors.

Example 1

ALTERNATE APPROACH
Using Place-holders You may wish to encourage students to write 0-coefficients as place-holders to help them correctly line up *like* terms when using the vertical formats. For example, in part **a**, they may want to write:

$$-n^3 + 2n^2 - n + 4$$
$$2n^3 + 0n^2 + 3n + 6$$

Remind students of the Distributive Property for integers, namely, $a \cdot (b+c) = a \cdot b + a \cdot c$. Use integer values for variables *a*, *b*, and *c* to illustrate the relationship. Now apply the Distributive Property to the subtraction of polynomials by showing students that you can rewrite the given problem as follows: $(3x^2 - 1 + 2x) - (-2x^2 + 5 - 7x)$ is the same as $(3x^2 - 1 + 2x) + (-1)(-2x^2 + 5 - 7x)$. The distributive property can now be used to simplify the second polynomial, which becomes $2x^2 - 5 + 7x$. The entire expression becomes $3x^2 - 1 + 2x + 2x^2 - 5 + 7x$. When we say we are using the distributive property to subtract, we are mentally performing the step of rewriting the expression as shown above.

Example 2

Review why rectangular regions can be used to represent multiplication. Then remind students how to multiply variables. Remember that some students benefit from writing in the "invisible 1" that is the exponent of the expression *x*.

Communicating about MATHEMATICS

Challenge students to describe a real-life situation that can be represented by the figure in Example 2.

Writing Prompt

I could really use help with . . .

Answer to Communicating

A. $(x^2 + 3x) - (x^2 - 6x)$
$= (9^2 + 3 \cdot 9) - (9^2 - 6 \cdot 9)$
$= (81 + 27) - (81 - 54)$
$= 108 - 27$
$= 81$ units^2

B. $9x = 9 \cdot 9$
$= 81$ units^2

Answers vary, Way B requires much less computation.

Goal 2 Subtracting Polynomials

To subtract two polynomials, you can use the Distributive Property. For instance, you can subtract $x^2 - x + 3$ from $3x^2 - x + 5$ as follows.

$$(3x^2 - x + 5) - (x^2 - x + 3) = 3x^2 - x + 5 - x^2 + x - 3$$
$$= 3x^2 - x^2 - x + x + 5 - 3$$
$$= 2x^2 + 2$$

A vertical format for this subtraction is shown at the left. Notice that the vertical format requires two steps.

Subtract
$$\begin{array}{r} 3x^2 - x + 5 \\ -(x^2 - x + 3) \\ \hline \end{array}$$

Distribute
$$\begin{array}{r} 3x^2 - x + 5 \\ -x^2 + x - 3 \\ \hline 2x^2 \quad\quad + 2 \end{array}$$

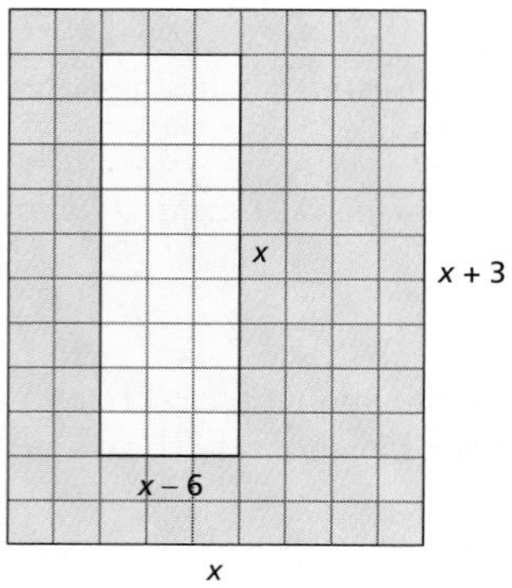

Example 2 *Subtracting Polynomials*

Connections **Geometry**

Find an expression that represents the area of the green region at the left.

Solution The area of the larger rectangle is

Area $= x(x + 3) = x^2 + 3x$.

The area of the smaller rectangle is

Area $= x(x - 6) = x^2 - 6x$.

To find the area of the green region, subtract the area of the smaller rectangle from the area of the larger rectangle.

$$(x^2 + 3x) - (x^2 - 6x) = x^2 + 3x - x^2 + 6x$$
$$= x^2 - x^2 + 3x + 6x$$
$$= 9x$$

■

Communicating about MATHEMATICS

SHARING IDEAS about the Lesson

Evaluating Polynomials In Example 2, find the area of the green region when $x = 9$ in the following two ways. Which way do you prefer? Explain. See margin.

A. Substitute 9 for *x* in the expression for the area of each rectangle. Then subtract the area of the smaller from the area of the larger.

B. Substitute 9 for *x* in the expression for the area of the green region.

OPTION: Extra Examples

Here are additional examples similar to Example 1.

Adding Polynomials

Add the polynomials.

a. $(n^3 - 3n^2 + 4n - 6) + (n^3 + n^2 + 5)$
b. $(-x^3 + 6x^2 - 3x) + (5x^3 + 3x - 4)$

Solution

You can use either a horizontal or vertical format. The horizontal format is shown below.

a. $(n^3 - 3n^2 + 4n - 6) + (n^3 + n^2 + 5)$
$= n^3 + n^3 - 3n^2 + n^2 + 4n - 6 + 5$
$= 2n^3 - 2n^2 + 4n - 1$

b. $(-x^3 + 6x^2 - 3x) + (5x^3 + 3x - 4)$
$= -x^3 + 5x^3 + 6x^2 - 3x + 3x - 4$
$= 4x^3 + 6x^2 - 4$

EXERCISES

Guided Practice

▶ **CHECK for Understanding**

In Exercises 1 and 2, use a horizontal format to find the sum or difference.

1. $(3x^2 - 7x + 5) + (3x^2 - 10)$ $6x^2 - 7x - 5$

2. $(n^2 + 8n - 7) - (-n^2 + 8n - 12)$ $2n^2 + 5$

In Exercises 3 and 4, use a vertical format to find the sum or difference.

3.
$$\begin{array}{r} 2y^3 + y^2 - 4y + 3 \\ + \quad y^3 - 5y^2 + 2y - 6 \\ \hline 3y^3 - 4y^2 - 2y - 3 \end{array}$$

4.
$$\begin{array}{r} 2y^3 + y^2 - 4y + 3 \\ - \quad y^3 - 5y^2 + 2y - 6 \\ \hline y^3 + 6y^2 - 6y + 9 \end{array}$$

Independent Practice

Error Analysis   **In Exercises 5 and 6, find and correct the error.**

5.
$$\begin{array}{r} -4z^3 + z^2 + \qquad 7 \\ + \quad 3z^3 \qquad 6z - 5 \\ \hline -z^3 + z^2 + 6z + 2 \end{array}$$
$$\begin{array}{r} -4z^3 + z^2 \qquad + 7 \\ + \quad 3z^3 \qquad - 6z - 5 \\ \hline -z^3 + z^2 - 6z + 2 \end{array}$$

✪ 6.
$$\begin{array}{r} 4x^3 + 3x^2 + 4x + 3 \\ -(2x^3 + x^2 + 2x + 1) \\ \hline 2x^3 + 4x^2 + 6x + 4 \end{array}$$
$$\begin{array}{r} 4x^3 + 3x^2 + 4x + 3 \\ -(2x^3 + x^2 + 2x + 1) \\ \hline 2x^3 + 2x^2 + 2x + 2 \end{array}$$

In Exercises 7 and 8, add the polynomials. (Use a horizontal format.)

7. $(-x^2 + 9x - 5) + (6x^2 - 2x + 16)$
   $5x^2 + 7x + 11$

8. $(-8a^3 + a^2 + 17) + (6a^2 - 3a + 9)$
   $-8a^3 + 7a^2 - 3a + 26$

In Exercises 9 and 10, subtract the polynomials. (Use a horizontal format.)

9. $(-b^3 + 4b^2 - 1) - (7b^3 + 4b^2 + 3)$
   $-8b^3 - 4$

10. $(-5x^3 - 13x + 4) - (-3x^3 + x^2 + 10x - 9)$
   $-2x^3 - x^2 - 23x + 13$

In Exercises 11 and 12, add the polynomials. (Use a vertical format.)

11.
$$\begin{array}{r} x^3 + 4x^2 - 9x + 2 \\ + \quad -2x^3 + 5x^2 + x - 6 \\ \hline -x^3 + 9x^2 - 8x - 4 \end{array}$$

12.
$$\begin{array}{r} 2n^4 + 2n^3 - n^2 - 4n + 6 \\ + \quad n^4 + 3n^3 - 3n^2 - 5n + 2 \\ \hline 3n^4 + 5n^3 - 4n^2 - 9n + 8 \end{array}$$

In Exercises 13 and 14, subtract the polynomials. (Use a vertical format.)

13.
$$\begin{array}{r} 3t^3 + 4t^2 + t - 5 \\ - \quad (t^3 + 2t^2 - 9t + 1) \\ \hline 2t^3 + 2t^2 + 10t - 6 \end{array}$$

14.
$$\begin{array}{r} x^4 + 3x^3 + x^2 + 2x + 5 \\ - (x^4 + 2x^3 + 3x^2 + 4x - 4) \\ \hline x^3 - 2x^2 - 2x + 9 \end{array}$$

In Exercises 15–18, perform the indicated operations.

15. $(2x^2 + 9x - 4) + (-8x^2 + 3x + 6) + (x^2 - 5x - 7)$ $-5x^2 + 7x - 5$

16. $(-5y^3 - 4y^2 - 1) + (12y^3 + 3y - 11) - (10y^2 + y - 3)$ $7y^3 - 14y^2 + 2y - 9$

17. $(z^2 - 5) - (-z^3 + 2z^2 + 3) + (-z^3 - 4z + 8)$ $-z^2 - 4z$

18. $(4x^2 + x - 17) - (x^2 - 15x + 7) - (-7x^2 + x + 6)$ $10x^2 + 15x - 30$

✪ More difficult exercises
P Portfolio Opportunity

14.6 • *Adding and Subtracting Polynomials*   **661**

EXERCISE Notes

ASSIGNMENT GUIDE

*Basic/Average:
   Day 1: Ex. 5–13 odd, 26–31
   Day 2: Ex. 15–25, 32–34

Above Average:
   Ex. 5–17 odd, 19–25, 32–35

Advanced: Ex. 5–17 odd, 19–25, 32–35

Selected Answers: Ex. 1–4, 5–27 odd

*You may wish to omit this lesson for these students.

Guided Practice

Use these exercises in class. Ask students which format they prefer and have them explain why.

Independent Practice

▶ **Ex. 7–14**   Students may prefer one format over the other. Let them use their preference.

▶ **Ex. 15–18**   Refer students to Goal 2, page 660. For Ex. 18, caution students that subtracting the quantity must be performed twice.

Extra Practice

Extra Practice **14.6** Name _____

In Exercises 1 and 2, find and correct the error. 1-2. See back of supplement.

1.
$$\begin{array}{r} -4x^3 + 2x^2 \qquad 4 \\ + \qquad 3x^3 + 2x + 8 \\ \hline -4x^3 - x^2 + 2x + 4 \end{array}$$

2.
$$\begin{array}{r} 3x^3 + 2x^2 - 6x + 3 \\ -(2x^3 - 6x^2 - 4x + 8) \\ \hline x^3 - 4x^2 - 10x - 5 \end{array}$$

In Exercises 3 and 4, add or subtract the polynomials, as indicated. (Use a horizontal format.)

3. $(-3x^2 + 4x - 7) + (8x^2 - 3x - 3)$
   $5x^2 + x - 10$

4. $(-k^3 - 2k + 1) - (3k^2 - 4k - 11)$
   $-k^3 - 3k^2 + 2k + 12$

In Exercises 5 and 6, add the polynomials. (Use a vertical format.)

5.
$$\begin{array}{r} w^3 - 3w^2 + 8w - 11 \\ + 3w^3 + 2w^2 - 10w - 7 \\ \hline 4w^3 - w^2 - 2w - 18 \end{array}$$

6.
$$\begin{array}{r} 3d^4 - 3d^3 + 2d^2 - 16d - 11 \\ + -5d^4 + 2d^3 - 11d^2 + 10d - 7 \\ \hline -2d^4 - d^3 - 9d^2 - 6d - 18 \end{array}$$

In Exercises 7 and 8, subtract the polynomials. (Use a vertical format.)

7.
$$\begin{array}{r} 3x^3 - 2x^2 + 5x - 11 \\ - (-3x^3 + 11x^2 - 7x - 6) \\ \hline 6x^3 - 13x^2 + 12x - 5 \end{array}$$

8.
$$\begin{array}{r} 2y^4 - 11y^3 - 2y^2 + 5y - 11 \\ - (-y^4 + 6y^3 + 11y^2 - 7y + 10) \\ \hline 3y^4 - 17y^3 - 13y^2 + 12y - 21 \end{array}$$

In Exercises 9–12, perform the indicated operations.

9. $(3x^2 - 7x + 5) + (-4x^2 - 6x + 11) + (x^2 - 3x + 7)$ $-16x + 23$

10. $(-5k^2 - 11k + 10) + (3k^2 - 7k + 11) - (7k^2 - 4k + 3)$ $-9k^2 - 14k + 18$

11. $(-w^2 + 5) - (w^2 - 11w + 2) + (3w^2 - 11)$ $w^2 + 11w - 8$

12. $(4x^3 - 7x + 2) - (x^2 - 4x + 6) - (3x^3 - 2x^2 + 7x + 5)$ $x^3 + x^2 + 4x - 9$

In Exercises 13 and 14, find the perimeter of the polygon. Then evaluate when $x = 8$.

13.
$3x^2 + 9x - 34$, 230

14. $x^2 + 7x + 4$, 124

In Exercises 15 and 16, find an expression that represents the area of the unshaded region. Then evaluate the area when $x = 3$.

15.
$7x^2 + 11x$, 96

16.
$-3x^2 + 36x + 80$, 161

Windows   *14.6* • *Adding or Subtracting Polynomials* **115**

Reteaching

Reteach Chapter 14   Name _____

What you should learn:

14.6	How to add polynomials and how to subtract polynomials

Correlation to Pupil's Textbook:
Chapter Test (p. 678)
Exercises 12, 13

Examples *Adding Polynomials and Subtracting Polynomials*

a. Use a horizontal format to add the polynomials $12p^3 - 5p^2 - 3p + 2$ and $4p^3 + 9p - 6$.

You can add two polynomials by combining like terms.

$(12p^3 - 5p^2 - 3p + 2) + (4p^3 + 9p - 6) = 12p^3 - 5p^2 - 3p + 2 + 4p^3 + 9p - 6$
$= 12p^3 + 4p^3 - 5p^2 - 3p + 9p + 2 - 6$
$= 16p^3 - 5p^2 + 6p - 4$

b. Use a horizontal format to subtract $-2a^2 + a - 6$ from $a^2 + a + 3$.

To subtract two polynomials, you can use the Distributive Property.

$(a^2 + a + 3) - (-2a^2 + a - 6) = a^2 + a + 3 + 2a^2 - a + 6$
$= a^2 + 2a^2 + a - a + 3 + 6$
$= 3a^2 + 9$

c. Use a vertical format to subtract $f^2 - 2f$ from $8f^2 - 2f + 3$.

You must use two steps when you use the vertical format for subtraction.

Subtract
$$\begin{array}{r} 8f^2 - 2f + 3 \\ -(f^2 - 6f + 5) \end{array}$$
Distribute
$$\begin{array}{r} 8f^2 - 2f + 3 \\ -f^2 + 6f - 5 \\ \hline 7f^2 + 4f - 2 \end{array}$$

Guidelines:
- The degree of a polynomial is its largest exponent.
- Any two polynomials (with the same or different degrees) can be added or subtracted.
- When you use a vertical format to add or subtract two polynomials, be sure that you line up the like terms.

EXERCISES

1. Use a vertical format to add the polynomials.
$$\begin{array}{r} 8y^3 - 4y^2 + y - 9 \\ -y^3 + 2y^2 - y + 5 \\ \hline 7y^3 - 2y^2 - 4 \end{array}$$

2. Use a vertical format to subtract the polynomials.
$$\begin{array}{r} 5m^4 + 3m^3 + m^2 - 2m + 7 \\ -(-3m^4 + 8m^3 + m^2 + 3m - 2) \\ \hline 8m^4 - 5m^3 - 5m + 9 \end{array}$$

In Exercises 3 and 4, perform the indicated operations. (Use a horizontal format.)

3. $(x^2 - 4x + 8) - (3x^2 - 6x + 1) + (4x^2 + 8x + 9)$ $2x^2 + 10x + 16$

4. $(6t^3 + 2t^2 - t + 10) - (5t^3 + 7t + 7) - (9t^2 - t - 2)$ $t^3 - 7t^2 - 7t + 5$

Windows   *Chapter 14* • *Exploring Data and Polynomials* **115**

Lesson 14.6 **661**

► **Ex. 19, 20** Ask students whether or not they should simplify first, and have them explain their response.
► **Ex. 21, 22** These exercises are similar to the area model provided in Example 2, page 660.
► **Ex. 23–25** Use these exercises as an in-class teacher-led activity.

Integrated Review

These exercises help to maintain the skill of interpreting data.

Geometry **In Exercises 19 and 20, find the perimeter of the polygon. Then evaluate the perimeter when $x = 3$.**

19.

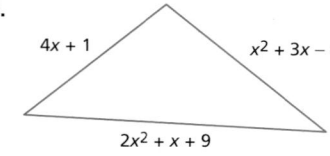

$4x + 1$ $x^2 + 3x - 4$
$2x^2 + x + 9$

$3x^2 + 8x + 6$, 57

20.

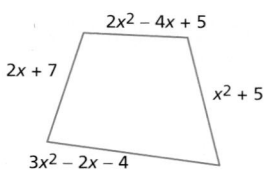

$2x^2 - 4x + 5$
$2x + 7$
$x^2 + 5$
$3x^2 - 2x - 4$

$6x^2 - 4x + 13$, 55

In Exercises 21 and 22, find an expression that represents the area of the green region. Then evaluate the area when $x = 5$.

✪ **21.**

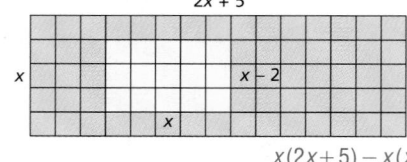

$2x + 5$
x
$x - 2$
x

$x(2x+5) - x(x-2)$; 60

✪ **22.**

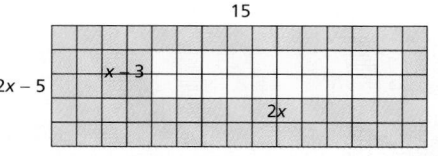

15
$2x - 5$
$x - 3$
$2x$

$15(2x-5) - 2x(x-3)$; 55

Profit **In Exercises 23–25, use the following information.**

You spend $500 to start a small business selling a computer software program you wrote. Each program costs you $2.50 to produce (for the discs and package). You sell each program for $12.50. Your income and expense for producing and selling x programs are

$$\text{Income} = 12.50x \qquad \text{and} \qquad \text{Expense} = 2.50x + 500.$$

✪ **23.** Write a polynomial model for the profit you make for selling x programs. $10x - 500$

✪ **24.** How much profit will you make if you sell 200 programs? $1500

✪ **25.** *Think about It*   Will you make twice as much profit if you sell 400
Ⓟ   programs? Explain.
No; you will make more than twice as much, $3500.

Integrated Review   *Making Connections within Mathematics*

Low-Calorie **In Exercises 26–28, use the figure at the right showing the number of people who bought low-calorie foods and beverages from 1978 to 1993.** *(Source: Caloric Control Council)*

26. How many more people bought low-calorie food and drink in 1993 than in 1978?   67 million

27. Estimate the number who bought low-calorie food and drink in 1986. In 1990.   79 million, 98 million

28. Estimate the number of people who will buy low-calorie food and drink in 1995.   118 million

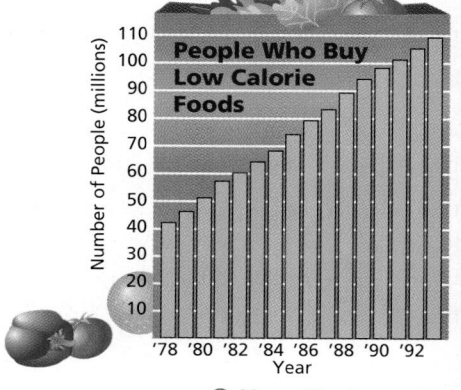

People Who Buy Low Calorie Foods

Number of People (millions)

'78 '80 '82 '84 '86 '88 '90 '92
Year

✪ More difficult exercises
Ⓟ Portfolio Opportunity

Exploration and Extension

Guess, Check, and Revise   **In Exercises 29–34, each of the equations has two solutions. Use a guess, check, and revise strategy to find both solutions.**

29. $x^2 - 3x + 2 = 0$ 1, 2

⭐ 30. $x^2 - 5x + 6 = 0$ 2, 3

31. $x^2 - 7x + 12 = 0$ 3, 4

⭐ 32. $x^2 - 9x + 20 = 0$ 4, 5

33. $x^2 - 11x + 30 = 0$ 5, 6

⭐ 34. $x^2 - 13x + 42 = 0$ 6, 7

35. *Patterns*   Use the pattern from Exercises 29–34 to write a polynomial equation that has 7 and 8 as its solutions. Check your result by substituting. $x^2 - 15x + 56 = 0$

Mixed REVIEW

In Exercises 1–6, use the similar triangles at the right. (11.1)

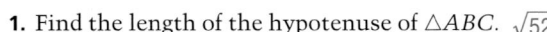

1. Find the length of the hypotenuse of $\triangle ABC$. $\sqrt{52}$
2. Find the length of the hypotenuse of $\triangle DEF$. $\sqrt{117}$
3. What is the scale factor of $\triangle DEF$ to $\triangle ABC$?   1.5
4. Find the area of each triangle.   12 units², 27 units²
5. Find the perimeter of each triangle. $10 + \sqrt{52}$, $15 + \sqrt{117}$
6. Describe the relationship between the scale factor, the perimeters, and the areas.
   The scale factor is the same for perimeters but is squared for areas.

In Exercises 7 and 8, the following data gives the number in thousands of cellular phone subscribers from 1987 through 1992. (5.1, 5.2)

1987: 1,231;   1988: 2,069;   1989: 3,509;   See margin.
1990: 5,283;   1991: 7,557;   1992: 11,033

(Source: Cellular Telecommunications Industry Association)

7. Draw a picture graph of the data.   8. Draw a bar graph of the data.

In Exercises 9–14, simplify. (7.4, 7.5)

9. $\frac{2}{3} + \frac{1}{6}$ $\frac{5}{6}$

10. $\frac{5}{8} - \frac{3}{4}$ $-\frac{1}{8}$

11. $\frac{12}{15} \times \frac{2}{5}$ $\frac{8}{25}$

12. $-\frac{13}{21} \times \left(-\frac{4}{81}\right)$ $\frac{52}{1701}$

13. $\frac{16}{21} \div \frac{4}{7}$ $\frac{4}{3}$

14. $\frac{6}{19} \div 2$ $\frac{3}{19}$

In Exercises 15–18, solve the inequality. (9.6)

15. $5y + 13 \geq 28$ $y \geq 3$

16. $3 - 2r < 6$ $r > -\frac{3}{2}$

17. $\frac{1}{2} < \frac{1}{4} - \frac{1}{3}s$ $s < -\frac{3}{4}$

18. $4x + 3 \leq 2x$ $x \leq -\frac{3}{2}$

In Exercises 19 and 20, add the polynomials. (14.6)

19. $(3x^2 + 2x + 1) + (x^2 + 2x + 3)$ $4x^2 + 4x + 4$

20. $(6x^3 - x^2 + 2) + (3x^2 + 2)$ $6x^3 + 2x^2 + 4$

Enrichment

Point A is the center of the circle. $AR = 3$ and $AK = 4$. Find the radius of the circle.

5

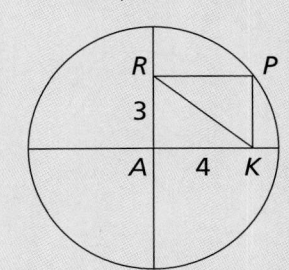

Exploration and Extension

Have students investigate Ex. 29–34 with a graphing calculator, using a spreadsheet or a table feature as in the *TI-82*.

Portfolio Opportunity: Math Log

It is standard practice to write a polynomial in descending order (i.e. the term with the largest exponent is written first, the term with the second largest exponent second, etc.). Must a polynomial be written in descending order? Explain your answer.

Also available as a copymaster, page 44, Ex. 6

Short Quiz

Covers Lessons 14.5 and 14.6

Available as a copymaster, page 232

Answers

7.

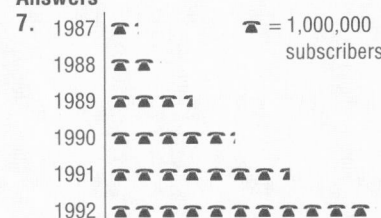

8.

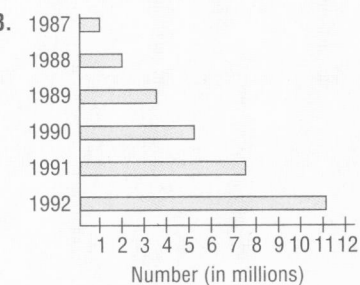

Materials

Teaching Tools
Algebra tiles, pp. T4, C5

Use this investigation to help students visually explore the nature of polynomial multiplication. This connects to investigations in the Distributive Property (Lessons 2.1 and 4.4) and in area (Lesson 11.1).

Materials Needed: algebra tiles

In this investigation, you will use algebra tiles to explore polynomial multiplication.

Example   *Exploring Polynomial Multiplication*

Use algebra tiles to represent the product of the polynomials $3x$ and $x + 4$. Then write the polynomial that is represented by the entire group of algebra tiles.

Solution   You can represent the product of the two polynomials as follows:

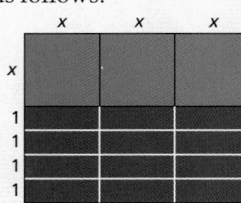

Length $= 3x$
Width $= x + 4$
Area $=$ (Length)(Width)
$\qquad = 3x(x + 4)$

The combined group represents the polynomial $3x^2 + 12x$. The result can be written as the *polynomial equation*

$$3x(x + 4) = 3x^2 + 12x.$$ ■

Exercises

In Exercises 1–4, write the polynomial equation indicated by the algebra tiles.   See margin.

1.

2.

3.

4.

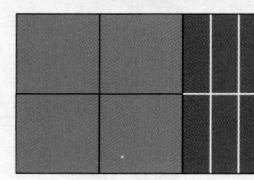

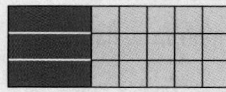

P In Exercises 5–8, use algebra tiles to find the product.   Check students' work.

5. $2x(3x + 2)$ $6x^2 + 4x$ 6. $x(4x + 3)$ $4x^2 + 3x$ 7. $3x(x + 1)$ $3x^2 + 3x$ 8. $4x(2x + 3)$
$\qquad\qquad\qquad\qquad\qquad\qquad\qquad\qquad\qquad\qquad\qquad\qquad\qquad\qquad\qquad\qquad\qquad 8x^2 + 12x$

Answers

1. $(x + 5)x = x^2 + 5x$ or $x(x + 5)$
$\quad = x^2 + 5x$
2. $(x + 5)3 = 3x + 15$ or $3(x + 5)$
$\quad = 3x + 15$
3. $(2x + 3)2x = 4x^2 + 6x$ or $2x(2x + 3)$
$\quad = 4x^2 + 6x$
4. $3x(3 + x) = 9x + 3x^2$ or $(3 + x)3x$
$\quad = 9x + 3x^2$

14.7 Multiplying Polynomials

PACING the Lesson

Suggested Number of Days
Basic/Average 0   Above Average 0
Advanced 2

PLANNING the Lesson

Lesson Plan 14.7, p. 116

What you should learn:

Goal 1 How to multiply a polynomial by a monomial

Goal 2 How to use polynomial multiplication to solve geometry problems

Why you should learn it:

You can use polynomial multiplication to solve geometry problems, such as finding the area of a region.

Study Tip...
When multiplying polynomials, be sure to check that the signs of the product are correct. One of the most common errors in algebra is to forget to "distribute negative signs."

Incorrect

$$-x(2x^2 - 3x + 1)$$
$$= -2x^3 - 3x^2 + x$$

Correct

$$-x(2x^2 - 3x + 1)$$
$$= -2x^3 + 3x^2 - x$$

Goal 1   Multiplying Polynomials

In this lesson, you will learn how to multiply a polynomial by a monomial. Example 1 reviews the types of polynomials that you already know how to multiply.

Example 1   *Multiplying Polynomials*

a. $2(3x + 5) = 6x + 10$ *Distributive Property (Lesson 2.1)*

b. $n(n - 3) = n^2 - 3n$ *Distributive Property (Lesson 3.4)*

c. $(y^2)(y^3) = y^5$ *Property of Exponents (Lesson 6.7)* ∎

Each of the products in Example 1 is an example of multiplying a polynomial by a *monomial.* The general rule for finding this type of product is stated below.

> **Multiplying a Polynomial by a Monomial**
> To multiply a polynomial by a monomial, multiply each term of the polynomial by the monomial.

Example 2   *Multiplying a Polynomial by a Monomial*

a. $3x(x^2 + 2x - 5) = 3x(x^2) + 3x(2x) - 3x(5)$ *Distribute.*
$$= 3x^3 + 6x^2 - 15x$$ *Simplify.*

b. $n^2(-2n^3 + 4n) = n^2(-2n^3) + n^2(4n)$ *Distribute.*
$$= -2n^5 + 4n^3$$ *Simplify.*

c. $2b^2(-4b^4 + b + 6) = 2b^2(-4b^4) + 2b^2(b) + 2b^2(6)$
$$= -8b^6 + 2b^3 + 12b^2$$

d. $-5y(3y^2 + y - 7) = -5y(3y^2) + (-5y)(y) - (-5y)(7)$
$$= -15y^3 - 5y^2 + 35y$$ ∎

14.7 • Multiplying Polynomials **665**

ORGANIZER

Starters (reproduced below)
  Problem of the Day 14.7, p. 42
  Warm-Up Exercises 14.7, p. 42
Lesson Resources
  Color Transparencies
    Diagram for Example 3, p.59
  Math Log, p. 44
  Answer Masters 14.7, p. 285
  Extra Practice Copymaster 14.7, p. 116
  Reteaching Copymaster 14.7, p. 116
Special Populations
  Suggestions, Teacher's Edition, p. 632D

LESSON Notes

Emphasize the importance of the Distributive Property in multiplying polynomials. You can help students remember to distribute a factor to all the terms of an expression by using the analogy of a teacher passing out (distributing) exam papers who says, "I mustn't forget to give a paper to that last person in the last row."

Example 1

Have students record in their math journals the rules for multiplying powers and using the Distributive Property. Encourage students to use examples to clarify their statements of these rules.

Example 2

Students may find it helpful to see that the original expression evaluated for a given value of x (in part **a**) gives the same result as when the simplified expression is evaluated for the same value of x. Repeat this check for parts **b**, **c**, and **d**.

STARTER: Problem of the Day

If a dart lands on this target, what is the probability that it will land in the shaded area?

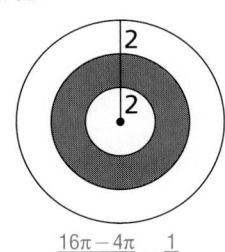

$$\frac{16\pi - 4\pi}{36\pi} = \frac{1}{3}$$

Also available as a copymaster, page 42

STARTER: Warm-Up Exercises

1. What does the Distributive Property of Multiplication over Addition state?
$a \bullet (b + c) = (a \bullet b) + (a \bullet c)$

2. Provide three examples of each of the following.
a. binomials **b.** trinomials **c.** monomials
Answers will vary.

3. Simplify each expression.
a. $3x^2 - 3x + 8x^2 + 9x$
b. $-12m^3 + 23m^2 + 16m^3 - 8$
a. $11x^2 + 6x$, **b.** $4m^3 + 23m^2 - 8$

Also available as a copymaster, page 42

Frequently, geometric problems are expressed using algebraic variables. In such situations, the connection between geometry and algebra is often very useful.

Example 3

This example shows how algebra can be used to get geometric information. You may wish to review the area formulas for various polygons before beginning.

Communicating about **MATHEMATICS**

Challenge students to generate examples from science or math of multiplying polynomials.

Writing Prompt
The most important thing I learned about math this week is . . .

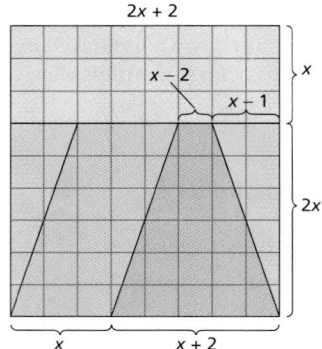
Connections
Geometry

Goal 2 **Using Polynomial Multiplication**

Example 3 *Using Polynomial Multiplication*

The rectangle at the left is divided into five regions. Write an expression for the area of each region. Then write an expression for the area of the entire region.

Solution

Polygon	Expression for Area	Simplify
Rectangle	Area $= x(2x + 2)$	$2x^2 + 2x$
Parallelogram	Area $= x(2x)$	$2x^2$
Trapezoid	Area $= \frac{1}{2}(2x)([x - 2] + [x + 2])$	$2x^2$
Each triangle	Area $= \frac{1}{2}(2x)(x - 1)$	$x^2 - x$

To find an expression for the area of the entire region, you can add the expressions for the areas of the five regions.

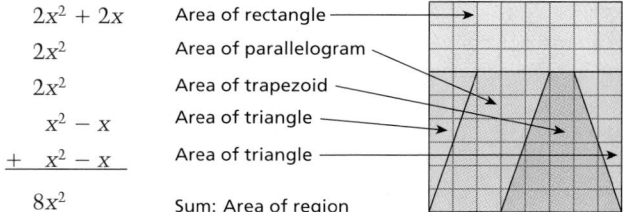

$$2x^2 + 2x \quad \text{Area of rectangle}$$
$$2x^2 \quad \text{Area of parallelogram}$$
$$2x^2 \quad \text{Area of trapezoid}$$
$$x^2 - x \quad \text{Area of triangle}$$
$$+ \ \ x^2 - x \quad \text{Area of triangle}$$
$$8x^2 \quad \text{Sum: Area of region}$$

Communicating about **MATHEMATICS**

Cooperative Learning

▶ **SHARING IDEAS about the Lesson**

Guess, Check, and Revise

A. The area of the entire region in Example 3 can be modeled with the expression

$$\text{Area} = (\text{Length})(\text{Width}) = (3x)(2x + 2).$$

Show how you can use the rule for multiplying a polynomial by a monomial to simplify this product. $6x^2 + 6x$

B. The expression for the area of the entire region obtained in Part A is not the same as that obtained in Example 3. Find a value of x that makes both expressions equal. What is the area of the entire region?

0 and 3, but for $x = 0$ the figure becomes a point; 72 units^2

OPTION: Extra Examples

Here is an additional example similar to Example 2.
Multiplying a Polynomial by a Monomial

a. $4x(x^2 - x + x^2)$
$= 4x(x^2) - 4x(x) + 4x(2)$ Distribute.
$= 4x^3 - 4x^2 + 8x$ Simplify.

b. $a^2 - (3a + 6)$
$= a^2 - (3a) + a^2(6)$ Distribute.
$= 3a^3 + 6a^2$ Simplify.

c. $- 5y(2y^3 - y - 3)$
$- 5y(2y^3) - (- 5y)(y) - (- 5y)(3)$ Distribute.
$= - 10y^4 + 5y^2 + 15y$ Simplify.

EXERCISES

Guided Practice

▶ **CHECK for Understanding**

In Exercises 1 and 2, find the product.

1. $4n(2n^2 - 3n + 5)$ $8n^3 - 12n^2 + 20n$

2. $-3y^2(y^2 + 2y - 5)$ $-3y^4 - 6y^3 + 15y^2$

Geometry   **In Exercises 3–7, use the figure at the right.**
See margin.

3. Write an expression for the area of each region.

4. Use the results of Exercise 3 to write an expression for the area of the entire region. $24x^2$

5. Write expressions for the length and width of the entire region. $6x, 4x$

6. Use the result of Exercise 5 to write an expression for the area of the entire region. $24x^2$

7. Compare the expressions obtained in Exercises 4 and 6.
They are the same.

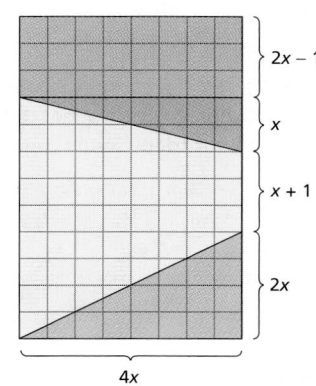
$2x - 1$
x
$x + 1$
$2x$
$4x$

Independent Practice

12. $-8b^6 - 10b^5 + b^4$ **13.** $-8t^3 + 12t^2 - 4t$

In Exercises 8–16, multiply.

12., 13. See above.
$4x^3 - 8x^2 - 4x$ $-6x^2 - 12x + 16$

8. $2y(y^2 + 1)$ $2y^3 + 2y$

9. $4x(x^2 - 2x - 1)$

10. $-2(3x^2 + 6x - 8)$

11. $8t^2(-6t - 5)$ $-48t^3 - 40t^2$

12. $-b^4(8b^2 + 10b - 1)$

13. $2t(-4t^2 + 6t - 2)$

14. $y(-7y^3 + 8y - 4)$
$-7y^4 + 8y^2 - 4y$

15. $-4z(2z^5 - z^3 + 10)$
$-8z^6 + 4z^4 - 40z$

16. $n^3(-n^4 + n^3 - n^2 + n - 1)$
$-n^7 + n^6 - n^5 + n^4 - n^3$

Geometry   **In Exercises 17–20, use the figure at the right.**   See margin.

17. Write an expression for the area of each region.

18. Use the results of Exercise 17 to write an expression for the area of the entire region.   **18., 19.** $8x^2 - 6x$

19. Use the formula for the area of a rectangle to write an expression for the area of the entire region.

20. Compare the expressions obtained in Exercise 18 and 19.   They are the same.

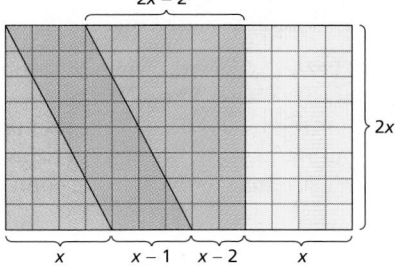
$2x - 2$
$2x$
x $x - 1$ $x - 2$ x

In Exercises 21 and 22, translate the verbal phrase to an algebraic expression. Then multiply.

21. The product of a number and one more than that number $n(n + 1), n^2 + n$

22. The cube of a number times the difference of the number and 2 $n^3(n - 2), n^4 - 2n^3$

✪ More difficult exercises

EXERCISE Notes

ASSIGNMENT GUIDE
*Basic/Average:
  Day 1: Ex. 9–15 odd, 17–20
  Day 2: Ex. 21, 22, 29–35 odd, 37
*Above Average:
  Day 1: Ex. 9–15 odd, 17–20
  Day 2: Ex. 21–26, 29–37 odd
Advanced: Day 1: Ex. 8–20
              Day 2: Ex. 21–26, 27–37 odd
Selected Answers: Ex. 1–7, 9–35 odd
* You may wish to omit this lesson for these students.

Guided Practice

Use these exercises as an in-class summary activity. An excellent connection for polynomial operations is the concept of area in geometry. This connection also provides students with a visual understanding of polynomials.

Independent Practice

▶ **Ex. 8–16**   Refer students to the Study Tip on page 665.
▶ **Ex. 17–20**   Assign these exercises as additional practice similar to Ex. 3–7.

Extra Practice

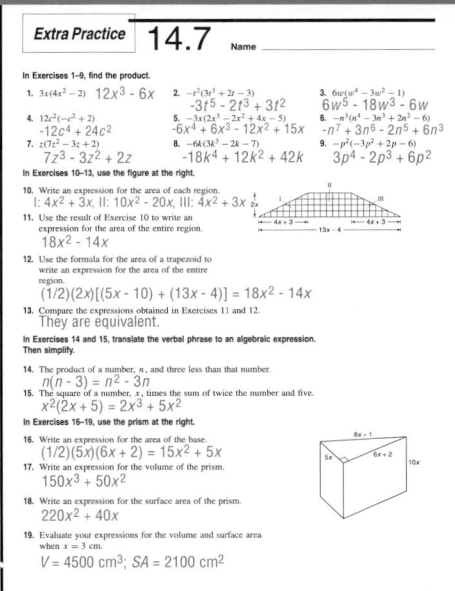

Reteaching

Answers
3. Rectangle: $8x^2 - 4x$, small triangle: $2x^2$, trapezoid: $10x^2 + 4x$, large triangle: $4x^2$

17. Triangle: x^2, parallelogram: $2x^2 - 2x$, trapezoid: $3x^2 - 4x$, rectangle: $2x^2$

Surface Area and Volume   **In Exercises 23–26, use the rectangular prism at the right.**

23. Write an expression for the area of the base of the prism. $3x^2 + x$

24. Write an expression for the volume of the prism. $6x^3 + 2x^2$

25. Write an expression for the surface area of the prism. $22x^2 + 6x$

✪ **26.** The surface area of the prism is 216 square units. What is the volume? Explain your reasoning.   180 units³
$22x^2 + 6x = 216$, so $11x^2 + 3x = 108$. $x = 3$ by trial and error.
$6x^3 + 2x^2 = 6(3)^3 + 2(3)^2 = 180$.

P *You Be the Teacher*   **In Exercises 27 and 28, you are helping a friend. Your friend's solution is given. What did your friend do wrong? What could you say to help your friend avoid the error?**   Answers vary.

✪ **27.** $7t^2(-t^3 + 3t^2 - 8t) = 7t^2(-t^3) + 7t^2(3t^2) - 7t^2(-8t)$
$= -7t^6 + 21t^4 + 58t^3$

$7t^2(-t^3) = -7t^5$
$-7t^2(8t) = -56t^3$

✪ **28.** $-3x^3(2x^2 - 5x + 9) = -3x^3(2x^2) - 3x^3(5x) + 3x^3(9)$
$= -6x^6 - 15x^4 + 24x^3$

$-3x^3(2x^2) = -6x^5$
$-(-3x^3)(5x) = +15x^4$
$-3x^3(9) = -27x^3$

Integrated Review   *Making Connections within Mathematics*

In Exercises 29–32, write the expression without using exponents.

29. 4^0 1

30. 2^{-1} $\frac{1}{2}$

31. $3^3 \cdot 3^2$ 243

32. $5^{-1} \cdot 5^4$ 125

In Exercises 33–36, use the Distributive Property to rewrite the expression.

33. $2(6 + x)$
$12 + 2x$

34. $-3(t + 4)$
$-3t - 12$

35. $5(2x + 3)$
$10x + 15$

36. $4(3x - 5)$
$12x - 20$

Exploration and Extension

✪ **37.** *Puzzle*   Copy the four points on a piece of paper. Then show how to draw three line segments through the four points without retracing or lifting your pencil. You must return to the starting point.

✪ **38.** *Puzzle*   Copy the nine points on a piece of paper. Then draw four line segments through the nine points without retracing or lifting your pencil. You do not need to return to the starting point.

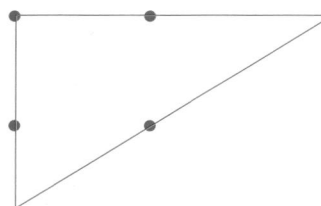

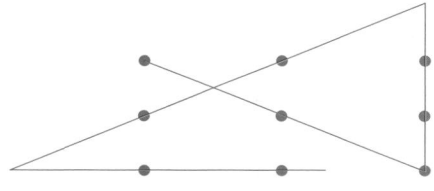

✪ More difficult exercises
P Portfolio Opportunity

Materials Needed: algebra tiles

In this investigation, you will use algebra tiles to explore multiplication of a binomial by a binomial.

Example **Multiplying Two Binomials**

Use algebra tiles to represent the product of the binomials $2x + 1$ and $x + 3$. Then write the polynomial that is represented by the entire group of algebra tiles.

Solution You can represent the product of the two polynomials as follows.

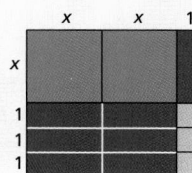

Length $= 2x + 1$

Width $= x + 3$

Area $= ($Length$)($Width$)$

$= (2x + 1)(x + 3)$

The combined group represents the polynomial $2x^2 + 7x + 3$. The result can be written as the *polynomial equation*

$(2x + 1)(x + 3) = 2x^2 + 7x + 3.$ ■

Exercises

In Exercises 1–4, write the polynomial equation indicated by the algebra tiles. $(2x + 3)(x + 1) = 2x^2 + 5x + 3$ $(x + 5)(x + 1) = x^2 + 6x + 5$

1.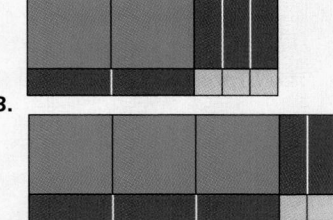

2.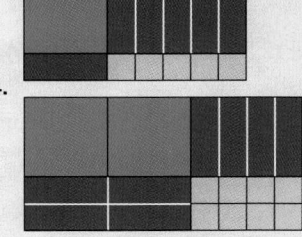

3. **4.**

$(3x + 2)(x + 2) = 3x^2 + 8x + 4$ $(2x + 4)(x + 2) = 2x^2 + 8x + 8$

In Exercises 5–8, use or sketch algebra tiles to find the product. For sketches, see margin.

5. $(x + 2)(3x + 1)$ **6.** $(x + 1)(4x + 3)$ **7.** $(x + 1)^2$ **8.** $(x + 2)^2$

$3x^2 + 7x + 2$ $4x^2 + 7x + 3$ $x^2 + 2x + 1$ $x^2 + 4x + 4$

Materials
Teaching Tools
  Algebra tiles, pp. T4, C5

EXTENSION
Extend the investigation by asking students to model the square $(x + 1)^2$, the square $(x + 2)^2$, the square $(x + 3)^2$, and the square $(x + 4)^2$ with algebra tiles. Then ask students:
a. What tiles were added to the $(x + 1)^2$ figure to form $(x + 2)^2$? 2 x-tiles and 3 1-tiles
b. What tiles were added to the $(x + 2)^2$ figure to form $(x + 3)^2$? 2 x-tiles and 5 1-tiles
c. What tiles were added to the $(x + 3)^2$ figure to form $(x + 4)^2$? 2 x-tiles and 7 1-tiles
d. Is there a pattern to the number of tiles added to the previous square? You add 2 x-tiles and 2 1-tiles more than the previous addition.

Answers
5.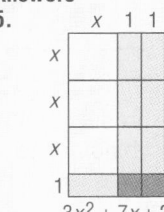

$3x^2 + 7x + 2$

6.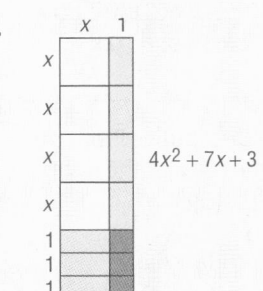

$4x^2 + 7x + 3$

7.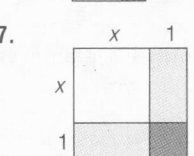

$x^2 + 2x + 1$

8.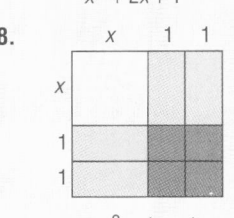

$x^2 + 4x + 4$

ORGANIZER

Starters (reproduced below)
    Problem of the Day 14.8, p. 42
    Warm-Up Exercises 14.8, p. 42
Lesson Resources
    Color Transparencies
        Picture for Example 3, p. 60
        Picture for Ex. 28, p. 60
    Math Log, p. 44
    Answer Masters 14.8, pp. 286, 287
    Extra Practice Copymaster 14.8, p. 117
    Reteaching Copymaster 14.8, p. 117
    Enrichment Projects, pp. 75, 76
Special Populations
    Suggestions, Teacher's Edition, p. 632D

LESSON Notes

Explain to students that multiplying binomials is very similar to multiplying a monomial and polynomial, except that the Distributive Property is used twice (instead of once) when multiplying binomials.

Example 1

ALTERNATE APPROACH
An alternative way to find the product is to distribute each term of the first binomial to the second binomial:
$(x+1)(2x+3) = x(2x+3) + 1(2x+3)$.
After this first step, apply the Distributive Property again to $x(2x+3)$ and $1(2x+3)$.

Example 2

Emphasize that the Distributive Property applies both from the left and the right:
$(a+b)(c+d) = a(c+d) + b(c+d)$
or
$(a+b)(c+d) = (a+b)c + (a+b)d$.
Encourage students to apply the distributive property from the direction they feel most comfortable with (left or right). Have them record their preferences (along with a rationale) in their math journals.

14.8 More about Multiplying Polynomials

What you should learn:

Goal 1 How to multiply a binomial by a binomial

Goal 2 How to use polynomial multiplication to solve real-life problems

Why you should learn it:
You can use polynomial multiplication to solve real-life problems, such as finding the dimensions of a picture frame.

Goal 1   Multiplying Two Binomials

In the *Lesson Investigation* on page 669, you learned how to use algebra tiles to model the product of two binomials. In this lesson, you will learn how to use the Distributive Property to multiply two binomials.

Example 1   *Multiplying Two Binomials*

Find the product of $(x + 1)$ and $(2x + 3)$.

Solution   In the following solution, notice that the Distributive Property is used in the first step *and* in the second step.

$$(x + 1)(2x + 3) = (x + 1)(2x) + (x + 1)(3)$$
$$= (x)(2x) + (1)(2x) + (x)(3) + (1)(3)$$
$$= 2x^2 + 2x + 3x + 3$$
$$= 2x^2 + 5x + 3 \qquad \blacksquare$$

Notice in Example 1 that the first use of the Distributive Property is to distribute the binomial $(x + 1)$ over the binomial $(2x + 3)$ to obtain

$$(x + 1)(2x) + (x + 1)(3).$$

Then the Distributive Property is used again to rewrite the expressions $(x + 1)(2x)$ and $(x + 1)(3)$.

Study Tip...
Another way to multiply two binomials is to use a vertical format, as shown below.

$$
\begin{array}{r}
x + 1 \\
2x + 3 \\
\hline
3x + 3 \\
2x^2 + 2x \\
\hline
2x^2 + 5x + 3
\end{array}
$$

Example 2   *Multiplying Two Binomials*

Find the product of $(4x + 2)$ and $(3x + 1)$.

Solution

$$(4x + 2)(3x + 1) = (4x + 2)(3x) + (4x + 2)(1)$$
$$= (4x)(3x) + (2)(3x) + (4x)(1) + (2)(1)$$
$$= 12x^2 + 6x + 4x + 2$$
$$= 12x^2 + 10x + 2 \qquad \blacksquare$$

STARTER: Problem of the Day

On your thirtieth birthday you announce "I'm one billion seconds old today!" Is this true?
No; 30 years ≈ 946,700,000 seconds

Also available as a copymaster, page 42

STARTER: Warm-Up Exercises

1. Multiply.
a. $3x(5x + 3)$ **b.** $-3(6x - 2)$
a. $15x^2 + 9x$, **b.** $-18x + 6$
2. Multiply.
a. $(2x - 11)3x^2$ **b.** $(-8x + 5)(-2x)$
a. $6x^3 - 33x^2$, **b.** $16x^2 - 10x$

Also available as a copymaster, page 42

Goal 2 Solving Real-Life Problems

Example 3 Guess, Check, and Revise

Real Life
Art

The area of the picture at the left, including the frame, is 80 square inches. What are the dimensions of the frame?

Solution One way to solve the problem is to begin by writing a model for the total area.

Verbal Model

| Area | = | Length | • | Width |

Labels
Area = 80   (square inches)
Length = $2x + 7$ (inches)
Width = $2x + 5$ (inches)

Algebraic Model
$$80 = (2x + 7)(2x + 5)$$
$$= (2x + 7)(2x) + (2x + 7)(5)$$
$$= (2x)(2x) + (7)(2x) + (2x)(5) + (7)(5)$$
$$= 4x^2 + 14x + 10x + 35$$
$$= 4x^2 + 24x + 35$$

Using this model, you can use *Guess, Check, and Revise* to find the value of x for which $4x^2 + 24x + 35$ is equal to 80.

Let $x = 1$: $4(1)^2 + 24(1) + 35 = 4 + 24 + 35 = 63$

Let $x = 2$: $4(2)^2 + 24(2) + 35 = 16 + 48 + 35 = 99$

Let $x = 1.5$: $4(1.5)^2 + 24(1.5) + 35 = 9 + 36 + 35 = 80$

Because $x = 1.5$, the frame is 8 inches by 10 inches. ∎

The next generation may only know the douc langur from photographs. Environmental changes in Southeast Asia have made it an endangered species.

P *Communicating* about **MATHEMATICS**

▶ **SHARING IDEAS about the Lesson**

The FOIL Method The *FOIL Method* for multiplying two binomials is shown below. Use this method to find the products. Then use the Distributive Property to check your work.

$$(2x + 7)(2x + 5) = 4x^2 + 10x + 14x + 35 = 4x^2 + 24x + 35$$

First: (2x)(2x)   Outer: (2x)(5)   Inner: (7)(2x)   Last: (7)(5)

A. $(2x + 3)(x + 4)$ **B.** $(3x + 5)(x + 2)$

$2x^2 + 11x + 12$ $3x^2 + 11x + 10$

Example 3

Remind students that the 7 and 5 are in inches. There are many ways to guess solutions. Students might try factoring 80 in several ways to solve for *x*:
$80 = 4 \times 20$, 8×10, 2×40, or 16×5.
Each product represents possible side lengths for a painting that is 80 in². Ask students which side lengths are possible, given that we know the sides are *more than* 5 inches and 7 inches. The etching must be 8×10. We can then reason that since $7 + 3 = 10$ and $5 + 3 = 8$, then $2x = 3$, and $x = 1.5$

Communicating about **MATHEMATICS**

Note that distributing the terms of the first binomial over the second gives the same results as FOIL:
$(2x + 7)(2x + 5) = 2x(2x + 5) + 7(2x + 5)$
$= (2x)(2x) + (2x)(5) + (7)(2x) + (7)(5)$
       First   Outer   Inner   Last

Addressing Misconceptions

Some students who simply memorize the FOIL algorithm without understanding that FOIL is the result of distributing the terms of the first binomial over the second have trouble relating multiplication of binomials to multiplication of polynomials. The FOIL technique does not apply to multiplying polynomials with more than two terms, so some students incorrectly believe they need to learn a new method. You may wish to illustrate that the same basic technique used in FOIL (distributing the terms of the first polynomial over the second) can be used also with larger polynomials.
$(3x^2 + 2x + 7)(2x + 5) = (3x^2)(2x + 5) + (2x)$
$(2x + 5) + (7)(2x + 5)$

Writing Prompt
Describe the images that come to mind when you think of polynomials.

OPTION: Extra Examples

Here are additional examples similar to those of the lesson.
Multiplying Two Binomials
a. Find the product of $(3x + 4)$ and $(6x + 1)$.
b. Find the product of $(4x + 5)$ and $(2x + 3)$.
Solution
In the following solutions, notice that the Distributive Property is used in the first step and in the second step.

a. $(3x + 4)(6x + 1) = (3x + 4)(6x) + (3x + 4)(1)$
$= (3x)(6x) + (4)(6x) + (3x)(1) + (4)(1)$
$= 18x^2 + 24x + 3x + 4$
$= 18x^2 + 27x + 4$

b. $(4x + 5)(2x + 3) = (4x + 5)(2x) + (4x + 5)(3)$
$= (4x)(2x) + (5)(2x) + (4x)(3) + (5)(3)$
$= 8x^2 + 10x + 12x + 15$
$= 8x^2 + 22x + 15$

ASSIGNMENT GUIDE

*Basic/Average:
  Day 1: Ex. 7–17 odd, 18–24
  Day 2: Ex. 25–28, 29–39 odd

*Above Average:
  Ex. 7–17 odd, 25, 28, 30–40 even

Advanced: Ex. 7–21 odd, 25, 28, 30–40 even

Selected Answers: Ex. 1–6, 7–33 odd

*You may wish to omit this lesson for these students.

Guided Practice

▶ **Ex. 1, 2** Ask students to compare this use of the Distributive Property to their previous use of it.
▶ **Ex. 3–6** Assign these as an in-class readiness check for the Independent Practice exercises.

Independent Practice

▶ **Ex. 9–17** Encourage students to use different methods to check the answer. They can use tiles, "double distributive," or FOIL as outlined in the Communicating about Mathematics on page 671.

EXERCISES

Guided Practice

▶ **CHECK for Understanding**

In Exercises 1 and 2, use the Distributive Property to find the product.
Explain each step. For explanations, see margin.

1. $(x + 3)(3x + 2)$ $3x^2 + 11x + 6$

2. $(2x + 1)(4x + 5)$ $8x^2 + 14x + 5$

In Exercises 3–6, match the expression with its equivalent expression.

a. $12x^2 + 15x + 3$
b. $12x^2 + 52x + 16$
c. $12x^2 + 32x + 16$
d. $12x^2 + 17x + 6$

3. $(4x + 3)(3x + 2)$ d
4. $(2x + 8)(6x + 2)$ b
5. $(12x + 3)(x + 1)$ a
6. $(6x + 4)(2x + 4)$ c

Independent Practice

P *Error Analysis*   **In Exercises 7 and 8, find and correct the error.**

❂ **7.** $(x + 6)(2x + 5)$
$= (x + 6)(2x) + 5$ $(x + 6)(5)$
$= (x)(2x) + 6(2x) + 5$ $(x)(5) + 6(5)$
$= 2x^2 + 12x + 5$ $5x + 30$
$= 2x^2 + 17x + 30$

❂ **8.** $(3x + 4)(4x + 3)$ $(3x + 4)(3)$
$= (3x + 4)(4x) + (4x + 3)(4)$
$= 3x(4x) + 4(4x) + (4x)(4) + 3(4)$
$9x = 12x^2 + 16x + 16x + 12$ $(3x)(3) + 4$
$= 12x^2 + 32x + 12$
$25x$

In Exercises 9–17, find the product using the Distributive Property.

   $8x^2 + 36x + 36$
9. $(x + 3)(8x + 12)$

   $5x^2 + 16x + 12$
10. $(5x + 6)(x + 2)$

   $18x^2 + 23x + 7$
11. $(2x + 1)(9x + 7)$

   $20x^2 + 41x + 20$
12. $(4x + 5)(5x + 4)$

13. $(10x + 10)(2x + 2)$

14. $(3x + 8)(3x + 2)$

15. $(2x + 3)(4x + 1)$
   $8x^2 + 14x + 3$

16. $(2x + 4)(7x + 9)$
   $14x^2 + 46x + 36$

17. $(6x + 5)(3x + 5)$

13. $20x^2 + 40x + 20$

In Exercises 18–20, multiply using a vertical format. Then check the result by using a horizontal format.

14. $9x^2 + 30x + 16$

17. $18x^2 + 45x + 25$

18. $(3x + 2)(6x + 8)$
   $18x^2 + 36x + 16$

19. $(9x + 6)(3x + 1)$
   $27x^2 + 27x + 6$

20. $(x + 10)(4x + 15)$
   $4x^2 + 55x + 150$

Geometry   **In Exercises 21–24, find the area of the figure. Then evaluate the area when $x = 2$.**

21.

$4x + 1$

$x + 12$

$4x^2 + 49x + 12$, 126 units²

22.

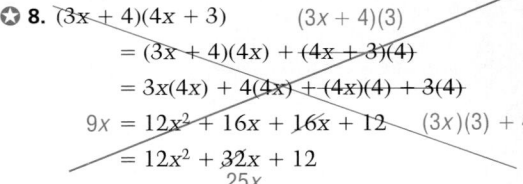

$\dfrac{5x^2 + 29x + 42}{2}$, 60 units²

$x + 3$

$5x + 14$

❂ More difficult exercises
P Portfolio Opportunity

Extra Practice

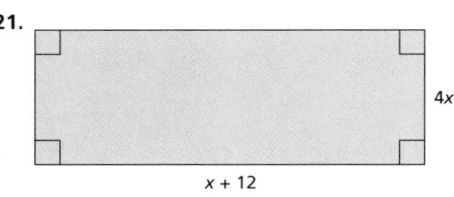

Extra Practice **14.8** Name ___

1. Find and correct the error. $(3x + 5)(2x + 4) = (3x + 5)(2x) + (3x + 5)(4)$
$(3x + 5)(2x + 4) = (3x + 5)(2x) + (5)(2x + 4)$ $= 6x^2 + 10x + 12x + 20$
$= 6x^2 + 10x + 10x + 20$ $= 6x^2 + 22x + 20$
$= 6x^2 + 20x + 20$

In Exercises 2–7, find the product using the Distributive Property.
2. $(x + 2)(5x + 1)$ **3.** $(3x + 4)(x + 5)$ **4.** $(2x + 7)(x + 4)$
   $5x^2 + 11x + 2$ $3x^2 + 19x + 20$ $2x^2 + 15x + 28$
5. $(4x + 2)(3x + 6)$ **6.** $(2x + 9)(x + 4)$ **7.** $(3x + 2)(5x + 3)$
   $12x^2 + 30x + 12$ $2x^2 + 17x + 36$ $15x^2 + 19x + 6$

In Exercises 8–10, multiply using a vertical format. Then check the results by using the Distributive Property.
8. $(3x + 9)(4x + 8)$ **9.** $(5x + 9)(4x + 11)$ **10.** $(6x + 10)(7x + 12)$
   $12x^2 + 60x + 72$ $20x^2 + 91x + 99$ $42x^2 + 142x + 120$

In Exercises 11–13, find the area of the figure.
11.

$x^2 + \dfrac{15}{2}x + 9$

12.

$5x^2 + \dfrac{35}{2}x + 15$

13.

$6x^2 + 11x + 4$

In Exercises 14 and 15 find the area of the shaded region.
14.

$x^2 + 14x + 30$

15.

$8x + 18$

In Exercises 16 and 17, find the area of the mosaic made up of tiles by, first, writing its dimensions and, then, multiplying. $(4x + 5)$ by $(3x + 4)$; $A = 12x^2 + 31x + 20$
16.   **17.**

$(4x + 2)$ by $(3x + 2)$; $A = 12x^2 + 14x + 4$

Reteaching

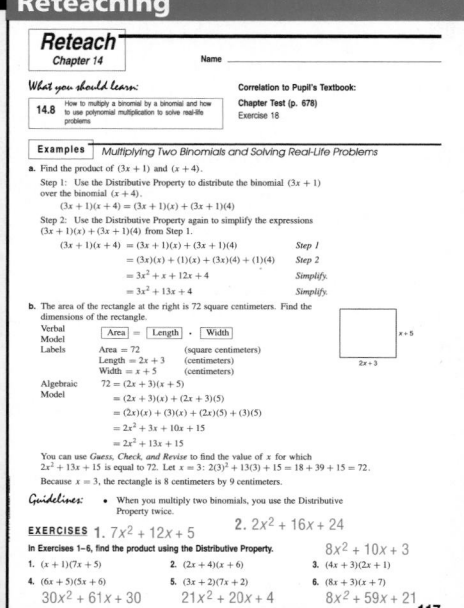

Reteach **Chapter 14** Name ___

What you should learn: **Correlation to Pupil's Textbook:**
14.8 How to multiply a binomial by a binomial and how   **Chapter Test (p. 678)**
     to use polynomial multiplication to solve real-life   **Exercise 18**
     problems

Examples *Multiplying Two Binomials and Solving Real-Life Problems*

a. Find the product of $(3x + 1)$ and $(x + 4)$.

Step 1: Use the Distributive Property to distribute the binomial $(3x + 1)$ over the binomial $(x + 4)$.

$(3x + 1)(x + 4) = (3x + 1)(x) + (3x + 1)(4)$

Step 2: Use the Distributive Property again to simplify the expressions $(3x + 1)(x) + (3x + 1)(4)$ from Step 1.

$(3x + 1)(x + 4) = (3x + 1)(x) + (3x + 1)(4)$ *Step 1*
$= (3x)(x) + (1)(x) + (3x)(4) + (1)(4)$ *Step 2*
$= 3x^2 + x + 12x + 4$ *Simplify.*
$= 3x^2 + 13x + 4$ *Simplify.*

b. The area of the rectangle at the right is 72 square centimeters. Find the dimensions of the rectangle.

Verbal
Model   Labels | Area | = | Length | ⋅ | Width |
Labels   Area = 72   (square centimeters)
     Length = $2x + 3$ (centimeters)
     Width = $x + 5$ (centimeters)
Algebraic
Model $72 = (2x + 3)(x + 5)$
     $= (2x + 3)(x) + (2x + 3)(5)$
     $= (2x)(x) + (3)(x) + (2x)(5) + (3)(5)$
     $= 2x^2 + 3x + 10x + 15$
     $= 2x^2 + 13x + 15$

You can use *Guess, Check, and Revise* to find the value of x for which
$2x^2 + 13x + 15$ is equal to 72. Let $x = 3$: $2(3)^2 + 13(3) + 15 = 18 + 39 + 15 = 72$.
Because $x = 3$, the rectangle is 8 centimeters by 9 centimeters.

Guidelines: • When you multiply two binomials, you use the Distributive Property twice.

EXERCISES **1.** $7x^2 + 12x + 5$ **2.** $2x^2 + 16x + 24$
In Exercises 1–6, find the product using the Distributive Property.
1. $(x + 1)(7x + 5)$ **2.** $(2x + 4)(x + 6)$ **3.** $(4x + 3)(2x + 1)$
                                                 $8x^2 + 10x + 3$
4. $(6x + 5)(5x + 6)$ **5.** $(3x + 2)(7x + 2)$ **6.** $(8x + 3)(x + 7)$
   $30x^2 + 61x + 30$ $21x^2 + 20x + 4$ $8x^2 + 59x + 21$

Answers
1. $(x + 3)(3x + 2)$
$= (x + 3)(3x) + (x + 3)(2)$
$= (x)(3x) + (3)(3x) + (x)(2) + (3)(2)$
$= 3x^2 + 9x + 2x + 6$
$= 3x^2 + 11x + 6$
2. $(2x + 1)(4x + 5)$
$= (2x + 1)(4x) + (2x + 1)(5)$
$= (2x)(4x) + (1)(4x) + (2x)(5) + (1)(5)$
$= 8x^2 + 4x + 10x + 5$
$= 8x^2 + 14x + 5$

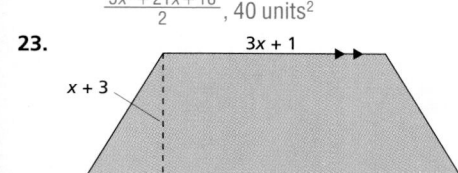

$\dfrac{5x^2+21x+18}{2}$, 40 units²

23.

3x + 1

x + 3

2x + 5

$10x^2 + 11x + 3$, 65 units²

24.

2x + 1

5x + 3

25. Multiply $(x + 15)$ by $(2x + 1)$. Then multiply $(2x + 1)$ by $(x + 15)$. What can you conclude? What property does this illustrate?   See margin.

Ⓟ *Algebra Tiles*   **In Exercises 26 and 27, use algebra tiles (or a sketch) to model the product. Then use the Distributive Property to confirm your result.**   See margin.

✪ **26.** $(1 + 2x)(2 + 3x)$ ✪ **27.** $(4 + x)(3 + 2x)$

Ⓟ **28.** *Designing a Mosaic*   You are designing a mosaic that is to have an area of 180 square feet. The mosaic is a rectangle and is made up of rectangular enameled tiles that are each x feet by 1 foot. The mosaic is $(4x + 2)$ feet wide and $(7x + 4)$ feet high. Find the dimensions of the mosaic.
10 ft by 18 ft

Mexican Art   **About 7.5 million stones make up the Juan O'Gorman mosaic found at Mexico's National Autonomous University. It depicts scenes from the history of Mexico.**

Integrated Review

29. $2x^2 + 16x + 30$, c   **30.** $2x^2 + 8x + 6$, a   **31.** $3x^2 + 18x + 15$, b

In Exercises 29–31, multiply the binomials. Then match the result with the product that yields the same result.

a. $(2x + 2)(x + 3)$ **b.** $(x + 5)(3x + 3)$ **c.** $(2x + 10)(x + 3)$
29. $(2x + 6)(x + 5)$ **30.** $(2x + 6)(x + 1)$ **31.** $(3x + 15)(x + 1)$

32. *Estimation*   Which of the following best estimates the weight (in pounds) of a 12-fluid-ounce can of soda pop?   a
a. 1   **b.** 6   **c.** 12   **d.** 20

33. *Estimation*   Which of the following best estimates the height (in centimeters) of a 12-fluid-ounce can of soda pop?   c
a. 1   **b.** 6   **c.** 12   **d.** 20

Exploration and Extension

Making Connections within Mathematics

✪ *Binomial Pattern*   **In Exercises 34–39, multiply.**

34. $(x + 1)(x + 1)$ $x^2 + 2x + 1$ **35.** $(x + 2)(x + 2)$ $x^2 + 4x + 4$ **36.** $(x + 3)(x + 3)$ $x^2 + 6x + 9$

37. $(x + 4)(x + 4)$ $x^2 + 8x + 16$ **38.** $(x + 5)(x + 5)$ $x^2 + 10x + 25$ **39.** $(x + 6)(x + 6)$ $x^2 + 12x + 36$

✪ **40.** *Binomial Pattern*   Each of the products in Exercises 34–39 is an example of a "binomial pattern." Describe the pattern. Then use your description to find the product of $(x + 7)$ and $(x + 7)$. Use the Distributive Property to check your result. $(x + a)(x + a) = x^2 + 2ax + a^2$, $x^2 + 14x + 49$

▶ **Ex. 26, 27**   Assign these in class using algebra tiles.
▶ **Ex. 28**   This is similar to the model provided by Example 3 on page 671.

Integrated Review

Ex. 29–31   These exercises may help students realize that trinomials may have more than one pair of factors.

Exploration and Extension

EXTENSION
Ask students to examine the pattern in the products for:
$(x+1)(x-1)$ $(x+3)(x-3)$ $(x+5)(x-5)$
$(x+2)(x-2)$ $(x+4)(x-4)$ $(x+6)(x-6)$
The first term is x^2, there is no linear (middle) term, and the constant term is a square.

Portfolio Opportunity: Math Log
What is wrong with the following calculation? Correct it.
$(x+3)^2 = x^2 + 9$

Also available as a copymaster, page 44, Ex. 8

Short Quiz
Covers Lessons 14.7 and 14.8

Available as a copymaster, page 233

Alternative Assessment
A cooperative learning project in which students develop polynomial multiplication skills.

Available as a copymaster, page 42

Answers
25. The products are equal, the commutative property of multiplication
26.

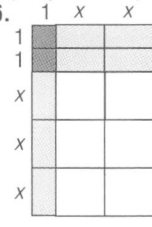

$2 + 7x + 6x^2$

27.

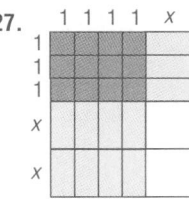

$12 + 11x + 2x^2$

SUMMARY and REVIEW

COOPERATIVE LEARNING

Encourage students to study together. Emphasize the importance of teaching a classmate how to perform a skill or how to recall a procedure. When students work together, everyone wins. The students receiving help get additional instruction, and the students giving help gain a deeper understanding of the skills and concepts involved.

Chapter SUMMARY

Recommend that students read the section on this page of the pupil text entitled "How does it fit into the bigger picture of mathematics?"

Lessons 14.1–14.3 dealt with the techniques for ordering data such as a stem-and-leaf plot or a box-and-whisker plot, so that the data can be more readily interpreted and analyzed for measures of central tendency, frequency distributions, and so on. Lesson 14.4 presented matrices as a further technique for arranging data so that arithmetic operations can be applied to the data according to well-defined rules.

Lessons 14.5 and 14.6 developed the concept of polynomials. Students learned the technique of adding and subtracting polynomials. Lessons 14.7 and 14.8 showed students how to apply the Distributive Property to the multiplication of a polynomial by a monomial and, finally, to the multiplication of two binomials.

14

Chapter Summary

What did you learn?

Skills

1. Find the mean, median, and mode of a collection of numbers. **(14.1)**
2. Draw a stem-and-leaf plot for a collection of numbers. **(14.2)**
3. Find the quartiles of a collection of numbers. **(14.3)**
   - Draw a box-and-whisker plot for a collection of numbers. **(14.3)**
4. Use matrices to organize data. **(14.4)**
   - Add and subtract matrices. **(14.4)**
5. Identify different types of polynomials. **(14.5)**
   - Simplify polynomials by combining like terms. **(14.5)**
6. Add and subtract polynomials. **(14.6)**
7. Multiply polynomials. **(14.7, 14.8)**
   - Multiply a polynomial by a monomial. **(14.7)**
   - Multiply two binomials. **(14.8)**

Problem-Solving Strategies

8. Use data plots, matrices, and polynomials to model and solve real-life problems. **(14.1–14.8)**

Exploring Data

9. Use tables and graphs to solve problems. **(14.1–14.8)**

Why did you learn it?

In many areas of real life, you will encounter data. Data is much easier to interpret when it is organized. In this chapter, you learned how stem-and-leaf plots and box-and-whisker plots can be used to compare characteristics of different populations, and how matrices can be used to analyze the success of a business. You also studied about polynomials, and you learned that they can be used to model areas of regions.

How does it fit into the bigger picture of mathematics?

If someone were to ask you, "What did you study in math this year?" what would you say? We hope you would say that you were introduced to the two main parts of mathematics: algebra and geometry. We also hope you would say you learned that mathematics is not just a collection of formulas that need to be memorized. Instead, you learned that mathematics is a language that can be used to model and solve real-life problems.

Of course, there is much more to algebra and geometry than is possible to put in this book. You can think of the fourteen chapters in this book as "windows" that give you glimpses of the algebra and geometry that you might be studying in the next two or three years.

In Exercises 1–7, use the table, which lists the National League teams' home run totals through the first part of the 1994 season. *(Source: USA Today)* **(14.1–14.3)**

Team	Home Run Total	Team	Home Run Total
Cincinnati	38	Houston	44
Los Angeles	42	Philadelphia	32
Atlanta	48	Chicago	36
Colorado	52	St. Louis	36
Montreal	21	New York	49
Pittsburgh	16	San Francisco	35
Florida	34	San Diego	34

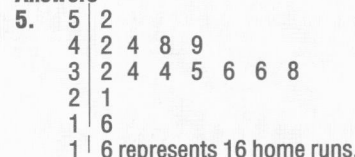

With 755 home runs, Henry (Hank) Aaron holds the major league lifetime record. Babe Ruth holds second place with 714.

1. Find the mean home run total. $36\frac{13}{14}$
2. Find the median home run total.   36
3. Find the mode of the home run totals.   None
4. Which measure of central tendency do you think best represents the data? Explain.   Answers vary.
5. Make a stem-and-leaf plot to organize the data.   See margin.
6. Use the results of the stem-and-leaf plot to draw a histogram for the table.   See margin.
7. Draw a box-and-whisker plot for the data in the table.   See margin.

In Exercises 8–10, find the first, second, and third quartiles for the numbers. (14.3)

8. 5, 8, 9, 12, 16, 18, 21, 22, 25, 27   9, 17, 22
9. 79, 71, 65, 69, 73, 61, 68, 77, 81, 62, 84, 67   66, 70, 78
10. 35, 67, 95, 21, 16, 100, 47, 82, 50, 0, 89, 71, 31, 54   31, 52, 82

In Exercises 11–13, use the matrix at the right. (14.4)

$$\begin{bmatrix} 5 & -6 & 8 & 3 & 1 \\ -2 & -7 & 9 & 4 & 2 \\ 10 & 7 & -4 & -8 & 11 \\ 9 & 0 & 6 & -1 & -3 \end{bmatrix}$$

11. How many rows and columns does the matrix have?   4, 5
12. Identify the entry in the third row and second column.   7
13. Identify the entry in the second row and fourth column.   4

In Exercises 14 and 15, find the sum and difference of the matrices. (14.4)

14. $\begin{bmatrix} 0 & -4 \\ 3 & 6 \end{bmatrix}, \begin{bmatrix} 8 & 7 \\ 4 & -6 \end{bmatrix}$ $\begin{bmatrix} 8 & 3 \\ 7 & 0 \end{bmatrix}, \begin{bmatrix} -8 & -11 \\ -1 & 12 \end{bmatrix}$

15. $\begin{bmatrix} -1 & 5 & 9 \\ 2 & -8 & 1 \\ -5 & 4 & -3 \end{bmatrix}, \begin{bmatrix} 3 & -1 & 2 \\ 6 & -5 & 8 \\ 4 & -7 & 0 \end{bmatrix}$ $\begin{bmatrix} 2 & 4 & 11 \\ 8 & -13 & 9 \\ -1 & -3 & -3 \end{bmatrix}, \begin{bmatrix} -4 & 6 & 7 \\ -4 & -3 & -7 \\ -9 & 11 & -3 \end{bmatrix}$

⊙ 16. Give an example of two matrices that cannot be added together.
Answers vary. $\begin{bmatrix} 1 & 1 \\ 1 & 1 \end{bmatrix}$ and $\begin{bmatrix} 1 & 1 & 1 \\ 1 & 1 & 1 \end{bmatrix}$

✪ More difficult exercises

Have students begin this Review in class and complete it as a homework assignment.

ASSIGNMENT GUIDE
*Basic/Average
   Ex. 1–7, 9–27 odd, 29–33, 35-39
*Above Average:
   Ex. 1–7, 9–33 odd, 35–39, 41-59
Advanced:
   Ex. 1–7, 9–33 odd, 35–39, 41-59

*For these students, you will need to limit assignments to cover only those lessons you chose to teach from this chapter.

Resources
Teaching Tools
   Crossword for Ex. 59, p. C33
Answer Masters, pp. 288, 289

Answers
5.
```
5 | 2
4 | 2 4 8 9
3 | 2 4 4 5 6 6 8
2 | 1
1 | 6
1 | 6 represents 16 home runs.
```

6.
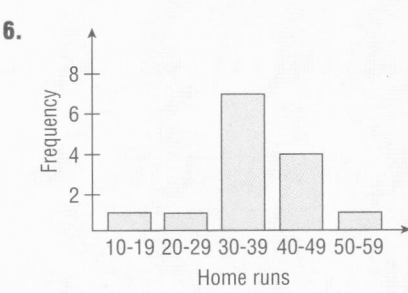

7.

17. $-7x$, monomial   **18.** $6z^2 - 10z - 3$, trinomial

In Exercises 17–22, simplify the polynomial. Then state whether the result is a monomial, a binomial, or a trinomial. (14.5)

$-4n^2 + 5n + 8$, trinomial

17. $-10x - 7 + 3x + 7$ **18.** $6z^2 - 4 - 10z + 1$ **19.** $8 + 3n^2 + 5n - 7n^2$

20. $-12 - 9y + 6 + 2y$ **21.** $4t^2 - 6t + t^2 + 9t$ **22.** $8a - a^3 - 8a + 2a^3$
    $-7y - 6$, binomial $5t^2 + 3t$, binomial a^3, monomial

In Exercises 23 and 24, add the polynomials. (14.6)

23. $(6x^2 - 3x - 7) + (x^2 + 3x - 9)$ **24.** $(-4n^2 + 6n + 2) + (8n^3 - 14)$
    $7x^2 - 16$ $8n^3 - 4n^2 + 6n - 12$

In Exercises 25 and 26, subtract the polynomials. (14.6)

25. $(5n^2 + 2n - 11) - (2n^2 - 6n - 8)$ **26.** $(2x^3 - 4x^2 + x - 1) - (-7x^2 - x)$
    $3n^2 + 8n - 3$ $2x^3 + 3x^2 + 2x - 1$

In Exercises 27 and 28, find the perimeter of the polygon. (14.6)

27.

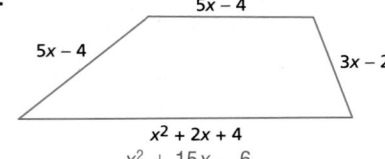

$x^2 + 15x - 6$

28.

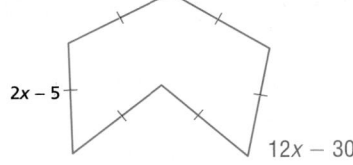

$12x^2 + 16z + 5$

In Exercises 29–34, multiply the polynomials. (14.7, 14.8)

$12z^2 + 16z + 5$

29. $x(x^2 + x)$ $x^3 + x^2$ **30.** $(y + 8)(y + 6)$ $y^2 + 14y + 48$ **31.** $(2z + 1)(6z + 5)$

32. $n^2(n^3 + 4)$ $n^5 + 4n^2$ **33.** $3t(2t^2 + 4t + 5)$ **34.** $(4x + 3)(4x + 3)$
                                              $6t^3 + 12t^2 + 15t$ $16x^2 + 24x + 9$

Swimming Pool   **In Exercises 35–38, use the diagram of the swimming pool at the right. (14.6, 14.7)**

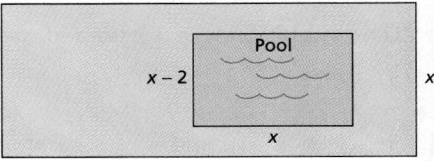

35. Write an expression for the area of the pool. $x^2 - 2x$

36. Write an expression for the area of the entire yard, including the pool. $4x^2 - 7x$

37. Use polynomial subtraction to find an expression for the area of the lawn. $3x^2 - 5x$

38. The pool is 10 meters by 8 meters. What is the area of the lawn?   250m²

In Exercises 39 and 40, write an expression for the area of the entire region. (14.6, 14.8)

✪ **39.**

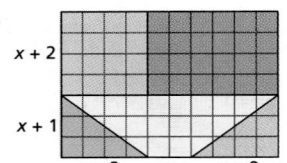

$6x^2 + 17x + 12$

✪ **40.**

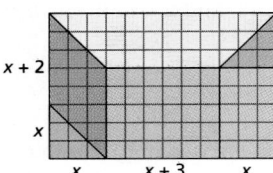

$6x^2 + 12x + 6$

In Exercises 41–58, use the stem-and-leaf plot, the box-and-whisker plot, and the matrix to determine the number for each animal.

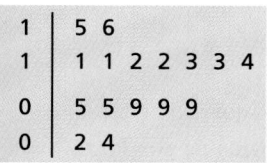

1	5 6
1	1 1 2 2 3 3 4
0	5 5 9 9 9
0	2 4

1 | 5 represents 15

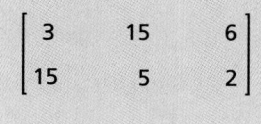

$$\begin{bmatrix} 3 & 15 & 6 \\ 15 & 5 & 2 \end{bmatrix}$$

41. Mean *Rhinoceros* 10
42. 3rd quartile *Horse* 13
43. 1st quartile *Bat* 7
44. Mode *Fish* 9
45. Maximum *Bear* 16
46. Median *Platypus* 11

47. 3rd quartile *Elephant* 12
48. Minimum *Cat* 1
49. Median *Giraffe* 8
50. Maximum *Tiger* 14
51. 1st quartile *Ostrich* 4
52. 2nd quartile *Goat* 8

53. 1st row, 3rd col. *Porcupine* 6
54. 2nd row, 3rd col. *Rabbit* 2
55. 2nd row, 2nd col. *Albatross* 5
56. 1st row, 2nd col. *Dog* 15
57. 2nd row, 1st col. *Deer* 15
58. 1st row, 1st col. *Cow* 3

⊙ **59.** *Animal Facts* Fill in the crossword puzzle (Hint: The answers correspond to the numbers found in Exercises 41–58.)

ACROSS See margin.

5. Seabird with 11-foot wingspan
7. Flying mammal
8. Angora breed raised for its wool
11. Mammal with bill and webbed feet
12. Has ears that are 4 ft across
15. Has bones called antlers
16. Weighs $\frac{1}{2}$ lb to 1 lb at birth

DOWN

1. Has keen sense of balance
2. It hops
3. Has stomach with 14 compartments
4. Runs up to 44 mph
6. Has sharp quills
8. Has 18-inch tongue
9. Has no eyelids
10. Has 3 toes on each foot
13. Requires 10–12 gal water per day
14. Adult has a 3-foot long tail
15. First tamed animal

Chapter Review **677**

Answer 59.

		¹C		²R		³C		⁴O
	⁵A	L	B	A	T	R	O	S	S
		T		B		W		T
⁶P				⁷B	A	T		R
O				I				I
R		⁸G	O	A	T			C
C		I			⁹F			H
U		R			I		¹⁰R	
¹¹P	L	A	T	Y	P	U	S	H
I		F			S	H		I
N		F			H		N	
¹²E	L	E	P	¹³H	A	N	¹⁴T	O
				O		I		C
¹⁵D	E	E	R			G		E
O			S		¹⁶B	E	A	R
G			E		R		O	
							S	

In Exercises 1–4, the numbers (in millions) of people camping for the years 1983–1990 are given below. *(Source: U.S. Bureau of Land Management)* (14.1, 14.3)

1983: 84.1	1984: 73.0	1985: 65.3	1986: 95.2
1987: 195.3	1988: 178.7	1989: 173.6	1990: 165.4

1. What is the first quartile?   78.55 million

2. What is the second quartile?   130.3 million

3. What is the third quartile?   176.15 million

4. Create a box-and-whisker plot for the data.
          See margin.

In Exercises 5–7, use {77, 79, 84, 93, 93, 96, 99, 99, 99, 102, 102} (14.1)

5. What is the mean of the data?   93

6. What is the median of the data?   96

7. What is the mode of the data?   99

In Exercises 8 and 9, find the sum or difference. (14.4)

$$\begin{bmatrix} 2 & 10 & 8 \\ -2 & 12 & 9 \\ 16 & 42 & -11 \end{bmatrix}$$

8. $\begin{bmatrix} 18 & 12 \\ 4 & 22 \end{bmatrix} + \begin{bmatrix} 6 & 2 \\ 14 & 9 \end{bmatrix}$ $\begin{bmatrix} 24 & 14 \\ 18 & 31 \end{bmatrix}$

9. $\begin{bmatrix} 3 & 18 & 12 \\ 16 & 12 & 15 \\ 12 & 21 & 11 \end{bmatrix} - \begin{bmatrix} 1 & 8 & 4 \\ 18 & 0 & 6 \\ -4 & -21 & 22 \end{bmatrix}$

In Exercises 10 and 11, simplify and write in standard form. (14.5)

10. $2p^2 - p^3 + p + 2p^3$ $p^3 + 2p^2 + p$

11. $3n^3 + 4 - n^2 - n^3 - n$ $2n^3 - n^2 - n + 4$

In Exercises 12 and 13, add or subtract the polynomials and simplify. (14.6) $3p^3 + p^2 + 1$

12. $(3x^2 + 2x + 5) + (7x^2 - 4x + 2)$
          $10x^2 - 2x + 7$

13. $(4p^3 + 6p - 4) - (p^3 - p^2 + 6p - 5)$

In Exercises 14–16, use the stem-and-leaf plot. (14.1–14.3)

14. What is the mean for each group? $88\frac{13}{16}, 88\frac{13}{16}$

15. Construct a box-and-whisker plot for the Group 1 data.

16. Construct a box-and-whisker plot for the Group 2 data.
          15., 16. See margin.

	Group 1						Group 2			
		0	7	8	5	10	1	4	2	4
			3	8	2	9	7	9	2	1	4
6	9	4	1	7		8	7	3	8
			4	2	8	7	7	4
					7	6	6	2

5|10|1 represents 105 and 101

In Exercises 17 and 18, multiply the polynomials. (14.7, 14.8)

17. $2y(3y^2 + 2y + 1)$ $6y^3 + 4y^2 + 2y$

18. $(3p + 1)(2p + 3)$ $6p^2 + 11p + 3$

In Exercises 19 and 20, the data in Matrix 1 gives the numbers of dollars deposited into savings accounts at 2 different banks. Matrix 2 shows how much money is in the accounts after 1 year. (14.4)

19. Write a matrix that shows how much interest was earned in each account.   See margin.

20. Write a matrix that shows the percent of interest that each account earned.   See margin.

Deposits		Balances After One Year	
Bank 1	Bank 2	Bank 1	Bank 2
100	150	108	164
450	300	480	325
600	1000	648	1100

Answers

4.

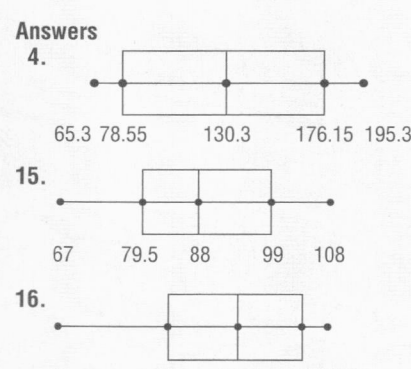

65.3 78.55   130.3   176.15 195.3

15.

67   79.5   88   99   108

16.

62   80   91.5   100 104

19.   Interest

	Bank 1	Bank 2
	8	14
	30	25
	48	100

20.   Percent of Interest

	Bank 1	Bank 2
	8	≈ 9.3
	≈ 6.7	≈ 8.3
	8	10

Formal Assessment ▶

Three **Chapter Tests.** Form A is of average difficulty, Form B is of average difficulty in multiple choice format, and Form C is more challenging.

Available as copymasters, pages 234–242

678   Chapter 14

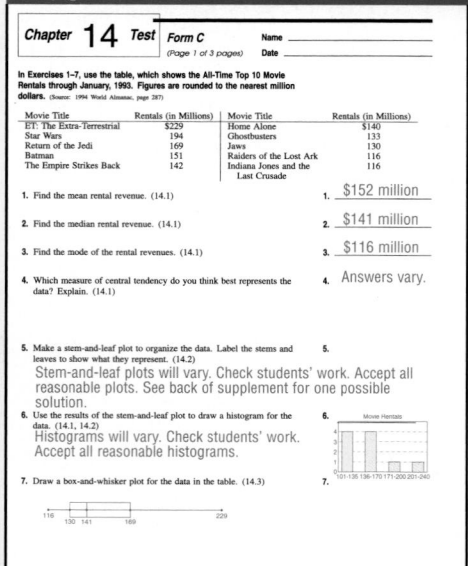

Student Handbook

Table of Contents

THE METRIC SYSTEM

■ Length

10 millimeters (mm) = 1 centimeter (cm)

10 centimeters = 1 decimeter (dm)

100 centimeters = 1 meter (m)

1000 meters = 1 kilometer (km)

100,000 centimeters = 1 kilometer

■ Capacity

1000 milliliters (mL) = 1 liter (L)

10 deciliters (dL) = 1 liter

■ Mass

1000 milligrams (mg) = 1 gram (g)

1000 grams = 1 kilogram (kg)

■ Area

$100 \text{ mm}^2 = 1 \text{ cm}^2$

$100 \text{ cm}^2 = 1 \text{ dm}^2$

$100 \text{ dm}^2 = 1 \text{ m}^2$

$1,000,000 \text{ m}^2 = 1 \text{ km}^2$

■ Volume

$1000 \text{ cm}^3 = 1 \text{ dm}^3$

$1000 \text{ dm}^3 = 1 \text{ m}^3$

$1 \text{ cm}^3 = 1 \text{ mL}$

$1 \text{ dm}^3 = 1 \text{ L}$

■ Converting Units

In the metric system, the units are related by powers of 10.

Table of Units				
Prefix	**Power of 10**	**Length**	**Capacity**	**Mass**
kilo (k)	1000 units	kilometer	kiloliter*	kilogram
hecto (h)	100 units	hectometer*	hectoliter*	hectogram*
deka (dk)	10 units	dekameter*	dekaliter*	dekagram*
——	1 unit	meter	liter	gram
deci (d)	0.1 unit	decimeter*	deciliter*	decigram*
centi (c)	0.01 unit	centimeter	centiliter*	centigram*
milli (m)	0.001 unit	millimeter	milliliter	milligram

*These units are seldom used.

Study Tip...

When you change from a larger unit to a smaller unit, you multiply.

$$0.24 \text{ m} = \boxed{?} \text{ cm}$$

In the Table of Units, there are 2 steps from meters to centimeters, so multiply by 10^2, or 100.

$$0.24 \times 100 = 24$$

$$0.24 \text{ m} = 24 \text{ cm}$$

Study Tip...

When you change from a smaller unit to a larger unit, you divide.

$$3500 \text{ mg} = \boxed{?} \text{ kg}$$

In the Table of Units, there are 6 steps from milligrams to kilograms, so divide by 10^6, or 1,000,000.

$$3500 \div 1,000,000 = 0.0035$$

$$3500 \text{ mg} = 0.0035 \text{ kg}$$

THE CUSTOMARY SYSTEM

■ Length

12 inches (in.) = 1 foot (ft)

3 feet = 1 yard (yd)

36 inches = 1 yard

5280 feet = 1 mile (mi)

1760 yards = 1 mile

■ Capacity

1 cup (c) = 8 fluid ounces (fl oz)

2 cups = 1 pint (pt)

2 pints = 1 quart (qt)

2 quarts = 1 half-gallon

4 quarts = 1 gallon

■ Weight

16 ounces (oz) = 1 pound (lb)

2000 pounds = 1 ton

■ Area

144 in.^{2} = 1 ft^2

9 ft^2 = 1 yd^2

640 acres = 1 square mile

■ Volume

1728 in.^{3} = 1 ft^3

27 ft^3 = 1 yd^3

■ Time

60 seconds (sec) = 1 minute (min)

3600 seconds = 1 hour (hr)

60 minutes = 1 hour

24 hours = 1 day

7 days = 1 week

360 days = 1 business year

365 days = 1 year

366 days = 1 leap year

10 years = 1 decade

10 decades = 1 century = 100 years

■ Unit Analysis

When you convert from one unit to another, you can use conversion fractions.

Study Tip...

To change 45 miles per hour to feet per second:

$$\frac{45 \text{ miles}}{\text{hour}} \times \frac{5280 \text{ feet}}{1 \text{ mile}} \times \frac{1 \text{ hour}}{3600 \text{ seconds}}$$

$$= \left(\frac{45 \times 5280}{3600}\right) \frac{\text{feet}}{\text{second}} = 66 \text{ ft/sec}$$

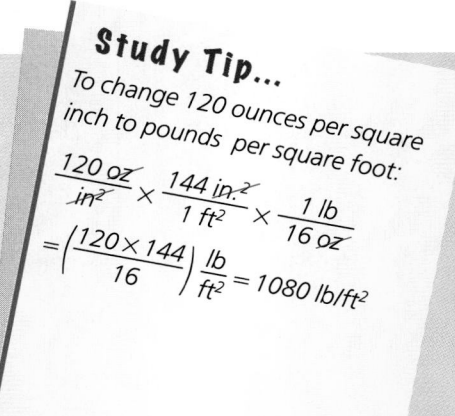

Study Tip...

To change 120 ounces per square inch to pounds per square foot:

$$\frac{120 \text{ oz}}{\text{in}^2} \times \frac{144 \text{ in.}^2}{1 \text{ ft}^2} \times \frac{1 \text{ lb}}{16 \text{ oz}}$$

$$= \left(\frac{120 \times 144}{16}\right) \frac{\text{lb}}{\text{ft}^2} = 1080 \text{ lb/ft}^2$$

Table of Squares and Approximate Square Roots

Find 54^2 and $\sqrt{54}$.

Find 54 in the column labeled **n**. Read across on that line to the columns labeled **n^2** and **$\sqrt{n}$**.

n	n^2	$\sqrt{n}$
51	2601	7.141
52	2704	7.211
53	2809	7.280
54	2916	7.348
55	3025	7.416
56	3136	7.483

$$54^2 = 2916 \qquad \sqrt{54} \approx 7.348$$

Table of Trigonometric Ratios

Find sin 48°, cos 48°, and tan 48°.

Find 48° in the **Angle** column. Read across on that line to the columns labeled **Sine, Cosine,** and **Tangent.**

Angle	Sine	Cosine	Tangent
46°	0.7193	0.6947	1.0355
47°	0.7314	0.6820	1.0724
48°	0.7431	0.6691	1.1106
49°	0.7547	0.6561	1.1504
50°	0.7660	0.6428	1.1918

$$\sin 48° \approx 0.7431 \qquad \cos 48° \approx 0.6691 \qquad \tan 48° \approx 1.1106$$

TABLE OF SQUARES AND APPROXIMATE SQUARE ROOTS

n	n^2	$\sqrt{n}$	n	n^2	$\sqrt{n}$
1	1	1.000	51	2601	7.141
2	4	1.414	52	2704	7.211
3	9	1.732	53	2809	7.280
4	16	2.000	54	2916	7.348
5	25	2.236	55	3025	7.416
6	36	2.449	56	3136	7.483
7	49	2.646	57	3249	7.550
8	64	2.828	58	3364	7.616
9	81	3.000	59	3481	7.681
10	100	3.162	60	3600	7.746
11	121	3.317	61	3721	7.810
12	144	3.464	62	3844	7.874
13	169	3.606	63	3969	7.937
14	196	3.742	64	4096	8.000
15	225	3.873	65	4225	8.062
16	256	4.000	66	4356	8.124
17	289	4.123	67	4489	8.185
18	324	4.243	68	4624	8.246
19	361	4.359	69	4761	8.307
20	400	4.472	70	4900	8.367
21	441	4.583	71	5041	8.426
22	484	4.690	72	5184	8.485
23	529	4.796	73	5329	8.544
24	576	4.899	74	5476	8.602
25	625	5.000	75	5625	8.660
26	676	5.099	76	5776	8.718
27	729	5.196	77	5929	8.775
28	784	5.292	78	6084	8.832
29	841	5.385	79	6241	8.888
30	900	5.477	80	6400	8.944
31	961	5.568	81	6561	9.000
32	1024	5.657	82	6724	9.055
33	1089	5.745	83	6889	9.110
34	1156	5.831	84	7056	9.165
35	1225	5.916	85	7225	9.220
36	1296	6.000	86	7396	9.274
37	1369	6.083	87	7569	9.327
38	1444	6.164	88	7744	9.381
39	1521	6.245	89	7921	9.434
40	1600	6.325	90	8100	9.487
41	1681	6.403	91	8281	9.539
42	1764	6.481	92	8464	9.592
43	1849	6.557	93	8649	9.644
44	1936	6.633	94	8836	9.695
45	2025	6.708	95	9025	9.747
46	2116	6.782	96	9216	9.798
47	2209	6.856	97	9409	9.849
48	2304	6.928	98	9604	9.899
49	2401	7.000	99	9801	9.950
50	2500	7.071	100	10000	10.000

TABLE OF TRIGONOMETRIC RATIOS

Angle	Sine	Cosine	Tangent	Angle	Sine	Cosine	Tangent
1°	0.0175	0.9998	0.0175	46°	0.7193	0.6947	1.0355
2°	0.0349	0.9994	0.0349	47°	0.7314	0.6820	1.0724
3°	0.0523	0.9986	0.0524	48°	0.7431	0.6691	1.1106
4°	0.0698	0.9976	0.0699	49°	0.7547	0.6561	1.1504
5°	0.0872	0.9962	0.0875	50°	0.7660	0.6428	1.1918
6°	0.1045	0.9945	0.1051	51°	0.7771	0.6293	1.2349
7°	0.1219	0.9925	0.1228	52°	0.7880	0.6157	1.2799
8°	0.1392	0.9903	0.1405	53°	0.7986	0.6018	1.3270
9°	0.1564	0.9877	0.1584	54°	0.8090	0.5878	1.3764
10°	0.1736	0.9848	0.1763	55°	0.8192	0.5736	1.4281
11°	0.1908	0.9816	0.1944	56°	0.8290	0.5592	1.4826
12°	0.2079	0.9781	0.2126	57°	0.8387	0.5446	1.5399
13°	0.2250	0.9744	0.2309	58°	0.8480	0.5299	1.6003
14°	0.2419	0.9703	0.2493	59°	0.8572	0.5150	1.6643
15°	0.2588	0.9659	0.2679	60°	0.8660	0.5000	1.7321
16°	0.2756	0.9613	0.2867	61°	0.8746	0.4848	1.8040
17°	0.2924	0.9563	0.3057	62°	0.8829	0.4695	1.8807
18°	0.3090	0.9511	0.3249	63°	0.8910	0.4540	1.9626
19°	0.3256	0.9455	0.3443	64°	0.8988	0.4384	2.0503
20°	0.3420	0.9397	0.3640	65°	0.9063	0.4226	2.1445
21°	0.3584	0.9336	0.3839	66°	0.9135	0.4067	2.2460
22°	0.3746	0.9272	0.4040	67°	0.9205	0.3907	2.3559
23°	0.3907	0.9205	0.4245	68°	0.9272	0.3746	2.4751
24°	0.4067	0.9135	0.4452	69°	0.9336	0.3584	2.6051
25°	0.4226	0.9063	0.4663	70°	0.9397	0.3420	2.7475
26°	0.4384	0.8988	0.4877	71°	0.9455	0.3256	2.9042
27°	0.4540	0.8910	0.5095	72°	0.9511	0.3090	3.0777
28°	0.4695	0.8829	0.5317	73°	0.9563	0.2924	3.2709
29°	0.4848	0.8746	0.5543	74°	0.9613	0.2756	3.4874
30°	0.5000	0.8660	0.5774	75°	0.9659	0.2588	3.7321
31°	0.5150	0.8572	0.6009	76°	0.9703	0.2419	4.0108
32°	0.5299	0.8480	0.6249	77°	0.9744	0.2250	4.3315
33°	0.5446	0.8387	0.6494	78°	0.9781	0.2079	4.7046
34°	0.5592	0.8290	0.6745	79°	0.9816	0.1908	5.1446
35°	0.5736	0.8192	0.7002	80°	0.9848	0.1736	5.6713
36°	0.5878	0.8090	0.7265	81°	0.9877	0.1564	6.3138
37°	0.6018	0.7986	0.7536	82°	0.9903	0.1392	7.1154
38°	0.6157	0.7880	0.7813	83°	0.9925	0.1219	8.1443
39°	0.6293	0.7771	0.8098	84°	0.9945	0.1045	9.5144
40°	0.6428	0.7660	0.8391	85°	0.9962	0.0872	11.4301
41°	0.6561	0.7547	0.8693	86°	0.9976	0.0698	14.3007
42°	0.6691	0.7431	0.9004	87°	0.9986	0.0523	19.0811
43°	0.6820	0.7314	0.9325	88°	0.9994	0.0349	28.6363
44°	0.6947	0.7193	0.9657	89°	0.9998	0.0175	57.2900
45°	0.7071	0.7071	1.0000				

■ Arithmetic and Algebra

$=$	Is equal to
$\neq$	Is not equal to
$>$	Is greater than
$<$	Is less than
$\geq$	Is greater than or equal to
$\leq$	Is less than or equal to
$\approx$	Is approximately equal to
ab or $a(b)$	a times b
a^n	A number a raised to the nth power
a^{-n}	$\frac{1}{a^n}$
a^0	1
$(\,),\{\,\},[\,]$	Grouping symbols
5 or $+5$	Positive 5
-5	Negative 5
$|a|$	Absolute value of a number a
$\sqrt{a}$	The principal (positive) square root of a number a
$a:b$ or $\frac{a}{b}$	Ratio of a to b
$P(A)$	Probability of the outcome A
$n!$	n-factorial

■ Geometry

(a, b)	Ordered pair a, b
$\sim$	Is similar to
$\cong$	Is congruent to
$\triangle ABC$	Triangle ABC
$\overleftrightarrow{AB}$	Line AB
AB	Segment AB
AB	Measure of segment AB
$\overrightarrow{AB}$	Ray AB
$\angle A$	Angle A
$m\angle A$	Measure of angle A
π	Pi

■ Right Triangle

$\sin A$	Sine of angle A
$\cos A$	Cosine of angle A
$\tan A$	Tangent of angle A

■ Miscellaneous:

$d = rt$ — Distance formula (25)

$F = \frac{9}{5}C + 32$ — Temperature conversion to degrees Fahrenheit (123)

$C = \frac{5}{9}(F - 32)$ — Temperature conversion to degrees Celsius (589)

$A = P(1 + r)^n$ — The balance in a savings account (331)

$d^2 = \frac{3}{2}h$ — Distance to the horizon (393)

$0 = -16t^2 + s$ — Falling objects (393)

$a^2 + b^2 = c^2$ — Pythagorean Theorem (400)

■ Perimeter:

$P = 4s$ — Perimeter of a square (12)

$P = 2(l + w)$ — Perimeter of a rectangle (16)

$C = \pi d$ or $C = 2\pi r$ — Circumference of a circle (539)

■ Area:

$A = s^2$ — Area of a square (12)

$A = lw$ — Area of a rectangle (25)

$A = bh$ — Area of a parallelogram (488)

$A = \frac{1}{2}bh$ — Area of a triangle (37)

$A = \frac{1}{2}h(b_1 + b_2)$ — Area of a trapezoid (45)

$A = \pi r^2$ — Area of a circle (540)

■ Surface Area:

$S = 6s^2$ — Surface area of a cube (14)

$S = 2B + Ph$ — Surface area of a prism (549)

$S = 2B + Ch$ — Surface area of a cylinder (549)

$S = 4\pi r^2$ — Surface area of a sphere (572)

■ Volume:

$V = lwh$ — Volume of a rectangular prism (554)

$V = s^3$ — Volume of a cube (14)

$V = Bh$ — Volume of a prism (554)

$V = \pi r^2 h$ — Volume of a cylinder (559)

$V = \frac{1}{3}Bh$ — Volume of a pyramid (564)

$V = \frac{1}{3}\pi r^2 h$ — Volume of a cone (564)

$V = \frac{4}{3}\pi r^3$ — Volume of a sphere (569)

■ Coordinate Geometry:

$m = \frac{y_2 - y_1}{x_2 - x_1}$ — The Slope of a Line (604)

$d = \sqrt{(x_2 - x_1)^2 + (y_2 - y_1)^2}$ — The Distance Formula (623)

$\text{Midpoint} = \left(\frac{x_1 + x_2}{2}, \frac{y_1 + y_2}{2}\right)$ — The Midpoint Formula (624)

SYMBOLS FORMULAS

Estimation

When should you estimate rather than find an exact answer?

- An estimate can solve a *yes* or *no* problem.

    Do I have enough money to buy these items?

    Did I really get a 25% savings on my total bill?

- An estimate can be used when you want to know about how long or about how much.

    How much of a tip should I leave?

    About how many miles can I drive on a full tank of gasoline?

- An estimate can be used to eliminate possibilities in multiple-choice situations.

Choose the best answer.	$<$, $>$, **or** $=$ **?**
$\frac{7}{8} + \frac{13}{14}$ **a.** 1 **b.** 2 **c.** $1\frac{1}{2}$	49% of 37 $\boxed{?}$ 15

- An estimate can be used to check the reasonableness of an answer, especially when using calculators.

    I used a calculator to find $0.17\overline{)1.3685}$ and I got 80.5 as an answer.

    Did I make any mistakes in entering the numbers?

Here are some examples that can help you decide when and how to estimate.

Estimating Sums and Differences

A quick and easy method of estimating some sums is clustering.

Example I	*Estimating by Clustering*

Estimate.
$79.1 + 75.6 + 82.3 + 85.0 + 88.2 + 69.7$

Solution If all the values you want to add or subtract are close to each other, try clustering. Since 79, 75, and 69 are all less than 80, and 82, 85, and 88 are all greater than 80, you can reasonably say all the numbers in the list are close to 80. So, the sum is close to $6 \cdot 80 = 480$. Since the actual sum is 479.9, the estimate is very reasonable. ∎

Warning! Clustering is a fast and easy method for estimating sums, but clustering is only valid when the numbers are *really* close to the number you pick! For most estimating situations, you will have to use combinations of the following methods.

Marla's Test Scores

79.1 75.6   82.3
85.0 88.2   69.7

Grades:

A 570+
B 510+
C 450

What score did Marla get?

Example 2   *Estimating by Rounding*

Estimate. $52,764 - 36,195 + 7,326$

Solution Rounding is often the best method to use for estimating sums and differences. For this problem, round each number to the nearest thousand:

$53,000 - 36,000 + 7,000$

Regroup the numbers to be able to use mental math to find the total:

$$53,000 - 36,000 + 7,000 = 53,000 + 7,000 - 36,000$$
$$= 60,000 - 36,000 = 24,000$$

The actual value is 23,895, so the estimate is reasonable. ■

Example 3   *Front-End Estimation with Adjustments*

Estimate. $\$20.00 - (\$3.46 + \$8.95 + \$1.33 + \$0.32)$

Solution For many addition-subtraction situations, front-end estimating with adjustment produces the most accurate estimates.

Start at the front-end. Estimate the sum using only the front-end (in this case, the dollars) digits:

$\$3 + \$8 + \$1 + \$0 = \$12$

Look at the rest of the values. $\$0.46 + \$0.33 + \$0.32$ is a little more than $1.00. $0.95 is a little less than $1.00.
Put them together. The estimated sum is $\$12 + \$1 + \$1 = \$14$.
So, the estimated value is $\$20 - \$14 = \$6$.
The actual value is $5.94, so the estimate is reasonable. ■

```
******Sales Receipt******
      ARNIE'S ART
         GOODS
         $3.46
         $8.95
         $1.33
         $0.32
```

Can I buy a poster that costs $3.95 with the change from a $20 bill?

Estimating Products and Quotients

Example I   *Estimating Products by Rounding*

Estimate. $152.6 \cdot 48.9$

Solution Rounding is the most common strategy used in estimating products. For this example, round each value to the nearest 10.

Estimate: $150 \cdot 50 = 7500$
Actual value: 7462.14 ■

<, >, or =?

$152.6 \cdot 48.9$? 8000

Example 2   *Rounding and Adjusting*

Estimate.   **a.** $25.05 \cdot 36.8$ **b.** $34.1 \cdot 63.5$

Solution By rounding, the estimates are **a.** $30 \cdot 40 = 1200$ and **b.** $30 \cdot 60 = 1800$. Notice that in part **a**, both factors are rounded up, so you know the estimate is too large. In part **b**, both factors are rounded down, so you know the estimate is too small.

Actual values: **a.** 921.84 **b.** 2165.35
When you use rounding, you should not be locked into rigid rules. There are many ways to get more accurate estimates. For example, in part **a** above, it helps to think of 25 as $\frac{100}{4}$ So, $25.05 \cdot 36.8 \approx \frac{100}{4} \cdot 36 = 100 \cdot 9 = 900$. How would you adjust the estimate in part **b**? Try some methods of your own.

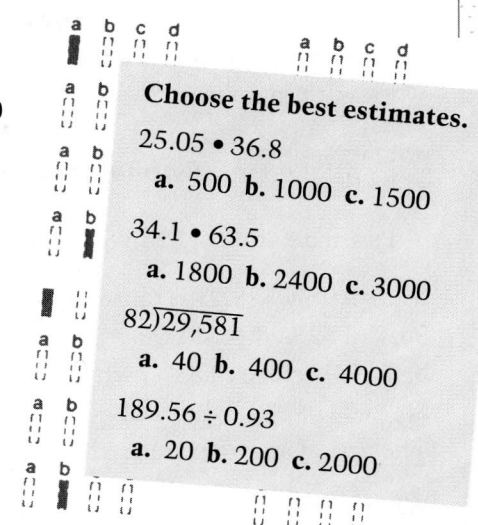

Choose the best estimates.

$25.05 \cdot 36.8$
   a. 500   **b.** 1000   **c.** 1500

$34.1 \cdot 63.5$
   a. 1800   **b.** 2400   **c.** 3000

$82)\overline{29{,}581}$
   a. 40   **b.** 400   **c.** 4000

$189.56 \div 0.93$
   a. 20   **b.** 200   **c.** 2000

Example 3   *Estimating Quotients*

Estimate.   **a.** $82)\overline{29{,}581}$ **b.** $189.56 \div 0.93$

Solution **a.** If you are using estimating in division only to help you find a "first guess," then use front-end estimating. Think $8)\overline{29} \approx 3^+$, so $82)\overline{29{,}581} \approx 300^+$.

If you need a more accurate estimate, consider a combination of techniques. Start off by rounding the divisor to 80. You could round 29,581 up to 30,000. But it would be difficult to divide 30,000 by 80 mentally. Consider using "compatible' or "nice" numbers, that is, numbers you can compute mentally.

Multiples of 8: 8, 16, 24, 32, 40, etc.

Think: 29,581 is closest to 32,000.
So, $82)\overline{29{,}581} \approx 80)\overline{32{,}000} = 400$, which is a reasonable estimate when compared to the actual answer of 360 R 61.

b. When the problem involves decimals, you need to consider whether to make the divisor and dividend whole numbers first and then use compatible numbers , or whether you can just estimate from the given problem
$$0.93)\overline{189.56} = 93)\overline{18{,}956} \approx 90)\overline{18{,}000} = 200 \text{ or } 0.93)\overline{189.56} \approx 1)\overline{190} = 190.$$
The actual answer is ≈ 203.83, so both estimates are reasonable. ■

HINTS FOR
ESTIMATING

Estimating with Fractions and Percents

When multiplying with rational numbers and percents, the easiest and fastest method of estimating is to substitute compatible numbers that are easy to work with mentally.

Example 1   *Estimating Products*

Estimate. **a.** $\frac{3}{7}$ of \$28.98.   **b.** 26% of 239.

Solution **a.** \$28.98 is close to \$28. $\frac{1}{7}$ of \$28 = \$4.

So, $\frac{3}{7}$ of \$28.98 $\approx$ \$12.00.

b. 26% is close to 25%, which equals $\frac{1}{4}$. 239 is close to 240.

So, 26% of 239 $\approx \frac{1}{4}$ of 240 = 60.

The actual answers are **a.** \$12.42 and **b.** 62.14. The estimates are reasonable. ■

When estimating sums and differences of fractions, it is often convenient to use the numbers 0, $\frac{1}{2}$, and 1 as benchmarks.

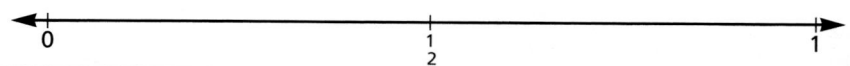

• A fraction is close to 0 if its numerator is very small compared to its denominator.	• A fraction is close to $\frac{1}{2}$ if its numerator is about half its denominator.	• A fraction is close to 1 if its numerator and denominator are about equal.

(You can draw number lines or use fraction strips to help you decide whether a fraction is about 0, about $\frac{1}{2}$ or about 1.)

Example 2   *Estimating Sums and Differences of Fractions*

Estimate. **a.** $\frac{9}{10} + \frac{1}{6} + \frac{2}{5}$ **b.** $8\frac{4}{5} - 1\frac{2}{3} - \frac{7}{9}$

Solution **a.** $\frac{9}{10}$ is about 1, $\frac{1}{6}$ is about 0, and $\frac{2}{5}$ is about $\frac{1}{2}$. So, $\frac{9}{10} + \frac{1}{6} + \frac{2}{5}$

$\approx 1 + 0 + \frac{1}{2} = 1\frac{1}{2}$, which is close to the actual answer of $1\frac{7}{15}$.

b. When you estimate with mixed numbers, you can separate the whole number parts from the fraction parts, or you can consider the numbers as a whole and use front-end estimation. In this problem, all the fraction parts are close to 1, so a first estimate is $9 - 2 - 1 = 6$. Since both of the subtracted numbers were rounded up, and since $\frac{2}{3}$ is not very close to 1, you might consider refining your estimate by rounding $\frac{2}{3}$ down to $\frac{1}{2}$.

So, $8\frac{4}{5} - 1\frac{2}{3} - \frac{7}{9} \approx 9 - 1\frac{1}{2} - 1 = (9 - 1) - 1\frac{1}{2} = 8 - 1\frac{1}{2} = 6\frac{1}{2}$ which is closer to the actual answer of $6\frac{16}{45}$. ■

absolute value (101) The distance between the number and 0 on a number line. For example, $|3| = 3, |-3| = 3, |0| = 0$.

abundant number (279) A natural number with the sum of its factors, except itself, greater than the number.

acute angle (443) An angle whose measure is between 0° and 90°.

acute triangle (458) A triangle with three acute angles.

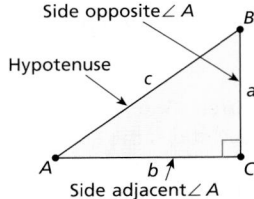

addition (7) A basic number operation specified by the symbol "$+$".

Addition Property of Equality (65) Adding the same number to each side of an equation produces an equivalent equation. If $a = b$, then $a + c = b + c$.

adjacent side (522) In $\triangle ABC$, side $\overline{AC}$ is adjacent to $\angle A$.

Side opposite $\angle A$
Hypotenuse
Side adjacent $\angle A$

algebraic model (25) An algebraic expression or equation used to represent a real-life situation.

alternate interior angles (451) Angles that lie between lines l and m on opposite sides of a line. For example, angles 3 and 6.

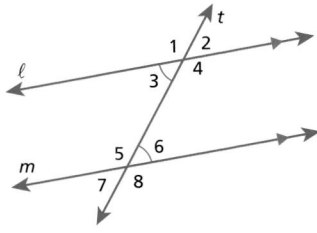

angle (36, 443) A figure consisting of two different rays that begin at the same point. The rays are the *sides* of the angle and the point is the *vertex* of the angle.

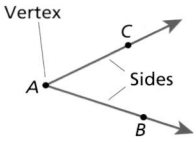

approximate (12) To express a numerical value to different degrees of accuracy. For example, $\sqrt{2}$ can be approximated as 1.41.

area (8) A measure of how much surface is covered by a figure. Areas are measured in square units.

arithmetic mean (127) Another name for the average.

Associative Property of Addition (66) Changing the grouping of the addends does not change the sum. For example, $(a + b) + c = a + (b + c)$.

Associative Property of Multiplication (66) Changing the grouping of the factors does not change the product. For example, $(ab)c = a(bc)$.

average (127, 634) The sum of the numbers in a list divided by the *number* of numbers in the list.

bar graph (29, 199) A graph that organizes a collection of data by using horizontal or vertical bars to display how many times each event or number occurs in the collection.

base of a percent (358) The number from which a portion is to be found, for example, in the percent equation $\frac{a}{b} = \frac{p}{100}$, the base is b.

base of a power (11) The number or expression that is used as a factor in the repeated multiplication. For example, in the expression 4^6, 4 is the base.

binomial (654, 669) A polynomial that has two terms.

bisect (497) Divide into two equal parts.

box-and-whisker plot (642) A graphical display that uses a box to represent the middle quartiles of a set of data and segments drawn to the extremes at both ends to display the first and fourth quartiles.

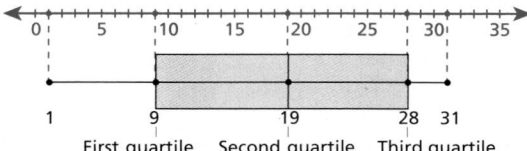

canceling (71, 259) Using slashes to indicate dividing a numerator and a denominator by a common factor.

center of a circle (538, 539) The point inside the circle that is the same distance from all points on the circle.

certain event (229) An event with a probability of 1.

circle (538) The set of all points in a plane that are the same distance from a given point called the center.

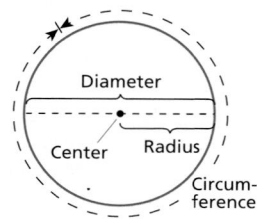

circle graph (300, 323) A graph that displays portions of data collections as parts of a circular region. The parts are often labeled using fractions or percents.

circumference (539) The distance around a circle.

coefficient (110, 654) The numerical factor of an algebraic term. For example, in the term $3x^2$, the coefficient of x^2 is 3.

collecting like terms (55) A procedure for simplifying the sum and difference of like terms in algebraic expressions.

common factor (71, 250) A number that is a factor of two or more numbers. For example, 2 is a common factor of 4 and 6 because 2 is a factor of both 4 and 6.

common multiple (255) A number that is a multiple of two or more numbers. For example, 60

is a common multiple of 5 and 6 because it is a multiple of both 5 and 6.

Commutative Property of Addition (55) Changing the order of the addends does not change the sum. For example, $a + b = b + a$.

Commutative Property of Multiplication (51) Changing the order of the factors does not change the product. For example, $ab = ba$.

complementary angles (155) Two angles whose measures have a sum of 90°.

composite number (245) A natural number that has three or more factors.

concave polygon See *nonconvex polygon*.

conditional equations (59) Equations that are not true for all values of the variables they contain.

cone (545) A solid that has a circular base, a vertex, and a lateral surface.

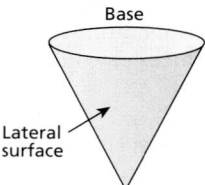

congruent angles (443) Angles that have the same measure.

congruent figures (356) Figures having exactly the same size and same shape.

congruent polygons (467) Two polygons that are exactly the same size and the same shape.

Converse of the Pythagorean Theorem (408) In a triangle, if the sum of the squares of two side lengths is equal to the square of the third side length, then the triangle is a right triangle.

convex polygon (37) A polygon is convex if a segment joining any two interior points lies completely within the polygon.

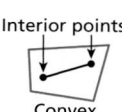

coordinate plane (135) A plane formed by two real number lines called axes that intersect at a right angle; a plane used for locating a point whose coordinates are known.

coordinates (135) An ordered pair of numbers that locate a point on a coordinate graph.

cosine of an angle (522)
The cosine of an acute angle in a right triangle is the ratio of the length of the leg adjacent to the acute angle to the length of the hypotenuse. For example, $\cos A = \frac{b}{c}$.

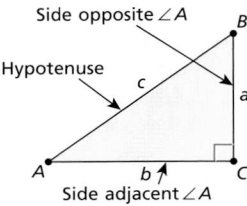

Counting Principle (373) If one event can occur in m ways and another event can occur in n ways, then the two events can occur in mn ways.

Cross-Product Property (349) For two ratios, if $\frac{a}{b} = \frac{c}{d}$, then $ad = bc$.

cross section (487) The exposed surface of a solid cut by a plane.

cube (14) A rectangular prism whose six faces are congruent squares.

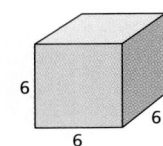

cubic numbers (41) Numbers in the set 1, 8, 27, ..., n^3.

cubic units (554) Standard measures of volume.

cylinder (545) A solid figure with congruent circular bases that lie in parallel planes.

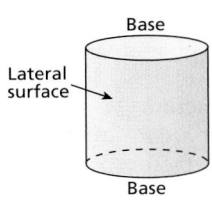

data (28) The facts, or numbers, that describe something.

decagon (34) A polygon that has ten sides.

deficient number (279) A natural number with the sum of its factors, except itself, less than the number.

degree of a polynomial (659) The largest exponent of a polynomial.

diagonal (35) A segment that connects two vertices of a polygon and is not a side.

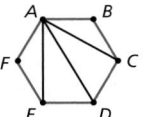

Three diagonals of this hexagon are $\overline{AC}$, $\overline{AD}$, and $\overline{AE}$.

diameter (538) The distance across the circle through its center. The length of the diameter is twice the length of the radius.

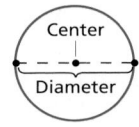

difference (7, 24) The result obtained when numbers or expressions are subtracted. The difference of a and b is $a - b$.

digits (10) The basic symbols used to write numerals. In our base-ten decimal system, the digits are 0, 1, 2, 3, 4, 5, 6, 7, 8, and 9.

dimensions (16) The measure of the magnitude or size of an object. For example, the dimensions of a rectangle are its length and its width.

discount (364) The difference between the regular price and the sale price of an item.

Distributive Property (51) The product of a number and the sum of two numbers is equal to the sum of the two products. For example,
$a(b + c) = ab + ac$ and $ab + ac = a(b + c)$.

Dividing Powers Property (270) To divide two powers with the same base, subtract the exponent of the denominator from the exponent of the numerator, that is, $\frac{a^m}{a^n} = a^{m-n}$.

divisible (8, 240) One natural number is divisible by another natural number if the second divides evenly into the first, that is, if there is a 0 remainder after division. For example, 84 is divisible by 2, since 84 ÷ 2 leaves no remainder.

Division Property of Equality (71) Dividing both sides of an equation by the same nonzero number produces an equivalent equation. If $a = b$, then $\frac{a}{c} = \frac{b}{c}$.

Glossary **693**

693

edge (14, 544) The segment formed when two faces of a solid figure meet.

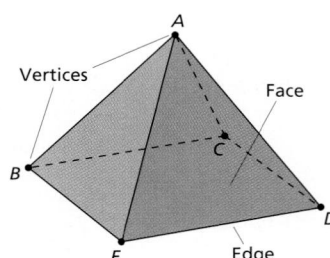

endpoint (34) The point at the end of a line segment or ray.

equally likely outcomes (229) Two or more possible outcomes of a given situation that have the same probability.

equal matrices (648) Two matrices are equal if all the entries in corresponding positions are equal.

equation (59) A statement formed when an equality symbol is placed between two expressions. For example, $3 \times 9 = 27$ and $8 + x = 10$ are equations.

equiangular triangle (458) A triangle in which all three angles have the same measure.

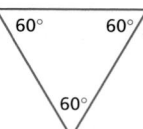

equilateral triangle (170, 457) A triangle in which all three sides have the same length.

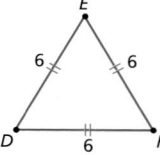

equivalent equations (59) Equations that have the same solutions.

equivalent expressions (51) Expressions that have the same values when numbers are substituted for the variables.

equivalent fractions (259) Fractions that have the same decimal form: $\frac{1}{2}, \frac{2}{4}, \frac{3}{6}$ are equivalent fractions because each is equal to 0.5.

evaluate an algebraic expression (24) To find the value of an expression by replacing each variable in an expression with numbers.

evaluate a numerical expression (17) To perform operations to obtain a single number or value.

even number (10) A whole number that is divisible by 2.

exponent (11) A number or variable that represents the number of times the base is used as a factor. For example, in the expression 2^3, 3 is the exponent.

expression (17, 24) A symbol or combination of symbols that represent a mathematical relationship.

exterior angles (472) Exterior angles are formed when the sides of a polygon are extended.

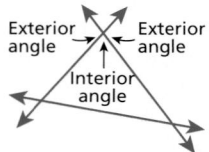

face (14, 544) The flat surface of a solid figure; one of the polygons that make up a polyhedron.

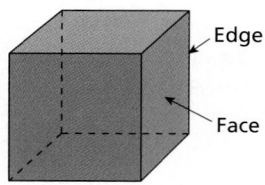

factored form (241) A natural number is factored when it is written as the product of two or more natural numbers.

factorial (376) The product of the numbers from 1 to n is called n-factorial and is denoted by $n!$.

factors (24) Numbers or variable expressions that are multiplied. For example, 4 and x are the factors of $4x$.

favorable outcome (229) An outcome of an experiment for which you are interested in measuring the probability.

Fibonacci Sequence (41) An unending sequence such as 1, 1, 2, 3, 5, 8, 13, 21, … in which the first two terms are fixed and the other terms are the sum of the two preceding terms.

FOIL pattern (671) A method used to multiply two binomials in a single step. Find the sum of the products of the **F**irst terms, **O**uter terms, **I**nner terms, and **L**ast terms. For example, to find $(2x + 3)(x - 5)$, find

Outer: $(2x)(-5)$ Inner: $(3)(x)$

$$2x^2 + (-10x) + 3x + (-15)$$

First: $(2x)(x)$ Last: $(3)(-5)$

formula (25) An algebraic expression that represents a general way of expressing a relationship in real-life situations.

frequency distribution (200) Organizing data by displaying the number of items or events that occur in an interval.

geometry (34) The study of shapes and their measures.

graph of a linear equation (593) The graph of all its solutions, a line.

graph of a linear inequality (620) The half-plane that consists of all points on one side of the line that is the graph of the corresponding linear equation. For example, this is the graph of the inequality $y > 2x - 4$.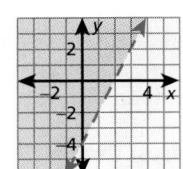

greatest common factor, GCF (250) The largest common factor of two numbers or algebraic expressions. For example, $4a$ is the GCF of $20ab^2$ and $24a^2$.

half-plane (620) In a plane, the region on one side of a line.

height (37, 488, 549) The perpendicular distance between parallel bases of a parallelogram, trapezoid, prism, or cylinder or the distance from a vertex to an opposite side of a triangle, pyramid, or cone.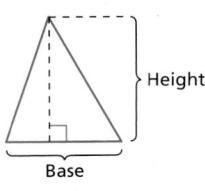

hemisphere (569) One of the two halves of a sphere.

heptagon (34) A polygon with seven sides.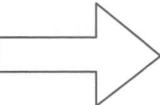

hexagon (34) A polygon with six sides.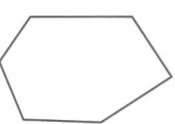

histogram (200) A bar graph in which the bars represent intervals.

hypotenuse (400) The side of a right triangle that is opposite the right angle. It is the longest side of a right triangle.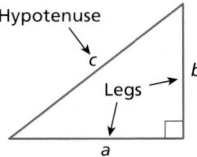

icosahedron (547) A polyhedron with 20 triangular faces.

identities (59) Equations that are true for all values of the variable. For example, the identities $a + 0 = a$ and $a \cdot 1 = a$ are true for all numbers.

image (462, 497, 502, 506) The new figure formed by the transformation of a given figure.

inequality (89) A mathematical sentence that contains a symbol such as $\neq$, $>$, $<$, $\geq$, or $\leq$.

integers (100) The set of numbers . . . $-3, -2, -1, 0, 1, 2, 3, \ldots$.

interest (331) A percent of the money on deposit (the principal) paid to a lender or depositor for the use of the principal.

interior angle (36, 472) An angle of a polygon formed by two adjacent sides.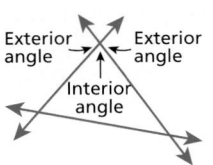

intersecting lines (439) Lines that cross or meet at a common point.

intersection of sets, ∩ (162) Contains only the elements found in both of two sets.

inverse operations (131) Operations that undo each other. For example, addition and subtraction are inverse operations, as are multiplication and division.

irrational number (265, 395) A real number that cannot be expressed as the quotient of two integers. For example, the square roots of numbers that are not perfect squares like $\sqrt{2}$, π, and nonterminating nonrepeating decimals like 0.100100010001 . . . are all irrational numbers.

isosceles trapezoid (462) A trapezoid whose nonparallel sides have the same length.

isosceles triangle (401, 457) A triangle with at least two sides that have the same length.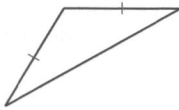

kite (462) A quadrilateral that is not a parallelogram but has two pairs of sides of equal lengths.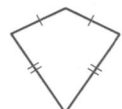

lateral (171) Side.

least common denominator, LCD (299) The least common denominator of two fractions is the least common multiple of their denominators.

least common multiple, LCM (255) The least common multiple of two numbers or algebraic expressions is the smallest of their common multiples. $6a^2b$ is the LCM of $2ab$ and $3a^2$.

Left-to-Right Rule (18) Operations having the same priority in an expression are evaluated from left to right.

leg of a right triangle (400) Either of the two shorter sides of a right triangle.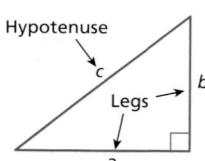

like fractions (294) Fractions that have the same denominator.

like terms (55) Two or more terms in an expression that have the same variable factors raised to the same powers.

linear equation (423, 588) An equation in two variables whose graph is a straight line.

linear inequality (423, 619) An inequality in two variables for which the graph is a half-plane above or below the corresponding linear equation.

linear relationship (614) Two quantities that can be modeled with a linear equation.

line of symmetry (453) A line that divides a figure into two parts, each of which is the mirror image of the other.

line plot (219) A diagram showing the frequency of data on a number line.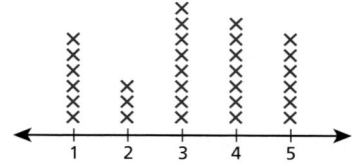

line segment (34, 439) Part of a line consisting of two endpoints and all the points between them.

lowest terms (259) A fraction is in lowest terms if the greatest common factor of the numerator and denominator is 1.

markup (50) The amount a store adds to the wholesale price to get the retail price.

matrix (125, 648) A rectangular array of numbers or data in rows and columns.

mean (127, 634) The average of all the numbers in a set.

measures of central tendency (634) Numbers that can be used to represent a group of numbers. The mean, median, and mode of a distribution.

median (634) The middle number (or the average of the two middle numbers) of a group of numbers listed in order.

midpoint (624) The halfway point on a line segment.

mode (634) The number that occurs most often in a given collection of numbers.

monomial (654) A polynomial with only one term; variable, a number, or a product of variables and numbers.

multiple (255) The product of a given number and any whole number. For example, 8 is a multiple of 1, 2, 4, and 8.

Multiplication Property of Equality (71) Multiplying both sides of an equation by the same nonzero number produces an equivalent equation. If $a = b$, then $ac = bc$.

Multiplying Powers Property (270) To multiply two powers with the same base, add their exponents; that is, $a^m \cdot a^n = a^{m+n}$.

natural number (11, 38) The set of numbers 1, 2, 3, 4, ...

negative correlation (224) Data points on a scatter plot whose y-coordinates tend to decrease as the x-coordinates increase.

negative integer (100) An integer that is less than 0.

negative slope (605) A line in the coordinate plane has a negative slope if it slants downward as you move from left to right.

net (442, 544) A flat pattern that can be folded to form a solid. For example, these nets can be folded to cubes.

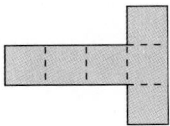 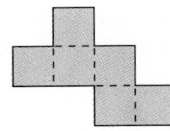

nonagon (34) A polygon with nine sides.

nonconvex polygon (37) A polygon that is not convex because one or more segments joining any two interior points does not lie completely within the polygon.

Not convex

n-gon (34) A polygon with n sides.

nonrepeating decimal (266) A decimal that neither terminates nor repeats.

numerical expression (17) A collection of numbers, operations, and grouping symbols.

obtuse angle (443) An angle that measures between 90° and 180°.

obtuse triangle (458) A triangle with an obtuse angle.

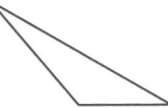

octagon (34) A polygon with eight sides.

octahedron (547) A polyhedron with eight triangular faces.

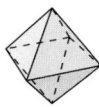

odd number (10) A whole number that is not divisible by 2. The numbers 1, 3, 5, 7, ... are odd.

opposites (101) Two numbers that have the same absolute value but opposite signs; any two numbers whose sum is 0.

opposite side (522) In $\triangle ABC$, side $\overline{BC}$ is opposite $\angle A$.

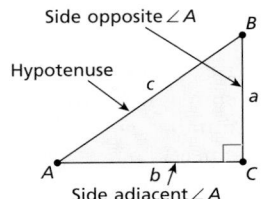

ordered pair (136, 588, 619) A pair of numbers or coordinates used to locate a point in a coordinate plane. The solution of an equation or an inequality in two variables.

Order of Operations (17, 18) A procedure for evaluating an expression involving more than one operation.
1. First do operations that occur within grouping symbols.
2. Then evaluate powers.
3. Then do multiplications and divisions from left to right.
4. Then do additions and subtractions from left to right.

GLOSSARY

origin (135) The point of intersection in the coordinate plane of the horizontal axis and the vertical axis. The point (0, 0).

outcome (229) A possible result of an event; for example, obtaining heads is an outcome of tossing a coin.

parallel lines (439) Lines in the same plane that do not intersect.

parallelogram (185, 462) A quadrilateral with opposite sides parallel.

pentagon (34) A polygon with five sides.

percent, % (268, 318) A way of expressing hundredths; that is, a fraction whose denominator is 100. *Percent* means "per hundred." 5% (5 percent) equals $\frac{5}{100}$.

Percent Equation (358) The statement "*a* is *p* percent of *b*" is equivalent to the equation $\frac{a}{b} = \frac{p}{100}$.

percent of increase or decrease (367) An indication of how much a quantity has increased or decreased.

perfect number (279) A natural number with the sum of its factors, except itself, equal to the number. For example 6 is a perfect number since $1 + 2 + 3 = 6$.

perfect square (12) A number whose square root can be written as an exact decimal.

perimeter of a polygon (16) The distance around a figure; the sum of the lengths of the sides.

perpendicular lines (443) Two lines that meet at a right angle.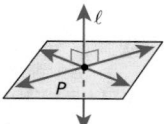

pi (539) The number that is the ratio of the circumference of a circle to its diameter. It is represented by the Greek letter π and is approximately equal to 3.1416.

plotting a point (100, 135) Locating a point that corresponds to a number on a number line or that corresponds to an ordered pair in the coordinate plane.

polygon (34) A closed plane figure that is made up of straight line segments that intersect at their endpoints.

polyhedron (544) A solid that is bounded by polygons, which are called faces.

polynomial (653, 654) A monomial or the sum or difference of monomials.

population (230) A group of people (or objects or events) that fit a particular description.

portion (318) A fraction that compares the measure of part of a quantity to the measure of the whole quantity.

positive correlation (224) Data points on a scatter plot whose *y*-coordinates tend to increase as the *x*-coordinates increase.

positive integer (100) The numbers 1, 2, 3, 4, . . . are positive integers.

positive slope (605) A line in the coordinate plane has a positive slope if it slants upward as you move from left to right.

possible outcomes (229) All the different ways an event can turn out.

power (11) An expression such as 4^2 that has a base (4) and an exponent (2).

prime factorization (245) Expression of a composite number as a product of prime factors. The prime factorization of 18 is $2 \cdot 3 \cdot 3$.

prime number (245) A natural number that has exactly two factors, itself and 1. The numbers 2, 3, 5, 7, 11, 13, and so on, are prime numbers.

principal (331) The amount of money loaned by a bank to a borrower or the amount of money on deposit in a bank.

prism (544) A polyhedron that has two parallel, congruent faces called bases.

probability of an event (228) A measure of the likelihood that the event will occur.

GLOSSARY

product (7, 24) The result obtained when numbers or expressions are multiplied. The product of a and b is $a \cdot b$ or ab.

proportion (349) An equation stating that two ratios are equal. If a is to b as c is to d, then $\frac{a}{b} = \frac{c}{d}$.

protractor (443) A measuring device that can be used to approximate the measure of an angle.

pyramid (441, 544) A space figure whose base is a polygon and whose other faces are triangles that share a common vertex.

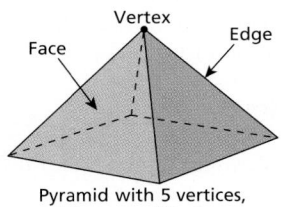

Pyramid with 5 vertices, 5 faces, and 8 edges

Pythagorean Theorem (400) For any right triangle, the sum of the squares of the lengths of the legs, a and b, equals the square of the length of the hypotenuse, c. $a^2 + b^2 = c^2$

Pythagorean triple (401) A set of three natural numbers that represent the sides of a right triangle.

quadrant (135) In the coordinate plane, one of the four parts into which the axes divide the plane.

quadrilateral (34, 462) A polygon with four sides.

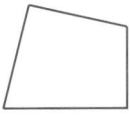

quartile (642) The first, second, and third quartiles roughly divide a collection of ordered numbers into four equal groups.

quotient (7, 24) The result obtained when numbers or expressions are divided. The quotient of a and b is $\frac{a}{b}$.

radical (12) The square root symbol, $\sqrt{}$.

radius of a circle (539) A segment that has the center as one endpoint and a point on the circle as the other endpoint.

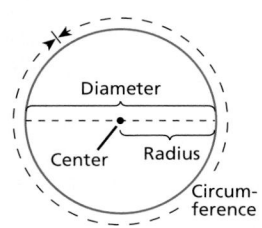

random sample (230) A sample in which every person (or object or event) in the population has an equal chance of having the characteristics of the larger group.

rate (344) The relationship $\frac{a}{b}$ of two quantities a and b that have different units of measure.

ratio (345) The relationship $\frac{a}{b}$ of two quantities a and b that have the same unit of measure.

rational number (265, 395) A number that can be written as the quotient of two integers.

raw data (218) Unorganized data from an experiment or survey.

ray (439) Part of a line that has one endpoint and extends forever in only one direction.

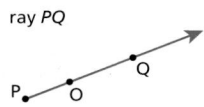

ray PQ

real numbers (62, 395) The set of all rational numbers and irrational numbers together.

reciprocal (130) The reciprocal of a nonzero number a is $\frac{1}{a}$. The product of two reciprocals is 1.

Reciprocal Property (349) For ratios $\frac{a}{b}$ and $\frac{c}{d}$, if $\frac{a}{b} = \frac{c}{d}$ then $\frac{b}{a} = \frac{d}{c}$.

rectangle (8) A parallelogram that has four right angles.

rectangular prism (551) A prism whose bases are rectangles.

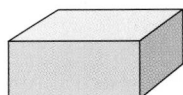

reflection (497) A transformation that flips a figure about a line onto its mirror image on the opposite side of the line.

GLOSSARY

reflection line (497) In a reflection, a line that is perpendicular to and bisects each segment that joins an original point to its image.

regular polygon (36, 468) A polygon with each of its sides having the same length and each of its angles having the same measure.

relatively prime (251) Two natural numbers are relatively prime if their greatest common factor is one.

repeating decimal (38, 395) A decimal in which a digit or group of digits repeats forever. Repeating digits are indicated by a bar.

$$0.3333\ldots = 0.\overline{3}$$
$$1.47474747\ldots = 1.\overline{47}$$

retail price (50) The amount you pay for any item in a store.

rhombus (462) A parallelogram with four sides of equal length.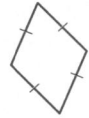

right angle (400) An angle whose measure is 90°.

right triangle (400, 458) A triangle that has a right angle.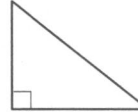

rotation (502) A transformation that turns a figure a given angle and direction about a point.

rotational symmetry (454) A figure has rotational symmetry if it coincides with itself after rotating 180° or less about a point.

round a number (12) To replace a number by another one of approximately the same value that is easier to use.

round-off error (178) The error produced when a number is rounded in a computation.

sample space (229) The set of all possible outcomes of an event.

scale factor (512) In two similar polygons or two similar solids, the **scale factor** is the ratio of corresponding linear measures.

scalene quadrilateral (462) A quadrilateral whose four sides all have different lengths.

scalene triangle (457) A triangle whose three sides all have different lengths.

scatter plot (224) The graph of a collection of ordered pairs (x, y).

scientific notation (274) A short form of writing numbers whose absolute values are very large or very small. A number is written in scientific notation if it has the form $c \times 10^n$, where c is greater than or equal to 1 and less than 10, and where n is an integer.

segment See *line segment*.

sequence (3) An ordered list of numbers.

set (162) A well-defined collection of objects.

side of a polygon (34) One of the straight line segments that make up the polygon.

similar figures (356, 512) Figures that have the same shape but not necessarily the same size.

similar solids (573) Solids that have the same shape with their corresponding lengths proportional.

similar triangles (350) Two triangles that have the same angle measures. For example, triangle ABC is similar to triangle DEF.

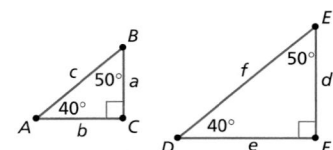

simplest form (259) A fraction (or mixed number) is in simplest form if the fraction (or fraction-part of the mixed number) is less than 1 and in lowest terms (reduced form).

simulation (377) An experiment that models a real-life situation.

sine of an angle (522) The sine of an acute angle in a right triangle is the ratio of the length of the leg opposite the acute angle to the length of the hypotenuse. For example, $\sin A = \frac{a}{c}$.

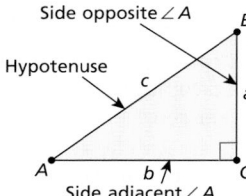

slope (603) The ratio of the difference in y-coordinates to the difference in x-coordinates for any two points on the graph of a linear equation. Also defined as the rise over the run.

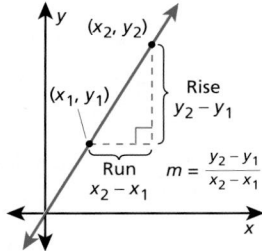

slope-intercept form of an equation (610) A linear equation in x and y that has the form $y = mx + b$, where m is the slope of the line and b is the y-intercept.

solution (59, 89, 136, 619) A number (or ordered pair of numbers) that produces a true statement when substituted for the variable(s) in an equation or an inequality.

solving an equation (59) Finding all the values of the variable that make the equation true.

solving an inequality (89) Finding all the values of the variable that make the inequality true.

solving a right triangle (401) Determining the measures of all six parts; that is, the lengths of the three sides and the measures of the three angles.

spreadsheet (75) A computer program that creates tables.

square (12) A rectangle with four sides of equal length.

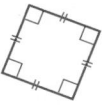

square number (11) The set of numbers 1, 4, 9, ..., n^2.

square root of a number (12, 390) The number that when squared will produce the given number. Both 7 and –7 are square roots of 49, because $7^2 = 49$ and $(-7)^2 = 49$.

square root symbol See *radical.*

standard form of a polynomial (654) A polynomial written so that the powers of the variable decrease from left to right.

statistics (218) A branch of mathematics that organizes large collections of data in ways that can be used to understand trends and make predictions.

stem-and-leaf plot (638–639) A method of organizing data in increasing or decreasing order.

straight angle (443) An angle whose measure is 180°.

substituting (24) Replacing a variable in an expression by a number.

Subtraction Property of Equality (65) Subtracting the same number from both sides of an equation produces an equivalent equation. If $a = b$, then $a - c = b - c$.

sum (7, 24) The result obtained when numbers or expressions are added. The sum of a and b is $a + b$.

Sum of Opposites Property (105) The sum of any two opposites is zero.

supplementary angles (67) Two angles whose measures have a sum of 180°.

surface area (14, 548) The sum of the areas of all the faces of a solid figure.

tangent of an angle (522) The tangent of an acute angle in a right triangle is the ratio of the length of the leg opposite the acute angle to the length of the leg adjacent to that acute angle. For example, $\tan A = \frac{a}{b}$.

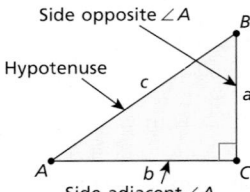

Side opposite ∠A

Hypotenuse

Side adjacent ∠A

terminating decimal (38) A decimal, that contains a finite number of digits, for example, 0.5.

terms of an expression (24, 116, 654) The terms of an expression are separated by addition signs. In the expression $3x + (-2)$, the terms are $3x$ and -2.

tetrahedron (547, 565) A pyramid with four triangular faces.

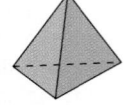

time line (196) A graph on a number line of the dates of several occurrences.

transformations in geometry (502) An operation such as a reflection (flip), rotation (turn), or translation (slide) that maps or moves a figure from an original position (preimage) to a new position (image).

translation (506) A transformation that slides each point of a figure the same distance in a given direction.

trapezoid (45, 462) A quadrilateral with only one pair of parallel sides.

tree diagram (245, 373) A diagram that shows all the prime factors of a number or the possible outcomes of an event.

triangle (34) A polygon with three sides.

Triangle Inequality (90, 425) The sum of the lengths of any two sides of a triangle is greater than the length of the third side of the triangle.

triangular numbers (39) The set of numbers $1, 3, 6, \ldots, \frac{n(n+1)}{2}$.

triangular prism (551) A prism whose bases are triangles.

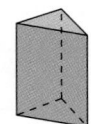

trigonometric ratio (522) A ratio of the lengths of two sides of a right triangle; for example: sine, cosine, and tangent.

trinomial (654) A polynomial that has only three terms.

two-step equation (149) An equation whose solution involves two transformations.

union of sets, ∪ (162) All the elements found in either or both of two sets.

unit analysis (72) A technique that can be used to decide the unit of measure assigned to a product or quotient.

unlike fractions (299) Fractions that do not have the same denominator.

variable (24, 29) A symbol, usually a letter, that is used to represent one or more numbers in an algrebraic expression, for example, x is a variable in the expression $8x + 19$.

Venn diagram (162, 265) A diagram that shows the relationships among sets of numbers or objects.

vertex (34, 443, 544) The point at the corner of an angle, plane figure, or solid figure.

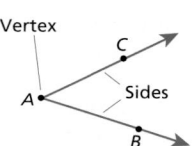

Vertex

Sides

vertical angles (448) Angles whose sides form two pairs of opposite rays.

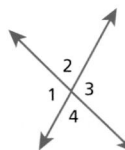

Vertical angles:
∠1 and ∠3, ∠2 and ∠4

volume (14, 554) The measure of the amount of space that an object occupies, or how much it will hold.

whole number (38) Any of the numbers 0, 1, 2, 3, 4, ...

wholesale price (50) The amount that a store paid for an item.

x-axis (135) The horizontal number line in the coordinate plane.

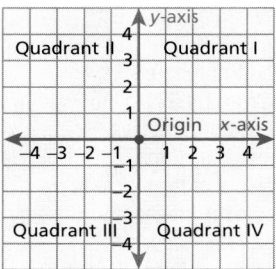

x-coordinate (135) The first number of an ordered pair, the position of the point relative to the horizontal axis.

x-intercept (598) The x-coordinate of the point where a graph crosses the x-axis; the value of x when $y = 0$.

y-axis (135) The vertical number line in the coordinate plane.

y-coordinate (135) The second number of an ordered pair, the position of the point relative to the vertical axis.

y-intercept (598) The y-coordinate of the point where a graph crosses the y-axis; the value of y when $x = 0$.

Zero Property of Addition (105) When zero is added to any number, the sum is the same number. $a + 0 = a$ and $0 + a = a$

CHAPTER 1

1.1 Independent Practice pp. 4–5

To get the next number:

5. Name next consecutive odd number.
6. Name next consecutive multiple of 5.
7. Add 2, add 3, add 4, etc., to preceding number.
8. Subtract 3, subtract 4, subtract 5, etc., from preceding number.
9. Add 1 to both numerator and denominator of preceding number.
10. Add 2 to both numerator and denominator of preceding number.
11. Add 3_2 to preceding number.
12. Name next smaller perfect square; or subtract 19, subtract 17, subtract 15, etc., from previous number.
13. Multiply preceding number by 3.
14. Divide preceding number by 4; or name next smaller power of 4; or name next smaller even power of 2.

To get the next letter:

15. Name second consecutive letter.
16. In every odd-numbered position: Name the letter of the alphabet in that position. In every even-numbered position: Subtract the position number from 27 and name the letter of the alphabet in that numbered position.
17. In every odd-numbered position, except the first: Name the letter of the alphabet that precedes the letter in the preceding odd-numbered position. In every even-numbered position, except the first: Name the letter of the alphabet that follows the letter in the preceding even-numbered position.

18. In every odd-numbered position, except the first: Name the letter of the alphabet that follows the letter in the preceding odd-numbered position. In every even-numbered position, except the first: Name the letter of the alphabet that follows the letter in the preceding even-numbered position.
19. Write the initial letter in the name of the next counting number.
20. *One description* In every odd-numbered position, except the first: Write T if S is in the previous odd-numbered position, and vice-versa. In every even-numbered position, except the first: Name the letter of the alphabet that precedes the letter in the preceding even-numbered position. *Another description* Write the initial letter in the name of the next even counting number.

23.

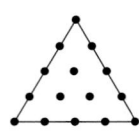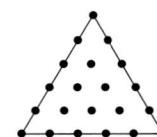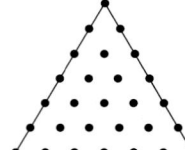

24.

25. The first number is minutes and the second number is seconds. So you ran the race in 2 minutes and 39.4 seconds, while your friend ran the race in 2 minutes and 41.8 seconds.
26. Your friend jumped 2 inches farther than you did.
28. Answers vary. Identify objects: Rides and buildings numbered on displayed maps, cars of roller coasters and Ferris wheels numbered on their sides. Measure objects: Time it takes to run a film, maximum number of people (or maximum weight) allowed in a car on a ride.

1.3 Mixed Review p. 15

To get the next number:

1. Add 2 to preceding number.
2. Subtract 3 from preceding number.
3. Add 5 to preceding number.
4. Divide preceding number by 3; or multiply preceding number by $\frac{1}{3}$.
5. Raise 2 to the power of the preceding number's position and add it to the preceding number; or add 2 times the difference of the two preceding numbers to the preceding number; or raise 2 to the power of the number's position and subtract 1; or add 1 to the product of 2 and the preceding number.
6. Raise 3 to the power of the preceding number's position and add it to the preceding number; or add 3 times the difference of the two preceding numbers to the preceding number; or subtract 1 from the product of 3 and the preceding number.

1.6 Independent Practice p. 30

7.

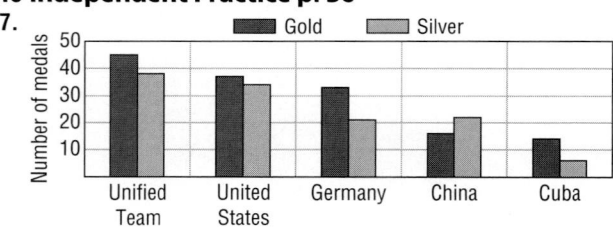

A bar graph is preferable because there are no connections among the numbers of medals won by the various teams.

11.

Side	1	2	3	4	5	6	7
Perimeter	4	8	12	16	20	24	28
Area	1	4	9	16	25	36	49

12.

n	1	2	3	4	5	6	7
$n+2$	3	4	5	6	7	8	9
Perimeter	8	12	16	20	24	28	32
Area	3	8	15	24	35	48	63

1.6 Independent Practice p. 31

13.

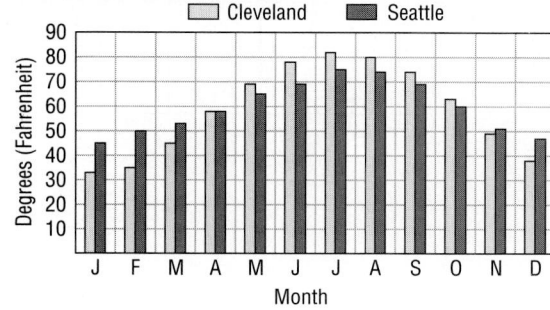

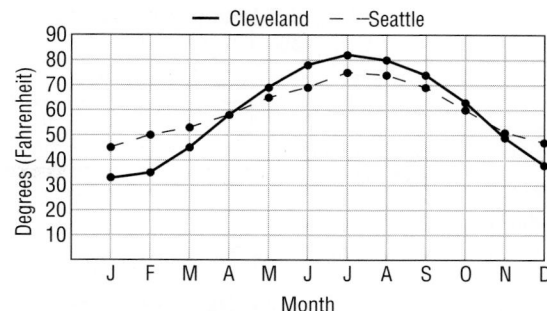

1.8 Independent Practice p. 40

3.

n	1	2	3	4
$192 \div n$	192	96	64	48

4.

n	0	1	2	3	4	5	6	7	8
$75n$	0	75	150	225	300	375	450	525	600

5.

n	1	2	3	4	5	6	7	8	9
$\frac{n}{3}$	$0.\overline{3}$	$0.\overline{6}$	1	$1.\overline{3}$	$1.\overline{6}$	2	$2.\overline{3}$	$2.\overline{6}$	3

6.

n	1	2	3	4	5	6	7	8	9
$\frac{2}{n}$	2	1	$0.\overline{6}$	0.5	0.4	$0.\overline{3}$	$0.\overline{285714}$	0.25	$0.\overline{2}$

Repeating decimals are produced when $n = 3, 6, 7,$ and 9.

7.

n	0	1	2	3	4	5	6
$\frac{n^2}{2}$	0	0.5	2	4.5	8	12.5	18

8.

n	1	2	3	4	5
$\frac{n}{n+1}$	0.5	$0.\overline{6}$	0.75	0.8	$0.8\overline{3}$

9. Each number, after the first, is 10 times the preceding number plus 1 less than the units digit of the preceding number.

10. Each number, after the first, is 111111 more than the preceding number.

11. Each number, after the first, is 0.2 more than the preceding number.

12. Each number, after the first, is 3 more than the preceding number.

Calculator key sequences depend on the brand and model of calculator. For T1 calculators with $\boxed{K}$ keys, you would enter the operation and $\boxed{K}$ as in $8 \boxed{+} \boxed{K}$ 1, $13 \boxed{-} \boxed{K}$ 100, $3 \boxed{\times} \boxed{K}$ 5, and $5 \boxed{\div} \boxed{K}$ 1025, etc. For many Casio models, you double the operation key as in $8 \boxed{+} \boxed{+}$ 1, $13 \boxed{-} \boxed{-}$ 100, $3 \boxed{\times} \boxed{\times}$ 5, and $5 \boxed{\div} \boxed{\div}$ 1025.

13. $1 \boxed{+} 8 \boxed{=} \boxed{=} \boxed{=} \boxed{=} \boxed{=} \boxed{=} \boxed{=}$; 33, 41, 49, 57

14. $100 \boxed{-} 13 \boxed{=} \boxed{=} \boxed{=} \boxed{=} \boxed{=} \boxed{=} \boxed{=}$; 48, 35, 22, 9

*15. $5 \boxed{\times} 3 \boxed{=} \boxed{=} \boxed{=} \boxed{=} \boxed{=} \boxed{=} \boxed{=}$; 405, 1215, 3645, 10935

16. $1025 \boxed{\div} 5 \boxed{=} \boxed{=} \boxed{=} \boxed{=} \boxed{=} \boxed{=} \boxed{=}$; 1.64, 0.328, 0.0656, 0.01312

17. $1008 \boxed{\div} 10 \boxed{=} \boxed{=} \boxed{=} \boxed{=} \boxed{=} \boxed{=} \boxed{=}$; 1.008, 0.1008, 0.01008, 0.001008

*18. $12.3 \boxed{\times} 2 \boxed{=} \boxed{=} \boxed{=} \boxed{=} \boxed{=} \boxed{=} \boxed{=}$; 98.4, 196.8, 393.6, 787.2

*On some *TI* calculator models you need to reverse the order of the keys for multiplication, that is, enter $3 \boxed{\times} 5$ and $2 \boxed{\times} 12.3$.

1.8 Independent Practice p. 41

19.

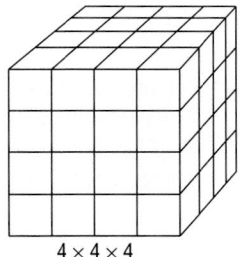

$4 \times 4 \times 4$

CHAPTER 2

2.1 Independent Practice p. 53

9.

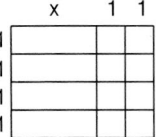

11.

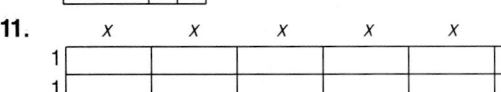

10.

12.

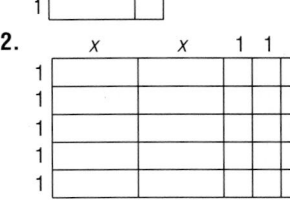

2.2 Independent Practice p. 57

41. The expressions are not equivalent.
1st perimeter: $5x + 4$, 2nd perimeter: $6x + 4$
If the expressions were equivalent, then the perimeters would be the same for all values of x. But, other than 0, there are no such values.

42. The expressions are not equivalent.
1st perimeter: $5x + 7$, 2nd perimeter: $5x + 5$
If the expressions were equivalent, then the perimeters would be the same for all values of x. But there are no such values.

2.2 Independent Practice p. 58

43.

x	1	2	3	4	5
Perimeter, $18x$	18	36	54	72	90

44.

x	1	2	3	4	5
Perimeter, $8x$	8	16	24	32	40

43., 44. Each perimeter, after the first, is $\binom{18}{8}$ more than the preceding perimeter.

2.5 Independent Practice p. 73

35.

36.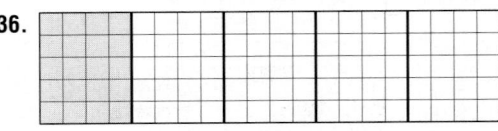

2.8 Independent Practice p. 88

13. Sales commission = Commission rate × Annual sales

14. Sales commission: x (dollars)
Commission rate: $\frac{1}{20}$
Annual sales: $150,000

2.9 Independent Practice p. 92

55. c.

Last-place time in minutes	− Minutes <	First-place time in minutes

$85 - m < 69$
$16 < m$

d.

Cruisin' Kids' time in minutes	− Minutes ≤	Brave Bikers' time in minutes

$76 - m \leq 71$
$5 \leq m$

CHAPTER 3

3.2 Independent Practice p. 107

11. $11 + 15 = 26$
12. $-8 + (-2) = -10$
13. $-13 + (-13) = -26$
14. $10 + 24 = 34$
15. $10 + (-10) = 0$
16. $-8 + 8 = 0$
17. $-13 + 13 = 0$
18. $24 + (-24) = 0$
19. $13 + 0 = 13$
20. $-7 + 0 = -7$
21. $0 + 15 = 15$
22. $0 + (-33) = -33$
23. $2 + (-9) = -7$
24. $39 + (-21) = 18$
25. $-16 + 12 = -4$
26. $-17 + 13 = -4$

3.3 Independent Practice p. 111

5. $4 + (-5) + 6 = 5$
6. $3 + (-9) + 13 = 7$
7. $-7 + 1 + (-8) = -14$
8. $-6 + 2 + (-15) = -19$
9. $-8 + 12 + (-1) = 3$
10. $-10 + 16 + (-4) = 2$
11. $-12 + (-4) + (-8) = -24$
12. $-11 + (-7) + (-3) = -21$
13. $5 + (-6) + (-13) = -14$
14. $4 + (-8) + 9 + (-2) = 3$
15. $-7 + (-6) + 2 + (-7) = -18$
16. $-12 + (-4) + 20 = 4$

3.4 Independent Practice p. 117

11. $23 - (-8) = 31$
12. $2 - (-4) = 6$
13. $-10 - 7 = -17$
14. $-3 - 3 = -6$
15. $-5 - (-5) = 0$
16. $-16 - (-8) = -8$
17. $-5 - 5 = -10$
18. $-16 - 8 = -24$

3.6 Mixed Review p. 130

11. Every number, after the first, is -2 times the preceding number.
12. Every number, after the first, is -3 times the preceding number.
13. Every number, after the first, is $-\frac{1}{2}$ times the preceding number.
14. Every number, after the first, is $-\frac{1}{5}$ times the preceding number.

3.8 Communicating about Mathematics p. 136

x	3	2	1	0	−1	−2	−3
y	0	1	2	3	4	5	6
(x, y)	(3, 0)	(2, 1)	(1, 2)	(0, 3)	(−1, 4)	(−2, 5)	(−3, 6)

The graph is a straight line.

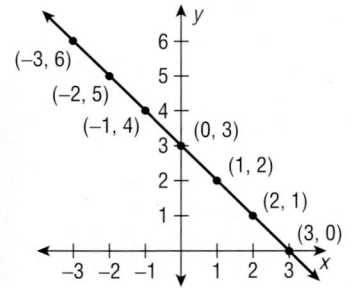

3.8 Independent Practice pp. 137–138

29.

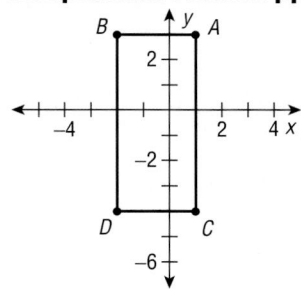

30.

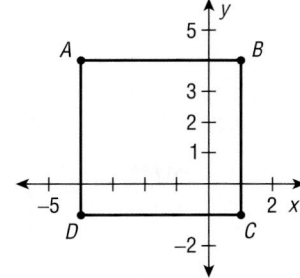

34.

x	0	1	2
y	4	3	2
(x, y)	(0, 4)	(1, 3)	(2, 2)

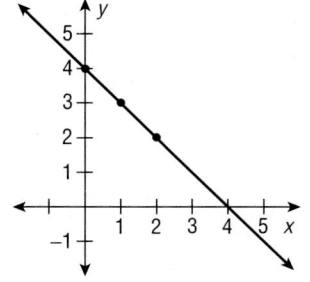

The graph is a straight line.

35.

x	−1	0	1
y	5	0	−5
(x, y)	(−1, 5)	(0, 0)	(1, −5)

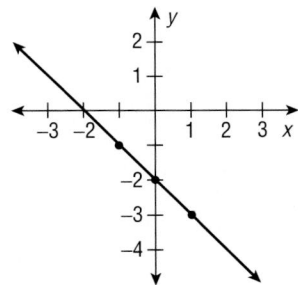

The graph is a straight line.

36.

x	0	1	2
y	−1	1	3
(x, y)	(0, −1)	(1, 1)	(2, 3)

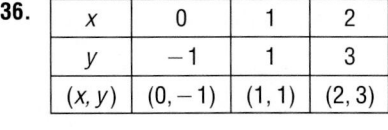

The graph is a straight line.

37.

x	0	2	4
y	3	4	5
(x, y)	(0, 3)	(2, 4)	(4, 5)

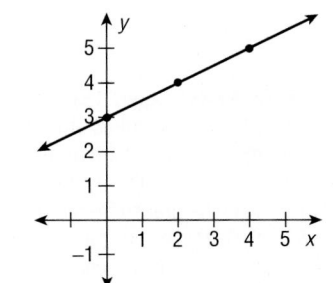

The graph is a straight line.

38.

x	−1	0	1
y	−1	−2	−3
(x, y)	(−1, −1)	(0, −2)	(1, −3)

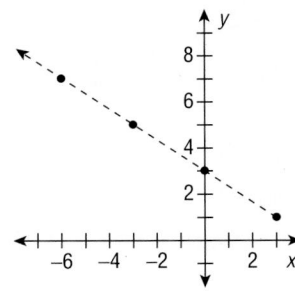

The graph is a straight line.

39.

x	0	1	2
y	−2	1	4
(x, y)	(0, −2)	(1, 1)	(2, 4)

The graph is a straight line.

51. a. (0, 0), (1, 1), (2, 2), (3, 3), etc.

b.

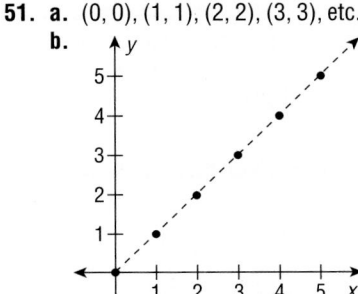

c. The points lie on the same straight line.

52. a. (3, 1), (0, 3), (−3, 5), (−6, 7), etc.

b.

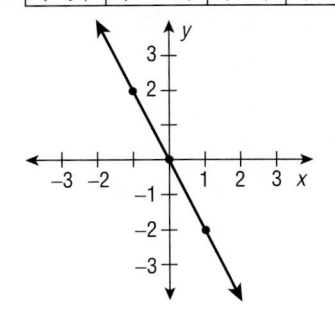

c. The points lie on the same straight line.

3.8 Chapter Review p. 141

69.

x	−1	0	1
y	2	0	−2
(x, y)	(−1, 2)	(0, 0)	(1, −2)

The graph is a straight line.

70.

x	−1	0	1
y	2	1	0
(x, y)	(−1, 2)	(0, 1)	(1, 0)

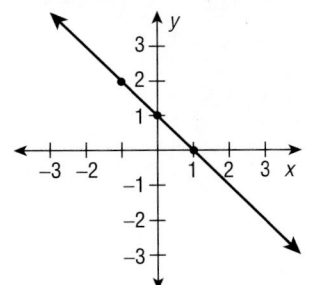

4.1 Independent Practice pp. 151–152

24.

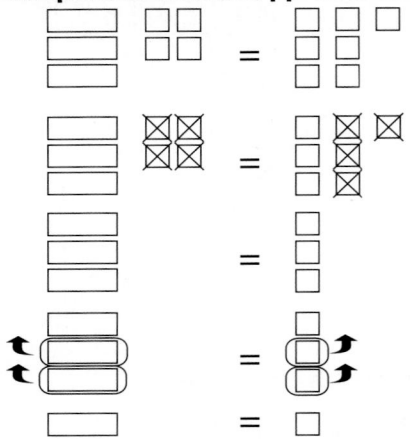

25. $3n + 7 = 34$ **26.** $8n + 12 = 100$

27. $\frac{1}{4}n - 2 = 5$ **28.** $\frac{1}{2}n + 13 = 30$

29. $21 + 7x = -14$ **30.** $84 + \frac{x}{2} = -36$

31. $57 - 9n = 129$ **32.** $\frac{5y}{4} = 25$

35. Both of you will leave the museum, walk 2 blocks west to the subway, and ride the subway downtown. Then you and your friend will part at your apartment.

36. a.

Cost of 1st minute	+	Cost of each additional minute	×	Number of additional minutes	=	Money you have

b. Cost of 1st minute = 25 (cents)
Cost of each additional minute = 15 (cents)
Number of additional minutes = n
Money you have = 95 (cents)

c. $25 + 15n = 95, n = 4\frac{2}{3}$

d. Since you would be charged 15 cents for any part of a minute, you can talk only 4 additional minutes. You can talk 1 minute + 4 minutes or 5 minutes.
Check: $25 + 15(4) = 75 < 95$
$25 + 15(5) = 100 > 95$

4.2 Independent Practice p. 156

29. $-14, -7, 0, 7, 14$; each number, after the first, is 7 more than the preceding number.

30. $-16, -8, 0, 8, 16$; each number, after the first, is 8 more than the preceding number.

31. $-27, -15, -3, 9, 21$; each number, after the first, is 12 more than the preceding number.

32. $0, 3, 6, 9, 12$; each number, after the first, is 3 more than the preceding number.

33. $22, 11, 0, -11, -22$; each number, after the first, is 11 less than the preceding number.

34. $10, 5, 0, -5, -10$; each number, after the first, is 5 less than the preceding number.

35.

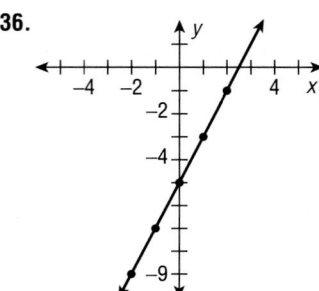

The graph is a straight line.

36.

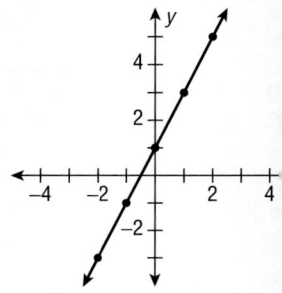

The graph is a straight line.

37.

The graph is a straight line.

4.5 Communicating About Mathematics p. 170

	x	0	1	2	3	4	5	6
Rectangle's perimeter:	$4x + 6$	6	10	14	18	22	26	30
Triangle's perimeter:	$3x + 9$	9	12	15	18	21	24	27

4.6 Independent Practice p. 175

6.

Time (P.M.)	3:00	4:00	5:00	6:00	7:00	8:00	9:00
Santa Fe temp.	86°	83°	80°	77°	74°	71°	68°
Minot temp.	56°	58°	60°	62°	64°	66°	68°

at 9 P.M.

7.

Temp. in Santa Fe	−	Santa Fe rate	×	Time for temp. to be the same	=	Temp. in Minot	+	Minot rate	×	Time for temp. to be the same

8. Temp. in Santa Fe = 86 (degrees Fahrenheit)
Santa Fe rate = 3 (degrees per hour)
Time for temp. to be the same = h (hours)
Temp. in Minot = 56 (degrees Fahrenheit)
Minot rate = 2 (degrees per hour)

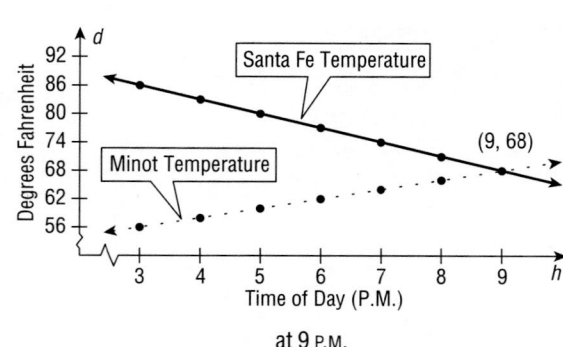

at 9 P.M.

4.6 Independent Practice p. 176

14.

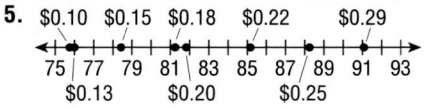

The cost of the CD club is less when you buy more than 5 CD's.

4.7 Independent Practice p. 181

23.

Cost of 1st oz	+	Cost of each additional oz	×	Number of additional oz	=	Total cost

24.

Additional oz	1	2	3	4	5	6	7	8
Cost ($)	0.52	0.75	0.98	1.21	1.44	1.67	1.90	2.13

25.

Initial Fee	+	Cost per mile	×	Number of miles	=	Total cost

26.

Miles	100	200	300	400	450	455	456
Cost ($)	58	81	104	127	138.50	139.65	139.88

CHAPTER 5

5.1 Independent Practice pp. 197–198

5.

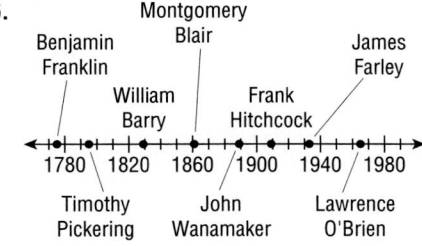

6.

11.

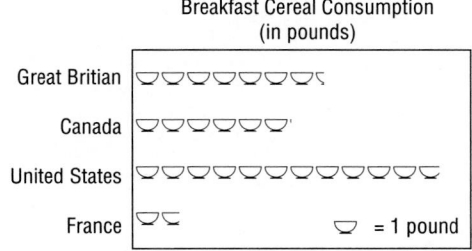

16.

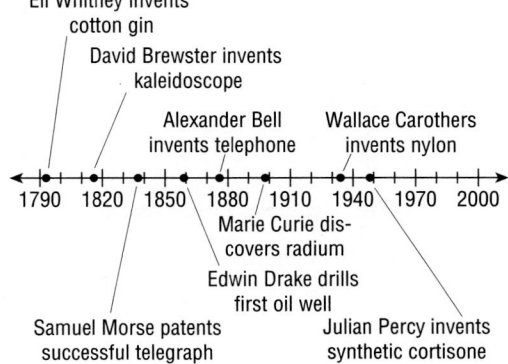

5.2 Independent Practice p. 202

15. Answers vary but may include the following conclusion. For the last three age brackets, there are large increases from 1995 to 2005.

16.

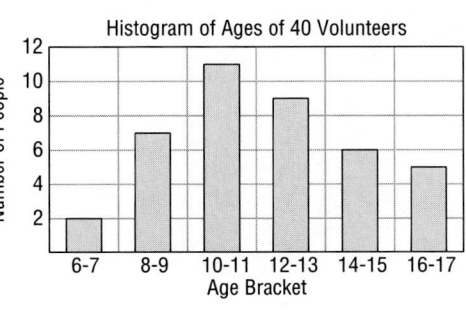

5.2 Integrated Review p. 202

17.

Perimeter	Number of squares
4	16
8	9
12	4
16	1

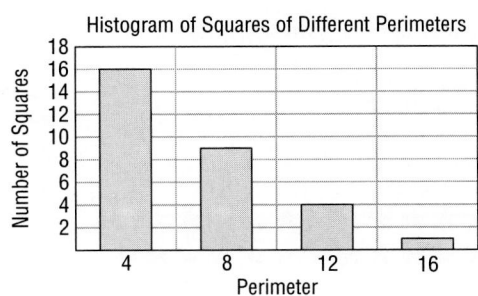

18.

Area	Number of rectangles
1	16
2	24
3	16
4	17
6	12
8	6
9	4
12	4
16	1

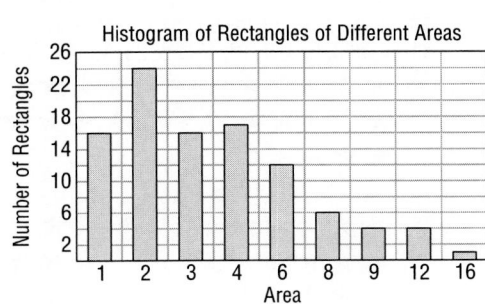

5.2 Exploration and Extension p. 202

19.

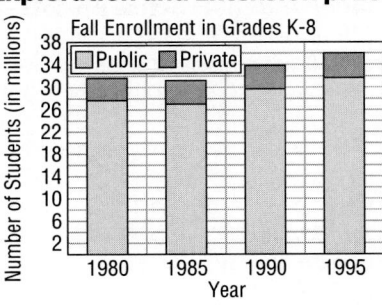

5.3 Independent Practice p. 205

14.

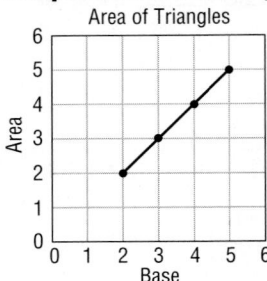

Area of Triangles

15.

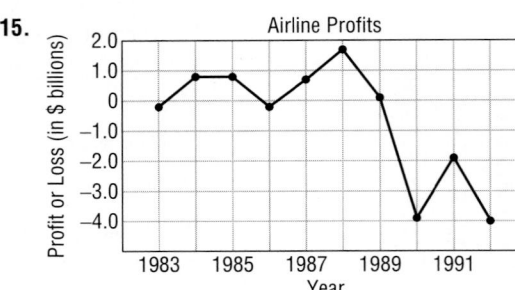

Airline Profits

5.5 Independent Practice p. 216

6.

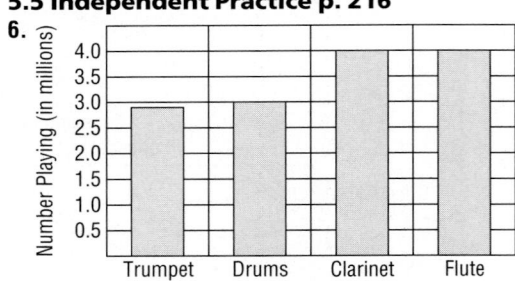

10.

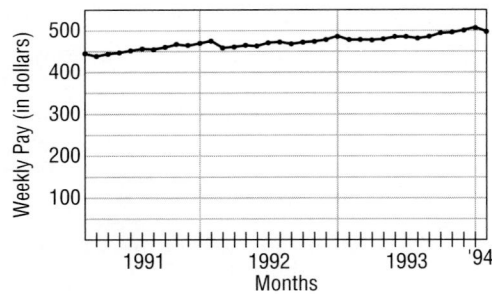

5.7 Independent Practice p. 227

21.

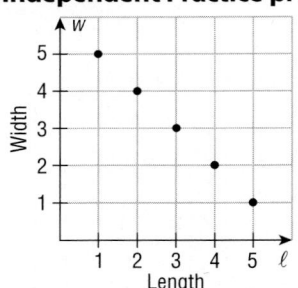

Negative Correlation

5.7 Exploration and Extension p. 227

26.

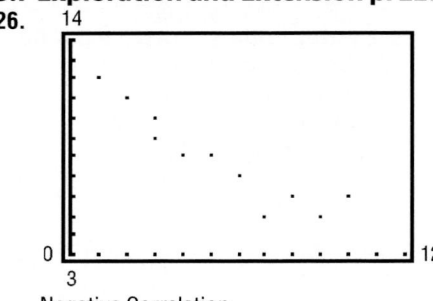

Negative Correlation

27.

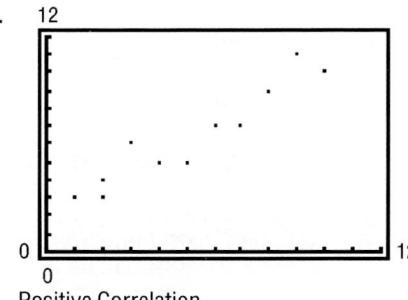

Positive Correlation

CHAPTER 6

6.1 Independent Practice pp. 242–243

23. 2^3 is divisible by 2, 4, and 8; 3^2 is divisible by 3 and 9; 5 is divisible by 5; 2×3 is divisible by 6. So $2^3 \times 3^2 \times 5$ is divisible by 2, 3, 4, 5, 6, 8, and 9; and $2^3 \times 3^2 \times 5 = 360$.

24. Let $a = 3x$ and $b = 3y$, and let x and y be any integers. Then

  a. $a + b = 3x + 3y = 3(x+y)$
  b. $a - b = 3x - 3y = 3(x-y)$
  c. $a\,b = (3x)(3y)$
  d. $\dfrac{a}{b} = \dfrac{3x}{3y} = \dfrac{x}{y}$

In **a**, **b**, and **c**, the expressions are always divisible by 3. In **d**, $\dfrac{x}{y}$ may be a fraction or an integer that is not divisible by 3.

33. $2 \times 3 \times 4$ or $2 \times 2 \times 6$

34. $2 \times 2 \times 9$ or $2 \times 3 \times 6$ or $3 \times 3 \times 4$

35. $2 \times 3 \times 35, 2 \times 5 \times 21, 2 \times 7 \times 15,$ $3 \times 5 \times 14, 3 \times 7 \times 10,$ or $5 \times 6 \times 7$

36. $2 \times 2 \times 36, 2 \times 3 \times 24, 2 \times 4 \times 18,$ $2 \times 6 \times 12, 2 \times 8 \times 9, 3 \times 3 \times 16,$ $3 \times 4 \times 12, 3 \times 6 \times 8, 4 \times 4 \times 9,$ or $4 \times 6 \times 6$

39. No, $15 = 3 \times 5$ and 3 is not a factor of 350

40. 1 ft $\times$ 1600 ft, 2 ft $\times$ 800 ft, 4 ft $\times$ 400 ft, 5 ft $\times$ 320 ft, 8 ft $\times$ 200 ft, 10 ft $\times$ 160 ft, 16 ft $\times$ 100 ft, 20 ft $\times$ 80 ft, 25 ft $\times$ 64 ft, 32 ft $\times$ 50 ft, and 40 ft $\times$ 40 ft

6.2 Independent Practice p. 248

37. No, by the answers to Exercises **33.–36.**

38. No. Let $x =$ the smallest integer; then the perimeter $= x + (x + 1) + (x + 2) = 3x + 3 = 3(x + 1)$, which is divisible by 3.

39. Answers vary. $20 = 3 + 17, 22 = 3 + 19, 24 = 5 + 19, 26 = 3 + 23,$ $28 = 5 + 23, 30 = 7 + 23, 32 = 3 + 29, 34 = 3 + 31, 36 = 5 + 31,$ $38 = 7 + 31, 40 = 3 + 37$

40. 17 and 19, 29 and 31, 41 and 43, 59 and 61, 71 and 73

41. 1, 2, 3, 5, 6, 9, 10, 15, 18, 25, 30, 45, 50, 75, 90, 150, 225, 450

43.

45.

44.

46.

6.3 Exploration and Extension p. 253

47.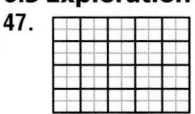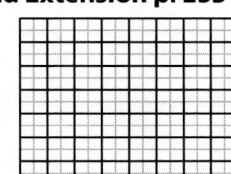

48.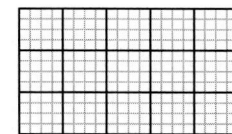

6.4 Independent Practice pp. 257–258

9. 3, 6, 9, 12, 15, 18, 21
7, 14, 21

10. 7, 14, 21, 28, 35, 42, 49, 56
8, 16, 24, 32, 40, 48, 56

11. 6, 12, 18, 24
8, 16, 24

12. 3, 6, 9
9

13. 8, 16, 24, 32, 40
10, 20, 30, 40

14. 10, 20, 30
15, 30

15. 10, 20, 30, 40, 50, 60, 70, 80, 90, 100, 110, 120, 130
26, 52, 78, 104, 130

16. 4, 8, 12, 16, 20, 24, 28, 32, 36, 40, 44
22, 44

17. 3, 6, 9, 12, 15, 18, 21, 24, 27, 30, 33, 36
4, 8, 12, 16, 20, 24, 28, 32, 36
18, 36

18. 3, 6, 9, 12, 15, 18
6, 12, 18
9, 18

19. 5, 10, 15, 20
10, 20
20

20. 6, 12, 18
9, 18
18

21. $90 = 2 \cdot 3^2 \cdot 5$
$108 = 2^2 \cdot 3^3$
$2^2 \cdot 3^3 \cdot 5 = 540$

22. $7 = 7$
$8 = 2^3$
$2^3 \cdot 7 = 56$

23. $125 = 5^3$
$500 = 2^2 \cdot 5^3$
$2^2 \cdot 5^3 = 500$

24. $160 = 2^5 \cdot 5$
$432 = 2^4 \cdot 3^3$
$2^5 \cdot 3^3 \cdot 5 = 4320$

25. $135 = 3^3 \cdot 5$
$375 = 3 \cdot 5^3$
$3^3 \cdot 5^3 = 3375$

26. $225 = 3^2 \cdot 5^2$
$324 = 2^2 \cdot 3^4$
$2^2 \cdot 3^4 \cdot 5^2 = 8100$

27. $144 = 2^4 \cdot 3^2$
$162 = 2 \cdot 3^4$
$2^4 \cdot 3^4 = 1296$

28. $16x = 2^4 \cdot x$
$32x^4 = 2^5 \cdot x^4$
$2^5 \cdot x^4 = 32x^4$

29. $7s^2t = 7 \cdot s^2 \cdot t$
$49st^2 = 7^2 \cdot s \cdot t^2$
$7^2 \cdot s^2 \cdot t^2 = 49s^2t^2$

30. $2x^3y = 2 \cdot x^3 \cdot y$
$3xy^5 = 3 \cdot x \cdot y^5$
$2 \cdot 3 \cdot x^3 \cdot y^5 = 6x^3y^5$

31. $3m^4n^4 = 3 \cdot m^4 \cdot n^4$
$7m^6n^2 = 7 \cdot m^6 \cdot n^2$
$3 \cdot 7 \cdot m^6 \cdot n^4 = 21m^6 \cdot n^4$

32. $4a^6b^3 = 2^2 \cdot a^6 \cdot b^3$
$8a^7b^5 = 2^3 \cdot a^7 \cdot b^5$
$2^3 \cdot a^7 \cdot b^5 = 8a^7b^5$

6.4 Integrated Review p. 258

To get the next number:

46. Add 4, add 6, add 8, etc., to the preceding number.

47. Add 8, add 12, add 16, etc., to the preceding number.

6.6 Communicating about Mathematics p. 266

A. $x = 0.6666\ldots$ — Let x represent the number.
$10x = 6.666\ldots$ — Multiply each side by 10.
$9x = 6$ — Subtract 1st equation from 2nd.
$x = \dfrac{6}{9}$ — Divide each side by 9.
$x = \dfrac{2}{3}$ — Simplify.

B. $x = 1.6666\ldots$ — Let x represent the number.
$10x = 16.666\ldots$ — Multiply each side by 10.
$9x = 15$ — Subtract 1st equation from 2nd.
$x = \dfrac{15}{9}$ — Divide each side by 9.
$x = \dfrac{5}{3}$ — Simplify.

C. $2.25 = \dfrac{225}{100} = \dfrac{9 \cdot 25}{4 \cdot 25} = \dfrac{9}{4}$

D. $x = 0.2222\ldots$ — Let x represent the number.
$10x = 2.222\ldots$ — Multiply each side by 10.
$9x = 2$ — Subtract 1st equation from 2nd.
$x = \dfrac{2}{9}$ — Divide each side by 9.

6.9 Independent Practice p. 281

5.

n	1	2	3	4	5	6
$n^2 + 1$	2	5	10	17	26	37

6.

n	1	2	3	4	5	6
$n^2 + n$	2	6	12	20	30	42

7.

n	1	2	3	4	5	6
2^{n-1}	1	2	4	8	16	32

8.

n	1	2	3	4	5	6
2^{1-n}	1	$\dfrac{1}{2}$	$\dfrac{1}{4}$	$\dfrac{1}{8}$	$\dfrac{1}{16}$	$\dfrac{1}{32}$

15. 15, 21

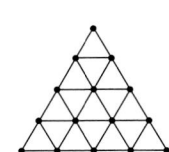 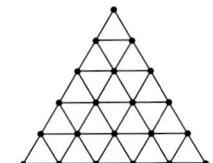

16. 25, 36

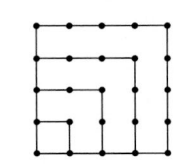 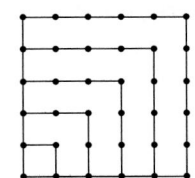

17. 35, 51

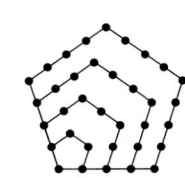

18. 45, 66

 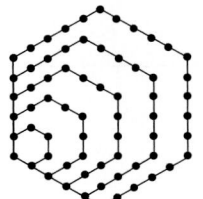

ADDITIONAL ANSWERS

7.2 Exploration and Extension p. 302

43.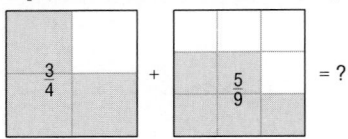

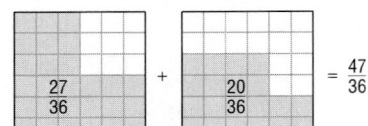

44.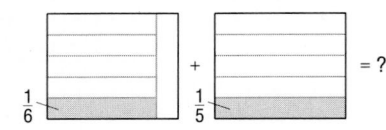

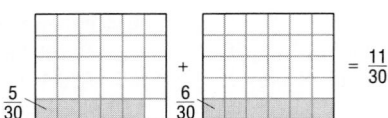

45.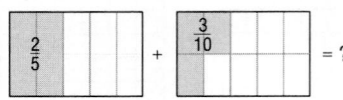

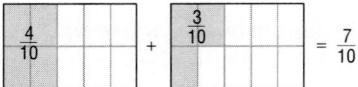

46.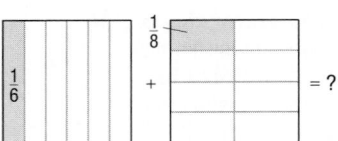

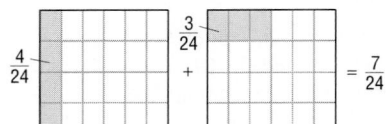

7.3 Independent Practice p. 305

11.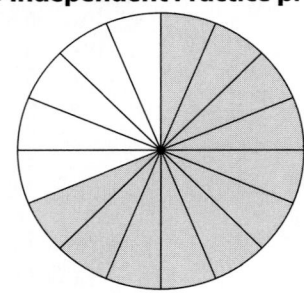

12.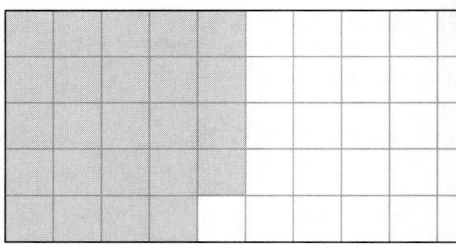

13.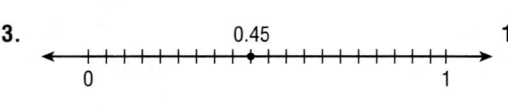

14.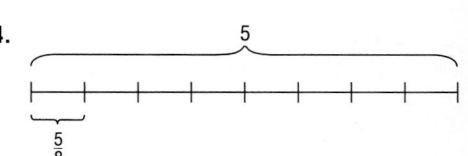

7.5 Communicating About Mathematics p. 313

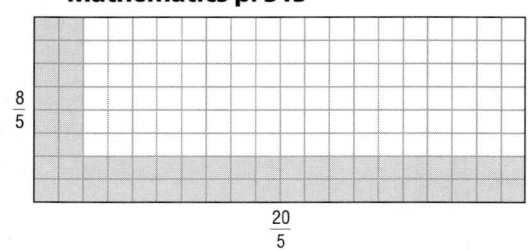

$4 \cdot 10 = 40$

7.7 Independent Practice p. 325

60.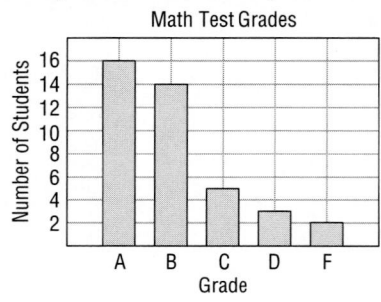

7.8 Independent Practice p. 329

16.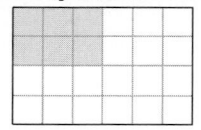

17.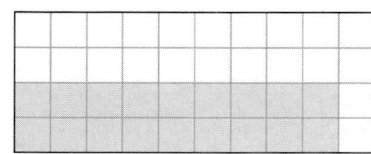

18.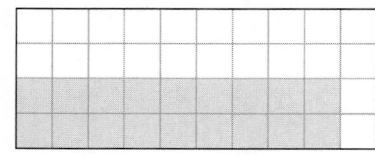

7.9 Chapter Review p. 339

83.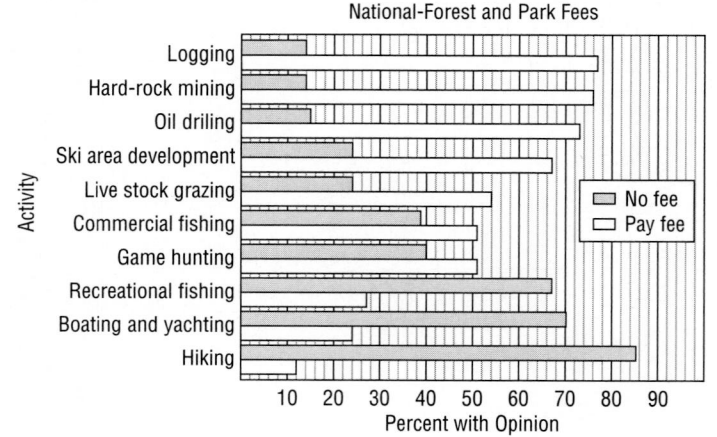

8.4 Independent Practice p. 360

23. 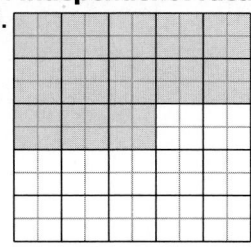 **24.** 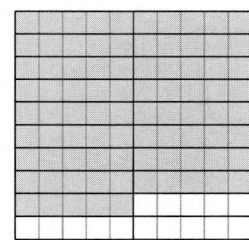 **25.**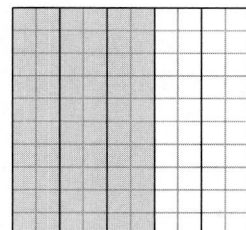

8.3 Exploration and Extension p. 356

21. 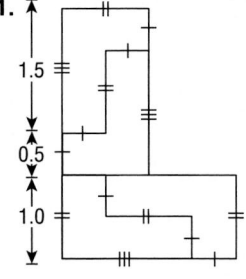 **22.** 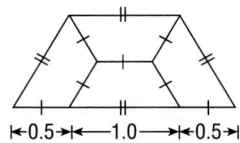 **23.** 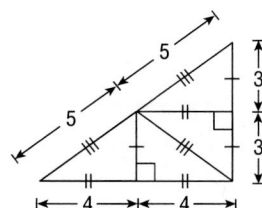 **24.**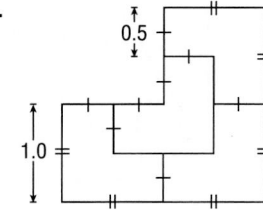

8.6 Exploration and Extension p. 371

37. 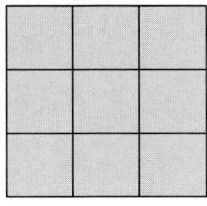 **38.** 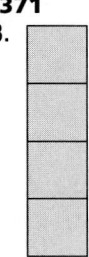 **39.** 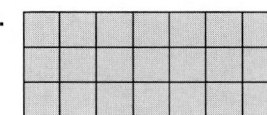 **40.**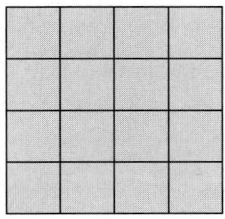

8.7 Independent Practice p. 376

10.b.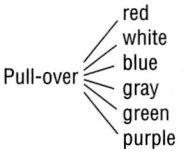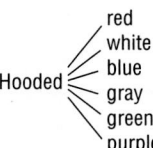

9.2 Integrated Review p. 398

46.

	Natural	Whole	Integers	Rational	Irrational	Real
-5			✓	✓		✓
$\frac{15}{12}$				✓		✓
$\sqrt{9}$	✓	✓	✓	✓		✓
$-\sqrt{\frac{6}{5}}$					✓	✓
$\sqrt{11}$					✓	✓
0		✓	✓	✓		✓

9.3 Independent Practice pp. 402–403

15. 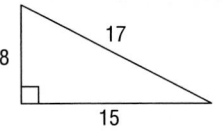 **16.** 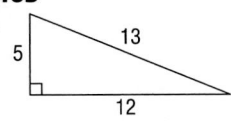 **20.**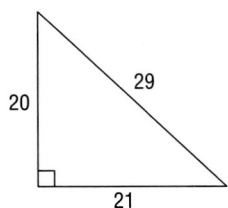

9.3 Independent Practice pp. 402–403 *(continued)*

31.

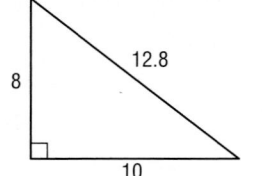 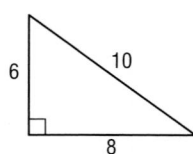

32.

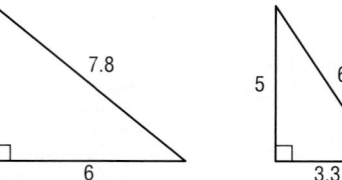

9.3 Integrated Review p. 403

33.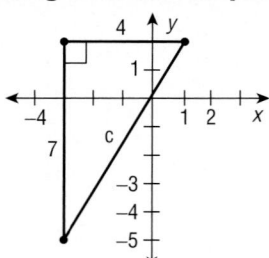

34.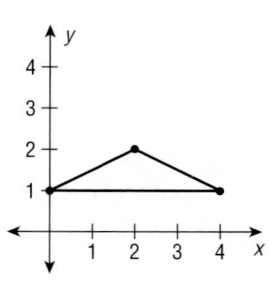

35.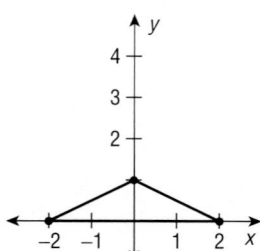

36.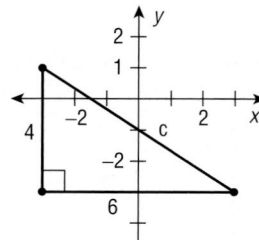

37.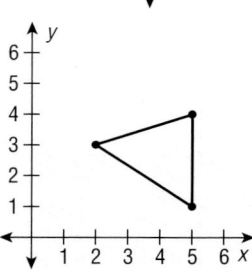

38.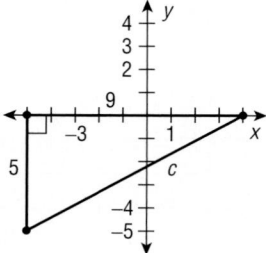

9.6 Independent Practice p. 418

20.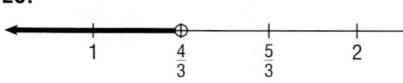

21.

22.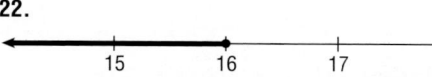

23.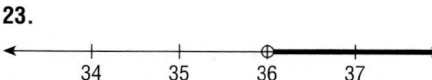

24.

25.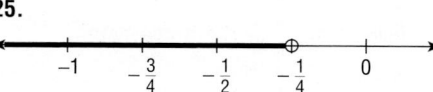

26.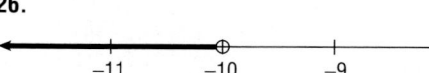

27.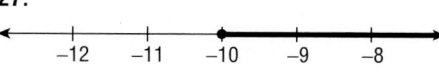

28.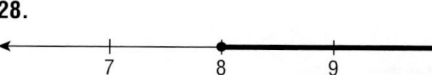

29.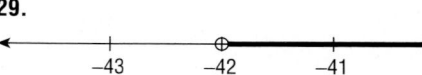

30.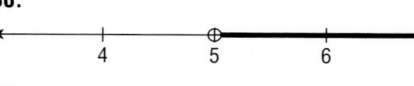

31.

32.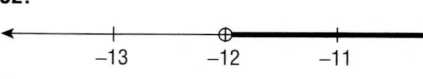

33.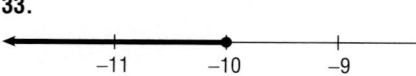

34.

35.

9.7 Independent Practice p. 423

33.

Number of tickets bought	4	8	12	16	20	24	28	32	36	40
Total cost in dollars	11	12	13	14	15	16	17	18	19	20

39.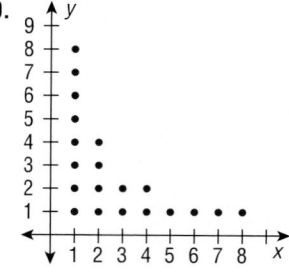

40.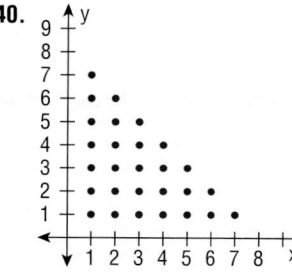

10.1 Independent Practice p. 441

21.  22. 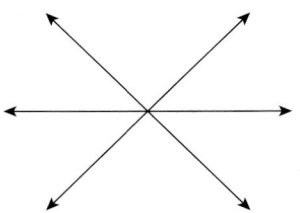 23. 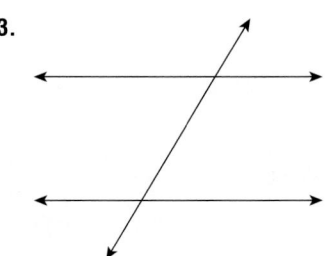 24.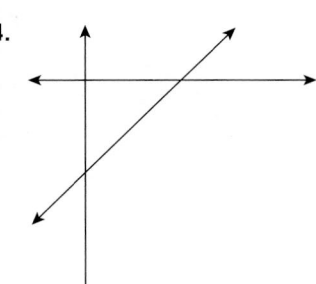

10.1 Integrated Review p. 442

31.

$\overleftrightarrow{AB}$

32.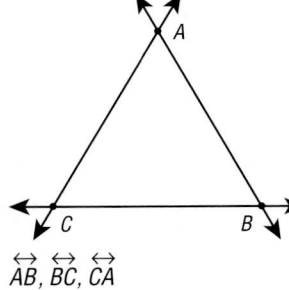

$\overleftrightarrow{AB}, \overleftrightarrow{BC}, \overleftrightarrow{CA}$

33.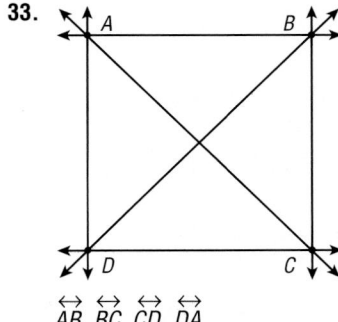

$\overleftrightarrow{AB}, \overleftrightarrow{BC}, \overleftrightarrow{CD}, \overleftrightarrow{DA},$
$\overleftrightarrow{AC}, \overleftrightarrow{BD}$

34.

$\overleftrightarrow{AB}, \overleftrightarrow{BC}, \overleftrightarrow{CD}, \overleftrightarrow{DE}, \overleftrightarrow{EA},$
$\overleftrightarrow{AC}, \overleftrightarrow{AD}, \overleftrightarrow{BD}, \overleftrightarrow{BE}, \overleftrightarrow{CE}$

10.3 Communicating about Mathematics p. 449

$\angle 1 \cong \angle a, \angle a \cong \angle b$, and $\angle b \cong \angle 3$;
so $\angle 1 \cong \angle 3$.
$\angle 2 \cong \angle c, \angle c \cong \angle d$, and $\angle d \cong \angle 4$;
so $\angle 2 \cong \angle 4$.
$m\angle 2 = 96°, m\angle 3 = 84°, m\angle 4 = 96°$.

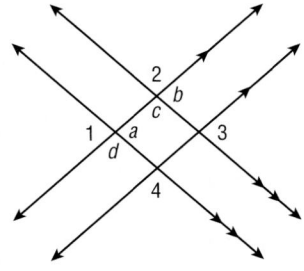

10.5 Guided Practice p. 459

1. c; all sides have different lengths.
   d; one angle is obtuse.

2. a; at least two sides have the same length.
   d; one angle is obtuse.

3. c; all sides have different lengths.
   f; one angle is right.

4. c; all sides have different lengths.
   g; all three angles are acute.

5. a; at least two sides have the same length.
   b; all three angles have the same measure.
   e; all three sides have the same length.
   g; all three angles are acute.

6. c; all sides have different lengths.
   g; all three angles are acute.

7. a; at least two sides have the same length.
   b; all three angles have the same measure.
   e; all three sides have the same length.
   g; all three angles are acute.

8. a; at least two sides have the same length.
   f; one angle is right.

10.5 Independent Practice p. 459

21.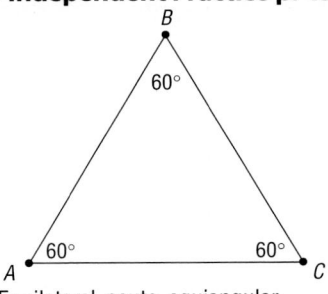

Equilateral, acute, equiangular, isosceles

22.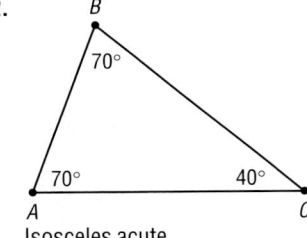

Isosceles acute

23.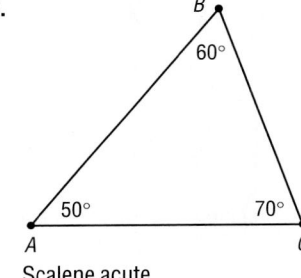

Scalene acute

Independent Practice p. 459 (continued)

24.

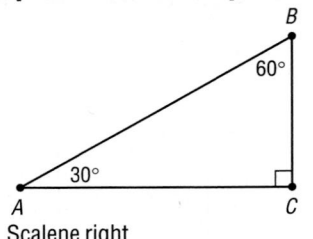

Scalene right

25.

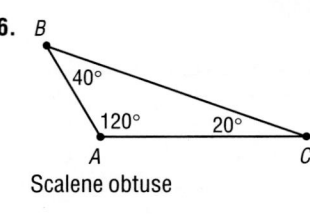

Isosceles right

26.

Scalene obtuse

10.5 Integrated Review p. 460

36.

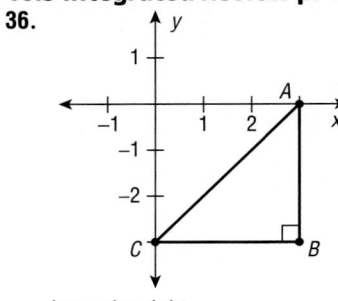

Isosceles right

37.

Isosceles obtuse

38.

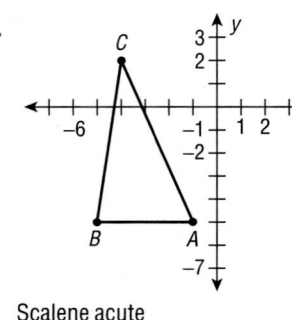

Scalene acute

39.

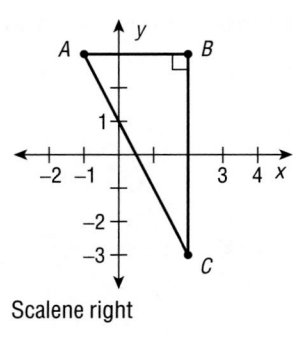

Scalene right

10.5 Exploration and Extension p. 460

40.

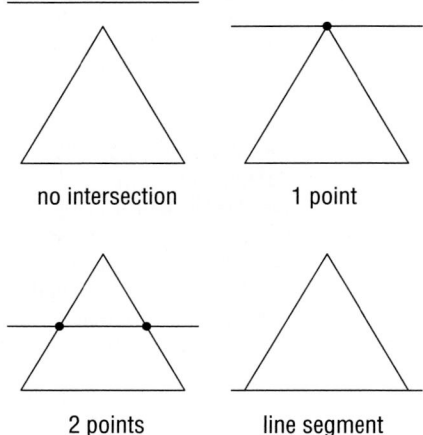

no intersection   1 point

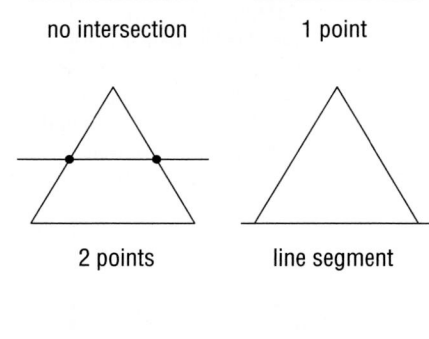

2 points   line segment

41.

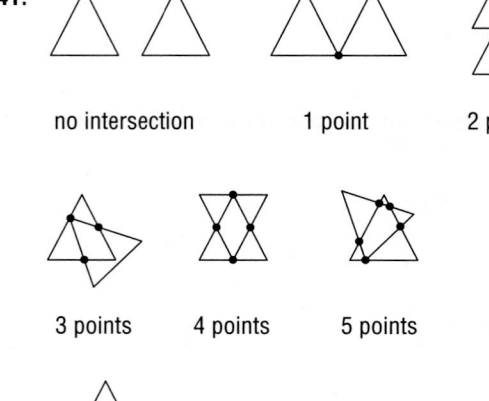

no intersection   1 point   2 points

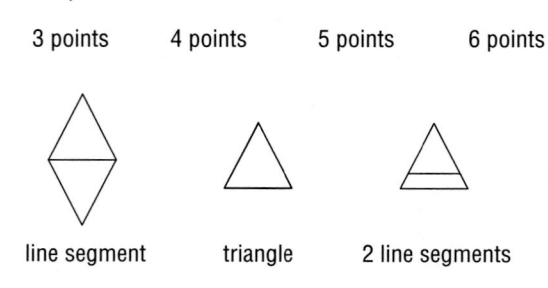

3 points   4 points   5 points   6 points

line segment   triangle   2 line segments

42.

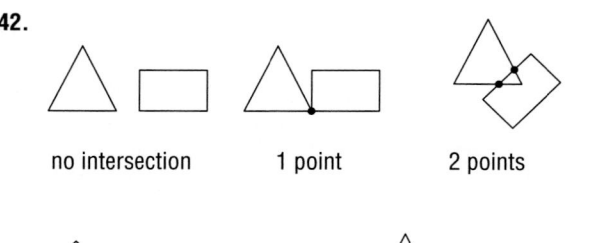

no intersection   1 point   2 points

3 points   4 points   5 points

6 points   line segment   2 line segments

43.

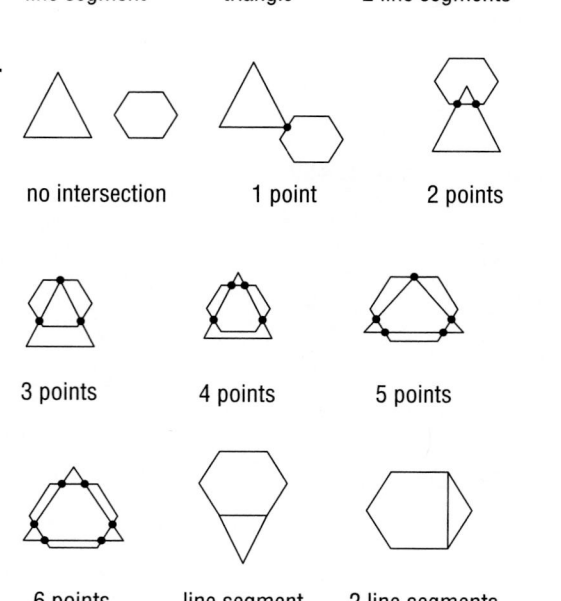

no intersection   1 point   2 points

3 points   4 points   5 points

6 points   line segment   2 line segments

10.6 Integrated Review p. 465

41.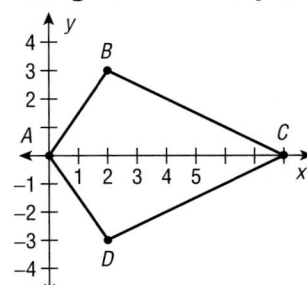

42.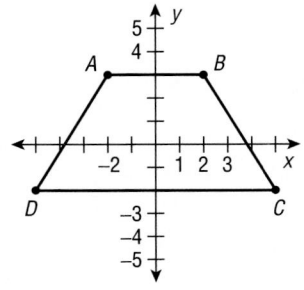

43.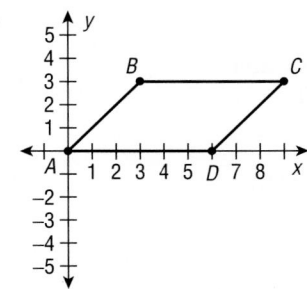

44.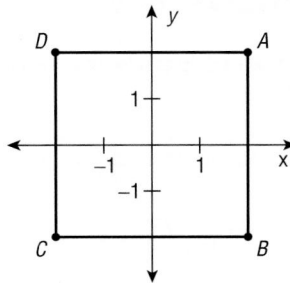

10.6 Mixed Review p. 466

1.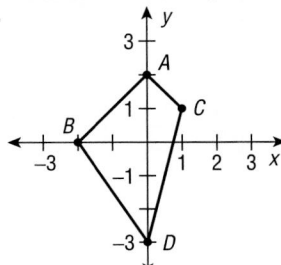

2.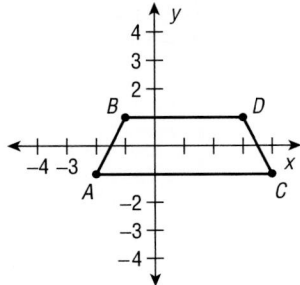

3.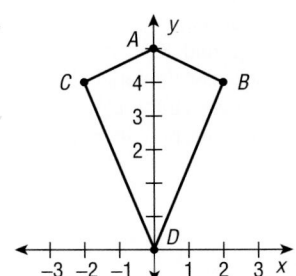

10.9 Independent Practice pp. 479–480

14.–17. The smallest angle is opposite the shortest side.

14. $BC \approx 8.01$, so $\overline{BC}$ is the shortest side.

15. $AC \approx 6.01$, so $\overline{BC}$ is the shortest side.

16. $BC \approx 6.00$, so $\overline{AC}$ is the shortest side.

17. $AC \approx 19.00$, so $\overline{AC}$ is the shortest side.

18.–21. The shortest side is opposite the smallest angle and the longest side is opposite the largest angle.

18. $\angle C = 53°$, so $\angle C$ is the smallest angle and $\angle B$ is the largest angle.

19. $\angle DEF = 60°$ and $\angle F = 50°$, so $\angle F$ is the smallest angle and $\angle D$ is the largest angle.

20. $\angle ABC = 72°$ and $\angle A = 60°$, so $\angle C$ is the smallest angle and $\angle ABC$ is the largest angle.

21. $\angle D = 48°$, so $\angle D$ is the smallest angle and $\angle E$ is the largest angle.

26.–30. If a triangle has three sides of the same length, then it has three angles of the same measure; so Exercise 27 matches with c. If no two sides of a triangle have the same length, then no two angles have the same measure; so Exercise 29 matches with b. If a triangle has a shortest side and no longest side, then it has a smallest angle and no largest angle; so Exercise 30 matches with a. The longest side in Exercise 26 is less than 50% longer than the shorter sides, while the longest side in Exercise 28 is more than 80% longer than the shorter sides; so the largest angle in Exercise 26 is smaller than the largest angle in Exercise 28; so Exercise 26 matches with d. Then Exercise 28 matches with e.

10.9 Exploration and Extension p. 480

37.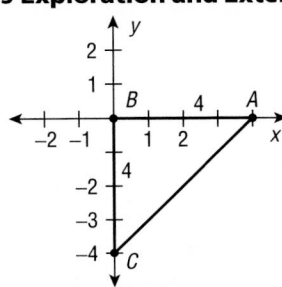

$AB = 4$, $BC = 4$, $AC \approx 5.7$; none, $\angle B$

38.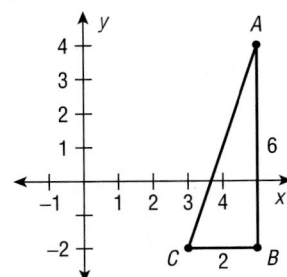

$AB = 6$, $BC = 2$, $AC \approx 6.3$; $\angle A$, $\angle B$

39.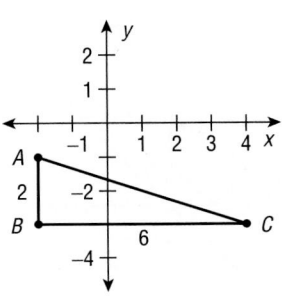

$AB = 2$, $BC = 6$, $AC \approx 6.3$; $\angle C$, $\angle B$

40.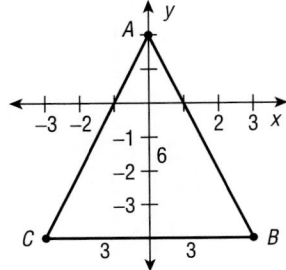

$AB \approx 6.7$, $BC = 6$, $AC \approx 6.7$; $\angle A$, none

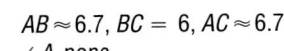

11.1 Independent Practice pp. 490–491

10.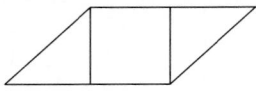

11.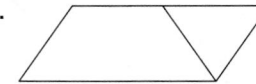

12.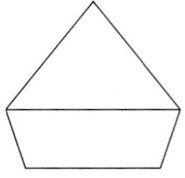

13.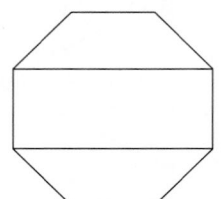

14.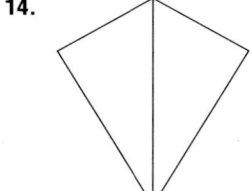

15. A: Trapezoid, B: Isosceles right triangle, C: Scalene obtuse triangle, D: Kite, E: Parallelogram, F: Square, G: Trapezoid, H: Rectangle, I: Isosceles right triangle, J: Isosceles trapezoid, K: Isosceles right triangle

16. A: 10.5 units^2, B: 8 units^2, C: 6 units^2, D: 12 units^2, E: 15 units^2, F: 9 units^2, G: 6 units^2, H: 8 units^2, I: 9 units^2, J: 12 units^2, K: 4.5 units^2

19. b.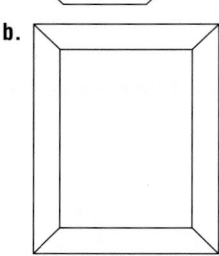

11.1 Integrated Review p. 491

23.

height (x)	1	2	3	4	5
area (y)	3	6	9	12	15

For every unit that the height increases, the area increases by 3 units^2.

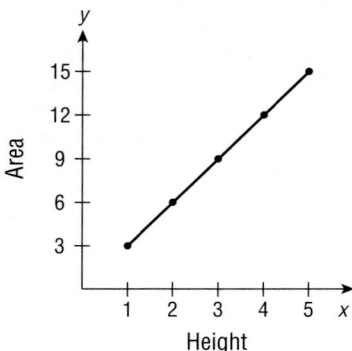

24.

height (x)	5	6	7	8	9
area (y)	35	42	49	56	63

For every unit that the height increases, the area increases by 7 units^2.

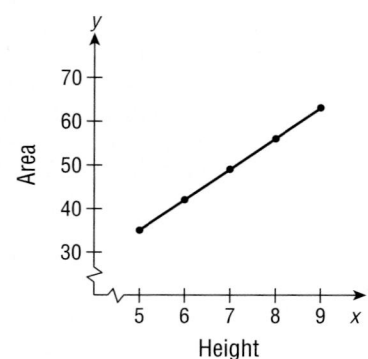

11.3 Independent Practice pp. 499–500

11.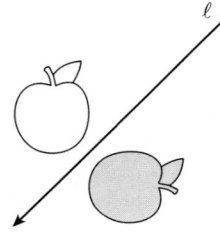

13.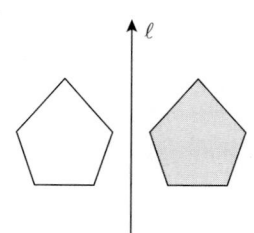

15.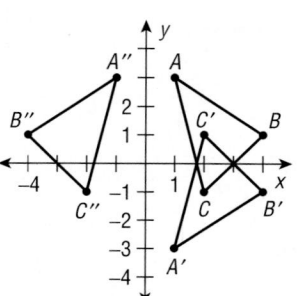

16.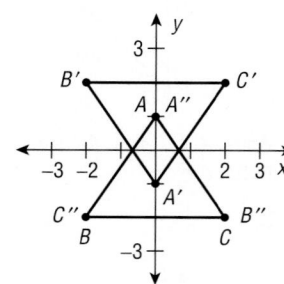

17.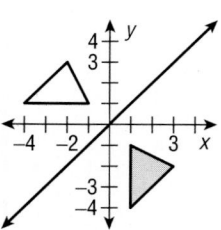

18.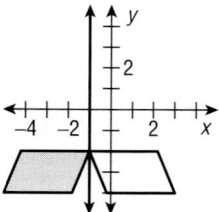

19.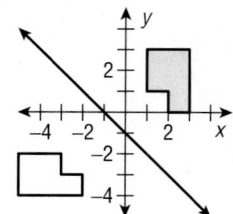

20.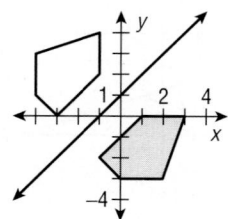

11.5 Independent Practice p. 508

13.
a.
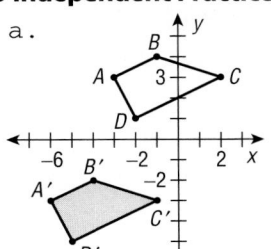

b.
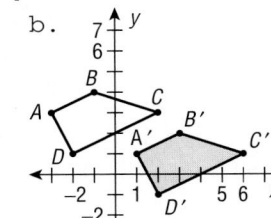

c.
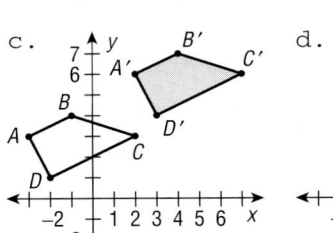

d.
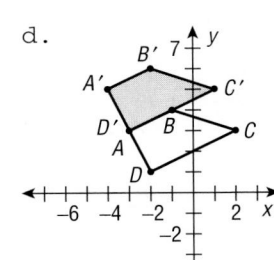

11.7 Exploration and Extension p. 520

17.
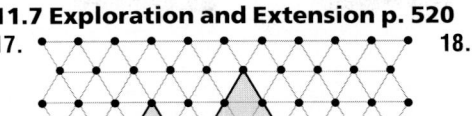
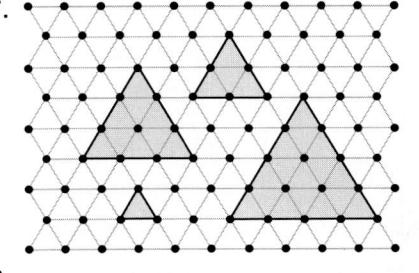

18.
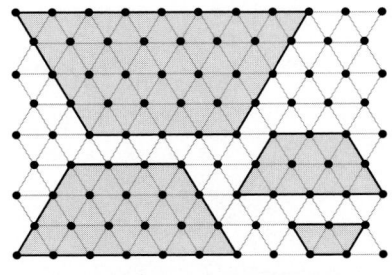

19.
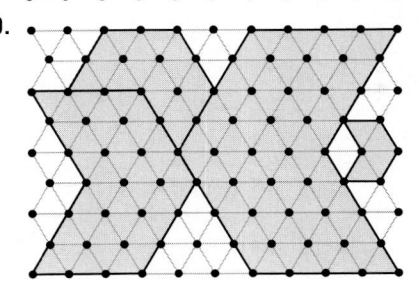

20.
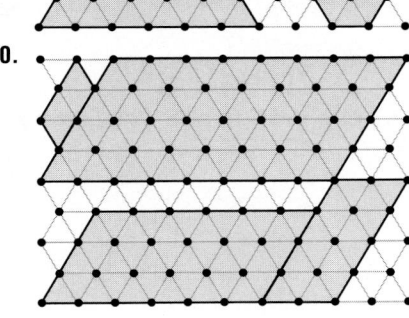

CHAPTER 12

12.1 Independent Practice p. 542

19.

Radius	1	2	3	4	5	6
Circumference	6.28	12.56	18.84	25.12	31.40	37.68

For every one-unit increase in the radius, the circumference increases 6.28 units.

20.

Radius	1	2	3	4	5	6
Area	3.14	12.56	28.26	50.24	78.50	113.04

For every one-unit increase in the radius after the first increase, the area increases by the square of the ratio of the radius to the previous radius.

21. The circumference doubles; $C_1 = \pi d$, $C_2 = \pi(2d) = 2(\pi d)$. The area quadruples; $A_1 = \pi r^2$, $A_2 = \pi(2r)^2 = 4(\pi r^2)$.

12.1 Integrated Review p. 542

29.
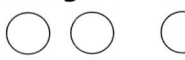 

no points   1 point   2 points   all points

30.
  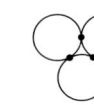

no points 1 point 2 points 2 points 3 points 3 points

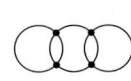 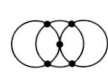 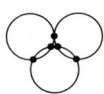

3 points 4 points 5 points 5 points 6 points 6 points

2 circles coincide   3 circles coincide   2 circles coincide and intersect the third circle in 1 point   2 circles coincide and intersect the third circle in 2 points

12.1 Exploration and Extension p. 542

31.

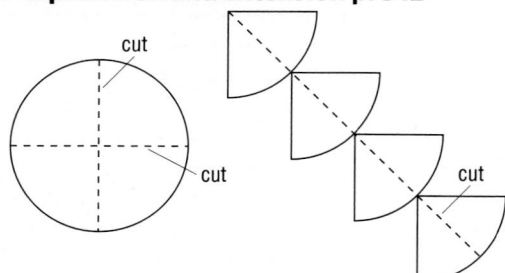

32.

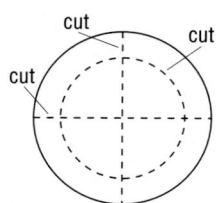

The curved cut is about $\frac{7}{10}$ of the way from the center of the pie.

12.3 Exploration and Extension p. 552

23.

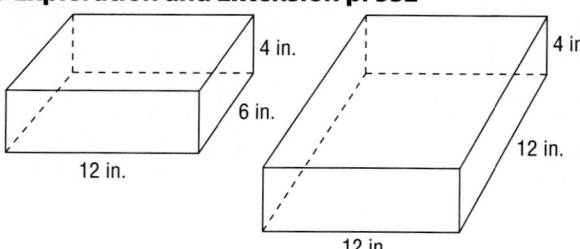

24.

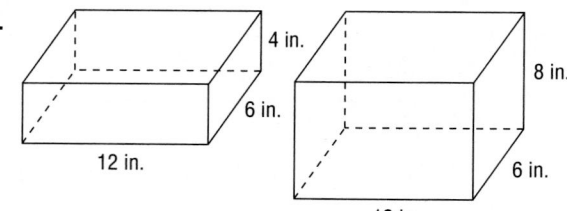

25.

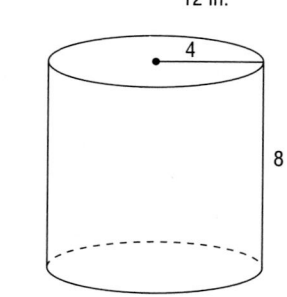

26.

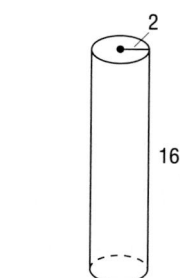

CHAPTER 13

13.2 Independent Practice pp. 595–596

19.

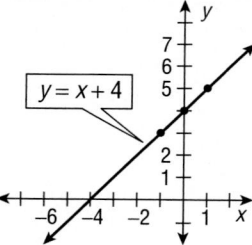

$y = x + 4$

20.

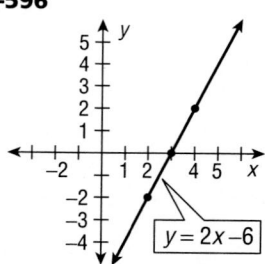

$y = 2x - 6$

21.

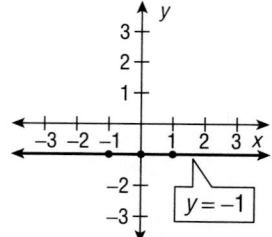

$y = -1$

22.

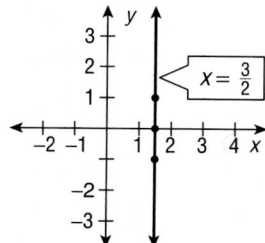

$x = \frac{3}{2}$

23.

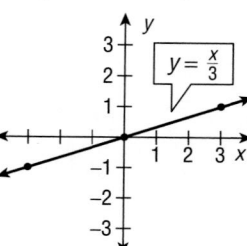

$y = \frac{x}{3}$

24.

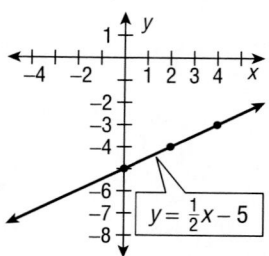

$y = \frac{1}{2}x - 5$

25.

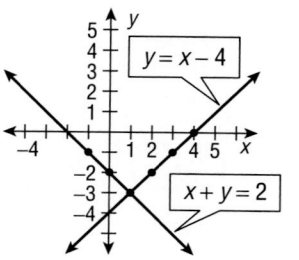

$y = x - 4$

$x + y = 2$

26.

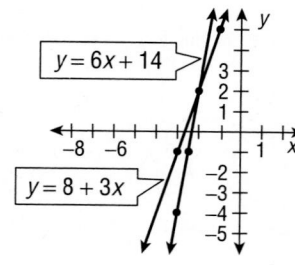

$y = 6x + 14$

$y = 8 + 3x$

27.

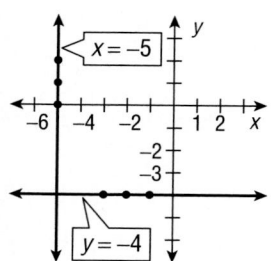

$x = -5$

$y = -4$

30.

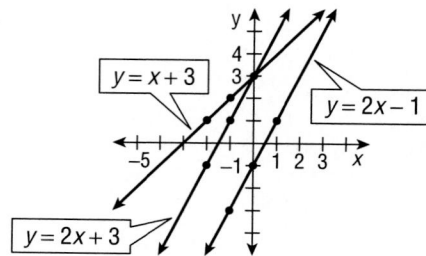

$y = x + 3$

$y = 2x - 1$

$y = 2x + 3$

32.

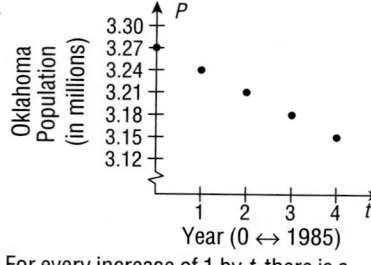

For every increase of 1 by t, there is a corresponding decrease of 0.03 by P. Yes, the points lie on a line.

33.

m	1	2	3	4	5	6	7	8
t	35.9	40.9	50.3	60.4	68.4	76.7	82.0	81.1

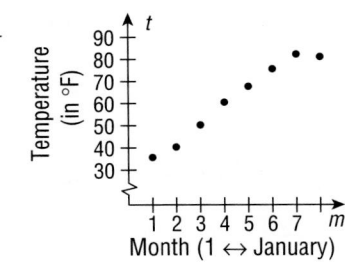

For an increase in *m,* there is an increase in *t* (with one exception). No, the points do not all lie on the same line.

13.2 Integrated Review p. 596

34.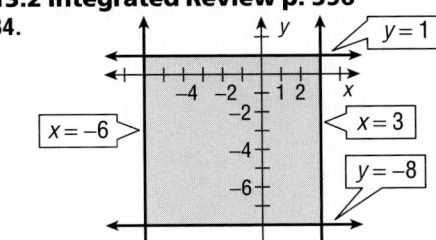

35.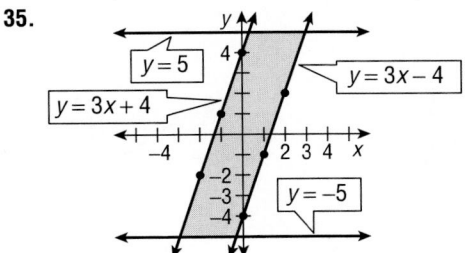

36.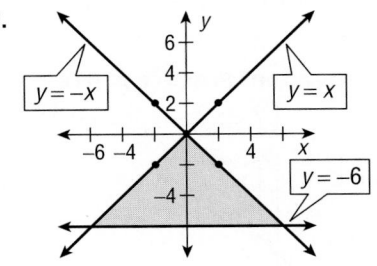

37.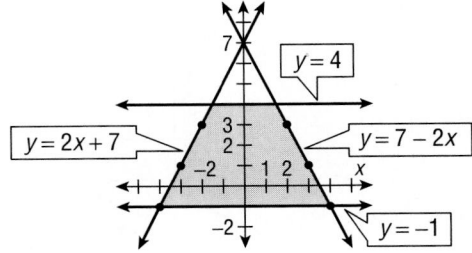

13.3 Guided Practice p. 600

3.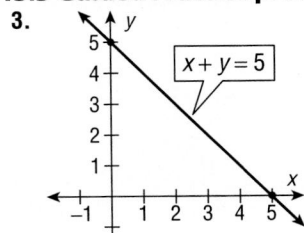

4.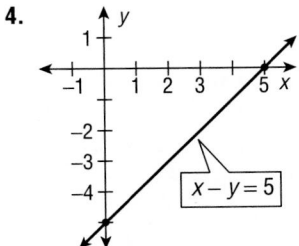

5.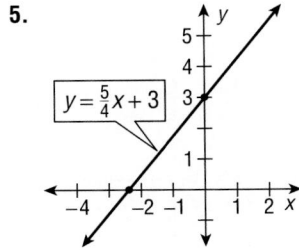

6.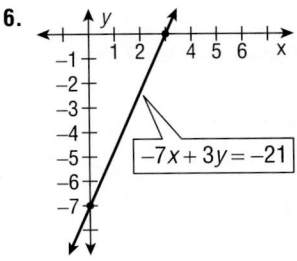

13.3 Independent Practice p. 600

11.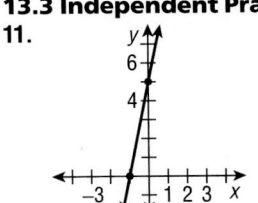

12.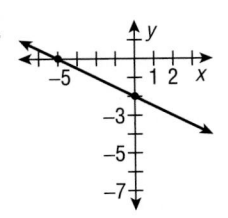

13.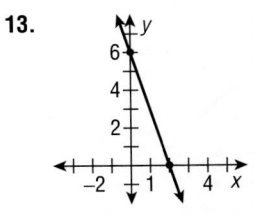

14.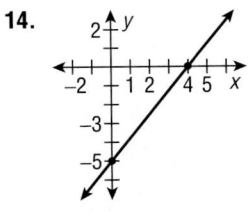

19.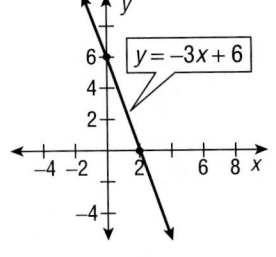

x	0	1	2	3	4
y	6	3	0	−3	−6

20.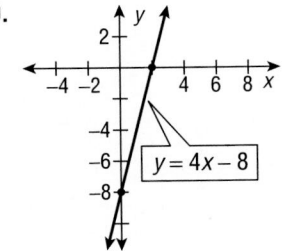

x	0	1	2	3	4
y	−8	−4	0	4	8

21.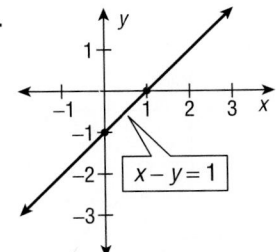

x	0	1	2	3	4
y	−1	0	1	2	3

22.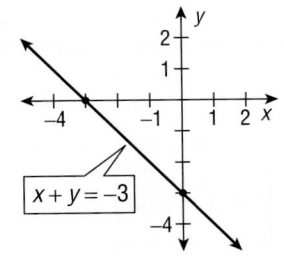

x	−3	−2	−1	0	1
y	0	−1	−2	−3	−4

13.3 Independent Practice p. 600 (continued)

23.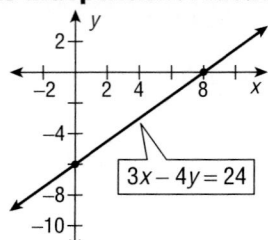

x	8	4	0	-4	-8
y	0	-3	-6	-9	-12

24.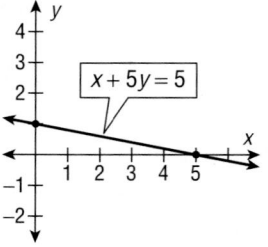

x	-10	-5	0	5	10
y	3	2	1	0	-1

25.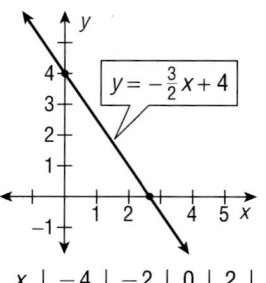

x	-4	-2	0	2	4
y	10	7	4	1	-2

26.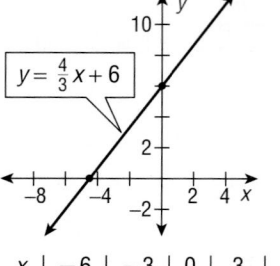

x	-6	-3	0	3	6
y	-2	2	6	10	14

13.5 Independent Practice p. 612

8.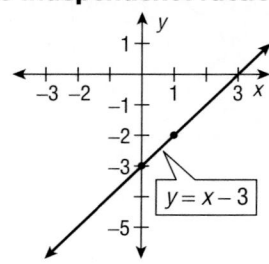

9.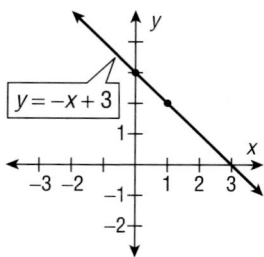

10.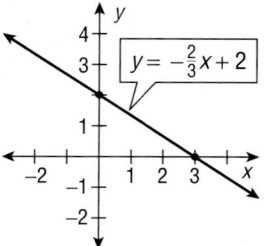

11.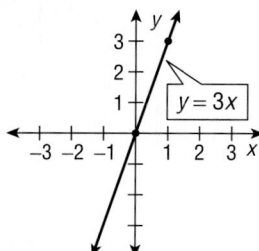

12.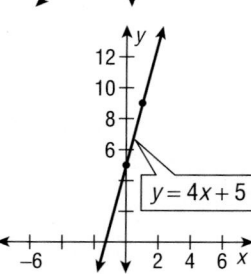

13.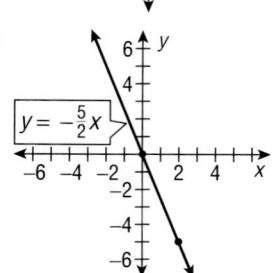

14.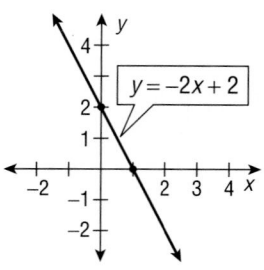

15.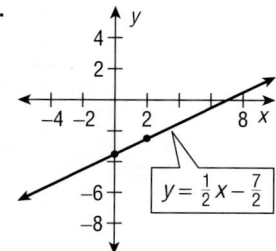

13.7 Independent Practice pp. 621–622

21.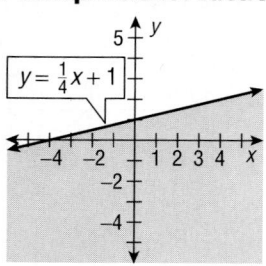

22.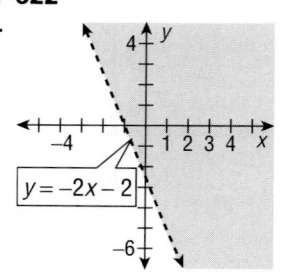

23.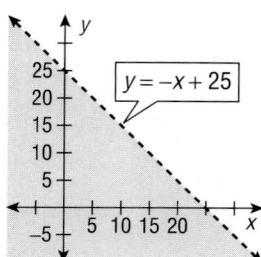

24.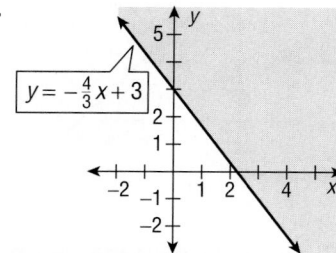

26.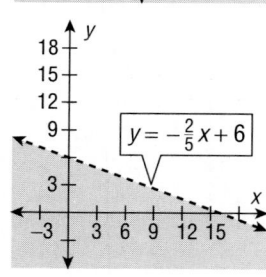

28.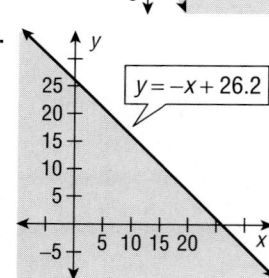

13.7 Exploration and Extension p. 622

37.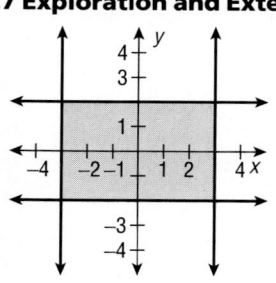

38.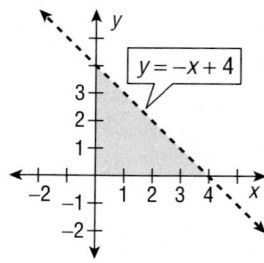

39.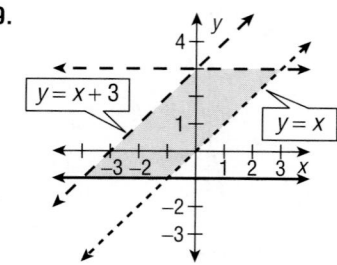

40.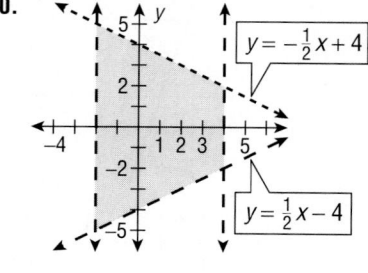

13.8 Chapter Review p. 628

13.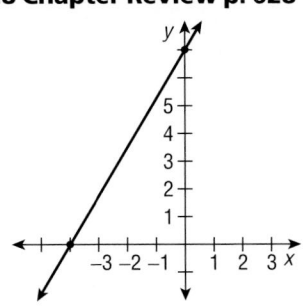

14.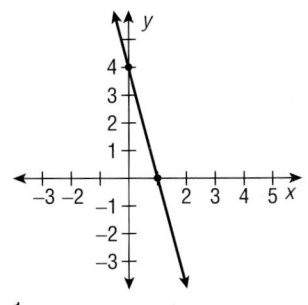

15.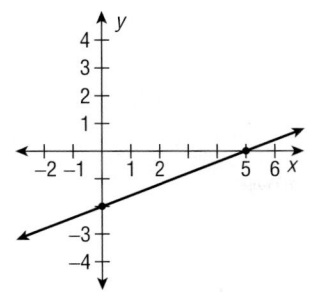

16.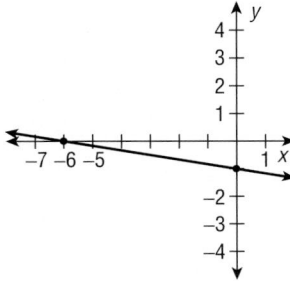

17.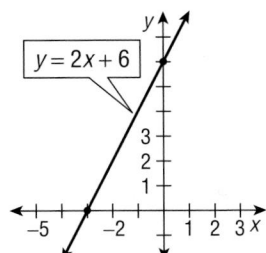

$y = 2x + 6$

18. 1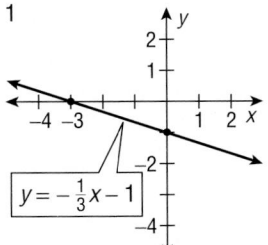

$y = -\frac{1}{3}x - 1$

19.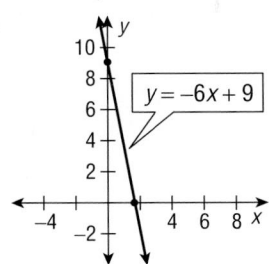

$y = -6x + 9$

20.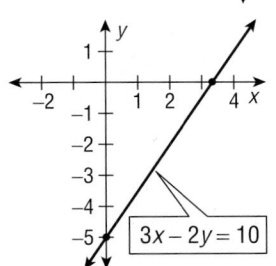

$3x - 2y = 10$

CHAPTER 14

14.2 Independent Practice pp. 640-641

4.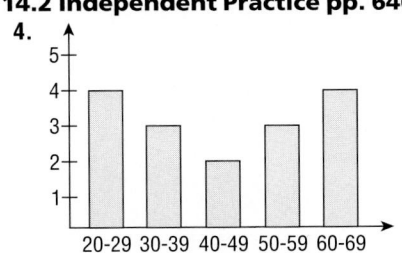

5.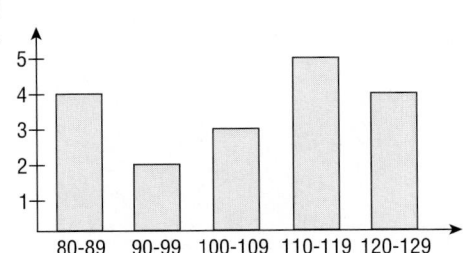

6.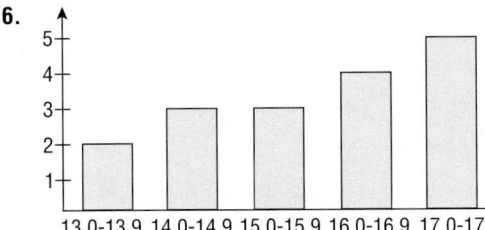

8.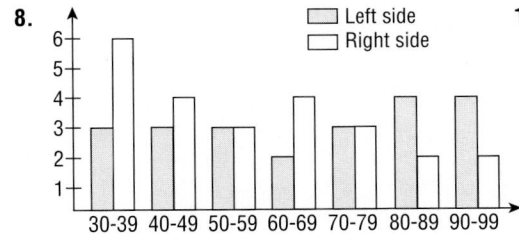

11.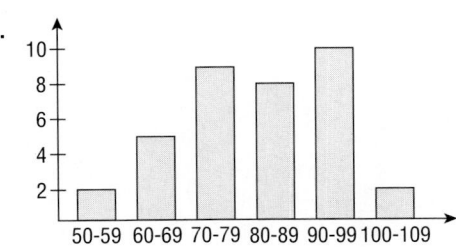

13.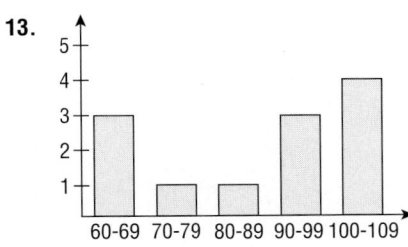

4.4 Independent Practice p. 651

21.

Income	Store 1	Store 2
May	231,450	206,210
June	265,985	319,754
July	303,442	321,615
August	324,570	256,419

Expenses	Store 1	Store 2
May	208,345	200,926
June	247,913	296,575
July	287,500	306,480
August	317,940	238,212

23.

Profit	Store 1	Store 2
May	$23,105	$5,284
June	$18,072	$23,179
July	$15,942	$15,135
August	$6,630	$18,207

25.

	Side 1	Side 2	Side 3
Triangle 1	5	7	10
Triangle 2	9	12	15
Triangle 3	0.9	4	4.1
Triangle 4	5	6	9.2

14.4 Exploration and Extension p. 651

30. $\begin{bmatrix} 3 & 8 & 4 \\ 7 & 6 & 2 \\ 5 & 1 & 9 \end{bmatrix}$ or $\begin{bmatrix} 3 & 8 & 4 \\ 5 & 1 & 9 \\ 7 & 6 & 2 \end{bmatrix}$

31. $\begin{bmatrix} 4 & 8 & 3 \\ 2 & 6 & 7 \\ 9 & 1 & 5 \end{bmatrix}$ or $\begin{bmatrix} 9 & 1 & 5 \\ 2 & 6 & 7 \\ 4 & 8 & 3 \end{bmatrix}$

32. $\begin{bmatrix} 6 & 8 & 1 \\ 7 & 3 & 5 \\ 2 & 4 & 9 \end{bmatrix}$ or $\begin{bmatrix} 8 & 6 & 1 \\ 3 & 7 & 5 \\ 4 & 2 & 9 \end{bmatrix}$

33. $\begin{bmatrix} 3 & 8 & 4 \\ 5 & 1 & 9 \\ 7 & 6 & 2 \end{bmatrix}$ or $\begin{bmatrix} 3 & 4 & 8 \\ 5 & 9 & 1 \\ 7 & 2 & 6 \end{bmatrix}$

PROFESSIONAL HANDBOOK

In this handbook, fellow educators share their thoughts and experiences on the following topics:

- **Cooperative Learning Takes Teamwork**
- **Writing to Learn Mathematics**
- **Teaching and Technology—a Partnership for the Future**
- **Using Manipulatives**
- **Special Populations**
- **Assessing Student Progress**
- **Community Connections**

One of the joys of teaching is the opportunity for continual professional development. This development could include gradually implementing some of the ideas in the following pages which are directed at improving student learning. Some of these ideas can be just as effective for teachers as they are for students. For example, teachers working and planning cooperatively, in pairs or larger groups depending on the situation, can be more effective than teachers working alone. And teachers can benefit from writing journals about teaching mathematics just as much as students can benefit from writing about learning mathematics. For further information, refer to the NCTM publications Professional Standards for Teaching Mathematics and its accompanying handbooks.

COOPERATIVE LEARNING TAKES TEAMWORK

Christine S. Losq
Math Consultant, Author
The Whole Math™ Project
Palo Alto, California

Cooperative group learning is a powerful teaching and learning tool. To make it work for you:

- **create a cooperative climate in your classroom**

- **model sharing and listening skills**

- **communicate your goals and purposes**

- **decide on a grouping strategy appropriate for your goals and the needs of your class**

- **assess group work for mathematical content and for cooperative skills**

Create a cooperative climate

Set the stage by emphasizing that we all learn from each other, so everybody benefits when working in a group. Prepare students for different participation styles. Some people get ideas quickly. Others need time to think, collect more data, and listen to others before their own ideas gel. Therefore, both sharing and listening are important skills when working in a group. Arrange desks and chairs into pods of four or six to encourage cooperative interaction. When facing one another, students can better develop listening skills. As students work with a partner or a group, their cooperative skills will develop.

Set clear limits on group behavior. If a group is not on task, consider splitting it into partners. As a last resort, have students work alone. Point out that when working alone

Prepare students for different participation styles.

they lose the valuable resources of the group.

Model sharing and listening skills

Occasionally model speaking and listening skills through role play. For example, have students consider the following student dialogue.

Student 1: "How did you figure that out? I got a different answer."
Student 2: "Well, like, I don't know. I just kind of put this number here and then it all came out. Oh, and I punched some buttons on the calculator."
Student 1: "I'll write down what I did. You write down what you did. Then, let's compare."

Ask students what other follow-up questions they could ask to stay on task.

Then model a listening strategy called *feedback*. Have students analyze what is going on in this situation:

Student 1: "Well first I figured out that there was more information than I needed. So I reread the problem and wrote up the question in my own words."
Student 2: "I heard you say that you first rewrote the problem in your own words. I did that, too, but I

think we're supposed to be finding out something different."

Ask the class for suggestions about what these two students could do next.

Communicate your goals and purposes

Assess your own purposes for using cooperative learning groups. They may include:
- assessing or developing students' interactive skills
- helping students construct their own understanding of a math concept
- helping students develop and explain a procedure or problem-solving strategy
- developing communication skills by requiring a group presentation of a project
- creating a peer tutoring situation

Decide on a grouping strategy

There is no formula for grouping students to maximize learning. Sometimes groups of four to six work well. Sometimes partners are more effective. Be flexible and try different arrangements until you find the ones that work best with a given class.

Change groups at least monthly so that students get a chance to work with a variety of classmates.

Sometimes there are one or two students that others feel they cannot get along with. Role play a difficult situation and ask the class to help find solutions that would enable the group to work together. Emphasize that difficult situations require an effort on *everyone's* part.

Grouping Options	Purpose	Type of Task	Teacher's Role
Teacher-selected random grouping	Assess student's learning styles and interactive skills	Tasks that involve data collection and analysis	Circulate and observe. Coach for sharing and listening skills.
Self-selected or teacher-selected groups (Group students who are thinking about a problem in similar ways.)	Develop understanding of a concept or a problem-solving strategy	Developing solution processes (Compare strategies when each group is ready to explain their idea.)	Circulate and observe. Ask questions as needed to help students articulate their thinking.
Teacher-selected or self-selected partners	Peer tutoring	Tasks that involve explaining and giving feedback	Circulate and observe. Listen for articulate explanations and good questioning strategies.

Once you have decided on your purpose for grouping, communicate your objectives clearly to your students. Then, as students work together, circulate and coach as needed. You may find it helpful to keep some open-ended questions in mind that will help students take responsibility for their own learning.

Questioning Strategies
- What are you trying to find out?
- What do you already know that can be used?
- What have you tried so far? What worked? What didn't work?
- What did you learn from what you tried so far? What can you try next?
- How did you get this result? Walk me through your process.
- Is there more than one way to solve this problem?
- Could there be more than one right answer? Why or why not?

Assess group products

Include teacher, peer, and self assessments to determine a final grade. One grade might measure the quality of the mathematical thinking and communicating. A second grade might measure how well the group worked together. Ask students to grade themselves and each other. In assigning their grades, students should explain how each group member contributed to the product.

Cooperative group learning can be a powerful learning tool. By having students work together in a collaborative climate, everyone will benefit.

References

"Strategies for Cooperative Group Work" in *Inspiring Active Learning* by Merrill Harmin, ASCD: Alexandria, VA, 1994.

Davidson, Nell (editor), *Cooperative Learning in Mathematics, A Handbook for Teachers*, Addison Wesley: Menlo Park, CA, 1990.

Writing to Learn Mathematics

Marsha W. Lilly
Alief Independent School District
Alief, TX

Why write in mathematics?

Writing is a powerful learning tool and a rich source of information about students' thinking. Although oral language is invaluable within the classroom for collaborative reflection, social development of thought, and creating a community of learners, it is written language that requires all students to think.

Asking students to "ink" their thinking develops and deepens their understanding of mathematics. Students derive a personalized mode of learning that enhances their ability to question, to wonder, to think for themselves, and to reflect.

How do students write?

Students write in a variety of genres. They write
- freely, creatively, formally, informally
- in journals, in learning logs
- about mathematics, assessments, and themselves

What are the benefits of writing?

Writing helps students
- identify what they can and cannot do
- link their learnings (past to present)
- summarize their understandings
- question new ideas
- think about what they know
- pose problems
- "see and hear" their thinking on paper

Writing helps teachers
- foster communication
- actively engage students
- learn what students know
- establish instructional decisions
- "hear" all of their students' voices

Writing helps students and teachers communicate.

What are examples of mathematics writing?

Pre-Assessments
Have students write a few words (write five words that have to do with squares) or a list (write everything you know about squares). This initial assessment helps provide criteria for entry-level instruction.

Learning Logs
Have students fold their pages in half. The left side of the page is reserved for their "thinking aloud," the right side for problem set-up, format, sketches, calculations. The "think aloud on paper" allows the student to record initial questions, comments, concerns, etc. With practice, students use this space to record metacognitive reflections.

Lesson Closures/"Exit Slips"

Close lessons with **writing prompts** that can also serve as journal entries:

- I discovered that . . .
- I changed my mind about _____ because . . .
- I agree with _____ and can add that . . .
- I disagree with _____ because . . .
- What surprised me was . . .
- The most significant thing I learned today was . . .
- As I think about the ideas we discussed in our group, it makes me think about . . .

Journal Entries

For a more reflective portrait, have students write about:

- the advantages and disadvantages of the strategies they have used
- the topics or ideas they find most challenging/difficult and why
- the way their ideas have changed
- their ability to keep on task when solving a problem
- their skills in working with others in collaborative problem solving

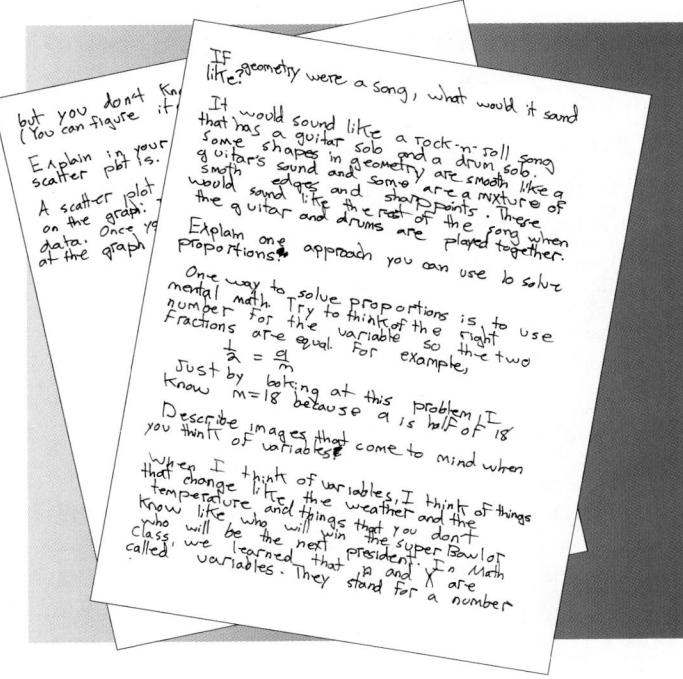

Quick Writes (Wet Ink)

A **quick write** is a short, immediate response to a particular topic. It can be exploratory, introspective, or self-assessing.

- Provide initial assessment by asking students to write what they know about _____ . The purpose is to collect information about the range of understanding and experience of the class.
- Following instruction, ask students to write again as they did at the beginning what they know about _____ . The purpose this time is

to show everything they have learned about _____ from the unit.

- To reflect, have students compare their initial response with their most recent one and do a quick write assessing their learning.

What are some uses of writing?

The emphasis in writing in mathematics classes is on thoughtful meaning rather than grammatical correctness. The primary purpose is to provide an environment in which students can construct new learnings by making connections between new information and what is already known. Additional instructional strategies that have proven effective learning tools are:

"How To" Summaries

Have students write directions on how to

- solve one-step equations
- add integers
- find the area and perimeter of quadrilaterals
- find the least common multiple/greatest common factor

Admit Slips

Have students anonymously record their concerns, identify areas of difficulty, and ask questions that need to be addressed.

Mathographies

Have students reflect on their personal experiences in mathematics by having them write a biographical narrative. This is often considered as a portfolio entry.

What are examples of teacher comments?

Writing allows teacher and student to dialogue on paper. The comments placed on student work have a greater impact than a numerical grade. These questions, affirmations, and observations have instructional implications:

> Interesting approach to solving this problem
> Is this the only solution?
> Where would you go from here?
> Can you think of a related problem?
> What about/if . . .?
> Wow, I'm impressed with your thinking!

Assessing what students know and understand is an ongoing, dynamic, and often informal process. As teachers, we can learn what our students know from reading their written work and responding to their thinking.

Teaching and Technology
—a Partnership for the Future

John A. Carter
West Chicago Community High School
West Chicago, Illinois

Technology can help teachers meet the needs of today's students and better prepare them for future challenges. Proponents of technology often speak of freeing students from the rote and mundane activities that accompanied traditional mathematics courses in the past. They speak of exploring, making and testing conjectures, and of the teacher as moderator—phrases that did not describe the traditional classroom. The transition to creative uses of technology can be accomplished gradually and painlessly.

When to Use Technology

Here are some suggestions for both beginners and experienced users of technology in the classroom.

If you are just beginning to use technology, ask yourself the following questions at the outset of each chapter:
- How often do I want the students using technology in this chapter?
- Are there topics in this chapter that lend themselves to calculators or computers?
- Can I think of a better way to present any of these topics using technology?

If you are an experienced user of technology, these questions become:
- Can I get the students to use technology more often and more appropriately this year?
- Are there topics that I have not integrated with technology yet?
- How can I use technology more effectively in my presentations?

You do not need to use technology every day. There may be topics for which it offers no significant advantage. Reflect on your curriculum and plan appropriately. Set realistic goals and stick to them.

The Classroom Environment

The use of technology in a classroom can change the content and structure of a lesson as is shown in the following vignette.

Ms. Laych-Rauco started her algebra class with an opening activity. She gave each student a copy of the following table to complete by evaluating each expression at the top of the column for the value at the left.

	$6x + x$	$6x^2$	$6x$	$7x$	$7x^2$
$x = 5$					
$x = -73$					
$x = 103$					
$x = 1135$					

The students used their calculators to evaluate the expressions and fill in the boxes.

Then Ms. Laych-Rauco displayed a spreadsheet on the overhead projector and created the table for the class to see. She asked students to examine the columns and name the two that were always equal in value. "Do you think this will work for all numbers?" The class response was split. She asked for another value of x and created another row in the spreadsheet for that value of x. She asked each student to supply a different x-value. Student responses ranged from -100 to $1,000,000$. "Why do you think $6x + x$ is always the same as $7x$ and not the same as the others?" The class discussion went on. . .

Each student is involved in an exploration.

By using the calculator, students are concentrating on the task rather than on the performance of the arithmetic.

The spreadsheet gives instantaneous feedback to each student's response and allows rapid testing of all kinds of numbers.

Technology provided the experience and set the stage for a meaningful discussion, which led to understanding the equivalence of algebraic expressions.

Technology can efficiently provide students with many opportunities to view the connections between arithmetic and algebra.

knowledge using technology and not just their ability to use technology.

Involving Parents and Administrators in the Classroom

Parents and administrators are deeply concerned with providing the best possible mathematics education to students. Keep them informed and involved. Invite parents and administrators to visit your classroom and observe the integration of technology with the traditional curriculum. Parents sometimes fear that by using technology their students will not know the basics. Give them the opportunity to take part in classroom activities to help ease these concerns. Sponsor a mathematics parent night. A well-planned evening presentation can inform parents about the NCTM Standards and research on the integration of technology, and can provide some hands-on experience with the technology. Choose a topic that illustrates the power of the technology, put parents into groups, and give them some time to feel like a student again. Give them a copy of the student's edition and lead them through an activity. This evening provides parents with a first-hand view of the changes that are taking place in mathematics education.

Choosing Appropriate Technology

There is a variety of technology available for the classroom— scientific calculators, graphing calculators, spreadsheets, computer drawing programs, and projection devices for classroom demonstrations. Each has its ideal uses. Do not avoid overhead demonstrations just because students have their own calculators. There are times when the efficiency of your demonstration can make a stronger impact than having students try to do it all themselves.

Some schools require students to purchase their own calculators. If this is out of the question, ask the school to buy a class set, at least one calculator for every two students.

Also seek support from local businesses or parent groups to help defray the cost of hardware and software.

Assessing Student Performance Using Technology

As technology becomes an important and integral part of instruction in your classroom, it should become integrated in the assessment process too. From teacher-made tests to alternative assessment projects, students should be allowed to use technology. Take care to assess students' mathematics

Using
MANiPULATiVES

Linda Gojak
Hawken School
Lyndhurst, Ohio

Using manipulative materials to introduce and model concepts supports the goals of developing connections, communication, problem solving, and reasoning.

Connections

Manipulative materials are tools that enable students to begin connecting their previous experiences to the abstract ideas and symbols of algebra and geometry.

Communication

Manipulative materials, used properly, aid students in communicating their ideas by relating their thoughts to physical and visual models. With teacher guidance, the language and symbols of algebra develop. Activities with concrete materials set the stage for oral and written discourse by individuals or within cooperative groups.

Problem Solving

As early as kindergarten, students begin to solve mathematical problems with strategies including act it out, make a model, and draw a diagram. Throughout elementary and middle school, students begin to develop algebraic ideas through problem solving with the use of models. It is reasonable, then, that modeling activities be a vital part of the preparation for formal algebra. Experiences with a variety of concrete materials will enable students to relate abstract problems to the physical world.

Reasoning

Research shows that students who construct their own knowledge internalize and retain concepts. Activity-based lessons that focus on doing, not just manipulating symbols by rote memorization of an algorithm, give the learner the opportunity to reason mathematically. In doing so, students clarify the meaning of a concept in their own minds and begin bridging from the concrete to symbolic notation.

Classroom Procedures

When using manipulatives, the classroom becomes a laboratory in which students explore, discover, and make conjectures. As new materials are introduced, allow time for students to explore and make discoveries. Ask carefully constructed questions to help students see relationships between the structure of the material and mathematical ideas. Plan worthwhile tasks that enable students to connect the use of the material to the mathematical problem or concept.

At the beginning of each activity, discuss its goal and set the stage for the connection between the concrete and abstract. This will help keep students focused as they work. They begin to view the manipulatives as a learning tool much like a calculator or a computer. The ability to make connections between concrete and abstract will vary among students. Some will need more time to work with materials, while others will make the connection with ease. Flexibility in the use of materials can help meet individual needs within a classroom.

Commercially available products abound, but the expense can be prohibitive in obtaining classroom sets. It is important for each student to handle and experience the materials. An overhead set, while helpful, is not enough. One way to overcome the budgetary problem of obtaining manipulatives is to have students construct their own materials. Patterns for many manipulatives are provided on copymasters in *Teaching Tools*. When students make their own materials, they feel they have ownership of the materials, each student can have an ample

supply, and lost materials are easily replaced. Good organization and management of the materials can minimize the time needed for distribution and collection. Sandwich-size zipper bags are ideal for storing student sets of materials. Gallon-size bags can be used to store classroom sets. Large boxes from reams of copy paper can be used to store quantities of materials and are easily obtained from school offices or office supply companies. Storing together sets of materials related to the same general topic and labeling boxes make it easy to locate the appropriate material for each unit.

Windows to Algebra and Geometry carefully incorporates the use of manipulative materials to help you plan lessons that will allow students to make connections between concrete models and abstract ideas. This enables you to meet a wide range of abilities and learning styles and provides a broad yet solid foundation for further study in algebra and geometry.

Ellen Silbert
Adlai E. Stevenson High School
Linconshire, Illinois

The Limited English Proficient Student Profile

Defining the characteristics of Limited English Proficient (LEP) students may be more complex than explaining the educational approaches a teacher should take to educate these students. Some LEP students are able to express themselves in English but may not be proficient in their native language. Others are proficient in writing but unable to speak, often due to being self-conscious in front of peers. Some LEP students have periods of absence from school. However, all LEP students share one common denominator: English is not spoken in their homes. Therefore, they depend largely on their teachers to explain what they need to know in order to comprehend, process, and learn mathematics.

LEP students bring to class a multitude of cultural

and educational experiences. In some countries, raising a hand, shouting out answers, or bringing attention to the individual is considered in poor taste and may result in punishment. Correcting a teacher or asking questions that are not initiated by a teacher may also be considered rude. Therefore, learning classroom behavior is a large part of an LEP student's education. A classroom setting with a low anxiety level creates a stage for a healthy classroom atmosphere that allows LEP students to flourish in their new environment.

Helpful hints for working with LEP students:

- Give oral directions facing the class in addition to printing instructions on the chalkboard. Many students cannot read cursive letters.
- Allow LEP students extra time to complete assignments. Translation between the native language and the target language is time consuming.
- Encourage LEP students to bring a native language dictionary to class. Students can create their own mathematics dictionary by including pictures or diagrams in a math notebook to give further explanation of problems, theories, etc.
- Keep explanations short and uncomplicated and accompanied by visuals and manipulatives.
- Enlist peer tutors. Using students as aides often results in fewer anguished moments.
- Do not assume that LEP students have mastered material covered by the mainstream. Often LEP students are much further behind.
- Explain how to use a calculator. Most countries do not allow their students to use calculators.
- Don't forget—a smile goes a long way!

Special Populations

AT RISK STUDENTS

Ileene Paul
Adlai E. Stevenson High School
Linconshire, Illinois

Teaching special needs students who display various learning styles requires no "bag of tricks," but rather good teaching strategies. Explaining, modeling, interacting, and practicing are fundamental teaching methods for all students.

Communication is of primary concern in teaching mathematics to students requiring multiple learning styles. Emphasis on both expressive and receptive language is essential in delivering clear, understandable explanations of basic mathematical concepts. The mathematics vocabulary must be simple, precise and related to words students already know. This is especially important for abstract terms. We cannot take it for granted that a special needs student understands our mathematical language.

The following strategies will facilitate understanding:

1. Ensure that instructions are not ambiguous. Concepts such as "greater than" can be vague to students and can be replaced by more concrete phrases such as "bigger than" or "more than."

2. Have students speak in mathematical terms as often as possible. The more concrete the language, the greater the possibility of understanding.

3. Reinforce concepts through auditory and visual cues. Repetition and expansion of examples and answers give students more time to process new material. Color coding key terms calls attention to concepts to be emphasized.

4. Teach techniques for analyzing problems.

Mathematical procedures need to be broken down into small, sequential steps.

5. If neccesary, show students illustrations, diagrams, or other graphic explanations of mathematical concepts.

6. Use tactile approaches such as touching and handling manipulatives to reinforce oral explanations. Algebra tiles, chips, and number lines provide hands-on activities for students who require learning through multiple modalities.

In short, it is essential to employ as many avenues of mental functioning as possible in teaching and reinforcing each new concept. The greater the number of sensory modalities, the greater the chance for success.

Underachieving students with no diagnosed disability may benefit from a multi-modality teaching approach; but they may also need additional emphasis on motivation and achieving success. Negative attitudes and behaviors may gradually diminish with the implementation of confidence-

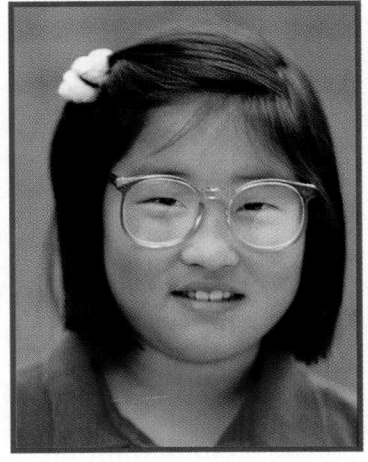

building activities and a positive classroom approach. Daily lessons built on previous knowledge, carefully engineered to insure student success, keep students motivated. Mathematics related to sporting events, cartoons, movies, cars, and food, as well as games and activities that require active student involvement, keep interest piqued. Capitalizing on students' personal strengths in teaching new concepts helps engage the reluctant learner. Students' ability to work in groups or lead activities should be incorporated into daily planning. Through promotion of positive student attitudes, successful learning experiences, and high expectations, students will be more apt to take risks and attempt new, more difficult concepts.

STUDENT PROGRESS

Marianne Weber
Author, Mathematics Consultant
Chesterfield, Missour

Are you familiar with the term "alternative assessment" yet sometimes wonder what it really means? Do you find yourself interested in learning about more effective ways to measure students' understanding of mathematics, but are concerned about time constraints? Perhaps the following dialogue between Chris and Yolande, two middle school mathematics teachers, can help you with this dilemma.

CHRIS	YOLANDE
Have you ever felt that the way we evaluate our students doesn't really give an accurate picture of their ability in mathematics?	Yes, I know what you mean. Just yesterday I asked a student to explain his wrong answer to a multiple-choice question. He had interpreted the question differently. His answer made sense based on his interpretation of the question.
We learn so much more when we ask students to explain their thinking. We really need to do more than evaluate the marks they put on paper.	
I've heard a lot about alternative assessment, portfolios, rubrics for scoring open-ended questions, and a myriad of other ways to assess students. I must say, I'm a little overwhelmed and confused by it all!	You aren't the only one. I've heard that there are a host of effective methods of evaluating students' knowledge of mathematics.
	Portfolios and rubrics are just two of the many assessment "tools" we have to choose from. There are others, such as math journals, projects, and partner quizzes, to name a few. But where do you begin?
My students and I have been experimenting with math journals.	What motivated you to start with math journals?
I started with journal writing because I, too, was frustrated with the little information I obtained from multiple-choice and short-answer tests.	
I asked them to write about *how* they would determine the amount of sod needed to cover the infield of a baseball field.	How did your students react? Didn't they complain?

CHRIS

The fact that they had to step back and write about their plan to solve the problem before performing the necessary "number crunching" was exciting for some and bewildering for others.

No, but asking them to write about how they would solve the problem made them more aware of what they understood or misunderstood about the problem, and about the mathematics needed to solve it.

We're finding that journal writing is equally enlightening to students and teachers.

Yes, it is. But I do get bogged down sometimes reading each student's journal every week. It's pretty time consuming.

It looks as though you've just reduced my workload, Yolande. The journal writing I'm obtaining from my students could be part of a bigger assessment picture, called portfolios.

I think I'm beginning to feel overwhelmed again!

I guess you're right. The key is to start with an alternative assessment strategy you're interested in, and build from there. You know, some parents are excited about this, too. They also gain more knowledge about their child's thinking and feelings.

Talking with you about assessment makes me feel good that I've taken this first step, and encourages me to consider taking others.

Really? Which one?

Just think of how much information we would gather about our students from listening to them discuss problems and pose solutions!

YOLANDE

So some of them didn't like writing, did they?

It sounds like this alternative assessment method is quite powerful!

Perhaps you're trying to evaluate too much of their writing, Chris. It might be better to identify key mathematics topics or particularly rich problems you want student insights about.

Exactly. In addition to journal entries, alternative assessment can include research projects, open-ended questions, problems, tasks, and much, much more!

There's no need to. You've already taken a major step. You've tried a new assessment strategy, and its giving you much more information about your students' mathematical abilities. That's what we're after.

Come to think of it, Chris, we've been implementing an alternative assessment strategy as we've discussed this issue.

Group assessment. We've been sharing our ideas about how to change traditional assessment to obtain more knowledge about our students' mathematical ability. We've discussed problems and formulated solutions based on our discussions.

I think I'll start with Partner Quizzes. I've heard that other teachers have had success with them. It's time for me to get my feet wet!

Partner Quizzes are provided on copymasters in the supplement Alternative Assessment. *That booklet also contains copymasters for projects and information on using portfolios, error notebooks, math journals, and daily quizzes. You can work from that booklet on your own, but it can be more enjoyable and more effective to work with one or more of your colleagues. Good luck.*

Community Connections

Clementine Sherman
Dade County Public Schools
Miami, Florida

Most educators agree that the job of educating children belongs not only to the school but also to the parents and the community at large. Even with state-of-the-art research-based content and pedagogy, the teaching and learning of mathematics cannot be improved without the assistance of parents and the real world. Mathematics is often thought of as too abstract to be useful anywhere but in the classroom. Fortunately, reform in the mathematics curriculum and advances in technology make the learning of mathematics more fun and more relevant to children's lives. Therefore, it is very important that we as educators reach out to parents, the business community, professional organizations, churches, political groups, the media, and other stake holders to improve children's success in mathematics.

Positive communication with parents about their children's experiences in mathematics is essential to establish rapport with parents. During the first few weeks of the school term, parents are most anxious about what their children are learning in school and what progress, if any, their children will make during the year. Many parents are uncomfortable with mathematics. They may be unaware of the new expectations of more content, the use of technology, new ways of assessing students, and new instructional strategies. Therefore, they may not be able to assist their children with homework assignments. New and improved mathematics textbooks such as this one can pose a challenge for parents because they do not see the extensive drill and practice exercises that were in their mathematics books.

The following is a list of things that teachers can do to obtain and maintain parent and community involvement in the teaching and learning of mathematics.

- Develop school programs to assist parents who may not be able to help their children.
- Design home assignments that include activities that would permit parents to learn alongside their children.
- Capitalize on the high percentage of homes that have multimedia computers, high-tech toys, and other resources in the home.
- Be sensitive to the number of children who do not have computers, technology, books, trips to education supportive environments, scientists, engineers, or other highly successful people in their immediate environment.

Activities for Making Parent and Community Connections

Teachers or groups of teachers can:
- Help parent groups, churches, and community organizations set up homework centers.
- Conduct awareness workshops about the importance of doing well in mathematics and science.
- Organize a back-to-school career night for the family using community volunteers.
- Have students write letters to the newspaper about the importance of mathematics and some of the things that they are doing in mathematics.
- Get the media involved—local radio, television, newspapers, newsletters, and other forms for communicating with parents and community.
- Seek parent volunteers to assist in the classroom. Plan and design the training for parent volunteers to assist teachers in mathematics classrooms.
- Design newsletters for parents about things that are happening in the classroom. This newsletter can be a project for students. Include pictures, copies of completed projects, and ideas for parents to help their children with mathematics. Activities should be very practical things: shopping for food, goods, and services; household repair; nutrition and food preparation; family vacations; household budgets, taxes, investments savings, and entertainment.

Parents can:
- Provide a quiet, comfortable study area for children.
- Help students with effective time management to include time for study, entertainment, and family time.
- Be familiar with new teaching strategies, state-of-the art instructional materials, and new assessment techniques.
- Share with students how mathematics is used in their daily lives.
- Expose children to libraries, science museums, laboratories, and other interesting places that increase their awareness and knowledge of mathematics, science, and technology.
- Take part in school activities, and serve as role models or mentors for students. Volunteer to assist teachers with routine tasks so that teachers may have more time to work with students.

- Help children learn to value education and success in mathematics.
- Volunteer to help organize and maintain homework centers in the community.

The community can:
- Provide mentors and internship opportunities for students and teachers.
- Support field trips and guest speakers for mathematics classes.

- Support training for teachers that allows them to do summer work in business and industry in order to find out what students really need to know in mathematics when they apply for jobs or seek higher education.
- Help raise funds to support projects or reward students for outstanding performance in mathematics.

Conclusion

An effective mathematics teacher helps students make connections between what is taught in the classroom and the real world. The content of this textbook makes it easy to make these connections because it is rich in real-world applications. However, many of the students in your class lack role models and do not identify with success in algebra and geometry. Explore intervention strategies and programs that students at this level may enter after school, on Saturdays, and during the summer. Seek programs to match students with successful professionals in mathematics and science.

Expose children to interesting places that increase their awareness.

PROFESSIONAL

HANDBOOK

INDEX

as solutions of linear equations, 136–138, 156, 588, 590–591, 593

as solutions of inequalities, 423, 619

Ordered-pair solution, 136

Ordering integers, 102

Ordering numbers, 10

Ordering by volume, 571

Organizing data, 28–31, 56, 176, 194–206, 208–212, 218–227, 234–237

in a matrix, 648

in scatter plots, 224–227, 291

Origin, 135, 502

Outcome, 229

P

Pacing Charts, T18–T19, TE1, TE48, TE98, TE146, TE192, TE238, TE292, TE342, TE388, TE436, TE486, TE536, TE586, TE632

Paper cutting and folding, 185, 443, 453, 471, 472, 497, 509, 514

Parallel lines, 439

and angle congruences, 448

and slope, 605, 607, 613

Parallelogram, 185, 451, 456, 462, 520, 626

area of, 185, 488–491, 673

base and height of, 488

Parentheses, 129

as grouping symbols, 18, 20

in multiplication, 7

Pascal's Triangle, 372, 374–376, 385, 441

Pattern(s), 2, 15, 23, 372

addition, 107

Braille alphabet, TE5

coordinate graphs, 135–138, 280, 281, 393, 591, 607

correlations, 224–227

decimal, 314

describing, 3–5

digit, 38, 40

division, 128, 243

drawing a diagram to find, 39, 41

Enrichment Activities, TE393, TE591

factor, 244

fraction, 268, 296, 302

geometric, 23, 34–37, 56–58, 204–205, 348, 441, 471, 567, 573, 576

integer, 128

look for a, 3–5, 16, 23, 35, 39, 41, 56, 58, 164, 373, 526

measurement, 541

mosaic, 467, 473, 673

multiplication, 122

number, 3–5, 38, 40–41, 241–243, 245, 247, 249, 256, 258, 268, 272, 279–282, 302, 369

in Pascal's triangle, 372, 374–376, 385

percents, 321, 330

perimeter, 56

and predictions, 10, 13, 15, 164, 243, 281

prime number, 258

star, 473

subtraction, 115

sum and difference, 673

trigonometric, 526

using tables to find, 15, 56–58, 164

visualizing, 4

Payroll tax, 332, 334

Pentagon, 34, 451, 474

diagonals of, 35

sides and angles, 204, 471

Percent(s), 268, 318–321, 582

of an area, 327, 329, 330

calculator, 369

commonly used, 323

comparing, 318, 324, 328

estimating with, 321, 324–326, 690

forms of, 268, 318–319, 332, 358–361

fractions, decimals, and, 318–325

of increase or decrease, 359–361, 367, 435

mental math, 327, 329

modeling, 317–321, 324–330, 338, 358–361

of a number, 327–330

patterns, 321, 330

portion, 317–321, 324, 327–330

in problem solving, 322–325

symbol form, 318–320, 322

three cases of, 358–359

verbal form, 318, 319, 322

Percent Equation, 358–366, 368–371, 383–387, 434, 645

decimal solution, 359–361

error analysis, 360

mental math, 360

model for, 360

in problem solving, 363–366, 368–371

reciprocal solution, 359–361

Percent form, 322

Percent key, 327

Perfect numbers, 279, 281, 282

Perfect square, 12

Performance Assessment, T16

Perimeter, 12, 337, 338, 341, 347, 405–407, 431, 434, 470,

489–491, 493, 503, 518–520, 547, 626, 662

and area, 30, 33, 183, 518

estimating, 183

patterns, 56

of a polygon, 16, 37, 56–58, 62, 84

of rectangles, 84, 135, 160, 166, 170–172, 184–185, 227, 297, 301, 302, 329, 330, 651

of regular hexagons, 176

of squares, 12, 172, 175, 184–185, 202, 290

of a trapezoid, 498

of triangles, 160, 170–172, 423, 428, 629

Perpendicular lines, 443

and slope, 613

Pi, 539

Pi key, calculator, 543

Picture graph, 159, 195, 194, 195, 197, 198, 209, 210

Pixel, 356

Plane(s), 439–442

motion in the, 496

Plot(s), 100

box–and–whisker, 642

stem–and–leaf, 638

Plotting

integers, 100

irrational numbers, by construction, 410

the point (in the coordinate plane), 135, 280

Point(s), 135, 439–442

of intersections (linear equations), 592–595

Point symmetry, 453, 455–456

Polygon(s), 34

angles of, 36, 467–475

congruence, 467–470

congruent, 356, 467, 492

convex, 37, 462

in the coordinate plane, 135, 137, 456, 465, 480, 495, 496, 500, 512, 596, 625, 629

decagons, 471

diagonals of, 35

dividing into triangles, 204, 470

drawing, 36

as faces of solids, 14, 544

heptagon, 34, 204, 471

hexagons, 34, 176, 204, 471

identifying, 34, 36

interior and exterior angles of, 36, 472–475

intersections, 460

measure of angles of, 155, 166, 204–205, 290, 471

naming, 34

n-gons, 34, 471

solving a, 401–403, 435, 527
    solving by trigonometry, 527–530
    trigonometric ratio, 522–525
Rise, 587, 604
RND function, 641
Rotational symmetry, 454–456
Rotations, 502–505
    angle of, 502
Rounded solution, 157
Rounding decimals, 15, 232, 296
Rounding numbers, 12, 157, 178, 180, 189
    in estimation, 12, 15, 688–690
Round-off error, 178
Row of matrix, 648
Rubik's cube, 270, 272
Run, 587, 604

S

Salaries and wages, 72, 86, 164, 216, 237, 262, 366, 616, 635
Sale price, 364
Sales tax, 332, 334, 339, 361
Sample space, 229
Scale dimensions 353
Scale drawings and models, 344, 347, 353, 355, 356, 517–520, 574, 607
Scale factor, 512, 515, 516, 573, 576
Scalene, 457
Scalene quadrilateral, 462
Scalene triangle, 457
Scatter plot, 224–227, 291, 475, 615
    best fit line, 224
    correlations, 224
    graphing calculator, 223, 227
    and linear relationships, 615
    ordered pairs, 224
Scientific notation, 274–278
    on a calculator, 278
    multiplying and dividing in, 275–278
Second quartile, 642
Segment, midpoint of, 624
Sequence(s), 3, 130, 252, 272, 281, 285, 369
    coordinate, 138
    describing patterns, 3
    Fibonacci, 41, 279, 281, **TE161, TE206**
    fraction, 302
    generating by using a calculator, 38, 40
    Group Investigation, 41
    number, 38–41
Sets, 162
Shape of Things, 441, 456, 460, 514

Side(s), 171
    of angles, 443
    classify triangle by, 457–460
    corresponding congruent, 492–495
    corresponding similar, 512–515
    lengths of, and angle measures, 477–480
    of a polygon, 34
    of a rectangle, 135, 272
    of right triangles, 347, 521
    of a square, 12
    of a triangle, 395, 400, 424–428, 477
    ratios of, 347, 522–525
Similar figures, 356, 511–515
    enlargements or magnifications, 352, 356
    ratio of sides, 350–352, 356, 383, 385, 387, 521
    scale drawings and models, 344, 347, 353, 355, 356
Similar solids, 573–576, 579, 581
Similar triangles, 350–352, 356, 383, 385, 387, 405, 451, 525
    corresponding parts of, 350–352
    properties of, 512
Similarity, 512
Simplest form, 259, 261
Simplified expression, 55
Simplifying
    algebraic expressions, 55–58, 80
    algebraic fractions, 259, 267
    equations, 153, 163
    expressions, 110–111
    fractions (canceling), 71, 259, 261, 262, 267
    polynomials, 654
Simulations, 377–381
Sine (sin), 522
Sketching a quick–graph of a line, 599
Slide, 496, 506
Slope of a line, 587, 603–607, 610–613
    and misleading graphs, 607
    and parallel and perpendicular lines, 605, 607, 613
    and y-intercepts, 609
Slope-intercept form of the equations of a line, 610–613
    and quick graphs, 611
Solid(s),
    base and lateral surface, 545
    cube, 14
    faces, edges, 14
    height of, 549
    nets for, 442, 544, 554, 547, 557, 562, 565
    similar, 573–576, 579, 581

    vertices of, 544
    visualizing, 547, 557
Solution(s)
    checking, 59, 149, 178–181
    of an equation, 59
    half-planes as, 620
    of an inequality, 89, 411–423
    of a linear equation, 136, 588–591
    of a linear inequality, 619–622
    of multi-variable equations, 156
    ordered pairs as, 136, 423, 588
    organizing the, 589
    of polynomial equations, 663
    of power equations, 271, 583
    rounded, 157, 178–181
    of square root equations, 390–393
    tables, 156, 589–591, 593, 594, 615–617
Solving equations, 59–62, 64–68, 70–74, 84, 131, 133, 148–157, 168–172, 176, 187–191, 273
    with absolute values, 166, 172, **TE423**
    addition or subtraction, 65–68
    algebra tile model for, 64, 70, 148, 151, 168
    approximating solutions, 178–181
    area model for, 71
    checking solutions for, 59, 157
    error analysis, 151, 165, 180, 189, 360
    with fractions, 295–297, 303–305
    by inverse operations, 131, 149, 153, 163
    by isolating the variable, 64, 70, 131, 133, 149
    linear equations, 588–591
    by mental math, 60–62, 103, 124, 128, 143, 222, 271, 289, 311, 414
    more than one solution, 107, 156
    more than one way to solve, 158, 161, 163
    multiplication or division, 70–74
    multi-step equations, 153–157
    ordered pairs as solutions, 135–138
    by packaging and unpackaging x, TE149
    Percent Equation, 358–366, 368–371
    powers in, 271, 583
    by properties of equality, 65, 71, 131, 133
    proportions, 349–356
    round-off errors, 178
    simplifying using the Distributive Property, 163–165
    square roots, 390–393

Appreciation to the staff at Larson Texts, Inc:
who assisted with proofreading the manuscript and
preparing and proofreading the art package.

*Appreciation to the following art/photo
production staff:*
Art: Joan Williams
Photographs: Susan Doheny
Cover design: Linda Fishborne.
Cover photos: Y. Gladu/Photo Researchers;
inset, DeSciose/The Stock Broker.

ILLUSTRATION CREDITS

Kathy Meisl: 142, 167, 194, 196, 198, 213, 217, 234(b),
260, 297, 365(b), 370, 375(b), 386, 408, 439, 517, 553, 589,
655.
Patrice Rossi: 10, 45, 62, 69, 108, 110, 134, 154, 159, 195,
210, 262, 290, 302, 335, 365(c), 368, 435, 480, 530, 567,
582, 591, 617, 662.

PHOTOGRAPHY CREDITS

CHAPTER 1   1: Guy Spangenberg. **2:** Billy Barnes/
Tony Stone Images. **3:** Ken O'Donoghue © D.C.
Heath. **5:** Dagmar Fabricius/Stock Boston.
7: Museum of The History of Science, Oxford
University. **14:** Steve Elmore/Stock Market. **21:**
Stuart McCall/Tony Stone Images. **22:** Lester
Lefkowitz/Tony Stone Images. **25:** NASA. **27:**
Phillips-Ramsey. **28:** Jonathan Daniel/Allsport.
31: George Wuerthner. **32:** Nash Baker © D.C.
Heath. **34:** Jeff Foott. **39:** Steve Umland. **41:**
Keith Thompson/Tony Stone Images. **43:** Barbara Von
Hoffmann/Tom Stack & Associates.
46: NASA.

CHAPTER 2   48-9: John Senzer /Fashion Institute of
Technology. **54:** Michael Newman/Photo Edit.
58: Dan McCoy/Rainbow. **60:** Henry Hilliard.
63: From The World Book Encyclopedia © 1994 World
Book, Inc. By permission of the publisher.
68: Jonathan Rawle/Stock Boston. **72:** Michael
Newman/Photo Edit. **74:** Stephen Dunn/Allsport.
77: Ken O'Donoghue © D.C. Heath. **82:** Ken O'Donoghue
© D.C. Heath. **84:** Tom Pantages.
86: Darell Lane. **87:** William Johnson/Stock
Boston. **92:** David Madison. **94:** Vasamuseet - The Vasa
Museum. **95:** David Lissy/Picture Cube.
96: Lawrence Migdale/Tony Stone Images.

CHAPTER 3   98-9: Dance Theatre of Harlem.
101: George Ranalli/ Photo Researchers. **103:** Bob
Daemmrich. **106:** Mark Segal/Tony Stone Images.
108: Mike Powell/Allsport. **112:** Mark Wagner/
Tony Stone Images. **112:** Mark Wagner/Tony Stone
Images. **113:** Anthony Salamone © D.C.
Heath. **119:** NASA. **120:** Michael Norton/Adstock
Photos. **127:** Bob Daemmrich/Stock Boston. **129:**

William R. Sallaz/Duomo. **132:** Paul Avis © D.C.
Heath. **134:** AP/Wide World Photos. **141:** Mitchell
Layton/Duomo. **142:** Vandystadt Agence de
Presse/Allsport. **143:** Michael Newman/Photo
Edit. **145:** Daniel L. Feicht/Cedar Point.

CHAPTER 4   146-47: Tom & Pat Leeson/DRK.
150: Barrie Rokeach. **152:** Peabody Museum, Harvard
University. Photograph by Hillel Burger.
156: Courtesy of Nantucket Nectars. **161:** Tom
Walker/Stock Boston. **162:** The Bettmann Archive.
164: David Sams/Stock Boston. **166:** David Young-
Wolff/Photo Edit. **171:** Ken O'Donoghue © D.C.
Heath. **172:** Jeff Foott. **175:** Tom Bean. **176:** David Young-
Wolff/Photo Edit. **179:** Ken O'Donoghue © D.C.
Heath. **181:** Duomo. **183:** W. Cody/Westlight.
184: Paul Avis © D. C. Heath. **188:** Jan Petter Lynaw/Scan
Foto. **190:** Jeff Foott.

CHAPTER 5   192-93: David Nunuk/Westlight.
196: United Airlines. **199:** Jeff Watts. **203:** Mark O.
Thiessen © National Geographic Society. **204:**
From A Treasury of Amish Quilts by Rachel and Kenneth
Pellman. © 1991 by Good Books, Intercourse,
Pennsylvania. Quilt from the collection of Barbara S.
Janos. Used by permission. All rights
reserved.. **207:** Anthony Salamone © D.C.
Heath. **209:** Janice Fullman/Picture Cube. **210:** Ken
Straiton/Stock Market. **214:** Kindra Clineff/Picture
Cube. **216:** Ken O'Donoghue © D.C. Heath. **218:**
Stephen J. Krasemann/DRK. **219:** Kolvoord/Image
Works. **220:** Al Zwiazek/Tony Stone Images. **225:**
Tony Stone Images. **226:** Ken O'Donoghue © D.C.
Heath. **228:** Bob Daemmrich/Tony Stone Images.
229: Ken O'Donoghue © D.C. Heath. **230:** Susan
Doheny. **235:** J. Pickerell/FPG. **236:** David Young-
Wolff/Photo Edit.

CHAPTER 6   238-39: Tony Friedkin/FASE. **243:**
W. Cody/Westlight. **246:** W. Cody/Westlight.
248: Jasper Johns *Three Flags* 1958. Encaustic on canvas.
30 7/8x1/2x5 in. (78.4x115.6x12.7 cm.) Collection of
Whitney Museum of American Art, 50th Anniversary
Gift of the Gilman Foundation, Inc., The Lauder
Foundation, A. Alfred Taubman, an anonymous donor,
and purchase 80.32. **251:**
Wayne Hoy/Picture Cube. **253:** Zigy Kaluzny/Tony Stone
Images. **254:** Metropolitan Museum of Art,
56.171.38. **258:** t, Fukuhara, Inc./Weslight; b, Chuck
Keeler/Tony Stone Images. **259:** Bruno De Hogues/Tony
Stone Images. **262:** Oddo & Sinibaldi/Stock
Market. **268:** Ken O'Donoghue
© D.C. Heath. **270:** Larry Ulrich/Tony Stone Images.
273: F. Robert Masini/Phototake. **275:**
Lindenmeyr Munroe. **277:** NASA. **279:** Margaret
Courtney-Clarke. **280:** Gabe Palmer/Stock Market.
282: Ken Shung © 1993 The Walt Disney Co. Reprinted
with permission of Discover Magazine.
285: Steve Wilkings/Stock Market. **286:** Michele
McDonald. **287:** Frank Siteman/Picture Cube.

CHAPTER 7 **292-93:** Jeff Gnass. **295:** Ian Howarth. **300:** MacDonald Photography/Unicorn Stock Photos. **307:** Anthony Salamone © D.C. Heath. **309:** Courtesy of Four Seasons Sunrooms. **311:** t, Peter Menzel; b, Ken O'Donoghue © D.C. Heath. **313:** Judy Nemeth/Picturesque. **316:** Dan McCoy/Rainbow. **319:** Bridgeman/Art Resource. **323:** Stephen Whalen/Picturesque. **329:** AP/Wide World. **331:** Peter Menzel. **333:** Courtesy of Hispanic Market Connections. **334:** Arthur Tilley/FPG. **339:** Stephen Gorman. **340:** Jeff Gnass. **341:** Bob Daemmrich/Stock Boston.

CHAPTER 8 **342-43:** Paul Avis/Liaison International. **345:** Richard Nowitz. **347:** A. Borrel/Liaison International. **352:** AP/Wide World. **353:** Ken O'Donoghue © D.C. Heath. **354:** Bob Thomason/Tony Stone Images. **355:** Bob Daemmrich. **357:** British Library/The Bridgeman Art Library. **361:** UPI/Bettmann. **362:** Dave Jacobs/Tony Stone Images. **364:** Ken O'Donoghue © D.C. Heath. **374:** Myrleen Ferguson/Photo Edit. **379:** Robert W. Ginn/Picture Cube. **380:** Ken O'Donoghue © D.C. Heath. **381:** Peter Correz/Tony Stone Images. **384:** P.A. Harrington/Peter Arnold, Inc. **385:** Herb Snitzer/Stock Boston. **386:** Ed Lallo/Liaison International. **387:** L.L.T. Rhodes/Tony Stone Images.

CHAPTER 9 **388-89:** Tony Stone Images. **391:** The Woman That Fell from The Sky "Falling Star" by Robert Orduño, Oil on linen, 60"x60". **393:** Susan Lapides. **404:** Chel Beeson © D.C. Heath. **406:** Reuters/Bettmann. **411:** Burk Uzzle. **414:** UPI/Bettmann. **417:** Anne Heimann/Stock Market. **419:** Robert W. Ginn/The Picture Cube. **421:** Ken O'Donoghue © D.C. Heath. **423:** Dan L. Feicht/Cedar Point. **426:** Bohdan Hrynewych/Stock Boston. **432:** t, Alex Bartel/Picture Cube; b, Lionel Delevingne/Stock Boston.

CHAPTER 10 **436-37:** Brian Parker/Tom Stack & Associates. **440:** Peter Yates. **443:** British Museum. **444:** Jim Pickerell/Westlight. **449:** Tony Stone Images. **452:** David Cornwell/Pacific Stock. **454:** Mittet Foto/Tony Stone Images. **456:** l, Mitch Reardon/Tony Stone Image; c, Superstock; r, Art Wolfe/Allstock. **457:** Superstock. **461:** Visuals Unlimited. **463:** Gerry Ellis Nature Photography. **464:** Ken O'Donoghue © D.C. Heath. **467:** Craig Aurness/Westlight. **468:** Vladpans/Leo de Wys. **473:** Rick Strange/The Picture Cube. **475:** Courtesy of Four Seasons Sunrooms. **478:** Telegraph Colour Library/FPG. **484:** l, James Solliday/Biological Photo Service; c, Tom Myers; r, Charles Seaborn/Odyssey.

CHAPTER 11 **486-87:** NASA. **493:** Comstock. **495:** Ken Straiton/Stock Market. **498:** Nancy Sheehan © D.C. Heath. **499:** Richard Hutchings/Photo Edit. **501:** NASA-Ames Research Center. **503:** Steve Gottlieb. **507:** Chris Alan Wilton/Image Bank. **510:** Michele Burgess/The Stock Market. **511:** Joe McDonald/Global Pictures. **513:** Ken O'Donoghue © D.C. Heath. **515:** David Weintraub/West Stock. **519:** Nippondenso Co., Ltd.. **520:** Julie Kramer Cole. **528:** t, Mark Sasahara; b, Ken O'Donoghue © D.C. Heath. **533:** Roger Tully/Tony Stone Images. **534:** t, © Kelly Freas 1954, 1973, 1993, 1996; b, NASA.

CHAPTER 12 **536-37:** Anthony Salamone © D.C. Heath, inset; Ken O'Donoghue © D.C. Heath. **539:** Ken O'Donoghue © D.C. Heath. **540:** The White House. **545:** Ken O'Donoghue © D.C. Heath. **547:** The *Polyhedron Earth* was designed and invented by R. Buckminster Fuller. © 1938, 1967, 1982, & 1992 Buckminster Fuller Institute, Santa Barbara, CA. All rights reserved. Globe distributed by Shasta Visions, Mt. Shasta, CA. (800) 800.3693. Photo © Hugh Barton. **552:** Peabody Museum, Harvard University. Photograph by Hillel Burger. **553:** The Bettmann Archive. **555:** Jules Allen. **560:** Ken O'Donoghue © D.C. Heath. **563:** Ringette Canada. **567:** Sheila Beougher/Liaison International. **570:** Nikolay Zurek/FPG. **572:** Peter Tatiner/Leo de Wys. **573:** Mark J. Barrett/Allstock. **574:** Sava Cvek Associates. **580:** Bruce Benedict/The Stock Broker. **581:** NASA/Tom Stack.

CHAPTER 13 **586-87:** David Leip, MIT Solar Electric Vehicle Team. **596:** H.P. Smith Jr./Academy of Natural Sciences, Philadelphia/VIREO. **601:** Katherine Lambert. **602:** Anthony Salamone © D.C. Heath. **606:** Len Clifford/Natural Selection. **608:** Richard Laird/FPG. **613:** J. Faircloth/Transparencies, Inc. **618:** Richard Wood/The Picture Cube. **622:** Owen Franken/Stock Boston. **629:** Henley & Savage/The Stock Market. **630:** Mark Snyder/Tony Stone Images.

CHAPTER 14 **632-33:** Ron Garrison/Zoological Society of San Diego. **635:** Raymond Barnes/Tony Stone Images. **636:** Jim Brandenburg/Minden Pictures. **637:** Bill Bachmann/Leo de Wys. **638:** Beatriz Terrazas. **639:** Gary Irving/Tony Stone Images. **643:** Jay Paris. **645:** Doug Wechsler/VIREO. **651:** /Animals Animals. **655:** John Yurka/The Picture Cube. **657:** Steve Vidler/Leo de Wys. **671:** Art Wolfe. **673:** Robert Frerck/Odyssey Productions. **675:** UPI/Bettmann. **677:** John Cancalosi/Natural Selection.

PHOTOGRAPHY CREDITS, TE

726: Susan Lapides. **728:** Robert W. Ginn/Photo Edit. **729:** Mary Kate Denny/Photo Edit. **730:** Elliott Smith. **731:** David Young-Wolfe/Photo Edit. **732:** David Young-Wolfe/Photo Edit. **733:** Ken O'Donoghue © D.C. Heath. **734:** t, David Young-Wolfe/Tony Stone Images; c, Michael Newman/Photo Edit; b, Don Smetzer/Tony Stone Images. **735:** t, David Young-Wolfe/Photo Edit; b, Lawrence Migdale. **736:** Carol Lee/Picture Cube. **737:** Jeff Greenberg/Picture Cube. **738:** Marc Pokempner/Tony Stone Images. **739:** Chip Henderson/Tony Stone Images.

Keystrokes for page 223

The following steps show the keystrokes for the *TI-80, TI-81,* the *Casio fx-7700G,* and the *Sharp EL-9300C* that would be used for creating a bar graph for the data given below.

Age of Deer	1	2	3	4	5	6	7	8	9	10	11	12
Number of Deer	18	14	10	7	6	4	3	3	2	1	2	2

TI-80

Window   XMIN = 0   YMIN = −1
          XMAX = 13   YMAX = 20
          XSCL = 1   YSCL = 1

STAT   ENTER (Edit)

L1(1) = 1   L2(1) = 18   L1(7) = 7   L2(7) = 3
L1(2) = 2   L2(2) = 14   L1(8) = 8   L2(8) = 3
L1(3) = 3   L2(3) = 10   L1(9) = 9   L2(9) = 2
L1(4) = 4   L2(4) = 7   L1(10) = 10   L2(10) = 1
L1(5) = 5   L2(5) = 6   L1(11) = 11   L2(11) = 2
L1(6) = 6   L2(6) = 4   L1(12) = 12   L2(12) = 2

2nd   STAT PLOT   ENTER (Plot1)

Choose the following:
   On, Type: ⊞ , XL: L1, F: L2

GRAPH

TI-81

Range   Xmin = 0   Ymin = −1
        Xmax = 13   Ymax = 20
        Xscl = 1   Yscl = 1

2nd   STAT , cursor to DATA, ENTER

x1 = 1   y1 = 18   x7 = 7   y7 = 3
x2 = 2   y2 = 14   x8 = 8   y8 = 3
x3 = 3   y3 = 10   x9 = 9   y9 = 2
x4 = 4   y4 = 7   x10 = 10   y10 = 1
x5 = 5   y5 = 6   x11 = 11   y11 = 2
x6 = 6   y6 = 4   x12 = 12   y12 = 2

2nd   STAT , cursor to DRAW, ENTER
(Hist) ENTER

Casio *fx-7700G*

Range   Xmin = 0   Ymin = −1
        Xmax = 13   Ymax = 20
        Xscl = 1   Yscl = 1

MODE ✕ (SD)

MODE SHIFT 3 (DRAW)

SHIFT Defm 12 EXE

1 F3 18 F1   7 F3 3 F1
2 F3 14 F1   8 F3 3 F1
3 F3 10 F1   9 F3 2 F1
4 F3 7 F1   10 F3 1 F1
5 F3 6 F1   11 F3 2 F1
6 F3 4 F1   12 F3 2 F1

GRAPH EXE

Sharp *El-9300C*

Range   Xdlt = 1
        n = 1
        Xmin = 1   Ymin = −1
        Xmax = 13   Ymax = 20
        Xscl = 1   Yscl = 1

▤ MENU , cursor to DEL, 2, ENTER , 2

X1 = 1   W1 = 18   X7 = 7   W7 = 3
X2 = 2   W2 = 14   X8 = 8   W8 = 3
X3 = 3   W3 = 10   X9 = 9   W9 = 2
X4 = 4   W4 = 7   X10 = 10   W10 = 1
X5 = 5   W5 = 6   X11 = 11   W11 = 2
X6 = 6   W6 = 4   X12 = 12   W12 = 2

2nd F ⦂⦂ ENTER

TECHNOLOGY

Keystrokes for page 597

The following steps show the keystrokes for the *TI-80, TI-81,* and the *Casio fx-7700G* that would be used to sketch the graph of the equation.

$$y = 1.5x - 2.$$

TI-80

WINDOW (Set range.)
XMIN = −10
XMAX = 10
XSCL = 1
YMIN = −10
YMAX = 10
YSCL = 1

Y= 1.5 X,T ☐ 2
:$Y_1 = 1.5X - 2$
:$Y_2 =$
:$Y_3 =$
:$Y_4 =$

GRAPH
CLEAR (Clear screen)

TI-81

RANGE (Set range.)
Xmin = −10
Xmax = 10
Xscl = 1
Ymin = −10
Ymax = 10
Yscl = 1

Y= 1.5 X|T ☐ 2
:$Y_1 = 1.5X - 2$
:$Y_2 =$
:$Y_3 =$
:$Y_4 =$

GRAPH
CLEAR (Clear screen)

Casio fx-7700G

RANGE (Set range.)
Xmin = −10
  max = 10
  scl = 1
Ymin = −10
  max = 10
  scl = 1

EXE RANGE
SHIFT F5 (Cls) EXE
GRAPH 1.5 X, θ, T ☐ 2
Graph Y = 1.5 X − 2
EXE
SHIFT F5 (Cls) EXE

Tech 2

Keystrokes for page 646

The following steps show the keystrokes for the *TI-80* that would be used to sketch the box and whisker plot for the data below.

22, 65, 23, 19, 42, 62, 38, 29, 50, 46, 28, 36, 25, 40

TI-80

WINDOW

XMIN = 15	YMIN = 700
XMAX = 70	YMAX = 1000
XSCL = 1	YSCL = 50

STAT ENTER (Edit)

L1(1) = 22	ENTER	L1(8) = 29	ENTER
L1(2) = 65	ENTER	L1(9) = 50	ENTER
L1(3) = 23	ENTER	L1(10) = 46	ENTER
L1(4) = 19	ENTER	L1(11) = 28	ENTER
L1(5) = 42	ENTER	L1(12) = 36	ENTER
L1(6) = 62	ENTER	L1(13) = 25	ENTER
L1(7) = 38	ENTER	L1(14) = 40	ENTER

2nd STAT PLOT ENTER (Plot1)

Choose the following:
On, Type: ⊢□⊣, XL: L1, F: 1

GRAPH

To find the minimum, maximum, first quartile, median, and third quartile:
TRACE and ▷ or ◁

(Before completing the exercises, set XMIN = 10 and XMAX = 85.)

TECHNOLOGY